Dan
Trebisky

Automatic Sprinkler Systems Handbook

Automatic Sprinkler Systems Handbook

NINTH EDITION

EDITED BY

Christian Dubay, P.E.
Senior Fire Protection Engineer
National Fire Protection Association

With the complete text of the 2002 edition of NFPA 13, *Standard for the Installation of Sprinkler Systems;* NFPA 13D, *Standard for the Installation of Sprinkler Systems in One- and Two-Family Dwellings and Manufactured Homes;* and NFPA 13R, *Standard for the Installation of Sprinkler Systems in Residential Occupancies up to and Including Four Stories in Height*

National Fire Protection Association
NFPA Quincy, Massachusetts

Product Manager: Brad Gray/Debra Rose
Developmental Editor: Dana Richards
Project Editor: Irene Herlihy
Copy Editor: Kim Cervantes
Composition: Omegatype Typography, Inc.
Art Coordinator: Cheryl Langway

Cover Designer: Cameron, Inc.
Manufacturing Manager: Ellen Glisker
Printer: R. R. Donnelley/Willard

Copyright © 2002
National Fire Protection Association, Inc.
One Batterymarch Park
Quincy, Massachusetts 02269

Notice Concerning Liability: Publication of this handbook is for the purpose of circulating information and opinion among those concerned for fire and electrical safety and related subjects. While every effort has been made to achieve a work of high quality, neither the NFPA nor the contributors to this handbook guarantee the accuracy or completeness of or assume any liability in connection with the information and opinions contained in this handbook. The NFPA and the contributors shall in no event be liable for any personal injury, property, or other damages of any nature whatsoever, whether special, indirect, consequential, or compensatory, directly or indirectly resulting from the publication, use of, or reliance upon this handbook.

This handbook is published with the understanding that the NFPA and the contributors to this handbook are supplying information and opinion but are not attempting to render engineering or other professional services. If such services are required, the assistance of an appropriate professional should be sought.

Notice Concerning Code Interpretations: This ninth edition of *Automatic Sprinkler Systems Handbook* is based on the 2002 editions of NFPA 13, *Standard for the Installations of Sprinkler Systems;* NFPA 13D, *Standard for the Installation of Sprinkler Systems in One- and Two-Family Dwellings and Manufactured Homes;* and NFPA 13R, *Standard for the Installation of Sprinkler Systems in Residential Occupancies up to and Including Four Stories in Height.* All NFPA codes, standards, recommended practices, and guides are developed in accordance with the published procedures of the NFPA by technical committees comprised of volunteers drawn from a broad array of relevant interests. The handbook contains the complete text of NFPA 13, NFPA 13D, and NFPA 13R and any applicable Formal Interpretations issued by the Association. These documents are accompanied by explanatory commentary and other supplementary materials.

The commentary and supplementary materials in this handbook are not a part of the Standard and do not constitute Formal Interpretations of the NFPA (which can be obtained only through requests processed by the responsible technical committees in accordance with the published procedures of the NFPA). The commentary and supplementary materials, therefore, solely reflect the personal opinions of the editor or other contributors and do not necessarily represent the official position of the NFPA or its technical committees.

NFPA No.: 13HB02
ISBN: 0-87765-549-9
Library of Congress Control Number: 2002114312

Printed in the United States of America
03   04   05   06   07   5   4   3   2   1

This handbook is dedicated to the memory of Rolf H. Jensen, P.E.

Rolf served on the Automatic Sprinkler Committee from 1966 until his death in August of 2002. During this time he chaired the New Technology Subcommittee as well as chairing the Residential Subcommittee during the period when residential sprinkler technology was being developed and tested ultimately leading to the publication of NFPA 13D. In addition, he also served on the NFPA Board of Directors from 1990 until 1993.

His experience, expertise, numerous contributions, and knowledge remain an integral part of the standards on automatic sprinklers and this handbook. Rolf's tireless committee service and dedication will be deeply missed by all those involved.

Contents

Annexes

PART THREE

**NFPA 13R, *Standard for the Installation
of Sprinkler Systems in Residential Occupancies
up to and Including Four Stories in Height,
2002 Edition, with Commentary*   845**

Annexes

PART FOUR

Supplements   909

Preface

The first automatic fire extinguishing system on record was patented in England in 1723 and consisted of a cask of water, a chamber of gunpowder, and a system of fuses. In about 1852 the perforated pipe system represented the first form of a sprinkler system used in the United States. In 1874, Henry S. Parmelee of New Haven, Connecticut, patented the first practical automatic sprinkler.

C. J. H. Woodbury of the Boston Manufacturers Mutual Fire Insurance Company and F. E. Cabot of the Boston Board of Fire Underwriters completed a study on the performance of sprinklers for the Factory Mutual Fire Insurance Company in 1884. This study was the basis for the first set of rules for the installation of automatic sprinkler systems that were developed by John Wormald of the Mutual Fire Insurance Corporation of Manchester, England, in 1885. In 1887, similar rules were prepared in the United States by the Factory Improvement Committee of the New England Insurance Exchange.

By 1895, the commercial growth and development of sprinkler systems were so rapid that a number of different installation rules had been adopted by various insurance organizations. Within a few hundred miles of Boston, Massachusetts, nine radically different standards for the size of piping and sprinkler spacing were being used. This problem led to the creation of NFPA 13 and the formation of the National Fire Protection Association in 1896.

In many respects, the issues that led to the development of the first edition of NFPA 13 are relevant today. The unprecedented development of sprinkler system products, design techniques, and installation practices over the past several years is offering numerous options for effective system design. While this increased flexibility provides numerous advantages, it also requires more diligence by those designing, installing, and approving sprinkler systems as the rules for various system components become less uniform.

As has been the case for over 100 years, the intent of NFPA 13 is to provide a means for analyzing sprinkler system information and presenting it in a form that will lead to effective system designs and installations. This task continues to become increasingly demanding as scientific and other discoveries generate information at an increasingly accelerated rate. In response to these challenges, NFPA expanded the scope of NFPA 13 so that it is the most comprehensive document addressing sprinkler systems.

NFPA 13 addresses sprinkler system installations for all types of facilities regardless of the type of fire hazards present. NFPA 13 contains sprinkler system design and installation information from over 40 NFPA codes and standards. The 2002 edition of NFPA 13 further continues the reorganization and restructuring begun with the 1999 edition. A major part of this effort included the incorporation of the NFPA Manual of Style which resulted in several new chapters dedicated to Administration (Chapter 1), Referenced Publications (Chapter 2), Definitions (Chapter 3), and General Requirements (Chapter 4). The design and installation criteria were further expanded to include several new chapters including Underground Piping (Chapter 10), Design Approaches (Chapter 11), Storage (Chapter 12), and Special Occupancy Requirements (Chapter 13). Additionally, numerous technical changes have been incorporated.

As the scope of NFPA 13 has expanded, so has that of the *Automatic Sprinkler Systems Handbook*. This edition includes new and updated commentary on underground piping installation, rack and on-floor storage applications of various commodities including plastics, rubber tires, baled cotton, wooden and plastic pallets, and roll paper as well as commentary on many of the extracted special occupancies. In addition, the handbook includes updated commentary on those portions of NFPA 13 that have been revised. Two new supplements addressing microbiologically influenced corrosion and large orifice sprinkler applications have been added to the current supplement addressing the history of sprinklers, sprinkler systems, and NFPA sprinkler standards.

Acknowledgments

Over the past several years I have had the good fortune to work with some of the most knowledgeable and experienced people in the sprinkler industry. The help of these individuals has been invaluable in completing this handbook. I would especially like to acknowledge and thank the following people for their efforts with this project:

Ed Budnick	Kerry Bell
Randy Eberly	Russ Fleming
James Golinveaux	Roland Huggins
Ken Isman	Larry Keeping
George Laverick	Ken Linder
Dan Madrzykowski	Bill Thomas

I would also like to acknowledge those who contributed their time, effort, and knowledge in developing previous editions of the handbook. Many are still involved with the sprinkler project. Their work has created the solid foundation on which to build this and future editions.

I would be remiss if I did not acknowledge others at NFPA with whom I worked very closely on this project. Dana Richards, Kim Cervantes, and Irene Herlihy provided key input throughout various stages of the book's development and showed great patience in working with a new editor.

I would like to acknowledge several individuals who have had a significant impact on my life and my career in fire protection engineering: Jim Lathrop, Dick Morris, and Ron Pringle, each of whom taught me that knowledge and expertise are not gained through title or rank, but are only gained with experience, training, and perspective. I also want to acknowledge my mom, who has taught me to enjoy each moment and stage that life brings you. Finally, I would like to thank my father who taught me among many things the character traits of respect, accountability, and integrity. I am indebted to him as a father, a mentor, and a friend.

I am particularly grateful to my amazing wife, Andrea, and my sons Benjamin, Nicholas, and Silas who remind me on a daily basis where to place my priorities and focus while providing me with continual energy and amusement.

In closing, sprinkler systems have established an enviable record for achieving life safety and property protection. This handbook is intended to provide a better understanding of the requirements of NFPA 13, 13D, and 13R and how to implement them. I hope that this edition helps people make better decisions about fire safety and that it advances the legacy of automatic sprinkler systems worldwide.

Christian Dubay, P.E.

PART ONE

NFPA 13, *Standard for the Installation of Sprinkler Systems,* 2002 Edition, with Commentary

Part One of this handbook includes the complete text of the 2002 edition of NFPA 13, *Standard for the Installation of Sprinkler Systems,* which is made up of 18 mandatory chapters and five nonmandatory annexes. The text and illustrations from the standard are printed in black and are the official requirements of NFPA 13. Line drawings and photographs from the standard are labeled "Figures."

Paragraphs that begin with the letter "A" are extracted from Annex A of the standard. Although printed in black ink, this nonmandatory material is purely explanatory in nature. For ease of use, this handbook places Annex A material immediately after the standard paragraph to which it refers.

Part One also includes one Formal Interpretation on NFPA 13 in Chapter 8. Formal Interpretations are not part of the standard and are printed in shaded gray boxes.

In addition to the standard text, annexes, and Formal Interpretations, Part One includes commentary that provides the history and other background information for specific paragraphs in the standard. This insightful commentary takes the reader behind the scenes, into the reasons underlying the requirements.

To make commentary material readily identifiable, commentary text, captions, and tables are printed in blue. Line drawings and photographs in the commentary are labeled "Exhibits."

This edition of the handbook includes a new Frequently Asked Questions feature. The marginal FAQs are based on the most commonly asked questions of the NFPA 13 staff.

This edition of the handbook also features a tool designed to help users easily identify important elements in the text. Icons, which represent special information, have been added in the margins of the book next to the material they are identifying. These icons represent the following material:

 Annex A paragraphs   Referenced publications

 New material of special interest   Calculations

Administration

Chapter 1 provides the administrative text and requirements for NFPA 13. Chapter 1 covers the Scope, Purpose, Application, Retroactivity, Equivalency, New Technology, and Units and Symbols. The 2002 edition of NFPA 13 has been restructured to comply with the *NFPA Manual of Style,* and Chapter 1 is provided for the administrative text of the document.

Chapter 1 provides the user with some of the basic assumptions and principles when applying the requirements of NFPA 13 so that he or she will have a clear understanding of the limitations of NFPA 13 and the proper use and application of the requirements contained in NFPA 13.

1.1* Scope

This standard shall provide the minimum requirements for the design and installation of automatic fire sprinkler systems and exposure protection sprinkler systems covered within this standard.

A.1.1 This standard provides a range of sprinkler system approaches, design development alternatives, and component options that are all acceptable. Building owners and their designated representatives are advised to carefully evaluate proposed selections for appropriateness and preference.

NFPA 13, as stated in Section 1.1, addresses the design and installation of sprinkler systems employing automatic or open sprinklers that discharge water to suppress or control a fire. NFPA 13 provides only the minimum requirements for satisfactory sprinkler system performance during a fire. The overall level of fire protection provided by sprinkler systems can be enhanced through the use of additional provisions, such as supplemental supervisory signaling systems.

As an installation standard, NFPA 13 does not specify the buildings or structures that require sprinkler systems. The purpose of NFPA 13 is to provide for the proper design and installation of a sprinkler system and to specify acceptable system components when a sprinkler system is required. In other words, NFPA 13 specifies how to properly design and install a sprinkler system using the proper components. The standard does not identify when a system is required. The local building code; *NFPA 5000™, Building Construction and Safety Code™*; NFPA *101®, Life Safety Code®* (see Exhibit 1.1); or insurance regulations typically specify the buildings and structures that require sprinkler systems.

To the extent possible, all requirements pertaining to the design and installation of automatic sprinkler systems have been centralized in NFPA 13. The scope of NFPA 13 now includes sprinkler system design and installation requirements for storage facilities, which were formerly located in the NFPA 231 series of documents. The design and installation requirements for underground piping and private fire service mains, which are also found in NFPA

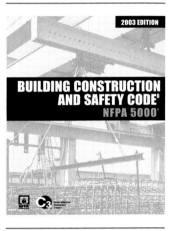

EXHIBIT 1.1 NFPA 5000™, Building Construction and Safety Code™, 2003 Edition.

◀ **FAQ**
Does my building require a sprinkler system?

◀ **FAQ**
Where are the design and installation requirements for underground piping and private fire service mains?

24, *Standard for the Installation of Private Fire Service Mains and Their Appurtenances,* have been included in Chapter 10.

     Chapter 13 of NFPA 13 incorporates and consolidates the sprinkler system information that has been extracted from other NFPA standards to assist NFPA 13 users with the design and installation of automatic sprinkler systems for hazards and facilities not previously addressed by NFPA 13. Sprinkler system information from over 40 NFPA codes, standards, and recommended practices is extracted in Chapter 13 and its annex. For example, 13.6.1 and 13.6.2 contain sprinkler system design and installation criteria from NFPA 40, *Standard for the Storage and Handling of Cellulose Nitrate Film.* In a few instances where extracted text could be confusing or misleading, NFPA 13 only references the appropriate NFPA standard. For example, 13.2.1 references only NFPA 30, *Flammable and Combustible Liquids Code,* rather than extract specific sprinkler system discharge criteria from NFPA 30.

     NFPA 13 also references other documents that address equipment that is essential to the proper and effective operation of the sprinkler system. For example, Chapter 15 establishes the types of acceptable water supply sources. However, Chapter 15 does not contain installation or performance requirements for those water supply sources. Other NFPA standards such as NFPA 20, *Standard for the Installation of Stationary Pumps for Fire Protection,* and NFPA 22, *Standard for Water Tanks for Private Fire Protection,* provide specific installation requirements for fire pumps and water storage tanks.

Since NFPA 13 only pertains to sprinkler systems, other NFPA standards should be referenced for design and installation requirements of other types of water-based fire protection systems. The following list identifies some of these standards:

NFPA 11, *Standard for Low-, Medium-, and High-Expansion Foam*

NFPA 11A, *Standard for Medium- and High-Expansion Foam Systems*

NFPA 13D, *Standard for the Installation of Sprinkler Systems in One- and Two-Family Dwellings and Manufactured Homes*

NFPA 13R, *Standard for the Installation of Sprinkler Systems in Residential Occupancies up to and Including Four Stories in Height*

NFPA 14, *Standard for the Installation of Standpipe, Private Hydrant, and Hose Systems*

NFPA 15, *Standard for Water Spray Fixed Systems for Fire Protection*

NFPA 16, *Standard for the Installation of Foam-Water Sprinkler and Foam-Water Spray Systems*

NFPA 750, *Standard on Water Mist Fire Protection Systems*

1.2* Purpose

 A.1.2 Since its inception, this document has been developed on the basis of standardized materials, devices, and design practices. However, Section 1.2 and other subsections such as 6.3.6 and 8.4.9 allow the use of materials and devices not specifically designated by this standard, provided such use is within parameters established by a listing organization. In using such materials or devices, it is important that all conditions, requirements, and limitations of the listing be fully understood and accepted and that the installation be in complete accord with such listing requirements.

1.2.1 The purpose of this standard shall be to provide a reasonable degree of protection for life and property from fire through standardization of design, installation, and testing requirements for sprinkler systems, including private fire service mains, based on sound engineering principles, test data, and field experience.

In 1.2.1, the purpose of NFPA 13 is to "provide a reasonable degree of protection for life and property from fire…" However, as with most life safety systems, it is difficult to precisely quantify the overall level of protection to life and property provided by sprinkler systems. For example, accurate mathematical predictions that everyone exposed to a rapidly spreading flammable liquids fire in a fully sprinklered processing plant would escape without harm or that property damage could be limited to a specific dollar value or to a percentage of the overall building area cannot be made. However, life safety and property protection in buildings are both known to be greatly enhanced by the presence of an automatic sprinkler system complying with NFPA 13.

Fire data collected and analyzed by NFPA's Fire Analysis and Research Division (see Exhibit 1.2) has lead to the following conclusions:

> When sprinklers are present, the chances of dying in a fire and the average property loss per fire are both cut by one-half to two-thirds, compared to fires where sprinklers are not present. What's more, this simple comparison understates the potential value of sprinklers because it lumps together all sprinklers, regardless of type, coverage, or operational status, and is limited to fires reported to fire departments. If unreported fires could be included and if complete, well maintained, and properly installed and designed systems could be isolated, sprinkler effectiveness would be seen as even more impressive. [Rohr 1998]

Furthermore, "NFPA has no record of a fire killing more than two people in a completely sprinklered building where the system was properly operating, except in an explosion or flash fire or where industrial fire brigade members or employees were killed during fire suppression operations" [Rohr 1998]. In some cases, victims of fatal fires in sprinklered properties were either involved in the ignition of the fire and received their injuries prior to the operation of the sprinklers or were unable to escape due to a physical or mental impairment.

With regard to unsatisfactory sprinkler system performance, the cited NFPA data indicates that this occurrence is rare, and that the reason almost always involves some type of human error. Examples of human error include failure to properly maintain the system or failure to upgrade an existing system when the hazard or occupancy in which it is located changes. Overall, the NFPA study states that the major reason a sprinkler system would not operate satisfactorily is that the water supply was shut off. See Commentary Table 1.1.

COMMENTARY TABLE 1.1 *Leading Reasons for Unsatisfactory Sprinkler Performance*

Cause of Failure	Percentage of Cases
Water shut off	35.4
Inadequate maintenance	8.4
Obstruction to water distribution	8.2
System frozen	1.4

Note: Table statistics based on 3134 fires reported to NFPA during 1925 to 1969 for which sprinkler performance was deemed unsatisfactory. Of these reported fires, 75 percent were in industrial facilities, 12 percent were in storage facilities, 5.6 percent were in stores, and 7.4 percent were in all other properties.

Source: Rohr, K. D., "U.S. Experience with Sprinklers: Who Has Them? How Well Do They Work?," National Fire Protection Association Fire and Analysis and Research Division, 1998.

1.2.2 Sprinkler systems and private fire service mains are specialized fire protection systems and shall require knowledgeable and experienced design and installation.

EXHIBIT 1.2 *NFPA's One Stop Data Shop.*

The requirements of NFPA 13 were developed through the application of engineering principles, fire test data, and field experience. During its 100-plus-year history, the technical committees on automatic sprinkler systems have reviewed, analyzed, and evaluated sprinkler system–related information and presented it in a useful form. Although those who developed and updated NFPA 13 possess numerous credentials regarding their ability to design, install, review, or evaluate sprinkler systems, NFPA 13 does not specify particular qualifications for its users beyond those stated in 1.2.2. However, as with any specialized subject, a good understanding of the basic principles as well as a continued effort to keep current with developing technologies is essential. NFPA 13 is a design and installation standard. It is not a how-to manual or a textbook.

FAQ ▶
Who sets the qualifications for those who design and install sprinkler systems?

Although NFPA 13 does not specify qualifications for those who design and install sprinkler systems, state and local government agencies typically do. For example, some states require that sprinkler system designers be registered fire protection engineers or be certified as National Institute for Certification of Engineering Technicians (NICET) and that those who install sprinkler systems be licensed. These requirements are similar to the required qualifications for those who design and install electrical systems that affect public safety.

1.3 Application

1.3.1 This standard shall apply to:

(1) Character and adequacy of water supplies
(2) Selection of sprinklers
(3) Fittings
(4) Piping
(5) Valves
(6) All materials and accessories, including the installation of private fire service mains

1.3.2 This standard shall also apply to "combined service mains" used to carry water for both fire service and other uses as well as mains for fire service use only.

1.4 Retroactivity Clause

The provisions of this standard reflect a consensus of what is necessary to provide an acceptable degree of protection from the hazards addressed in this standard at the time the standard was issued. Unless otherwise specified, the provisions of this standard shall not apply to facilities, equipment, structures, or installations that existed or were approved for construction or installation prior to the effective date of this standard. Where specified, the provisions of this standard shall be retroactive. In those cases where the authority having jurisdiction determines that the existing situation presents an unacceptable degree of risk, the authority having jurisdiction shall be permitted to apply retroactively any portions of this standard deemed appropriate.

The retroactivity clause, as shown in Section 1.4, appears in many NFPA codes and standards. Its main purpose is to reinforce the premise that any sprinkler system installed in accordance with the applicable edition of NFPA 13 is considered to comply with the standard for the system's lifetime as long as no system modifications are made and the fire hazard remains unchanged. In other words, an existing system is not required to be reviewed for compliance with every new edition of the standard. For example, the 2002 edition requires that means be provided downstream of pressure-reducing valves so that flow tests at system demand can be conducted. This requirement is not intended to retroactively apply to a system that was installed in accordance with previous editions of the standard that did not contain the requirement.

Omission of this retroactivity clause would require building owners, code enforcers, insurance companies, and installers to undertake the never-ending task of updating and revising their sprinkler systems every time a new edition of NFPA 13 was published. Although newer editions often include updated requirements that enhance the level of protection, older editions should not be interpreted as unsafe. In those instances where a severe deficiency is discovered, the last sentence of Section 1.4 provides latitude for the authority having jurisdiction (AHJ). For example, it could be discovered that an existing system would not be able to perform satisfactorily for the fire hazard presented.

Where the hazard within a sprinklered building or space has changed, an evaluation of the existing sprinkler system needs to be conducted to verify its adequacy. For example, it is highly unlikely that a sprinkler system designed and installed to protect 8-ft (2.4-m) high on-floor storage would be capable of protecting 18-ft (5.4-m) high rack storage of the same commodity. Sprinkler protection for the high rack storage arrangement needs to be upgraded in compliance with the latest NFPA 13 provision for such storage.

Routine inspections and testing of a sprinkler system in accordance NFPA 25, *Standard* *for the Inspection, Testing, and Maintenance of Water-Based Fire Protection Systems,* uncover many of the impairments that lead to unsuccessful sprinkler system performance. Proper knowledge of system design and installation requirements as well as a vigilant maintenance program are also critical in ensuring that sprinkler systems remain one of the most reliable and effective defenses against fire.

1.5 Equivalency

Nothing in this standard is intended to prevent the use of systems, methods, or devices of equivalent or superior quality, strength, fire resistance, effectiveness, durability, and safety over those prescribed by this standard. Technical documentation shall be submitted to the authority having jurisdiction to demonstrate equivalency. The system, method, or device shall be approved for the intended purpose by the authority having jurisdiction.

In Section 1.5, the equivalency statement allows that products and system arrangements not specifically covered by the standard can be used, provided it can be demonstrated that these products or arrangements do not lower the level of safety provided by the standard or alter the standard's intent.

1.6 New Technology

Scientific understanding of fire, sprinklers, and their interaction continues to increase, and Section 1.6 provides for this advance in technology. This knowledge allows for better system performance and the development of more effective new products. For example, residential sprinklers were developed to protect people in the room of fire origin within a dwelling unit who are not intimate with ignition, provided the fire load is typical of that found in a residential-type occupancy. More information on residential sprinklers is provided in NFPA 13D, *Standard for the Installation of Sprinkler Systems in One- and Two-Family Dwellings and Manufactured Homes.* Another example includes the development of early suppression fast-response (ESFR) sprinklers with various K-factors (see Exhibit 1.3). The application of this technology allows for fire suppression of various commodities stored up to 40 ft (12.2 m) in height with relatively low discharge pressures. See Chapter 12 for more information.

EXHIBIT 1.3 *Upright-Type ESFR Sprinkler.*

1.6.1 Nothing in this standard shall be intended to restrict new technologies or alternate arrangements, provided the level of safety prescribed by this standard is not lowered.

NFPA 13 encourages innovative and economically feasible measures that provide life safety and property protection. Paragraph 1.6.1 allows for the use of increasingly available specially listed materials and products and promotes the continued development of new sprinkler-related technologies.

1.6.2 Materials or devices not specifically designated by this standard shall be utilized in complete accord with all conditions, requirements, and limitations of their listings.

NFPA 13 encourages innovative and economically feasible measures that provide life safety and property protection. Paragraph 1.6.2 allows for the use of increasingly available specially listed materials and products and promotes the continued development of new sprinkler-related technologies. Exhibit 1.4 shows various types of special sprinklers.

EXHIBIT 1.4 Listed Special Sprinklers.

FAQ ▶
When using a specially listed product are the only installation requirements those contained within NFPA 13?

Paragraph 1.6.2 alerts the NFPA 13 user that specialized products often have specific requirements or limitations, which are not addressed by NFPA 13. For all listed products, the listing information and the relevant manufacturer's literature must be referenced.

For example, nonmetallic pipe is an acceptable alternative to traditional materials, such as steel or copper, for certain applications. Initially tested and listed in 1984 for use only in systems designed in accordance with NFPA 13D, nonmetallic pipe is now listed for use in any light hazard occupancy (see Exhibit 1.5).

EXHIBIT 1.5 Listed Plastic Pipe.

1.7 Units and Symbols

1.7.1 Units.

Subsection 1.7.1 discusses the use of units in NFPA 13. The English units for sprinkler design densities are gallons per minute per square foot (gpm/ft^2). The direct metric equivalent to these English units is liters per minute per square meter [(L/min)/m^2]. However, the more common units for measuring sprinkler discharge densities in those countries that employ the metric system are millimeters per minute (mm/min), and this designation is used throughout the standard.

1.7.1.1 Metric units of measurement in this standard are in accordance with the modernized metric system known as the International System of Units (SI).

1.7.1.2 Two units (liter and bar), outside of but recognized by SI, are commonly used in international fire protection.

1.7.1.3 These units are listed in Table 1.7.1.3 with conversion factors.

TABLE 1.7.1.3 *SI Units and Conversion Factors*

Name of Unit	Unit Symbol	Conversion Factor
liter	L	1 gal = 3.785 L
millimeter per minute	mm/min	1 gpm/ft^2 = 40.746 mm/min = 40.746 (L/min)/m^2
cubic decimeter	dm^3	1 gal = 3.785 dm^3
pascal	Pa	1 psi = 6894.757 Pa
bar	bar	1 psi = 0.0689 bar
bar	bar	1 bar = 10^5 Pa

Note: For additional conversions and information, see ASTM SI 10, *Standard for Use of the International System of Units (SI): The Modern Metric System.*

1.7.1.4 If a value for measurement as given in this standard is followed by an equivalent value in other units, the first stated is to be regarded as the requirement.

1.7.2 Symbols.

The standard abbreviations in Table 1.7.2 shall be used on the hydraulic calculation form discussed in Chapter 11.

TABLE 1.7.2 *Hydraulic Symbols*

Symbol or Abbreviation	Item
p	Pressure in psi
gpm	U.S. gallons per minute
q	Flow increment in gpm to be added at a specific location
Q	Summation of flow in gpm at a specific location
P_t	Total pressure in psi at a point in a pipe
P_f	Pressure loss due to friction between points indicated in location column
P_e	Pressure due to elevation difference between indicated points. This can be a plus value or a minus value. If minus, the (−) shall be used; if plus, no sign need be indicated.
P_v	Velocity pressure in psi at a point in a pipe
P_n	Normal pressure in psi at a point in a pipe
E	90-degree ell
EE	45-degree ell
Lt.E	Long-turn elbow
Cr	Cross
T	Tee-flow turned 90 degrees
GV	Gate valve
BV	Butterfly (wafer) check valve
Del V	Deluge valve
ALV	Alarm valve
DPV	Dry pipe valve
CV	Swing check valve
WCV	Butterfly (wafer) check valve
St	Strainer
psi	Pounds per square inch
v	Velocity of water in pipe in feet per second

SUMMARY

In addition to the administrative text of NFPA 13, Chapter 1 gives the user an introduction into the use and application of NFPA 13 and to sprinkler system design and review. In addition, some of the basic assumptions and principles when applying the requirements of NFPA 13 are also provided. Chapter 1 additionally provides the important allowance for new technologies that are developed and specified in new designs and installations.

 ## REFERENCES CITED IN COMMENTARY

National Fire Protection Association, 1 Batterymarch Park, P.O. Box 9101, Quincy, MA 02269-9101

NFPA 11, *Standard for Low-, Medium-, and High-Expansion Foam,* 2002 edition
NFPA 11A, *Standard for Medium- and High-Expansion Foam Systems,* 2002 edition
NFPA 13D, *Standard for the Installation of Sprinkler Systems in One- and Two-Family Dwellings and Manufactured Homes,* 2002 edition
NFPA 13R, *Standard for the Installation of Sprinkler Systems in Residential Occupancies up to and Including Four Stories in Height,* 2002 edition
NFPA 14, *Standard for the Installation of Standpipe, Private Hydrant, and Hose Systems,* 2000 edition
NFPA 15, *Standard for Water Spray Fixed Systems for Fire Protection,* 2001 edition
NFPA 16, *Standard for the Installation of Foam-Water Sprinkler and Foam-Water Spray Systems,* 1999 edition
NFPA 20, *Standard for the Installation of Stationary Pumps for Fire Protection,* 1999 edition
NFPA 22, *Standard for Water Tanks for Private Fire Protection,* 1998 edition
NFPA 24, *Standard for the Installation of Private Fire Service Mains and Their Appurtenances,* 2002 edition
NFPA 25, *Standard for the Inspection, Testing, and Maintenance of Water-Based Fire Protection Systems,* 2002 edition
NFPA 30, *Flammable and Combustible Liquids Code,* 2000 edition
NFPA 40, *Standard for the Storage and Handling of Cellulose Nitrate Film,* 2001 edition
NFPA *101*®, *Life Safety Code*®, 2000 edition
NFPA 750, *Standard on Water Mist Fire Protection Systems,* 2000 edition
NFPA 5000™, *Building Construction and Safety Code*™, 2003 edition
Rohr, K. D. "U.S. Experience with Sprinklers: Who Has Them? How Well Do They Work?," Quincy, MA: National Fire Protection Association Fire Analysis and Research Division, 1998

CHAPTER 2

Referenced Publications

2.1 General

The documents or portions thereof listed in this chapter are referenced within this standard and shall be considered part of the requirements of this document.

2.2 NFPA Publications

National Fire Protection Association, 1 Batterymarch Park, P.O. Box 9101, Quincy, MA 02269-9101.

NFPA 11A, *Standard for Medium- and High-Expansion Foam Systems,* 1999 edition.

NFPA 14, *Standard for the Installation of Standpipe, Private Hydrant, and Hose Systems,* 2000 edition.

NFPA 15, *Standard for Water Spray Fixed Systems for Fire Protection,* 2001 edition.

NFPA 20, *Standard for the Installation of Stationary Pumps for Fire Protection,* 1999 edition.

NFPA 22, *Standard for Water Tanks for Private Fire Protection,* 1998 edition.

NFPA 25, *Standard for the Inspection, Testing, and Maintenance of Water-Based Fire Protection Systems,* 2002 edition.

NFPA 30, *Flammable and Combustible Liquids Code,* 2000 edition.

NFPA 30B, *Code for the Manufacture and Storage of Aerosol Products,* 2002 edition.

NFPA 40, *Standard for the Storage and Handling of Cellulose Nitrate Film,* 2001 edition.

NFPA 42, *Code for the Storage of Pyroxylin Plastic,* 2002 edition.

NFPA 45, *Standard on Fire Protection for Laboratories Using Chemicals,* 2000 edition.

NFPA 51, *Standard for the Design and Installation of Oxygen–Fuel Gas Systems for Welding, Cutting, and Allied Processes,* 2002 edition.

NFPA 51A, *Standard for Acetylene Cylinder Charging Plants,* 2001 edition.

NFPA 51B, *Standard for Fire Prevention During Welding, Cutting, and Other Hot Work,* 1999 edition.

NFPA 55, *Standard for the Storage, Use, and Handling of Compressed and Liquefied Gases in Portable Cylinders,* 1998 edition.

NFPA 59, *Utility LP-Gas Plant Code,* 2001 edition.

NFPA 59A, *Standard for the Production, Storage, and Handling of Liquefied Natural Gas (LNG),* 2001 edition.

NFPA 70, *National Electrical Code®,* 2002 edition.

NFPA 72®, National Fire Alarm Code®, 2002 edition.

NFPA 75, *Standard for the Protection of Electronic Computer/Data Processing Equipment,* 1999 edition.

NFPA 82, *Standard on Incinerators and Waste and Linen Handling Systems and Equipment,* 1999 edition.

NFPA 86C, *Standard for Industrial Furnaces Using a Special Processing Atmosphere,* 1999 edition.

NFPA 96, *Standard for Ventilation Control and Fire Protection of Commercial Cooking Operations,* 2001 edition.

NFPA *101®, Life Safety Code®,* 2000 edition.

NFPA 170, *Standard for Fire Safety Symbols,* 2002 edition.

NFPA 214, *Standard on Water-Cooling Towers,* 2000 edition.

NFPA 251, *Standard Methods of Tests of Fire Endurance of Building Construction and Materials,* 1999 edition.

NFPA 259, *Standard Test Method for Potential Heat of Building Materials,* 1998 edition.

NFPA 307, *Standard for the Construction and Fire Protection of Marine Terminals, Piers, and Wharves,* 2000 edition.

NFPA 409, *Standard on Aircraft Hangars,* 2001 edition.

NFPA 430, *Code for the Storage of Liquid and Solid Oxidizers,* 2000 edition.

NFPA 703, *Standard for Fire Retardant Impregnated Wood and Fire Retardant Coatings for Building Materials,* 2000 edition.

NFPA 1963, *Standard for Fire Hose Connections,* 1998 edition.

2.3 Other Publications

2.3.1 ASME Publications.

American Society of Mechanical Engineers, Three Park Avenue, New York, NY 10016-5990.

ASME A17.1, *Safety Code for Elevators and Escalators,* 2000.

ASME B1.20.1, *Pipe Threads, General Purpose (Inch),* 2001.

ASME B16.1, *Cast Iron Pipe Flanges and Flanged Fittings, Classes 25, 125, and 250,* 1998.

ASME B16.3, *Malleable Iron Threaded Fittings, Classes 150 and 300,* 1998.

ASME B16.4, *Cast Iron Threaded Fittings, Classes 125 and 250,* 1998.

ASME B16.5, *Pipe Flanges and Flanged Fittings,* 1996.

ASME B16.9, *Factory-Made Wrought Steel Buttwelding Fittings,* 2001.

ASME B16.11, *Forged Steel Fittings, Socket-Welding and Threaded,* 1996.

ASME B16.18, *Cast Copper Alloy Solder Joint Pressure Fittings,* 1994.

ASME B16.22, *Wrought Copper and Copper Alloy Solder Joint Pressure Fittings,* 1995.

ASME B16.25, *Buttwelding Ends,* 1997.

ANSI/ASME B31.1, *Code for Power Piping,* 2001.

ANSI/ASME B36.10M, *Welded and Seamless Wrought Steel Pipe,* 2000.

2.3.2 ASTM Publications.

American Society for Testing and Materials, 100 Barr Harbor Drive, West Conshohocken, PA 19428-2959.

ANSI/ASTM A 53, *Standard Specification for Pipe, Steel, Black and Hot-Dipped, Zinc-Coated, Welded and Seamless,* 2001.

ASTM A 135, *Standard Specification for Electric-Resistance-Welded Steel Pipe,* 2001.

ASTM A 153, *Standard Specification for Zinc Coating (Hot Dip) on Iron and Steel Hardware,* 2001.

ASTM A 234/A 234M, *Standard Specification for Piping Fittings of Wrought-Carbon Steel and Alloy Steel for Moderate and High Temperature Service,* 2001.

ASTM A 795, *Standard Specification for Black and Hot-Dipped Zinc-Coated (Galvanized) Welded and Seamless Steel Pipe for Fire Protection Use,* 2000.

ASTM B 32, *Standard Specification for Solder Metal,* 2000.

ASTM B 75, *Standard Specification for Seamless Copper Tube,* 1999.

ASTM B 88, *Standard Specification for Seamless Copper Water Tube,* 1999.

ASTM B 251, *Standard Specification for General Requirements for Wrought Seamless Copper and Copper-Alloy Tube,* 1997.

ASTM B 446, *Standard Specification for Nickel-Chromium-Molybdenum-Columbium Alloy (UNSN 06625) and Nickel-Chromium-Molybdenum-Silicon Alloy (UNSN 06219) Rod and Bar,* 2000.

ASTM B 813, *Standard Specification for Liquid and Paste Fluxes for Soldering Applications of Copper and Copper-Alloy Tube,* 2000.

ASTM B 828, *Standard Practice for Making Capillary Joints by Soldering of Copper and Copper Alloy Tube and Fittings,* 2000.

ASTM D 3309, *Standard Specification for Polybutylene (PB) Plastic Hot- and Cold-Water Distribution Systems,* 1996.

ASTM E 119, *Standard Test Methods for Fire Tests of Building Construction and Materials,* 2000.

ASTM E 136, *Standard Test Method for Behavior of Materials in a Vertical Tube Furnace at 750°C,* 1999.

ASTM F 437, *Standard Specification for Threaded Chlorinated Poly (Vinyl Chloride) (CPVC) Plastic Pipe Fittings, Schedule 80,* 1999.

ASTM F 438, *Standard Specification for Socket-Type Chlorinated Poly (Vinyl Chloride) (CPVC) Plastic Pipe Fittings, Schedule 40,* 2001.

ASTM F 439, *Standard Specification for Socket-Type Chlorinated Poly (Vinyl Chloride) (CPVC) Plastic Pipe Fittings, Schedule 80,* 2001.

ASTM F 442, *Standard Specification for Chlorinated Poly (Vinyl Chloride) (CPVC) Plastic Pipe (SDR-PR),* 1999.

ASTM F 1121, *Standard Specification for International Shore Connections for Marine Fire Applications,* 1998.

ASTM SI 10, *Standard for Use of the International System of Units (SI): The Modern Metric System,* 1997.

2.3.3 AWS Publications.

American Welding Society, 550 N.W. LeJeune Road, Miami, FL 33126.

AWS A5.8, *Specification for Filler Metals for Brazing and Braze Welding,* 1992.

AWS B2.1, *Specification for Welding Procedure and Performance Qualification,* 2000.

AWS D10.9, *Specification for Qualification of Welding Procedures and Welders for Piping and Tubing,* 1980.

2.3.4 AWWA Publications.

American Water Works Association, 6666 West Quincy Avenue, Denver, CO 80235.

AWWA C104, *Cement Mortar Lining for Ductile Iron Pipe and Fittings for Water,* 1995.

AWWA C105, *Polyethylene Encasement for Ductile Iron Pipe Systems,* 1999.

AWWA C110, *Ductile Iron and Gray Iron Fittings, 3-in. Through 48-in. (76 mm Through 1219 mm), for Water and Other Liquids,* 1998.

AWWA C111, *Rubber Gasket Joints for Ductile Iron Pressure Pipe and Fittings,* 2000.

AWWA C115, *Flanged Ductile Iron Pipe with Ductile Iron or Gray Iron Threaded Flanges,* 1999.

AWWA C150, *Thickness Design of Ductile Iron Pipe,* 1996.

AWWA C151, *Ductile Iron Pipe, Centrifugally Cast for Water,* 1996.

AWWA C200, *Steel Water Pipe 6 in. (150 mm) and Larger,* 1997.

AWWA C203, *Coal-Tar Protective Coatings and Linings for Steel Water Pipelines Enamel and Tape—Hot Applied,* 1997.

AWWA C205, *Cement-Mortar Protective Lining and Coating for Steel Water Pipe 4 in. (100 mm) and Larger—Shop Applied,* 2000.

AWWA C206, *Field Welding of Steel Water Pipe,* 1997.

AWWA C207, *Steel Pipe Flanges for Waterworks Service—Sizes 4 in. Through 144 in. (100 mm Through 3,600 mm),* 1994.

AWWA C208, *Dimensions for Fabricated Steel Water Pipe Fittings,* 1996.

AWWA C300, *Reinforced Concrete Pressure Pipe, Steel-Cylinder Type, for Water and Other Liquids,* 1997.

AWWA C301, *Prestressed Concrete Pressure Pipe, Steel-Cylinder Type, for Water and Other Liquids,* 1999.

AWWA C302, *Reinforced Concrete Pressure Pipe, Non-Cylinder Type, for Water and Other Liquids,* 1995.

AWWA C303, *Reinforced Concrete Pressure Pipe, Steel-Cylinder Type, Pretensioned, for Water and Other Liquids,* 1995.

AWWA C400, *Standard for Asbestos-Cement Distribution Pipe, 4 in. Through 16 in. (100 mm Through 400 mm), for Water and Other Liquids,* 1998.

AWWA C401, *Standard Practice for the Selection of Asbestos-Cement Water Pipe, 4 in. Through 16 in. (100 mm Through 400 mm),* 1998.

AWWA C600, *Standard for the Installation of Ductile Iron Water Mains and Their Appurtenances,* 1999.

AWWA C602, *Cement-Mortar Lining of Water Pipe Lines 4 in. (100 mm) and Larger—in Place,* 2000.

AWWA C603, *Standard for the Installation of Asbestos-Cement Water Pipe,* 1996.

AWWA C900, *Polyvinyl Chloride (PVC) Pressure Pipe, 4 in. Through 12 in. (100 mm Through 300 mm), for Water and Other Liquids,* 1997.

AWWA M11, *A Guide for Steel Pipe Design and Installation,* 3rd edition, 1989.

2.3.5 IEEE Publication.

Institute of Electrical and Electronics Engineers, 445 Hoes Lane, P.O. Box 1331, Piscataway, NJ 08855-1331.

IEEE 45, *Recommended Practice for Electric Installations on Shipboard,* 1998.

2.3.6 UL Publication.

Underwriters Laboratories Inc., 333 Pfingsten Road, Northbrook, IL 60062.

UL 300, *Standard for Safety Fire Testing of Fire Extinguishing Systems for Protection of Restaurant Cooking Areas,* 1998.

2.3.7 U.S. Government Publications.

U.S. Government Printing Office, Washington, DC 20402.

Title 46, *Code of Federal Regulations,* Parts 54.15-10 Safety and Relief Valves, 56.20 Valves, 56.20-5(a) Marking, 56.50-95 Overboard Discharges and Shore Connections, 56.60 Materials, and 58.01-40 Machinery, Angle of Inclination.

Title 46, *Code of Federal Regulations,* Subchapter F, "Marine Engineering."

Title 46, *Code of Federal Regulations,* Subchapter J, "Electrical Engineering."

CHAPTER 3

Definitions

Many of the terms used throughout NFPA 13 are unique to sprinkler systems and are defined in Chapter 3. Due to the large number and types of terms used throughout this standard, the terms are organized into one of eight categories to facilitate their search. These categories include terms specific to NFPA (Section 3.2), terms associated with general fire protection (Section 3.3), terms describing various types of sprinkler systems (Section 3.4), terms addressing individual sprinkler system components (Section 3.5), terms specific to the automatic sprinklers (Section 3.6), terms that characterize building construction features (Section 3.7), terms pertaining to private water supply piping (Section 3.8), and terms related to storage operations (Section 3.9).

For the 2002 edition of NFPA 13 all of the definitions were relocated from Chapter 1 to Chapter 3. Additionally, all of the Marine Definitions (Section 3.14) were copied into Chapter 3. Due to their specific application, the marine definitions also remain in Chapter 17, Marine Systems.

3.1 General

The definitions contained in this chapter shall apply to the terms used in this standard. Where terms are not included, common usage of the terms shall apply.

3.2 NFPA Official Definitions

3.2.1* Approved. Acceptable to the authority having jurisdiction.

A.3.2.1 Approved. The National Fire Protection Association does not approve, inspect, or certify any installations, procedures, equipment, or materials; nor does it approve or evaluate testing laboratories. In determining the acceptability of installations, procedures, equipment, or materials, the authority having jurisdiction may base acceptance on compliance with NFPA or other appropriate standards. In the absence of such standards, said authority may require evidence of proper installation, procedure, or use. The authority having jurisdiction may also refer to the listings or labeling practices of an organization that is concerned with product evaluations and is thus in a position to determine compliance with appropriate standards for the current production of listed items.

In the context of NFPA 13, the term *approved,* as defined in 3.2.1, has a different meaning from the term *listed,* which is defined in 3.2.3. A component that is approved is not necessarily listed. Components critical to the proper operation of a sprinkler system, such as alarm valves, dry pipe valves, sprinklers, and hangers, must be both listed and approved. Noncritical components, such as drain valves, are not required to be listed but are required to be approved. (See the commentary following A.3.2.3 for more information on the term *listed.*)

Components that are required to be approved are necessary to maintain an acceptable level of system reliability. However, their impairment would not render the sprinkler system

◄ FAQ
What is the difference between Listed and Approved?

out of service. Components such as pressure gauges, drain valves, and water meters fit into this category.

3.2.2* Authority Having Jurisdiction (AHJ). The organization, office, or individual responsible for approving equipment, materials, an installation, or a procedure.

 A.3.2.2 Authority Having Jurisdiction (AHJ). The phrase "authority having jurisdiction," or its acronym AHJ, is used in NFPA documents in a broad manner, since jurisdictions and approval agencies vary, as do their responsibilities. Where public safety is primary, the authority having jurisdiction may be a federal, state, local, or other regional department or individual such as a fire chief; fire marshal; chief of a fire prevention bureau, labor department, or health department; building official; electrical inspector; or others having statutory authority. For insurance purposes, an insurance inspection department, rating bureau, or other insurance company representative may be the authority having jurisdiction. In many circumstances, the property owner or his or her designated agent assumes the role of the authority having jurisdiction; at government installations, the commanding officer or departmental official may be the authority having jurisdiction.

The *authority having jurisdiction,* as defined in 3.2.2, is that person or office enforcing the standard. In cases where the standard is to be legally enforced, the authority having jurisdiction is usually a fire marshal or building official. It is common for multiple authorities having jurisdiction to review the same project, enforcing this standard, other standards, or all. In many cases where NFPA 13 is utilized, the insuring agency for the facility may have requirements that differ or exceed the requirements contained in NFPA 13. For all designs and applications it is important to communicate with all of the appropriate "authorities" to determine the proper criteria.

3.2.3* Listed. Equipment, materials, or services included in a list published by an organization that is acceptable to the authority having jurisdiction and concerned with evaluation of products or services, that maintains periodic inspection of production of listed equipment or materials or periodic evaluation of services, and whose listing states that either the equipment, material, or service meets appropriate designated standards or has been tested and found suitable for a specified purpose.

 A.3.2.3 Listed. The means for identifying listed equipment may vary for each organization concerned with product evaluation; some organizations do not recognize equipment as listed unless it is also labeled. The authority having jurisdiction should utilize the system employed by the listing organization to identify a listed product.

Most components that are critical to system performance must be *listed,* which is defined in 3.2.3. Such components include, but are not limited to, pipe, alarm valves, hangers, and sprinklers. However, this rule has some exceptions. Steel pipe, for example, that meets specific industry standards is not required to be listed because it has a long-established track record of acceptable performance.

FAQ ▶
Is listed the same as classified?

One listing agency uses the designation *classified* to indicate that a specific product meets its testing and evaluation requirements. Materials with this designation meet the intent of *listed.* As indicated in A.3.2.3, evaluation of the product should address reliable operation for the intended function.

3.2.4 Shall. Indicates a mandatory requirement.

The term *shall,* which is defined in 3.2.4, indicates a requirement of this standard and mandates that a specific provision of NFPA 13 be followed. When the term *shall* is attached to a specific provision of the standard, compliance with that provision is not optional. For example, 6.2.5.1 states that sprinklers shall have their frame arms color coded a certain way. Color coding of the deflector instead of the frame arms is not permitted. The term *should,* which is the next term discussed (defined in 3.2.5), refers to a recommendation of this standard rather than a requirement.

Any allowance to modify a base requirement is specifically stated in subsequent paragraphs. With regard to color coding of sprinkler frame arms, NFPA 13 permits the deflector to be color coded under specific conditions as described in 6.2.5.2. This specific paragraph indicates that it is only under the specific conditions of the paragraph that sprinkler deflectors are permitted to be painted. Mandatory requirements of NFPA 13 are found in the main body of the standard—that is, Chapters 1 through 18.

3.2.5 Should. Indicates a recommendation or that which is advised but not required.

The term *should,* as defined in 3.2.5, indicates a recommendation, not a requirement, of this standard. A provision of this standard associated with the term *should* is advisory, and its use is limited to the annexes. The term *should* identifies a good idea or a better practice. If the recommendation is not followed, the sprinkler system is still expected to perform satisfactorily.

For example, A.8.16.4.2 recommends that the inspector's test connection be installed at the end of the hydraulically most remote branch line for a wet pipe sprinkler system. Placing the inspector's test connection at some other location will not negatively impact the performance of the system. An arrangement where the inspector's test is not at the end of the hydraulically most remote branch line is still in compliance with the standard.

Any section number preceded by a letter is an annex item. Terms such as *should* and *recommend* are prevalent in these sections.

3.2.6 Standard. A document, the main text of which contains only mandatory provisions using the word "shall" to indicate requirements and which is in a form generally suitable for mandatory reference by another standard or code or for adoption into law. Nonmandatory provisions shall be located in an appendix or annex, footnote, or fine-print note and are not to be considered a part of the requirements of a standard.

3.3 General Definitions

3.3.1 Automatic Sprinkler. A fire suppression or control device that operates automatically when its heat-activated element is heated to its thermal rating or above, allowing water to discharge over a specified area.

The term *automatic sprinkler,* as defined in 3.3.1, was added to provide a definition for this fundamental component. Additionally, this definition helps to clarify the difference between an automatic sprinkler and an open sprinkler (see 3.6.2.6).

3.3.2 Automotive Components on Portable Racks. Automotive components on portable racks are defined as the following: instrument panels, windshields, metal and plastic gasoline tanks, heater housings, door panels, interior trim, bumper facia, wiring harnesses, sheet metal, body components, engines, driveline components, steering mechanisms, auxiliary motors, and lighting—all with or without expanded plastic donnage. This definition does not include the storage of air bags, tires, and seats on portable racks.

The term *automotive components on portable racks,* as defined in 3.3.2, was added to properly address the new design arrangements (see 12.7.1) for protecting these components. This term only applies to the protection criteria outline in 12.7.1 for the protection of these components and storage arrangements.

3.3.3* Bathroom. Within a dwelling unit, any room or compartment containing a lavatory dedicated to personal hygiene, or a water closet, or bathing capability such as a shower or tub, or any combination of facilities thereof.

A.3.3.3 Bathroom. A room is still considered a bathroom if it contains just a toilet. Additionally, two bathrooms can be adjacent to each other and are considered separate rooms provided they are enclosed with the required level of construction.

The term *bathroom,* as defined in 3.3.3, was added to NFPA 13 to help identify and clarify the physical boundaries and characteristics of a bathroom. This definition provides clarification when applied to 8.14.8.1 for the omission of sprinklers in some bathrooms. Many modern dwelling units contain several small adjacent rooms that together provide the basic requirements for the term *bathroom.* These individual rooms or compartments should be treated as bathrooms as defined by 3.3.3.

 3.3.4 Ceiling Height. The distance between the floor and the underside of the ceiling above (or roof deck) within the area.

 3.3.5 Ceiling Types.

Definitions of ceiling types, as defined in 3.3.5.1 through 3.3.5.4, were added to NFPA 13 to clarify that where used throughout NFPA 13 these terms have specific meanings that impact the use of specific sprinklers. In many cases these terms provide limits on the applications of specific types of sprinklers and must be understood when choosing a specific sprinkler type.

 3.3.5.1 Flat Ceiling. A continuous ceiling in a single plane.

The term *flat ceiling,* as defined in 3.3.5.1, does not mean that ceiling is horizontal. In many instances and applications flat ceilings will have some type of slope.

 3.3.5.2 Horizontal Ceiling. A ceiling with a slope not exceeding 2 in 12.

A *horizontal ceiling,* as defined in 3.3.5.2, is limited to a ceiling plane where the slope of the ceiling plane does not exceed 2 units of rise for every 12 units of run. Exhibit 3.1 illustrates how to determine ceiling slope.

EXHIBIT 3.1 *Ceiling Slope.*

 3.3.5.3 Sloped Ceiling. A ceiling with a slope exceeding 2 in 12.

A *sloped ceiling,* as defined in 3.3.5.2, is limited to a ceiling plane where the slope of the ceiling plane exceeds 2 units of rise for every 12 units of run. Exhibit 3.1 illustrates how to determine ceiling slope.

 3.3.5.4 Smooth Ceiling. A continuous ceiling free from significant irregularities, lumps, or indentations.

The term *smooth ceiling,* as defined in 3.3.5.4, applies to the actual surface of the ceiling and is applicable to each type of ceiling defined in 3.3.5.1, 3.3.5.2, and 3.3.5.3.

3.3.6 Compartment. A space completely enclosed by walls and a ceiling. The compartment enclosure is permitted to have openings to an adjoining space if the openings have a minimum lintel depth of 8 in. (203 mm) from the ceiling.

The term *compartment,* as defined in 3.3.6, is primarily associated with the use of fast-response sprinklers. For a system using residential sprinklers in a compartment, 8.3.3.2 requires that all the sprinklers within the compartment be of the fast-response type. Additionally, the term *compartment* is applied to areas where light hazard systems are converted to use quick-response or residential sprinklers (see 8.3.3.4) or in areas where the area of operation reduction is taken in accordance with the requirements of 11.2.3.2.3.1.

Openings in a compartment cannot extend to the ceiling. A minimum 8-in. (203-mm) lintel ensures that heat from a fire collects at the ceiling in the room where the fire operates and results in faster operation of the sprinklers nearest to the fire.

3.3.7 Drop-Out Ceiling.
A suspended ceiling system, which is installed below the sprinklers, with listed translucent or opaque panels that are heat sensitive and fall from their setting when exposed to heat.

A *drop-out ceiling,* as defined in 3.3.7, allows the installation of a false ceiling beneath an existing sprinkler system. Drop-out ceilings provide an alternative to relocating sprinklers beneath a new ceiling.

Drop-out ceilings are evaluated to ensure that they do not contribute to fire growth and that they do not significantly delay the operation of the sprinkler system. Once installed, building owners must ensure that any ceiling panels replaced during the life of the system are of the same type originally installed.

3.3.8 Dwelling Unit.
One or more rooms arranged for the use of one or more individuals living together, as in a single housekeeping unit normally having cooking, living, sanitary, and sleeping facilities. For purposes of this standard, dwelling unit includes hotel rooms, dormitory rooms, apartments, condominiums, sleeping rooms in nursing homes, and similar living units.

Dwelling units, as defined in 3.3.8, are a series of connected rooms within a residential occupancy. Residential occupancies are identified in A.5.2 as light hazard. The residential classification encompasses all dwelling units included in the definition. The residential classification allows for the use of listed residential sprinklers. In addition, some spaces within a dwelling unit are identified by certain exceptions as not requiring sprinkler coverage. NFPA 13 precisely defines those spaces in those specific types of residential occupancies, such as hotels, in which sprinkler coverage can be omitted.

The definition of the term *dwelling unit* within NFPA 13 is broader than in other codes and standards, and this definition should only be used within the context of NFPA 13. See 8.14.8 for more information on dwelling units.

3.3.9 Fire Control.
Limiting the size of a fire by distribution of water so as to decrease the heat release rate and pre-wet adjacent combustibles, while controlling ceiling gas temperatures to avoid structural damage.

Since the inception of the first sprinkler system in the 1870s, the focus of most sprinkler systems has been to control a fire rather than to extinguish it. (The term *fire control* is defined in 3.3.9.) Although sprinkler systems have extinguished numerous fires, sprinkler systems generally are designed to limit the size of a developing fire and prevent it from growing and spreading beyond its general area of origin. In some cases fires are shielded from sprinkler system discharge, which makes complete extinguishment difficult.

A sprinkler system's ability to extinguish or suppress a fire has not been widely discussed until fairly recently because the interaction between sprinkler discharge and a fire had not been sufficiently understood. Phenomena associated with fire growth rates, mass loss of the burning fuel package, and the rate of heat release produced by a fire need to be considered. Only within the past two decades have research efforts provided a greater understanding of these phenomena. The result was the development of nontraditional sprinkler devices such as the large drop sprinkler and the early suppression fast-response (ESFR) sprinkler.

3.3.10 Fire Suppression. Sharply reducing the heat release rate of a fire and preventing its regrowth by means of direct and sufficient application of water through the fire plume to the burning fuel surface.

The concept of suppression was fully realized in sprinkler system technology in the spring of 1988 when the first ESFR sprinkler was introduced. The definition of *fire suppression,* as defined in 3.3.10, is qualitative in nature because it does not specify to what extent—for example, 10 percent or 50 percent—the rate of heat release must be reduced in order to achieve suppression.

A sprinkler can achieve a 100 percent reduction of the heat release rate—that is, complete extinguishment—of a free-burning cellulose material, such as wood, located in the center of a room, if the fire, especially the area near the ignition, is not shielded from sprinkler discharge. In contrast, if a plasticized product stored 10 ft (3 m) high is burning with the ignition source near the floor, and the fire is partially shielded from the sprinkler because the material is stored on wood pallets, then a less than 100 percent reduction in the heat release rate is more likely. The degree to which a fire is shielded from the sprinkler and its discharge is a key factor affecting a sprinkler system's ability to suppress a fire.

Exhibit 3.2 shows a simplified heat release rate curve and how it would be impacted by a sprinkler system designed for fire control versus one designed for fire suppression. Currently, the only device that can achieve fire suppression is the ESFR sprinkler.

3.3.11 High-Challenge Fire Hazard. A fire hazard typical of that produced by fires in combustible high-piled storage.

The occupancy hazard descriptions given in Sections 5.2, 5.3, and 5.4 are a means of categorizing the types of fires that can be protected by sprinkler systems installed in accordance with the occupancy hazard requirements of NFPA 13. To a large degree, occupancy hazard classification depends on the function of the space. Occupancy hazards have been the basis for the sprinkler design criteria found in NFPA 13 since 1947. Section 5.1 provides additional information on occupancy hazard classifications.

Since about 1947, the quantity and arrangement of materials stored in buildings have changed quite dramatically. For example, warehouses that accommodate 70-ft (21-m) high rack storage now exist, as do warehouse-type spaces used for bulk retail operations. These buildings can contain a wide range and a large quantity of commodities such as plastics, flam-

EXHIBIT 3.2 Simplified Fire Control/Fire Suppression Analogy.

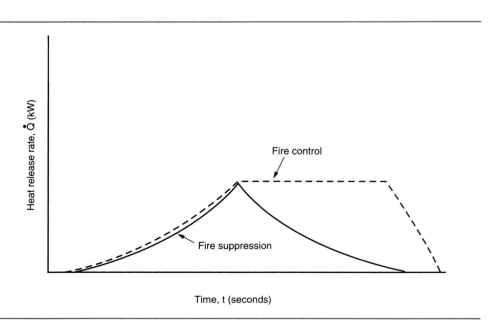

mable liquids, aerosols, and automobile tires. These kinds of facilities often create fire hazards that exceed the hazards characterized by the occupancy hazard descriptions.

Rather than categorizing the associated fire hazards in storage facilities according to the occupancy hazard approach, the hazards are categorized according to the types of commodities stored. See Chapter 5 and Chapter 12 for additional information. With regard to hazards presented by other commodities, processes, or occupancies, the appropriate sprinkler system information is now either cited or referenced in NFPA 13. For example, where aerosols are stored, 13.3.1 references NFPA 30B, *Code for the Manufacture and Storage of Aerosol Products*.

Unless specifically stated to the contrary, regulations governing specific installation requirements and information pertaining to hydraulic calculations are the same for systems protecting high-challenge fire hazards, as defined in 3.3.11, as they are for light, ordinary, and extra hazard occupancies. For example, rules for positioning sprinklers, techniques for hydraulic calculations, selection of appropriate pipe materials, and requirements for determining the coverage area for a sprinkler are the same.

The term *high challenge* implies that provisions in excess of those required for light, ordinary, and extra hazard occupancies are necessary to achieve fire control or fire suppression. An additional provision could include the need for higher sprinkler discharge densities, a larger design area, or the installation of additional devices or components.

3.3.12 High-Piled Storage. Solid-piled, palletized, rack storage, bin box, and shelf storage in excess of 12 ft (3.7 m) in height.

Storage heights exceeding 12 ft (3.7 m) are considered high piled by NFPA 13, as defined in 3.3.12. See Section 5.6 and Chapter 12 for the relevant sprinkler system criteria. Exhibit 3.3 illustrates an example of high-piled storage consisting of on-floor, palletized, and future rack storage.

EXHIBIT 3.3 Example of High-Pile Storage.

3.3.13 Hydraulically Designed System. A calculated sprinkler system in which pipe sizes are selected on a pressure loss basis to provide a prescribed water density, in gallons per minute per square foot (mm/min), or a prescribed minimum discharge pressure or flow per sprinkler, distributed with a reasonable degree of uniformity over a specified area.

A sprinkler system designed using hydraulic analysis is preferable over those systems designed using a pipe schedule approach. (*Hydraulically designed system* is defined in 3.3.13.) Hydraulic designs provide for a more accurate analysis of the piping system and allow for the selection of the most suitable pipe sizes. A hydraulic analysis also demonstrates if the water supply is adequate for the sprinkler system demand. The availability of an increasing number of product-specific sprinkler system components all but necessitates the hydraulic design of sprinkler systems.

A hydraulic analysis determines the sprinkler system's demand and the necessary water supply. An acceptable system is one in which the system's demand is less than the available water supply. The results of hydraulic analysis are often presented in graphical form. Graphical representation of the hydraulic analysis provides easier review and evaluation. The graph usually contains two curves—one that represents the system demand and the other that represents the available water supply. Figure A.14.3.2(d) illustrates this graphical representation. Where fire pumps or other equipment supplement the available water supply, their effect on the water supply must also be presented graphically, resulting in additional curves on the graph.

To hydraulically design a sprinkler system, the following information must be obtained:

1. The design density and the anticipated area of sprinkler system operation. For light, ordinary (Groups 1 and 2), and extra hazard (Groups 1 and 2) occupancies, this information can be obtained from Figure 11.2.3.1.5. For the protection of storage, the design density and anticipated area of operation are found in Chapter 12. For the types of hazards where the requirements have been extracted into NFPA 13, the design density and anticipated area of sprinkler system operation are found in Chapter 13 under the applicable hazard heading. In a few instances, such as for flammable and combustible liquids (NFPA 30, *Flammable and Combustible Liquids Code*) and aerosol products (NFPA 30B), references are made to specific NFPA standards for this information. Some insurance companies set their own requirements for sprinkler discharge densities and area of sprinkler system operation for the properties they insure. This topic is discussed in more detail in Chapters 11, 12, 13, and 14.

2. The characteristics of the available water supply. The types of acceptable water supplies (see also Chapter 15) are summarized as follows:

   a. Connection to a waterworks system. Information on the characteristics of the water supply can be obtained from the water department, fire department, or insurance companies or by conducting a waterflow test as described in A.15.2.1.

   b. Gravity tanks. The available pressure is determined by the tank's height. The friction loss through the water distribution system is based on the required flow and is calculated through hydraulic analysis. The determination of water supply characteristics for gravity tanks is not considered to be a complicated procedure due to the basic hydraulic principle of utilizing elevation to develop the required pressure. More information on gravity tanks can be found in NFPA 22, *Standard for Water Tanks for Private Fire Protection*.

   c. Fire pumps. A fire pump increases the pressure and flow from an available water supply such as a municipal water supply system. The effect of the fire pump on the available municipal water supply curve can be presented graphically, as shown in Exhibit 3.4.

   It is important to note that fire pumps do not create additional water capacity but rather boost the pressure and flow of an existing water supply. For example, if a fire pump is connected to a municipal water supply, the fire pump cannot create a larger quantity of water than what already exists in the municipal supply. Instead, the fire pump will boost the pressure from the municipal supply so that additional flow is available. The function of the fire pump is to raise the water supply curve in terms of pressure and flow so that it exceeds the sprinkler system demand (see Exhibit 3.4).

   In the case of a suction tank located on the ground, the fire pump provides all the necessary pressure and resultant waterflow. The water tank provides the necessary quantity of water. When pumps take suction from tanks, the elevation of the bottom of the tank with respect to the elevation of the fire pump needs to be considered since

FAQ ▶
How does a fire pump affect the water supply performance?

EXHIBIT 3.4 Fire Pump and Water Supply Performance.

the effects of gravity impact overall performance. Where pump suction is from water mains, the fire pump curve is added to the water supply curve for the water main. This addition can be done mathematically or graphically (see Exhibit 3.4). NFPA 20, *Standard for the Installation of Stationary Pumps for Fire Protection,* provides more information about fire pumps.

d. Pressure tanks. In this type of water supply, the designer defines the characteristics required, chooses a tank of proper volume, and establishes the air pressure from the procedure given in A.15.2.3.3. For more information see NFPA 22.

NFPA 13 does not require a safety factor to be applied to either the water supply or the system demand. A safety factor ensures that there be more water available than required. The use of a safety factor is considered good practice but is not required. Although NFPA 13 does not specifically require the application of safety factors in any part of a sprinkler system design or installation, safety factors are implicitly imbedded in many of the document's requirements. However, it is important to note that when comparing the system demand to the available water supply, the designer should determine the reasonable worst-case available supply.

Some designers, however, leave a certain margin between the water supply and the system demand to account for future use or deterioration of the water supply. For instance, the construction of additional buildings drawing water from a common municipal supply can negatively impact the available water supply. This situation could result in a sprinkler system deficiency because the water supply can no longer meet the system demand. Designers who do not account for future potential development by leaving a margin between the system demand and the water supply run an increased risk of having an inadequate sprinkler system in future years.

In addition, some areas of the United States develop critical water shortages during certain times of the year, causing some water purveyors to initiate water supply reduction programs. In other cases, available water distribution system pressures and flows are intentionally reduced by trimming pumps and valves, which results in lower static and residual pressures. A safety factor increases the likelihood that these systems will perform adequately if gradual reductions in the water supply occur during the life of the sprinkler system.

◄ **FAQ**
Does NFPA 13 require a safety factor for the water supply?

◄ **FAQ**
What other factors should be considered when evaluating a water supply?

An appropriate size for the safety factor takes into account the existing water supply and any anticipated future development of the site.

3.3.14 Limited-Combustible Material. A building construction material that does not comply with the definition of noncombustible material that, in the form in which it is used, has a potential heat value not exceeding 3500 Btu per lb (8141 kJ/kg) *(see NFPA 359, Standard Test Method for Potential Heat of Building Materials),* and that complies with either of the following, (a) or (b). Materials subject to increase in combustibility or flame spread rating beyond the limits herein established through the effects of age, moisture, or other atmospheric condition shall be considered combustible. (a) Materials having a structural base of noncombustible material, with a surfacing not exceeding a thickness of ⅛ in. (3.2 mm) that has a flame spread rating not greater than 50. (b) Materials, in the form and thickness used, other than as described in (a), having neither a flame spread rating greater than 25 nor evidence of continued progressive combustion and of such composition that surfaces that would be exposed by cutting through the material on any plane would have neither a flame spread rating greater than 25 nor evidence of continued progressive combustion.

The definition of *limited-combustible material* given in 3.3.14 is from NFPA 220, *Standard on Types of Building Construction,* and is used in portions of Chapter 8, specifically Section 8.14, where describing those areas in which sprinklers are not required. The presence of wall materials that are noncombustible or limited-combustible is necessary to meet many of the exceptions that allow for the omission of sprinklers in certain areas.

3.3.15* Miscellaneous Storage. Storage that does not exceed 12 ft (3.66 m) in height and is incidental to another occupancy use group. Such storage shall not constitute more than 10 percent of the building area or 4000 ft² (372 m²) of the sprinklered area, whichever is greater. Such storage shall not exceed 1000 ft² (93 m²) in one pile or area, and each such pile or area shall be separated from other storage areas by at least 25 ft (7.62 m).

A.3.3.15 Miscellaneous Storage. The sprinkler system design criteria for miscellaneous storage at heights below 12 ft (3.7 m) is covered by this standard in Chapter 12. Chapter 12 describes design criteria and Section 8.2 describes installation requirements (area limits). These requirements apply to all storage of 12 ft (3.7 m) or less in height.

The miscellaneous storage concept applies to a building in which storage constitutes only a part of the building's use, such as the back room of a mercantile facility. Limitations are imposed on the amount and arrangement of storage that is permitted. The requirements for the protection of miscellaneous storage, as defined in 3.3.15, are contained in 12.1.10.

The concept of miscellaneous storage was developed to address those situations where only a relatively small portion of a building is used for storage and where such storage does not exceed 12 ft (3.7 m) in height. One example is a manufacturing operation that uses a portion of its facility to store small amounts of finished product and raw materials. As with most facilities, the fire hazard associated with the storage is likely to differ from that of the manufacturing operation. Prior editions of NFPA 13 only addressed storage if it was considered miscellaneous. However, this edition of NFPA 13 treats storage under 12 ft (3.7 m) in height and miscellaneous storage virtually the same, both of which are addressed in Chapter 12, subsection 12.1.10.

The 10 percent limit is taken from certain accessory use definitions as found in the model building codes. The 4000-ft² (372-m²) limit is derived by taking 10 percent of the maximum allowable area of coverage for a sprinkler system riser protecting high-piled storage. (See Section 8.2 for system protection area limitations.)

3.3.16 Noncombustible Material. A material that, in the form in which it is used and under the conditions anticipated, will not ignite, burn, support combustion, or release flammable vapors when subjected to fire or heat. Materials that are reported as passing ASTM E 136,

Standard Test Method for Behavior of Materials in a Vertical Tube Furnace at 750°C, shall be considered noncombustible materials.

The definition of *noncombustible material,* as given in 3.3.16, is from NFPA 220. The use of noncombustible or limited-combustible materials is necessary to meet many of the requirements that allow for the omission of sprinklers in certain areas—for example 8.14.1.2, Concealed Spaces Not Requiring Sprinkler Protection. Construction materials that fall under this category include certain types of acoustical ceiling tiles and insulation materials.

3.3.17 Pipe Schedule System. A sprinkler system in which the pipe sizing is selected from a schedule that is determined by the occupancy classification and in which a given number of sprinklers are allowed to be supplied from specific sizes of pipe.

A pipe schedule system, as defined in 3.3.17, describes one of the design approaches permitted by Chapter 11 and is the oldest design approach. A version of it appeared in the first edition of NFPA 13 in 1896. Although still permitted by the standard under limited conditions, pipe schedule systems are much less common than they used to be.

Hydraulically designed systems, which were introduced in 1969, have become more popular because they allow for a more thorough and accurate analysis of the system, which typically leads to more effective and cost-efficient designs. Computer technology and the availability of numerous sprinkler hydraulic programs have also contributed to the decline of pipe schedule systems.

A pipe schedule design is often referred to as a cookbook design approach because the pipe size is predetermined based on the number of sprinklers being supplied.

3.3.18* Reinforced Plastic Pallet. A plastic pallet incorporating a secondary reinforcing material (such as steel or fiberglass) within the pallet.

A.3.3.18 Reinforced Plastic Pallet. See Figure A.3.3.18(a) and Figure A.3.3.18(b).

Exhibits 3.5 and 3.6 show examples of reinforced and non-reinforced plastic pallets. The pallets shown in the exhibits are four-way pallets.

3.3.19 Shop-Welded. As used in this standard, *shop* in the term *shop-welded* means either (1) a sprinkler contractor's or fabricator's premise or (2) an area specifically designed or authorized for welding, such as a detached outside location, maintenance shop, or other area (either temporary or permanent) of noncombustible or fire-resistive construction free of combustible and flammable contents and suitably segregated from adjacent areas.

Paragraph 6.5.2.2 requires sprinkler system piping to be shop-welded, as defined in 3.3.19. However, under carefully controlled circumstances, as permitted by NFPA 13, the pipe can be welded in place. The definition of *shop-welded* establishes the necessary criteria for the shop-welding of pipe.

3.3.20 Small Rooms. A room of light hazard occupancy classification having unobstructed construction and floor areas not exceeding 800 ft^2 (74.3 m^2) that are enclosed by walls and a ceiling. Openings to the adjoining space are permitted if the minimum lintel depth is 8 in. (203 mm) from the ceiling.

It is important to note that the design allowances in 8.6.3.2.4 are only permitted to be utilized in light hazard occupancies as indicated in the definition of the term small room, which is given in 3.3.20.

Fires in small rooms of a light hazard occupancy present a lesser challenge to the sprinkler system. As a result, sprinklers installed in rooms that meet the criteria of small rooms are given an exception to the spacing rules of 8.6.3.2.4. For applications of small room provisions, see Figure A.8.6.3.2.4(a) through Figure A.8.6.3.2.4(d).

◄ FAQ
In what occupancies can the design allowances for small rooms be utilized?

Reinforcements

FIGURE A.3.3.18(a) Cut-Away Reinforced Plastic Pallet.

Reinforcements

FIGURE A.3.3.18(b) Assembled Reinforced Plastic Pallet.

FAQ ▶
Do openings from small rooms require doors in order for the room to be classified as a small room?

Small room openings do not need to be protected with doors if the openings are equipped with lintels that have a minimum depth of 8 in. (203 mm). A lintel with a depth of at least 8 in. (203 mm) ensures adequate collection of the heat from a fire at the ceiling of the room of fire origin and promotes faster operation of the sprinklers nearest to the fire.

3.3.21* Sprinkler System. For fire protection purposes, an integrated system of underground and overhead piping designed in accordance with fire protection engineering standards. The installation includes one or more automatic water supplies. The portion of the sprinkler system aboveground is a network of specially sized or hydraulically designed piping installed in a building, structure, or area, generally overhead, and to which sprinklers are attached in a systematic pattern. The valve controlling each system riser is located in the system riser or its supply piping. Each sprinkler system riser includes a device for actuating an alarm when the system is in operation. The system is usually activated by heat from a fire and discharges water over the fire area.

  A.3.3.21 Sprinkler System. A sprinkler system is considered to have a single system riser control valve. The design and installation of water supply facilities such as gravity tanks, fire pumps, reservoirs, or pressure tanks are covered by NFPA 20, *Standard for the Installation of Stationary Pumps for Fire Protection,* and NFPA 22, *Standard for Water Tanks for Private Fire Protection.*

An individual sprinkler system is denoted by the presence of an alarm check valve or a waterflow device and a control valve. It is important to note that the sprinkler system definition given in 3.3.21 includes water supplies and underground piping. Although design and installation requirements for tanks and pumps are covered by other standards, these components are used in connection with sprinkler piping and are considered an integral part of the sprinkler system. Tanks and pumps are critical to successful sprinkler system performance and must be given serious consideration.

Sprinkler systems can be designed according to hydraulic calculation techniques or according to predetermined pipe sizes conforming to pipe schedules (see Chapter 14). However, NFPA 13 severely restricts the use of pipe schedule systems.

3.3.22 System Working Pressure. The maximum anticipated static (nonflowing) or flowing pressure applied to sprinkler system components exclusive of surge pressures.

The term *system working pressure,* as defined in 3.3.22, is intended to apply to the pressure in the sprinkler system when installed. The term is not intended to be used as criteria for evaluating individual system components.

3.3.23 Thermal Barrier. A material that will limit the average temperature rise of the unexposed surface to not more than 250°F (121°C) after 15 minutes of fire exposure, which complies with the standard time-temperature curve of NFPA 251, *Standard Methods of Tests of Fire Endurance of Building Construction and Materials.*

The term *thermal barrier,* as defined in 3.3.23, is used in 8.14.8.1.1 to establish a condition necessary to omit sprinklers from certain types of dwelling unit bathrooms.

3.4 Sprinkler System Type Definitions

3.4.1 Antifreeze Sprinkler System. A wet pipe sprinkler system employing automatic sprinklers that are attached to a piping system that contains an antifreeze solution and that are connected to a water supply. The antifreeze solution is discharged, followed by water, immediately upon operation of sprinklers opened by heat from a fire.

An antifreeze sprinkler system, as defined in 3.4.1, is often considered auxiliary to a wet pipe system and is installed on the system side of the control valve of a wet pipe system. The antifreeze sprinkler system is considered part of a wet pipe system, and the two systems as a whole must satisfy all appropriate rules, such as those pertaining to protection area limitations and hydraulic calculations, for the wet pipe system. In addition, all requirements for the antifreeze system must also be satisfied. Each auxiliary antifreeze system requires its own separate control valve, drains, and so forth. Alarms on the wet pipe system might not be adequate for the auxiliary system, necessitating additional alarms. The use of antifreeze systems will usually be regulated by the municipal water department. See Section 7.5 for specific requirements pertaining to antifreeze systems.

3.4.2 Circulating Closed-Loop Sprinkler System. A wet pipe sprinkler system having non–fire protection connections to automatic sprinkler systems in a closed-loop piping arrangement for the purpose of utilizing sprinkler piping to conduct water for heating or cooling, where water is not removed or used from the system but only circulated through the piping system.

The possibility of using sprinkler system piping for other building functions has been contemplated for quite some time. The definition of *circulating closed-loop sprinkler system,* given in 3.4.2, allows sprinkler piping to be used for functions other than fire protection, such as the heating and air-conditioning of a building. A basic criterion used in the development of this definition was that the auxiliary functions be added in such a manner and with sufficient controls to ensure that there would be no reduction in overall fire protection. It was determined that this criterion could be controlled more adequately with totally closed systems. The inherent characteristics of a closed system provide a means of ensuring the necessary system performance. See 7.6.1 for specific requirements pertaining to circulating closed-loop systems. Also see Figure A.14.1.5(a) and Figure A.14.1.5(b).

Closed-loop systems possess a self-supervisory feature. System problems often become obvious to building occupants when, for example, building temperatures become too hot or too cold, and building occupants become uncomfortable and complain. This situation would typically result in the dispatch of maintenance personnel to make repairs while ensuring that the sprinkler system remained in service.

Closed-loop systems are often heat pump systems in which water is circulated through heating and air-conditioning equipment, using sprinkler pipe as the primary means of circulating water. Heat is either added to or removed from the circulating water as dictated by requirements of the system. Water, on the other hand, is neither added to nor removed from the piping system.

3.4.3 Combined Dry Pipe-Preaction Sprinkler System. A sprinkler system employing automatic sprinklers attached to a piping system containing air under pressure with a supplemental detection system installed in the same areas as the sprinklers. Operation of the detection system actuates tripping devices that open dry pipe valves simultaneously and without loss of air pressure in the system. Operation of the detection system also opens listed air exhaust valves at the end of the feed main, which usually precedes the opening of sprinklers. The detection system also serves as an automatic fire alarm system.

Combined dry pipe-preaction sprinkler systems, defined in 3.4.3 (see Section 7.4), are employed primarily where more than one dry pipe system is required due to the size of the space, and where it is not possible to install supply piping to each dry pipe valve through a heated or protected space. Primary examples where combined dry pipe-preaction systems are used include piers, wharves, and very large cold storage warehouses. These systems are special application systems and should be used as such. Many cold storage rooms can be adequately protected with a conventional dry pipe system or a double interlock preaction system.

3.4.4 Deluge Sprinkler System. A sprinkler system employing open sprinklers that are attached to a piping system that is connected to a water supply through a valve that is opened by the operation of a detection system installed in the same areas as the sprinklers. When this valve opens, water flows into the piping system and discharges from all sprinklers attached thereto.

A deluge system's mode of activation is similar to that for a preaction system (*deluge sprinkler system* is defined in 3.4.4). With the exception of the non-interlock preaction system, the activation of these two types of systems depends on the operation of a supplemental detection system. The difference between the two types of systems is that preaction systems employ automatic sprinklers that respond to heat, and deluge systems use open sprinklers that have no fusible element. Operation of the detection system in a preaction system fills the system piping with water once certain interlocks are triggered. Water is not discharged from the system until a sprinkler operates. For a deluge system, operation of the detection system results in flow from all system sprinklers. Deluge systems are normally used for high-hazard areas requiring an immediate application of water over the entire hazard. An aircraft hangar is an example of a facility that is likely to use deluge systems. Exhibit 3.7 illustrates an example of a deluge system using a supplemental electronic heat or smoke detection system.

3.4.5 Dry Pipe Sprinkler System. A sprinkler system employing automatic sprinklers that are attached to a piping system containing air or nitrogen under pressure, the release of which (as from the opening of a sprinkler) permits the water pressure to open a valve known as a dry pipe valve, and the water then flows into the piping system and out the opened sprinklers.

FAQ ▶
Where are dry pipe sprinkler systems required?

Dry pipe sprinkler systems, defined in 3.4.5, should only be installed where pipe is subject to freezing. Paragraph 8.15.3.1.1 requires dry pipe systems to be installed where the building environment cannot be maintained at or above 40°F (4°C).

Dry pipe systems should not be used to reduce water damage from pipe breakage or leakage, since they operate too quickly to be of value for this purpose. A single or double interlock preaction system should be used for this purpose.

EXHIBIT 3.7 *Deluge System.*

A dry pipe system is typically filled with compressed air or nitrogen and is activated when a drop in pressure occurs. A drop in pressure can be caused by the activation of a single sprinkler or by damage to the sprinkler system piping. A drop in pressure causes the dry pipe valve to open and allows water to flow through the system. Exhibit 3.8 illustrates an example of a dry pipe system.

EXHIBIT 3.8 *Dry Pipe System. (Courtesy of Viking Corporation)*

1 Main drain piping
2 Ball drip
3 Fire department connection (FDC)
4 Check valve for FDC
5 Water motor alarm drain
6 Main drain valve
7 Dry pipe valve
8 Priming water fill cup
9 Water motor alarm
10 Air pressure maintenance device
11 Accelerator
12 Air supply
13 Pressure switch (hidden)
14 Heated room or enclosure
15 OS&Y valve
16 System check valve
17 Upright sprinkler
18 Inspector's test valve
19 Inspectors's test connection
20 Thrust block

3.4.6* Gridded Sprinkler System. A sprinkler system in which parallel cross mains are connected by multiple branch lines. An operating sprinkler will receive water from both ends of its branch line while other branch lines help transfer water between cross mains.

 A.3.4.6 Gridded Sprinkler System. See Figure A.3.4.6.

Grid-type systems (see Figure A.3.4.6) are preferred by some designers because of their attractive hydraulic characteristics. Since a number of flow paths to the sprinklers are available, pressure drops through the system piping are lower in a gridded system compared to other system configurations. Due to the very complex nature of the hydraulic calculations involved, the use of computer hydraulic programs is almost always necessary in evaluating the piping grid and determining the pressure requirements of the system.

Although the gridded system possesses highly advantageous hydraulic characteristics, certain limitations and design conditions are associated with its use.

For example, gridded systems are not permitted for dry pipe systems and certain preaction systems because excessive amounts of air can remain trapped in the system piping, which significantly delays water from reaching the operating sprinklers (see 7.2.3.5 and 7.3.2.5).

Gridded systems must be "peaked" to verify that the hydraulically most demanding combination of sprinklers was selected (see 14.4.4.2).

FAQ ▶
Why is a relief valve required on a gridded sprinkler system?

Gridded systems must be equipped with a relief valve to remove trapped air from the piping. In addition to removing trapped air, the relief valve allows for pressure fluctuations associated with the thermal expansion of the water within the piping. In a tree system, the air trapped within the branch lines absorbs these increases in pressure. However, in a gridded system there is no such room for expansion due to water filling all sections of pipe. (See 7.1.2.)

3.4.7* Looped Sprinkler System. A sprinkler system in which multiple cross mains are tied together so as to provide more than one path for water to flow to an operating sprinkler and branch lines are not tied together.

 A.3.4.7 Looped Sprinkler System. See Figure A.3.4.7.

Looped sprinkler systems, as defined in 3.4.7, possess better hydraulic characteristics than do tree systems. Tree systems are the most basic of sprinkler pipe layout where the cross mains and the branch lines are not tied together, providing only one path for the water to flow to an operating sprinkler. While looped systems hydraulically perform better than tree systems, their hydraulic characteristics are not as good as those of a gridded system. The hydraulic calculations associated with a looped system are not as tedious and complicated as those for a

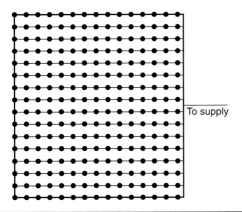

FIGURE A.3.4.6 Gridded System.

gridded system. The calculations for a looped system can be conducted without the use of a computer program, although the hand calculation process can be quite laborious. Additionally, looped systems do not have the same limitations and design considerations as do gridded systems.

3.4.8* Preaction Sprinkler System.
A sprinkler system employing automatic sprinklers that are attached to a piping system that contains air that might or might not be under pressure, with a supplemental detection system installed in the same areas as the sprinklers.

A.3.4.8 Preaction Sprinkler System. The actuating means of the valve are described in 7.3.2.1. Actuation of the detection system and sprinklers in the case of double-interlocked systems opens a valve that permits water to flow into the sprinkler piping system and to be discharged from any sprinklers that are open.

The three types of preaction systems are indicated in 7.3.2.1. (Preaction sprinkler system is defined in 3.4.8.) The user should be aware that the double interlock version is subject to the same time delay problems as a dry pipe system and, likewise, is subject to comparable dry pipe system limitations.

Double interlock reaction systems are normally used to protect properties where accidental water discharge is a significant concern. Even though accidental or premature discharge of sprinkler systems is extremely rare, some property owners still prefer these systems in electronic equipment areas.

Exhibit 3.9 shows an example of a double interlock preaction system with electric activation. Preaction systems can also be activated through pneumatic means—that is, a dry pilot sprinkler line. Section 7.3 addresses the requirements for preaction systems.

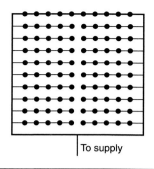

To supply

FIGURE A.3.4.7 Looped System.

◀ **FAQ**
Where are double interlock preaction systems normally used?

1 System control valve
2 Deluge valve
3 Basic trim kit (deluge valve)
4 Check valve (preaction)
5 Waterflow pressure switch
6 Mechanical alarm
7 Releasing control panel (optional)
8 Alarm annunciator (optional)
9 Trouble annunciator (optional)
10 Manual emergency station (optional)
11 Detector (optional)
12 Automatic sprinkler
13 Air compressor
14 Accelerator (optional)
15 Pressure maintenance device
16 Pressure switch

EXHIBIT 3.9 Example of a Preaction System. (Courtesy of The Reliable Automatic Sprinkler Co., Inc.)

3.4.9 Wet Pipe Sprinkler System. A sprinkler system employing automatic sprinklers attached to a piping system containing water and connected to a water supply so that water discharges immediately from sprinklers opened by heat from a fire.

Wet pipe sprinkler systems, defined in 3.4.9, are the simplest and most reliable of all sprinkler systems. Operation of one sprinkler activates a wet pipe system. It is important to note that only those sprinklers activated by the heat from fire discharge water. Exhibit 3.10 illustrates an example of a wet pipe system using an alarm check valve. Section 7.1 addresses requirements for wet pipe systems.

All other types of systems addressed by NFPA 13 require the use of additional equipment such as dry pipe valves, preaction valves, or supplemental detectors for successful operation. As the number of events needed for system activation increases—that is, the activation of both sprinklers and heat detectors or the use of more elaborate devices such as dry pipe valves— the greater the need for a comprehensive inspection, testing, and maintenance program. In other words, the more complicated a system, the greater the likelihood that something can go wrong and the greater the effort needed to keep the system in proper working order.

Wet pipe systems should always be the first type of system considered. Only where a wet pipe system could not properly protect a space should another type of system be contemplated. For example, a wet pipe system is not a good candidate for a cold storage room because the cold temperature is likely to cause the water in the sprinkler piping to freeze, resulting in damage to the piping and an impairment of the sprinkler system. A dry pipe or an antifreeze system is a better choice for the protection of cold storage rooms.

EXHIBIT 3.10 Wet Pipe Sprinkler Riser with Alarm Check Valve.

1 Alarm valve trim	8 Check valve
2 Automatic drip valve	9 Water motor alarm
3 Fire department connection	10 Alarm check valve
4 Retard chamber	11 Main drain valve
5 Alarm line strainer	12 Alarm test shut-off valve
6 Alarm pressure switch	13 Main drain piping
7 System side water gauge	14 Underground supply

3.5* System Component Definitions

A.3.5 See Figure A.3.5.

A System riser D Riser nipple
B Feed main   E Branch lines
C Cross main   F Underground
                 supply

FIGURE A.3.5 *Building Elevation Showing Parts of Sprinkler Piping System.*

Section 3.5 contains system component definitions. Exhibit 3.11 shows a complete system with components identified.

EXHIBIT 3.11 Complete System. (Adapted from FM Global Systems)

3.5.1 Branch Lines. The pipes in which the sprinklers are placed, either directly or through risers.

Branch lines, as defined in 3.5.1 and as identified in Exhibit 3.11, are usually the smallest diameter pipes installed on a system and normally have sprinklers attached to them.

3.5.2 Cross Mains.   The pipes supplying the branch lines, either directly or through risers.

3.5.3 Feed Mains.   The pipes supplying cross mains, either directly or through risers.

3.5.4 Flexible Listed Pipe Coupling.   A listed coupling or fitting that allows axial displacement, rotation, and at least 1 degree of angular movement of the pipe without inducing harm on the pipe. For pipe diameters of 8 in. (203.2 mm) and larger, the angular movement shall be permitted to be less than 1 degree but not less than 0.5 degree.

Flexible listed pipe coupling, as defined in 3.5.4, is specified for use by 9.3.2 to maintain system integrity during seismic events. However, its use for other applications requiring flexibility, such as some industrial and manufacturing processes, is also possible. Listed flexible couplings will permit differential movement of the pipe, thereby reducing the potential for pipe breakage.

3.5.5 Risers.   The vertical supply pipes in a sprinkler system.

3.5.6 Sprig-up.   A line that rises vertically and supplies a single sprinkler.

3.5.7 Supervisory Device.   A device arranged to supervise the operative condition of automatic sprinkler systems.

NFPA 13 requires that certain elements and conditions of the sprinkler system be supervised to decrease the likelihood of a system impairment. (*Supervisory device* is defined in 3.5.7.) For example, a planned or inadvertent closure of one of the valves that controls water supply to the sprinkler system would render the system inoperative. Therefore, these valves must be supervised.

      Although several means of valve supervision are permitted by NFPA 13, a more sophisticated means includes the use of an electronically monitored tamper switch that sounds an alarm at a constantly attended location. The installation of this type of device is addressed by *NFPA 72*®, *National Fire Alarm Code*®. Other system conditions that are required to be supervised include the air pressure in a dry pipe or preaction system and the water temperature in a circulating closed-loop system.

3.5.8 System Riser.   The aboveground horizontal or vertical pipe between the water supply and the mains (cross or feed) that contains a control valve (either directly or within its supply pipe) and a waterflow alarm device.

A system riser, defined in 3.5.8, is more than just a subset of the term *riser,* which is broadly defined as any vertical piping within the sprinkler system.

FAQ ▶
Must a system riser be vertical to be defined as a system riser?

As indicated by the definition, a system riser can be any aboveground pipe in a vertical or horizontal orientation installed between the water supply and the system mains that contains specific devices.

3.6 Sprinkler Definitions

Section 3.6 places sprinkler definitions into one of the following categories:

1. Characteristics that define a sprinkler's ability to control or suppress a fire
2. Thermal response

3. Spray distribution
4. Coverage area
5. Occupancy use or limitations
6. Orientation

As little as 25 years ago, most sprinklers were of the upright, pendent, or sidewall type and were classified as having either frangible bulb or solder link operating mechanisms. Since then, many advances have been made with regard to our scientific understanding of fire, sprinklers, and their interaction.

These technological advances are responsible for the production of an increasingly large variety of sprinkler types and styles. Sprinklers are now manufactured and designed to allow systems to perform specific functions. Section 3.6 describes the features that differentiate sprinklers from one another.

3.6.1* General. The following are characteristics of a sprinkler that define its ability to control or extinguish a fire. (a) Thermal sensitivity. A measure of the rapidity with which the thermal element operates as installed in a specific sprinkler or sprinkler assembly. One measure of thermal sensitivity is the response time index (RTI) as measured under standardized test conditions. (1) Sprinklers defined as fast response have a thermal element with an RTI of 50 (meters-seconds)$^{1/2}$ or less. (2) Sprinklers defined as standard response have a thermal element with an RTI of 80 (meters-seconds)$^{1/2}$ or more. (b) Temperature rating. (c) Orifice size *(see Chapter 6).* (d) Installation orientation *(see 3.6.3).* (e) Water distribution characteristics (i.e., application rate, wall wetting). (f) Special service conditions *(see 3.6.4).*

A.3.6.1 General. The response time index (RTI) is a measure of the sensitivity of the sprinkler's thermal element as installed in a specific sprinkler. It is usually determined by plunging a sprinkler into a heated laminar airflow within a test oven. The plunge test is not currently applicable to certain sprinklers.

The RTI is calculated using the following:

(1) The operating time of the sprinkler
(2) The operating temperature of the sprinkler's heat-responsive element (as determined in a bath test)
(3) The air temperature of the test oven
(4) The air velocity of the test oven
(5) The sprinkler's conductivity *(c)* factor, which is the measure of conductance between the sprinkler's heat-responsive element and the sprinkler oven mount

Other factors affecting response include the temperature rating, sprinkler position, fire exposure, and radiation.

ISO standard 6182-1 currently recognizes the RTI range of greater than 50 (meters-seconds)$^{1/2}$ and less than 80 (meters-seconds)$^{1/2}$ as special response. Such sprinklers can be recognized as special sprinklers under 8.4.9.1.

It should be recognized that the term *fast response* (like the term *quick response* used to define a particular type of sprinkler) refers to the thermal sensitivity within the operating element of a sprinkler, not the time of operation in a particular installation. There are many other factors, such as ceiling height, spacing, ambient room temperature, and distance below ceiling, that affect the time of response of sprinklers. In most fire scenarios, sprinkler activation times will be shortest where the thermal elements are located 1 in. (25.4 mm) to 3 in. (76.2 mm) below the ceiling. A fast response sprinkler is expected to operate quicker than a standard response sprinkler in the same installation orientation. For modeling purposes, concealed sprinklers can be considered equivalent to pendent sprinklers having a similar thermal response sensitivity installed 12 in. (305 mm) below smooth unobstructed ceilings, and recessed sprinklers can be considered equivalent to pendent sprinklers having a similar thermal response sensitivity installed 8 in. (203 mm) below smooth unobstructed ceilings.

The key characteristics that affect a sprinkler's ability to control or suppress a fire are specifically addressed by this standard. These characteristics, as stated in 3.6.1, include temperature rating, orifice size, installation orientation, water distribution patterns, hydraulic criteria, wall-wetting characteristics, and thermal sensitivity.

Because sprinkler manufacturers and researchers investigated the effect of modifying certain sprinkler characteristics, sprinklers with faster operating times, broader spray patterns, and deeper water penetration capabilities are becoming more widely available.

With regard to item (a) of 3.6.1, thermal sensitivity is considered a measure of the rapidity with which the sprinkler's thermal element operates when mounted within the sprinkler frame. A common measure of thermal sensitivity is the response time index (RTI). This value is usually determined by plunging a sprinkler into a heated laminar (nonturbulent) airflow within a test oven. However, this test is not readily applicable to certain sprinklers such as recessed or concealed sprinklers.

As indicated in A.3.6.1, RTI is not necessarily a measure of the responsiveness of a given sprinkler when installed in the field. The RTI of a sprinkler is a function of the convective heat transfer coefficient, specific heat of the operating element, mass of the operating element, and the surface area of the operating element. Other factors that can affect a sprinkler's thermal sensitivity in the field include temperature rating, position from the ceiling, attachment to piping, and anticipated fire exposure. However, a fast-response sprinkler can be expected to operate faster than a standard response sprinkler given the same conditions. RTI is used to comparatively describe the sensitivity of the sprinkler link for any given sprinkler.

NFPA 13 addresses the concept of thermal sensitivity by classifying sprinklers as either fast response or standard response. Fast-response sprinklers, such as the one shown in Exhibit 3.12, include those sprinklers that have a thermal element with an RTI of 50 (meters-seconds)$^{1/2}$ [90 (ft-sec)$^{1/2}$] or less. Standard response sprinklers (see Exhibit 3.12) include those sprinklers that have a thermal element with an RTI of 80 (meters-seconds)$^{1/2}$ [145 (ft-sec)$^{1/2}$] or more.

FAQ ▶

What classification is given to sprinklers with RTIs of greater than 50 (meters-seconds)$^{1/2}$ [90 (ft-sec)$^{1/2}$] but less than 80 (meters-seconds)$^{1/2}$ [145 (ft-sec)$^{1/2}$]?

Sprinklers having operating elements with an RTI of greater than 50 (meters-seconds)$^{1/2}$ [90 (ft-sec)$^{1/2}$] but less than 80 (meters-seconds)$^{1/2}$ [145 (ft-sec)$^{1/2}$] are considered special sprinklers. This RTI classification is consistent with that of the International Standards Organization (ISO), which considers these sprinklers as "special response." The gap between these two RTI values is intentional in order to provide a clear distinction between fast-response and standard-response sprinklers.

EXHIBIT 3.12 Grinnell Model A Standard-Response Spray Sprinkler (left) and Viking Model A Quick-Response Standard Spray Sprinkler (right). (Courtesy of TYCO and Viking)

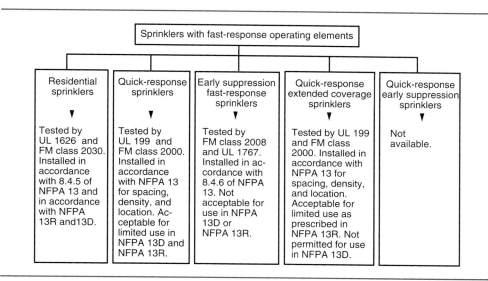

EXHIBIT 3.13 *Comparison of Sprinklers with Fast-Response Operating Elements.*

The definitions of several sprinkler types such as quick response, residential, and early suppression fast response clearly reflect the emphasis on a sprinkler's thermal sensitivity. Exhibit 3.13 compares the various types of fast-response sprinklers.

With regard to item (c) of 3.6.1, the size of a sprinkler's orifice influences certain performance features such as the amount of water discharging from the sprinkler and the size of the water droplets. The size and shape of the orifice are indicated through the sprinkler's K-factor. A provision in Chapter 6 provides a means of control with respect to the manufacture and listing of sprinklers with K-factors different from the ones currently identified in the standard. See 6.2.3.1 and Table 6.2.3.1 for sprinkler discharge characteristics.

In addition, NFPA 13 requires that large-drop and ESFR sprinklers have a K-factor of at least 11.2. This limitation establishes a level of consistency with regard to these sprinkler's operational features and functional objectives.

3.6.2 Sprinkler Types. The following sprinklers are defined according to design and performance characteristics.

3.6.2.1* Early Suppression Fast-Response (ESFR) Sprinkler. A type of fast-response sprinkler that meets the criteria of 3.6.1(a)(1) and is listed for its capability to provide fire suppression of specific high-challenge fire hazards.

A.3.6.2.1 Early Suppression Fast-Response (ESFR) Sprinkler. It is important to realize that the effectiveness of these highly tested and engineered sprinklers depends on the combination of fast response and the quality and uniformity of the sprinkler discharge. It should also be realized that ESFR sprinklers cannot be relied upon to provide fire control, let alone suppression, if they are used outside the guidelines specified in Chapter 12.

ESFR sprinklers, defined in 3.6.2.1, evolved by examining how the effects of sprinkler sensitivity and water distribution characteristics could be combined to achieve early fire suppression. The concept is that if a sufficient amount of water can be discharged in the early phases of a fire and penetrate the developing fire plume, then fire suppression can be achieved. Once the fire plume reaches a significant size, the likelihood of suppression is greatly reduced.

A fast and hot fire plume can frustrate suppression efforts in two ways. A strong updraft is characteristic of a severe fire plume, which decreases the amount of water that can reach the burning area. Water droplets traveling through this fire plume are either vaporized before they reach the fire or blown away from the fire. A severe fire plume can also cause sprinklers distant from the fire area to open. These excessive sprinkler actuators result in a decreased amount of water being delivered from the sprinklers nearest to the fire. Since the discharge from sprinklers operating at a distance from the fire source cannot reach the fire or prewet the area immediately around it, these sprinklers do not help to achieve fire suppression.

Because other types of sprinklers operate more slowly and do not have the same water distribution characteristics as ESFR sprinklers, sprinklers such as spray sprinklers operate on the concept of fire control. With spray sprinklers, a more significant fire plume develops prior to the operation of the first sprinkler. The intensity of the fire can also remain at an elevated state until fire control is achieved. The concept of fire control is to provide sufficient sprinkler discharge so that the fire does not spread beyond the sprinkler system design area. Spray sprinklers are expected to prevent the fire from spreading by slowly reducing its intensity and by sufficiently prewetting the surrounding combustibles so they do not ignite. Concurrently, the sprinkler discharge is expected to absorb heat and cool the surrounding space, including the area containing structural members, thus preventing building collapse.

ESFR sprinklers, on the other hand, operate earlier in the fire than standard sprinklers and provide adequate discharge to suppress the fire before a severe fire plume develops. In principle, early suppression is determined by the following three factors:

1. Thermal sensitivity
2. Required delivered density (RDD)
3. Actual delivered density (ADD)

An ESFR sprinkler must possess specific properties related to these three factors, and systems that have not been designed to address all three of these factors cannot be relied on to achieve early fire suppression. All three of these factors can be independently measured.

FAQ ▶
What is thermal sensitivity and RTI?

Thermal sensitivity is a measurable expression of the sensitivity or responsiveness of a sprinkler's operating element when exposed to fire conditions. The most common measure of thermal sensitivity is the RTI, as indicated in the commentary to A.3.6.1. The more responsive the element is to the effects of a fire, the lower the RTI value. The RTI of a sprinkler generally varies little with the sprinkler's temperature rating. (See A.3.6.1.)

A sprinkler's response time for a given fire situation is a function of the thermal sensitivity of its operating element, its temperature rating, and its distance relative to the fire. Because of the thermal lag associated with the mass of the operating element, however, the gas temperature near the sprinkler can reach a value that is higher than the temperature rating of the sprinkler prior to the activation of the sprinkler. This can negatively affect the ability of a sprinkler with a high RTI to achieve early fire suppression, because the fire has had a chance to develop a significant fire plume before the activation of the first sprinkler.

Smaller fires are generally easier to suppress than larger ones. The sooner the sprinkler operates, the less the amount of water needed to suppress the fire. For sprinklers with the same temperature rating, those with a lower RTI value will operate sooner in a rapidly growing fire than sprinklers with a higher RTI value.

FAQ ▶
What is RDD?

Required delivered density (RDD) is the measure of the amount of water needed to suppress a fire. The value of required delivered density depends on the size of the fire at the time of sprinkler operation.

FAQ ▶
What is ADD?

Actual delivered density (ADD) is a measurement of the amount of water discharged from the sprinklers that actually reaches the fire. ADD is determined during a fire test by measuring the amount of water that collects in a pan on the top horizontal surface of a burning combustible array. ADD is a means of characterizing a sprinkler's distribution pattern and droplet penetration capability during a fire event. The longer it takes a sprinkler to actuate, the faster the fire grows and the smaller the value of ADD. ADD is a function of fire plume velocity, water drop momentum and size, and the distance the water drops must travel from the sprinkler.

These three measurements—RTI, RDD, and ADD—are the controlling factors that define the time-dependent nature of early fire suppression. In theory, the earlier the water is applied to a growing fire, the lower the RDD will be and the higher the ADD will be. In other words, the faster the sprinkler response (lower RTI), the lower the RDD will be and the higher the ADD will be. Conversely, the later the water is applied (higher RTI), the higher the RDD will be and the lower the ADD will be. When the ADD is less than the RDD, the sprinkler discharge is no longer effective enough to achieve early fire suppression. Thus, it is clear that early fire suppression depends on the correct installation of ESFR sprinklers that have been shown to meet the performance criteria related to the RTI, ADD, and RDD factors for the hazard being protected. Exhibit 3.14 shows the generalized concept that early suppression is achieved when the ADD exceeds the RDD. Implicit in the preceding theory is the expectation that water discharging from the first operating ESFR sprinkler reaches the burning material. It is critical with suppression mode sprinklers that the requirements of 8.12.5 be followed to minimize obstructions.

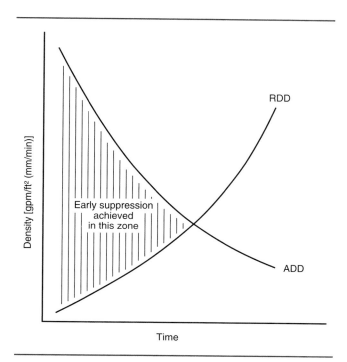

EXHIBIT 3.14 Generalized RDD-ADD Relationship.

ESFR sprinklers are predominantly used to protect storage occupancies. Caution must be exercised to avoid confusing ESFR sprinklers with other types of sprinklers that are equipped with fast-response operating elements. A non-ESFR sprinkler with a fast-response element is not specifically designed to achieve fire suppression. The relationship among thermal sensitivity, ADD, and RDD needs to be considered.

Several types of ESFR sprinklers available are illustrated in Exhibits 3.15 and 3.16. Exhibit 3.15 shows three pendent-type ESFR sprinklers. The sprinklers on the right have a nominal K-factor of 14, while the sprinkler on the left has a nominal K-factor of 25.2. Exhibit 3.16 illustrates an upright ESFR sprinkler with a nominal K-factor of 11.2. It is important to note that the installation and discharge criteria for these different ESFR sprinklers are not uniform. See Chapters 8 and 12 for additional information.

3.6.2.2 Extended Coverage Sprinkler. A type of spray sprinkler with maximum coverage areas as specified in Sections 8.8 and 8.9 of this standard.

Extended coverage (EC) sprinklers, defined in 3.6.2.2, are available in the pendent, upright, and sidewall configurations. The advantage of EC sprinklers is that their areas of coverage are

EXHIBIT 3.15 Pendent-Type ESFR Sprinklers.

greater than those established for standard spray and sidewall sprinklers. Exhibits 3.17 and 3.18 illustrate pendent and sidewall types of EC sprinklers. EC sprinklers can look similar to standard coverage sprinklers, so the listing information should be consulted to confirm that the sprinklers used are, in fact, extended coverage sprinklers.

EXHIBIT 3.17 Pendent-Type Extended Coverage Sprinklers.

EXHIBIT 3.18 Sidewall-Type Extended Coverage Sprinkler.

EXHIBIT 3.16 Upright-Type ESFR Sprinkler. (Courtesy of Viking Corporation)

3.6.2.3 Large Drop Sprinkler. A type of specific application control mode sprinkler that is capable of producing characteristic large water droplets and that is listed for its capability to provide fire control of specific high-challenge fire hazards.

A large drop sprinkler, defined in 3.6.2.3, is a control mode sprinkler primarily used for the protection of storage facilities. Exhibit 3.19 illustrates a large drop sprinkler.

EXHIBIT 3.19 *Viking Large Drop Sprinkler. (Courtesy of Viking Corporation)*

3.6.2.4 Nozzles. A device for use in applications requiring special water discharge patterns, directional spray, or other unusual discharge characteristics.

Nozzles, such as the one shown in Exhibit 3.20, are special application devices that have unique characteristics designed to meet specific needs. (Nozzles are defined in 3.6.2.4.) These devices are equipped with heat-responsive elements or are open to the atmosphere. Nozzles are designed to spray water in a specific direction. NFPA 15, *Standard for Water Spray Fixed Systems for Fire Protection,* provides more information on these devices.

3.6.2.5 Old-Style/Conventional Sprinkler. A sprinkler that directs from 40 percent to 60 percent of the total water initially in a downward direction and that is designed to be installed with the deflector either upright or pendent.

Old-style/conventional sprinklers, defined in 3.6.2.5, were predominantly used in North America prior to the development of spray sprinklers. The major difference between old-style/conventional and standard spray sprinklers is the design of their deflectors. Old-style/conventional sprinklers, whether upright or pendent, direct approximately 40 percent of their water discharge up against the ceiling, with the remaining discharge directed downward as indicated in Exhibit 3.21. Spray sprinklers direct 100 percent of their water discharge downward as indicated in Exhibit 3.22.

Old-style/conventional sprinklers are still available and are used in Europe. These sprinklers are also used in North America for special applications in which an upward sprinkler discharge is desired, such as for fur storage vaults and for pier and wharf protection.

3.6.2.6 Open Sprinkler. A sprinkler that does not have actuators or heat-responsive elements.

Open sprinklers, such as the one shown in Exhibit 3.23, are used predominantly on deluge or water spray systems. (*Open sprinkler* is defined in 3.6.2.6.)

EXHIBIT 3.20 *Grinnell Automatic Protectospray™ Nozzle. (Courtesy of TYCO/Grinnell)*

EXHIBIT 3.21 *Principal Distribution Pattern of Water from Old-Style/Conventional Sprinklers (Used Before 1953).*

EXHIBIT 3.22 *Principal Distribution Pattern of Water from Spray Sprinklers (Introduced in 1953).*

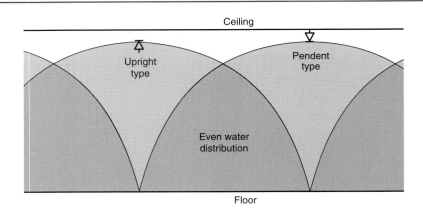

3.6.2.7* Quick-Response Early Suppression (QRES) Sprinkler. A type of quick-response sprinkler that meets the criteria of 3.6.1(a)(1) and is listed for its capability to provide fire suppression of specific fire hazards.

 A.3.6.2.7 Quick-Response Early Suppression (QRES) Sprinkler. Research into the development of QRES sprinklers is continuing under the auspices of the National Fire Protection Research Foundation. It is expected that the proposed design criteria will be added to the standard when a thorough analysis of the test data is completed.

The concept of a quick-response early suppression sprinkler, defined in 3.6.2.7, was proposed some time ago. The definition and annex material appear in NFPA 13 to introduce the concept, since the sprinkler itself does not exist. The concept of the QRES sprinkler is based largely on information discovered in developing the ESFR sprinkler. The QRES sprinkler is intended to bring fire suppression to occupancies such as office buildings and manufacturing facilities.

A four-sprinkler design concept was targeted. The relevant combinations of fuel load, ceiling height, operating pressure, and sprinkler spacing need to be verified. Once any data becomes available and the sprinkler committees are able to review the results, an amendment to NFPA 13 will likely be considered.

3.6.2.8 Quick-Response Extended Coverage Sprinkler. A type of quick-response sprinkler that meets the criteria of 3.6.1(a)(1) and complies with the extended protection areas defined in Chapter 8.

A quick-response extended coverage sprinkler, defined in 3.6.2.8, is specifically listed as having a fast-response operating element. Some standard response EC sprinklers use fast-

EXHIBIT 3.23 *Grinnell Open Sprinkler. (Courtesy of TYCO/Grinnell)*

response operating elements in order to achieve a desired performance. However, those EC sprinklers must be considered standard response unless specifically listed as quick-response extended coverage sprinklers. Exhibit 3.24 illustrates a type of listed quick-response extended coverage sprinkler.

3.6.2.9 Quick-Response (QR) Sprinkler. A type of spray sprinkler that meets the criteria of 3.6.1(a)(1) and is listed as a quick-response sprinkler for its intended use.

Quick-response (QR) sprinkler technology was developed from residential sprinkler technology. QR sprinklers, defined in 3.6.2.9, are similar to standard spray sprinklers except that they possess a fast-response operating element. QR sprinklers are tested against the same criteria as standard-response sprinklers. The commentary to A.3.6.1 provides additional discussion on thermal sensitivity and fast-response technology. Exhibit 3.12 shows a QR sprinkler adjacent to a standard-response sprinkler. The difference in the size of the operating elements should be noted. Where glass bulbs are used for standard spray sprinklers, the bulb of a QR sprinkler is typically thinner than that of a standard-response sprinkler. Where a metallic alloy is used, the operating element is usually larger in a QR sprinkler.

3.6.2.10 Residential Sprinkler. A type of fast-response sprinkler that meets the criteria of 3.6.1(a)(1) that has been specifically investigated for its ability to enhance survivability in the room of fire origin and is listed for use in the protection of dwelling units.

The residential sprinkler, defined in 3.6.2.10, was introduced in the early 1980s with the primary objective of achieving life safety in dwelling units. Residential sprinklers are installed to provide a tenable space for a period of time necessary for an occupant to evacuate. Additionally, these sprinklers are intended to protect persons in the room of fire origin who are not intimate with ignition. This sprinkler possesses a fast-response operating element and produces a spray pattern that discharges water higher than the standard spray sprinkler.

Residential sprinklers are tested for their ability to meet a specified life safety criterion. This criterion includes temperature, oxygen, and carbon monoxide levels measured at a height 5 ft (1.5 m) above the floor. The commentary to NFPA 13D, *Standard for the Installation of Sprinkler Systems in One- and Two-Family Dwellings and Manufactured Homes,* in Part Two of this handbook further describes the testing and developmental programs that led to the introduction of the residential sprinkler. Exhibit 3.25 shows a listed residential sprinkler.

3.6.2.11 Special Sprinkler. A sprinkler that has been tested and listed as prescribed in 8.4.9.

NFPA 13 provides detailed information for special sprinklers, defined in 3.6.2.11. This type of sprinkler does not fall into the other categories as it is usually intended to protect specific hazards or construction features. Special sprinklers must be evaluated and listed for their intended purpose. Fire test performance, spray pattern distribution with respect to both the wetting of walls and floors, operation with obstructions, thermal sensitivity, and performance under horizontal or sloped ceilings all need to be considered. While a good deal of latitude is provided for the development of special sprinklers, their K-factor and temperature rating must comply with the provisions identified by this standard. Also, their maximum area of coverage cannot exceed 400 ft^2 (36 m^2) for light and ordinary hazard occupancies and 196 ft^2 (18.2 m^2) for extra hazard occupancies and high-piled storage applications.

The special sprinkler category often serves as a starting point for the introduction of a new kind of sprinkler. Once a sufficient comfort level and overall acceptance of a special sprinkler is achieved, the need to establish a new sprinkler category is evident. Establishing a new sprinkler category is also desirable because special sprinklers do not always receive broad-based acceptance as mainstream devices. This was the case with the EC sprinkler, which is no longer considered a special sprinkler according to NFPA 13. Another example is the upright ESFR sprinkler, which in the past was classified as a special sprinkler. Examples of special sprinklers include specific application and cycling sprinklers. Exhibit 1.6 shows listed special sprinklers.

EXHIBIT 3.24 *Quick-Response Extended Coverage Sprinkler.*

EXHIBIT 3.25 *Viking Listed Residential Sprinkler. (Courtesy of Viking)*

3.6.2.12* Specific Application Control Mode Sprinkler (for Storage Use). A type of spray sprinkler listed at a minimum operating pressure with a specific number of operating sprinklers for a given protection scheme.

A.3.6.2.12 Specific Application Control Mode Sprinkler (for Storage Use). Examples include large drop sprinklers or listed at a minimum operating pressure or density with a specific number of operating sprinklers—for example, specific application sprinklers.

3.6.2.13 Spray Sprinkler. A type of sprinkler listed for its capability to provide fire control for a wide range of fire hazards.

The spray sprinkler, defined in 3.6.2.13, was introduced in the early 1950s and was the successor to the old-style/conventional sprinkler. The old-style sprinkler continues to serve the sprinkler industry. Standard spray, pendent, standard spray upright, sidewall, EC, and EC sidewall sprinklers are categories of spray sprinklers.

3.6.2.14 Standard Spray Sprinkler. A spray sprinkler with maximum coverage areas as specified in Sections 8.6 and 8.7 of this standard.

This control mode spray sprinkler defined in 3.6.2.14 is installed in accordance with the coverage area limitations in Sections 8.6 and 8.7. It is available in pendent, upright, and sidewall configurations. Because the standard spray sprinkler is proven to be effective for a broad range of hazards and applications, it is very popular and, to a certain degree, serves as the benchmark for sprinkler measurement and performance. Exhibit 3.26 illustrates a standard spray upright sprinkler and a standard spray pendent sprinkler.

EXHIBIT 3.26 Viking Model M Glass Bulb Standard Spray Upright and Pendent Sprinklers. (Courtesy of Viking)

3.6.3 Installation Orientation. The following sprinklers are defined according to orientation.

The devices described in 3.6.3 are based on the geometry of how the sprinkler is installed. Representative discharge patterns for these devices allow them to be categorized as concealed, flush, pendent, and recessed sprinklers, all of which have similar discharge patterns and are mounted to the bottom of a branch line or pipe drop. Sidewall sprinklers are typically installed along a wall or lintel and discharge water away from the wall into the room or space. Sidewall sprinklers can be mounted on the side, bottom, or top of a branch line, as specified in their listings. Upright sprinklers have a spray pattern that appears similar to that of a pendent sprinkler. The difference is that upright sprinklers are mounted to the top of branch lines or sprigs.

3.6.3.1 Concealed Sprinkler. A recessed sprinkler with cover plates.

Exhibit 3.27 illustrates a concealed sprinkler. The cover plate drops away when exposed to a certain amount of heat. The fusible elements holding the cover plate are designed to operate prior to the activation of the sprinkler's thermal element. The cover plate is included as part of the listing.

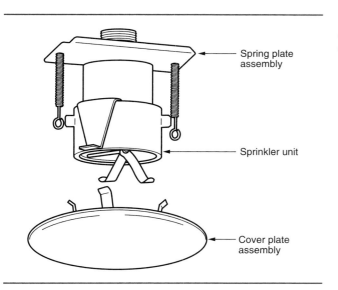

EXHIBIT 3.27 *Standard Model G Concealed Ceiling Sprinkler.*

Spring plate assembly

Sprinkler unit

Cover plate assembly

EXHIBIT 3.28 *Viking Model H Standard Spray Pendent Flush-Mount Sprinkler. (Courtesy of Viking)*

3.6.3.2 Flush Sprinkler. A sprinkler in which all or part of the body, including the shank thread, is mounted above the lower plane of the ceiling.

Exhibit 3.28 illustrates a flush sprinkler, which is defined in 3.6.3.2.

3.6.3.3 Pendent Sprinkler. A sprinkler designed to be installed in such a way that the water stream is directed downward against the deflector.

Exhibit 3.29 illustrates a standard spray pendent sprinkler, which is defined in 3.6.3.3.

3.6.3.4 Recessed Sprinkler. A sprinkler in which all or part of the body, other than the shank thread, is mounted within a recessed housing.

Exhibit 3.30 shows a recessed sprinkler, defined in 3.6.3.4.

3.6.3.5 Sidewall Sprinkler. A sprinkler having special deflectors that are designed to discharge most of the water away from the nearby wall in a pattern resembling one-quarter of a sphere, with a small portion of the discharge directed at the wall behind the sprinkler.

Exhibit 3.31 illustrates a horizontal sidewall sprinkler, defined in 3.6.3.5.

3.6.3.6 Upright Sprinkler. A sprinkler designed to be installed in such a way that the water spray is directed upwards against the deflector.

Exhibit 3.32 illustrates several upright sprinklers, defined in 3.6.3.6.

3.6.4 Special Service Conditions. The following sprinklers are defined according to special application or environment.

The devices described in 3.6.4 are intended for use in specific environments. These devices are either covered with a special coating or are designed for a specific function. Only the sprinkler manufacturer can apply coatings.

3.6.4.1 Corrosion-Resistant Sprinkler. A sprinkler fabricated with corrosion-resistant material, or with special coatings or platings, to be used in an atmosphere that would normally corrode sprinklers.

EXHIBIT 3.29 *Standard Spray Pendent Sprinkler. (Courtesy of Viking)*

EXHIBIT 3.30 *Recessed Sprinkler.*

EXHIBIT 3.31 Horizontal Sidewall Sprinkler. (Courtesy of Viking)

EXHIBIT 3.32 Upright Sprinklers.

Corrosion-resistant sprinklers, defined in 3.6.4.1, are usually standard sprinklers with a corrosion-resistant coating, such as wax or lead, applied to them.

Any coating of this type can only be applied by the manufacturer.

Exhibit 3.33 illustrates a wax-coated corrosion-resistant sprinkler.

FAQ ▶
Who can apply corrosion-resistance coatings to sprinklers?

3.6.4.2* Dry Sprinkler. A sprinkler secured in an extension nipple that has a seal at the inlet end to prevent water from entering the nipple until the sprinkler operates.

A.3.6.4.2 Dry Sprinkler. Under certain ambient conditions, wet pipe systems having dry-pendent (or upright) sprinklers can freeze due to heat loss by conduction. Therefore, due consideration should be given to the amount of heat maintained in the heated space, the length of the nipple in the heated space, and other relevant factors.

Dry sprinklers are intended to extend into an unheated area from a wet pipe system or to be used on a dry pipe system.

Exhibit 3.34 shows a dry-pendent sprinkler (*dry sprinkler* is defined in 3.6.4.2). When the glass bulb is heated, it breaks apart. The inner tube, which also serves as an orifice, drops to a predetermined position, allowing the sealing elements to pass through the tube and away from the sprinkler. Water flows through the tube and strikes the deflector, which distributes it in a spray pattern comparable to a standard spray sprinkler. The dry upright sprinkler is similar to the dry pendent, except that the upright uses an upright deflector.

3.6.4.3 Intermediate Level Sprinkler/Rack Storage Sprinkler. A sprinkler equipped with integral shields to protect its operating elements from the discharge of sprinklers installed at higher elevations.

EXHIBIT 3.33 Central Model A Upright Wax-Coated Corrosion-Resistant Sprinkler.

3.6.4.4 Ornamental/Decorative Sprinkler. A sprinkler that has been painted or plated by the manufacturer.

Some ornamental sprinklers, defined in 3.6.4.4, can be nothing more than corrosion-resistant sprinklers with a special coating similar in color to that of the interior building finish. The same holds true for the covers of concealed sprinklers.

    As noted in 6.2.6, any coating for decorative or protective purposes must be applied only by the sprinkler manufacturer.

◄ **FAQ**
Who can apply coatings to sprinklers?

3.7 Construction Definitions

Section 3.7 contains construction definitions. Ceiling construction impacts sprinkler installation, as it is a factor in determining the position of the sprinkler deflector in relation to the ceiling and in determining the allowable area of coverage for a given sprinkler.

    Sprinklers must be positioned so that they are located in the hot gas layer that develops near the ceiling during a fire. This sprinkler placement allows for timely operation. Depending on the ceiling construction type, sprinklers are permitted to be located various distances from the ceiling so that they activate shortly after the fire begins.

    Sprinklers must also be positioned so that their discharge pattern is not adversely impacted by construction elements at the ceiling. If water cannot reach the combustible surfaces, the effectiveness of the sprinkler system is compromised. To a large degree, potential obstructions to sprinkler discharge are addressed by the obstruction rules of 8.5.5.

    Ceiling construction also impacts sprinkler discharge. Therefore, the maximum area of coverage for a specific type of sprinkler depends on the type of ceiling construction under which the sprinkler is installed.

    The numerous construction terms in NFPA 13 fall into two basic categories: obstructed construction and unobstructed construction. The construction types identified in A.3.7.1 and A.3.7.2 aid in determining whether a given ceiling construction should be classified as either obstructed or unobstructed. The annex material also describes particular ceiling features that influence the placement of sprinklers.

EXHIBIT 3.34 Viking Model E Dry-Pendent Sprinkler. (Courtesy of Viking)

3.7.1* Obstructed Construction. Panel construction and other construction where beams, trusses, or other members impede heat flow or water distribution in a manner that materially affects the ability of sprinklers to control or suppress a fire.

A.3.7.1 Obstructed Construction. The following are examples of obstructed construction. The definitions are provided to assist the user in determining the type of construction feature.

(1) *Beam and Girder Construction.* The term *beam and girder construction* as used in this standard includes noncombustible and combustible roof or floor decks supported by wood beams of 4 in. (102 mm) or greater nominal thickness or concrete or steel beams spaced 3 ft to 7½ ft (0.9 m to 2.3 m) on center and either supported on or framed into girders. [Where supporting a wood plank deck, this includes semi-mill and panel construction, and where supporting (with steel framing) gypsum plank, steel deck, concrete, tile, or similar material, this includes much of the so-called noncombustible construction.]

Beam and girder construction, which is discussed in A.3.7.1(1), consists of roof or floor decks supported by beams spaced 3 ft to 7½ ft (0.9 m to 2.3 m) on center that are either framed onto or into girders. This construction type results in the formation of ceiling bays or panels. Exhibit 3.35 illustrates an example of beam and girder construction in which the beams are framed into the girders. Exhibit 3.36 shows the bays formed by the beams.

    The close spacing of the beams creates a greater likelihood of sprinkler spray pattern interference. Therefore, the positioning and maximum area of coverage rules for obstructed construction are different than the rules for unobstructed construction.

EXHIBIT 3.35 *Beam and Girder Construction.*

EXHIBIT 3.36 *Bays Formed by Beam and Girder Construction.*

Beam and girder construction causes heat from a fire to accumulate within the bays or panels formed by the supporting members. As a fire continues to generate heat, the heat flows down the length of the members, activating only sprinklers within that bay or panel. Once the capacity of the bays or panels is reached, fire gases spill over into adjacent bays or panels and allow sprinklers in other bays and panels to activate. Because of this phenomenon, the deflector positioning rules in Chapter 8 provide a degree of flexibility in positioning the deflector in relation to the ceiling and the supporting members.

(2) *Concrete Tee Construction.* The term *concrete tee construction* as it is used in this standard refers to solid concrete members with stems (legs) having a nominal thickness less than the nominal height. See Figure A.3.7.1(a) for examples of concrete tee construction.

FIGURE A.3.7.1(a) *Typical Concrete Tee Construction.*

(3) *Composite Wood Joist Construction.* The term *composite wood joist construction* refers to wood beams of "I" cross section constructed of wood flanges and solid wood web, supporting a floor or roof deck. Composite wood joists can vary in depth up to 48 in. (1.2 m), can be spaced up to 48 in. (1.2 m) on centers, and can span up to 60 ft (18 m) between supports. Joist channels should be firestopped to the full depth of the joists with material equivalent to the web construction so that individual channel areas do not exceed 300 ft² (27.9 m²). [*See Figure A.3.7.1(b) for an example of composite wood joist construction.*]

FIGURE A.3.7.1(b) *Typical Composite Wood Joist Construction.*

NFPA 13 provides guidance on the placement of sprinklers under composite wood joists only where the joists do not exceed a total depth of 22 in. (559 mm). [Composite wood joist construction is discussed in A.3.7.1(3).]

The firestopping between the composite wood joists that form the 300-ft^2 (27.9-m^2) pocket is needed to trap the heat and accelerate sprinkler operation. [See Figure A.3.7.1(b).]

Composite wood joists are typically referred to as wood "I" beams. The predominant use of these members was initially found in western North America, but now they are quite common in other areas as well.

 (4) *Panel Construction.* The term *panel construction* as used in this standard includes ceiling panels formed by members capable of trapping heat to aid the operation of sprinklers and limited to a maximum of 300 ft^2 (27.9 m^2) in area. There should be no unfilled penetrations in the cross sectional area of the bounding structural members including the interface at the roof. Beams spaced more than 7½ ft (2.3 m) apart and framed into girders qualify as panel construction, provided the 300-ft^2 (27.9-m^2) area limitation is met.

FAQ ▶
Can panel construction with members spaced more than 7½ ft (2.3 m) apart be considered obstructed construction?

Panel construction, which is discussed in A.3.7.1(4), can be considered a version of beam and girder construction in which beams are framed into girders and form a ceiling panel with a maximum area of 300 ft^2 (27.9 m^2). Panel construction with members spaced more than 7½ ft (2.3 m) apart can be considered obstructed construction, provided the ceiling panels do not exceed an area of 300 ft^2 (27.9 m^2). Where ceiling panels consist of an area in excess of 300 ft^2 (27.9 m^2), they cannot be considered obstructed construction. See Exhibits 3.35 and 3.36.

(5) *Semi-Mill Construction.* The term *semi-mill construction* as used in this standard refers to a modified standard mill construction, where greater column spacing is used and beams rest on girders.

(6) *Wood Joist Construction.* The term *wood joist construction* refers to solid wood members of rectangular cross section, which can vary from 2 in. to 4 in. (51 mm to 102 mm) nominal width and can be up to 14 in. (356 mm) nominal depth, spaced up to 3 ft (0.9 m) on centers, and can span up to 40 ft (12 m) between supports, supporting a floor or roof deck. Solid wood members less than 4 in. (102 mm) nominal width and up to 14 in. (356 mm) nominal depth, spaced more than 3 ft (0.9 m) on centers, are also considered as wood joist construction.

Can composite wood joists and wood trusses be considered wood joist construction?
FAQ ▶

Wood joist construction, a type of light combustible construction that is discussed in A.3.7.1(6), uses nominal 2-in. to 4-in. (51-mm to 102-mm) wide solid wood members on edge to support a ceiling or roof deck. Sheathing such as drywall cannot be fastened to the underside of the joists. Sheathed joists are considered unobstructed construction. Most construction assemblies that use solid wood members less than 4 in. (102 mm) thick are classified as wood joists.

Composite wood joists and wood trusses should not be considered solid wood members.

 (7) *Bar Joist Construction with Fireproofing.* In order to meet building codes, bar joists are often covered with fireproofing materials. In such an event, if greater than 30 percent of the area of the joist is obstructed, it should be considered obstructed construction.

3.7.2* Unobstructed Construction. Construction where beams, trusses, or other members do not impede heat flow or water distribution in a manner that materially affects the ability of sprinklers to control or suppress a fire. Unobstructed construction has horizontal structural members that are not solid, where the openings are at least 70 percent of the cross-section area and the depth of the member does not exceed the least dimension of the openings, or all construction types where the spacing of structural members exceeds 7½ ft (2.3 m) on center.

Unobstructed construction, which is defined in 3.7.2, does not contain features that are expected to impede the flow of heat from a fire. Additionally, once the sprinklers have activated, the likelihood of their spray pattern being interrupted by construction features at or near the ceiling is greatly reduced. Examples of traditional unobstructed construction are identified in A.3.7.2.

A.3.7.2 Unobstructed Construction. The following are examples of unobstructed construction. The definitions are provided to assist the user in determining the type of construction feature.

(1) *Bar Joist Construction.* The term *bar joist construction* refers to construction employing joists consisting of steel truss-shaped members. Wood truss-shaped members, which consist of wood top and bottom chord members not exceeding 4 in. (102 mm) in depth with steel tube or bar webs, are also defined as bar joists. Bar joists include noncombustible or combustible roof or floor decks on bar joist construction. [*See Figure A.3.7.2(a) and Figure A.3.7.2(b) for examples of bar joist construction.*]

Also known as open-web steel joist construction, bar joist construction, which is discussed in A.3.7.2(1), utilizes a top and bottom wood or steel chord. Unlike solid wood or composite wood joists, this construction type allows heat and fire gases to pass though it and spread out across the ceiling. Obstruction to water distribution is minimal as inferred by the spacing and positioning rules of Chapter 8. The maximum protection area per sprinkler for standard spray upright and pendent sprinklers under unobstructed construction can be as high as 200 ft^2 (18.6 m^2) for pipe schedule systems and 225 ft^2 (20.9 m^2) for hydraulically calculated systems [see Table 8.6.2.2.1(a)]. Figure A.3.7.2(a), Figure A.3.7.2(b), and Exhibit 3.37 show examples of bar joist construction.

(2) *Open-Grid Ceilings.* The term *open-grid ceilings* as used in this standard are ceilings in which the openings are ¼ in. (6.4 mm) or larger in the least dimension, the thickness of the ceiling material does not exceed the least dimension of the openings, and the openings constitute at least 70 percent of the ceiling area.

(3) *Smooth Ceiling Construction.* The term *smooth ceiling construction* as used in this standard includes the following:

    (a) Flat slab, pan-type reinforced concrete

    (b) Continuous smooth bays formed by wood, concrete, or steel beams spaced more than 7½ ft (2.3 m) on centers—beams supported by columns, girders, or trusses

    (c) Smooth roof or floor decks supported directly on girders or trusses spaced more than 7½ ft (2.3 m) on center

    (d) Smooth monolithic ceilings of at least ¾ in. (19 mm) of plaster on metal lath or a combination of materials of equivalent fire-resistive rating attached to the underside of wood joists, wood trusses, and bar joists

    (e) Open-web-type steel beams, regardless of spacing

    (f) Smooth shell-type roofs, such as folded plates, hyperbolic paraboloids, saddles, domes, and long barrel shells

FIGURE A.3.7.2(a) *Wood Bar Joist Construction.*

FIGURE A.3.7.2(b) *Open-Web Bar Joist Construction.*

(g) Suspended ceilings of combustible or noncombustible construction
(h) Smooth monolithic ceilings with fire resistance less than that specified under item (d) attached to the underside of wood joists, wood trusses, and bar joists

In general, smooth ceiling construction, which is discussed in A.3.7.2(3), does not incorporate supporting members that are less than 7½ ft (2.3 m) on center or have members that would interfere with the distribution of water from sprinklers. The 7½-ft (2.3-m) length serves as a threshold value. This length is the maximum dimension a standard spray sprinkler can be placed from a wall for light hazard and ordinary hazard occupancies. In small rooms standard spray sprinklers can be placed up to 9 ft (2.7 m) from one wall. (See 8.6.3.2.3 and 8.6.3.2.4.) Exhibit 3.38 illustrates smooth ceiling construction consisting of a suspended ceiling.

Exhibit 3.39 illustrates smooth ceiling construction consisting of flat slab, pan-type reinforced concrete. Although this type of construction is typically considered smooth ceiling, it

EXHIBIT 3.39 *Flat Slab, Pan-Type Reinforced Concrete Ceiling.*

is not considered a smooth, flat ceiling as required for sidewall or extended coverage sprinklers. See 8.4.2 and 8.4.3 for specific requirements.

Combustible or noncombustible floor decks are permitted in the construction specified in A.3.7.2(3)(b) through (f). Item (b) would include standard mill construction.

(4) *Standard Mill Construction.* The term *standard mill construction* as used in this standard refers to heavy timber construction as defined in NFPA 220, *Standard on Types of Building Construction.*

(5) *Wood Truss Construction.* The term *wood truss construction* refers to parallel or pitched wood chord members connected by open wood members (webbing) supporting a roof or floor deck. Trusses with steel webbing, similar to bar joist construction, having top and bottom wood chords exceeding 4 in. (102 mm) in depth, should also be considered wood truss construction. *[See Figure A.3.7.2(c).]*

Greater than 4 in. (102 mm)

Floor truss

Continuous 2 times load share bridging
[minimum size 2 in. × 6 in. (50 mm × 152 mm) #2 spruce pine fir]

FIGURE A.3.7.2(c) *Examples of Wood Truss Construction.*

EXHIBIT 3.40 *Heavy Timber
Construction of the
Laminated Floor and Beam
Type. (Courtesy of National
Forest Products Association)*

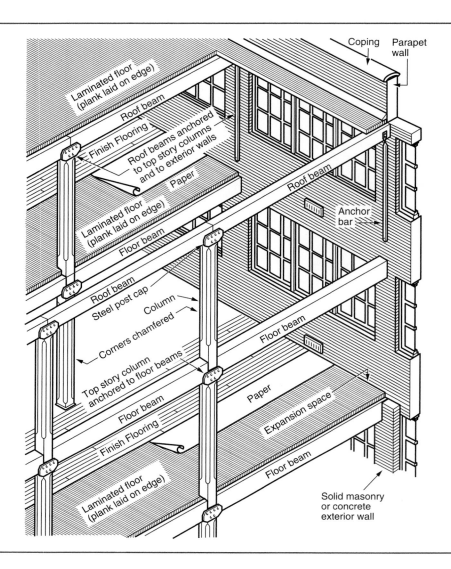

Wood truss construction, which is discussed in A.3.7.2(5), is similar to bar joist construction except that the top and bottom chords are typically of a heavier wood construction and the chords are typically connected by wood or steel web members rather than steel bars.

Past editions of NFPA 13 included wood truss construction in the same category as bar joist construction. This classification caused some confusion, and separate definitions were introduced in the 1989 edition. However, with only two broad categories of construction considered by NFPA 13, the differences between wood truss and bar joist construction in terms of sprinkler system installation became less important.

Exhibits 3.40 and 3.41 illustrate different types of heavy timber construction.

3.8 Private Water Supply Piping Definitions

3.8.1* Private Fire Service Main. Private fire service main, as used in this standard, is that pipe and its appurtenances on private property (1) between a source of water and the base

EXHIBIT 3.41 Components of a Heavy Timber Building That Shows Floor Framing with Components of a Type Known as Semi-Mill Identified.

of the system riser for water-based fire protection systems, (2) between a source of water and inlets to foam-making systems, (3) between a source of water and the base elbow of private hydrants or monitor nozzles, and (4) used as fire pump suction and discharge piping, (5) beginning at the inlet side of the check valve on a gravity or pressure tank.

A.3.8.1 Private Fire Service Main. See Figure A.3.8.1.

In the context of sprinkler systems, a private fire service main, which is defined in 3.8.1 and shown in Exhibit 3.11, is the piping that is either buried or above ground, connecting the water supply to the sprinkler system. A private fire service main is also the piping that supplies water to private hydrants and other devices used for manual fire fighting. It should be noted that the requirements for private fire service mains were intended to apply to the portion of the piping system on private property that is dedicated to fire protection or combined use.

A

◀ **FAQ**
What portion of the piping is considered the private fire service main?

3.9 Palletized, Solid Pile, Bin Box, and Shelf Storage Definitions

3.9.1 Array.

3.9.1.1 Closed Array. A storage arrangement where air movement through the pile is restricted because of 6-in. (152-mm) or less vertical flues.

FIGURE A.3.8.1 *Typical Private Fire Service Main.*

3.9.1.2* Open Array. A storage arrangement where air movement through the pile is enhanced because of vertical flues larger than 6 in. (152 mm).

A.3.9.1.2 Open Array. Fire tests conducted to represent a closed array utilized 6-in. (152-mm) longitudinal flues and no transverse flues. Fire tests conducted to represent an open array utilized 12-in. (305-mm) longitudinal flues.

3.9.2* Available Height for Storage. The maximum height at which commodities can be stored above the floor and still maintain adequate clearance from structural members and the required clearance below sprinklers.

A.3.9.2 Available Height for Storage. For new sprinkler installations, the maximum height of storage is the height at which commodities can be stored above the floor where the minimum required unobstructed space below sprinklers is maintained. For the evaluation of existing situations, the maximum height of storage is the maximum existing height, if space between the sprinklers and storage is equal to or greater than required.

3.9.3 Bin Box Storage. Storage in five-sided wood, metal, or cardboard boxes with open face on the aisles. Boxes are self-supporting or supported by a structure so designed that little or no horizontal or vertical space exists around boxes.

3.9.4 Clearance. The distance from the top of storage to the ceiling sprinkler deflectors.

3.9.5 Commodity. Combinations of products, packing material, and container upon which the commodity classification is based.

3.9.6* Compartmented. The rigid separation of the products in a container by dividers that form a stable unit under fire conditions.

A.3.9.6 Compartmented. Cartons used in most of the Factory Mutual—sponsored plastic tests involved an ordinary 200-lb (90.7-kg) test of outside corrugated cartons with five layers of vertical pieces of corrugated carton used as dividers on the inside. There were also single horizontal pieces of corrugated carton between each layer.

    Other tests sponsored by the Society of Plastics Industry, Industrial Risk Insurers, Factory Mutual, and Kemper used two vertical pieces of carton (not corrugated) to form an "X" in the carton for separation of product. This arrangement was not considered compartmented, as the pieces of carton used for separations were flexible (not rigid), and only two pieces were used in each carton.

3.9.7* Container (Shipping, Master, or Outer Container). A receptacle strong enough, by reason of material, design, and construction, to be shipped safely without further packaging.

A.3.9.7 Container (Shipping, Master, or Outer Container). The term *container* includes items such as cartons and wrappings. Fire-retardant containers or tote boxes do not by themselves create a need for automatic sprinklers unless coated with oil or grease. Containers can lose their fire-retardant properties if washed. For obvious reasons, they should not be exposed to rainfall.

3.9.8 Encapsulation. A method of packaging consisting of a plastic sheet completely enclosing the sides and top of a pallet load containing a combustible commodity or a combustible package or a group of combustible commodities or combustible packages. Combustible commodities individually wrapped in plastic sheeting and stored exposed in a pallet load also are to be considered encapsulated. Totally noncombustible commodities on wood pallets enclosed only by a plastic sheet as described are not covered under this definition. Banding (i.e., stretch-wrapping around the sides only of a pallet load) is not considered to be encapsulation. Where there are holes or voids in the plastic or waterproof cover on the top of the carton that exceed more than half of the area of the cover, the term *encapsulated* does not apply. The term *encapsulated* does not apply to plastic-enclosed products or packages inside a large, nonplastic, enclosed container.

The chairs shown in Exhibit 3.42 are considered encapsulated since the chairs are completely enclosed by the plastic sheet. (Encapsulation is defined in 3.9.8.) The wrapped commodities in Exhibit 3.43 are not considered encapsulated because the plastic does not cover the top of the pallet loads.

◀ **FAQ**
What is the difference between encapsulation and wrapped in plastic?

3.9.9 Expanded (Foamed or Cellular) Plastics. Those plastics, the density of which is reduced by the presence of numerous small cavities (cells), interconnecting or not, dispersed throughout their mass.

3.9.10 Exposed Group A Plastic Commodities. Those plastics not in packaging or coverings that absorb water or otherwise appreciably retard the burning hazard of the commodity. (Paper wrapped or encapsulated, or both, should be considered exposed.)

EXHIBIT 3.42 *Encapsulated Chairs.*

EXHIBIT 3.43 *Commodity Wrapped in a Plastic Sheet.*

3.9.11 Free-Flowing Plastic Materials. Those plastics that fall out of their containers during a fire, fill flue spaces, and create a smothering effect on the fire. Examples include powder, pellets, flakes, or random-packed small objects [e.g., razor blade dispensers, 1-oz to 2-oz (28-g to 57-g) bottles].

3.9.12 Packaging. A commodity wrapping, cushioning, or container.

3.9.13 Palletized Storage. Storage of commodities on pallets or other storage aids that form horizontal spaces between tiers of storage.

3.9.14* Pile Stability, Stable Piles. Those arrays where collapse, spillage of content, or leaning of stacks across flue spaces is not likely to occur soon after initial fire development.

A.3.9.14 Pile Stability, Stable Piles. Pile stability performance has been shown to be a difficult factor to judge prior to a pile being subjected to an actual fire. In the test work completed, compartmented cartons *(see A.3.9.6, Compartmented)* have been shown to be stable under fire conditions. Tests also indicated cartons that were not compartmented tended to be unstable under fire conditions.

Storage on pallets, compartmented storage, and plastic components that are held in place by materials that do not deform readily under fire conditions are examples of stable storage.

3.9.15* Pile Stability, Unstable Piles. Those arrays where collapse, spillage of contents, or leaning of stacks across flue spaces occurs soon after initial fire development.

A.3.9.15 Pile Stability, Unstable Piles. Leaning stacks, crushed bottom cartons, and reliance on combustible bands for stability are examples of potential pile instability under a fire condition. An increase in pile height tends to increase instability.

Pile stability is defined in 3.9.14 and 3.9.15. Pile collapse needs to occur before or within 1 to 2 minutes after the first sprinkler operates to be a positive factor in fire control.

3.9.16 Roof Height. The distance between the floor and the underside of the roof deck within the storage area.

3.9.17 Shelf Storage. Storage on structures less than 30 in. (76.2 cm) deep with shelves usually 2 ft (0.6 m) apart vertically and separated by approximately 30-in. (76.2-cm) aisles.

Shelf storage is defined in 3.9.17. The 30-in. (76.2-cm) maximum width is measured from aisle to aisle, as indicated in Exhibit 3.44.

As an example, two back-to-back shelves with an overall width greater than 30 in. (76.2 cm) should be considered solid shelf racks.

◀ **FAQ**
How should multiple shelf units be addressed?

3.9.18 Solid Unit Load of a Nonexpanded Plastic (Either Cartoned or Exposed). A load that does not have voids (air) within the load and that burns only on the exterior of the load; water from sprinklers might reach most surfaces available to burn.

3.9.19 Storage Aids. Commodity storage devices, such as pallets, dunnage, separators, and skids.

3.9.20 Unit Load. A pallet load or module held together in some manner and normally transported by material handling equipment.

EXHIBIT 3.44 Shelf Storage.

3.10 Rack Storage Definitions

3.10.1* Aisle Width. The horizontal dimension between the face of the loads in racks under consideration. *(See Figure A.3.10.1.)*

 A.3.10.1 Aisle Width. See Figure A.3.10.1.

FIGURE A.3.10.1 Illustration of Aisle Width.

3.10.2 Bulkhead. A vertical barrier across the rack.

3.10.3 Cartoned. A method of storage consisting of corrugated cardboard or paperboard containers fully enclosing the commodity.

3.10.4* Conventional Pallets. A material-handling aid designed to support a unit load with openings to provide access for material-handling devices. *(See Figure A.3.10.4.)*

 A.3.10.4 Conventional Pallets. See Figure A.3.10.4.

3.10.5 Face Sprinklers. Standard sprinklers that are located in transverse flue spaces along the aisle or in the rack, are within 18 in. (0.46 m) of the aisle face of storage, and are used to oppose vertical development of fire on the external face of storage.

Conventional pallet

Solid flat bottom
wood pallet (slave pallet)

FIGURE A.3.10.4 *Typical Pallets.*

Face sprinklers, defined in 3.10.5, must be located at transverse flues within racks. Face sprinklers are not effective if located outside the flue space, even if they are within 18 in. (0.46 m) of the rack face. Exhibit 3.45 illustrates a face sprinkler that is not located directly in the transverse flue. Note the wood slat and pallet load just above the sprinkler.

EXHIBIT 3.45 *Face Sprinkler Not Properly Located Within the Transverse Flue.*

3.10.6 Horizontal Barrier. A solid barrier in the horizontal position covering the entire rack, including all flue spaces at certain height increments, to prevent vertical fire spread.

3.10.7* Longitudinal Flue Space. The space between rows of storage perpendicular to the direction of loading. *(See Figure A.3.10.7.)*

FIGURE A.3.10.7 *Typical Double-Row (Back-to-Back) Rack Arrangement.*

A **A.3.10.7 Longitudinal Flue Space.** See Figure A.3.10.7.

3.10.8* Rack. Any combination of vertical, horizontal, and diagonal members that supports stored materials. Some rack structures use solid shelves. Racks can be fixed, portable, or movable. Loading can be either manual—using lift trucks, stacker cranes, or hand placement—or automatic—using machine-controlled storage and retrieval systems.

A **A.3.10.8 Rack.** Rack storage as referred to in this standard contemplates commodities in a rack structure, usually steel. Many variations of dimensions are found. Racks can be single-row, double-row, or multiple-row, with or without solid shelves. The standard commodity used in most of the tests was 42 in. (1.07 m) on a side. The types of racks covered in this standard are as follows:

(1) *Double-Row Racks.* Pallets rest on two beams parallel to the aisle. Any number of pallets can be supported by one pair of beams. *[See Figure A.3.10.8(a) through Figure A.3.10.8(d).]*

(2) *Automatic Storage-Type Rack.* The pallet is supported by two rails running perpendicular to the aisle. *[See Figure A.3.10.8(e).]*

(3) *Multiple-Row Racks More than Two Pallets Deep, Measured Aisle to Aisle.* These racks include drive-in racks, drive-through racks, flow-through racks, portable racks arranged in the same manner, and conventional or automatic racks with aisles less than 42 in. (1.07 m) wide. *[See Figure A.3.10.8(f) through Figure A.3.10.8(k).]*

(4) *Movable Racks.* Movable racks are racks on fixed rails or guides. They can be moved back and forth only in a horizontal, two-dimensional plane. A moving aisle is created as abutting racks are either loaded or unloaded, then moved across the aisle to abut other racks. *[See Figure A.3.10.8(k).]*

(5) *Solid Shelving.* Conventional pallet racks with plywood shelves on the shelf beams *[see Figure A.3.10.8(c) and Figure A.3.10.8(d)]*. These racks are used in special cases. *(See Chapter 12.)*

(6) *Cantilever Rack.* The load is supported on arms that extend horizontally from columns. The load can rest on the arms or on shelves supported by the arms. *[See Figure A.3.10.8(j).]*

End View
Double Row   **Aisle View**

L Longitudinal flue space
T Transverse flue space

FIGURE A.3.10.8(a) Conventional Pallet Rack.

A Load depth	G Pallet
B Load width	H Rack depth
E Storage height	L Longitudinal flue space
F Commodity	T Transverse flue space

FIGURE A.3.10.8(b) Double-Row Racks Without Solid or Slatted Shelves.

A Shelf depth	H Rack depth
B Shelf height	L Longitudinal flue space
E Storage height	T Transverse flue space
F Commodity	

FIGURE A.3.10.8(c) Double-Row Racks with Solid Shelves.

A Shelf depth	H Rack depth
B Shelf height	L Longitudinal flue space
E Storage height	T Transverse flue space
F Commodity	

FIGURE A.3.10.8(d) Double-Row Racks with Slatted Shelves.

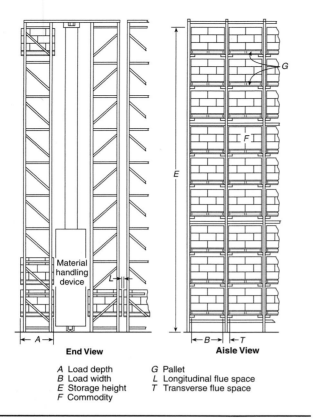

End View

A Load depth   G Pallet
B Load width   L Longitudinal flue space
E Storage height T Transverse flue space
F Commodity

FIGURE A.3.10.8(e) *Automatic Storage-Type Rack.*

End View

L Longitudinal flue space

FIGURE A.3.10.8(f) *Multiple-Row Rack to Be Served by a Reach Truck.*

End View

Aisle View

T Transverse flue space

FIGURE A.3.10.8(g) *Flow-Through Pallet Rack.*

End View

Aisle View

T Transverse flue space

FIGURE A.3.10.8(h) *Drive-In Rack—Two or More Pallets Deep (Fork Truck Drives into the Rack to Deposit and Withdraw Loads in the Depth of the Rack).*

FIGURE A.3.10.8(i) *Flow-Through Racks (Top) and Portable Racks (Bottom).*

FIGURE A.3.10.8(j) *Cantilever Rack.*

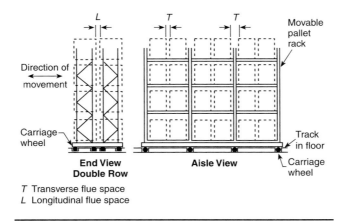

FIGURE A.3.10.8(k) *Movable Rack.*

Load depth in conventional or automatic racks should be considered a nominal 4 ft (1.22 m). *[See Figure A.3.10.8(b).]*

3.10.8.1 Double-Row Racks. Two single-row racks placed back-to-back having a combined width up to 12 ft (3.7 m), with aisles at least 3.5 ft (1.1 m) on each side.

3.10.8.2 Movable Racks. Racks on fixed rails or guides. They can be moved back and forth only in a horizontal, two-dimensional plane. A moving aisle is created as abutting racks are either loaded or unloaded, then moved across the aisle to abut other racks.

3.10.8.3 Multiple-Row Racks. Racks greater than 12 ft (3.7 m) wide or single- or double-row racks separated by aisles less than 3.5 ft (1.1 m) wide having an overall width greater than 12 ft (3.7 m).

3.10.8.4 Portable Racks. Racks that are not fixed in place. They can be arranged in any number of configurations.

3.10.8.5 Single-Row Racks. Racks that have no longitudinal flue space and that have a width up to 6 ft (1.8 m) with aisles at least 3.5 ft (1.1 m) from other storage.

3.10.9 Slave Pallet. A special pallet captive to a material-handling system. *(See Figure A.3.10.4.)*

 3.10.10 Solid Shelving. Solid shelving is fixed in place, slatted, wire mesh or other type of shelves located within racks. The area of a solid shelf is defined by perimeter aisle or flue space on all four sides. Solid shelves having an area equal to or less than 20 ft^2 shall be defined as open racks. Shelves of wire mesh, slates, or other materials more than 50 percent open and where the flue spaces are maintained shall be defined as open racks.

Exhibit 3.46 illustrates a storage rack with solid shelving, which is defined in 3.10.10.

EXHIBIT 3.46 *Storage Rack with Solid Shelving.*

3.10.11 Transverse Flue Space. The space between rows of storage parallel to the direction of loading. *(See Figure A.3.10.7.)*

3.11 Rubber Tire Storage Definitions

3.11.1 Banded Tires. A storage method in which a number of tires are strapped together.

3.11.2 Horizontal Channel. Any uninterrupted space in excess of 5 ft (1.5 m) in length between horizontal layers of stored tires. Such channels can be formed by pallets, shelving, racks, or other storage arrangements.

3.11.3 Laced Tire Storage. Tires stored where the sides of the tires overlap, creating a woven or laced appearance. *[See Figure A.3.11.9(g).]*

3.11.4* Miscellaneous Tire Storage. The storage of rubber tires that is incidental to the main use of the building. Storage areas shall not exceed 2000 ft² (186 m²). On-tread storage piles, regardless of storage method, shall not exceed 25 ft (7.6 m) in the direction of the wheel holes. Acceptable storage arrangements include (a) on-floor, on-side storage up to 12 ft (3.7 m) high; (b) on-floor, on-tread storage up to 5 ft (1.5 m) high; (c) double-row or multirow fixed or portable rack storage on-side or on-tread up to 5 ft (1.5 m) high; (d) single row fixed or portable rack storage on-side or on-tread up to 12 ft (3.7 m) high; and (e) laced tires in racks up to 5 ft (1.5 m) in height.

A.3.11.4 Miscellaneous Tire Storage. The limitations on the type and size of storage are intended to identify those situations where tire storage is present in limited quantities and incidental to the main use of the building. Occupancies such as aircraft hangars, automobile dealers, repair garages, retail storage facilities, automotive and truck assembly plants, and mobile home assembly plants are types of facilities where miscellaneous storage could be present.

3.11.5 On-Side Tire Storage. Tires stored horizontally or flat.

3.11.6 On-Tread Tire Storage. Tires stored vertically or on their treads.

3.11.7 Palletized Tire Storage. Storage on portable racks of various types utilizing a conventional pallet as a base.

3.11.8 Pyramid Tire Storage. On-floor storage in which tires are formed into a pyramid to provide pile stability.

3.11.9* Rubber Tire Rack Illustrations. See Figure A.3.11.9(a) through Figure A.3.11.9(g).

A.3.11.9 Rubber Tire Rack Illustrations. Figure A.3.11.9(a) through Figure A.3.11.9(g) do not necessarily cover all possible rubber tire storage configurations.

3.11.10 Rubber Tires. Pneumatic tires for passenger automobiles, aircraft, light and heavy trucks, trailers, farm equipment, construction equipment (off-the-road), and buses.

3.12 Baled Cotton Definitions

3.12.1* Baled Cotton. A natural seed fiber wrapped and secured in industry-accepted materials, usually consisting of burlap, woven polypropylene or sheet polyethylene, and secured with steel, synthetic or wire bands, or wire; can also include linters (lint removed from the cottonseed) and motes (residual materials from the ginning process). *(See Table A.3.12.1.)*

FIGURE A.3.11.9(a)
Typical Open Portable Tire Rack Unit.

FIGURE A.3.11.9(b) *Typical Palletized Portable Tire Rack Units.*

FIGURE A.3.11.9(c) *Open Portable Tire Rack.*

A Load depth	G Pallet
B Load width	H Rack depth
E Storage height	L Longitudinal flue space
F Commodity	T Transverse flue space

FIGURE A.3.11.9(d) *Double-Row Fixed Tire Rack Storage.*

FIGURE A.3.11.9(e) *Palletized Portable Tire Rack, On-Side Storage Arrangement (Banded or Unbanded).*

FIGURE A.3.11.9(f) *On-Floor Storage; On-Tread, Normally Banded.*

FIGURE A.3.11.9(g) *Typical Laced Tire Storage.*

A.3.12.1 Baled Cotton. See Table A.3.12.1.

A

3.12.2 Block Cotton Storage. The number of bales closely stacked in cubical form and enclosed by aisles or building sides, or both.

3.12.3 Cold Cotton. Baled cotton five or more days old after the ginning process.

3.12.4 Fire-Packed. A bale within which a fire has been packed as a result of a process, with ginning being the most frequent cause.

3.12.5 Naked Cotton Bale. A bale secured with wire or steel straps without wrapping.

3.13 Roll Paper Definitions

3.13.1 Array (Paper).

3.13.1.1 Closed Array (Paper). A vertical storage arrangement in which the distances between columns in both directions are short [not more than 2 in. (50 mm) in one direction and 1 in. (25 mm) in the other].

TABLE A.3.12.1 *Typical Cotton Bale Types and Approximate Sizes*

	Dimensions		Average Weight		Volume		Density	
Bale Type	in.	mm	lb	kg	ft³	m³	lb/ft³	kg/m³
Gin, flat	55 × 45 × 28	1397 × 1143 × 711	500	226.8	40.1	1.13	12.5	201
Modified gin, flat	55 × 45 × 24	1397 × 1143 × 610	500	226.8	34.4	0.97	14.5	234
Compressed, standard	57 × 29 × 23	1448 × 736 × 584	500	226.8	22.0	0.62	22.7	366
Gin, standard	55 × 31 × 21	1397 × 787 × 533	500	226.9	20.7	0.58	24.2	391
Compressed, universal	58 × 25 × 21	1475 × 635 × 533	500	226.8	17.6	0.50	28.4	454
Gin, universal	55 × 26 × 21	1397 × 660 × 533	500	226.8	17.4	0.49	28.7	463
Compressed, high density	58 × 22 × 21	1473 × 559 × 533	500	226.8	15.5	0.44	32.2	515

3.13.1.2 Open Array (Paper). A vertical storage arrangement in which the distance between columns in both directions is lengthy (all vertical arrays other than closed or standard).

3.13.1.3* Standard Array (Paper). A vertical storage arrangement in which the distance between columns in one direction is short [1 in. (25 mm) or less] and is in excess of 2 in. (50 mm) in the other direction.

A **A.3.13.1.3 Standard Array (Paper).** The occasional presence of partially used rolls on top of columns of otherwise uniform diameter rolls does not appreciably affect the burning characteristics.

3.13.2 Banded Roll Paper Storage. Rolls provided with a circumferential steel strap [⅜ in. (9.5 mm) or wider] at each end of the roll.

3.13.3 Column. A single vertical stack of rolls.

3.13.4 Core. The central tube around which paper is wound to form a roll.

3.13.5 Paper (General Term). The term for all kinds of felted sheets made from natural fibrous materials, usually vegetable but sometimes mineral or animal, and formed on a fine wire screen from water suspension.

3.13.6 Roll Paper Storage.

3.13.6.1 Horizontal Roll Paper Storage. Rolls stored with the cores in the horizontal plane (on-side storage).

3.13.6.2 Vertical Roll Paper Storage. Rolls stored with the cores in the vertical plane (on-end storage).

3.13.6.3* Wrapped Roll Paper Storage. Rolls provided with a complete heavy kraft covering around both sides and ends.

A **A.3.13.6.3 Wrapped Roll Paper Storage.** Rolls that are completely protected with a heavy-weight kraft wrapper on both sides and ends are subject to a reduced degree of fire hazard. Standard methods for wrapping and capping rolls are outlined in Figure A.3.13.6.3.

In some cases, rolls are protected with laminated wrappers, using two sheets of heavy kraft with a high-temperature wax laminate between the sheets. Where using this method, the overall weight of wax-laminated wrappers should be based on the basis weight per 1000 ft^2 (92.9 m^2) of the outer sheet only, rather than on the combined basis weight of the outer and inner laminated wrapper sheets. A properly applied wrapper can have the effect of changing the class of a given paper to essentially that of the wrapper material. The effect of applying a wrapper to tissue has not been determined by test.

3.13.7* Roll Paper Storage Height. The maximum vertical distance above the floor at which roll paper is normally stored.

A **A.3.13.7 Roll Paper Storage Height.** The size of rolls and limitations of mechanical handling equipment should be considered in determining maximum storage height.

3.14 Marine Definitions

These definitions apply to Chapter 17 only.

 3.14.1 A-Class Boundary. A boundary designed to resist the passage of smoke and flame for 1 hour when tested in accordance with ASTM E 119, *Standard Test Methods for Fire Tests of Building Construction and Materials.*

Wrapper
Exterior wrapper
Body wrapper

General term for protective wrapping of sides and ends on roll.

Body wrap
Sleeve wrap
Wrap — do not cap

Wrapper placed around circumference of roll. No heads or caps needed.

Heads
Headers

Protection applied to the ends of the rolls (*A* and *B*). Heads do not lap over the end of the roll.

Inside heads

Protection applied to the ends of the rolls next to the roll itself (*B*). The wrapper of the rolls is crimped down over these heads.

Outside heads

Protection applied to the ends of the rolls on the outside (*A*). This head is applied after the wrapper is crimped.

Edge protectors
Edge bands

Refers to extra padding to prevent damage to roll edges (*C*).

Overwrap

The distance the body wrap or wrapper overlaps itself (*D*).

Roll cap

A protective cover placed over the end of a roll. Edges of cap lap over the end of the roll and are secured to the sides of the roll.

FIGURE A.3.13.6.3 *Wrapping and Capping Terms and Methods.*

3.14.2 B-Class Boundary. A boundary designed to resist the passage of flame for ½ hour when tested in accordance with ASTM E 119, *Standard Test Methods for Fire Tests of Building Construction and Materials.*

3.14.3 Central Safety Station. A continuously manned control station from which all of the fire control equipment is monitored. If this station is not the bridge, direct communication with the bridge shall be provided by means other than the ship's service telephone.

The central safety station, which is defined in 3.14.3, is typically the bridge.

3.14.4* Heat-Sensitive Material. A material whose melting point is below 1700°F (926.7°C).

A.3.14.4 Heat-Sensitive Material. The backbone of the fire protection philosophy for U.S. flagged vessels and passenger vessels that trade internationally is limiting a fire to the compartment of origin by passive means. Materials that do not withstand a 1-hour fire exposure when tested in accordance with ASTM E 119, *Standard Test Methods for Fire Tests of Building Construction and Materials,* are considered "heat sensitive." *(See Figure A.3.14.4.)*

FIGURE A.3.14.4 *International Shore Fire Connection.*

 Ships are highly compartmentalized by passive fire barrier systems, such as bulkheads (walls) and decks (floors). Overall, shipboard fire protection places a greater emphasis on passive fire safety systems than on active fire suppression systems, such as automatic sprinklers. An assembly that is not expected to withstand fire exposure for 1 hour in accordance with the time—temperature profile of ASTM E 119, *Standard Test Methods for Fire Tests of Building Construction and Materials,* is considered heat sensitive. The fire endurance of materials, such as piping, that penetrate fire barriers on ships must be tested dry so that a failure of the sprinkler system would not cause a failure of the passive system.

3.14.5 Heel. The inclination of a ship to one side.

3.14.6 Heel Angle. The angle defined by the intersection of a vertical line through the center of a vessel and a line perpendicular to the surface of the water.

Exhibit 3.47 illustrates measurement of the heel angle, which is defined in 3.14.6.

 3.14.7 International Shore Connection. A universal connection complying with ASTM F 1121, *Standard Specification for International Shore Connections for Marine Fire Applications,* to which shoreside fire-fighting hose are to be connected.

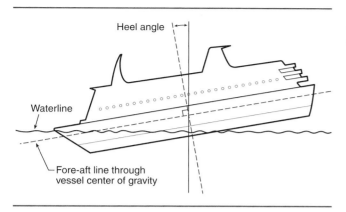

EXHIBIT 3.47 *Measurement of the Heel Angle. (Courtesy of Morgan Hurley)*

3.14.8* Marine System. A sprinkler system installed on a ship, boat, or other floating structure that takes its supply from the water on which the vessel floats.

A.3.14.8 Marine System. Some types of sprinkler systems can closely resemble marine systems, such as a system installed on a floating structure that has a permanent water supply connection to a public main. For these types of systems, judgment should be used in determining if certain aspects of Chapter 17 are applicable.

Marine system is defined in 3.14.8. Although originally intended only for application to ships, other types of waterborne structures were recognized to more closely resemble ships than buildings. Examples include restaurants and casinos that are built on permanently moored barges. Where a sprinkler system on a floating structure takes its water supply from the water on which the structure floats, as opposed to from a permanent water main, the sprinkler system must comply with Chapter 17.

3.14.9* Marine Thermal Barrier. An assembly that is constructed of noncombustible materials and made intact with the main structure of the vessel, such as shell, structural bulkheads, and decks. A marine thermal barrier shall meet the requirements of a B-Class boundary. In addition, a marine thermal barrier shall be insulated such that, if tested in accordance with ASTM E 119, *Standard Test Methods for Fire Tests of Building Construction and Materials,* for 15 minutes, the average temperature of the unexposed side does not rise more than 250°F (193°C) above the original temperature, nor does the temperature at any one point, including any joint, rise more than 405°F (225°C) above the original temperature.

A.3.14.9 Marine Thermal Barrier. A marine thermal barrier is typically referred to as a B-15 boundary.

3.14.10 Supervision. A visual and audible alarm signal given at the central safety station to indicate when the system is in operation or when a condition that would impair the satisfactory operation of the system exists. Supervisory alarms shall give a distinct indication for each individual system component that is monitored.

3.14.11 Survival Angle. The maximum angle to which a vessel is permitted to heel after the assumed damage required by stability regulations is imposed.

The survival angle, defined in 3.14.11, for a ship is typically calculated when the ship is designed. A sprinkler designer would likely need to consult with a vessel's representative, such as the captain or naval architect, to determine the survival angle. The sprinkler system equipment is selected to remain functional at this angle of inclination.

◀ **FAQ**
Do the requirements of Chapter 17 apply to float structures such as restaurants and casinos that are either mobile or permanently moored?

3.14.12 Type 1 Stair. A fully enclosed stair that serves all levels of a vessel in which persons can be employed.

3.14.13 Marine Water Supply. The supply portion of the sprinkler system from the water pressure tank or the sea suction of the designated sprinkler system pump up to and including the valve that isolates the sprinkler system from these two water sources.

SUMMARY

Many of the terms used throughout NFPA 13 are unique to sprinkler systems and have been defined in Chapter 3 to assist with the use and application of NFPA 13. The terms defined in Chapter 3 are an integral part of using and applying the requirements of NFPA 13. Where a term has been defined in Chapter 3, it is important to ensure that the use and application of that term matches the defined term in Chapter 3.

 ## REFERENCES CITED IN COMMENTARY

National Fire Protection Association, 1 Batterymarch Park, P.O. Box 9101, Quincy, MA 02269-9101

NFPA 13D, *Standard for the Installation of Sprinkler Systems in One- and Two-Family Dwellings and Manufactured Homes,* 2002 edition
NFPA 15, *Standard for Water Spray Fixed Systems for Fire Protection,* 2001 edition
NFPA 20, *Standard for the Installation of Stationary Pumps for Fire Protection,* 1999 edition
NFPA 22, *Standard for Water Tanks for Private Fire Protection,* 1998 edition
NFPA 30, *Flammable and Combustible Liquids Code,* 2000 edition
NFPA 30B, *Code for the Manufacture and Storage of Aerosol Products,* 2002 edition
NFPA 72®, National Fire Alarm Code®, 2002 edition
NFPA 220, *Standard of Types of Building Construction,* 1999 edition
NFPA 5000™, Building Construction and Safety Code™, 2003 edition

American Society for Testing and Materials, 100 Barr Harbor Drive, West Conshohocken, PA 19428-2959

ASTM E 119, *Standard Test Methods for Fire Tests of Building Construction and Materials,* 2000 edition

General Requirements

Chapter 4 was created during the *Manual of Style* reformatting of NFPA 13. Chapter 4 contains the general requirements that apply to all of NFPA 13. Items covered in Chapter 4 include level of protection, limited area systems, and owners' certificates.

4.1 Level of Protection

A building, where protected by an automatic sprinkler system installation, shall be provided with sprinklers in all areas except where specific sections of this standard permit the omission of sprinklers.

The oldest and most important design rule of NFPA 13, as stated in Section 4.1, is that sprinklers should be installed in all areas of a building. The few exceptions to this rule are associated with specific conditions and are relatively new revisions to the standard. Some of those who use NFPA 13 are under the impression that certain areas, such as electrical equipment rooms, closets, bank vaults, or walk-in coolers and freezers, do not require sprinklers. However, unless a specific paragraph in Chapter 5 gives explicit permission to omit sprinklers, sprinklers are required in all spaces of a building.

The success of a sprinkler system largely depends on the size of the fire when the first few sprinklers activate. If the fire grows to a relatively large size before sprinklers operate, the likelihood of successful sprinkler system performance in terms of fire control or fire suppression is significantly reduced. Sprinkler systems designed in accordance with NFPA 13 are not intended to prevent a fire in an unsprinklered area from spreading into a sprinklered area.

◀ FAQ
If NFPA 13 does not specifically state that sprinklers are required in a particular area, are sprinklers required?

4.2 Limited Area Systems

Section 4.2 acknowledges that certain codes or local ordinances might permit the installation of a partial or limited area sprinkler system. For example, NFPA *101®*, *Life Safety Code®*, recognizes a limited area sprinkler system in certain residential occupancies. This type of system is installed in the corridors along with one sprinkler just inside the door of each dwelling unit. This system is intended to provide additional time for the occupants to escape. Such a system cannot be expected to control a fire so as to minimize property damage, and therefore property damage would most likely be quite severe.

4.2.1 When partial sprinkler systems are installed, the requirements of this standard shall be used insofar as they are applicable.

4.2.2 The authority having jurisdiction shall be consulted in each case.

4.3 Owners' Certificate

The owner(s) of a building or structure where the fire sprinkler system is going to be installed or their authorized agent shall provide the sprinkler systems installer with the following information prior to the layout and detailing of the fire sprinkler system (*See Figure A.14.1(b)*):

(1) Intended use of the building including the materials within the building and the maximum height of any storage

(2) A preliminary plan of the building or structure along with the design concepts necessary to perform the layout and detail for the fire sprinkler system

(3) Any special knowledge of the water supply including known environmental conditions that might be responsible for microbiologically influenced corrosion (MIC)

 The owner's certificate described in Section 4.3 improves communication between the owner or owner's agent and the installing contractor. [See Figure A.14.1(b) for an example of an owner's certificate.] For any sprinkler system installation, the owner is in the best position to determine the intended use of the building, and it is important that such use be established in advance to ensure that the capability of the sprinkler system is adequate to address the hazard. Professional designers acting in the capacity of owner's agents must be sure that they have been given complete information so they can accurately fill out the certificate. The questions relating to special occupancies, materials, and areas emphasize the need to reference appropriate sprinkler discharge criteria, whether found within this standard or in NFPA 30, *Flammable and Combustible Liquids Code;* NFPA 30B, *Code for the Manufacture and Storage of Aerosol Products;* or NFPA 409, *Standard on Aircraft Hangars.*

The owner's certificate can be used to accompany preliminary plans, which generally contain the design concept and are part of the construction documents submitted for new construction. New model building codes make the distinction between construction documents and fire protection system shop drawings. Construction documents are submitted to obtain building permits. Fire protection system shop drawings are submitted for approval prior to the start of system installation and contain the detailed information required by this standard.

The owner's certificate should also ask if there is any evidence that would suggest that water supplies should be specially treated against microbiologically influenced corrosion (MIC). This is a fairly rare but severe phenomenon occurring in metallic piping systems that appears related to specific characteristics of a water supply. Water treatment systems are available to help prevent MIC from occurring and can be considered where there has been prior adverse experience of this type. See Supplement 2 for more information on microbiologically influenced corrosion.

SUMMARY

Chapter 4 covers NFPA 13 general requirements. Level of protection, limited use systems, and owners' certificates are described herein.

 REFERENCES CITED IN COMMENTARY

National Fire Protection Association, 1 Batterymarch Park, P.O. Box 9101, Quincy, MA 02269-9101

NFPA 30, *Flammable and Combustible Liquids Code,* 2000 edition
NFPA 30B, *Code for the Manufacture and Storage of Aerosol Products,* 2002 edition
NFPA *101*®, *Life Safety Code*®, 2000 edition
NFPA 409, *Standard on Aircraft Hangars,* 2001 edition

Classification of Occupancies and Commodities

Chapter 5 provides information on the classification of occupancy hazards previously found in Chapter 2 of the 1999 edition of NFPA 13 and the description of storage commodities formerly found in NFPA 231, NFPA 231C, and NFPA 231F. To a large degree, the occupancy hazard classifications form the basis of the design and installation criteria of NFPA 13. The occupancy hazards provide a convenient means of categorizing the fuel loads and fire severity associated with certain building operations. The classifications also present a relationship between the burning characteristics of these fuels and the ability of a sprinkler system in controlling the associated types of fires. The likelihood of ignition is not considered in the occupancy classifications.

5.1* Classification of Occupancies

A.5.1 Occupancy examples in the listings as shown in the various hazard classifications are intended to represent the norm for those occupancy types. Unusual or abnormal fuel loadings or combustible characteristics and susceptibility for changes in these characteristics, for a particular occupancy, are considerations that should be weighed in the selection and classification.

The light hazard classification is intended to encompass residential occupancies; however, this is not intended to preclude the use of listed residential sprinklers in residential occupancies or residential portions of other occupancies.

5.1.1 Occupancy classifications for this standard shall relate to sprinkler design, installation, and water supply requirements only.

5.1.2 Occupancy classifications shall not be intended to be a general classification of occupancy hazards.

The occupancy hazards mentioned in 5.1.2 and presented in NFPA 13 should not be interpreted as a generic description or quantification of fire hazards and are not intended to parallel those identified in other fire safety regulations such as NFPA *101®, Life Safety Code®, NFPA 5000™, Building Construction and Safety Code™,* or other building codes.

A specific operation might present more or less of a hazard, depending on the combustibility, quantity, and arrangement of the building contents. For instance, paperback books in boxes stacked to a height of 6 ft (1.83 m) in the back room of a bookstore present a lower fire hazard than the same books stacked to a height of 12 ft (3.7 m) throughout a warehouse. Accordingly, NFPA 13 categorizes the 6-ft (1.83-m) high stockpile as an ordinary hazard (Group 1) occupancy. The 12-ft (3.7-m) high warehouse storage is considered a Class III commodity and needs to be protected in accordance with the criteria for ordinary hazard (Group II) occupancies.

Proper classification of a fire hazard is critical to the overall success of the sprinkler system. The determination of the type of occupancy hazard influences system design and installation considerations such as sprinkler discharge criteria, sprinkler spacing, and water supply

Are the occupancy hazards contained in NFPA 13 the same as the hazards presented in other NFPA documents?

◀ FAQ

requirements. The operations of a given facility can vary significantly over time and change the overall fire hazard. These potential fluctuations in building operations must be properly accounted for when designing a new sprinkler system or when evaluating the adequacy of an existing sprinkler system.

FAQ ▶
How should occupancy classification be determined?

The proper occupancy hazard classification for a given building operation should be determined by carefully reviewing the descriptions of each occupancy hazard and by evaluating the quantity, combustibility, and heat release rate of the associated contents. To aid in the classification of a building operation, examples for each type of occupancy hazard are provided in Annex A (see A.5.2, A.5.3.2, A.5.3.2, A.5.4.1, and A.5.4.2.) Experience and good judgment play a critical role in properly determining the hazard classification, just as they do in evaluating the adequacy of the entire sprinkler system.

FAQ ▶
Who makes the final determination or acceptability of the occupancy classification?

The final determination or acceptability of the occupancy classification is up to the authority having jurisdiction.

The occupancy hazard classifications are presented as qualitative descriptions rather than quantifiable measurements. Ideally, quantification of key factors such as the fire safety goals of the standard, the likely hazards contained within a specific space, the effect of building geometry and ventilation, and the interaction of sprinkler discharge with the fire would form the basis for NFPA 13. Under a performance-based approach, designers and enforcers would have more flexibility in complying with NFPA 13. Although much of the technology needed for a generic widespread performance-based approach for sprinkler system design is not yet available, testing and research continue to fill the gaps. For instance, performance-based-type approaches have been applied in the development of new types of sprinklers such as the early suppression fast-response (ESFR) sprinkler and residential sprinklers.

5.2* Light Hazard Occupancies

Light hazard occupancies shall be defined as occupancies or portions of other occupancies where the quantity and/or combustibility of contents is low and fires with relatively low rates of heat release are expected.

A.5.2 Light hazard occupancies include occupancies having uses and conditions similar to the following:

> Churches
> Clubs
> Eaves and overhangs, if of combustible construction with no combustibles beneath
> Educational
> Hospitals
> Institutional
> Libraries, except large stack rooms
> Museums
> Nursing or convalescent homes
> Offices, including data processing
> Residential
> Restaurant seating areas
> Theaters and auditoriums, excluding stages and prosceniums
> Unused attics

Of the five occupancy hazard classifications, light hazard occupancies, as described in Section 5.2, represent the least severe fire hazard since the fuel loads associated with these occupancies are low, and relatively small rates of heat release are expected. Generally, no processing, manufacturing, or storage operations are included, and fixtures and furniture remain in fairly permanent arrangements. Light hazard occupancies typically consist of institutional, educational, religious, residential, and office facilities. Sprinkler systems designed to protect against light hazard occupancies, therefore, have less demanding water supply requirements. Additionally, more design flexibility is possible.

5.3 Ordinary Hazard Occupancies

Prior to the 1991 edition, NFPA 13 included three categories of ordinary hazard occupancies, which are described in Section 5.3. The technical committee believed that the small differences between the "old" ordinary 2 and 3 curves had little impact on fire control. See the density/area curve comparison in Exhibit 5.1. The wide range of occupancies addressed by the overall ordinary hazard classification and the associated water supply requirements are better served by two categories of ordinary hazard rather than three.

    Within the ordinary hazard classification, Group 1 occupancies present the least severe fire. Group 1 occupancies are mostly light manufacturing and service industries where the use of flammable and combustible liquids or gases is either nonexistent or very limited. Stockpiles of combustible commodities typically found within an ordinary hazard (Group 1) occupancy cannot exceed a height of 8 ft (2.4 m). Additionally, the quantity and arrangement of the stockpiles cannot exceed the limitations of miscellaneous storage as defined in Chapter 3. If the miscellaneous storage limitations are exceeded, then the Chapter 12 provisions related to storage apply.

    The ordinary hazard (Group 2) classification addresses those ordinary hazard occupancies that do not meet the criteria of the Group 1 classification. Group 2 occupancies present a more severe fire hazard and demand more from the sprinkler system to achieve fire control than do Group 1 and light hazard occupancies. Ordinary hazard (Group 2) occupancies include those types of manufacturing and processing operations in which the amount and combustibility of contents is greater than that for Group 1. The Group 2 category also addresses the miscellaneous storage of contents stored up to and including 12 ft (3.7 m) in height.

5.3.1* Ordinary Hazard (Group 1). Ordinary hazard (Group 1) occupancies shall be defined as occupancies or portions of other occupancies where combustibility is low, quantity of combustibles is moderate, stockpiles of combustibles do not exceed 8 ft (2.4 m), and fires with moderate rates of heat release are expected.

◀ **FAQ**
What happened to the requirements for ordinary hazard (Group 3) occupancies?

EXHIBIT 5.1 Density/Area Curve Comparison.

For SI units, 1 ft² = 0.092 m²; 1 gpm/ft² = 40.746 (L/min)/m².

A.5.3.1 Ordinary hazard occupancies (Group 1) include occupancies having uses and conditions similar to the following:

> Automobile parking and showrooms
> Bakeries
> Beverage manufacturing
> Canneries
> Dairy products manufacturing and processing
> Electronic plants
> Glass and glass products manufacturing
> Laundries
> Restaurant service areas

5.3.2* Ordinary Hazard (Group 2). Ordinary hazard (Group 2) occupancies shall be defined as occupancies or portions of other occupancies where the quantity and combustibility of contents are moderate to high, stockpiles do not exceed 12 ft (3.7 m), and fires with moderate to high rates of heat release are expected.

 A.5.3.2 Ordinary hazard occupancies (Group 2) include occupancies having uses and conditions similar to the following:

> Cereal mills
> Chemical plants—ordinary
> Confectionery products
> Distilleries
> Dry cleaners
> Feed mills
> Horse stables
> Leather goods manufacturing
> Libraries—large stack room areas

FAQ ▶
What is meant by "Libraries—large stack room areas" and what should be classified as a large stack room area?

The segregation between the ordinary hazard (Group 2) category for library stack rooms, listed in A.5.3.2, and the light hazard occupancy category for library reading areas is not an appropriate separation in most situations. The light hazard separation is based on the library having an area composed of tables, chairs, and perhaps some magazine racks and individual bookshelves. When this type of seating area exists, the rules for light hazard apply. Those areas of the library used primarily for book storage on shelves are considered stack areas, and the rules for ordinary hazard apply.

> Machine shops
> Metal working
> Mercantile
> Paper and pulp mills
> Paper process plants
> Piers and wharves
> Post offices
> Printing and publishing
> Repair garages
> Resin application area
> Stages
> Textile manufacturing
> Tire manufacturing
> Tobacco products manufacturing
> Wood machining
> Wood product assembly

5.4 Extra Hazard Occupancies

Extra hazard occupancies, described in Section 5.4, represent the most severe fire conditions addressed under the occupancy hazard classifications in NFPA 13 and present the most severe challenge to sprinkler protection. The extra hazard (Group 1) occupancies include those with hydraulic machinery or systems with flammable or combustible hydraulic fluids under pressure. Ruptures and leaks in piping or fittings have resulted in fine spray discharge of such liquids, causing intense fires. Those occupancies with process machinery that use flammable or combustible fluids in closed systems are extra hazard (Group 1). Also in this group are occupancies that have dust and lint in suspension or that contain moderate amounts of combustible cellular foam materials. Buildings used for textile manufacturing are an example of an extra hazard occupancy.

Extra hazard (Group 2) occupancies contain more than small amounts of flammable or combustible liquids, usually in open systems where rapid evaporation can occur when these liquids are subjected to high temperatures.

The extra hazard (Group 2) occupancy classification also applies where ceiling sprinklers are severely obstructed by occupancy, not structural, conditions and where water discharged by sprinklers may not reach the burning material because of the shielding.

The extra hazard occupancy examples are classified on the basis of actual field experience with sprinkler system operations in occupancies having conditions similar to those identified.

5.4.1* Extra Hazard (Group 1). Extra hazard (Group 1) occupancies shall be defined as occupancies or portions of other occupancies where the quantity and combustibility of contents are very high and dust, lint, or other materials are present, introducing the probability of rapidly developing fires with high rates of heat release but with little or no combustible or flammable liquids.

A.5.4.1 Extra hazard occupancies (Group 1) include occupancies having uses and conditions similar to the following:

Aircraft hangars (except as governed by NFPA 409, *Standard on Aircraft Hangars*)
Combustible hydraulic fluid use areas
Die casting
Metal extruding
Plywood and particle board manufacturing
Printing [using inks having flash points below 100°F (38°C)]
Rubber reclaiming, compounding, drying, milling, vulcanizing
Saw mills
Textile picking, opening, blending, garnetting, or carding, combining of cotton,
    synthetics, wool shoddy, or burlap
Upholstering with plastic foams

5.4.2* Extra Hazard (Group 2). Extra hazard (Group 2) occupancies shall be defined as occupancies or portions of other occupancies with moderate to substantial amounts of flammable or combustible liquids or occupancies where shielding of combustibles is extensive.

A.5.4.2 Extra hazard occupancies (Group 2) include occupancies having uses and conditions similar to the following:

Asphalt saturating
Flammable liquids spraying
Flow coating
Manufactured home or modular building assemblies (where finished enclosure
    is present and has combustible interiors)

Open oil quenching
Plastics processing
Solvent cleaning
Varnish and paint dipping

5.5* Special Occupancy Hazards

A.5.5 Other NFPA standards contain design criteria for fire control or fire suppression *(see Section 5.5 and Chapter 2).* While these can form the basis of design criteria, this standard describes the methods of design, installation, fabrication, calculation, and evaluation of water supplies that should be used for the specific design of the system.

Other NFPA standards contain sprinkler system design criteria for fire control or suppression of specific hazards. This information has been either referenced or copied into Chapter 13 using NFPA's extract policy.

Special occupancy hazards are described in Section 5.5. NFPA 13 was reorganized in 1999 to provide the basis for methods of sprinkler system design, installation, fabrication, calculation, and evaluation of water supplies for specific designs. Under this reorganization, a detailed review of the fire sprinkler design requirements in other NFPA standards was performed by the sprinkler technical committees. As a result of these reviews, information from these other standards is cited or referenced in Chapter 13 to facilitate the user's access to relevant requirements and related information.

Many buildings now contain several different types of occupancies. A simple example of this is a restaurant, where for purposes of sprinkler protection, food preparation areas are treated as ordinary hazard (Group 1), while the public seating areas are handled as light hazard. On a larger scale, a grocery store contains a public shopping area, which is usually treated as an ordinary hazard (Group 2) occupancy. In many cases, however, the back room areas not within the mercantile operation will likely contain some quantity of bulk storage. Although it is reasonable to expect that a higher degree of fire protection would be needed in the back room, older editions of NFPA 13 did not provide guidance.

The storage of bulk items in a back room is similar to a warehouse operation, although on a smaller scale, and requires special consideration. Depending on the size of the back room area and the type, quantity, and arrangement of items stored, the space needs to be protected in accordance with the provisions for miscellaneous storage in 12.1.10 or protected in accordance with the storage requirements of Chapter 12. The concept of miscellaneous storage is included to allow for correlation between occupancy and commodity classifications.

The protection schemes shown in Table 12.1.10 were developed by completing a comparative analysis of design curves for 12-ft (3.7-m) storage of the appropriate commodity classes as defined in 5.6.3. In all cases, the design criteria for commodity storage could be approximated by a design point in Figure 12.1.10.

For example, wood window frames are stored in cardboard boxes on wood pallets to a height of 10 ft (3 m). This storage is incidental to another occupancy (a hardware store).

According to Table A.5.6.3, wood window frames are considered a Class III commodity. Assuming the use of 165°F (74°C) sprinklers, the design criteria from 12.1.10 result in a density/area protection scheme of 0.19 gpm/ft^2 [7.74 (L/min)/m^2] over a 2000-ft^2 (186-m^2) area of operation. It is important to note that an adjustment was made to the density for a 12-ft (3.7-m) storage height, since the criteria in 12.1.10 terminate at a 12-ft (3.7-m) minimum storage height.

Table 12.1.10 refers the designer to the criteria for curve 3 of Figure 12.1.10, which requires a density of 0.19 gpm/ft^2 [7.74 (L/min)/m^2] for a 2000-ft^2 (186-m^2) area of operation.

While the methodology used to establish the information contained in Table 12.1.10 is not exact, it does provide a good correlation between the commodity storage requirements and the general occupancy hazard requirements for most commodity classes. Some of the protection rows were intentionally left blank because no test data supports the use of any precise design criteria for certain combinations of storage and clearance.

5.6* Commodity Classification

See Section C.2.

A.5.6 Specification of the type, amount, and arrangement of combustibles for any commodity classification is essentially an attempt to define the potential fire severity, based on its burning characteristics, so the fire can be successfully controlled by the prescribed sprinkler protection for the commodity class. In actual storage situations, however, many storage arrays do not fit precisely into one of the fundamental classifications; therefore, the user needs to make judgments after comparing each classification to the existing storage conditions. Storage arrays consist of thousands of products, which make it impossible to specify all the acceptable variations for any class. As an alternative, a variety of common products are classified in this appendix based on judgment, loss experience, and fire test results.

Table A.5.6 provides examples of commodities not addressed by the classifications in Section 5.6.

TABLE A.5.6 *Examples of Commodities Not Addressed by the Classifications in Section 5.6*

Boxes, Crates
 —Empty, wood slatted*

Lighters (butane)
 —Loose in large containers (Level 3 aerosol)

*Should be treated as idle pallets.

EXHIBIT 5.2 *Standard Class II Commodity. (Courtesy of FM Global)*

Table A.5.6.3 is an alphabetized list of commodities with corresponding classifications.

Table A.5.6.3.1 through Table A.5.6.3.4 and Table A.5.6.4.1 provide examples of commodities within a specific class.

5.6.1 General.

Subsection 5.6.1 describes the classification of commodities. Protection standards for stored commodities are based on testing that primarily involves the standard Class II and standard plastic commodities. The standard Class II commodity is a double tri-wall corrugated cardboard carton with a metal liner on a wood pallet, as shown in Exhibit 5.2. The standard plastic commodity is polystyrene cups in a compartmented corrugated cardboard carton on a wood pallet (see Exhibit 5.3).

Protection for Class I, III, and IV commodities is based on limited testing and extrapolation from testing on Class II commodities. (No Class I tests, two Class III tests, and two Class IV tests were done.)

Classification of actual commodities is primarily based on comparing the commodity to the definitions for the various commodity classes. Commodity classification can also be done by testing, but it is important that such testing involve sprinklers or some other method to simulate water application by sprinklers and be large enough in scale to produce meaningful results. Bench-scale testing is not useful for making precise commodity classifications.

5.6.1.1* Classification of Commodities.

A.5.6.1.1 Commodity classification is governed by the types and amounts of materials (e.g., metal, paper, wood, plastics) that are a part of a product and its primary packaging. However,

EXHIBIT 5.3 *Standard Plastic Commodity. (Courtesy of FM Global)*

in a storage or warehousing situation, classification is also affected by such factors as the primary storage or shipping container material, the amount of air space, and the location of the more hazardous materials within the container. For example, a Group A plastic product enclosed in a five- or six-sided metal container can be considered Class II, while a ceramic product heavily wrapped in tissue paper and placed in a corrugated carton could be Class III.

5.6.1.1.1 Commodity classification and the corresponding protection requirements shall be determined based on the makeup of individual storage units (i.e., unit load, pallet load).

5.6.1.1.2 When specific test data of commodity classification by a nationally recognized testing agency are available, the data shall be permitted to be used in determining classification of commodities.

5.6.1.2 Mixed Commodities.

5.6.1.2.1 Protection requirements shall not be based on the overall commodity mix in a fire area.

5.6.1.2.2 Unless the requirements of 5.6.1.2.3 or 5.6.1.2.4 are met, mixed commodity storage shall be protected by the requirements for the highest classified commodity and storage arrangement.

5.6.1.2.3 The protection requirements for the lower commodity class shall be permitted to be utilized where all of the following are met:

(1) Up to 10 pallet loads of a higher hazard commodity, as described in 5.6.3 and 5.6.4, shall be permitted to be present in an area not exceeding 40,000 ft^2 (3716 m^2).
(2) The higher hazard commodity shall be randomly dispersed with no adjacent loads in any direction (including diagonally).
(3) Where the ceiling protection is based on Class I or Class II commodities, the allowable number of pallet loads for Class IV or Group A plastics shall be reduced to five.

5.6.1.2.4 Mixed Commodity Segregation. The protection requirements for the lower commodity class shall be permitted to be utilized in the area of lower commodity class, where the higher hazard material is confined to a designated area and the area is protected to the higher hazard in accordance with the requirements of this standard.

Mixed commodity segregation is discussed in 5.6.1.2.4. The fire area anticipated during sprinkler design is often mistakenly assumed to be the same as the sprinkler operating area. In fact, the fire area for successfully controlled storage fires seldom exceeds 200 ft^2 (18.6 m^2) in testing, and often is less than 100 ft^2 (9.3 m^2). Regardless of the overall mix of commodities in a storage area, the possibility that 100 ft^2 to 200 ft^2 (9.3 m^2 to 18.6 m^2) of the highest hazard commodity will accumulate always exists.

FAQ ▶
What are the effects of mixed commodities?

FM Global did testing to evaluate the effect of mixing commodities in rack storage. In one test, 20 ft (6.1 m) of storage, encompassing four tiers, consisted of the standard plastic commodity in the bottom tier with the standard Class II commodity in the top three tiers. The second test was similar to the first, except that the plastic commodity was located in the top tier rather than the bottom. In the third test, plastic and Class II commodities were homogeneously mixed in the rack. The testing showed that protection for plastic commodities was needed for all three cases.

5.6.2 Pallet Types.

5.6.2.1 When loads are palletized, the use of wooden or metal pallets shall be assumed in the classification of commodities.

In addition to wood and metal, as described in 5.6.2.1, pallets are constructed of various reinforced and unreinforced plastics. The effect on the commodity classification of the "plastic" type pallets exhibiting different fire characteristics requires consideration. The requirements set forth in 5.6.2.2 through 5.6.2.7 reflect the results of available test data regarding this issue.

5.6.2.2 For Class I through Class IV, when unreinforced polypropylene or high-density polyethylene plastic pallets are used, the classification of the commodity unit shall be increased one class (e.g., Class III will become Class IV and Class IV will become cartoned unexpanded Group A plastics).

5.6.2.3 For Class I through Class IV, when reinforced polypropylene or high-density polyethylene plastic pallets are used, the classification of the commodity unit shall be increased two classes (e.g., Class II will become Class IV and Class III will become cartoned unexpanded Group A plastic commodity). Reinforced polypropylene or reinforced high-density polyethylene plastic pallets shall be marked with a molded symbol to indicate that the pallet is reinforced.

5.6.2.4 For Class I through Class IV when other than polypropylene or high-density polyethylene plastic pallets are used, the classification of the commodity unit shall be determined by specific testing conducted by a national testing laboratory or shall be increased two classes.

5.6.2.5 No increase in the commodity classification shall be required for Group A plastic commodities stored on plastic pallets.

The requirements associated with the impact of the use of plastic pallets on commodity class have been expanded based on available test results. Several types of plastic pallets, including reinforced and unreinforced polypropylene and high-density polyethylene pallets, have been tested using large scale calorimeter fire testing.

Test results from two series of tests reported in UL Project No. 01NK31019, NC4354 and UL Project No. 01NK20682, R18834 provided relevant input regarding necessary commodity adjustments associated with commodities supported on different types of plastic pallets. The test results indicated a range from no increase in commodity class to as much as a two-class increase, depending on the type of plastic pallet tested. Generally, unreinforced polypropylene or high-density polyethylene plastic pallets exhibited a one-class increase in commodity classification. Reinforced polypropylene or high-density polyethylene plastic pallets demonstrated up to a two-class increase.

Exhibit 5.4 illustrates a nonreinforced plastic pallet. See also Exhibits 3.5 and 3.6 for other plastic pallets.

EXHIBIT 5.4 Nonreinforced Plastic Pallet. (Courtesy of ORBIS CORPORATION/ Nucon Beverage Products Group)

5.6.2.6 For ceiling-only sprinkler protection, the requirements of 5.6.2.2 and 5.6.2.3 shall not apply where plastic pallets are used and where the sprinkler system uses spray sprinklers with a K-factor of 16.8.

Available full-scale test data for K-16.8 orifice sprinkler devices demonstrated no need for an increase in commodity classification for plastic pallets, as stated in 5.6.2.6.

5.6.2.7 The requirements of 5.6.2.2 through 5.6.2.4 shall not apply to nonwood pallets that have demonstrated a fire hazard that is equal to or less than wood pallets and are listed as such.

 FAQ ▶
Where can plastic pallets be protected as if they were wood pallets?

Paragraph 5.6.2.7 refers to nonwood pallets that have demonstrated a fire hazard that is equal to or less than wood pallets. Plastic pallets presented a unique challenge for sprinkler protection. Recent studies and product development, along with significant fire testing, have shown that some plastic pallets have been tested and have demonstrated a fire hazard that is equivalent to or less than the fire hazard presented by wood pallets. Plastic pallets meeting these requirements are specifically listed as such. The requirements for adjustments in the commodity classification due to the use of different types of plastic pallets are based on UL 2335 and FM 4995, large-scale calorimeter tests. There are "listed" plastic pallets that exhibit similar fire performance to wood pallets in these tests, and can be treated as equivalent to wood pallets for commodity classification (see Exhibit 5.5). Actual fire test data, from recognized testing laboratories such as FM Global and UL, should be reviewed and taken into account when determining if any unique design requirements are needed when protecting a specific plastic pallet.

EXHIBIT 5.5 *Classified Fire Retardant Plastic Pallet (40 in. × 48 in.) Equivalent to Wood Pallet. (Courtesy of ORBIS CORPORATION/ Nucon Beverage Products Group)*

5.6.3* Commodity Classes.

A.5.6.3 See Table A.5.6.3.

5.6.3.1* Class I. A Class I commodity shall be defined as a noncombustible product that meets one of the following criteria:

(1) Placed directly on wooden pallets
(2) Placed in single-layer corrugated cartons, with or without single-thickness cardboard dividers, with or without pallets
(3) Shrink-wrapped or paper-wrapped as a unit load with or without pallets

A.5.6.3.1 See Table A.5.6.3.1.

5.6.3.2* Class II. A Class II commodity shall be defined as a noncombustible product that is in slatted wooden crates, solid wood boxes, multiple-layered corrugated cartons, or equivalent combustible packaging material, with or without pallets.

A.5.6.3.2 See Table A.5.6.3.2.

5.6.3.3* Class III.

A.5.6.3.3 See Table A.5.6.3.3.

5.6.3.3.1 A Class III commodity shall be defined as a product fashioned from wood, paper, natural fibers, or Group C plastics with or without cartons, boxes, or crates and with or without pallets.

5.6.3.3.2 A Class III commodity shall be permitted to contain a limited amount (5 percent by weight or volume or less) of Group A or Group B plastics.

TABLE A.5.6.3 *Alphabetized Listing of Commodity Classes*

Commodity	Commodity Class
Aerosols	
Cartoned or uncartoned	
—Level 1	Class III
Alcoholic Beverages	
Cartoned or uncartoned	
—Up to 20 percent alcohol in metal, glass, or ceramic containers	Class I
—Up to 20 percent alcohol in wood containers	Class II
Ammunition	
Small arms, shotgun	
—Packaged, cartoned	Class IV
Appliances, Major (e.g., stoves, refrigerators)	
—Not packaged, no appreciable plastic exterior trim	Class I
—Corrugated, cartoned (no appreciable plastic trim)	Class II
Baked Goods	
Cookies, cakes, pies	
—Frozen, packaged in cartons[1]	Class II
—Packaged, in cartons	Class III
Batteries	
Dry cells (nonlithium or similar exotic metals)	
—Packaged in cartons	Class I
—Blister-packed in cartons	Class II
Automobile	
—Filled[2]	Class I
Truck or larger	
—Empty or filled[2]	Group A plastics
Beans	
Dried	
—Packaged, cartoned	Class III
Bottles, Jars	
Empty, cartoned	
—Glass	Class I
—Plastic PET (polyethylene terephthalate)	Class IV
Filled noncombustible powders	
—Plastic PET	Class II
—Glass, cartoned	Class I
—Plastic, cartoned [less than 1 gal (3.8 L)]	Class IV
—Plastic, uncartoned (other than PET), any size	Group A plastics
—Plastic, cartoned or exposed [greater than 1 gal (3.8 L)]	Group A plastics
—Plastic, solid plastic crates	Group A plastics
—Plastic, open plastic crates	Group A plastics
Filled noncombustible liquids	
—Glass, cartoned	Class I
—Plastic, cartoned [less than 5 gal (18.9 L)]	Class I
—Plastic, open or solid plastic crates[3]	Group A plastics
—Plastic, PET	Class I
Boxes, Crates	
—Empty, wood, solid walls	Class II
—Empty, wood, slatted[4]	Outside of scope
Bread	
Wrapped cartoned	Class III
	(Continues)

TABLE A.5.6.3 *Continued*

Commodity	Commodity Class
Butter	
Whipped spread	Class III
Candles	
Packaged, cartoned	
—Treat as expanded plastic	Group A plastics
Candy	
Packaged, cartoned	Class III
Canned Foods	
In ordinary cartons	Class I
Cans	
Metal	
—Empty	Class I
Carpet Tiles	
Cartoned	Group A plastics
Cartons	
Corrugated	
—Unassembled (neat piles)	Class III
—Partially assembled	Class IV
Wax coated, single walled	Group A plastics
Cement	
Bagged	Class I
Cereals	
Packaged, cartoned	Class III
Charcoal	
Bagged	
—Standard	Class III
Cheese	
—Packaged, cartoned	Class III
—Wheels, cartoned	Class III
Chewing Gum	
Packaged, cartoned	Class III
Chocolate	
Packaged, cartoned	Class III
Cloth	
Cartoned and not cartoned	
—Natural fiber, viscose	Class III
—Synthetic[5]	Class IV
Cocoa Products	
Packaged, cartoned	Class III
Coffee	
—Canned, cartoned	Class I
—Packaged, cartoned	Class III
Coffee Beans	
Bagged	Class III
Cotton	
Packaged, cartoned	Class III
Diapers	
—Cotton, linen	Class III
—Disposable with plastics and nonwoven fabric (in cartons)	Class IV
—Disposable with plastics and nonwoven fabric (uncartoned), plastic wrapped	Group A plastics

TABLE A.5.6.3 *Continued*

Commodity	Commodity Class
Dried Foods	
Packaged, cartoned	Class III
Fertilizers	
Bagged	
—Phosphates	Class I
—Nitrates	Class II
Fiberglass Insulation	
—Paper-backed rolls, bagged or unbagged	Class IV
File Cabinets	
Metal	
—Cardboard box or shroud	Class I
Fish or Fish Products	
Frozen	
—Nonwaxed, nonplastic packaging	Class I
—Waxed-paper containers, cartoned	Class II
—Boxed or barreled	Class II
—Plastic trays, cartoned	Class III
Canned	
—Cartoned	Class I
Frozen Foods	
Nonwaxed, nonplastic packaging	Class I
—Waxed-paper containers, cartoned	Class II
—Plastic trays	Class III
Fruit	
Fresh	
—Nonplastic trays or containers	Class I
—With wood spacers	Class I
Furniture	
Wood	
—No plastic coverings or foam plastic cushioning	Class III
—With plastic coverings	Class IV
—With foam plastic cushioning	Group A plastics
Grains—Packaged in Cartons	
—Barley	Class III
—Rice	Class III
—Oats	Class III
Ice Cream	Class I
Leather Goods	Class III
Leather Hides	
Baled	Class II
Light Fixtures	
Nonplastic	
—Cartoned	Class II
Lighters	
Butane	
—Blister-packed, cartoned	Group A plastics
—Loose in large containers (Level 3 aerosol)	Outside of scope
Liquor	
100 proof or less, 1 gal (3.8 L) or less, cartoned	
—Glass (palletized)[6]	Class IV
—Plastic bottles	Class IV

(Continues)

TABLE A.5.6.3 *Continued*

Commodity	Commodity Class
Marble	
Artificial sinks, countertops	
—Cartoned, crated	Class II
Margarine	
—Up to 50 percent oil (in paper or plastic containers)	Class III
—Between 50 percent and 80 percent oil (in any packaging)	Group A plastics
Matches	
Packaged, cartoned	
—Paper	Class IV
—Wood	Group A plastics
Mattresses	
—Standard (box spring)	Class III
—Foam (in finished form)	Group A plastics
Meat, Meat Products	
—Bulk	Class I
—Canned, cartoned	Class I
—Frozen, nonwaxed, nonplastic containers	Class I
—Frozen, waxed-paper containers	Class II
—Frozen, expanded plastic trays	Class II
Metal Desks	
—With plastic tops and trim	Class I
Milk	
—Nonwaxed-paper containers	Class I
—Waxed-paper containers	Class I
—Plastic containers	Class I
—Containers in plastic crates	Group A plastics
Motors	
—Electric	Class I
Nail Polish	
—1-oz to 2-oz (29.6-ml to 59.1-ml) glass, cartoned	Class IV
—1-oz to 2-oz (29.6-ml to 59.1-ml) plastic bottles, cartoned	Group A plastics
Nuts	
—Canned, cartoned	Class I
—Packaged, cartoned	Class III
—Bagged	Class III
Paints	
Friction-top cans, cartoned	
—Water-based (latex)	Class I
—Oil-based	Class IV
Paper Products	
—Books, magazines, stationery, plastic-coated paper food containers, newspapers, cardboard games, or cartoned tissue products	Class III
—Tissue products, uncartoned and plastic wrapped	Group A plastics
Paper, Rolled	
In racks or on side	Class III
—Medium- or heavyweight	
In racks	Class IV
—Lightweight	
Paper, Waxed	
Packaged in cartons	Class IV

TABLE A.5.6.3 *Continued*

Commodity	Commodity Class
Pharmaceuticals	
Pills, powders	
—Glass bottles, cartoned	Class II
—Plastic bottles, cartoned	Class IV
Nonflammable liquids	
—Glass bottles, cartoned	Class II
Photographic Film	
—Motion picture or bulk rolls of film in polycarbonate, polyethylene, or metal cans; polyethylene bagged in cardboard boxes	Class II
—35-mm in metal film cartridges in polyethylene cans in cardboard boxes	Class III
—Paper, in sheets, bagged in polyethylene, in cardboard boxes	Class III
—Rolls in polycarbonate plastic cassettes, bulk wrapped in cardboard boxes	Class IV
Plastic Containers (except PET)	
—Noncombustible liquids or semiliquids in plastic containers less than 5 gal (18.9 L) capacity	Class I
—Noncombustible liquids or semiliquids (such as ketchup) in plastic containers with nominal wall thickness of ¼ in. (6.4 mm) or less and larger than 5 gal (18.9) capacity	Class II
—Noncombustible liquids or semiliquids (such as ketchup) in plastic containers with nominal wall thickness greater than ¼ in. (6.4 mm) and larger than 5 gal (18.9 L) capacity	Group A plastics
Polyurethane	
—Cartoned or uncartoned expanded	Group A plastics
Poultry Products	
—Canned, cartoned	Class I
—Frozen, nonwaxed, nonplastic containers	Class I
—Frozen (on paper or expanded plastic trays)	Class II
Powders	
Ordinary combustibles—free flowing	
—In paper bags (e.g., flour, sugar)	Class II
PVA (polyvinyl alcohol) Resins	
PVC (polyvinyl chloride)	
—Flexible (e.g., cable jackets, plasticized sheets)	Class III
—Rigid (e.g., pipe, pipe fittings)	Class III
—Bagged resins	Class III
Rags	
Baled	
—Natural fibers	Class III
—Synthetic fibers	Class IV
Rubber	
—Natural, blocks in cartons	Class IV
—Synthetic	Group A plastics
Salt	
—Bagged	Class I
—Packaged, cartoned	Class II
Shingles	
—Asphalt-coated fiberglass	Class III
—Asphalt-impregnated felt	Class IV
Shock Absorbers	
—Metal dust cover	Class II
—Plastic dust cover	Class III

(Continues)

TABLE A.5.6.3 *Continued*

Commodity	Commodity Class
Signatures	
Books, magazines	
—Solid array on pallet	Class II
Skis	
—Wood	Class III
—Foam core	Class IV
Stuffed Toys	
Foam or synthetic	Group A plastics
Syrup	
—Drummed (metal containers)	Class I
—Barreled, wood	Class II
Textiles	
Natural fiber clothing or textile products	Class III
Synthetics (except rayon and nylon)—50/50 blend or less	
—Thread, yarn on wood or paper spools	Class III
—Fabrics	Class III
—Thread, yarn on plastic spools	Class IV
—Baled fiber	Group A plastics
Synthetics (except rayon and nylon)—greater than 50/50 blend	
—Thread, yarn on wood or paper spools	Class IV
—Fabrics	Class IV
—Baled fiber	Group A plastics
—Thread, yarn on plastic spools	Group A plastics
Rayon and nylon	
—Baled fiber	Class IV
—Thread, yarn on wood or paper spools	Class IV
—Fabrics	Class IV
—Thread, yarn on plastic spools	Group A plastics
Tobacco Products	
In paperboard cartons	Class III
Transformers	
Dry and oil filled	Class I
Vinyl-Coated Fabric	
Cartoned	Group A plastics
Vinyl Floor Coverings	
—Tiles in cartons	Class IV
—Rolled	Group A plastics
Wax-Coated Paper	
Cups, plates	
—Boxed or packaged inside cartons (emphasis on packaging)	Class IV
—Loose inside large cartons	Group A plastics
Wax	
Paraffin/petroleum wax, blocks, cartoned	Group A plastics
Wire	
—Bare wire on metal spools on wood skids	Class I
—Bare wire on wood or cardboard spools on wood skids	Class II
—Bare wire on metal, wood, or cardboard spools in cardboard boxes on wood skids	Class II
—Single- or multiple-layer PVC-covered wire on metal spools on wood skids	Class II
—Insulated (PVC) cable on large wood or metal spools on wood skids	Class II
—Bare wire on plastic spools in cardboard boxes on wood skids	Class IV

TABLE A.5.6.3 *Continued*

Commodity	Commodity Class
Wire	
—Single- or multiple-layer PVC-covered wire on plastic spools in cardboard boxes on wood skids	Class IV
—Single, multiple, or power cables (PVC) on large plastic spools	Class IV
—Bulk storage of empty plastic spools	Group A plastics
Wood Products	
—Solid piles—lumber, plywood, particleboard, pressboard (smooth ends and edges)	Class II
—Spools (empty)	Class III
—Toothpicks, clothespins, hangers in cartons	Class III
—Doors, windows, wood cabinets, and furniture	Class III
—Patterns	Class IV

[1]The product is presumed to be in a plastic-coated package in a corrugated carton. If packaged in a metal foil, it can be considered Class I.

[2]Most batteries have a polypropylene case and, if stored empty, should be treated as a Group A plastic. Truck batteries, even where filled, should be considered a Group A plastic because of their thicker walls.

[3]As the openings in plastic crates become larger, the product behaves more like a Class III commodity. Conversely, as the openings become smaller, the product behaves more like a plastic.

[4]These items should be treated as idle pallets.

[5]Tests clearly indicate that a synthetic or synthetic blend is considered greater than Class III.

[6]When liquor is stored in glass containers in racks, it should be considered a Class III commodity; where it is palletized, it should be considered a Class IV commodity.

5.6.3.4* Class IV.

A.5.6.3.4 See Table A.5.6.3.4.

5.6.3.4.1 A Class IV commodity shall be defined as a product, with or without pallets, that meets one of the following criteria:

(1) Constructed partially or totally of Group B plastics
(2) Consists of free-flowing Group A plastic materials
(3) Contains within itself or its packaging an appreciable amount (5 percent to 15 percent by weight or 5 percent to 25 percent by volume) of Group A plastics

Where the designer is considering classifying a commodity mixed with plastics, the designer needs to consider the location of the plastic commodity within a carton. A cartoned commodity that is 15 percent plastic by weight where all of the nonplastic content is surrounded by plastic behaves as a plastic commodity in a fire. Likewise, a heavy metal item encased in expanded plastic packaging that occupies 25 percent of the carton behaves as an expanded plastic commodity in a fire.

5.6.3.4.2 The remaining materials shall be permitted to be metal, wood, paper, natural or synthetic fibers, or Group B or Group C plastics.

5.6.4* Classification of Plastics, Elastomers, and Rubber. Plastics, elastomers, and rubber shall be classified as Group A, Group B, or Group C.

A.5.6.4 The categories listed in 5.6.4.1, 5.6.4.2, and 5.6.4.3 are based on unmodified plastic materials. The use of fire- or flame-retarding modifiers or the physical form of the material could change the classification.

TABLE A.5.6.3.1 *Examples of Class I Commodities*

Alcoholic Beverages
  Cartoned or uncartoned
  —Up to 20 percent alcohol in metal, glass, or ceramic containers
Appliances, Major (e.g., stoves, refrigerators)
  —Not packaged, no appreciable plastic exterior trim
Batteries
  Dry cells (nonlithium or similar exotic metals)
  —Packaged in cartons
  Automobile
  —Filled*
Bottles, Jars
  Empty, cartoned
  —Glass
  Filled noncombustible liquids
  —Glass, cartoned
  —Plastic, cartoned [less than 5 gal (18.9 L)]
  —Plastic, PET
  Filled noncombustible powders
  —Glass, cartoned
Canned Foods
  In ordinary cartons
Cans
  Metal
  —Empty
Cement
  Bagged
Coffee
  Canned, cartoned
Fertilizers
  Bagged
  —Phosphates
File Cabinets
  Metal
  —Cardboard box or shroud
Fish or Fish Products
  Frozen
  —Nonwaxed, nonplastic packaging
  Canned
  —Cartoned

Frozen Foods
  Nonwaxed, nonplastic packaging
Fruit
  Fresh
  —Nonplastic trays or containers
  —With wood spacers
Ice Cream
Meat, Meat Products
  —Bulk
  —Canned, cartoned
  —Frozen, nonwaxed, nonplastic containers
Metal Desks
  —With plastic tops and trim
Milk
  —Nonwaxed-paper containers
  —Waxed-paper containers
  —Plastic containers
Motors
  —Electric
Nuts
  —Canned, cartoned
Paints
  Friction-top cans, cartoned
  —Water-based (latex)
Plastic Containers
  —Noncombustible liquids or semiliquids in plastic containers less than 5 gal (18.9 L) capacity
Poultry Products
  —Canned, cartoned
  —Frozen, nonwaxed, nonplastic containers
Salt
  Bagged
Syrup
  Drummed (metal containers)
Transformers
  Dry and oil filled
Wire
  Bare wire on metal spools on wood skids

*Most batteries have a polypropylene case and, if stored empty, should be treated as a Group A plastic. Truck batteries, even where filled, should be considered a Group A plastic because of their thicker walls.

TABLE A.5.6.3.2 *Examples of Class II Commodities*

Alcoholic Beverages
Up to 20 percent alcohol in wood containers
Appliances, Major (e.g., stoves)
Corrugated, cartoned (no appreciable plastic trim)
Baked Goods
Cookies, cakes, pies
—Frozen, packaged in cartons*
Batteries
Dry cells (nonlithium or similar exotic metals) in blister
pack in cartons
Bottles, Jars
Filled noncombustible powders
—Plastic PET
Boxes, Crates
Empty, wood, solid walls
Fertilizers
Bagged
—Nitrates
Fish or Fish Products
Frozen
—Waxed-paper containers, cartoned
—Boxed or barreled
Frozen Foods
Waxed-paper containers, cartoned
Leather Hides
Baled
Light Fixtures
Nonplastic
—Cartoned
Marble
Artificial sinks, countertops
—Cartoned, crated
Meat, Meat Products
—Frozen, waxed-paper containers
—Frozen, expanded plastic trays
Pharmaceuticals
Pills, powders
—Glass bottles, cartoned
Nonflammable liquids
—Glass bottles, cartoned

Photographic Film
—Motion picture or bulk rolls of film in polycarbonate,
polyethylene, or metal cans; polyethylene bagged in cardboard
boxes
Plastic Containers
Noncombustible liquids or semiliquids (such as ketchup) in
plastic containers with nominal wall thickness of ¼ in. (6.4
mm) or less and larger than 5 gal (18.9 L) capacity
Poultry Products
Frozen (on paper or expanded plastic trays)
Powders (ordinary combustibles—free flowing)
In paper bags (e.g., flour, sugar)
Salt
Packaged, cartoned
Shock Absorbers
Metal dust cover
Signatures
Book, magazines
—Solid array on pallet
Syrup
Barreled, wood
Wire
—Bare wire on wood or cardboard spools on wood skids
—Bare wire on metal, wood, or cardboard spools in cardboard
boxes on wood skids
—Single- or multiple-layer PVC-covered wire on metal spools
on wood skids
—Insulated (PVC) cable on large wood or metal spools on
wood skids
Wood Products
Solid piles
—Lumber, plywood, particle board, pressboard (smooth ends
and edges)

*The product is in a plastic-coated package in a corrugated carton. If packaged in a metal foil, it can be considered Class I.

TABLE A.5.6.3.3 *Examples of Class III Commodities*

Aerosols
  Cartoned or uncartoned
  —Level 1
Baked Goods
  Cookies, cakes, pies
  —Packaged, in cartons
Beans
  Dried
  —Packaged, cartoned
Bread
  Wrapped, cartoned
Butter
  Whipped spread
Candy
  Packaged, cartoned
Cartons
  Corrugated
  —Unassembled (neat piles)
Cereals
  Packaged, cartoned
Charcoal
  Bagged
  —Standard
Cheese
  —Packaged, cartoned
  —Wheels, cartoned
Chewing Gum
  Packaged, cartoned
Chocolate
  Packaged, cartoned
Cloth
  Cartoned and not cartoned
  —Natural fiber, viscose
Cocoa Products
  Packaged, cartoned
Coffee
  Packaged, cartoned
Coffee Beans
  Bagged
Cotton
  Packaged, cartoned
Diapers
  Cotton, linen
Dried Foods
  Packaged, cartoned
Fish or Fish Products
  Frozen
  —Plastic trays, cartoned
Frozen Foods
  Plastic trays

Furniture
  Wood
  —No plastic coverings or foam plastic cushioning
Grains—Packaged in Cartons
  —Barley
  —Rice
  —Oats
Margarine
  Up to 50 percent oil (in paper or plastic containers)
Mattresses
  Standard (box spring)
Nuts
  —Packaged, cartoned
  —Bagged
Paper Products
  Books, magazines, stationery, plastic-coated paper food containers, newspapers, cardboard games, cartoned tissue products
Paper, Rolled
  In racks or on side
  —Medium or heavyweight
Photographic Film
  —35-mm in metal film cartridges in polyethylene cans in cardboard boxes
  —Paper, in sheets, bagged in polyethylene, in cardboard boxes
PVC (polyvinyl chloride)
  —Flexible (e.g., cable jackets, plasticized sheets)
  —Rigid (e.g., pipe, pipe fittings)
  —Bagged resins
Rags
  Baled
  —Natural fibers
Shingles
  Asphalt-coated fiberglass
Shock Absorbers
  Plastic dust cover
Skis
  Wood
Textiles
  Natural fiber clothing or textile products
  Synthetics (except rayon and nylon)—
  50/50 blend or less
  —Thread, yarn on wood or paper spools
  —Fabrics
Tobacco Products
  In paperboard cartons
Wood Products
  —Spools (empty)
  —Toothpicks, clothespins, hangers in cartons
  —Doors, windows, wood cabinets, and furniture

TABLE A.5.6.3.4 *Examples of Class IV Commodities*

Ammunition
  Small arms, shotgun
  —Packaged, cartoned
Bottles, Jars
  Empty, cartoned
  —Plastic PET (polyethylene terephthalate)
  Filled noncombustible powders
  —Plastic, cartoned [less than 1 gal (3.8 L)]
Cartons
  Corrugated
  —Partially assembled
Cloth
  Cartoned and not cartoned
  —Synthetic[1]
Diapers
  Disposable with plastics and nonwoven fabric (in cartons)
Fiberglass Insulation
  —Paper-backed rolls, bagged or unbagged
Furniture
  Wood
  —With plastic coverings
Liquor
  100 proof or less, 1 gal (3.8 L) or less, cartoned
  —Glass (palletized)[2]
  —Plastic bottles
Matches
  Packaged, cartoned
  —Paper
Nail Polish
  1-oz to 2-oz (29.6-ml to 59.1-ml) glass, cartoned
Paints
  Friction-top cans, cartoned
  —Oil based
Paper, Rolled
  In racks
  —Lightweight
Paper, Waxed
  Packaged in cartons
Pharmaceuticals
  Pills, powders
  —Plastic bottles, cartoned

Photographic Film
  —Rolls in polycarbonate plastic cassettes, bulk wrapped in cardboard boxes
PVA (polyvinyl alcohol) Resins
  Bagged
Rags
  Baled
  —Synthetic fibers
Rubber
  Natural, blocks in cartons
Shingles
  Asphalt-impregnated felt
Skis
  Foam core
Textiles
  Synthetics (except rayon and nylon)—
  50/50 blend or less
  —Thread, yarn on plastic spools
  Synthetics (except rayon and nylon)—greater than 50/50 blend
  —Thread, yarn on wood or paper spools
  —Fabrics
  Rayon and nylon
  —Baled fiber
  —Thread, yarn on wood or paper spools
  —Fabrics
Vinyl Floor Coverings
  Tiles in cartons
Wax-Coated Paper
  Cups, plates
  —Boxed or packaged inside cartons (emphasis is on packaging)
Wire
  —Bare wire on plastic spools in cardboard boxes on wood skids
  —Single- or multiple-layer PVC-covered wire on plastic spools in cardboard boxes on wood skids
  —Single, multiple, or power cables (PVC) on large plastic spools
Wood Products
  Patterns

[1]Tests clearly indicate that a synthetic or synthetic blend is considered greater than Class III.

[2]Where liquor is stored in glass containers in racks, it should be considered a Class III commodity; where it is palletized, it should be considered a Class IV commodity.

5.6.4.1* Group A. The following materials shall be classified as Group A:

(1) ABS (acrylonitrile-butadiene-styrene copolymer)
(2) Acetal (polyformaldehyde)
(3) Acrylic (polymethyl methacrylate)
(4) Butyl rubber
(5) EPDM (ethylene-propylene rubber)
(6) FRP (fiberglass-reinforced polyester)
(7) Natural rubber (if expanded)
(8) Nitrile-rubber (acrylonitrile-butadiene-rubber)
(9) PET (thermoplastic polyester)
(10) Polybutadiene
(11) Polycarbonate
(12) Polyester elastomer
(13) Polyethylene
(14) Polypropylene
(15) Polystyrene
(16) Polyurethane
(17) PVC (polyvinyl chloride—highly plasticized, with plasticizer content greater than 20 percent) (rarely found)
(18) SAN (styrene acrylonitrile)
(19) SBR (styrene-butadiene rubber)

 A.5.6.4.1 See Table A.5.6.4.1.

5.6.4.2 Group B. The following materials shall be classified as Group B:

(1) Cellulosics (cellulose acetate, cellulose acetate butyrate, ethyl cellulose)
(2) Chloroprene rubber
(3) Fluoroplastics (ECTFE—ethylene-chlorotrifluoro-ethylene copolymer; ETFE—ethyl-ene-tetrafluoroethylene-copolymer; FEP—fluorinated ethylene-propylene copolymer)
(4) Natural rubber (not expanded)
(5) Nylon (nylon 6, nylon 6/6)
(6) Silicone rubber

5.6.4.3 Group C. The following materials shall be classified as Group C:

(1) Fluoroplastics (PCTFE—polychlorotrifluoroethylene; PTFE—polytetrafluoroethylene)
(2) Melamine (melamine formaldehyde)
(3) Phenolic
(4) PVC (polyvinyl chloride—flexible—PVCs with plasticizer content up to 20 percent)
(5) PVDC (polyvinylidene chloride)
(6) PVDF (polyvinylidene fluoride)
(7) PVF (polyvinyl fluoride)
(8) Urea (urea formaldehyde)

5.6.5* Classification of Rolled Paper Storage. For the purposes of this standard, the classifications of paper described in 5.6.5.1 through 5.6.5.4 shall apply and shall be used to determine the sprinkler system design criteria.

 A.5.6.5 Paper Classification. These classifications were derived from a series of large-scale and laboratory-type small-scale fire tests. It is recognized that not all paper in a class burns with exactly the same characteristics.

Paper can be soft or hard, thick or thin, or heavy or light and can also be coated with various materials. The broad range of papers can be classified according to various properties. One important property is basis weight, which is defined as the weight of a sheet of paper of a specified area. Two broad categories are recognized by industry—paper and paperboard. Pa-

TABLE A.5.6.4.1 *Examples of Group A Plastic Commodities*

Batteries
  Truck or larger
  —Empty or filled[1]
Bottles, Jars
  Empty, cartoned
  —Plastic (other than PET), any size
  Filled noncombustible liquids
  —Plastic, open or solid plastic crates[2]
  Filled noncombustible powders
  —Plastic, cartoned or uncartoned [greater than 1 gal (3.8 L)]
  —Plastic, solid plastic crates
  —Plastic, open plastic crates
Candles
  Packaged, cartoned
  —Treat as expanded plastic
Carpet Tiles
  Cartoned
Cartons
  Wax coated, single walled
Diapers
  Disposable with plastics and nonwoven fabric (uncartoned), plastic wrapped
Furniture
  Wood
  —With foam plastic cushioning
Lighters
  Butane
  —Blister-packed, cartoned
Margarine
  Between 50 percent and 80 percent oil (in any packaging)
Matches
  Packaged, cartoned
  —Wood
Mattresses
  Foam (in finished form)
Milk
  Containers in plastic crates

Nail Polish
  1-oz to 2-oz (29.6-ml to 59.1-ml) plastic bottles, cartoned
Paper Products
  Tissue products, uncartoned and plastic wrapped
Plastic Containers
  —Combustible or noncombustible solids in plastic containers and empty plastic containers
  —Noncombustible liquids or semiliquids (such as ketchup) in plastic containers with nominal wall thickness greater than ¼ in. (6.4 mm) and larger than 5 gal (18.9 L) capacity
Polyurethane
  Cartoned or uncartoned expanded
Rubber
  Synthetic
Stuffed Toys
  Foam or synthetic
Textiles
  Synthetics (except rayon and nylon)—50/50 blend or less
  —Baled fiber
  Synthetics (except rayon and nylon)—greater than 50/50 blend
  —Baled fiber
  —Thread, yarn on plastic spools
  Rayon and nylon
  —Thread, yarn on plastic spools
Vinyl-Coated Fabric
  Cartoned
Vinyl Floor Coverings
  Rolled
Wax-Coated Paper
  Cups, plates
  —Loose inside large cartons
Wax
  Paraffin/petroleum wax, blocks, cartoned
Wire
  Bulk storage of empty plastic spools

[1]Most batteries have a polypropylene case and, if stored empty, should be treated as a Group A plastic. Truck batteries, even where filled, should be considered a Group A plastic because of their thicker walls.

[2]As the openings in plastic crates become larger, the product behaves more like Class III. Conversely, as the openings become smaller, the product makeup behaves more like a plastic.

perboard normally has a basis weight of 20 lb (9.1 kg) or greater measured on a 1000-ft² (92.9-m²) sheet. Stock with a basis weight less than 20 lb/1000 ft² (9.1 kg/92.9 m²) is normally categorized as paper. The basis weight of paper is usually measured on a 3000-ft² (278.7-m²) sheet. The basis weight of paper can also be measured on the total area of a ream of paper, which is normally the case for the following types of printing and writing papers:

(1) *Bond paper*—500 sheets, 17 in. × 22 in. (432 mm × 559 mm) = 1300 ft² (120.8 m²) per ream

(2) *Book paper*—500 sheets, 25 in. × 38 in. (635 mm × 965 mm) = 3300 ft² (306.6 m²) per ream

(3) *Index paper*—500 sheets, 25½ in. × 30½ in. (648 mm × 775 mm) = 2700 ft^2 (250.8 m^2) per ream

(4) *Bristol paper*—500 sheets, 22½ in. × 35 in. (572 mm × 889 mm) = 2734 ft^2 (254 m^2) per ream

(5) *Tag paper*—500 sheets, 24 in. × 36 in. (610 mm × 914 mm) = 3000 ft^2 (278.7 m^2) per ream

For the purposes of this standard, all basis weights are expressed in lb/1000 ft^2 (kg/92.9 m^2) of paper. To determine the basis weight per 1000 ft^2 (92.9 m^2) for papers measured on a sheet of different area, the following formula should be applied:

$$\frac{\text{Base weight}}{1000 \text{ ft}^2} = \text{basis weight} \times 1000 \text{ measured area}$$

 Example: To determine the basis weight per 1000 ft^2 (92.9 m^2) of 16-lb (7.3-kg) bond paper:

$$\left(\frac{16 \text{ lb}}{1300 \text{ ft}^2}\right) 1000 = \frac{12.3 \text{ lb}}{1000 \text{ ft}^2}$$

Large- and small-scale fire tests indicate that the burning rate of paper varies with the basis weight. Heavyweight paper burns more slowly than lightweight paper. Full-scale roll paper fire tests were conducted with the following types of paper:

(1) *Linerboard*—42 lb/1000 ft^2 (19.1 kg/92.9 m^2) nominal basis weight
(2) *Newsprint*—10 lb/1000 ft^2 (4.5 kg/92.9 m^2) nominal basis weight
(3) *Tissue*—5 lb/1000 ft^2 (2.3 kg/92.9 m^2) nominal basis weight

The rate of firespread over the surface of the tissue rolls was extremely rapid in the full-scale fire tests. The rate of firespread over the surface of the linerboard rolls was slower. Based on the overall results of these full-scale tests, along with additional data from small-scale testing of various paper grades, the broad range of papers has been classified into three major categories as follows:

(1) *Heavyweight*—Basis weight of 20 lb/1000 ft^2 (9.1 kg/92.9 m^2) or greater
(2) *Mediumweight*—Basis weight of 10 lb to 20 lb/1000 ft^2 (4.5 kg to 9.1 kg/92.9 m^2)
(3) *Lightweight*—Basis weight of less than 10 lb/1000 ft^2 (4.5 kg/92.9 m^2) and tissues regardless of basis weight

The following SI units were used for conversion of English units:

1 lb   = 0.454 kg
1 in.   = 25.4 mm
1 ft   = 0.3048 m
1 ft^2 = 0.0929 m^2

The various types of papers normally found in each of the four major categories are provided in Table A.5.6.5.

The paragraphs in A.5.6.5 apply to the classification of large rolls of paper stored on end or on side in piles greater than 10 ft (3.1 m) high. This type of paper storage is typically found in the finished goods storage warehouses at paper mills, in the raw stock storage warehouses of manufacturing plants that convert paper into finished products, or in other warehouses of similar occupancy. Fire experience and full-scale fire testing of this type of paper storage, as indicated in Exhibits 5.6 and 5.7, demonstrate unique burning characteristics that vary with the type of paper and the method of wrapping. The classifications for this type of paper storage are based on a series of full-scale and small-scale fire tests as described in A.5.6.5.

5.6.5.1 Heavyweight Class. Heavyweight class shall be defined so as to include paperboard and paper stock having a basis weight [weight per 1000 ft^2 (92.9 m^2)] of 20 lb (9.1 kg).

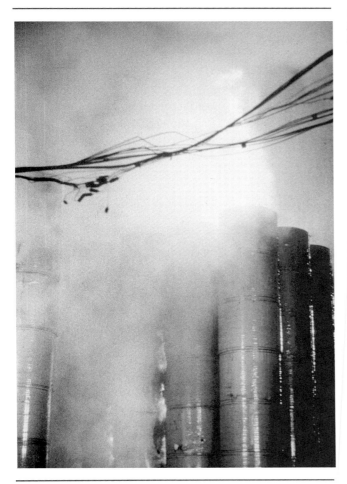

EXHIBIT 5.6 Fire Test of Roll Paper Using Large Drop Sprinklers.

EXHIBIT 5.7 Fire Test of Roll Paper Using Standard Spray Sprinklers.

TABLE A.5.6.5 *Paper Classification*

Heavyweight	Mediumweight	Lightweight	Tissue
Linerboards	Bond and reproduction	Carbonizing tissue	Toilet tissue
Medium	Vellum	Cigarette	Towel tissue
Kraft roll wrappers	Offset	Fruit wrap	
Milk carton board	Tablet	Onion skin	
Folding carton board	Computer		
Bristol board	Envelope		
Tag	Book		
Vellum bristol board	Label		
Index	Magazine		
Cupstock	Butcher		
Pulp board	Bag		
	Newsprint (unwrapped)		

5.6.5.2 Mediumweight Class. Mediumweight class shall be defined so as to include all the broad range of papers having a basis weight [weight per 1000 ft^2 (92.9 m^2)] of 10 lb to 20 lb (4.5 kg to 9.1 kg).

5.6.5.3 Lightweight Class. Lightweight class shall be defined so as to include all papers having a basis weight [weight per 1000 ft^2 (92.9 m^2)] of 10 lb (4.5 kg).

5.6.5.4 Tissue.

5.6.5.4.1 Tissue shall be defined so as to include the broad range of papers of characteristic gauzy texture, which, in some cases, are fairly transparent.

5.6.5.4.2 For the purposes of this standard, tissue shall be defined as the soft, absorbent type, regardless of basis weight—specifically, crepe wadding and the sanitary class including facial tissue, paper napkins, bathroom tissue, and toweling.

SUMMARY

Chapter 5 provides information on the classification of the various occupancy hazards addressed in NFPA 13. The occupancy hazards provide a convenient means of categorizing the fuel loads and fire severity associated with certain building operations. The classifications also present a relationship between the burning characteristics of these fuels and the ability of a sprinkler system in controlling the associated types of fires.

 ## REFERENCES CITED IN COMMENTARY

National Fire Protection Association, 1 Batterymarch Park, P.O. Box 9101, Quincy, MA 02269-9101

NFPA *101*®, *Life Safety Code*®, 2000 edition
NFPA 5000™, *Building Construction and Safety Code*™, 2003 edition

Factory Mutual Research Corporation, 1151 Boston-Providence Turnpike, Norwood, MA 02061

FMRC Publication 4995

Underwriters Laboratories Inc., 333 Pfingsten Road, Northbrook, IL 60062

UL Project No. 01NK31019, NC4354
UL Project No. 01NK20682, R18834
UL Publication 2335

System Components and Hardware

Chapter 6 identifies the types of materials and components that are acceptable for use in a sprinkler system and discusses their associated features and limitations. System components and hardware covered in Chapter 6 include sprinklers, aboveground pipe and tube, fittings, joining of pipe and fittings, valves, fire department connections, and waterflow alarms. Information concerning proper installation of system materials and components is contained in Chapter 8 and Chapter 9.

6.1 General

This chapter provides requirements for correct use of sprinkler system components.

6.1.1* Listing.

A.6.1.1 Included among items requiring listing are sprinklers, some pipe and some fittings, hangers, alarm devices, valves controlling flow of water to sprinklers, valve tamper switches, and gauges.

The ability of a sprinkler system to achieve fire control or suppression depends on a number of factors, including the use of effective and reliable system components. To ensure a sufficient degree of sprinkler system reliability and performance, NFPA 13, in 6.1.1, requires that those components critical to system performance during a fire be listed (see 3.2.3 for definition of *listed*). Components that would not adversely affect system performance if they were to malfunction during a fire are not required to be listed, but they must be approved (see 3.2.1 for definition of *approved*).

The requirement of listed products and materials is intended to increase the likelihood that the system will perform as it was designed when needed. For example, over 50 different types of tests are performed on a specific model of sprinkler during the listing process. These tests evaluate a number of performance features such as spray pattern distribution, operating temperature, response characteristics, exposure to corrosive atmospheres, ability to withstand pressure, orifice discharge characteristics, and the strength of the operating element.

6.1.1.1 Materials or devices not specifically designated by this standard shall be used in accordance with all conditions, requirements, and limitations of their special listing. All special listing requirements shall be included and identified in the product submittal literature and installation instructions.

When products are developed for sprinkler systems and their application is not specifically described in this standard, specific guidance for proper installation and use is to be described in the manufacturer's technical data or installation instructions. This information is required by 6.1.1.1 as part of the listing for these products.

6.1.1.2 Unless the requirements of 6.1.1.3, 6.1.1.4, or 6.1.1.5 are met, all materials and devices essential to successful system operation shall be listed.

6.1.1.3 Equipment as permitted in Table 6.3.1.1 and Table 6.4.1 shall not be required to be listed.

FAQ ▶
Does NFPA 13 require steel pipe and copper tubing to be listed for fire protection service?

Paragraph 6.1.1.3 does not require certain materials, such as Schedule 10, Schedule 30, and Schedule 40 steel pipe, copper tubing, and some of the fittings used with these pipes, to be listed for fire protection service. Pipe manufactured to specific ASTM standards and fittings made to specific ASME standards are considered sufficiently reliable. Additionally, many years of positive experience with these materials in sprinkler systems and in other types of mechanical systems supports their acceptable performance level. It should be noted that although listing of these materials is not required by NFPA 13, several manufacturers of these products have chosen to have their products listed.

6.1.1.4 Materials meeting the requirements of 9.1.1.2, 9.1.1.4.2, and 9.1.1.4.3 shall not be required to be listed.

Experience demonstrates that mild steel rods of the sizes specified in NFPA 13 do not need to be listed. Paragraph 6.1.1.4 recognizes that listed hangers may not be suitable for certain applications and permits hanger assemblies to be designed by a registered professional engineer for these special situations.

6.1.1.5 Components that do not affect system performance such as drain piping, drain valves, and signs shall not be required to be listed.

Paragraph 6.1.1.5 recognizes that the listing of all sprinkler system components not affecting system performance is unnecessary to increase overall system reliability during a fire. For example, a drain valve or a sign is not critical to system performance during a fire and does not require listing.

6.1.2 Reconditioned Components.

6.1.2.1 The use of reconditioned valves and devices as replacement equipment in existing systems shall be permitted.

6.1.2.2 Reconditioned sprinklers shall not be permitted to be utilized on any new or existing system.

Components such as valves may be reconditioned and reused.

FAQ ▶
Can reconditioned sprinklers be used?

FAQ ▶
Where can existing installed sprinklers be utilized?

As stated in 6.1.2.2, reconditioned sprinklers may not be used; only new sprinklers are to be used on any new or existing system. Unfavorable past experience with the use of reconditioned sprinklers provides the basis for this requirement.

However, when sprinklers have been installed in a building on a temporary basis—for example, prior to finish ceiling work—the same sprinklers can be used on that job. The same holds true for an existing system that is being lowered to accommodate a new ceiling provided the sprinklers are of the proper orientation and the associated hazard has not changed.

6.1.3 Rated Pressure. System components shall be rated for the maximum system working pressure to which they are exposed but shall not be rated at less than 175 psi (12.1 bar) for components installed aboveground and 150 psi (10.4 bar) for components installed underground.

A minimum pressure rating of 175 psi (12.1 bar), as specified in 6.1.3, historically has been the minimum strength criteria for aboveground system components. For underground system components, a minimum system pressure rating of 150 psi (10.4 bar) is specified in 6.1.3 based on satisfactory historical performance. Also, this reflects the pressure rating of the components typically used underground, such as piping, valves, and fittings.

Where system pressures are expected to exceed pressures of 150 psi and 175 psi, system components and materials manufactured and listed for higher pressures must be used. Systems that do not incorporate a fire pump or are not part of a combined standpipe system do not typically experience pressures exceeding 150 psi (10.4 bar) in underground piping and 175 psi (12.1 bar) in aboveground piping. However, each system must be evaluated on an individual basis because the presence of a fire department connection introduces the possibility of high pressures being applied by fire department apparatus.

6.2 Sprinklers

6.2.1 General. Only new sprinklers shall be installed.

Prompt sprinkler actuation during the early stages of a fire is critical to the successful performance of the entire sprinkler system. The sprinkler should not leak or rupture when installed, nor should it operate for any reason other than in response to heat from a fire. A new listed sprinkler has been thoroughly evaluated to ensure that it will operate only when needed and in an appropriate manner, which is the reason for the requirement in 6.2.1.

6.2.2* Sprinkler Identification.

A.6.2.2 The four- to six-character sprinkler identification number, with no intervening spaces, is intended to identify the sprinkler operating characteristics in lieu of the traditional laboratory approval marking (e.g., SSU, SSP, EC, QR, etc.). The number, marked on the deflector of most sprinklers and elsewhere on decorative ceiling sprinklers, consists of one or two characters identifying the manufacturer, followed by three or four digits.

Sprinkler manufacturers have identified their manufacturer designations for the listing organizations. Each change in orifice size, response characteristics, or deflector (distribution) characteristics results in a new sprinkler identification number. The numbers do not identify specific characteristics of sprinklers but can be referenced in the database information compiled by the listing organizations. At the plan review stage, the sprinkler identification number should be checked against such a database or the manufacturer's literature to ensure that sprinklers are being used properly and within the limitations of their listings. Field inspections can include spot checks to ensure that the model numbers on the plans are those actually installed.

6.2.2.1 All sprinklers shall be permanently marked with a one- or two-character manufacturer symbol, followed by three or four numbers, so as to identify a unique sprinkler identification for every change in orifice size or shape, deflector characteristic, pressure rating, and thermal sensitivity.

Sprinkler identification markings assist installers, building owners, and authorities in identifying sprinklers installed in the field and minimize the confusion resulting from the growing number and varieties of available sprinklers. The requirement in 6.2.2.1 became effective January 1, 2001, and all sprinklers are now designated with the sprinkler identification number (SIN). See Exhibit 6.1.

The sprinkler identification number associated with a particular sprinkler can be identified through sprinkler associations' web site(s) and through the listing organization's web site(s).

◀ **FAQ**
Where can information on specific sprinkler identification numbers be found?

6.2.2.2 The requirements of 6.2.2 shall become effective on January 1, 2001.

6.2.3 Sprinkler Discharge Characteristics.

6.2.3.1* General. Unless the requirements of 6.2.3.2, 6.2.3.3, or 6.2.3.4 are met, the K-factor, relative discharge, and marking identification for sprinklers having different orifice sizes shall be in accordance with Table 6.2.3.1.

EXHIBIT 6.1   Viking Sprinkler Showing SIN on Deflector. (Courtesy of Viking)

TABLE 6.2.3.1 *Sprinkler Discharge Characteristics Identification*

Nominal K-factor [gpm/(psi)$^{1/2}$]	K-factor Range [gpm/(psi)$^{1/2}$]	K-factor Range [dm^3/min/(kPa)$^{1/2}$]	Percent of Nominal K-5.6 Discharge	Thread Type
1.4	1.3–1.5	1.9–2.2	25	½ in. NPT
1.9	1.8–2.0	2.6–2.9	33.3	½ in. NPT
2.8	2.6–2.9	3.8–4.2	50	½ in. NPT
4.2	4.0–4.4	5.9–6.4	75	½ in. NPT
5.6	5.3–5.8	7.6–8.4	100	½ in. NPT
8.0	7.4–8.2	10.7–11.8	140	¾ in. NPT or ½ in. NPT
11.2	11.0–11.5	15.9–16.6	200	½ in. NPT or ¾ in. NPT
14.0	13.5–14.5	19.5–20.9	250	¾ in. NPT
16.8	16.0–17.6	23.1–25.4	300	¾ in. NPT
19.6	18.6–20.6	27.2–30.1	350	1 in. NPT
22.4	21.3–23.5	31.1–34.3	400	1 in. NPT
25.2	23.9–26.5	34.9–38.7	450	1 in. NPT
28.0	26.6–29.4	38.9–43.0	500	1 in. NPT

A **A.6.3.2.1** See Table A.6.3.2.1

The 1999 edition required sprinkler orifice sizes to be identified only according to the sprinkler's nominal K-factor. The nominal orifice sizes specified in NFPA 13 prior to the 1999 edition are retained in Table A.6.2.3.1 to assist the user in making the transition from nominal orifice sizes to nominal K-factors.

Any given sprinkler will have a specific K-factor that differs from the nominal K-factor sizes. However, the K-factor must lie within the ranges provided in Table 6.2.3.1. The nominal K-factor indicated in the table must be used to determine the sprinkler's flow rate at a particular pressure. This use of the nominal K-factor is of major importance for hydraulically designed systems. (See Chapter 11.)

TABLE A.6.2.3.1 *Nominal Sprinkler Orifice Sizes*

Nominal K-factor	Nominal Orifice Size		Nominal K-factor	Nominal Orifice Size	
	in.	*mm*		*in.*	*mm*
1.4	¼	6.4	14.0	¾	19.0
1.9	5/16	8.0	16.8	—	—
2.8	⅜	9.5	19.6	—	—
4.2	7/16	11.0	22.4	—	—
5.6	½	12.7	25.2	—	—
8.0	17/32	13.5	28.0	—	—
11.2	⅝	15.9			

Exhibits 6.2 and 6.3 illustrate the differences in orifice sizes among sprinklers with K-factors of 2.8, 5.6, and 25.2.

Prior to the 1999 edition, sprinklers with a nominal K-factor of other than 5.6 and a ½-in. (12.7-mm) National Pipe Thread (NPT) or sprinklers with a nominal K-factor of other than 8.0 and a ¾-in. pipe thread were identified with pintles. A pintle is a small metal protrusion extending from the sprinkler's deflector. It serves no function other than to provide some indication of the sprinkler's orifice size. Because so many sprinkler sizes are produced, the pintle is virtually meaningless and is no longer required to be used.

◄ **FAQ**
Why are pintles no longer required by NFPA 13?

EXHIBIT 6.2 *Sprinklers with K-factors of 5.6, 25.2, and 2.8.*

EXHIBIT 6.3 *Comparison of Orifices of Sprinklers with K-factors of 5.6, 25.2, and 2.8.*

6.2.3.2 Pipe Threads. Listed sprinklers having pipe threads different from those shown in Table 6.2.3.1 shall be permitted.

6.2.3.3 K-Factors Greater Than 28. Sprinklers listed with nominal K-factors greater than 28 shall increase the flow by 100 percent increments when compared with a nominal K-5.6 sprinkler.

This requirement in 6.2.3.3 was included to provide guidance for the future development of sprinklers that have orifices larger than K-28. These sprinklers will need to be manufactured in increments that represent a 100 percent increase in flow when compared to a sprinkler with a nominal K-factor of 5.6. This requirement is an effort by the technical committee to encourage new technology, while at the same time it addresses the need for interchangeability between product lines. Specifying the K-factors that can be used by sprinklers in the future removes the possibility of the manufacture of odd sprinkler sizes that would present replacement problems.

6.2.3.4 Residential Sprinklers. Residential sprinklers shall be permitted with K-factors other than those specified in Table 6.2.3.1.

Because residential sprinklers are intended for specific life safety objectives in certain building occupancies, these sprinklers are not subject to the K-factor range limitation specified in Table 6.2.3.1, as stated in 6.2.3.4.

6.2.3.5 Large Drop and ESFR K-Factors. Large drop and ESFR sprinklers shall have a minimum nominal K-factor of 11.2.

Paragraph 6.2.3.5 specifies a minimum nominal K-factor for large drop and ESFR sprinklers. This requirement establishes a degree of consistency with regard to these sprinklers' performance objectives.

6.2.3.6 ESFR Orifice Size. ESFR sprinkler orifice size shall be selected as appropriate for the hazard. *(See Chapter 12.)*

The reference to Chapter 12 in 6.2.3.6 alludes to the fact that there are different varieties of ESFR sprinklers and that they are not all intended to protect against the same types of hazards. Obviously, the application of an ESFR sprinkler beyond the limitations of its listing is very likely to result in an unfavorable outcome. Exhibits 3.15 and 3.16 illustrate ESFR sprinklers, and Exhibit 3.19 illustrates a large drop sprinkler.

6.2.4 Occupancy Limitations. Unless the requirements of 6.2.4.1 or 6.2.4.2 are met, sprinklers shall not be listed for protection of a portion of an occupancy classification.

6.2.4.1 Residential Sprinklers. Residential sprinklers shall be permitted to be listed for portions of residential occupancies as defined in 8.4.5.1.

6.2.4.2 Special Sprinklers. Special sprinklers shall be permitted to be listed for protection of a specific construction feature in a portion of an occupancy classification. *(See 8.4.9.)*

NFPA 13 encourages the development of new technologies and allows for a sufficient degree of flexibility for the pursuit of new products. However, a balance must be achieved between flexibility and practicality. The requirements of 6.2.4, 6.2.4.1, and 6.2.4.2 attempt to define this balance. The intent of the requirements is to minimize unnecessary complexities by limiting the development of devices that are narrowly limited in their application.

FAQ ▶
Can a sprinkler be listed to protect a specific portion of an occupancy classification?

Paragraph 6.2.4 requires that a sprinkler be listed and usable for all hazards addressed by an occupancy classification, such as light hazard occupancies. For instance, a sprinkler cannot be listed for the protection of only hospitals or offices but must instead be listed for all types of light hazard occupancies.

FAQ ▶
Can residential sprinklers be used throughout all light hazard occupancies?

Paragraph 6.2.4.1 acknowledges that residential sprinklers are developed specifically for life safety purposes in dwelling units and their adjoining corridors. Residential sprinklers cannot be used in other light hazard occupancies, and this limitation has always been associated with their listing.

The purpose of 6.2.4.2 is to allow for the development and use of sprinklers that address specific hazards or construction features, such as for protection of attics, interstitial combustible concealed spaces, and windows, when used in accordance with the listing limitations. Exhibit 1.4 identifies some of these special sprinklers.

6.2.5* Temperature Characteristics.

A.6.2.5 Information regarding the highest temperature that can be encountered in any location in a particular installation can be obtained by use of a thermometer that will register the highest temperature encountered; it should be hung for several days in the location in question, with the plant in operation.

The requirements in 6.2.5 specify the type of marking required to identify the temperature rating of the sprinkler. The temperature rating of a sprinkler plays a critical role in achieving fire control or suppression. The selection criteria for the temperature rating of a given sprinkler are a function of the occupancy classification and ambient ceiling temperatures expected in the vicinity of the sprinkler. Determination of the highest ambient ceiling temperatures influences the selection of the proper sprinkler temperature rating and minimizes the chance of a non-fire sprinkler operation, which is typically an extremely rare event.

If sprinklers with different temperature ratings are randomly installed throughout a compartment, sprinklers remote from the fire may operate prior to sprinklers in the immediate vicinity of the fire. This phenomenon is referred to as *skipping*, which can negatively impact system performance. For this reason, sprinklers with the same temperature ratings should be used in a given area, unless otherwise specified by 8.3.2.

A sprinkler's thermal sensitivity is another factor to consider. Note the warning in A.8.4 against mixing standard-response and quick-response sprinklers in the same compartment unless a specific design objective is being addressed. As a general rule, quick-response sprinklers operate significantly faster than standard-response sprinklers under the same conditions. The user must be aware of the possibility of skipping if quick-response and standard-response sprinklers of the same temperature rating are mixed in a compartment.

◄ FAQ
Why are all sprinklers installed throughout a compartment required to be of the same temperature range?

◄ FAQ
Besides temperature range selection, what other factor can affect skipping?

6.2.5.1 Automatic sprinklers shall have their frame arms, deflector, coating material, or liquid bulb colored in accordance with the requirements of Table 6.2.5.1 or the requirements of 6.2.5.2, 6.2.5.3, 6.2.5.4, or 6.2.5.5.

Sprinklers are color coded in accordance with Table 6.2.5.1 to provide a ready means of identifying the temperature classifications of their operating elements. Table 6.2.5.1 indicates the temperature ranges for sprinklers in each classification and the maximum ceiling temperatures for which each classification may be installed.

TABLE 6.2.5.1 Temperature Ratings, Classifications, and Color Codings

Maximum Ceiling Temperature		Temperature Rating		Temperature Classification	Color Code	Glass Bulb Colors
°F	°C	°F	°C			
100	38	135–170	57–77	Ordinary	Uncolored or black	Orange or red
150	66	175–225	79–107	Intermediate	White	Yellow or green
225	107	250–300	121–149	High	Blue	Blue
300	149	325–375	163–191	Extra high	Red	Purple
375	191	400–475	204–246	Very extra high	Green	Black
475	246	500–575	260–302	Ultra high	Orange	Black
625	329	650	343	Ultra high	Orange	Black

6.2.5.2 A dot on the top of the deflector, the color of the coating material, or colored frame arms shall be permitted for color identification of corrosion-resistant sprinklers.

6.2.5.3 Color identification shall not be required for ornamental sprinklers such as factory-plated or factory-painted sprinklers or for recessed, flush, or concealed sprinklers.

Paragraph 6.2.5.3 recognizes that traditional color codes are not applicable to specially coated sprinklers, such as decorative or ornamental sprinklers. In some cases, in order to receive a particular color finish, these devices are listed as corrosion-resistant sprinklers.

The decorative or corrosion-resistant finish applied to some sprinklers as listed by the testing laboratories requires NFPA 13 to accommodate some special rules with respect to the color-coding identification. Paragraphs 6.2.5.3 and 6.2.5.4 provide such accommodation.

6.2.5.4 The frame arms of bulb-type sprinklers shall not be required to be color coded.

6.2.5.5 The liquid in bulb-type sprinklers shall be color coded in accordance with Table 6.2.5.1.

Many glass bulb sprinklers have coated frame arms for aesthetic reasons. This coating makes frame arm color coding rather confusing.

FAQ ▶
What is contained in the glass bulb of a sprinkler, and how does it control the operation of the sprinkler?

The temperature rating of glass bulb sprinklers is determined by the color of the encased liquid, which is usually a sugar solution that expands when heated. The temperature rating of this type of element is controlled by the size of a small air bubble that is trapped in the glass tube of the device. The relative size of this bubble establishes the temperature rating of the sprinkler.

A glass bulb sprinkler with a white frame arm finish but a red bulb, for example, is rated as ordinary temperature, according to Table 6.2.5.1.

Subsection 8.3.2 provides details on the use of sprinklers with differing temperature ratings, depending on the environment.

6.2.6 Special Coatings.

6.2.6.1* Corrosion Resistant.

A **A.6.2.6.1** Examples of such locations include the following:

(1) Paper mills
(2) Packing houses
(3) Tanneries
(4) Alkali plants
(5) Organic fertilizer plants
(6) Foundries
(7) Forge shops
(8) Fumigation, pickle, and vinegar works
(9) Stables
(10) Storage battery rooms
(11) Electroplating rooms
(12) Galvanizing rooms
(13) Steam rooms of all descriptions, including moist vapor dry kilns
(14) Salt storage rooms
(15) Locomotive sheds or houses
(16) Driveways
(17) Areas exposed to outside weather, such as piers and wharves exposed to salt air
(18) Areas under sidewalks
(19) Areas around bleaching equipment in flour mills
(20) All portions of cold storage buildings where a direct ammonia expansion system is used
(21) Portions of any plant where corrosive vapors prevail

6.2.6.1.1 Listed corrosion-resistant sprinklers shall be installed in locations where chemicals, moisture, or other corrosive vapors sufficient to cause corrosion of such devices exist.

In compliance with 6.2.6.1.1, sprinklers manufactured with corrosion-resistant materials or with special coatings or platings are specifically listed for use in atmospheres that would corrode an uncoated sprinkler.

6.2.6.1.2* Unless the requirements of 6.2.6.1.3 are met, corrosion-resistant coatings shall be applied only by the manufacturer of the sprinkler and in accordance with the requirements of 6.2.6.1.3.

A.6.2.6.1.2 Care should be taken in the handling and installation of wax-coated or similar sprinklers to avoid damaging the coating.

◄ FAQ
Why are only sprinkler manufacturers permitted to apply protective coatings?

An attempt by anyone other than the manufacturer to provide sprinklers with any type of protective coating will very likely result in ineffective protection by the sprinkler or serious impairment of its operation, which is the reason for the requirement in 6.2.6.1.2. The listing of sprinklers with protective or special coatings requires that the coatings be applied at the manufacturer's facility. Field application of these platings and coatings is prohibited.

Exhibit 3.33 illustrates a wax-coated corrosion-resistant sprinkler.

6.2.6.1.3 Any damage to the protective coating occurring at the time of installation shall be repaired at once using only the coating of the manufacturer of the sprinkler in the approved manner so that no part of the sprinkler will be exposed after installation has been completed.

6.2.6.2* Painting.

A.6.2.6.2 Painting of sprinklers can retard the thermal response of the heat-responsive element, can interfere with the free movement of parts, and can render the sprinkler inoperative. Moreover, painting can invite the application of subsequent coatings, thus increasing the possibility of a malfunction of the sprinkler.

◄ FAQ
What is loading, as it relates to sprinklers?

Painting, covered in 6.2.6.2, is the primary, but not the only, example of a problem known as *loading,* in which a buildup of foreign material on the sprinkler acts to delay or prevent proper sprinkler activation. For example, sprinklers in textile mills are subject to loading by lint-type materials, which are by-products of the cloth-manufacturing process. Another example includes sprinklers at the bottom of elevator shafts and underneath escalators, as they are subject to loading from hydraulic oils and lubricants. These two examples are indicative of events that occur after the system is in service. Any sprinkler subject to loading of materials that cannot be readily dusted or blown away must be replaced.

Sprinklers that have been painted in the field, however slight (including overspray), must not be cleaned of paint and must be replaced with new sprinklers.

◄ FAQ
Can sprinklers that have had paint applied to them be cleaned and left in service?

6.2.6.2.1 Sprinklers shall only be painted by the sprinkler manufacturer.

6.2.6.2.2 Where sprinklers have had paint applied by other than the sprinkler manufacturer, they shall be replaced with new listed sprinklers of the same characteristics, including orifice size, thermal response, and water distribution.

6.2.6.3 Ornamental Finishes.

Decorative coatings for ornamentation and other markings can only be applied by the manufacturer and in accordance with the sprinkler's listing. This restriction also applies to the cover plate assembly of a listed concealed sprinkler.

6.2.6.3.1 Ornamental finishes shall only be applied to sprinklers, and if applicable their concealed cover plates, by the sprinkler manufacturer.

6.2.6.3.2 Sprinklers shall be specifically listed with ornamental finishes where utilized.

6.2.6.4 Protective Coverings.

6.2.6.4.1 Sprinklers protecting spray areas and mixing rooms in resin application areas shall be protected against overspray residue so that they will operate in the event of fire.

6.2.6.4.2 Where protected in accordance with 6.2.6.4.1, cellophane bags having a thickness of 0.003 in. (0.076 mm) or less or thin paper bags shall be used.

6.2.6.4.3 Coverings shall be replaced periodically so that heavy deposits of residue do not accumulate.

6.2.6.4.4 Sprinklers that have been painted or coated shall be replaced in accordance with the requirements of 6.2.6.2.2.

6.2.7 Escutcheons and Cover Plates.

6.2.7.1 Nonmetallic escutcheons shall be listed.

6.2.7.2* Escutcheons used with recessed, flush-type, or concealed sprinklers shall be part of a listed sprinkler assembly.

 A.6.2.7.2 The use of the wrong type of escutcheon with recessed or flush-type sprinklers can result in severe disruption of the spray pattern, which can destroy the effectiveness of the sprinkler.

Components for escutcheon plates, including cover plates, if used, are integral to proper sprinkler performance. The listing of these components, as required in 6.2.7.2, ensures that the plates do not delay the response or impede the operation of the sprinkler and that any components that are designed to fall away or slide do so as intended. Concealed cover plates exist that will fit numerous concealed sprinklers. Paragraph 6.2.7.2 requires the concealed cover plates be listed only with specific sprinkler models. The cover plates are marked with the compatible sprinkler model or sprinkler identification number.

Exhibit 6.4 illustrates a concealed sprinkler with the escutcheon plate and the cover plate missing. Although the missing cover plate will not impair sprinkler performance, the lack of the escutcheon (sprinkler cup) can impair performance because the concealed sprinkler was listed for use with an escutcheon.

Instances have occurred where the dimensions of an unlisted recessed escutcheon and a sprinkler were such that the deflector was not clear of the escutcheon, which seriously impaired the spray pattern. Failure to follow all manufacturer's instructions and listing criteria can result in less than acceptable performance of the sprinkler.

6.2.7.3 Cover plates used with concealed sprinklers shall be part of the listed sprinkler assembly.

EXHIBIT 6.4 *Improperly Installed Concealed Sprinkler.*

6.2.8* Guards and Shields. Sprinklers subject to mechanical injury shall be protected with listed guards.

A.6.2.8 Sprinklers under open gratings should be provided with shields. Shields over automatic sprinklers should not be less, in least dimension, than four times the distance between the shield and fusible element, except special sprinklers incorporating a built-in shield need not comply with this recommendation if listed for the particular application.

Sprinkler guards, which are discussed in 6.2.8, are protective cages that surround a sprinkler. Exhibit 6.5 illustrates a sprinkler with a listed guard. Guards have the potential to obstruct spray patterns and should only be used where a sprinkler is in danger of being struck by an object. A sprinkler guard can minimize the impact from physical damage by a variety of objects, including pallet loads used in the rack storage facilities. These guards are also useful in protecting people from injury by sprinklers in areas where there is low clearance, as occurs under a stairwell.

EXHIBIT 6.5 *Sprinkler with Listed Guard.*

Any sprinkler that exhibits physical damage must be replaced. Damage, such as a bent deflector, can reduce the effectiveness of the sprinkler.

Sprinkler shields are flat plates above the sprinkler that prevent water from sprinklers above from cooling a sprinkler at a lower elevation. Sprinklers in racks and under open gratings are examples of intermediate-level sprinklers, which must be provided with a shield to ensure their operation is not delayed due to a sprinkler that may be operating above it.

Listed intermediate level sprinklers are equipped with integral shields and have been tested under a fire condition when the sprinkler above is operating. Listed intermediate level sprinklers are not required to follow the recommendation for shield sizing.

 ◀ FAQ
Are listed intermediate level sprinklers required to follow the recommendations for shield sizing?

6.2.9 Stock of Spare Sprinklers.

6.2.9.1* A supply of at least six spare sprinklers (never fewer than six) shall be maintained on the premises so that any sprinklers that have operated or been damaged in any way can be promptly replaced.

A.6.2.9.1 A minimum of two sprinklers of each type and temperature rating should be provided.

The stock of spare sprinklers required in 6.2.9.1 is a minimum. Spare sprinklers of all the types and ratings installed must be available. For a building with a variety of sprinklers, the number of spare sprinklers should be increased above the minimum. Having adequate stock is particularly critical where specially listed sprinklers such as those discussed in 8.4.9 are installed.

Good judgment must be used when applying the rules for the number of spare sprinklers to maintain on the premises. For instance, if a building contained 350 sprinklers, only two of which were standard spray upright sprinklers with a temperature rating of 286°F (141°C), it is not intended that 12 such sprinklers be provided in the spare sprinkler cabinet. Two spare sprinklers are practical and acceptable to maintain, since there is no need for more than that number. Subsection 5.4.1 of NFPA 25, *Standard for the Inspection, Testing, and Maintenance of Water-Based Fire Protection Systems,* provides more information in this regard. Exhibit 6.6 illustrates a spare sprinkler cabinet equipped with a stock of spare sprinklers and a special sprinkler wrench.

6.2.9.2 The sprinklers shall correspond to the types and temperature ratings of the sprinklers in the property.

6.2.9.3 The sprinklers shall be kept in a cabinet located where the temperature to which they are subjected will at no time exceed 100°F (38°C).

6.2.9.4 Where dry sprinklers of different lengths are installed, spare dry sprinklers shall not be required, provided that a means of returning the system to service is furnished.

EXHIBIT 6.6 *Spare Sprinkler Cabinet.*

Under the requirement in 6.2.9.4, in systems where dry type sprinklers of various lengths are installed, spare dry sprinklers are not required if the system can be temporarily placed back in service after a sprinkler activation. This can be accomplished by the installation of non–dry type sprinklers in areas that are temporarily not subjected to freezing temperatures or through the use of plugs in areas that will remain below freezing. Because dry sprinklers are manufactured to specific lengths, it would be impractical to require a set of replacement sprinklers on the premises.

6.2.9.5 The stock of spare sprinklers shall include all types and ratings installed and shall be as follows:

(1) For protected facilities having under 300 sprinklers—no fewer than six sprinklers
(2) For protected facilities having 300 to 1000 sprinklers—no fewer than 12 sprinklers
(3) For protected facilities having over 1000 sprinklers—no fewer than 24 sprinklers

6.2.9.6 A special sprinkler wrench shall be provided and kept in the cabinet to be used in the removal and installation of sprinklers. One sprinkler wrench shall be provided for each type of sprinkler installed.

6.3 Aboveground Pipe and Tube

The use of new pipe materials and the development of new methods for installing and joining pipe continue to grow. The subsections under Section 6.3 provide details on the applications of various pipe materials used in aboveground applications. NFPA 13 currently allows for various types of steel, copper, and nonmetallic pipe to be used.

6.3.1 General

6.3.1.1 Pipe or tube shall meet or exceed one of the standards in Table 6.3.1.1 or be in accordance with 6.3.6.

Paragraph 6.3.1.1 permits the use of steel pipe and copper tube materials made to standards other than those identified in Table 6.3.1.1, provided the requirements of any other piping standard meet or exceed the requirements of those standards specified in Table 6.3.1.1. Additionally, NFPA 13 permits the use of other types of piping materials not specifically identified, provided they are listed for fire protection service.

Table 6.3.6.1 identifies the ASTM standards used in the manufacturing process of nonmetallic pipe. Since nonmetallic pipe is not identified in Table 6.3.1.1, it is required to be listed for fire protection service.

TABLE 6.3.1.1 *Pipe or Tube Materials and Dimensions*

Materials and Dimensions	Standard
Ferrous Piping (Welded and Seamless)	
Specification for black and hot-dipped zinc-coated (galvanized) welded and seamless steel pipe for fire protection use	ASTM A 795
Specification for welded and seamless steel pipe	ANSI/ASTM A 53
Wrought steel pipe	ANSI/ASME B36.10M
Specification for electric-resistance-welded steel pipe	ASTM A 135
Copper Tube (Drawn, Seamless)	
Specification for seamless copper tube	ASTM B 75
Specification for seamless copper water tube	ASTM B 88
Specification for general requirements for wrought seamless copper and copper-alloy tube	ASTM B 251
Fluxes for soldering applications of copper and copper-alloy tube	ASTM B 813
Brazing filler metal (classification BCuP-3 or BCuP-4)	AWS A5.8
Solder metal, 95-5 (tin-antimony-Grade 95TA)	ASTM B 32
Alloy materials	ASTM B 446

Table 6.3.1.1 specifies the solders, brazing alloys, and fluxes to be used when joining copper tube. The techniques and materials identified have low-corrosive characteristics and are unlikely to cause leaks through the seats of sprinklers. Leakage was a problem with some other types of piping materials and joining techniques.

The selection of a particular pipe material is often subject to the environmental conditions of the space in which the pipe is installed. For example, some industrial environments could require a corrosion-resistant pipe material. The desire to achieve a certain aesthetic appearance could also influence material selection. For instance, when piping is installed exposed, copper tubing could be used to blend with the architectural features.

6.3.1.2 Steel pipe shall be in accordance with 6.3.2, 6.3.3, or 6.3.4.

6.3.1.3 Copper tube shall be in accordance with 6.3.5.

6.3.1.4 Chlorinated polyvinyl chloride (CPVC) and polybutylene pipe shall be in accordance with 6.3.6 and with the portions of the ASTM standards specified in Table 6.3.6.1 that apply to fire protection service.

6.3.2* Steel Pipe—Welded or Roll-Grooved. When steel pipe referenced in Table 6.3.1.1 is used and joined by welding as referenced in 6.5.2 or by roll-grooved pipe and fittings as referenced in 6.5.3, the minimum nominal wall thickness for pressures up to 300 psi (20.7 bar) shall be in accordance with Schedule 10 for pipe sizes up to 5 in. (127 mm), 0.134 in. (3.40 mm) for 6-in. (152-mm) pipe, and 0.188 in. (4.78 mm) for 8- and 10-in. (203- and 254-mm) pipe.

A.6.3.2 See Table A.6.3.2.

When Schedule 10 or thinner wall steel pipe is joined by welding or roll-grooved pipe and fittings, the groove forming or welding process cannot result in a thinner wall thickness, other than that due to the normal tolerances associated with the groove forming or welding, which is the reason for the requirement in 6.3.2. The term *minimum nominal wall thickness* recognizes that pipe standards permit minor tolerance variations greater or less than the stated wall thickness. Exhibit 6.7 illustrates a piece of pipe with one end roll-grooved.

EXHIBIT 6.7 *Section of Steel Pipe with One End Roll-Grooved.*

TABLE A.6.3.2 *Steel Pipe Dimensions*

Nominal Pipe Size (in.)	Outside Diameter		Schedule 5				Schedule 10[a]				Schedule 30				Schedule 40			
			Inside Diameter		Wall Thickness		Inside Diameter		Wall Thickness		Inside Diameter		Wall Thickness		Inside Diameter		Wall Thickness	
	in.	mm	in.	mm	in.	mm	in.	mm	in.	mm	in.	mm	in.	mm	in.	mm	in.	mm
½[b]	0.840	21.3	—	—	—	—	0.674	17.0	0.083	2.1	—	—	—	—	0.622	15.8	0.109	2.8
¾[b]	1.050	26.7	—	—	—	—	0.884	22.4	0.083	2.1	—	—	—	—	0.824	21.0	0.113	2.9
1	1.315	33.4	1.185	30.1	0.065	1.7	1.097	27.9	0.109	2.8	—	—	—	—	1.049	26.6	0.133	3.4
1¼	1.660	42.2	1.530	38.9	0.065	1.7	1.442	36.6	0.109	2.8	—	—	—	—	1.380	35.1	0.140	3.6
1½	1.900	48.3	1.770	45.0	0.065	1.7	1.682	42.7	0.109	2.8	—	—	—	—	1.610	40.9	0.145	3.7
2	2.375	60.3	2.245	57.0	0.065	1.7	2.157	54.8	0.109	2.8	—	—	—	—	2.067	52.5	0.154	3.9
2½	2.875	73.0	2.709	68.8	0.083	2.1	2.635	66.9	0.120	3.0	—	—	—	—	2.469	62.7	0.203	5.2
3	3.500	88.9	3.334	84.7	0.083	2.1	3.260	82.8	0.120	3.0	—	—	—	—	3.068	77.9	0.216	5.5
3½	4.000	101.6	3.834	97.4	0.083	2.1	3.760	95.5	0.120	3.0	—	—	—	—	3.548	90.1	0.226	5.7
4	4.500	114.3	4.334	110.1	0.083	2.1	4.260	108.2	0.120	3.0	—	—	—	—	4.026	102.3	0.237	6.0
5	5.563	141.3	—	—	—	—	5.295	134.5	0.134	3.4	—	—	—	—	5.047	128.2	0.258	6.6
6	6.625	168.3	6.407	162.7	0.109	2.8	6.357	161.5	0.134[c]	3.4	—	—	—	—	6.065	154.1	0.280	7.1
8	8.625	219.1	—	—	—	—	8.249	209.5	0.188[c]	4.8	8.071	205.0	0.277	7.0	7.981	—	0.322	—
10	10.750	273.1	—	—	—	—	10.370	263.4	0.188[c]	4.8	10.140	257.6	0.307	7.8	10.020	—	0.365	—
12	12.750	—	—	—	—	—	12.090	—	0.330	—	—	—	—	—	11.938	—	0.406	—

[a]Schedule 10 defined to 5-in. (127-mm) nominal pipe size by ASTM A 135, *Standard Specification for Electric-Resistance-Welded Steel Pipe.*

[b]These values applicable when used in conjunction with 8.14.19.3 and 8.14.19.4.

[c]Wall thickness specified in 6.3.2 and 6.3.3.

The nominal ½-in. and ¾-in. pipe information in Table A.6.3.2 is provided only for those applications specified in 8.14.19. In retrofit situations, 8.14.19 permits the use of short ½-in. or ¾-in. pipe nipples to supply sprinklers below a false ceiling from existing ½-in. or ¾-in. sprinkler outlets. This allowance for short ½-in. or ¾-in. pipe nipples applies to existing systems in nonseismic areas only.

6.3.3 Steel Pipe—Threaded. When steel pipe referenced in Table 6.3.1.1 is joined by threaded fittings referenced in 6.5.1 or by fittings used with pipe having cut grooves, the minimum wall thickness shall be in accordance with Schedule 30 pipe [in sizes 8 in. (203 mm) and larger] or Schedule 40 pipe [in sizes less than 8 in. (203 mm)] for pressures up to 300 psi (20.7 bar).

When pipe is threaded or grooves are cut into it, the use of Schedule 10 or thinner steel pipe can result in an insufficient pipe wall thickness between the inside pipe diameter and the root diameter of the thread or groove, which is the reason for the requirement in 6.3.3. An insufficient pipe wall thickness reduces the beam strength of the pipe at those threaded or cut-grooved areas and can result in failure of the pipe and fittings. Exhibit 6.8 illustrates pipe joined with threaded fittings.

6.3.4 Specially Listed Steel Pipe. Pressure limitations and wall thickness for steel pipe specially listed in accordance with 6.3.6 shall be permitted to be in accordance with the pipe listing requirements.

A threaded or cut-grooved assembly for pipe sizes and schedules other than those specified in NFPA 13 can be used to satisfy the requirement in 6.3.4, provided the assembly is investigated for suitability in automatic sprinkler installations and is listed for this service.

6.3.5* Copper Tube. Copper tube as specified in the standards listed in Table 6.3.1.1 shall have a wall thickness of Type K, Type L, or Type M where used in sprinkler systems.

EXHIBIT 6.8 Pipe Joined Using Threaded Fittings.

A.6.3.5 See Table A.6.3.5.

Type M copper tube, which is mentioned in 6.3.5, is the thinnest walled tubing so it has the largest inside diameter. This larger internal diameter offers a hydraulic advantage and is less expensive than other types of copper tube. These advantages make Type M tube an attractive copper material when pipe bending is not required.

6.3.6* Listed Pipe and Tubing.

A.6.3.6 Other types of pipe and tube that have been investigated and listed for sprinkler applications include lightweight steel pipe and thermoplastic pipe and fittings. While these products can offer advantages, such as ease of handling and installation, cost-effectiveness, reduction of friction losses, and improved corrosion resistance, it is important to recognize

TABLE A.6.3.5 Copper Tube Dimensions

Nominal Tube Size (in.)	Outside Diameter		Type K				Type L				Type M			
			Inside Diameter		Wall Thickness		Inside Diameter		Wall Thickness		Inside Diameter		Wall Thickness	
	in.	mm	in.	mm	in.	mm	in.	mm	in.	mm	in.	mm	in.	mm
¾	0.875	22.2	0.745	18.9	0.065	1.7	0.785	19.9	0.045	1.1	0.811	20.6	0.032	0.8
1	1.125	28.6	0.995	25.3	0.065	1.7	1.025	26.0	0.050	1.3	1.055	26.8	0.035	0.9
1¼	1.375	34.9	1.245	31.6	0.065	1.7	1.265	32.1	0.055	1.4	1.291	32.8	0.042	1.1
1½	1.625	41.3	1.481	37.6	0.072	1.8	1.505	38.2	0.060	1.5	1.527	38.8	0.049	1.2
2	2.125	54.0	1.959	49.8	0.083	2.1	1.985	50.4	0.070	1.8	2.009	51.0	0.058	1.5
2½	2.625	66.7	2.435	61.8	0.095	2.4	2.465	62.6	0.080	2.0	2.495	63.4	0.065	1.7
3	3.125	79.4	2.907	73.8	0.109	2.8	2.945	74.8	0.090	2.3	2.981	75.7	0.072	1.8
3½	3.625	92.1	3.385	86.0	0.120	3.0	3.425	87.0	0.100	2.5	3.459	87.9	0.083	2.1
4	4.125	104.8	3.857	98.0	0.134	3.4	3.905	99.2	0.110	2.8	3.935	99.9	0.095	2.4
5	5.125	130.2	4.805	122.0	0.160	4.1	4.875	123.8	0.125	3.2	4.907	124.6	0.109	2.8
6	6.125	155.6	5.741	145.8	0.192	4.9	5.845	148.5	0.140	3.6	5.881	149.4	0.122	3.1
8	8.125	206.4	7.583	192.6	0.271	6.9	7.725	196.2	0.200	5.1	7.785	197.7	0.170	4.3
10	10.130	257.3	9.449	240.0	0.338	8.6	9.625	244.5	0.250	6.4	9.701	246.4	0.212	5.4

that they also have limitations that are to be considered by those contemplating their use or acceptance.

Corrosion studies have shown that, in comparison to Schedule 40 pipe, the effective life of lightweight steel pipe can be reduced, the level of reduction being related to its wall thickness. Further information with respect to corrosion resistance is contained in the individual listings for such pipe.

With respect to thermoplastic pipe and fittings, exposure of such piping to elevated temperatures in excess of that for which it has been listed can result in distortion or failure. Accordingly, care must be exercised when locating such systems to ensure that the ambient temperature, including seasonal variations, does not exceed the rated value.

The upper service temperature limit of currently listed CPVC sprinkler pipe is 150°F (65.5°C) at 175 psi (12.1 bar). The upper service temperature limit of currently listed polybutylene sprinkler pipe is 120°F (49°C) at 175 psi (12.1 bar).

 Not all pipe or tube made to ASTM F 442, *Standard Specification for Chlorinated Poly (Vinyl Chloride) (CPVC) Plastic Pipe (SDR-PR),* and ASTM D 3309, *Standard Specification for Polybutylene (PB) Plastic Hot- and Cold-Water Distribution Systems,* as described in 6.3.6, is listed for fire sprinkler service. Listed pipe is identified by the logo of the listing agency.

Not all fittings made to ASTM F 437, *Standard Specification for Threaded Chlorinated Poly (Vinyl Chloride) (CPVC) Plastic Pipe Fittings, Schedule 80;* ASTM F 438, *Standard Specification for Socket-Type Chlorinated Poly (Vinyl Chloride) (CPVC) Plastic Pipe Fittings, Schedule 40;* and ASTM F 439, *Standard Specification for Socket-Type Chlorinated Poly (Vinyl Chloride) (CPVC) Plastic Pipe Fittings, Schedule 80,* as described in 6.4.3, are listed for fire sprinkler service. Listed fittings are identified by the logo of the listing agency.

Consideration must also be given to the possibility of exposure of the piping to elevated temperatures during a fire. The survival of thermoplastic piping under fire conditions is primarily due to the cooling effect of the discharge from the sprinklers it serves. As this discharge might not occur simultaneously with the rise in ambient temperature and, under some circumstances, can be delayed for periods beyond the tolerance of the piping, protection in the form of a fire-resistant membrane is generally required. (Some listings do provide for the use of exposed piping in conjunction with residential or quick-response sprinklers, but only under specific, limited installation criteria.)

Where protection is required, it is described in the listing information for each individual product, and the requirements given must be followed. It is equally important that such protection must be maintained. Removal of, for example, one or more panels in a lay-in ceiling can expose piping in the concealed space to the possibility of failure in the event of a fire. Similarly, the relocation of openings through protective ceilings that expose the pipe to heat, inconsistent with the listing, would place the system in jeopardy. The potential for loss of the protective membrane under earthquake conditions should also be considered.

While the listings of thermoplastic piping do not prohibit its installation in combustible concealed spaces where the provision of sprinkler protection is not required, and while the statistical record of fire originating in such spaces is low, it should be recognized that the occurrence of a fire in such a space could result in failure of the piping system.

The investigation of pipe and tube other than described in Table 6.3.1.1 should involve consideration of many factors, including the following:

(1) Pressure rating
(2) Beam strength (hangers)
(3) Unsupported vertical stability
(4) Movement during sprinkler operation (affecting water distribution)
(5) Corrosion (internal and external), chemical and electrolytic
(6) Resistance to failure when exposed to elevated temperatures

(7) Methods of joining (strength, permanence, fire hazard)

(8) Physical characteristics related to integrity during earthquakes

NFPA does not limit aboveground sprinkler system piping materials to the steel and copper materials identified in Table 6.3.1.1. However, any other materials must be listed for use in sprinkler systems. Subsection 6.3.6 encourages development of other materials that offer cost or performance advantages. Historically, the development of new products and methods, such as threadable light wall steel pipe, copper tubing, and nonmetallic pipe, has occurred through the application of this subsection.

6.3.6.1 Other types of pipe or tube investigated for suitability in automatic sprinkler installations and listed for this service, including but not limited to polybutylene, CPVC, and steel, differing from that provided in Table 6.3.6.1 shall be permitted where installed in accordance with their listing limitations, including installation instructions.

TABLE 6.3.6.1 *Specially Listed Pipe or Tube Materials and Dimensions*

Materials and Dimensions	*Standard*
Nonmetallic piping specification for special listed chlorinated polyvinyl chloride (CPVC) pipe	ASTM F 442
Specification for special listed polybutylene (PB) pipe	ASTM D 3309

As indicated in 6.3.6.1, specially listed pipe must be installed in complete compliance with all conditions, requirements, and limitations of its listing.

Two nonmetallic piping materials have been listed for sprinkler system applications. These materials include CPVC pipe and polybutylene (PB) pipe, which have been listed for residential and light hazard occupancies. However, since April 1996, the resin used to manufacture polybutylene pipe is no longer available.

The listings of nonmetallic pipe, which is discussed in 6.3.6.1, include numerous restrictions. These restrictions include maximum and minimum temperature limits, use for wet pipe systems only, and use of fittings that are exclusively developed for use with the pipe.

Additionally, CPVC piping is not listed for use in ordinary hazard (except as allowed in 6.3.6.2) or extra hazard areas. Although A.6.3.6 provides some cautions pertaining to the use of nonmetallic pipe, the user must refer to the listing information, including installation instructions, to accomplish correct installation. (Also see the commentary following 6.4.3.)

When the product requires a protective membrane, readily available materials such as gypsum wallboard, ½-in. (12.7-mm) plywood, or acoustical panels would constitute acceptable protection. Throughout the life of the building, care should be taken to ensure that the integrity of the protective membrane materials remains intact—that is, no through penetrations and no removal of materials except at the sprinkler locations.

◄ FAQ
Can CPVC pipe be installed exposed?

CPVC pipe can be installed exposed under certain circumstances. The system must be installed using listed quick-response or listed residential sprinklers. If quick-response sprinklers are used, the deflectors must be installed within 8 in. (203 mm) of the ceiling. If residential sprinklers are used, the sprinklers must be installed in accordance with their listing. To obtain these special listings, piping materials are subject to rigorous fire-testing procedures. Successful completion of these tests demonstrates that the material will remain operable under certain fire conditions and will not contribute to the growth of the fire, thereby creating an acceptable confidence level with regard to these materials.

Although not shown in Table 6.3.1.1, some light wall steel pipe is listed for fire protection service, and its use is governed by 6.2.6.1. Light wall steel pipe is tested for its ability to provide performance characteristics similar to those of Schedule 40 steel pipe. These piping materials might be advantageous from a hydraulics standpoint since they have a larger interior diameter than other steel pipe materials. In addition, their weight is considerably less than that of Schedule 40 pipe, and their joining methods require less overall effort.

6.3.6.2 Pipe or tube listed for light hazard occupancies shall be permitted to be installed in ordinary hazard rooms of otherwise light hazard occupancies where the room does not exceed 400 ft^2 (37 m^2).

FAQ ▶

Can nonmetallic pipe be used in rooms of ordinary hazard occupancy in a predominately light hazard occupancy?

As stated in 6.3.6.2, it is the intent of NFPA 13 to permit the use of nonmetallic pipe in small rooms that do not exceed 400 ft^2, such as closets and mechanical rooms in otherwise light hazard occupancies.

6.3.6.3 Pipe or tube shall not be listed for portions of an occupancy classification.

6.3.6.4 Bending of listed pipe and tubing shall be permitted as allowed by the listing.

6.3.7 Pipe Bending.

6.3.7.1 Bending of Schedule 10 steel pipe, or any steel pipe of wall thickness equal to or greater than Schedule 10 and Types K and L copper tube, shall be permitted when bends are made with no kinks, ripples, distortions, or reductions in diameter or any noticeable deviations from round.

6.3.7.2 For Schedule 40 and copper tubing, the minimum radius of a bend shall be six pipe diameters for pipe sizes 2 in. (51 mm) and smaller and five pipe diameters for pipe sizes 2½ in. (64 mm) and larger.

6.3.7.3 For all other steel pipe, the minimum radius of a bend shall be 12 pipe diameters for all sizes.

Pipe bending is covered in 6.3.7.1 through 6.3.7.3. NFPA 13 permits bending of all types of Schedule 10 (thin wall) and thicker-walled steel pipe as indicated in Exhibit 6.9. The minimum bending radius for Schedule 40 (standard wall) pipe is less than it is for any of the thinner-walled products. Special listed pipe having a wall thickness less than Schedule 10 cannot be bent.

EXHIBIT 6.9 Bent Pipe.

Type M copper tube cannot be used for bending because the bending results in a wall that is too thin. However, the thicker Types K and L copper tubing can be used for bending because adequate material remains after bending. Without control over the bending radius of the pipe, excessive friction loss values for a given elbow, or similar segment of pipe that changes the direction of flow, can be expected.

6.3.8 Pipe Identification.

6.3.8.1 All pipe, including specially listed pipe allowed by 6.3.6, shall be marked continuously along its length by the manufacturer in such a way as to properly identify the type of pipe.

6.3.8.2 Pipe identification shall include the manufacturer's name, model designation, or schedule.

Pipe identification is covered in 6.3.8.1 and 6.3.8.2. All pipe used for sprinkler systems and not just pipe that is listed for use in sprinkler systems must be continuously marked. Not all pipe made to a particular manufacturing standard is listed. Listed piping is identified by the unique marking of the listing agency. One example of this identification is shown in Exhibit 6.10. In this case, the Underwriters Laboratories (UL) mark is clearly visible on the pipe. Exhibit 6.10 illustrates a piece of chlorinated polyvinyl chloride (CPVC) fire sprinkler system pipe. Nonmetallic piping that is not listed may be manufactured without the assurance of complying with the applicable specification and must not be used in sprinkler systems.

The variety of piping materials with varying wall thicknesses available to the sprinkler industry offers many benefits. Without the labeling requirements of 6.3.8.1 and 6.3.8.2, identification of pipe in the field would, in many instances, be extremely difficult.

The identification of some pipe materials is more obvious than others. For example, listed CPVC sprinkler pipe that has a characteristic orange and copper tube is easy to identify because of its color and appearance. The color schemes, however, need to be supplemented by the marking requirements established by 6.3.8.

◀ **FAQ**
Is all piping utilized for sprinkler systems required to be marked?

EXHIBIT 6.10 *Example of Plastic Pipe Showing the Marking of the Listing Agency.*

6.4 Fittings

6.4.1 Fittings used in sprinkler systems shall meet or exceed the standards in Table 6.4.1 or be in accordance with 6.4.2 or 6.4.3.

TABLE 6.4.1 *Fittings Materials and Dimensions*

Materials and Dimensions	Standard
Cast Iron	
Cast iron threaded fittings, Class 125 and 250	ASME B16.4
Cast iron pipe flanges and flanged fittings	ASME B16.1
Malleable Iron	
Malleable iron threaded fittings, Class 150 and 300 steel	ASME B16.3
Factory-made wrought steel buttweld fittings	ASME B16.9
Buttwelding ends for pipe, valves, flanges, and fittings	ASME B16.25
Specification for piping fittings of wrought carbon steel and alloy steel for moderate and elevated temperatures	ASTM A 234
Steel pipe flanges and flanged fittings	ASME B16.5
Forged steel fittings, socket welded and threaded copper	ASME B16.11
Wrought copper and copper alloy solder joint pressure fittings	ASME B16.22
Cast copper alloy solder joint pressure fittings	ASME B16.18

Paragraph 6.4.1 specifies the types of fittings permitted to be used in sprinkler systems. The fittings must be of the types and materials indicated in Table 6.4.1 and must be manufactured to the standards identified in the table or to other standards that meet or exceed these standards' requirements. Additionally, NFPA 13 permits the use of specially listed fittings.

The fittings specified in Table 6.4.1 are compatible with and intended for use with the piping materials listed in Table 6.3.1.1. If specially listed materials are used, then specially listed fittings complying with 6.4.2 and 6.4.3 should be used.

6.4.2 In addition to the standards in Table 6.4.1, CPVC fittings shall also be in accordance with 6.4.3 and with the portions of the ASTM standards specified in Table 6.4.3 that apply to fire protection service.

6.4.3* Other types of fittings investigated for suitability in automatic sprinkler installations and listed for this service including, but not limited to, polybutylene, CPVC, and steel differing from that provided in Table 6.4.3, shall be permitted when installed in accordance with their listing limitations, including installation instructions.

TABLE 6.4.3 *Specially Listed Fittings Materials and Dimensions*

Materials and Dimensions	Standard
Chlorinated polyvinyl chloride (CPVC) specification for schedule 80 CPVC threaded fittings	ASTM F 437
Specification for schedule 40 CPVC socket-type fittings	ASTM F 438
Specification for schedule 80 CPVC socket-type fittings	ASTM F 439

 A.6.4.3 Rubber-gasketed pipe fittings and couplings should not be installed where ambient temperatures can be expected to exceed 150°F (66°C) unless listed for this service. If the manufacturer further limits a given gasket compound, those recommendations should be followed.

Paragraph A.6.4.3 is similar to 6.3.1, which permits alternative types of listed pipe and tube. Innovations in the technology of new fittings can be linked to new piping materials. According to 6.4.3, any new fitting listed for use in a sprinkler system is permitted by NFPA 13. However, this requirement is not intended to mean that any listed fitting can be used with any listed pipe. The user must check the testing laboratory's fire protection equipment directory to ensure that the pipe and fitting are listed as compatible.

For example, one listed fitting is the specially designed "Press Fit," which can be used on certain types of specially listed thin-wall steel pipe. The Press Fit is not to be used with nonmetallic piping materials. Exhibit 6.11 illustrates a specially listed Press Fit tool. Exhibit 6.12 illustrates the pipe and fitting joined using this tool.

EXHIBIT 6.11 *Press Fit Tool.*

EXHIBIT 6.12 *Pipe and Fitting Joined Using the Press Fit Tool.*

6.4.4* Fitting Pressure Limits.

A.6.4.4 The rupture strength of cast-iron fittings 2 in. (50.8 mm) in size and smaller and malleable iron fittings 6 in. (152.4 mm) in size and smaller is sufficient to provide an adequate factor of safety.

6.4.4.1 Standard weight pattern cast-iron fittings 2 in. (51 mm) in size and smaller shall be permitted where pressures do not exceed 300 psi (20.7 bar).

6.4.4.2 Standard weight pattern malleable iron fittings 6 in. (152 mm) in size and smaller shall be permitted where pressures do not exceed 300 psi (20.7 bar).

6.4.4.3 Listed fittings shall be permitted for system pressures up to the limits specified in their listings.

6.4.4.4 Fittings not meeting the requirements of 6.4.4.1 through 6.4.4.3 shall be extra-heavy pattern where pressures exceed 175 psi (12.1 bar).

Fitting pressure limits are covered in 6.4.4.1 through 6.4.4.4. Paragraphs 6.4.4.1 and 6.4.4.2 permit cast-iron fittings 2 in. (51 mm) in size and smaller and malleable iron fittings 6 in. (152 mm) in size and smaller to be used in systems where pressures do not exceed 300 psi (20.7 bar). The design and rupture strength associated with these fittings provides an adequate level of performance. According to 6.4.4.3, fittings can be used in systems up to the pressure limitation of their listing.

6.4.5* Couplings and Unions.

A.6.4.5 Listed flexible connections are permissible and encouraged for sprinkler installations in racks to reduce the possibility of physical damage. Where flexible tubing is used, it should be located so that it will be protected against mechanical injury.

6.4.5.1 Screwed unions shall not be used on pipe larger than 2 in. (51 mm).

Screwed unions larger than 2 in. (51 mm) in size, as discussed in 6.4.5.1, present a maintenance problem because of their tendency to develop leaks. A variety of acceptable fittings are available for use in connecting various sizes of pipe. NFPA 13 permits the use of various joining methods throughout the system.

6.4.5.2 Couplings and unions of other than screwed-type shall be of types listed specifically for use in sprinkler systems.

6.4.6 Reducers and Bushings.

6.4.6.1 Unless the requirements of 6.4.6.2 or 6.4.6.3 are met, a one-piece reducing fitting shall be used wherever a change is made in the size of the pipe.

The intent of 6.4.6.1 prohibits the use of bushings where a one-piece reducing fitting is commercially available at the time the system is installed.

For other than the circumstance cited in 8.14.19.2, in which bushings are temporarily installed to facilitate an unrestricted flow to sprinklers installed below a future drop ceiling, bushings can be used only where reducing fittings are unavailable. Bushings have poorer flow characteristics than reducing fittings and have a greater tendency to leak.

The use of bushings under all but the most pressing conditions is discouraged. For example, a particular fitting may actually be manufactured but may be backordered for several months. If the proper reducing fitting cannot be obtained after an exhaustive effort, then the use of bushings can be considered. Exhibit 6.13 illustrates the use of a bushing in place of a one-piece reducing fitting.

EXHIBIT 6.13 *Hexagonal Bushing.*

6.4.6.2 Hexagonal or face bushings shall be permitted in reducing the size of openings of fittings when standard fittings of the required size are not available.

6.4.6.3 Hexagonal bushings as permitted in 8.14.19.2 shall be permitted to be used.

6.5 Joining of Pipe and Fittings

6.5.1 Threaded Pipe and Fittings.

6.5.1.1 All threaded pipe and fittings shall have threads cut to ASME B1.20.1, *Pipe Threads, General Purpose (Inch).*

Threaded pipe and fittings are addressed in 6.5.1.1. Poor workmanship can result in threads that allow pipe protrusions to partially obstruct fitting openings. If such joints are permitted, they can seriously restrict system flow and greatly increase the pressure lost to friction, thereby impairing system operation.

6.5.1.2* Steel pipe with wall thicknesses less than Schedule 30 [in sizes 8 in. (203 mm) and larger] or Schedule 40 [in sizes less than 8 in. (203 mm)] shall only be permitted to be joined by threaded fittings where the threaded assembly is investigated for suitability in automatic sprinkler installations and listed for this service.

A.6.5.1.2 Some steel piping material having lesser wall thickness than specified in 6.5.1.2 has been listed for use in sprinkler systems where joined with threaded connections. The service life of such products can be significantly less than that of Schedule 40 steel pipe, and it should be determined if this service life will be sufficient for the application intended.

All such threads should be checked by the installer using working ring gauges conforming to the "Basic Dimensions of Ring Gauges for USA (American) Standard Taper Pipe Threads, NPT," as per Table 8 of ASME B1.20.1, *Pipe Threads, General Purpose, (Inch).*

 FAQ ▶
What is CRR?

To alleviate concerns about the service life of listed thin-wall pipe, which is discussed in 6.5.1.2, part of its listing evaluation includes an examination of its corrosion resistance ratio (CRR) with respect to Schedule 40 steel pipe. The CRR relates to the ratio of pipe wall thickness of the thinnest wall cross section (usually the first exposed thread for threaded pipe) for the listed pipe when compared to Schedule 40 pipe measured at the same location. The CRR is calculated assuming that the environmental exposures are the same for both pipes and that the pipe will be perforated at the thinnest section by pit-type corrosion.

For example, a CRR of 0.21 indicates an anticipated service life of 21 percent, approximately one-fifth that of Schedule 40 pipe, when installed in wet systems in stable internal and external environmental conditions. These evaluation results are available in the listing information for a given product. Exhibit 6.8 shows steel pipe joined with a threaded fitting.

Paragraph 6.5.1.2 permits the use of threaded assemblies for thinner-walled pipe, provided the assembly is listed for use in sprinkler systems. Because of its pipe wall thickness, threading of listed thin-wall pipe requires careful workmanship and exceptional quality control.

6.5.1.3 Joint compound or tape shall be applied only to male threads.

Joint compound or tape that is applied to a fitting rather than to a male thread forms a ridge inside the pipe when the joint is made, which is the reason for the requirement in 6.5.1.3. The ridge reduces the inside diameter of the pipe and thereby obstructs water flow. The operation of systems other than wet systems involves a high-velocity flow when the valve trips. The impact of the water tends to break off pieces of joint compound and carry them in a mass to the opened sprinklers where they can obstruct the orifices.

◄ **FAQ**
Why is joint compound or tape only permitted to be applied to the male threads?

6.5.2* Welded Pipe and Fittings.

A.6.5.2 See Figure A.6.5.2(a) and Figure A.6.5.2(b).

A

Standard "vee" buttweld   *Flange connection*   *Slip-on flange*

Standard "vee"   *Hole in pipe cut to fit inner diameter of fitting*   *Welded outlet*

FIGURE A.6.5.2(a) *Acceptable Weld Joints.*

6.5.2.1 Welding methods that comply with the applicable requirements of AWS B2.1, *Specification for Welding Procedure and Performance Qualification,* shall be permitted as means of joining fire protection piping.

Welding of any sprinkler piping is subject to strict quality control procedures. Failure to adhere to the procedures outlined in 6.5.2.1 can result in an unsuccessful acceptance of the system. Although pipe welding can result in an excellent system installation, it requires special skills on the part of a qualified welder.

AWS B2.1, *Standard for Welding Procedure and Performance Qualification,* reflects the minimum welding requirements needed for the pressures found in sprinkler systems. AWS B2.1 is the American Welding Society's replacement of discontinued specification AWS D10.9.

6.5.2.1.1 Where outlets are welded in pipe using listed welding outlet fittings, partial joint penetration (groove/fillet) shall be acceptable when performed in accordance with the requirements of 6.5.2.1.

FIGURE A.6.5.2(b) Unacceptable Weld Joints.

6.5.2.1.2 Where slip-on flanges are welded to pipe, fillet welds shall be acceptable where such welds are used along both circumferences where the flange contacts the pipe.

6.5.2.2* Unless the requirements of 6.5.2.3 are met, sprinkler piping shall be shop welded.

A.6.5.2.2 Cutting and welding operations account for 4 percent of fires each year in nonresidential properties and 8 percent in industrial and manufacturing properties. In-place welding of sprinkler piping introduces a significant hazard that can normally be avoided by shop-welding the piping and installing the welded sections with mechanical fittings. As a result, the standard requires that all piping be shop-welded. When such situations cannot be avoided, the exceptions outline procedures and practices that minimize the increase in hazard.

Because the welding process introduces a potential ignition source, 6.5.2.2 of NFPA 13 requires shop-welding of all system piping unless certain conditions are met. If the provisions of NFPA 51B, *Standard for Fire Prevention During Welding, Cutting, and Other Hot Work,* are followed, the welding process can be expected to be safely accomplished in new installations. Since other mechanical system piping can be welded in place, it is logical to expect that sprinkler pipe can also be welded in place. Prior restrictions concerning welding of pipe in place were based on the occurrence of fires as a result of the welding process. NFPA 51B contains a number of precautions that, when followed, reduce or eliminate the ignition hazard.

6.5.2.3 Where the design specifications call for all or part of the piping to be welded in place, welding of sprinkler piping in place shall be permitted where the welding process is performed in accordance with NFPA 51B, *Standard for Fire Prevention During Welding, Cutting, and Other Hot Work,* and the mechanical fittings required by 8.14.16 and 8.14.21 are provided.

6.5.2.4 Welding of tabs for longitudinal earthquake bracing to in-place piping shall be permitted where the welding process is performed in accordance with NFPA 51B, *Standard for Fire Prevention During Welding, Cutting, and Other Hot Work.*

6.5.2.5 Welded fittings used to join pipe shall be listed fabricated fittings or manufactured in accordance with Table 6.4.1.

Unlisted fabricated fittings are not permitted under 6.5.2.5. A listed fabricated fitting has an identified equivalent length that identifies its hydraulic characteristics. The use of listed fabricated fittings also serves to increase overall system reliability.

6.5.2.6 Fittings referenced in 6.5.2.5 shall be joined in conformance with a qualified welding procedure as set forth in this section and shall be an acceptable product under this standard, provided that materials and wall thickness are compatible with other sections of this standard.

6.5.2.7 Fittings shall not be required where pipe ends are butt welded in accordance with the requirements of 6.5.2.1.

Paragraph 6.5.2.7 stipulates the only condition under which a manufactured fitting or a listed fabricated fitting need not be used, which is when two identical size pipe diameters are to be connected in the same plane with no change in direction. The pieces can then be buttwelded.

◀ **FAQ**
Under what conditions are manufactured fittings or listed fabricated fittings not required when joining pipe?

6.5.2.8 No welding shall be performed if there is impingement of rain, snow, sleet, or high wind on the weld area of the pipe product.

Welding must not be performed under conditions that introduce a hazard to the welder. Furthermore, welding performed in such adverse conditions as mentioned in 6.5.2.8 can also result in a structurally weak product.

6.5.2.9 When welding is performed, the following procedures shall be completed:

(1)* Holes in piping for outlets shall be cut to the full inside diameter of fittings prior to welding in place of the fittings.
(2) Discs shall be retrieved.
(3) Openings cut into piping shall be smooth bore, and all internal slag and welding residue shall be removed.
(4) Fittings shall not penetrate the internal diameter of the piping.
(5) Steel plates shall not be welded to the ends of piping or fittings.
(6) Fittings shall not be modified.
(7) Nuts, clips, eye rods, angle brackets, or other fasteners shall not be welded to pipe or fittings, except as permitted in 6.5.2.10.

A.6.5.2.9(1) Listed, shaped, contoured nipples meet the definition of fabricated fittings.

Past experience indicates that quality control can be a problem with welded sprinkler piping, which is the reason for the requirement in 6.5.2.9(1). Conditions that are not permitted are identified in 6.5.2.8.

When welded outlets are formed, some of the concerns addressed by these requirements are as follows:

1. The area of flow must not be restricted.
2. Holes should be cut in a manner that provides for disc retrieval to minimize obstructions in the waterway.
3. Rough edges cause turbulence, which increases friction loss, and welding residue could obstruct water flow through activated sprinklers.
4. Penetration beyond the internal diameter of the pipe restricts flow and causes turbulence.

Items 6.5.2.9(5), 6.5.2.9(6), and 6.5.2.9(7) represent poor practices within the industry and are not permitted by NFPA 13. Disc retrieval mentioned in 6.5.2.9(2) is best assured by attaching the disc to the piping at the point at which it was cut, as indicated in Exhibit 6.14.

EXHIBIT 6.14 Discs Attached to Piping from Which They Were Cut.

6.5.2.10 Tabs for longitudinal earthquake braces shall be permitted to be welded directly to the sprinkler pipe.

6.5.2.11 When the pipe size in a run of piping is reduced, a reducing fitting designed for that purpose shall be used in accordance with the requirements of 6.5.2.3.

Unlisted fabricated fittings are not permitted under 6.5.2.11. Such fittings do not have performance characteristics comparable to fittings specifically designed for this purpose.

6.5.2.12 Torch cutting and welding shall not be permitted as a means of modifying or repairing sprinkler systems.

Torch cutting and welding, which are addressed in 6.5.2.12, are restricted to new installations and only under those conditions specified by 6.5.2.3. This restriction reduces the possible introduction of ignition sources when the sprinkler system is impaired.

6.5.2.13 Qualifications.

6.5.2.13.1 A welding procedure shall be prepared and qualified by the contractor or fabricator before any welding is done.

 6.5.2.13.2 Qualification of the welding procedure to be used and the performance of all welders and welding operators shall be required and shall meet or exceed the requirements of

AWS B2.1, *Specification for Welding Procedure and Performance Qualification,* except as permitted by 6.5.2.13.3.

6.5.2.13.3 Successful procedure qualification of complete joint penetration groove welds shall qualify partial joint penetration (groove/fillet) welds and fillet welds in accordance with the provisions of this standard.

6.5.2.13.4 Welding procedures qualified under standards recognized by previous editions of this standard shall be permitted to be continued in use.

As indicated in 6.5.2.13.2, AWS B2.1 reflects the minimum welding requirements needed for the pressures found in sprinkler systems. The welding procedures and the performance of the welders must be in conformance with AWS B2.1. This standard is the American Welding Society's replacement of discontinued specification AWS D10.9. As indicated in paragraph 6.5.2.13.4, procedures qualified under AWS D10.9 are still applicable to work on sprinkler systems.

◀ **FAQ**
What happened to the requirements for AWS D10.9?

6.5.2.13.5 Contractors or fabricators shall be responsible for all welding they produce.

Contractors or fabricators are directly responsible for qualifying procedures and welders in accordance with 6.5.2.13.5 of NFPA 13, as well as for the quality of the welds performed by their employees.

6.5.2.13.6 Each contractor or fabricator shall have available to the authority having jurisdiction an established written quality assurance procedure ensuring compliance with the requirements of 6.5.2.9.

6.5.2.14 Records.

6.5.2.14.1 Welders or welding machine operators shall, upon completion of each weld, stamp an imprint of their identification into the side of the pipe adjacent to the weld.

The imprinted identification mentioned in 6.5.2.14.1 serves to record welds completed by a specific welder. Quality control problems or defective materials can be easily traced should a problem with the weld occur.

6.5.2.14.2 Contractors or fabricators shall maintain certified records, which shall be available to the authority having jurisdiction, of the procedures used and the welders or welding machine operators employed by them, along with their welding identification imprints.

6.5.2.14.3 Records shall show the date and the results of procedure and performance qualifications.

6.5.3 Groove Joining Methods.

6.5.3.1 Pipe joined with grooved fittings shall be joined by a listed combination of fittings, gaskets, and grooves.

6.5.3.2 Grooves cut or rolled on pipe shall be dimensionally compatible with the fittings.

Unlike threads, grooves are not fabricated to a national standard, which is the reason for the requirement in 6.5.3.2. Therefore, the listing of a grooved fitting (see Exhibit 6.15) includes information on the allowable groove type—cut or rolled—groove dimensions, and the compatible fitting and gasket.

6.5.3.3 Grooved fittings including gaskets used on dry pipe systems shall be listed for dry pipe service.

Gaskets on grooved couplings have a limited degree of fire endurance when used on dry pipe systems, which is the reason for the requirement in 6.5.3.3. Therefore, the listing requirements of some grooved couplings include an evaluation of the coupling's performance in dry

◀ **FAQ**
Why are gaskets used in dry pipe systems required to be listed?

EXHIBIT 6.15 Grooved Fitting.

pipe sprinkler applications. In addition, dry systems typically are exposed to extreme temperatures. Couplings for dry systems have their gaskets evaluated for their resistance to air leakage at the minimum temperatures referenced in the listing.

6.5.4* Brazed and Soldered Joints.

A.6.5.4 The fire hazard of the brazing and soldering processes should be suitably safeguarded.

Subsection 6.5.4 restricts the use of soldered joints to conditions under which the system piping is filled with water and in which heat from a fire will not reach a magnitude that can compromise the integrity of the joint.

6.5.4.1 Solder joints, where permitted, shall be fabricated in accordance with the methods and procedures listed in ASTM B 828, *Standard Practice for Making Capillary Joints by Soldering of Copper and Copper Alloy Tube and Fittings.*

Paragraph 6.5.4.1 provides guidance for the proper procedure for fabricating soldered joints. ASTM B 828 is the nationally recognized installation standard for soldering copper and copper alloy tube and fittings.

6.5.4.2 Unless the requirements of 6.5.4.3 or 6.5.4.4 are met, joints for the connection of copper tube shall be brazed.

6.5.4.3 Solder joints shall be permitted for exposed wet pipe systems in light hazard occupancies where the temperature classification of the installed sprinklers is of the ordinary- or intermediate-temperature classification.

6.5.4.4 Solder joints shall be permitted for wet pipe systems in light hazard and ordinary hazard (Group 1) occupancies where the piping is concealed, irrespective of sprinkler temperature ratings.

6.5.4.5* Soldering fluxes shall be in accordance with Table 6.3.1.1.

A.6.5.4.5 Soldering fluxes manufactured to the specifications required by Table 6.3.1.1 are unlikely to cause damage to the seats of sprinklers. When brazing flux is used, it must be of a type not likely to damage the seats of sprinklers.

Soldering fluxes are discussed in 6.5.4.5. Highly corrosive fluxes have been known to react with the metal in the seat of the sprinkler, resulting in leakage of the device. Solders meeting ASTM B 813, *Standard Specification for Liquid and Paste Fluxes for Soldering Applications of Copper and Copper-Alloy Tube,* minimize that risk.

6.5.4.6 Brazing fluxes, if used, shall not be of a highly corrosive type.

6.5.5 Other Joining Methods. Other joining methods investigated for suitability in automatic sprinkler installations and listed for this service shall be permitted where installed in accordance with their listing limitations, including installation instructions.

Paragraph 6.5.5 allows the use of joining methods not specifically described in NFPA 13, provided these methods are listed for use in sprinkler systems. Additionally, this paragraph encourages the development and application of new technology. The requirement is similar to 6.3.6 for pipe materials and 6.4.3 for fittings.

6.5.6 End Treatment.

6.5.6.1 After cutting, pipe ends shall have burrs and fins removed.

As stated in 6.5.6.1, pipe must be reamed and deburred to minimize the reduction of the inside diameter of the pipe and to remove any rough edges from the end of the pipe. Thin "fins" that occur after cutting are susceptible to corrosion and can dislodge causing obstructions in the waterway. The removal of irregular edges is particularly important when the fitting utilized has internal gaskets.

6.5.6.2 Pipe used with listed fittings and its end treatment shall be in accordance with the fitting manufacturer's installation instructions and the fitting's listing.

In recent years, a large variety of new fittings were introduced, including a number that join plain end pipe. The end treatment required in 6.5.6.2 varies, depending on the fitting that is used. For example, some mechanical-type fittings require that the varnish be removed from the exterior wall of the pipe entering the joint. Failure to follow the manufacturer's procedures and listing limitations can result in an unsatisfactory installation that tends to develop leaks.

6.6* Hangers

Hangers shall be in accordance with the requirements of Section 9.1.

A.6.6 See Section 9.1 for information pertaining to the type of hangers and hanger components acceptable for use on a sprinkler system.

Chapter 9 addresses the structural aspects of sprinkler systems. Information on hangers, as stated in Section 6.6, as well as earthquake bracing is contained in Chapter 9.

6.7 Valves

A closed valve is the primary reason why sprinkler systems do not perform adequately (see Commentary Table 1.1). The requirements in Section 6.7, as well as those in 8.15.1, are intended to minimize the occurrence of closed valves.

6.7.1 General.

6.7.1.1 Valve Pressure Requirements. When water pressures exceed 175 psi (12.1 bar), valves shall be used in accordance with their pressure ratings.

The minimum working pressure for system components is established in 6.1.3 as 175 psi (12.1 bar). When working pressures are expected to exceed this value, as discussed in 6.7.1.1, special components such as extra-heavy valves must be used. Listed valves that can accommodate higher pressures are currently available.

6.7.1.2 Valve Closure Time. Listed indicating valves shall not close in less than 5 seconds when operated at maximum possible speed from the fully open position.

The minimum valve closure time of 5 seconds that is given in 6.7.1.2 reduces the possibility of causing a "water hammer" in a system where water is flowing. A water hammer may instantaneously raise the pressure of the system well beyond the design pressure, which can result in damage to components or leakage. Water hammers, which sound like knocking in the pipes, are caused by quickly stopping the flow water, causing a pressure surge.

6.7.1.3 Listed Indicating Valves. Unless the requirements of 6.7.1.3.1, 6.7.1.3.2, or 6.7.1.3.3 are met, all valves controlling connections to water supplies and to supply pipes to sprinklers shall be listed indicating valves.

6.7.1.3.1 A listed underground gate valve equipped with a listed indicator post shall be permitted.

6.7.1.3.2 A listed water control valve assembly with a reliable position indication connected to a remote supervisory station shall be permitted.

6.7.1.3.3 A nonindicating valve, such as an underground gate valve with approved roadway box, complete with T-wrench, and where accepted by the authority having jurisdiction, shall be permitted.

All valves controlling the flow of water to sprinklers must be listed and must incorporate a method of readily determining that the valve is open, unless the valves meet the conditions of 6.7.1.3.1, 6.7.1.3.2, or 6.7.1.3.3. The means of indicating the valve's position can be part of the valve itself, such as a rising stem as indicated in Exhibit 6.16, or a feature of the assembly as illustrated in Exhibit 6.17.

EXHIBIT 6.16 Outside Stem and Yoke (OS&Y) Valve with Its Position Supervised by a Lock and Chain and a Tamper Switch.

EXHIBIT 6.17 Control Valve with a Position Indicator.

6.7.2 Wafer-Type Valves. Wafer-type valves with components that extend beyond the valve body shall be installed in a manner that does not interfere with the operation of any system components.

The discs of some listed wafer-type (butterfly) valves, which are discussed in 6.7.2, extend beyond the end of the valve body. Documented instances of such discs contacting other system components and partially obstructing the waterway exist. To avoid contact with other components in close proximity of the butterfly valve, the valves should be installed with piping before and after the valve to provide the required clearance. See Exhibit 6.18 for an example of a correctly installed butterfly valve.

EXHIBIT 6.18 Butterfly Valve.

6.7.3 Drain Valves and Test Valves. Drain valves and test valves shall be approved.

Drain valves and test valves are not considered essential for proper operation of the sprinkler system and are required to be approved only, as stated in 6.7.3. However, listed drain valves that have been investigated by a testing laboratory for their intended use are available for this application.

6.7.4* Identification of Valves.

A.6.7.4 The intent of 6.7.4 is to provide assistance in determining the area of a building served by a particular control valve.

Valve identification, as covered in 6.7.4, is beneficial in at least three ways. Valve identification permits the following:

1. Fire department personnel to locate and operate the valve
2. A contractor to readily shut off the system to make modifications
3. System valves to be easily identified during periodic inspections

6.7.4.1 All control, drain, and test connection valves shall be provided with permanently marked weatherproof metal or rigid plastic identification signs.

6.7.4.2 The identification sign shall be secured with corrosion-resistant wire, chain, or other approved means.

6.7.4.3 The control valve sign shall identify the portion of the building served.

This requirement in 6.7.4.3 was included in the 2002 edition to address the situation in which a valve room has numerous valves, making it difficult to determine which valve services the area or floor where the flow needs to be controlled.

6.8 Fire Department Connections

A fire department connection, which is described in Section 6.8, to any sprinkler system provides a desirable, auxiliary water supply to that system. Supplementing the automatic supply required by 15.1.1 increases overall system reliability. Fire department pump operators can also determine if any sprinklers have actually operated by using the fire department connection. If no water flows through the fire department connection into the system, it is likely that no sprinklers have operated. The other reason for no water flow is a closed sectional valve or piping obstruction.

6.8.1 Unless the requirements of 6.8.2 or 6.8.3 are met, the fire department connection(s) shall use an NH internal threaded swivel fitting(s) with an NH standard thread(s), where at least one of the connections shall be the "2.5–7.5 NH standard thread," as specified in NFPA 1963, *Standard for Fire Hose Connections.*

6.8.2 Where local fire department connections do not conform to NFPA 1963, *Standard for Fire Hose Connections,* the authority having jurisdiction shall be permitted to designate the connection to be used.

6.8.3 The use of threadless couplings shall be permitted where required by the authority having jurisdiction and where listed for such use.

All hose coupling threads in sprinkler systems and threads for hydrants on yard mains supplying sprinkler systems should match those of the first responding fire department. If fire department hose couplings are of the threadless type, which are discussed in 6.8.3, such as a quick connect, the sprinkler system connections should be compatible. Other types of compatible connections are permitted because some fire departments require their specified thread type and have not adopted the NH standard thread for couplings specified in NFPA 1963, *Standard for Fire Hose Connections.*

6.8.4 Fire department connections shall be equipped with listed plugs or caps, properly secured and arranged for easy removal by fire departments.

The reliability of the fire department connection depends on its relative ease of use, which is discussed in 6.8.4. This ease of use includes an evaluation of elements, such as the ability to efficiently remove the caps without special tools and to readily attach the hose. Missing caps must be replaced so the fire department connection does not become a receptacle for trash that can obstruct water flow into the system. Figure A.8.16.2(a) illustrates a fire department connection.

6.8.5 Fire department connections shall be of an approved type.

6.9 Waterflow Alarms

6.9.1 General. Waterflow alarm apparatus shall be listed for the service and so constructed and installed that any flow of water from a sprinkler system equal to or greater than that from a single automatic sprinkler of the smallest orifice size installed on the system will result in an audible alarm on the premises within 5 minutes after such flow begins and until such flow stops.

Does NFPA 13 require that water flow from the sprinkler system activate the building fire alarm system?
FAQ ▶

Paragraph 6.9.1 of NFPA 13 does not mandate the activation of a building fire alarm system when the sprinkler system is activated. If this feature is desired or specifically required by a building code, details, such as electrical circuit arrangement, time for alarm annunciation, and acceptable components, on this type of alarm system are contained in *NFPA 72®, National Fire Alarm Code®.*

If it is desired to indicate water flow on each floor of a multistory building, a floor control assembly can be used as indicated in Figure A.8.16.4.2(b). In addition to providing a means of waterflow indication, a floor control assembly also typically contains a control valve to isolate the system piping on the floor and a means to conduct flow testing and drainage of system piping on the floor. See Section 8.16 for additional information.

6.9.2 Waterflow Detecting Devices.

6.9.2.1 Wet Pipe Systems. The alarm apparatus for a wet pipe system shall consist of a listed alarm check valve or other listed waterflow-detecting alarm device with the necessary attachments required to give an alarm.

Waterflow detecting devices for wet pipe systems are addressed in 6.9.2.1. On a wet pipe system, an alarm check valve might be preferred to other listed waterflow-detecting alarm devices, particularly where fluctuating pressure water supplies are present. Fluctuating pressure can cause unwanted or nuisance alarms when other types of waterflow-detecting devices are used. On larger systems, an alarm check valve makes it possible to introduce an excess pressure higher than the supply on the system side of the alarm check valve. Water flow is then detected by a drop in pressure on the system side of the alarm check. In other instances, the alarm check valve serves to prevent waterflow alarms on risers not involved in an actual waterflow condition when fire pumps start or similar large fluctuations occur. In some instances, particularly when a system has both a large volume of dead-end piping and a backflow preventer, the alarm is not constant.

6.9.2.2 Dry Pipe Systems.

6.9.2.2.1 The alarm apparatus for a dry pipe system shall consist of listed alarm attachments to the dry pipe valve.

6.9.2.2.2 Where a dry pipe valve is located on the system side of an alarm valve, connection of the actuating device of the alarms for the dry pipe valve to the alarms on the wet pipe system shall be permitted.

Dry pipe systems are covered in 6.9.2.2.1 and 6.9.2.2.2. In some instances, small dry pipe systems are needed in areas of otherwise heated buildings, such as in areas under outside canopies, loading docks, unheated penthouses, and attics. In these cases, an auxiliary dry pipe system supplied from the building's wet pipe system can be more economical to install. Under these circumstances, the waterflow alarm from the dry pipe system can be connected into the wet pipe system alarm sounding or annunciating device.

6.9.2.3 Preaction and Deluge Systems. The alarm apparatus for deluge and preaction systems shall consist of alarms actuated independently by the detection system and the flow of water.

Because some preaction valves and deluge valves, which are discussed in 6.9.2.3, are not actuated by the operation of an automatic sprinkler, a supplemental detection system is required to actuate the valves. This detection system indicates conditions of fire prior to water flow in the system. The detection system can also be used to initiate other fire-related activities.

6.9.2.4* Paddle-Type Waterflow Devices. Paddle-type waterflow alarm indicators shall be installed in wet systems only.

A.6.9.2.4 The surge of water that occurs when the valve trips can seriously damage the device.

The use of paddle-type waterflow devices on dry pipe systems is prohibited by 6.9.2.4 due to the impact the activation of the dry pipe valve can have on the waterflow device. In addition to damaging the device itself, the impact from high-velocity water flow could totally disengage the paddle and carry it downstream until it lodged in the piping, causing an obstruction.

◀ **FAQ**
Can paddle-type waterflow devices be used on dry pipe sprinkler systems?

This restriction also applies to a situation in which a wet pipe system acts as the supply source for a preaction, deluge, or dry pipe system.

Exhibit 6.19 illustrates a paddle-type waterflow switch and Exhibit 6.20 illustrates a paddle-type waterflow switch installed on a wet pipe riser. The switch is located near the top of the riser.

EXHIBIT 6.19 Paddle-Type *Waterflow Switch.*

EXHIBIT 6.20 Paddle-Type *Waterflow Switch Installed on a Wet Pipe Riser.*

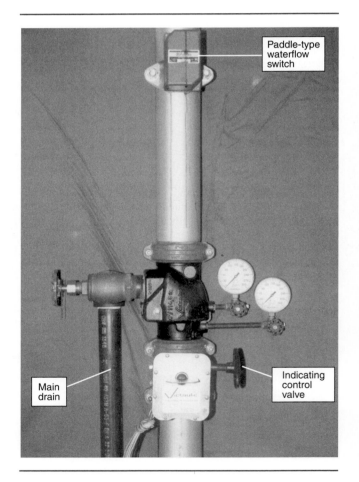

6.9.3 Attachments—General.

6.9.3.1* An alarm unit shall include a listed mechanical alarm, horn, or siren or a listed electric gong, bell, speaker, horn, or siren.

A.6.9.3.1 Audible alarms are normally located on the outside of the building. Listed electric gongs, bells, horns, or sirens inside the building, or a combination of such used inside and outside, are sometimes advisable.

Outside alarms can be omitted where the sprinkler system is used as part of a central station, auxiliary, remote station, or proprietary signaling fire alarm system utilizing listed audible inside alarm devices.

The audible local alarm required by 6.9.3.1 can be either mechanically or electrically operated. NFPA 13 does not stipulate whether the alarm's location be indoors or outdoors, since the location depends on site-specific conditions. The location and number of audible alarms are normally dictated by the purpose of the alarms, such as for water flow or evacuation. The location and number are also determined by normal operations within the protected premises and the locations at which the alarms would be expected to be heard. Exhibit 3.10 illustrates a water motor alarm. Paragraph 6.9.3.1 does not prohibit the use of visual alarm devices to supplement the audible alarm.

6.9.3.2* Outdoor water motor-operated or electrically operated bells shall be weatherproofed and guarded.

A.6.9.3.2 All alarm apparatus should be so located and installed that all parts are accessible for inspection, removal, and repair, and such apparatus should be substantially supported.

The water motor gong bell mechanism should be protected from weather-related elements such as rain, snow, or ice. To the extent practicable, it should also be protected from other influencing factors such as birds or other small animals that might attempt to nest in such a device.

Under the requirement of 6.9.3.2, internally moving parts of a water motor gong are expected to be adequately protected from a variety of problems such as snow, ice, birds' nests, and mechanical damage. The identified concerns are intended to give the user an idea of the types of problems to avoid. Some of these concerns can be difficult to guard against in all cases.

6.9.3.3 All piping to water motor-operated devices shall be galvanized or brass or other corrosion-resistant material acceptable under this standard and of a size not less than ¾ in. (19 mm).

Most listed alarm valves, listed dry pipe valves, and listed deluge valves in NFPA 13 contain supplemental trim and pre-piped outlets for alarm lines. In accordance with 6.9.3.3, the trim, outlets, and associated alarm piping must be verified to be corrosion resistant. The use of corrosion-resistant piping reduces the probability of clogging the orifice in the water motor.

6.9.3.4 Piping between the sprinkler system and a pressure actuated alarm-initiating device shall be galvanized or of nonferrous metal or other approved corrosion-resistant material of not less than ⅜ in. (9.5 mm) nominal pipe size.

6.9.4* Attachments—Electrically Operated.

A.6.9.4 Switches that will silence electric alarm-sounding devices by interruption of electric current are not desirable; however, if such means are provided, then the electric alarm-sounding device circuit should be arranged so that, when the sounding device is electrically silenced, that fact should be indicated by means of a conspicuous light located in the vicinity of the riser or alarm control panel. This light should remain in operation during the entire period of the electric circuit interruption.

6.9.4.1 Electrically operated alarm attachments forming part of an auxiliary, central station, local protective, proprietary, or remote station signaling system shall be installed in accordance with *NFPA 72®, National Fire Alarm Code®*.

6.9.4.2 Sprinkler waterflow alarm systems that are not part of a required protective signaling system shall not be required to be supervised and shall be installed in accordance with NFPA 70, *National Electrical Code®*, Article 760.

6.9.4.3 Outdoor electric alarm devices shall be listed for outdoor use.

6.9.5 Alarm Device Drains. Drains from alarm devices shall be so arranged that there will be no overflowing at the alarm apparatus, at domestic connections, or elsewhere with the sprinkler drains wide open and under system pressure. *(See 8.15.2.6)*

SUMMARY

Chapter 6 identifies the types of materials and components that are acceptable for use in a sprinkler system. The system components and hardware covered in Chapter 6 must be installed in compliance with the applicable sections of NFPA 13. Information concerning proper installation of system materials and components will be discussed in Chapter 8 and Chapter 9.

 ## REFERENCES CITED IN COMMENTARY

National Fire Protection Association, 1 Batterymarch Park, P.O. Box 9101, Quincy, MA 02269-9101

NFPA 25, *Standard for the Inspection, Testing, and Maintenance of Water-Based Fire Protection Systems,* 2002 edition
NFPA 51B, *Standard for Fire Prevention During Welding, Cutting, and Other Hot Work,* 1999 edition
NFPA 72®, National Fire Alarm Code®, 2002 edition
NFPA 1963, *Standard for Fire Hose Connections,* 1998 edition

American Society for Testing and Materials, 100 Barr Harbor Drive, West Conshohocken, PA 19428-2959

ASTM B 813, *Standard Specification for Liquid and Paste Fluxes for Soldering Applications of Copper and Copper-Alloy Tube,* 2000 edition
ASTM B 828, *Standard Practice for Making Capillary Joints by Soldering of Copper and Copper Alloy Tube and Fittings,* 2000 edition

American Welding Society, 550 N.W. LeJeune Road, Miami, FL 33126

AWS B2.1, *Standard for Welding Procedure and Performance Qualification,* 2000 edition

System Requirements

Chapter 7 provides the installation rules and characteristics that are unique to a particular type of system. The types of systems addressed by NFPA 13 include wet pipe, dry pipe, preaction, deluge, combined dry pipe preaction, antifreeze, circulating closed looped, outside systems for exposure protection, systems used in refrigerated spaces, and systems for commercial-type cooking equipment and ventilation. Chapter 7 covers information specific to each type of system. The information ranges from the relatively simple requirement for pressure gauges to limitations imposed on dry pipe system sizes to the design parameters for a circulating closed-loop system.

7.1 Wet Pipe Systems

Wet pipe sprinkler systems, which are covered in Section 7.1, are the simplest and the most common type of sprinkler system in use. In wet pipe systems, the piping contains water at all times and is connected to a water supply so that water discharges immediately from a sprinkler when the sprinkler activates. Because wet pipe systems have relatively few components, they have an inherently higher degree of reliability than other system types. Exhibits 3.10, 6.17, 8.29, and 8.31 illustrate some of the valves and other components found on a wet pipe system.

Dry sprinklers, as defined in 3.6.4.2, can also be used on wet pipe systems where individual sprinklers are extended into spaces that are subject to freezing. The extension of sprinklers into a freezer unit is one example of this application. A minimum length for the dry sprinkler's exposed portion outside the freezer is specified to avoid freezing water at the connection point to the branch line. These minimum lengths are specified by the sprinkler manufacturer. Dry sprinklers have a maximum length of up to 4 ft (1.2 m). Special applications using dry sprinklers in upright and other positions should be in accordance with their listings. For example, see Figure A.8.14.7 for the application of a dry pendent sprinkler under an exterior canopy.

7.1.1 Pressure Gauges.

7.1.1.1 A listed pressure gauge conforming to 8.16.3 shall be installed in each system riser.

7.1.1.2 Pressure gauges shall be installed above and below each alarm check valve or system riser check valve where such devices are present.

Pressure gauges are discussed in 7.1.1.1 and 7.1.1.2. At least one pressure gauge is required in each system riser. When any type of check valve is used, two gauges are required—one on the supply side of the check valve and one on the system side. It is not unusual for the gauge on the system side of the valve to read a higher pressure. Pressure surges are typically trapped in the system by the check valve. Readings from these gauges can be used to establish a database on the available pressure in the water supply. The gauge on the supply side is also used during the 2-in. (51-mm) drain test required by NFPA 25, *Standard for the Inspection, Testing, and Maintenance of Water-Based Fire Protection Systems,* to establish a database of residual pressures in the water supply.

7.1.2 Relief Valves.

7.1.2.1 Unless the requirements of 7.1.2.2 are met, a gridded wet pipe system shall be provided with a relief valve not less than ¼ in. (6.4 mm) in size set to operate at 175 psi (12.1 bar) or 10 psi (0.7 bar) in excess of the maximum system pressure, whichever is greater.

FAQ ▶
Why are relief valves required on gridded wet pipe systerms?

The requirement in 7.1.2.1 covers some situations that have occurred in which the pressure buildup in gridded wet pipe systems exceeded the working pressure of the system components, which is typically 175 psi (12.1 bar). For example, solar heating can increase temperature differentials in a building and, because wet pipe systems are closed systems, this solar heating can cause static pressures in the system to exceed 175 psi (12.1 bar). These pressures act on system components and can cause system failure if the pressures exceed the components' pressure ratings. The location of the relief valve will affect the pressure setting needed to protect the system, since it is necessary to account for elevation pressure experienced at the base of the riser. For an example of a relief valve installed on a gridded sprinkler system, see Exhibit 7.1.

EXHIBIT 7.1 *Relief Valve Installed on Gridded Sprinkler System.*

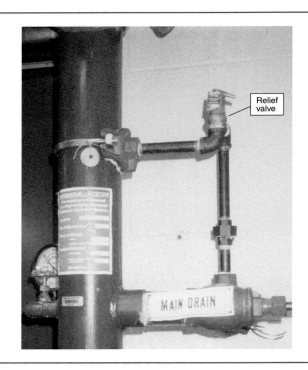

7.1.2.2 Where auxiliary air reservoirs are installed to absorb pressure increases, a relief valve shall not be required.

Since a limited number of air pockets typically exist in gridded systems, the auxiliary air reserves permitted by 7.1.2.2 need to be large enough to account for any pressure buildup in the system. One method is to use an expansion chamber as discussed in 7.5.3.3.

7.1.3 Auxiliary Systems. A wet pipe system shall be permitted to supply an auxiliary dry pipe, preaction, or deluge system, provided the water supply is adequate.

Paragraph 7.1.3 permits a combined system riser to be used when the available water supply is adequate to support such an arrangement. Exhibit 7.2 illustrates a combined system riser in which the water supply for the dry pipe system is taken from the wet pipe system. System protection area limitations specified in Section 8.2 apply when considering an auxiliary system. A control valve on the auxiliary system is desirable in order to facilitate maintenance and resetting of the system valve on the auxiliary system. The user needs to be aware that the combined system riser is not the same as a combined sprinkler/standpipe riser.

◀ **FAQ**
Can a wet pipe system supply an auxiliary system?

EXHIBIT 7.2 Example of a Combined System Riser.

7.2* Dry Pipe Systems

A.7.2 A dry pipe system should be installed only where heat is not adequate to prevent freezing of water in all parts of, or in sections of, the system. Dry pipe systems should be converted to wet pipe systems when they become unnecessary because adequate heat is provided. Sprinklers should not be shut off in cold weather.

Where two or more dry pipe valves are used, systems preferably should be divided horizontally to prevent simultaneous operation of more than one system and the resultant increased time delay in filling systems and discharging water and to prevent receipt of more than one waterflow alarm signal.

Where adequate heat is present in sections of the dry pipe system, consideration should be given to dividing the system into a separate wet pipe system and dry pipe system. Minimized use of dry pipe systems is desirable where speed of operation is of particular concern.

Dry pipe systems, which are covered in Section 7.2, are usually used in buildings or in areas that are subject to cold or freezing temperatures. Dry pipe systems are typically filled with pressurized air or nitrogen rather than water. As with wet pipe systems, automatic sprinklers are used. The operation of a sprinkler causes air pressure in the system to drop. This pressure drop activates a dry pipe valve and allows water to flow through the system. Dry pipe systems are more complex than wet pipe systems and require greater attention regarding their design, installation, and maintenance. Exhibit 3.8 provides an example of a dry pipe sprinkler system, and Exhibit 7.3 illustrates some of the components found on the system riser of a dry pipe system.

EXHIBIT 7.3 *Dry Pipe Valve and Associated Components.*

It is not the intent of NFPA 13 to require a building or portions of it to be heated to accommodate the sprinkler system. Although the intent of NFPA 13 is not to require portions of buildings to be heated in order to install wet systems, NFPA 13 does require that the valve rooms for dry pipe systems be heated (see 7.2.5.2.1).

7.2.1 Pressure Gauges. Listed pressure gauges conforming with 8.16.3 shall be connected as follows:

(1) On the water side and air side of the dry pipe valve
(2) At the air pump supplying the air receiver where one is provided
(3) At the air receiver where one is provided
(4) In each independent pipe from air supply to dry pipe system
(5) At exhausters and accelerators

Pressure gauges are discussed in 7.2.1. In a dry pipe system, pressure gauges are used to monitor water pressures in the system and in the water supply as well as air pressures in the system.

7.2.2 Sprinklers. The following types of sprinklers and arrangements shall be permitted for dry pipe systems:

(1) Upright sprinklers
(2)* Listed dry sprinklers

 A.7.2.2(2) Installation limitations of listed dry pendent sprinklers can vary with different products. Limitations should be included in product installation instructions to warn the user of the potential accumulation of water, scale, and sediment from collecting at the sprinkler.

(3) Pendent sprinklers and sidewall sprinklers installed on return bends, where the sprinklers, return bend, and branch line piping are in an area maintained at or above 40°F (4°C)

(4) Horizontal sidewall sprinklers, installed so that water is not trapped

Subsection 7.2.2 covers the types of sprinklers that are allowed for dry pipe systems. Since dry pipe systems are installed in areas that are subject to freezing, any water that remains in the piping after system operation should be quickly drained. The use of pendent sprinklers would allow a small amount of water to remain on the seat of the operating mechanism. This water would eventually freeze and impair the sprinkler. Therefore, pendent sprinklers are not permitted. However, if a sprinkler in the pendent position is needed, then 7.2.2(2) allows the use of listed dry sprinklers as an option. Dry sprinklers prevent water from accumulating on the sprinkler's operating mechanism and in the drop nipple. This arrangement minimizes the time it takes the system to be returned to its operating condition. A limit is placed on the size of the fitting used with a dry pendent sprinkler in order to avoid trapping water on the operating mechanism. To further aid in the drainage of dry pipe systems, 8.15.2.3 requires piping to be installed at a pitch.

Another consideration where using dry pipe systems is the need to minimize the obstruction potential from internal pipe scale that can break loose while the piping is being charged with water. The water velocities experienced when the dry pipe valve opens are likely to dislodge pipe scale and carry it to the open sprinklers. This concern still applies when corrosion-resistant pipe is used. The accumulation of material that could inhibit sprinkler operation includes sediment, mineral deposits, and scale from other piping such as valves, underground pipe, and water supplies. The use of pendent and sidewall sprinklers on return bends is permitted by 7.2.2(3) as an alternative to dry sprinklers when the return bend, branch line piping, and sprinkler are in a heated area that is maintained at or above 40°F (4°C). The return bend serves to minimize obstructions to water flow caused by pipe scale.

The conditions necessary to implement 7.2.2(3) are rather uncommon. One example is in a cold storage warehouse that is protected with a dry pipe system. If the warehouse contains an office that is heated, the sprinkler pipe in that area is also in a heated area and the return bend option could be used.

Paragraph 7.2.2(4) allows listed horizontal sidewall sprinklers in dry pipe, preaction, and combined dry pipe preaction systems, provided they are installed so that water is not trapped behind them. If these sprinklers are installed in such a manner as to avoid the accumulation of water, scale, and sediment, then no compelling reason to restrict their use in this application is evident.

7.2.3* Size of Systems—Volume Limitations.

A.7.2.3 The capacities of the various sizes of pipe given in Table A.7.2.3 are for convenience in calculating the capacity of a system.

7.2.3.1* Unless the requirements of 7.2.3.2 or 7.2.3.3 are met, not more than 750 gal (2839 L) system capacity shall be controlled by one dry pipe valve.

A.7.2.3.1 The 60-second limit does not apply to dry systems with capacities of 500 gal (1893 L) or less, nor to dry systems with capacities of 750 gal (2839 L) or less if equipped with a quick-opening device.

7.2.3.2 Piping volume shall be permitted to exceed the requirements of 7.2.3.1 where the system design is such that water is delivered to the system test connection in not more than 60 seconds, starting at the normal air pressure on the system and at the time of fully opened inspection test connection.

7.2.3.3 Piping volume shall be permitted to exceed the requirements of 7.2.3.1 where dry systems are calculated for water delivery in accordance with 11.2.3.9.

TABLE A.7.2.3 *Capacity of 1 ft of Pipe (Based on Actual Internal Pipe Diameter)*

Nominal Pipe Diameter (in.)	Pipe Schedule 40 (gal)	Pipe Schedule 10 (gal)	Nominal Pipe Diameter (in.)	Pipe Schedule 40 (gal)	Pipe Schedule 10 (gal)
¾	0.028		3	0.383	0.433
1	0.045	0.049	3½	0.513	0.576
1¼	0.078	0.085	4	0.660	0.740
1½	0.106	0.115	5	1.040	1.144
2	0.174	0.190	6	1.501	1.649[b]
2½	0.248	0.283	8	2.66[a]	2.776[c]

For SI units, 1 in. = 25.4 mm; 1 ft = 0.3048 m; 1 gal = 3.785 L.
[a]Schedule 30.
[b]0.134 wall pipe.
[c]0.188 wall pipe.

Paragraphs 7.2.3.1 and 7.2.3.2 discuss volume limitations of dry pipe systems. The water delay associated with dry pipe sprinkler systems is a significant disadvantage of their use. This delay consists of two parts—the time it takes for the dry pipe valve to operate and the time it takes for water to reach the open sprinkler once the valve operates. To compensate for these delays, NFPA 13 requires certain provisions such as limitations on system volume, the installation of quick-opening devices (see 7.2.4), the use of more conservative C factors for hydraulically calculated systems (see14.4.4.5), and a larger design area (see 11.2.3.2.5).

Dry pipe systems are limited to a maximum volume of 750 gal (2839 L). NFPA 13 offers two methods to increase the volume of a dry pipe system beyond 750 gal (2839 L). First, this volume limitation can be exceeded if water delivery to the inspector's test connection can be achieved in 60 seconds or less. When system volume exceeds 750 gal (2839 L), the only means to verify a delivery time of 60 seconds or less is by conducting a flow test through the inspector's test connection. Failure of this test can result in rejection of the system by the authority having jurisdiction. The 60-second water delivery is not required where the 750-gal (2839-L) volume limitation is not exceeded. Some dry pipe systems with capacities less than 750 gal (2839 L) can take up to 3 minutes to deliver water to the inspector's test connection, which is considered acceptable.

Secondly, NFPA 13 now provides the option for the designer to calculate the water delivery time utilizing a listed calculation method (see 7.2.3.3) and meeting the design requirements of 11.2.3.9. This calculation method takes advantage of recent research into dry pipe sprinkler systems using various piping configurations and water supplies. The testing has led to NFPA 13 permitting the use of listed calculation programs, which are capable of predicting the trip, transit, and compression time of a dry pipe sprinkler system.

Under the requirements of NFPA 25, water flow tests of dry systems must be conducted periodically. When conducting water flow tests in accordance with NFPA 25, the water delivery time to the inspector's test should be documented. The documented value is not intended to be a pass/fail criterion by NFPA 25, but to serve as a comparative basis to identify possible system malfunctions or impairments.

7.2.3.4 Check valves shall not be used to subdivide the dry pipe system.

FAQ ▶
Why is it prohibited to use check valves to subdivide dry pipe systems?

The requirement permitting the use of check valves to subdivide a system into volumes less than 750 gal (2839 L) was removed from NFPA 13 in 1987. Concern about air leaking by older check valves and delaying the trip time prompted this removal. Even though this practice is still identified for combined dry pipe and preaction systems (see 7.4.4), it is not applicable for dry pipe systems. Paragraph 7.2.3.4 of NFPA 13 prohibits the use of check valves to subdivide the dry pipe systems.

7.2.3.5 Gridded dry pipe systems shall not be installed.

Gridded dry pipe systems, which are addressed in 7.2.3.5, are subject to excessive time delays for water to reach the operating sprinkler. Past experience indicates that in many gridded dry pipe systems, the times for delivering water to the inspector's test connection were excessive—in some cases as long as 10 minutes. The multiple numbers of flow paths the water can take to fill the grid makes this piping configuration undesirable for dry pipe systems because of the associated time delays. Additionally, excessive amounts of air can become trapped in the system.

◀ **FAQ**
Why are gridded dry pipe systems prohibited?

   The restriction stipulated in 7.2.3.5 does not apply to a preaction system unless it is of the double interlock type. These types of preaction systems maintain air pressures typical to those of dry pipe systems.

   The use of a looped piping arrangement is not prohibited for a dry pipe system because the associated water delivery time delays are not as severe as for a gridded system.

7.2.4 Quick-Opening Devices.

Quick-opening devices, which are covered in 7.2.4, consist primarily of accelerators and exhausters. Accelerators cause the dry pipe valve to operate more quickly by redirecting system air into the valve's intermediate chamber, thus allowing water pressure to expel air from the activated sprinklers at a faster rate. Exhausters accelerate the rate at which air is discharged to atmosphere, thus reducing the time it takes for the dry pipe valve to operate and the time it takes for water to reach the open sprinklers. Exhibit 7.3 illustrates an accelerator attached to the dry pipe valve.

7.2.4.1 Unless the requirements of 7.2.4.2 are met, dry pipe valves shall be provided with a listed quick-opening device where system capacity exceeds 500 gal (1893 L).

7.2.4.2 A quick-opening device shall not be required where water is delivered to the system test connection in not more than 60 seconds, starting at the normal air pressure on the system and at the time of fully opened inspection test connection.

Even though quick-opening devices are not required where systems are of smaller capacity [less than 500 gal (1893 L)], they can be used whenever faster operating times are desired. Paragraph 7.2.4.2 allows omission of quick-opening devices when water delivery occurs at the inspector's test connection within 60 seconds or less. Omitting this device and failing to stay within established time constraints on larger systems creates the likelihood of a noncompliant system.

7.2.4.3 The quick-opening device shall be located as close as practical to the dry pipe valve.

7.2.4.4 To protect the restriction orifice and other operating parts of the quick-opening device against submergence, the connection to the riser shall be above the point at which water (priming water and back drainage) is expected when the dry pipe valve and quick-opening device are set, except where design features of the particular quick-opening device make these requirements unnecessary.

Protecting parts of the quick-opening device against submergence is covered in 7.2.4.4. Special circumstances can require a quick-opening device, such as an exhauster, to be located at a point remote from the dry pipe valve. In these instances, consideration should be given to protection of the device or its components against freezing. Remote devices should be accessible for servicing.

   Antiflooding devices are activated when the valve trips. The devices do not stop the submergence of operating parts from the priming water.

7.2.4.5 A soft disc globe or angle valve shall be installed in the connection between the dry pipe sprinkler riser and the quick-opening device.

The shutoff valve between the dry pipe sprinkler riser and the quick-opening device described in 7.2.4.5 is necessary since these devices require separate maintenance activities. It is very undesirable to have the entire system out of service because of a problem with the quick-opening device. However, because quick-opening devices can be shut off separately, they are frequently left out of service. Since system design is based on proper operation of the quick-opening device, it should be maintained in proper operating condition at all times, and any necessary repairs should be promptly completed.

7.2.4.6 A check valve shall be installed between the quick-opening device and the intermediate chamber of the dry pipe valve.

7.2.4.7 If the quick-opening device requires pressure feedback from the intermediate chamber, a valve type that will clearly indicate whether it is opened or closed shall be permitted in place of that check valve.

7.2.4.8 Where a valve is utilized in accordance with 7.2.4.7, the valve shall be constructed so that it can be locked or sealed in the open position.

The shutoff valve for a quick-opening device that requires pressure feedback from the intermediate chamber is much the same as the shutoff valve at the connection to the sprinkler riser. As stated in 7.2.4.8, the valve should always be maintained in the open position. The check valve allows flow only from the quick-opening device to the intermediate chamber.

7.2.4.9 Antiflooding Device.

7.2.4.9.1 Unless the requirements of 7.2.4.9.2 are met, a listed antiflooding device shall be installed in the connection between the dry pipe sprinkler riser and the quick-opening device.

7.2.4.9.2 A listed antiflooding device shall not be required where the quick-opening device has built-in antiflooding design features.

Antiflooding devices are covered in 7.2.4.9.1 and 7.2.4.9.2. Quick-opening devices and their accessory equipment, such as antiflooding devices, are often neglected when service and maintenance activities on the system are to be conducted. The manufacturer's instructions and NFPA 25 need to be carefully followed when resetting each dry pipe valve and quick-opening device. Impairments to the quick-opening device have been caused by not properly draining the equipment while resetting the dry pipe valve after it has operated. NFPA 25 contains a series of inspection, testing, and maintenance provisions that, when implemented, greatly improves the reliability of these devices.

7.2.5* Location and Protection of Dry Pipe Valve.

A.7.2.5 The dry pipe valve should be located in an accessible place near the sprinkler system it controls. Where exposed to cold, the dry pipe valve should be located in a valve room or enclosure of adequate size to properly service equipment.

The recommendations in A.7.2.5 serve to reduce the amount of piping in a dry pipe system and to help minimize system capacity. Long bulk mains from dry pipe valves to system piping can use a large portion of the available system capacity, which results in a rather small area of actual sprinkler coverage. To minimize the impact of the bulk main on the system's permitted capacity or water delivery time requirement, the installation of the bulk main as underground piping below floors and the relocation of the dry pipe valve in the center of the building are sometimes considered.

However, 10.6.1 places limitations on the installation of fire mains beneath buildings. Any leaks in the buried piping underneath the building could go undetected for long periods, and any corrective action would require penetration of the floor and relocation of any adjacent equipment. The location of system valves in the center of a building also places the system controls in the center of the building, which may not be desirable during a fire.

7.2.5.1* General. The dry pipe valve and supply pipe shall be protected against freezing and mechanical injury.

A.7.2.5.1 The dry pipe valve and supply piping should be in an area maintained at or above 40°F (4°C). It is the intent of the committee to protect the valves from freezing. The occasional exposure of valves to short exposures of air temperatures below 40°F (4°C) that would not cause the valves to freeze does not justify the construction of a valve room.

7.2.5.2 Valve Rooms.

7.2.5.2.1 Valve rooms shall be lighted and heated.

7.2.5.2.2 The source of heat shall be of a permanently installed type.

7.2.5.2.3 Heat tape shall not be used in lieu of heated valve enclosures to protect the dry pipe valve and supply pipe against freezing.

Heat tape is not considered a permanently installed heat source for heating the dry pipe valve and riser (see 7.2.5.2.3). A fixed heat source, such as a baseboard or unit heater, satisfies the requirements.

◄ FAQ
Can heat tape be utilized to heat the dry pipe valve and riser?

7.2.5.3 Supply. The supply for the sprinkler in the dry pipe valve enclosure shall be from the dry side of the system.

7.2.5.4 Low Differential Dry Pipe Valve. Protection against accumulation of water above the clapper shall be provided for a low differential dry pipe valve.

The requirement in 7.2.5.4 is critical for two reasons. If an accumulation of water extends beyond the heated enclosure, the potential for the system to freeze increases. In addition to this concern, a water column with a measurable head of pressure can develop, preventing operation of the dry pipe valve. The pressure of the water column can be greater than the pressure that would cause the valve to open.

7.2.5.5 High Water Level Device. An automatic high water level signaling device or an automatic drain device shall be permitted.

7.2.6 Air Pressure and Supply.

Proper air pressure, which is addressed in 7.2.6, should be maintained in the system at all times. It is important to follow manufacturer's instructions regarding the range of air pressures to be maintained. Low air pressures could result in accidental operation of the dry pipe valve. High air pressures result in slower operation because additional air must be exhausted from the system before water can be delivered to open sprinklers.

Traditional dry pipe valves normally have a differential in water pressure to air pressure at a trip point of approximately 5.5:1. A low differential dry pipe valve usually is an alarm check valve that has been converted to a dry pipe valve. The differential in water pressure and air pressure at the trip point of these valves is approximately 1.1:1.

7.2.6.1 Maintenance of Air Pressure. Air or nitrogen pressure shall be maintained on dry pipe systems throughout the year.

The use of either air or nitrogen in dry pipe systems, discussed in 7.2.6.1, is allowed. The use of nitrogen may be preferable in systems where severe accumulation of condensation from air in the system is likely.

Air pressure does not have to be automatically maintained or electrically supervised. The presence of such supervision, though, does impact the frequency of maintenance inspections.

7.2.6.2* Air Supply.

A.7.2.6.2 The compressor should draw its air supply from within the operating criteria allowed by the manufacturer of the compressor. Air piping should not be attached to the intake of the compressor unless acceptable to the compressor manufacturer and installed in accordance with 7.8.2.7. Damage, air reduction, or reduced life expectancy can result if guidelines are not followed.

A reliable and available air supply, which is discussed in 7.2.6.2, is necessary to allow the dry pipe system to stay in service and to maintain the necessary pressure differential between the water and air sides of the dry pipe valve. A compressor, a shop air supply, or a manifolded arrangement of nitrogen cylinders all constitute acceptable sources. The air maintenance device, if present, can be bypassed to meet the 30-minute filling criteria.

7.2.6.2.1 The compressed air supply shall be from a source available at all times.

7.2.6.2.2 The air supply shall have a capacity capable of restoring normal air pressure in the system within 30 minutes.

7.2.6.2.3 The requirements of 7.2.6.2.2 shall not apply in refrigerated spaces maintained below 5°F (–15°C), where normal system air pressure shall be permitted to be restored within 60 minutes.

7.2.6.3 Air Filling Connection.

7.2.6.3.1 The connection pipe from the air compressor shall not be less than ½ in. (13 mm) in diameter and shall enter the system above the priming water level of the dry pipe valve.

7.2.6.3.2 A check valve shall be installed in this air line, and a shutoff valve of the renewable disc type shall be installed on the supply side of this check valve and shall remain closed unless filling the system.

7.2.6.4 Relief Valve. A listed relief valve shall be provided between the compressor and controlling valve and shall be set to relieve at a pressure 10 psi (0.7 bar) in excess of the operating air pressure of the system.

A relief valve, discussed in 7.2.6.4, on manually operated systems is needed to reduce any excess air pressure in the system. Omission of the relief valve could result in higher pressures, thus resulting in slower operating times. Additionally, high pressures have the potential to damage some of the gasket materials used on the dry pipe valve. Air maintenance devices, if installed, also provide control of the pressure level (see 7.2.6.5).

The change from the 1999 edition of 5 psi to 10 psi in 2002 edition was made to address the proper performance of the relief valve. Setting of the relief valve within 5 psi of the maximum air pressure on the system resulted in the relief valve opening when not required. Setting the value to 10 psi will allow for small fluctuations in air pressure without the opening of the relief valve.

7.2.6.5 Shop Air Supply. Where the air supply is taken from a shop system having a normal pressure greater than that required for dry pipe system, an air maintenance device (regulator style) shall be used to regulate air pressure and flow to the system. A relief valve shall be installed between the outlet of the air maintenance device and dry system and set to relieve at 10 psi (0.7 bar) above the dry pipe system operating setpoint. *(See Figure 7.2.6.5.)*

The relief valve on a manual system that uses shop air supply, which is discussed in 7.2.6.5, should be set to prevent overpressurizing of the sprinkler system. As described in the com-

FIGURE 7.2.6.5 *Air Supply from Shop System.*

mentary to 7.2.6.4, high pressures are undesirable because they result in slower operation of the system and can negatively affect system components.

The 2002 edition now requires that the relief valve be set to operate at 20 psi above the dry pipe system's operating point. This 20-psi setting will allow for small fluctuations in air pressure without the opening of the relief valve, while at the same time ensuring that the system will not be overpressurized to the point that the dry pipe valve will not open and/or will be damaged.

7.2.6.6 Automatic Air Compressor.

7.2.6.6.1 Where a dry pipe system is supplied by an automatic air compressor or plant air system, any device or apparatus used for automatic maintenance of air pressure shall be of a type specifically listed for such service and capable of controlling the required air pressure on, and maximum airflow to, the dry pipe system.

7.2.6.6.2 Automatic air supply to more than one dry pipe system shall be connected to enable individual maintenance of air pressure in each system.

7.2.6.6.3 A check valve or other positive backflow prevention device shall be installed in the air supply to each system to prevent airflow or waterflow from one system to another.

7.2.6.6.4 Where the air compressor feeding the dry pipe system has less capacity than the discharge through a ⅛-in. orifice at 10 psig, no air maintenance device shall be required.

Automatic air compressors are covered in 7.2.6.6.1 through 7.2.6.6.4. Pumping air directly from an automatic air compressor through a fully opened supply pipe into the sprinkler system is not permitted. A restriction prevents the air supply system from adding air too quickly, thus preventing or slowing operation of the dry pipe valve. NFPA 13 does not require the use of a device to automatically maintain air pressure in the system. However, other means of maintaining the required air pressure can become overly burdensome.

Any device used for automatic air maintenance needs to be listed for such service. Listed air maintenance devices provide both restriction of the air flow and regulation of the air pressure. A compressor used in conjunction with the air maintenance device only needs to comply with the requirements of 7.2.6.2 and does not have to be listed.

Air compressors are available for use with and without air holding tanks. Compressors without air holding tanks are subject to more instances of short-cycling of the compressor.

◀ **FAQ**
Are the air maintenance device and the air compressor required to be listed?

Exhibit 7.4 illustrates an air compressor without an air holding tank, and an automatic air maintenance device.

EXHIBIT 7.4 *Air Compressor and Air Maintenance Device for a Dry Pipe System.*

7.2.6.7 System Air Pressure.

7.2.6.7.1 The system air pressure shall be maintained in accordance with the instruction sheet furnished with the dry pipe valve, or shall be 20 psi (1.4 bar) in excess of the calculated trip pressure of the dry pipe valve, based on the highest normal water pressure of the system supply.

7.2.6.7.2 The permitted rate of air leakage shall be as specified in 16.2.2.

7.2.6.8 Nitrogen. Where used, nitrogen shall be introduced through a pressure regulator set to maintain system pressure in accordance with 7.2.6.7.

7.3 Preaction Systems and Deluge Systems

Preaction systems, which are covered in Section 7.3, are more complex than wet pipe and dry pipe systems because they contain more components and equipment. Preaction systems require specialized knowledge and experience with their design and installation, and the inspection, testing, and maintenance activities needed to ensure their reliability and functionality are more involved. Manufacturer's specifications and listing restrictions must be strictly followed. Costs associated with the initial installation, use of supplemental equipment to operate the system, and maintenance should be thoroughly evaluated when considering a preaction system.

Since the first edition of this handbook was published in 1983, different types of valves have become available that are classified for use in preaction systems. The operating characteristics of these valves cause certain types of preaction systems to have qualities similar to that of a dry pipe system, such as a double interlock preaction system. Therefore, the same rules and restrictions that apply to dry pipe systems apply to double interlock preaction systems.

7.3.1* General.

A.7.3.1 Conditions of occupancy or special hazards might require quick application of large quantities of water, and, in such cases, deluge systems might be needed.

Fire detection devices should be selected to assure operation yet guard against premature operation of sprinklers based on normal room temperatures and draft conditions.

In locations where ambient temperature at the ceiling is high from heat sources other than fire conditions, heat-responsive devices that operate at higher than ordinary temperature and that are capable of withstanding the normal high temperature for long periods of time should be selected.

Where corrosive conditions exist, materials or protective coatings that resist corrosion should be used.

To help avoid ice formation in piping due to accidental tripping of dry pipe valves in cold storage rooms, a deluge automatic water control valve can be used on the supply side of the dry pipe valve. Where this method is employed, the following also apply:

(1) Dry systems can be manifolded to a deluge valve, with the protected area not exceeding 40,000 ft^2 (3716 m^2).
(2) Where a dry system is manifolded to a deluge valve, the distance between valves should be as short as possible to minimize water hammer.
(3) The dry pipe valves should be pressurized to 50 psi (3.4 bar) to reduce the possibility of dry pipe valve operation from water hammer.

Preaction systems and deluge systems are discussed in 7.3.1. The combination dry pipe and deluge valve was one of the older approaches for a double interlock preaction valve. Current designs use a single valve.

7.3.1.1 All components of pneumatic, hydraulic, or electrical systems shall be compatible.

The requirement in 7.3.1.1 for compatibility is necessary to ensure that all system compo- nents function as an integrated unit. The correct coordination of detection devices, releasing equipment, and the control panel is imperative for prompt and reliable operation of the system. Specific requirements on the design of hydraulic, pneumatic, and electrical detection systems are contained in *NFPA 72®, National Fire Alarm Code®*. The releasing panel or module is an essential component for system operation and is required to be listed (see 6.1.1.2).

7.3.1.2 The automatic water control valve shall be provided with hydraulic, pneumatic, or mechanical manual means for operation that is independent of detection devices and of the sprinklers.

In the event that the system does not automatically operate, a means for manually operating the system activation valve must be provided, as stated in 7.3.1.2. This feature is usually standard on valves listed for use in preaction or deluge systems. The manual release device must be a stand-alone arrangement whose operation is ensured regardless of the potential failure of the associated detection system.

7.3.1.3 Pressure Gauges. Listed pressure gauges conforming with 8.16.3 shall be installed as follows:

(1) Above and below preaction valve and below deluge valve
(2) On air supply to preaction and deluge valves

7.3.1.4 A supply of spare fusible elements for heat-responsive devices, not less than two of each temperature rating, shall be maintained on the premises for replacement purposes.

7.3.1.5 Hydraulic release systems shall be designed and installed in accordance with manufacturer's requirements and listing for height limitations above deluge valves or deluge valve actuators to prevent water column.

7.3.1.6 Location and Spacing of Detection Devices. Spacing of detection devices, including automatic sprinklers used as detectors, shall be in accordance with their listing and manufacturer's specifications.

Preaction and deluge systems are covered in 7.3.1.1 through 7.3.1.6. Various methods are available for activating a deluge or preaction system. Among these methods are pneumatic and hydraulic detection systems, smoke detectors, heat detectors, and detectors that respond to ultraviolet and infrared radiation. An automatic sprinkler is also recognized as a type of detector that can be used to activate an adjacent preaction or deluge system.

Although the definition of *sprinkler system* (see 3.3.21) states that these systems are "usually activated by heat," this definition should not be interpreted as prohibiting the use of smoke detection devices or other non-heat-sensing devices. Smoke and ultraviolet and infrared radiation are by-products of a fire, and their detection can be used to activate a preaction or deluge system.

 As stated in 7.3.1.6, detection systems are to be installed in accordance with their listing or as directed by the detection device manufacturer. The listing criteria for the detection devices are governed by *NFPA 72.*

In addition to permitting a range of options concerning the types of detection devices, various combinations of operation are permitted. See the commentary following 7.3.2.1.

7.3.1.7 Devices for Test Purposes and Testing Apparatus.

7.3.1.7.1 Where detection devices installed in circuits are located where not readily accessible for testing, an additional detection device shall be provided on each circuit for test purposes at an accessible location and shall be connected to the circuit at a point that will assure a proper test of the circuit.

7.3.1.7.2 Testing apparatus capable of producing the heat or impulse necessary to operate any normal detection device shall be furnished to the owner of the property with each installation.

7.3.1.7.3 Where explosive vapors or materials are present, hot water, steam, or other methods of testing not involving an ignition source shall be used.

7.3.1.8 Location and Protection of System Water Control Valves.

7.3.1.8.1 System water control valves and supply pipes shall be protected against freezing and mechanical injury.

7.3.1.8.2 Valve Rooms.

7.3.1.8.2.1 Valve rooms shall be lighted and heated.

7.3.1.8.2.2 The source of heat shall be of a permanently installed type.

7.3.1.8.2.3 Heat tape shall not be used in lieu of heated valve enclosure rooms to protect preaction and deluge valves and supply pipe against freezing.

FAQ ▶
Can heat tape be utilized to heat the preaction, and deluge valve and riser?

Heat tape is not considered a permanently installed heat source (see 7.3.1.8.2.3). A fixed heat source, such as a baseboard or unit heater, satisfies the requirements.

7.3.2 Preaction Systems.

Subsection 7.3.2 identifies the three basic types of preaction systems by identifying their means of operation. Specific terms that identify the mode of operation, such as *single interlock, non-interlock,* and *double interlock,* help differentiate between types of systems and allow for better reference. Besides the three basic types of systems, additional variations, such as the use of a cross-zoned smoke detection system, are possible. Other combinations can involve the use of additional devices such as an infrared detector. The detection systems for the single interlock and non-interlock systems typically have a lower temperature rating than the system sprinklers. When so configured, the single interlock and non-interlock systems are expected to operate more quickly than the double interlock or dry pipe systems. Exhibit 3.9 illustrates an example of a double interlock preaction system with electric activation.

7.3.2.1 Preaction systems shall be one of the following types:

(1) A single interlock system, which admits water to sprinkler piping upon operation of detection devices

(2) A non-interlock system, which admits water to sprinkler piping upon operation of detection devices or automatic sprinklers

(3) A double interlock system, which admits water to sprinkler piping upon operation of both detection devices and automatic sprinklers

Preaction systems are discussed in 7.3.2.1. Both the single interlock and non-interlock systems require only one event to occur before water is admitted to the system. The single interlock system is activated by the release of the detection system. Sprinkler activation does not affect this function. The non-interlock system is activated if either the detection system or a sprinkler operates.

The double interlock preaction system requires two events to occur before water is admitted to the system. One event consists of the activation of a device installed on the supplemental detection system. The other event includes the operation of a sprinkler that causes the maintained air pressure in the system to fall to a predetermined level, which is similar to that of a dry pipe system. When one of these events occurs, the system activation valve goes into a preset position. When the second event occurs, the valve opens, and water enters the system. Water does not enter the system until both events occur. These two events can occur in any order and result in the same outcome.

7.3.2.2 Size of Systems.

7.3.2.2.1 Not more than 1000 automatic sprinklers shall be controlled by any one preaction valve.

7.3.2.2.2 Unless the requirements of 7.3.2.2.3 are met, for preaction system types described in 7.3.2.1(3), not more than 750 gal (2839 L) shall be controlled by one preaction valve.

7.3.2.2.3 The system volume for preaction system types described in 7.3.2.1(3) shall be permitted to exceed 750 gal (2839 L) where the system is designed to deliver water to the system test connection in not more than 60 seconds, starting at the normal air pressure on the system, with the detection system operated and at the time of fully opened inspection test connection. Air pressure and supply shall comply with 7.2.6.

Preaction systems sizes are discussed in 7.3.2.2.1 through 7.3.2.2.3. Double interlock preaction systems are usually used for cold storage warehouses or flash-freeze facilities.

Because of the need to wait for the drop in air pressure, a double interlock system has characteristics that are similar to that of a dry pipe system. Double interlock preaction systems maintain air pressures similar to those found on dry pipe systems and, therefore, require the same restrictions as dry pipe systems. The restrictions include the 30 percent increase in design area (see 11.2.3.2.5), the 750-gal (2839-L) limit (see 7.2.3.1), and the prohibition of the gridded piping arrangement (see 7.2.3.5).

The volume of single interlock and non-interlock systems is not restricted. These systems are unrestricted because they are expected to operate more quickly than double interlock systems and do not rely on the discharge of system air in order to activate.

7.3.2.3* Supervision.

A.7.3.2.3 Supervision, either electrical or mechanical, as used in 7.3.2.3 refers to constant monitoring of piping and detection equipment to ensure the integrity of the system. Detection devices of listed flow cycling assemblies that cause an alarm during a single open or a single ground fault condition should be considered to satisfy the supervision requirement.

The term *supervision* in A.7.3.2.3 refers to a method of ensuring the overall integrity of the piping system. Pressurized air usually is introduced to the preaction system pipe network. A loss in air pressure indicates a sprinkler activation or a major leak in the system. Normal supervision status registers that the system piping and sprinklers are intact. This reading, however, is not meant to verify that the system is completely free of minor leaks. The air compressor

◀ **FAQ**
Are double interlock preaction systems required to meet the requirements and restrictions for dry pipe systems?

◀ **FAQ**
Do the volume limitations for dry pipe systems apply to single and non-interlock preaction systems?

and the air maintenance device could be able to maintain the necessary air pressure even where minor leaks exist.

A single interlock preaction system, as described in 7.3.2.1(1), with more than 20 sprinklers is still required to be supervised but not at a minimum pressure. A 7-psi (0.5-bar) minimum is required on the non-interlock and double interlock systems, since they can operate similarly to a dry pipe system in that water delivery time to the open sprinklers is delayed. The minimum supervisory pressure is necessary for proper operation of the sprinkler. Proper operation entails both the lifting of the cap so the air escapes and the clearing of the mechanisms so the water discharge pattern is not affected. A minimum operating pressure at the sprinkler is a critical part of the system's activation process.

Supervision of the associated electronic detection devices is very important since loss or failure of the detection system to an open circuit or ground fault can render the entire preaction system inoperative.

 Specifics on the supervision of fire detection system circuits, referred to as "monitoring the integrity of installation conductors," can be found in *NFPA 72*.

7.3.2.3.1 Sprinkler piping and fire detection devices shall be automatically supervised where there are more than 20 sprinklers on the system.

7.3.2.3.2 All preaction system types described in 7.3.2.1(2) and 7.3.2.1(3) shall maintain a minimum supervising air pressure of 7 psi (0.5 bar).

7.3.2.4 Sprinklers. The following types of sprinklers and arrangements shall be permitted for preaction systems:

(1) Upright sprinklers
(2)* Listed dry sprinklers

 A.7.3.2.4(2) See A.7.2.2(2).

Listed dry sprinklers are covered in 7.3.2.4(2). See the commentary for 7.2.2(4) for more information on the use of dry sprinklers, sprinklers on return bends, and horizontal sidewall sprinklers on preaction systems, where the same issues associated with their use on dry systems is applicable to their use in preaction systems.

(3) Pendent sprinklers and sidewall sprinklers installed on return bends, where the sprinklers, return bend, and branch line piping are in an area maintained at or above 40°F (4°C)
(4) Horizontal sidewall sprinklers, installed so that water is not trapped

7.3.2.5 System Configuration. Preaction systems of the type described in 7.3.2.1(3) shall not be gridded.

FAQ ►
Why are gridded double interlocked preaction systems prohibited?

The restriction in 7.3.2.5 prohibiting a gridded pipe arrangement for double interlock preaction systems reduces the likelihood of substantial delay in the delivery of water to the open sprinklers. The 1996 edition removed the 10-psi (0.7-bar) limit for double interlock systems that existed in previous editions. Since this type of preaction system can have the same time delays associated with a dry pipe system, even at pressures below 10 psi (0.7 bar), gridded arrangements are not permitted.

7.3.3* Deluge Systems.

 A.7.3.3 Where 8-in. (203-mm) piping is employed to reduce friction losses in a system operated by fire detection devices, a 6-in. (152-mm) preaction or deluge valve and a 6-in. (152-mm) gate valve between tapered reducers should be permitted.

 Deluge systems, which are covered in 7.3.3, are normally used in very high hazard areas. These systems have properties similar to those of a preaction system in that they rely on a supplemental detection system to operate them. However, these systems use open sprinklers and, therefore, are an open system. NFPA 409, *Standard on Aircraft Hangars,* requires the installation of foam-water deluge systems in certain aircraft hangars. NFPA does not limit the type of detection system to be used to activate a deluge system. Deluge systems may be operated by smoke, heat, ultraviolet (UV), or infrared (IR) detection systems. Exhibit 3.7 shows a schematic of a deluge system operated by electronic detectors. Exhibit 7.5 illustrates a deluge valve activated by a pneumatic dry pilot sprinkler line.

EXHIBIT 7.5 Deluge Valve.

7.3.3.1 The detection devices or systems shall be automatically supervised.

7.3.3.2 Deluge systems shall be hydraulically calculated.

Calculation of deluge systems is required in 7.3.3.2. Since all sprinklers are open, every sprinkler on the system discharges water simultaneously when the deluge valve operates. The determination of the system's area of operation is straightforward—it is the entire area protected by the deluge system.

◄ FAQ
What is the correct area of operation when calculating a deluge sprinkler system?

7.4 Combined Dry Pipe and Preaction Systems

Combined dry pipe and preaction systems, which are covered in Section 7.4, are not as common as they were several decades ago. The systems are intended to be applied to unusual structures, such as piers or wharves, that require unusually long runs of pipe.

7.4.1* General.

A.7.4.1 Systems described by Section 7.4 are special types of noninterlocking preaction systems intended for use in, but not limited to, structures where a number of dry pipe valves would be required if a dry pipe system were installed. These systems are primarily used in piers and wharves.

7.4.1.1* Combined automatic dry pipe and preaction systems shall be so constructed that failure of the detection system shall not prevent the system from functioning as a conventional automatic dry pipe system.

A.7.4.1.1 See Figure A.7.4.1.1.

See Figure A.7.4.3   See Figure A.7.4.3

Typical piping layout
(in one-story shed — 4-section system)

FIGURE A.7.4.1.1 *Typical Piping Layout for Combined Dry Pipe and Preaction Sprinkler System.*

Conventional automatic operation of the dry pipe valve, as discussed in 7.4.1.1, provides a highly reliable backup to the fire detection system. Since the primary purpose of the fire detection system is to cause piping to start filling sooner, loss of the detection system only results in a much slower operating mode. Although somewhat impaired, the system can still operate.

7.4.1.2 Combined automatic dry pipe and preaction systems shall be so constructed that failure of the dry pipe system of automatic sprinklers shall not prevent the detection system from properly functioning as an automatic fire alarm system.

Quite the opposite effect from that covered in 7.4.1.1 results when the detection system operates, but the dry pipe valve fails to open. With this type of failure, which is discussed in 7.4.1.2, no water flows to the piping system and sprinklers, and only the alarm activates.

7.4.1.3 Provisions shall be made for the manual operation of the detection system at locations requiring not more than 200 ft (61 m) of travel.

Manual operation of the fire detection system, which is discussed in 7.4.1.3, provides a prompt means of filling the system with water from remote locations throughout the protected area. Manual operation can be utilized in special circumstances where the danger of an incident is possible in order to fill the system piping so that in the event of a fire the system will operate as a wet pipe system.

7.4.1.4 Sprinklers. The following types of sprinklers and arrangements shall be permitted for combined dry pipe and preaction systems:

(1) Upright sprinklers
(2)* Listed dry sprinklers

A.7.4.1.4(2) See A.7.2.2(2).

Listed dry sprinklers are covered in 7.4.1.4(2). See the commentary for 7.2.2(4) for more information on the use of dry sprinklers, sprinklers on return bends, and horizontal sidewall sprinklers on preaction systems, where the same issues associated with their use on dry systems is applicable to their use in combined dry pipe and preaction systems.

(3) Pendent sprinklers and sidewall sprinklers installed on return bends, where both the sprinklers and the return bends are located in a heated area
(4) Horizontal sidewall sprinklers, installed so that water is not trapped

7.4.2 Dry Pipe Valves in Combined Systems.

7.4.2.1 Where the system consists of more than 600 sprinklers or has more than 275 sprinklers in any fire area, the entire system shall be controlled through two 6-in. (152-mm) dry pipe valves connected in parallel and shall feed into a common feed main.

7.4.2.2 Where parallel dry pipe valves are required by 7.4.2.1 these valves shall be checked against each other. *(See Figure 7.4.2.2.)*

Dry pipe valves in combined systems are discussed in 7.4.2.1 and 7.4.2.2. Although each dry pipe valve in a combined system serves as a backup valve, simultaneous operation of both valves is desirable to increase the system's flow characteristics.

7.4.2.3 Each dry pipe valve shall be provided with a listed tripping device actuated by the detection system.

7.4.2.4 Dry pipe valves shall be cross-connected through a 1-in. (25.4-mm) pipe connection to permit simultaneous tripping of both dry pipe valves.

7.4.2.5 The 1-in. (25.4-mm) cross-connection pipe shall be equipped with an indicating valve so that either dry pipe valve can be shut off and worked on while the other remains in service.

7.4.2.6 The check valves between the dry pipe valves and the common feed main shall be equipped with ½-in. (13-mm) bypasses so that a loss of air from leakage in the trimmings of a dry pipe valve will not cause the valve to trip until the pressure in the feed main is reduced to the tripping point.

7.4.2.7 An indicating valve shall be installed in each of these bypasses so that either dry pipe valve can be completely isolated from the main riser or feed main and from the other dry pipe valve.

7.4.2.8 Each combined dry pipe and preaction system shall be provided with listed quick-opening devices at the dry pipe valves.

7.4.3* Exhausters.

A.7.4.3 See Figure A.7.4.3.

Combined dry pipe and preaction systems have a very large air capacity. The exhausters, which are discussed in 7.4.3, serve to remove air at remote ends of the piping and allow water to fill the system at a faster rate. The exhausters should be located where they can be readily tested and maintained.

A listed exhauster, which is mechanically activated by a drop in air pressure, must be used. The tripping device activated by the detection system causes the drop in air pressure experienced by the exhauster. At the time of publication, no such listed tripping devices were available.

7.4.3.1 One or more listed exhausters of 2-in. (51-mm) or larger size controlled by operation of a fire detection system shall be installed at the end of the common feed main.

FIGURE 7.4.2.2 *Header for Dry Pipe Valves Installed in Parallel for Combined Systems; Standard Trimmings Not Shown. Arrows Indicate Direction of Fluid Flow.*

FIGURE A.7.4.3 *Arrangement of Air Exhaust Valves for Combined Dry Pipe and Preaction Sprinkler System.*

7.4.3.2 These air exhaust valves shall have soft-seated globe or angle valves in their intakes.

7.4.3.3 Approved strainers shall be installed between the globe valves and the air exhaust valves.

7.4.4 Subdivision of System Using Check Valves.

7.4.4.1 Where more than 275 sprinklers are required in a single fire area, the system shall be divided into sections of 275 sprinklers or fewer by means of check valves.

7.4.4.2 Where the system is installed in more than one fire area or story, not more than 600 sprinklers shall be supplied through any one check valve.

7.4.4.3 Each section shall have a 1¼-in. (33-mm) drain on the system side of each check valve supplemented by a dry pipe system auxiliary drain.

The requirements of 7.4.4.1 through 7.4.4.3 provide a cost-effective means to offset the large volume of air in these systems. The use of check valves is acceptable since air exhaust valves are still required to be used, and the system is a non-interlock preaction system, which is expected to be tripped by the detection system.

7.4.4.4 Section drain lines and dry pipe system auxiliary drains shall be located in heated areas or inside heated cabinets to enclose drain valves and auxiliary drains for each section.

7.4.4.5 Air exhaust valves at the end of a feed main and associated check valves shall be protected against freezing.

7.4.5 Time Limitation.

7.4.5.1 The sprinkler system shall be so constructed and the number of sprinklers controlled shall be so limited that water shall reach the farthest sprinkler within a period of time not exceeding 1 minute for each 400 ft (122 m) of common feed main from the time the heat-responsive system operates.

7.4.5.2 The maximum time permitted shall not exceed 3 minutes.

Time limitations are discussed in 7.4.5.1 and 7.4.5.2. Combined dry pipe and preaction systems have a combination of the features associated with both dry pipe and preaction systems and are intended for specific applications as indicated in the commentary to Section 7.4. The water delivery times associated with combined dry pipe and preaction systems, therefore, are different than those required for either dry pipe or preaction systems. Excessive delivery time for water should be reviewed with the authority having jurisdiction.

7.4.6 System Test Connection. The end section shall have a system test connection as required for dry pipe systems.

7.5 Antifreeze Systems

Antifreeze systems, which are covered in Section 7.5, are typically used as subsystems of a wet pipe system. Antifreeze systems are intended to protect small areas that could be exposed to freezing temperatures, such as outside loading docks. Antifreeze systems are also used for residential areas that are not protected against freezing temperatures, since residential sprinklers are currently listed only for wet pipe systems.

Antifreeze systems were once more attractive economically for protecting small areas than dry pipe systems. The reduction in size and cost of certain dry pipe valves combined with the added expense of backflow preventers and expansion chambers have made antifreeze systems somewhat less attractive. Even where a backflow preventer is not required, a larger area protected with a dry pipe system could still provide an economically more attractive option due to the cost of antifreeze for larger systems.

The potential effectiveness of antifreeze and water mixtures controlling a fire has come into question in the past. Antifreeze solutions are evaluated for their ability to allow for efficient fire control and to make sure that the solution does not serve as fuel for the fire. The concentrates identified in Tables 7.5.2.2 and 7.5.2.3 were tested for control mode spray sprinklers to ensure that they cause no such negative reaction.

The 2002 edition has been modified to only allow specific antifreeze solution listed for ESFR sprinkler systems to be utilized in ESFR applications.

7.5.1 General.

FAQ ▶
What happened to the recommended 40-gal (151-L) limit for antifreeze systems?

For the 2002 edition, the annex recommendation that systems be limited to 40 gal (151 L) has been deleted. It is important to note that while the committee has not set a limit on the size of antifreeze systems, in all cases they must be properly designed, installed, and maintained. When designing an antifreeze system, the designer should account for the impact the antifreeze solution will have on the design calculations and the impact on expansion chamber size due to the volume of solution. Additionally, the size of the antifreeze system will have an effect on the overall impact of regular inspection, testing, and maintenance of the system. The 2002 edition of NFPA 25 requires that the antifreeze solution be tested annually. In the event that the antifreeze solution needs to be remixed or drained and refilled, the impact of draining and refilling and large system could be significant.

7.5.1.1 The use of antifreeze solutions shall be in conformity with state and local health regulations.

The use of antifreeze solutions is addressed in 7.5.1.1. The current reaction by a number of water system purveyors to the use of antifreeze solutions in sprinkler systems has impacted the antifreeze system option, even though NFPA 13 only allows the use of nontoxic antifreeze solutions when the system is connected to the public water supply. Many local regulations require antifreeze systems to be equipped with a reduced-pressure zone backflow prevention device (see Exhibit 7.6) to guard against potential contamination of the public water supply. These local regulations have impacted the economic advantages offered by antifreeze systems to some degree.

EXHIBIT 7.6   Backflow Prevention Device Installed on an Antifreeze System.

A distinction is made between the use of additives for potable and nonpotable water. The solutions noted in Table 7.5.2.2 could be described as food-grade chemicals.

NFPA 13 does not place any limitations on the size of antifreeze systems. See commentary for 7.5.1 for additional information on antifreeze system size.

7.5.1.2 Antifreeze used in ESFR systems shall be specifically listed for ESFR applications.

In 7.5.1.2, NFPA 13 now requires that antifreeze utilized in ESFR sprinkler systems be specifically listed for ESFR applications. Testing completed by FM Global showed that the currently acceptable referenced antifreeze solutions could have a negative impaction on suppression sprinklers and should not be utilized for ESFR applications.

◄ FAQ
Does NFPA 13 limit the size of antifreeze systems?

◄ FAQ
Can an antifreeze system be utilized with ESFR applications?

7.5.2* Antifreeze Solutions.

A.7.5.2 Listed CPVC sprinkler pipe and fittings should be protected from freezing with glycerine only. The use of diethylene, ethylene, or propylene glycols are specifically prohibited. Laboratory testing shows that glycol-based antifreeze solutions present a chemical environment detrimental to CPVC.

7.5.2.1 Where sprinkler systems are supplied by potable water connections, the use of antifreeze solutions other than water solutions of pure glycerine (C.P. or U.S.P. 96.5 percent grade) or propylene glycol shall not be permitted.

7.5.2.2 Glycerine-water and propylene glycol–water mixtures shown in Table 7.5.2.2 shall be considered suitable for use.

7.5.2.3 If potable water is not connected to sprinklers, the commercially available materials indicated in Table 7.5.2.3 shall be permitted for use in antifreeze solutions.

7.5.2.4* An antifreeze solution shall be prepared with a freezing point below the expected minimum temperature for the locality.

A.7.5.2.4 Beyond certain limits, an increased proportion of antifreeze does not lower the freezing point of solution *(see Figure A.7.5.2.4).*

TABLE 7.5.2.2 *Antifreeze Solutions to Be Used if Potable Water Is Connected to Sprinklers*

Material	Solution (by volume)	Specific Gravity at 60°F (15.6°C)	Freezing Point	
			°F	°C
Glycerine	50% water	1.145	−20.9	−29.4
C.P. or U.S.P. grade*	40% water	1.171	−47.3	−44.1
	30% water	1.197	−22.2	−30.1
Hydrometer scale 1.000 to 1.200				
Propylene glycol	70% water	1.027	+9	−12.8
	60% water	1.034	−6	−21.1
	50% water	1.041	−26	−32.2
	40% water	1.045	−60	−51.1
Hydrometer scale 1.000 to 1.200 (subdivisions 0.002)				

*C.P.—chemically pure; U.S.P.—United States Pharmacopoeia 96.5%.

TABLE 7.5.2.3 *Antifreeze Solution to Be Used if Nonpotable Water Is Connected to Sprinklers*

Material	Solution (by volume)	Specific Gravity at 60°F (15.6°C)	Freezing Point	
			°F	°C
Glycerine	See Table 7.5.2.2.			
Diethylene glycol	50% water	1.078	−13	−25.0
	45% water	1.081	−27	−32.8
	40% water	1.086	−42	−41.1
Hydrometer scale 1.000 to 1.120 (subdivisions 0.002)				
Ethylene glycol	61% water	1.056	−10	−23.3
	56% water	1.063	−20	−28.9
	51% water	1.069	−30	−34.4
	47% water	1.073	−40	−40.0
Hydrometer scale 1.000 to 1.120 (subdivisions 0.002)				
Propylene glycol	See Table 7.5.2.2.			

Glycerine, diethylene glycol, ethylene glycol, and propylene glycol should never be used without mixing with water in proper proportions, because these materials tend to thicken near 32°F (0°C).

 It is critical to maintain the proper concentration of antifreeze solution at all times, which is the reason for the requirement in 7.5.2.4. Pressure surges and temperature fluctuations can alter the concentration because more water either has flowed into or out of the antifreeze system. NFPA 25 requires that the antifreeze concentrations be checked periodically.

Refractometers, such as the one shown in Exhibit 7.7, with scales that are calibrated for a particular antifreeze solution are available for testing the concentration of antifreeze solutions. Traditional types of refractometers require that a sample of the solution be placed onto the device so that the appropriate antifreeze concentration as indicated in Figure 7.5.2.5(a) can be verified. This type of refractometer is calibrated for a particular type of antifreeze solution, so a separate device needs to be used for each type of antifreeze.

EXHIBIT 7.7
Refractometer.

Flexible rubber
eyepiece

Includes dipstick and
pump tube

EXHIBIT 7.8   Digital
Refractometer.

9-Volt Battery
Good for more than
60 hours of use

Function Keys
Buttons are intuitive

Digital Accuracy
Alphanumeric display is
large and easy to read

Up to Five Scales
Up to five scales per
instrument, custom
scales available

Textured Surface
For secure grip

Smooth Surface
Repels liquid — easy to clean

Fiber-optic Sensor
Cutting-edge technology

Sapphire Window
Protects sensor
from damage

8.50 in.
(216 mm)

1.15 in.
(29.21 mm)

FIGURE A.7.5.2.4 *Freezing Points of Water Solutions of Ethylene Glycol and Diethylene Glycol.*

Digital refractometers (see Exhibit 7.8) contain a probe that is inserted into the antifreeze solution. These refractometers provide a reading of the appropriate antifreeze concentration as identified in Figure 7.5.2.5(b). Digital refractometers do not require that their scales be calibrated for each type of antifreeze, so a single device can be used to test all types of antifreeze.

Figure 7.5.2.5(c) was added to address the appropriate densities of aqueous glycerin solutions. This figure was added to assist the user where these solutions were utilized for freeze protection.

7.5.2.5 The specific gravity of the prepared solution shall be checked by a hydrometer, in accordance with Figure 7.5.2.5(a), Figure 7.5.2.5(b), and Figure 7.5.2.5(c), with suitable scale or a refractometer having a scale calibrated for the antifreeze solution involved.

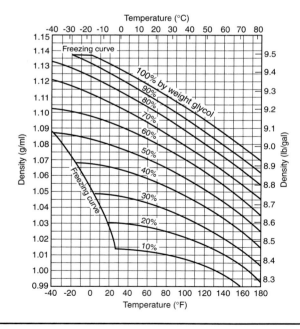

FIGURE 7.5.2.5(a) *Densities of Aqueous Ethylene Glycol Solutions (Percent by Weight).*

FIGURE 7.5.2.5(b) *Densities of Aqueous Propylene Glycol Solutions (Percent by Weight).*

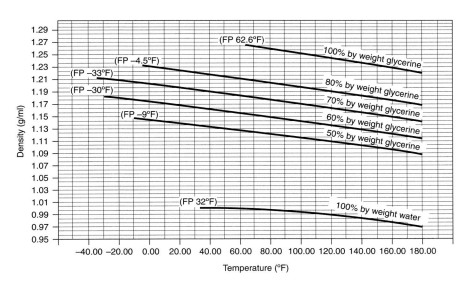

Data Sources:

1. Density data for 100% water was taken from Lange's *Handbook of Chemistry*, Revised Tenth Edition, page 1199. Temperatures have been converted from Celsius to Fahrenheit units, and data points at 10 degree Fahrenheit multiples have been determined by linear interpolation. Conversion from relative to absolute density was achieved by multiplying by 0.999973.

2. Densities of glycerine-water solutions at 0°C and above were taken from Table III (p. 6) in *Glycerol* by Anthony Armin Newman, C.R.C. Press, 1968. Densities for temperatures below 0°C were taken from Table IV. Temperatures have been converted from Celsius to Fahrenheit units, and data points at 10 degree Fahrenheit multiples have been determined by linear interpolation.

3. Density data for pure glycerine was taken from Table II (p. 6) in *Glycerol* by Anthony Armin Newman, C.R.C. Press, 1968, and derived from the thermal expansion data in Table 7-9 in *Gycerol* by Carl S. Miner and N.N. Dalton, Reinhold Publishing Corp., 1953 (American Chemical Society Monograph Series #117) using the density for 0°C as a base point. Temperatures have been converted from Celsius to Fahrenheit units, and data points at 10 degree Fahrenheit multiples have been determined by linear interpolation.

4. Freezing points were taken from the article, "Freezing Points of Glycerol and Its Aqueous Solution" by Leonard B. Lane in *Industrial and Engineering Chemistry*, volume 17 (1925), number 9, page 924. Temperatures have been converted from Celsius to Fahrenheit units.

FIGURE 7.5.2.5(c) *Densities of Aqueous Glycerine Solutions (Percent by Weight).*

7.5.3 Arrangement of Supply Piping and Valves.

7.5.3.1* Where the connection between the antifreeze system and the wet pipe system does not incorporate a backflow prevention device, piping and valves shall be installed as illustrated in Figure 7.5.3.1.

A.7.5.3.1 All permitted antifreeze solutions are heavier than water. At the point of contact (interface), the heavier liquid will be below the lighter liquid, preventing diffusion of water into the unheated areas.

Arrangement of supply piping and valves is discussed in 7.5.3.1. Since all permitted antifreeze solutions are heavier than water, an interface at which the water in the wet system will stay above the heavier antifreeze solution is created. If possible, the entire antifreeze system should be below the level of this interface, thus preventing the diffusion of water into low-temperature areas. When the antifreeze system is above the interface, alternative piping arrangements and additional system components as illustrated in Figures 7.5.3.1 and 7.5.3.2 are necessary.

Figure 7.5.3.1 shows an arrangement of supply piping and valves for an antifreeze system without a backflow device and with the sprinklers above the water/antifreeze interface.

FIGURE 7.5.3.1 *Arrangement of Supply Piping and Valves.*

In this arrangement, a check valve and a 5-ft (1.5-m) drop or U-loop is needed so that the antifreeze does not flow back into the wet pipe system. Additionally, because antifreeze solutions can expand with a rise in temperature and result in high pressures that can damage system components, a ¹⁄₃₂-in. (0.8-mm) hole drilled into the clapper of the check valve is needed. If the antifreeze system is entirely below the interface with the wet pipe system (shown at valve A), or a backflow device is used as indicated in 7.5.3.2, then the check valve and the 5-ft (1.5-m) drop are not needed.

Actual field conditions and practices could require some modification to the arrangement shown in Figure 7.5.3.1. For example, because the piping on the antifreeze system is at a higher elevation than the water supply, it is not practical to use a gravity-type filling cup at the illustrated supply location. If antifreeze is gravity-fed into the system, the filling cup should be relocated to the high point of the antifreeze system piping. As an alternative, antifreeze can be pumped into the system through the filling cup as presently located in Figure 7.5.3.1.

7.5.3.2* Where the connection between the antifreeze system and the wet pipe system incorporates a backflow prevention device, piping and valves shall be installed as illustrated in Figure 7.5.3.2.

 A.7.5.3.2 One formula for sizing the chamber is as follows. Other methods also exist.

$$\Delta L = S_V \left(\frac{D_L}{D_H} - 1 \right)$$

where:

ΔL = change in antifreeze solution volume (gal) due to thermal expansion

S_V = volume (gal) of antifreeze system, not including the expansion chamber

D_L = density (gm/ml) of antifreeze solution at lowest expected temperature

D_H = density (gm/ml) of antifreeze solution at highest expected temperature

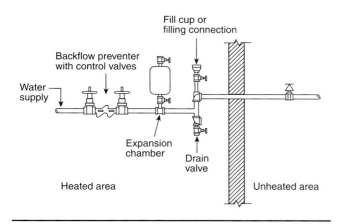

FIGURE 7.5.3.2 *Arrangement of Supply Piping with Backflow Device.*

This method is based on the following information:

$$\frac{P_0 \cdot V_0}{T_0} = \frac{P_1 \cdot V_1}{T_1} = \frac{P_2 \cdot V_2}{T_2}$$

where:

V_{EC} = minimum required volume (gal) of expansion chamber

V_0 = air volume (gal) in expansion chamber at precharge (before installation)

V_1 = air volume (gal) in expansion chamber at normal static pressure

V_2 = air volume (gal) in expansion chamber at post-expansion pressure (antifreeze at high temperature)

P_0 = absolute precharge pressure (psia) on expansion chamber before installation

P_1 = absolute static pressure (psi) on water (supply) side of backflow preventer

P_2 = absolute maximum allowable working pressure (psi) for antifreeze system

T_0 = temperature (°R) of air in expansion chamber at precharge

T_1 = temperature (°R) of air in expansion chamber when antifreeze system piping is at lowest expected temperature

T_2 = temperature (°R) of air in expansion chamber when antifreeze system piping is at highest expected temperature

This equation is one formulation of the ideal gas law from basic chemistry. The amount of air in the expansion chamber will not change over time. The pressure, temperature, and volume of the air at different times will be related in accordance with this formula.

$$V_2 = V_1 - \Delta L$$

The antifreeze in the system is essentially incompressible, so the air volume in the expansion chamber will decrease by an amount equal to the expansion of the antifreeze.

It is assumed that there is no trapped air in the system piping, so the only air in the system is in the expansion chamber. This is a conservative assumption, since more air is better. In reality, there will be at least some trapped air. However, only the air in the expansion chamber can be relied upon to be available when needed.

$$V_{EC} = V_0$$

At precharge, the chamber will be completely full of air.

$$V_{EC} = \frac{P_1 \cdot T_0 \cdot P_2 \cdot \Delta L \cdot T_1}{P_0 \cdot T_1 (P_2 \cdot T_1 - P_1 \cdot T_2)}$$

In cases where the normal static pressure on the sprinkler system is close to the maximum working pressure, antifreeze systems are not advisable if the connection to the wet pipe system will incorporate a backflow device. In these cases, expansion of the antifreeze solution during warm weather will cause the antifreeze system to exceed the maximum working pressure, regardless of the size of the expansion chamber. The normal static pressure is too close to the maximum working pressure if the formula for V_{EC} above yields a negative result. If this occurs, use a dry pipe system instead or install a pressure reducing valve before the backflow preventer.

A backflow device, discussed in 7.5.3.2, marks the interface between the wet pipe system and the antifreeze system. Because the backflow device prevents the flow of antifreeze back into the wet pipe system regardless of the elevation of the antifreeze system, the piping arrangement and valves indicated in 7.5.3.1 are not necessary.

FAQ ▶
Are there additional design considerations when utilizing a reduced-pressure backflow preventer?

A reduced-pressure backflow preventer contains a relief valve that discharges water to atmosphere under some circumstances. This discharge can be a significant amount of water, and appropriate drainage needs to be provided. The designer should determine from the backflow preventer manufacturer the anticipated flow from the relief valve should it discharge to atmosphere.

To account for pressure changes that can result because of temperature differences in the space protected by the antifreeze system, an expansion chamber with pre-charged air pressure is required. The expansion chamber is required rather than some other type of pressure-relieving device, such as a relief valve, because antifreeze solution is discharged from the system when the relief valve operates. The volume of solution lost is replaced by water when the temperature cools, thus diluting the concentration of the antifreeze solution below what is required.

As indicated by the equation in A.7.5.3.2, calculating the appropriate size of the expansion chamber requires some understanding of the overall process involved. The antifreeze system can be exposed to a seasonal temperature fluctuation—for example, winter to summer—that causes the antifreeze solution to expand and contract. The amount of expansion depends on the total temperature change and the density of the specific solution used. The type of antifreeze and the concentration used affects the overall density of the solution in the antifreeze system.

As the solution expands, some volume flows into the expansion chamber, compressing the air within the chamber. As the air compresses, a corresponding increase of the pressure on the system occurs. The air volume must be large enough to keep the system pressure below the pressure limitations of the system components. Factors other than the amount of thermal expansion that influence the required air volume (chamber size) include seasonal temperature changes of the air within the chamber, which are often different from the temperature change of the antifreeze solution, precharged air pressure level, and static pressure of the water supply. Fluctuations of air temperature within the expansion chamber can be different from the fluctuations of the temperature of the antifreeze system, since the chamber is often located within a temperature-controlled portion of the building.

Situations, such as with a high static pressure, occur in which the system pressure cannot be kept below 175 psi (12.1 bar) with an expansion chamber.

7.5.3.3 Where the connection between the antifreeze solution and the wet pipe system incorporates a backflow prevention device, a listed expansion chamber of appropriate size and precharged air pressure shall be provided to compensate for thermal expansion of the antifreeze solution as illustrated in Figure 7.5.3.2.

7.6 Automatic Sprinkler Systems with Non–Fire Protection Connections

7.6.1 Circulating Closed-Loop Systems.

7.6.1.1 System Components.

7.6.1.1.1 A circulating closed-loop system is primarily a sprinkler system and shall comply with all provisions of this standard such as those for control valves, area limitations of a system, alarms, fire department connections, sprinkler spacing, and so forth except as modified by Section 7.6.

7.6.1.1.2 Piping, fittings, valves, and pipe hangers shall meet the requirements specified in Chapter 6.

7.6.1.1.3 Unless the requirements of 7.6.1.1.4 are met, a dielectric fitting shall be installed in the junction where dissimilar piping materials are joined (e.g., copper to steel).

7.6.1.1.4 Dielectric fittings shall not be required in the junction where sprinklers are connected to piping.

Dielectric fittings are addressed in 7.6.1.1.4. The concern with dissimilar metals typically only applies where a system has a continuously moving fluid through it. The ionization of the area surrounding the two different materials is enhanced by the transition of the fluid across the surface of the metals. Since no other sprinkler system except a circulating closed-loop system has this condition, no further requirements concerning dielectric fittings are imposed on other systems. NFPA 13 only requires the use of dielectric fittings for circulating closed-loop systems. Exhibit 7.9 illustrates a dielectric fitting.

7.6.1.1.5 Other auxiliary devices shall not be required to be listed for sprinkler service; however, these devices, such as pumps, circulating pumps, heat exchangers, radiators, and luminaries, shall be pressure rated at 175 psi or 300 psi (12.1 bar or 20.7 bar) (rupture pressure of five times rated water system working pressure) to match the required rating of sprinkler system components.

EXHIBIT 7.9 Dielectric Fitting.

Although auxiliary equipment or components are not required to be listed, as stated in 7.6.1.1.5, they must be of materials acceptable in Chapter 6 and of sufficient quality in durability, suitability, and strength to be equal to all other sprinkler system components.

7.6.1.1.6 Auxiliary devices shall incorporate materials of construction and be so constructed that they will maintain their physical integrity under fire conditions to avoid impairment to the fire protection system.

7.6.1.1.7 Auxiliary devices, where hung from the building structure, shall be supported independently from the sprinkler portion of the system, following recognized engineering practices.

7.6.1.2* Hydraulic Characteristics. Piping systems for attached heating and cooling equipment shall have auxiliary pumps or an arrangement made to return water to the piping system in order to assure the following:

(1) Water for sprinklers shall not be required to pass through heating or cooling equipment.
(2) At least one direct path shall exist for waterflow from the sprinkler water supply to every sprinkler.
(3) Pipe sizing in the direct path shall be in accordance with the design requirements of this standard.
(4) No portions of the sprinkler piping shall have less than the sprinkler system design pressure, regardless of the mode of operation of the attached heating or cooling equipment.
(5) There shall be no loss or outflow of water from the system due to or resulting from the operation of heating or cooling equipment.
(6) Shutoff valves and a means of drainage shall be provided on piping to heating or cooling equipment at all points of connection to sprinkler piping and shall be installed in such a manner as to make possible repair or removal of any auxiliary component without impairing the serviceability and response to the sprinkler system.
(7) All auxiliary components, including the strainer, shall be installed on the auxiliary equipment side of the shutoff valves.

 A.7.6.1.2 Outlets should be provided at critical points on sprinkler system piping to accommodate attachment of pressure gauges for test purposes.

Paragraph 7.6.1.2(5) indicates that the flow to sprinklers cannot experience a reduction regardless of operation or presence of the auxiliary equipment. An enhancement of flow to the sprinkler system is allowed, but a reduction is not.

7.6.1.3 Water Temperature.

7.6.1.3.1 Maximum.

7.6.1.3.1.1 In no case shall maximum water temperature flowing through the sprinkler portion of the system exceed 120°F (49°C).

7.6.1.3.1.2 Protective control devices listed for this purpose shall be installed to shut down heating or cooling systems when the temperature of water flowing through the sprinkler portion of the system exceeds 120°F (49°C).

7.6.1.3.1.3 Where the water temperature exceeds 100°F (37.8°C), intermediate or higher temperature–rated sprinklers shall be used.

7.6.1.3.2 Minimum. Precautions shall be taken to ensure that temperatures below 40°F (4°C) are not permitted.

7.6.1.4 Obstruction to Discharge. Automatic sprinklers shall not be obstructed by auxiliary devices, piping, insulation, and so forth, from detecting fire or from proper distribution of water.

7.6.1.5 Signs. Caution signs shall be attached to all valves controlling sprinklers. The caution sign shall be worded as follows:

> This valve controls fire protection equipment.
> Do not close until after fire has been extinguished.
> Use auxiliary valves when necessary to
> shut off supply to auxiliary equipment.

> **Caution:** Automatic alarm will be sounded if this valve is closed.

7.6.1.6 Water Additives.

7.6.1.6.1 Materials added to water shall not adversely affect the fire-fighting properties of the water and shall be in conformity with any state or local health regulations.

Additives are usually necessary to extend the life of heating units, chillers, or companion equipment associated with the heating, ventilating, and air-conditioning (HVAC) systems. It is not the intent of 7.6.1.6.1 to prohibit the use of additives.

As a courtesy to fire suppression personnel, local fire departments with primary jurisdiction over the property should be made aware of the presence of and type of water additives included in the system.

7.6.1.6.2 Due care and caution shall be given to the use of additives that can remove or suspend scale from older piping systems.

7.6.1.6.3 Where additives are necessary for proper system operation, due care shall be taken to ensure that additives are replenished after alarm testing or whenever water is removed from the system.

7.6.1.7 Waterflow Detection.

7.6.1.7.1 The supply of water from sprinkler piping through auxiliary devices, circulatory piping, and pumps shall not under any condition or operation, transient or static, cause false sprinkler waterflow signals.

7.6.1.7.2 A sprinkler waterflow signal shall not be impaired when water is discharged through an opened sprinkler or through the system test connection while auxiliary equipment is in any mode of operation (on, off, transient, stable).

7.7 Outside Sprinklers for Protection Against Exposure Fires

These exposure systems discussed in Section 7.7 are usually installed on the exterior surface of a building to protect against exposure fires from an adjacent building or operation. An outside system typically has two performance objectives. One objective is to significantly limit the radiation or connective heat generated by an exposure fire from entering the building through windows, doors, and other openings in the exposed walls. This protection minimizes the likelihood of the ignition of building contents and other combustibles. The other objective is to minimize the likelihood of ignition of or heat damage to exterior combustible wall surfaces, including sheathing, eaves, and cornices.

Prompt sprinkler system discharge should occur by automatic actuation of the outside sprinklers. Delayed application of water to glass surfaces once they become sufficiently heated can result in breakage from thermal shock. Delayed application of water can also result in ignition of exterior combustible surfaces or damage to heat-sensitive materials.

Outside sprinkler systems might be required to compensate for lack of physical separation between adjacent structures. NFPA 80A, *Recommended Practice for Protection of Buildings from Exterior Fire Exposures,* allows the reduction of separation distances between buildings when proper exposure protection from sprinklers is provided.

7.7.1 Applications. Exposure protection systems shall be permitted on buildings regardless of whether the building's interior is protected by a sprinkler system.

7.7.2 Water Supply and Control.

7.7.2.1* Unless the requirements of 7.7.2.2 are met, sprinklers installed for protection against exposure fires shall be supplied from a standard water supply as outlined in Chapter 15.

A.7.7.2.1 The water supply should be capable of furnishing the total demand for all exposure sprinklers operating simultaneously for protection against the exposure fire under consideration for a duration of not less than 60 minutes.

Water supply is discussed in 7.7.2.1. Water should be continuously delivered at the required application rate to the outside sprinkler system for the duration of exposure fire expected from an adjacent building, structure, or other exposure source such as a flammable liquid storage tank or scrap tire storage. The required duration can exceed 60 minutes if hose streams cannot be applied in a sufficient amount of time or if the exposing fire cannot be contained during its developmental stages. Section 14.7 provides further guidance on the design parameters of an outside sprinkler system for exposure protection.

7.7.2.2 Where approved, other supplies, such as manual valves or pumps or fire department connections, shall be permitted to supply water to sprinklers for exposure protection.

Paragraph 7.7.2.2 permits a water supply other than the automatic water supply required in Chapter 15. The authority having jurisdiction must determine if this method of water supply, which includes fire department apparatus pumping into the fire department connection, is acceptable for the circumstances. This situation is the only one noted in NFPA 13 that does not require an automatic supply.

7.7.2.3 Where fire department connections are used for water supply, they shall be so located that they will not be affected by the exposing fire.

7.7.3 Control.

7.7.3.1 Each system of outside sprinklers shall have an independent control valve.

The division of sprinkler piping and sprinklers into separate systems, each of which needs to have an independent control valve as required in 7.7.3.1, should take into account the extent of a likely exposure fire from adjacent buildings or operations. Further division of sprinkler piping can be necessary if the surface to be protected is quite large.

The water supply can limit the area that can be protected by a single system. The system can be sized based on the assumption that any exposing fire will be confined to a certain size if the exposing building is compartmented by construction features such as fire walls, partitions, or enclosed stair shafts. In other words, it might not be necessary to assume that the entire exposed building wall will be engulfed in fire.

Flames from an adjacent building or structure will likely rise upward in a rectangular plume area. Each outside sprinkler system should be arranged to simultaneously discharge water over the corresponding rectangular plume area, assuming that the exposure will occur from ground level upward.

7.7.3.2 Manually controlled open sprinklers shall be used only where constant supervision is present.

Manually controlled sprinklers are discussed in 7.7.3.2. Where automatic actuation of outside sprinkler systems cannot be provided, prompt system operation should be ensured through manual means by the opening of strategically located and identified valves. Personnel assigned the responsibility for and instructed in the operation and importance of these systems need to constantly monitor the exposing operations.

7.7.3.3 Sprinklers shall be of the open or automatic type. Automatic sprinklers in areas subject to freezing shall be on dry pipe systems conforming to Section 7.2 or antifreeze systems conforming to Section 7.5.

7.7.3.4 Automatic systems of open sprinklers shall be controlled by the operation of fire detection devices designed for the specific application.

Fire detection devices, discussed in 7.7.3.4, with weatherproof fixtures should be located on the exterior of the exposed building in such a manner as to rapidly detect heat radiation or convection from an exposing fire. Spacing and location of detectors should be closer than that specified by the manufacturer if the line of sight of the exposing building or structure is obstructed.

7.7.4 System Components.

7.7.4.1 Drain Valves. Each system of outside sprinklers shall have a separate drain valve installed on the system side of each control valve, except where an open sprinkler, top-fed system is arranged to facilitate drainage.

7.7.4.2 Check Valves.

7.7.4.2.1 Where sprinklers are installed on two adjacent sides of a building, protecting against two separate and distinct exposures, with separate control valves for each side, the end lines shall be connected with check valves located so that one sprinkler around the corner will operate [see Figure 7.7.4.2.1(a) and Figure 7.7.4.2.1(b)].

7.7.4.2.2 The intermediate pipe between the two check valves shall be arranged to drain.

7.7.4.2.3 As an alternate solution, an additional sprinkler shall be installed on each system located around the corner from the system involved.

Check valves are covered in 7.7.4.2.1 through 7.7.4.2.3. The "trapped" section of pipe and sprinklers located between two check valves must be drained automatically to prevent water from freezing in the piping after system operation. Drainage can be accomplished by providing a downturned tee outlet and a K-2.8 sprinkler located in the piping at a low point. If the K-2.8

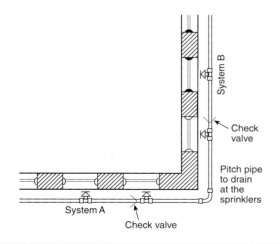

FIGURE 7.7.4.2.1(a) *Typical Arrangement of Check Valves.*

FIGURE 7.7.4.2.1(b) *Alternate Arrangement of Check Valves.*

sprinkler has not fused during sprinkler system operation, it must be removed to drain the piping and then replaced.

7.7.4.3 System Arrangement. Where one exposure affects two sides of the protected structure, the system shall not be subdivided between the two sides but rather shall be arranged to operate as a single system.

System arrangement is discussed in 7.7.4.3. Heat transfer from an exposing fire is typically accomplished by convection or radiation. Radiation is direct along a line of sight, while convection is via fire gases, which can be flaming and deflected by drafts or wind.

The convective gases are somewhat easier to cool due to the effect of the water spray from the sprinklers. Radiated heat is more difficult to block, since some of it can pass through the water spray and reach the exposed building. To account for this, systems should be designed so that a certain amount of water flows down the exposed building walls.

Outside sprinkler systems can be required to extend either beyond the wall area directly opposite the exposing building or structure or to surfaces other than those parallel to the exposing building wall or structure surface, or both.

7.7.5 Pipe and Fittings. Pipe and fittings installed on the exterior of the building shall be corrosion resistant.

Since outside sprinkler systems are exposed to environmental conditions, exterior surfaces of outside system components are subject to an accelerated rate of corrosion, which is the reason for the requirement in 7.7.5. The interior surfaces of the system are also subject to an accelerated rate of corrosion if the sprinklers are open, as in a manually or automatically controlled deluge system. Pipe scale, which forms in the interior of the system, could obstruct sprinkler orifices when the system activates. Therefore, galvanized pipe and fittings are normally used for this application. Corrosion of pipe is an important consideration, since sprinklers with nominal K-factors less than 4.2 can be used in these special systems. See 8.3.4 and its associated commentary.

7.7.6 Strainers. A listed strainer shall be provided in the riser or feed main that supplies sprinklers having nominal K-factors smaller than 2.8 (4.0).

Strainers are discussed in 7.7.6. Scale, mud, or debris can become dislodged from piping by fast-moving water traveling through dry pipe or deluge sprinkler systems. Sprinklers with nominal K-factors less than 2.8 are more susceptible to clogging. Strainers should be listed, located adjacent to the control valve, and capable of being flushed without stopping water flow while the outside sprinkler system is operating.

7.7.7 Gauge Connections. A listed pressure gauge conforming with 8.16.3 shall be installed immediately below the control valve of each system.

7.7.8 Sprinklers.

7.7.8.1 Only sprinklers of such type as are listed for window, cornice, sidewall, or ridge pole service shall be installed for such use, except where adequate coverage by use of other types of listed sprinklers and/or nozzles has been demonstrated.

Types of outside sprinklers are discussed in 7.7.8.1. Many sprinklers approved for use in outside sprinkler systems are automatic in operation, which means that they are equipped with heat-sensitive fusible elements. The use of automatic sprinklers allows for the installation of wet pipe systems in nonfreezing climates and the installation of dry pipe or antifreeze systems in areas where outside freezing conditions can occur.

Some sprinklers approved for use in outside sprinkler systems are not equipped with heat-sensitive fusible elements. Outside sprinkler systems that use open or non-automatic sprinklers must be of the deluge type.

Outside sprinkler systems provide fire protection by removing or mitigating the effects of heat that are transmitted from an exposing fire. Water sprays from sprinklers are shown to reduce radiated heat passing through them by 50 to 70 percent, depending on water flow rates. In addition, convected fire gases are cooled while passing through the sprinkler spray. A portion of the convected and radiated heat passes through the water spray and reaches the protected surface. However, a certain amount of sprinkler discharge should be directed so that it runs down the side of the building and cools the exposed surface. Provisions must be made so that the water remains in contact with the wall or window surface while running down the exposed surface. Additionally, consideration should be given to the effects of wind so that the surface can be properly wetted.

7.7.8.2 Small-orifice or large-orifice sprinklers shall be permitted.

7.8* Refrigerated Spaces

A.7.8 Careful installation and maintenance, and some special arrangements of piping and devices as outlined in this section, are needed to avoid the formation of ice and frost inside piping in cold storage rooms that will be maintained at or below 32°F (0°C). Conditions are particularly favorable to condensation where pipes enter cold rooms from rooms having temperatures above freezing.

Whenever the opportunity offers, fittings such as those specified in 7.8.2.1, as well as flushing connections, should be provided in existing systems.

Where possible, risers should be located in stair towers or other locations outside of refrigerated areas, which would reduce the probabilities of ice or frost formation within the riser (supply) pipe.

Cross mains should be connected to risers or feed mains with flanges. In general, flanged fittings should be installed at points that would allow easy dismantling of the system. Split ring or other easily removable types of hangers will facilitate the dismantling.

Because it is not practical to allow water to flow into sprinkler piping in spaces that might be constantly subject to freezing, or where temperatures must be maintained at or below 40°F (4.4°C), it is important that means be provided at the time of system installation to conduct trip tests on dry pipe valves that service such systems. NFPA 25, *Standard for the Inspection, Testing, and Maintenance of Water-Based Fire Protection Systems,* contains requirements in this matter.

Refrigerated spaces are covered in Section 7.8. Dry pipe systems installed in refrigerated spaces require special care and consideration, since temperatures are below freezing and frequently in subzero ranges. If a system trips accidentally and allows the piping to fill with water, the nature of the occupancy can preclude heating this space to allow melting of ice and repair of the system. Such systems may need to have the pipe dismantled and moved to a warm area where it would be thawed, emptied, and then reinstalled. Such operations are costly and result in long periods in which systems are out of service. Where conditions are particularly severe, double interlock preaction or other types of special systems should be considered.

In refrigerated spaces, the air supply for the preaction or dry pipe system needs to be sufficiently dry to prevent the accumulation of moisture and the subsequent development of ice plugs in the system piping. There have been occurrences where sprinkler systems protecting freezers maintained at 5°F (15°C) or less become plugged by ice or frost deposits have increased. The plugs found can create total blockage of the feed main and severely impair the system. Provisions for decreasing the chances of ice plug or ice block formation in the air supply line or in the sprinkler piping consist of arranging pipe and associated appurtenances in a manner that minimizes the moisture content in the air supply. Means of reducing the likelihood of ice plug formation include taking the air supply from the coldest freezer area, installing air dryers, or using a moisture-free gas such as nitrogen.

7.8.1 Spaces Maintained at Temperatures Above 32°F (0°C). Where temperatures are maintained above 32°F (0°C) in refrigerated spaces, the requirements in this section shall not apply.

7.8.2* Spaces Maintained at Temperatures Below 32°F (0°C).

 A.7.8.2 The requirements in 7.8.2 are intended to minimize the chances of ice plug formation inside sprinkler system piping protecting freezers.

7.8.2.1 General.

7.8.2.1.1 Where sprinkler pipe passes through a wall or floor into the refrigerated space, a section of pipe arranged for removal shall be provided immediately inside the space.

The removable section of pipe required in 7.8.2.1.1 as well as other fittings illustrated in Figures 7.8.2.7.1.1 and A.7.8.2.4 facilitate examination of piping to determine if ice formation is occurring. If inspections are conducted on a routine basis, the formation of ice plugs and their detrimental effect on system performance can be reduced.

7.8.2.1.2 The removable length of pipe required in 7.8.2.1.1 shall be a minimum of 30 in. (762 mm).

7.8.2.2 Low Air Pressure Alarm.

7.8.2.2.1 Unless the requirements of 7.8.2.2.2 are met, a low air pressure alarm to a constantly attended location shall be installed.

Low pressure alarms, which are discussed in 7.8.2.2.1, are intended to notify plant personnel that system air pressure is below acceptable limits. Plant personnel need to react to low pressure alarms by taking appropriate action to remedy the situation in order to avoid the system piping filling accidentally with water.

7.8.2.2.2 Systems equipped with local low pressure alarms and an automatic air maintenance device shall not be required to alarm to a constantly attended location.

7.8.2.3 Piping Pitch. Piping in refrigerated spaces shall be installed with pitch as outlined in 8.15.2.3.

Any water introduced to a system protecting a very cold environment can freeze in a matter of minutes. Piping is required by 7.8.2.3 to be pitched to aid in the prompt removal of water from the system.

7.8.2.4* Air or Nitrogen Supply. Air or nitrogen supply for systems shall be one of the following:

(1) Air from the room of lowest temperature to reduce the moisture content
(2) Air compressor/dryer package listed for the application utilizing ambient air
(3) Compressed nitrogen gas from cylinders used in lieu of compressed air

 A.7.8.2.4 A higher degree of preventing the formation of ice blocks can be achieved by lowering the moisture of the air supply entering the refrigerated space to a pressure dew point no greater than 20°F (–6.6°C) below the lowest nominal temperature of the refrigerated space. The pressure dew point of the air supply can cause moisture to condense and freeze in sprinkler pipe even when the air supply is from the freezer. One method of reducing the moisture content of the air by use of air drying systems is illustrated in Figure A.7.8.2.4.

Heated area

Refrigerated space

Two easily removed sections of pipe

30 in. (762 mm)

6 ft (1.9 m) minimum

P2

Normally open control valve

Check valve

Check valve with ³/₃₂ in. (2.4 mm) hole in clapper

Dry/preaction valve

Two easily removed air supply lines

Main control valve

Water supply

Pressure regulator

P1

Air dryer

Coalescer filter

Freezer air intake

Air compressor and tank

P1 Air pressure
     Air supply source

P2 Air pressure
     Water supply source

Notes:

1. If pressure gauge P1 and P2 do not indicate equal pressures, it could mean the air line is blocked or the air supply is malfunctioning.

2. Air dryer and coalescer filter not required when system piping capacity is less than 250 gal (946 L).

FIGURE A.7.8.2.4 *Refrigerator Area Sprinkler Systems Used to Minimize the Chances of Developing Ice Plugs.*

When compressors and dryers are used for an air supply, consideration should be given to pressure requirements of the regenerative dryers, compressor size, air pressure regulator capacity, and air fill rate. Application of these factors could necessitate the use of increased air pressures and a larger air compressor.

The compressed air supply should be properly prepared prior to entering a regenerative-type air dryer, such as minimum air pressure, maximum inlet air temperature, and proper filtration of compressed air.

Air or nitrogen supply is discussed in 7.8.2.4. Taking air supply from the coldest room and then compressing it does not guarantee moisture-free air. However, this arrangement usually provides a reasonable degree of protection against the formation of ice plugs. Paragraph A.7.8.2.4 includes additional information regarding the value in which the pressure dew point should be reduced. Additionally, the list in 7.8.2.4 allows other means for reducing the moisture content of air more reliably.

7.8.2.5* Control Valve. An indicating-type control valve for operational testing of the system shall be provided on each sprinkler riser outside of the refrigerated space.

A.7.8.2.5 A major factor contributing to the introduction of moisture into the system piping is excessive air compressor operation caused by system leakage. Where excessive compressor operation is noted or ice accumulates in the air supply piping, the system should be checked for leakage and appropriate corrective action should be taken.

7.8.2.6* Check Valve.

A.7.8.2.6 The purpose of the check valve is to prevent evaporation of prime water into the system piping.

The check valve, which is discussed in 7.8.2.6, is intended to prevent evaporated priming water from migrating into the piping located in the freezer and causing an ice plug to form. However, dry pipe and preaction valves are available that do not require priming water. If priming water is not necessary, then the check valve can be omitted as indicated by 7.8.2.6.2. Additionally, any residual water left in the system riser after a trip test can be drained out of the drain connection at the base of the freezer system water control valve.

7.8.2.6.1 Unless the requirements of 7.8.2.6.2 are met, a check valve with a ³⁄₃₂-in. (2.4-mm) diameter hole in the clapper shall be installed in the system riser below the test valve required in 7.8.2.5.

7.8.2.6.2 Check valves shall not be required where dry pipe or preaction valves are used and designed to completely drain all water above the seat and that are listed for installation without priming water remaining and where priming water is not used in the system riser.

7.8.2.7* Air or Nitrogen Supply Piping.

A.7.8.2.7 The dual lines feeding the system air entering the cold area are intended to facilitate continued service of the system when one line is removed for inspection. It should be noted that, when using a system as described in Figure A.7.8.2.4, differences in the pressures at gauge P1 and gauge P2 indicate blockage in the air supply line or other malfunctions.

7.8.2.7.1 The air or nitrogen supply piping entering the freezer area shall be as stated in 7.8.2.7.1.1 and 7.8.2.7.1.2.

7.8.2.7.1.1 Air Supply. The supply piping shall be equipped with two easily removable supply lines at least 6 ft (1.9 m) long and at least 1 in. (25.4 mm) in diameter as shown in Figure 7.8.2.7.1.1.

7.8.2.7.1.2 Nitrogen Supply. The supply piping shall be equipped with a single easily removable supply line at least 6 ft (1.9 m) long and at least 1 in. (25.4 mm) in diameter.

7.8.2.7.2 Each supply line shall be equipped with control valves located in the warm area.

7.8.2.7.3 Only one air supply line shall be open to supply the system air at any one time.

The requirement in 7.8.2.7.3 that one line is to be kept open while one line is to remain closed allows the system to remain in service while inspection, testing, and maintenance is completed. If a blockage occurs in the open line, the pressure gauges will show different pressures and the line with the blockage can be shut down and cleaned while the other line is opened.

7.9 Commercial-Type Cooking Equipment and Ventilation

The original requirements with respect to protection of cooking equipment and ventilation systems, which are found in Section 7.9, were developed as a result of test work done by a task group of the National Fire Sprinkler Association. The requirements were introduced in 1968. Automatic sprinklers are effective for extinguishing grease and cooking oil fires because the fine droplets of the water spray lower the temperatures to below the point at which the fire

Notes:
1. Check valve with ³⁄₃₂-in. (2.4-mm) hole in clapper not required if prime water not used.
2. Supply air to be connected to top or side of system pipe.
3. Each removable air line shall be a minimum of 1 in. (25 mm) diameter and a minimum of 6 ft (1.8 m) long.

FIGURE 7.8.2.7.1.1   *Refrigerator Area Sprinkler System Used to Minimize the Chances of Developing Ice Plugs.*

can sustain itself. The requirements of Section 7.9 are based on research and input from both the cooking equipment ventilation industry and the sprinkler manufacturing industry.

Large droplets sprayed onto a fire involving cooking oils in a deep fat fryer can result in sudden and rapid firespread due to the spattering effect caused by the large water droplets. In order to avoid this phenomenon, only specifically listed sprinklers can be used for the protection of deep fat fryers. (See 7.9.8.2.)

7.9.1 General. In cooking areas protected by automatic sprinklers, additional sprinklers or automatic spray nozzles shall be provided to protect commercial-type cooking equipment and ventilation systems that are designed to carry away grease-laden vapors unless otherwise protected. *(See NFPA 96, Standard for Ventilation Control and Fire Protection of Commercial Cooking Operations.)*

7.9.2* Sprinklers and Automatic Spray Nozzles.

A.7.9.2 See Figure A.7.9.2.

7.9.2.1 Unless the requirements of 7.9.2.2 are met, standard sprinklers or automatic spray nozzles shall be so located as to provide for the protection of exhaust ducts, hood exhaust duct collars, and hood exhaust plenum chambers.

A Exhaust fan
B Sprinkler or nozzle at top of vertical riser
C Sprinkler or nozzle at midpoint of each offset
D 5 ft 0 in. (1.5 m) maximum
E Horizontal duct nozzle or sprinkler
F 10 ft 0 in. (3 m) maximum
G Nozzle or sprinkler in hood or duct collar
H 1 in. (25 mm) minimum, 12 in. (305 mm) maximum
I Nozzle or sprinkler in hood plenum
J 1 in. (25 mm) maximum
K In accordance with the listing
L Deep fat fryer
M In accordance with the listing
N Cooking equipment nozzle or sprinkler
O Counter height cooking equipment
P Upright broiler or salamander broiler
Q Broiling compartment sprinkler or nozzle
R Broiling compartment
S Exhaust hood

*Listed for deep fat fryer protection

FIGURE A.7.9.2 *Typical Installation Showing Automatic Sprinklers or Automatic Nozzles Being Used for the Protection of Commercial Cooking Equipment and Ventilation Systems.*

7.9.2.2 Sprinklers or automatic spray nozzles in ducts, duct collars, and plenum chambers shall not be required where all cooking equipment is served by listed grease extractors.

Sprinklers are an effective way of controlling fires in cooking equipment, filters, and ducts if they are located to cover the cooking surfaces and all areas of an exhaust system to which fires could spread. If all cooking equipment is served by listed grease extractors, the sprinkler protection can be limited to the cooking surfaces, which is the reason for the requirement in 7.9.2.2. This arrangement is subject to acceptance by the authority having jurisdiction. Some manufacturers of exhaust systems that incorporate listed grease extractors provide listed built-in water spray fire protection for cooking surfaces in a pre-engineered package ready for connection to the sprinkler system.

7.9.3 Sprinkler and Automatic Spray Nozzle Location—Ducts.

7.9.3.1 Unless the requirements of 7.9.3.2 or 7.9.3.4 are met, exhaust ducts shall have one sprinkler or automatic spray nozzle located at the top of each vertical riser and at the midpoint of each offset.

7.9.3.2 Sprinklers or automatic spray nozzles shall not be required in a vertical riser located outside of a building, provided the riser does not expose combustible material or provided the interior of the building and the horizontal distance between the hood outlet and the vertical riser is at least 25 ft (7.6 m).

7.9.3.3 Unless the requirements of 7.9.3.4 are met, horizontal exhaust ducts shall have sprinklers or automatic spray nozzle devices located on 10 ft (3 m) centers beginning no more than 5 ft (1.5 m) from the duct entrance.

7.9.3.4 Sprinklers or automatic spray nozzles shall not be required where the entire exhaust duct is connected to a listed exhaust hood incorporating a specific duct collar and sprinkler (or automatic spray nozzle) assembly that has been investigated and been shown to protect an unlimited length of duct in accordance with UL 300, *Standard for Safety Fire Testing of Fire Extinguishing Systems for Protection of Restaurant Cooking Areas.*

UL 300, *Standard for Safety Fire Testing of Fire Extinguishing Systems for Protection of Restaurant Cooking Areas,* which is cited in 7.9.3.4, is currently used to determine adequate protection for ducts of unlimited length used for cooking applications. If a manufacturer successfully passes these tests with a specific sprinkler or spray nozzle assembly in a specific listed hood and duct collar, additional sprinklers or spray nozzles in the duct are not needed.

7.9.3.5 A sprinkler(s) or an automatic spray nozzle(s) in exhaust ducts subject to freezing shall be properly protected against freezing by approved means. *(See 8.15.3.1.)*

7.9.4 Sprinkler and Automatic Spray Nozzle Location—Duct Collar.

7.9.4.1 Each hood exhaust duct collar shall have one sprinkler or automatic spray nozzle located 1 in. minimum to 12 in. maximum (25.4 mm minimum to 305 mm maximum) above the point of duct collar connection in the hood plenum.

7.9.4.2 Hoods that have listed fire dampers located in the duct collar shall be protected with a sprinkler or automatic spray nozzle located on the discharge side of the damper and shall be so positioned as not to interfere with damper operation.

7.9.5 Sprinkler and Automatic Spray Nozzle Location—Exhaust Plenum Chambers.

7.9.5.1 Hood exhaust plenum chambers shall have one sprinkler or automatic spray nozzle centered in each chamber not exceeding 10 ft (3 m) in length.

7.9.5.2 Plenum chambers greater than 10 ft (3 m) in length shall have two sprinklers or automatic spray nozzles evenly spaced, with the maximum distance between the two sprinklers not to exceed 10 ft (3 m).

7.9.6 Sprinkler and Automatic Spray Nozzle Temperature Ratings and Orifice Sizes.

7.9.6.1 Where the exposed temperature is expected to be 300°F (149°C) or less, sprinklers, or automatic spray nozzles being used in duct, duct collar, and plenum areas shall be of the extra high–temperature classification [325°F to 375°F (163°C to 191°C)].

7.9.6.2 When use of a temperature-measuring device indicates temperatures above 300°F (149°C), a sprinkler or automatic spray nozzle of higher classification shall be used.

Under the circumstances described in 7.9.6.2, the sprinklers over the cooking surface must operate first so that water from the sprinklers in the plenum do not cool them and prevent their operation.

7.9.6.3 Sprinklers or automatic spray nozzles being used in duct, duct collar, and plenum areas shall have orifice with K-factors not less than 1.4 and not more than 5.6.

7.9.7 Sprinkler and Automatic Spray Nozzle.
Access shall be provided to all sprinklers or automatic spray nozzles for examination and replacement.

The access described in 7.9.7 should not jeopardize the integrity of the hood or duct. Refer to NFPA 96, *Standard for Ventilation Control and Fire Protection of Commercial Cooking Operations.*

7.9.8 Cooking Equipment.

7.9.8.1 General. Cooking equipment (such as deep fat fryers, ranges, griddles, and broilers) that is considered to be a source of ignition shall be protected in accordance with the provisions of 7.9.1.

7.9.8.2 Listed Sprinkler and Automatic Spray Nozzles.

7.9.8.2.1 A sprinkler or automatic spray nozzle used for protection of deep fat fryers shall be listed for that application.

As of the printing of this book, no listed sprinklers for the protection of deep fat fryers, which are required by 7.9.8.2.1, are available. The sprinklers that were previously listed for this function lost their listing following changes to UL 300. The remaining cooking equipment can still be protected with standard sprinklers.

7.9.8.2.2 The position, arrangement, location, and water supply for each sprinkler or automatic spray nozzle shall be in accordance with its listing.

7.9.8.3 Fuel and Heat Shut Off.

7.9.8.3.1 The operation of any cooking equipment sprinkler or automatic spray nozzle shall automatically shut off all sources of fuel and heat to all equipment requiring protection.

7.9.8.3.2 Any gas appliance not requiring protection but located under ventilating equipment shall also be shut off.

7.9.8.3.3 All shutdown devices shall be of the type that requires manual resetting prior to fuel or power being restored.

7.9.9 Indicating Valves.
A listed indicating valve shall be installed in the water supply line to the sprinklers and spray nozzles protecting the cooking and ventilating system.

7.9.10 Strainers.
A listed line strainer shall be installed in the main water supply preceding sprinklers or automatic spray nozzles having nominal K-factors smaller than 2.8 (4.0).

7.9.11 Test Connection. A system test connection shall be provided to verify proper operation of equipment specified in 7.9.8.3.

7.9.12 Sprinkler and Automatic Spray Nozzle Replacement.

7.9.12.1 Unless the requirements of 7.9.12.2 are met, sprinklers and automatic spray nozzles used for protecting commercial-type cooking equipment and ventilating systems shall be replaced annually.

7.9.12.2 Where automatic bulb-type sprinklers or spray nozzles are used and annual examination shows no buildup of grease or other material on the sprinklers or spray nozzles, such sprinklers or spray nozzles shall be permitted to be continued in use.

SUMMARY

Chapter 7 provides the installation rules and characteristics that are unique to each particular type of system. It is important for the designer to understand the limits and applications for each system to ensure that the proper system is chosen for the application. Chapter 7 provides information specific to each type of system. This information is vital when determining the correct system type.

REFERENCES CITED IN COMMENTARY

National Fire Protection Association, 1 Batterymarch Park, P.O. Box 9101, Quincy, MA 02269-9101

NFPA 25, *Standard for the Inspection, Testing, and Maintenance of Water-Based Fire Protection Systems,* 2002 edition

NFPA 72®, National Fire Alarm Code®, 2002 edition

NFPA 80A, *Recommended Practice for Protection of Buildings from Exterior Fire Exposures,* 2001 edition

NFPA 96, *Standard for Ventilation Control and Fire Protection of Commercial Cooking Operations,* 2001 edition

NFPA 409, *Standard on Aircraft Hangars,* 2001 edition

The SFPE Handbook of Fire Protection Engineering, second edition, 1995

Underwriters Laboratories Inc., 333 Pfingsten Road, Northbrook, IL 60062

UL 300, *Standard for Safety Fire Testing of Fire Extinguishing Systems for Protection of Restaurant Cooking Areas,* 1998 edition

Installation Requirements

Numerous factors, such as the available water supply, type of sprinkler, building construction features, and the anticipated fire hazards, must be considered in the design of automatic sprinkler systems. Chapter 8 deals exclusively with installation details, such as positioning, and location of system components, such as sprinklers and valves. The requirements in this chapter identify the location and positioning rules for system components and consider the impact of building construction and equipment on satisfactory sprinkler system performance.

8.1* Basic Requirements

A.8.1 The installation requirements are specific for the normal arrangement of structural members. There will be arrangements of structural members not specifically detailed by the requirements. By applying the basic principles, layouts for such construction can vary from specific illustrations, provided the maximums specified for the spacing and location of sprinklers (Section 8.4) are not exceeded.

Where buildings or portions of buildings are of combustible construction or contain combustible material, standard fire barriers should be provided to separate the areas that are sprinkler protected from adjoining unsprinklered areas. All openings should be protected in accordance with applicable standards, and no sprinkler piping should be placed in an unsprinklered area unless the area is permitted to be unsprinklered by this standard.

Water supplies for partial systems should be designed with consideration to the fact that in a partial system more sprinklers might be opened in a fire that originates in an unprotected area and spreads to the sprinklered area than would be the case in a completely protected building. Fire originating in a nonsprinklered area might overpower the partial sprinkler system.

Where sprinklers are installed in corridors only, sprinklers should be spaced up to the maximum of 15 ft (4.5 m) along the corridor, with one sprinkler opposite the center of any door or pair of adjacent doors opening onto the corridor, and with an additional sprinkler installed inside each adjacent room above the door opening. Where the sprinkler in the adjacent room provides full protection for that space, an additional sprinkler is not required in the corridor adjacent to the door.

Basic installation requirements are covered in Section 8.1. Sprinklers must be positioned with regard to other sprinklers, structural and architectural features at the ceiling, and other building elements such as ductwork and lighting. Failure to do so greatly increases the likelihood of delayed sprinkler activation and of skewed or obstructed sprinkler spray patterns. Limiting distances between sprinklers allows for their timely activation and results in the intended level of fire control or fire suppression. NFPA 13 also recognizes that building features that block the sprinkler discharge can negatively impact spray distribution patterns.

NFPA 13 requires that sprinklers be provided throughout the premises. However, certain sections permit sprinklers to be omitted from certain spaces where specific conditions are sat-

◄ **FAQ**
Are sprinklers required in all spaces?

isfied. These spaces include concealed spaces (see 8.14.1 and 8.14.6), vertical shafts (see 8.14.2), bathrooms and clothes closets in dwellings units (see 8.14.8.1 and 8.14.88.2), elevator shafts (see 8.14.5), and electrical equipment rooms (see 8.14.10). For the most part, these spaces must include noncombustible or limited-combustible construction where the introduction of combustible contents and storage is precluded by building usage. In some cases, a hazard exists but is it not considered practical to install sprinklers in the space.

The installation of sprinklers throughout the building ensures that the sprinkler system's effectiveness is not compromised by a fire originating in a noncompliant unsprinklered space. Fires originating in most unsprinklered areas where the combustible loading is not limited are likely to grow to a size where sprinklers in adjacent spaces have limited success in controlling them.

8.1.1* The requirements for spacing, location, and position of sprinklers shall be based on the following principles:

(1) Sprinklers shall be installed throughout the premises.
(2) Sprinklers shall be located so as not to exceed maximum protection area per sprinkler.
(3) Sprinklers shall be positioned and located so as to provide satisfactory performance with respect to activation time and distribution.
(4) Sprinklers shall be permitted to be omitted from areas specifically allowed by this standard.
(5) When sprinklers are specifically tested and test results demonstrate that deviations from clearance requirements to structural members do not impair the ability of the sprinkler to control or suppress a fire, their positioning and locating in accordance with the test results shall be permitted.
(6) Clearance between sprinklers and ceilings exceeding the maximums specified in this standard shall be permitted provided that tests or calculations demonstrate comparable sensitivity and performance of the sprinklers to those installed in conformance with these sections.

A.8.1.1 This standard contemplates full sprinkler protection for all areas including walk-in coolers, freezers, bank vaults, and similar areas. Other NFPA standards that mandate sprinkler installation might not require sprinklers in certain areas. The requirements of this standard should be used insofar as they are applicable. The authority having jurisdiction should be consulted in each case. A building is considered sprinklered throughout when protected in accordance with the requirements of this standard.

Principles for spacing, location, and position of sprinklers are found in 8.1.1. Unless NFPA 13 specifically permits the omission of sprinklers in a certain area, sprinklers are required. In some situations, this requirement can result in conflicts with other regulations.

 FAQ ▶

NFPA 101®, Life Safety Code®, permits the omission of sprinklers from certain sized closets in all residential occupancies, while NFPA 13 limits the omission of sprinklers in these closets to hotels and motels only. Why?

For example, NFPA *101®*, *Life Safety Code®*, allows sprinklers to be omitted from certain size closets in any type of residential occupancy. NFPA 13 restricts this omission to closets in hotels and motels only. Fires originating in these size closets in other types of residential occupancies can result in substantial property damage (see 8.14.8.2). The very small number of fires originating in these size closets that result in one or more fatalities justifies NFPA *101*'s broader exception. In other words, NFPA *101* addresses only life safety, while NFPA 13 addresses both life safety and property protection and can justify more stringent requirements.

NFPA 13 does not support the use of partial sprinkler systems. However, NFPA 13 recognizes that other regulations permit the use of partial systems (see Section 4.2). In such cases, NFPA 13 requirements should be followed to the extent possible. When considering partial sprinkler protection, it is important to recognize that a fire originating in an unsprinklered space is likely to grow and spread to the sprinklered area unless some other precautions are taken. Once the fire reaches the sprinklered space, it is likely to be of a size that cannot be controlled or suppressed by a partial system. Sprinkler systems designed and installed in accordance with NFPA 13 are intended to control or suppress fires during their early stages of development. When property protection is a primary concern and differences exist between NFPA 13 and other standards, the requirements of NFPA 13 should take precedence and sprinklers should be provided accordingly. If they are not, everyone involved must understand the ramifications of the decision from both a property and life safety perspective.

Proper placement of automatic sprinklers ensures that sprinklers operate in a timely manner and achieve effective fire control. To accomplish the basic goals indicated in 8.1.1(2) and 8.1.1(3), specific NFPA 13 requirements on spacing, position, coverage, and obstructions to sprinkler discharge must be followed (see Section 8.5). For example, depending on the type of sprinkler, specific dimensions on deflector positioning with respect to various ceiling features and types of obstructions are provided. In some cases, such as for unusual ceiling arrangements that contain deep pockets (see 8.6.7) or where heat and smoke vents are used, additional provisions could be necessary. Additionally, where tests or calculations indicate that other arrangements provide at least the same level of performance prescribed by this standard, then these other arrangements are permitted to be used in accordance with 8.1.1(5) and 8.1.1(6).

8.1.2* System valves and gauges shall be accessible for operation, inspection, tests, and maintenance.

A.8.1.2 The components need not be open or exposed. Doors, removable panels, or valve pits can satisfy this need. Such equipment should not be obstructed by such permanent features as walls, ducts, columns, or direct burial.

Access to critical system components, as discussed in 8.1.2, is necessary to allow for emergency shutdown after a fire and to check the operation of the system during a fire. Proper access also facilitates inspection, testing, and maintenance of the system in accordance with NFPA 25, *Standard for the Inspection, Testing, and Maintenance of Water-Based Fire Protection Systems*. Although valves and gauges are not required to be visible—that is, they can be located in valve pits or behind doors or removable panels—6.7.4 requires appropriate signage for valves, and 8.15.1.1.1.1 requires that the valves be in an accessible location. Additionally, 8.15.1.1.2.4 requires that where control valves are installed overhead, their indicating feature must be visible from the floor below.

8.2 System Protection Area Limitations

8.2.1 The maximum floor area on any one floor to be protected by sprinklers supplied by any one sprinkler system riser or combined system riser shall be as follows:

(1) Light hazard—52,000 ft^2 (4831 m^2)
(2) Ordinary hazard—52,000 ft^2 (4831 m^2)
(3) Extra hazard

    (a) Pipe schedule—25,000 ft^2 (2323 m^2)
    (b) Hydraulically calculated—40,000 ft^2 (3716 m^2)

(4) Storage—High-piled storage (as defined in 3.3.12) and storage covered by other NFPA standards—40,000 ft^2 (3716 m^2)

The maximum coverage area specified in 8.2.1 is the maximum floor area per system on any one floor in a given building. The maximum areas of coverage are not to be extended to other buildings as each building is to have its own sprinkler system.

NFPA 13 does not limit the number of floors that can be protected by a single riser, because each floor is considered a separate fire area. However, limitations are placed on the area of each floor.

Vertical openings are assumed to be protected as outlined in 8.14.4. In a single-story, 312,000-ft^2 (28,986-m^2) building of ordinary or light hazard occupancies, at least six systems

Does NFPA 13 limit the number of floors that a single riser can protect given each floor is less than the limits of 8.2.1?
◄ **FAQ**

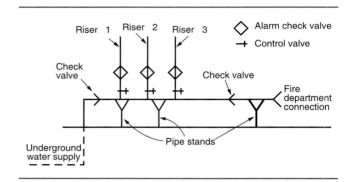

EXHIBIT 8.1 Manifold Riser Arrangement Consisting of Three Wet Pipe Systems.

would be required. If the building was six stories high with the floor area of each story not exceeding 52,000 ft^2 (4831 m^2), the building could be protected by a single system riser. If each story consisted of a floor area in excess of 52,000 ft^2 (4831 m^2), then more than one riser would be needed. Floor control valves, along with waterflow alarms, are often provided on each floor of a high-rise building to limit the area affected by a single impairment and to identify the floor or zone in which sprinkler operation occurred. Floor control valves and waterflow devices are not specifically required for each floor in a multistory building.

Where multiple risers are necessary to meet the system area limitations, a manifold riser arrangement can be considered as shown in Exhibits 8.1 and 8.2. For a building containing only light hazard or ordinary hazard occupancies, each of the three risers in Exhibits 8.1 and 8.2 could protect up to 52,000 ft^2 (4831 m^2) in a single-story, 156,000-ft^2 (14,470-m^2) building. If the building contained only extra hazard occupancies that were hydraulically designed or high-piled storage, each riser could protect up to 40,000 ft^2 (3716 m^2) in a single-story, 120,000-ft^2 (11,148-m^2) building. The total number of manifolded risers on a single header should be limited so that in the event of an impairment to the supply piping, the total area impaired is limited.

FAQ ▶
How was the 52,000-ft^2 (4831-m^2) limit established?

NFPA 13 formerly limited system size by the number of sprinklers on a system—for example, 400 sprinklers for ordinary hazard areas. The 52,000-ft^2 (4831-m^2) limitation is determined by multiplying the 400 sprinklers by the 130-ft^2 (12-m^2) maximum spacing. These area limitations are not related to the hydraulics or the operating characteristics of the system.

EXHIBIT 8.2 Manifold Riser Arrangement Consisting of Two Wet Pipe Systems and One Dry Pipe System.

Rather, the area limitations are based on judgmental factors concerning the maximum area within a single, vertical fire division that should be protected by a single system or that could be out of service at any given time.

8.2.2 The floor area occupied by mezzanines shall not be included in the area limits of 8.2.1.

Some confusion can result when tabulating the areas noted for each occupancy category.

Paragraph 8.2.2 does not require the additional area occupied by the mezzanine to be counted against the area limitation. Exhibits 8.3 and 8.4 show examples of the intent of this requirement. For high-piled storage, the area protected by one system riser cannot exceed 40,000 ft^2 (3716 m^2). When determining the area, the mezzanine area does not need to be added to the actual floor area.

◄ **FAQ**
When determining the area limitations for a single floor, is the additional area occupied by mezzanines required to be added to the floor area?

EXHIBIT 8.3 Mezzanine Used for Storage.

EXHIBIT 8.4 Mezzanine Storage Area in Warehouse.

8.2.3 Where single systems protect extra hazard, high-piled storage, or storage covered by other NFPA standards, and ordinary or light hazard areas, the extra hazard or storage area coverage shall not exceed the floor area specified for that hazard and the total area coverage shall not exceed 52,000 ft^2 (4831 m^2).

A single system protecting both ordinary or light hazard areas and solid-piled, palletized, or rack storage greater than 12 ft (3.7 m) high, or protecting extra hazard areas, can have a coverage area of up to 52,000 ft^2 (4831 m^2) as indicated by 8.2.3. However, not more than 40,000 ft^2 (3716 m^2) of that coverage area can be high-piled storage or hydraulically designed for extra hazard occupancies.

Where high-piled storage or extra hazard occupancies are mixed with light hazard or ordinary hazard occupancies, is it acceptable to exceed 40,000 ft^2 per floor?
◄ **FAQ**

The 40,000-ft^2 (3716-m^2) maximum extra hazard coverage area for hydraulically designed systems is consistent with the requirements for storage areas that have similar fire loading. If the potential exists to use the ordinary or light hazard areas for storage in the future, use of the lower system area 40,000 ft^2 (3716 m^2) as the allowable system protection area would be appropriate.

8.3 Use of Sprinklers

Use of sprinklers is covered in Section 8.3. Although numerous types of sprinklers are currently available, sprinkler technology continues to evolve, especially with regard to thermal sensitivity, spray pattern distribution characteristics, and droplet size. As a result, new types and styles of sprinklers with specific applications and installation requirements continue to be developed.

The requirements in Chapter 8 are organized by sprinkler types to better address their use and installation requirements. This standard provides use and installation requirements for the most common types of sprinklers, including standard spray upright and pendent, sidewall standard spray, extended coverage upright and pendent spray, extended coverage sidewall spray, residential, large drop, early suppression fast-response (ESFR), and in-rack sprinklers.

8.3.1 General.

8.3.1.1* Sprinklers shall be installed in accordance with their listing.

 A.8.3.1.1 The evaluation for usage should be based upon a review of available technical data.

Any limitations placed on a sprinkler, such as the hazard classification, location in which it can be used, restrictions on its position with respect to structural elements, or limitations placed on its temperature rating, are included as part of its listing. The requirement in 8.3.1.1 precludes the use of sprinklers for other than their intended use, unless that use has been tested and evaluated in accordance with 8.1.1(5) or 8.1.1(6). For example, some architects have insisted on the installation of sprinklers within a structure to achieve symmetry. These sprinklers are not connected to a water supply and are merely being used as a decorative feature—clearly not an intended use.

Some specially listed sprinklers, such as certain storage sprinklers, attic sprinklers, window sprinklers, on-off sprinklers, and institutional sprinklers, have unique use and installation requirements. These and other special sprinklers must be installed in accordance not only with NFPA 13 but also with any additional requirements specified by their listing. Subsection 8.4.9 addresses special sprinklers.

8.3.1.2 The requirements of 8.3.1.1 shall not apply where construction features or other special situations require unusual water distribution, and listed sprinklers shall be permitted to be installed in positions other than anticipated by their listing to achieve specific results.

8.3.1.3* Upright sprinklers shall be installed with the frame arms parallel to the branch line, unless specifically listed for other orientation.

 A.8.3.1.3 The purpose of this requirement is to minimize the obstruction of the discharge pattern.

The sprinkler's frame arm, which is discussed in 8.3.1.3, and the piping below the sprinkler both represent potential obstructions to the water distribution pattern and can prevent a uniform spray pattern. Even though the frame arm is designed to minimize this obstruction, the potential for obstruction cannot be completely eliminated. Installation of an upright sprinkler with its frame arm parallel to the branch line minimizes the likelihood of the water distribution pattern being obstructed by the frame arm. Exhibit 6.5 illustrates an upright sprinkler installed with its frame arm installed in the proper orientation.

8.3.1.4 Where solvent cement is used as the pipe and fittings bonding agent, sprinklers shall not be installed in the fittings prior to the fittings being cemented in place.

The solvent cement used to join some types of sprinkler piping, especially if used excessively, can drip onto the sprinkler and potentially block or plug the sprinkler orifice or otherwise prevent the sprinkler from operating properly. As stated in 8.3.1.4, to prevent dripping of excess solvent, the sprinkler should not be installed in the fitting until the fitting is connected to the pipe and any excess solvent is removed.

◀ **FAQ**
Why are sprinklers prohibited from being installed in fittings where solvent cement is utilized until the fittings have been cemented in place?

8.3.2 Temperature Ratings.

Temperature ratings of a sprinkler, which are covered in 8.3.2, are used as follows:

1. To keep sprinklers from operating accidentally if installed in a high ambient temperature area
2. To control the number of sprinklers operating in the design area

8.3.2.1* Unless the requirements of 8.3.2.2. 8.3.2.3, 8.3.2.4, or 8.3.2.5 are met, ordinary temperature–rated sprinklers shall be used throughout buildings.

A.8.3.2.1 For protection of baled cotton, limited tests and actual fire experience indicate an initial low heat release; thus, sprinklers in the ordinary temperature range should offer some advantage by opening faster than those of intermediate- or high-temperature classifications under similar conditions.

A

8.3.2.2 Where maximum ceiling temperatures exceed 100°F (38°C), sprinklers with temperature ratings in accordance with the maximum ceiling temperatures of Table 6.2.5.1 shall be used.

8.3.2.3 Intermediate- and high-temperature sprinklers shall be permitted to be used throughout ordinary and extra hazard occupancies and as allowed in this standard and other NFPA codes and standards.

8.3.2.4 Sprinklers of intermediate- and high-temperature classifications shall be installed in specific locations as required by 8.3.2.5.

Higher temperature classification sprinklers, which are discussed in 8.3.2.4, are preferable for some types of fast-developing fires. The use of ordinary temperature classification sprinklers to protect against fast-developing high heat release rate fires tends to result in the operation of sprinklers beyond the fire area. Sprinkler operation outside the fire area reduces the water discharge density available to the sprinklers directly adjacent to the fire, which reduces their effectiveness. In some high heat release fires with high thermal updrafts, the water discharged from sprinklers is carried back toward the ceiling as steam, where it condenses on ordinary temperature sprinklers and causes them to operate. This phenomenon is one of the reasons for sprinklers operating beyond the fire area.

◀ **FAQ**
Why are higher temperature sprinklers preferred or required in some locations?

Extra-high-temperature, very-extra-high-temperature, and ultra-high-temperature sprinklers identified in Table 6.2.5.1 can be used in areas immediately above equipment that produce large amounts of heat and high temperatures such as industrial and baking ovens, furnaces, and boilers.

8.3.2.5 The following practices shall be observed to provide sprinklers of other than ordinary-temperature classification unless other temperatures are determined or unless

TABLE 8.3.2.5(a) *Temperature Ratings of Sprinklers Based on Distance from Heat Sources*

Type of Heat Condition	Ordinary Degree Rating	Intermediate Degree Rating	High Degree Rating
(1) Heating ducts			
(a) Above	More than 2 ft 6 in.	2 ft 6 in. or less	
(b) Side and below	More than 1 ft 0 in.	1 ft 0 in. or less	
(c) Diffuser	Any distance except as shown under Intermediate Degree Rating column	*Downward discharge:* Cylinder with 1 ft 0 in. radius from edge extending 1 ft 0 in. below and 2 ft 6 in. above *Horizontal discharge:* Semicylinder with 2 ft 6 in. radius in direction of flow extending 1 ft 0 in. below and 2 ft 6 in. above	
(2) Unit heater			
(a) Horizontal discharge		*Discharge side:* 7 ft 0 in. to 20 ft 0 in. radius pie-shaped cylinder *(see Figure 8.3.2.5)* extending 7 ft 0 in. above and 2 ft 0 in. below heater; also 7 ft 0 in. radius cylinder more than 7 ft 0 in. above unit heater	7 ft 0 in. radius cylinder extending 7 ft 0 in. above and 2 ft 0 in. below unit heater
(b) Vertical downward discharge *(for sprinklers below unit heater, see Figure 8.3.2.5)*		7 ft 0 in. radius cylinder extending upward from an elevation 7 ft 0 in. above unit heater	7 ft 0 in. radius cylinder extending from the top of the unit heater to an elevation 7 ft 0 in. above unit heater
(3) Steam mains (uncovered)			
(a) Above	More than 2 ft 6 in.	2 ft 6 in. or less	
(b) Side and below	More than 1 ft 0 in.	1 ft 0 in. or less	
(c) Blowoff valve	More than 7 ft 0 in.		7 ft 0 in. or less

For SI units, 1 in. = 25.4 mm; 1 ft = 0.3048 m.

TABLE 8.3.2.5(b) *Ratings of Sprinklers in Specified Locations*

Location	Ordinary Degree Rating	Intermediate Degree Rating	High Degree Rating
Skylights		Glass or plastic	
Attics	Ventilated	Unventilated	
Peaked roof: metal or thin boards, concealed or not concealed, insulated or uninsulated	Ventilated	Unventilated	
Flat roof: metal, not concealed	Ventilated or unventilated	Note: For uninsulated roof, climate and insulated or uninsulated occupancy can necessitate intermediate sprinklers. Check on job.	
Flat roof: metal, concealed, insulated or uninsulated	Ventilated	Unventilated	
Show windows	Ventilated	Unventilated	

Note: A check of job condition by means of thermometers might be necessary.

high-temperature sprinklers are used throughout and temperature selection shall be in accordance with Table 8.3.2.5(a), Table 8.3.2.5(b), and Figure 8.3.2.5:

(1) Sprinklers in the high-temperature zone shall be of the high-temperature classification, and sprinklers in the intermediate-temperature zone shall be of the intermediate-temperature classification.
(2) Sprinklers located within 12 in. (305 mm) to one side or 30 in. (762 mm) above an uncovered steam main, heating coil, or radiator shall be of the intermediate-temperature classification.
(3) Sprinklers within 7 ft (2.1 m) of a low-pressure blowoff valve that discharges free in a large room shall be of the high-temperature classification.
(4) Sprinklers under glass or plastic skylights exposed to the direct rays of the sun shall be of the intermediate-temperature classification.
(5) Sprinklers in an unventilated, concealed space, under an uninsulated roof, or in an unventilated attic shall be of the intermediate-temperature classification.
(6) Sprinklers in unventilated show windows having high-powered electric lights near the ceiling shall be of the intermediate-temperature classification.
(7) Sprinklers protecting commercial-type cooking equipment and ventilation systems shall be of the high- or extra high–temperature classification as determined by use of a temperature-measuring device. *(See 7.9.6.)*
(8) Sprinklers protecting residential areas installed near specific heat sources identified in Table 8.3.2.5(c) shall be installed in accordance with Table 8.3.2.5(c).

The requirements specified in 8.3.2.5 relate to the use of sprinklers contained in Table 6.2.5.1. The temperature rating criteria allow the sprinklers to operate in response to a fire rather than to high ambient temperatures. Paragraph 8.3.2.5(8) was added to the 2002 edition to provide technical guidance when selecting the temperature rating of sprinklers protecting residential areas. The requirements of 8.3.2.5(8) and Table 8.3.2.5(c) provide guidance for all sprinklers utilized in residential areas, including residential sprinklers.

◀ **FAQ**
Is there any guidance for temperature selection for residential sprinklers?

8.3.2.6 In case of occupancy change involving temperature change, the sprinklers shall be changed accordingly.

TABLE 8.3.2.5(c) *Ratings of Sprinklers in Specified Residential Areas*

	Minimum Distance from Edge of Source to Ordinary-Temperature Sprinkler		Minimum Distance from Edge of Source to Intermediate-Temperature Sprinkler	
Heat Source	*in.*	*mm*	*in.*	*mm*
Side of open or recessed fireplace	36	914	12	305
Front of recessed fireplace	60	1524	36	914
Coal- or wood-burning stove	42	1067	12	305
Kitchen range	18	457	9	229
Wall oven	18	457	9	229
Hot air flues	18	457	9	229
Uninsulated heat ducts	18	457	9	229
Uninsulated hot water pipes	12	305	6	152
Side of ceiling- or wall-mounted hot air diffusers	24	607	12	305
Front of wall-mounted hot air diffusers	36	914	18	457
Hot water heater or furnace	6	152	3	76
Light fixture: 0 W–250 W	6	152	3	76
250 W–499 W	12	305	6	152

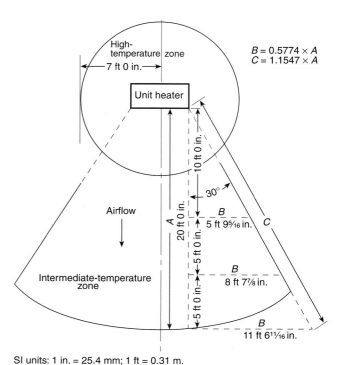

SI units: 1 in. = 25.4 mm; 1 ft = 0.31 m.

FIGURE 8.3.2.5 *High-Temperature and Intermediate-Temperature Zones at Unit Heaters.*

8.3.2.7* The minimum temperature rating of ceiling sprinklers in general storage, rack storage, rubber tire storage, roll paper storage, and baled cotton storage applications shall be 150°F (66°C).

A.8.3.2.7 Where high temperature–rated sprinklers are installed at the ceiling, high temperature–rated sprinklers also should extend beyond storage in accordance with Table A.8.3.2.7.

TABLE A.8.3.2.7 *Distance Beyond Perimeter of Storage for High-Hazard Occupancies Protected with High Temperature–Rated Sprinklers*

Design Area		Distance	
ft²	m²	ft	m
2000	186.0	30	9.1
3000	278.7	40	12.0
4000	371.6	45	13.7
5000	464.5	50	15.2
6000	557.4	55	16.7

8.3.3 Thermal Sensitivity.

8.3.3.1* Sprinklers in light hazard occupancies shall be one of the following:

(1) Quick-response type as defined in 3.6.2.9
(2) Residential sprinklers in accordance with the requirements of 8.4.5

(3) Standard response sprinklers used for modifications or additions to existing light hazard systems equipped with standard response sprinklers

(4) Standard response sprinklers used where individual standard response sprinklers are replaced in existing light hazard systems

A.8.3.3.1 When renovations occur in an existing building and no changes are made in the existing sprinkler system, this section is not intended to require the replacement of existing standard sprinklers with quick-response sprinklers.

The use of quick-response sprinklers, which are specified in 8.3.3.1(1), has been an option within NFPA 13 since the 1980 edition. Although quick-response sprinklers tend to enhance property protection and life safety, no requirements or incentives for their use were provided until the 1996 edition. The requirement that quick-response sprinklers be used in all light hazard occupancies, with appropriate exceptions to address existing systems, raises the baseline level of system performance. Existing systems are not required to be upgraded when renovations occur.

Quick-response sprinklers are considered necessary because of their life safety benefits. The evidence clearly indicates that using quick-response sprinklers rather than standard response sprinklers reduces the fire damage, all other factors being equal. Most of the sprinkler systems installed in light hazard occupancies, such as hospitals, hotels, and apartments, are installed for life safety purposes. However, even in those occupancies where life safety is not the primary reason for sprinkler system installation, such as in offices and restaurants, quick-response sprinklers are still considered important because they limit fire damage and the potential for injury or death of occupants and fire fighters. Given the current level of knowledge concerning the performance of quick-response sprinklers, the use of standard-response technology instead of quick-response technology in light hazard occupancies is considered inappropriate.

◀ **FAQ**
Why are quick-response sprinklers required in light hazard occupancies?

Like quick-response sprinklers, residential sprinklers have fast-response operating elements and can be used within some light hazard occupancies in accordance with 8.4.5.

In some occupancies that are traditionally considered light hazard, ordinary hazard designs are sometimes used due to an uncertainty in the fire loading (office buildings are an example). In these cases, quick response sprinklers should be used even though a higher sprinkler density is provided by using an ordinary hazard design.

◀ **FAQ**
Can residential sprinklers be used in light hazard occupancies where quick-response sprinklers are required?

8.3.3.2 Where quick-response sprinklers are installed, all sprinklers within a compartment shall be of the quick-response type.

8.3.3.3 Where circumstances require the use of other than ordinary temperature–rated sprinklers, standard response sprinklers shall be permitted to be used.

8.3.3.4 When existing light hazard systems are converted to use quick-response or residential sprinklers, all sprinklers in a compartmented space shall be changed.

The mixing of quick-response or residential sprinklers with standard response sprinklers in a light hazard occupancy (see 8.3.3.4) can cause more sprinklers to operate than necessary and change the order in which sprinklers operate—that is, those sprinklers further away from the fire could operate first. In that case, the sprinkler would provide some ceiling cooling but would allow the fire to grow larger than it would if the sprinklers closest to the fire operated first. Where the sprinklers in a light hazard occupancy are converted to quick-response or residential sprinklers, all sprinklers in the space must be of the quick-response or residential type.

◀ **FAQ**
Why are all sprinklers in a compartment required to be quick response?

8.3.4 Small Orifice Sprinklers.

Sprinklers with nominal K-factors less than 5.6 are commonly referred to as small-orifice sprinklers, which are discussed in 8.3.4. The 7-psi (0.5-bar) minimum pressure indicates that small-orifice sprinklers should only be used where the required sprinkler discharge is less than that provided by a sprinkler with a nominal K-factor of 5.6 operating at 7 psi (0.5 bar). The discharge pattern of small-orifice sprinklers becomes distorted at high pressures.

8.3.4.1 For light hazard occupancies not requiring as much water as is discharged by a sprinkler with a nominal K-factor of 5.6 operating at 7 psi (0.5 bar), sprinklers having a smaller orifice shall be permitted subject to the following restrictions:

(1) The system shall be hydraulically calculated.
(2) Sprinklers with K-factors of less than 5.6 shall be installed only in wet pipe sprinkler systems or in accordance with the limitations of 8.3.4.2.

FAQ ▶
Why are small-orifice sprinklers limited to light hazard occupancies and wet pipe systems only?

Restrictions on small-orifice sprinklers are found in 8.3.4.1(1) and 8.3.4.1(2). Small-orifice sprinklers are restricted to light hazard occupancies because they are not as effective in controlling a fire as are sprinklers with a nominal K-factor of at least 5.6. These sprinklers also do not pass the same fire tests that K-5.6 and larger sprinklers do. Small-orifice sprinklers are restricted to wet systems because of the likelihood that the sprinkler orifice will be obstructed by internal pipe scale and foreign material prevalent in dry pipe and preaction systems.

Exhibits 6.2 and 6.3 show a small-orifice sprinkler adjacent to a K-5.6 sprinkler.

FAQ ▶
Is it acceptable to install small-orifice sprinklers on an antifreeze system protecting a light hazard area?

It should be noted that the use of an antifreeze system within a light hazard occupancy does not affect the requirements of 8.3.4.1 since an antifreeze system is a type of wet pipe sprinkler system.

(3) A listed strainer shall be provided on the supply side of sprinklers with nominal K-factors of less than 2.8.

The strainer requirement in 8.3.4.1(3) serves to limit the introduction of foreign materials into the sprinkler system through the water supply. However, the strainer has no effect on scale buildup within the pipe and the possibility of scale being carried to the sprinkler.

As is indicated in the commentary on 6.2.3.1, actual orifice sizes may be slightly smaller than the sprinkler's size classification. The inclusion of the word *nominal* in 8.3.4.1(3) clarifies that a strainer is not required for a nominal K-2.8 sprinkler even if the actual orifice size is as small as 2.6.

8.3.4.2 Sprinklers with K-factors of less than 5.6 shall be permitted to be installed in conformance with 11.2.3.7 for protection against exposure fires.

8.3.5 Thread Size Limitations. Sprinklers having a K-factor exceeding 5.6 and having ½-in. (13-mm) National Pipe Thread (NPT) shall not be installed in new sprinkler systems.

Sprinklers that have nominal K-factors greater than 5.6 and that are equipped with a ½-in. (12.7-mm) National Pipe Thread (NPT), which are discussed in 8.3.5, are only intended for use on existing systems. Such a condition could exist when a system is being upgraded because the hazard in the building has changed. This approach allows an existing ½-in. (12.7-mm) line tee to be used to accommodate the retrofit of sprinklers with K-factors of either 8.0 or 11.2.

8.4* Application of Sprinkler Types

Sprinklers shall be selected for use as indicated in this section and shall be positioned and spaced as described in Section 8.5.

 A.8.4 The selection of a sprinkler type will vary by occupancy. Where more than one type of sprinkler is used within a compartment, sprinklers with similar response characteristics should be used (i.e., standard or quick response). However, some hazards might benefit from designs that include the use of both standard and quick-response sprinklers. Examples include rack storage protected by standard-response ceiling sprinklers and quick-response in-rack sprinklers. Another case might include opening protection using closely spaced quick-response sprinklers with standard-response sprinklers in the adjoining areas. Other designs can be compromised when sprinklers of differing sensitivity are mixed. An example is a system utilizing ESFR sprinklers adjacent to a system using high-temperature standard-response sprinklers as might be found in a warehouse. In this case, a fire occurring near the boundary might open ESFR sprinklers, which would not be contemplated in the standard-response system design.

Section 8.4 covers the application of sprinkler types. Today, there are many sprinklers from which to choose when designing a system. Chapter 8 covers many of the different types of sprinklers that are currently on the market. Criteria have been established to provide a degree of order over the types of sprinklers that can be developed and listed in the future. NFPA 13 categorizes sprinklers into several types. These categories include upright and pendent spray, sidewall spray, extended coverage, open, residential, early suppression fast-response, large drop, in-rack, and special sprinklers. Section 8.4 provides general information on where to use each type of sprinkler and outlines any restrictions in occupancy and construction that apply to each type of sprinkler.

Upright and pendent spray sprinklers are the most common sprinkler type and can be used in all occupancies and construction types. Other types of sprinklers have more specific limitations associated with them. For example, extended coverage and sidewall sprinklers can only be installed under smooth, flat ceilings. Another example is that sidewall spray sprinklers are limited to light hazard occupancies unless specifically listed for ordinary hazard occupancies. One of the most common design errors is the assumption that a sprinkler can be used in all building construction types for the protection of all occupancy hazard types.

◄ FAQ
Can all types of sprinklers be utilized to protect all occupancy hazards in all types of construction?

8.4.1 Standard Upright and Pendent Spray Sprinklers.

8.4.1.1 Upright and pendent spray sprinklers shall be permitted in all occupancy hazard classifications and building construction types.

8.4.1.2 Quick-response sprinklers shall not be permitted for use in extra hazard occupancies under the density-area design method.

Quick-response sprinklers cited in 8.4.1.2 operate faster and react to smaller fires than standard response sprinklers. This faster response often results in improved sprinkler system performance where all other factors remain constant.

Within extra hazard occupancies, fast-developing fires with large heat release rates can open a large number of quick-response sprinklers before the sprinklers have time to control the fire. The operation of a large number of sprinklers in a relatively short time period has the potential to overtax the system. For this reason, quick-response sprinklers using the area design method of Chapter 11 are not allowed for the protection of extra hazard occupancies.

◄ FAQ
Why are quick-response sprinklers prohibited from protecting extra hazard occupancies?

8.4.2 Sidewall Spray Sprinklers. Sidewall sprinklers shall only be installed as follows:

(1) Light hazard occupancies with smooth, horizontal or sloped, flat ceilings
(2) Ordinary hazard occupancies with smooth, flat ceilings where specifically listed for such use
(3) To protect areas below overhead doors

The discharge characteristics of sidewall sprinklers are not as effective as those of upright and pendent sprinklers for all applications. Accordingly, sidewall sprinklers are limited to light hazard occupancies unless the sprinkler is specifically listed for use in ordinary hazard occupancies. Several horizontal sidewall sprinklers are now listed for use in ordinary hazard occupancies.

In addition to being limited by the occupancy hazard classification, sidewall sprinklers are also limited to the ceiling configurations listed in 8.4.2.

Sidewall sprinklers are often used in retrofit situations where access to ceilings can be limited. System piping can be installed along the intersection of a wall and ceiling and covered with a built-up soffit with the sidewall sprinkler protruding through the soffit.

8.4.3 Extended Coverage Sprinklers. Extended coverage sprinklers shall only be installed as follows:

(1) Unobstructed construction consisting of flat, smooth ceilings with a slope not exceeding a pitch of one in six (a rise of two units in a run of 12 units, a roof slope of 16.7 percent)
(2) Unobstructed or noncombustible obstructed construction, where specifically listed for such use
(3) Within trusses or bar joists having web members not greater than 1 in. (25.4 mm) maximum dimension or where trusses are spaced greater than 7½ ft (2.3 m) on center and where the ceiling slope does not exceed a pitch of one in six (a rise of two units in a run of 12 units, a roof slope of 16.7 percent)
(4) Under smooth, flat ceilings that have slopes not exceeding a pitch of one in three (a rise of four units in a run of 12 units, a roof slope of 33.3 percent), where specifically listed for such use

Extended coverage (EC) sprinklers, which are covered in 8.4.3, are specifically listed as such. EC sprinklers cover an area that is larger than the area permitted for other types of sprinklers, such as standard spray and sidewall sprinklers. The extended coverage allows fewer sprinklers to be used. However, certain limitations are associated with the use of EC sprinklers.

FAQ ▶
Why are there additional limitations on extended coverage sprinklers?

The discharge from an EC sprinkler generally has a longer, flatter throw than a standard coverage sprinkler such as the standard spray upright. This flatter discharge pattern is affected by obstructions and the pitch of a ceiling more than other types of sprinklers. NFPA 13 limits the use of EC sprinklers to smooth, flat ceilings with relatively small slopes unless specific testing demonstrates their acceptability under greater slopes. Obstructions within bar joists and trusses are also limited to ensure proper distribution throughout the sprinkler's entire protection area.

8.4.4 Open Sprinklers.

8.4.4.1 Open sprinklers shall be permitted to be used in deluge systems to protect special hazards or exposures or in other special locations.

8.4.4.2 Open sprinklers shall be installed in accordance with all applicable requirements of this standard for their automatic counterpart.

Open sprinklers, which are covered in 8.4.4.1 and 8.4.4.2, are spray sprinklers with their operating elements removed. For information on open window or cornice sprinklers designed for outside exposure fire protection usage, see Chapters 11 and 14. Open sprinklers are also used in deluge systems, as discussed in Chapter 6. On a larger scale, NFPA 409, *Standard on Aircraft Hangars,* requires foam-water deluge systems, which utilize open sprinklers, as the predominant means of fire protection.

8.4.5 Residential Sprinklers.

FAQ ▶
Is the intent of 8.4.5 to allow residential sprinklers to be installed in corridors adjoining dwelling units, including corridors serving elevator lobbies and other spaces incidental to but serving the dwelling unit areas?

Residential sprinklers, which are covered in 8.4.5, are tested and listed in accordance with UL 1626, *Residential Sprinklers for Fire Protection Service* (see Exhibit 3.25). Because residential sprinklers are tested and listed using a residential fire scenario, they are permitted only in residential portions of all occupancies. In other portions of such occupancies, sprinklers must be listed for general usage and must be installed in accordance with the requirements of NFPA 13. Subsection 8.4.5 allows the use of residential sprinklers in corridors adjoining dwelling units and serving the incidental service areas for the dwelling units.

Beyond the use of residential sprinklers in NFPA 13, NFPA 13D, *Standard for the Installation of Sprinkler Systems in One- and Two-Family Dwellings and Manufactured Homes,* covers sprinkler system design in one- and two-family dwellings and manufactured homes and NFPA 13R, *Standard for the Installation of Sprinkler Systems in Residential Occupancies up to and Including Four Stories in Height,* covers sprinkler system design in certain low-rise residential facilities. For further discussion on the application, scope, and requirements of NFPA 13D and NFPA 13R, see the commentary for each document contained in Parts Two and Three of this handbook.

8.4.5.1* Residential sprinklers shall be permitted in dwelling units and their adjoining corridors provided they are installed in conformance with their listing.

In addition to the general sprinkler obstruction rules for residential sprinklers in this chapter, some residential sprinklers have specific obstruction requirements as part of the listing (see 8.4.5.1). These rules must also be followed.

A.8.4.5.1 The response and water distribution pattern of listed residential sprinklers have been shown by extensive fire testing to provide better control than spray sprinklers in residential occupancies. These sprinklers are intended to prevent flashover in the room of fire origin, thus improving the chance for occupants to escape or be evacuated.

The protection area for residential sprinklers is defined in the listing of the sprinkler as a maximum square or rectangular area. Listing information is presented in even 2-ft (0.65-m) increments from 12 ft to 20 ft (3.9 m to 6.5 m). When a sprinkler is selected for an application, its area of coverage must be equal to or greater than both the length and width of the hazard area. For example, if the hazard to be protected is a room 13 ft 6 in. (4.4 m) wide and 17 ft 6 in. (5.6 m) long, a sprinkler that is listed to protect a rectangular area of 14 ft × 18 ft (4.5 m × 5.8 m) or a square area of 18 ft × 18 ft (5.8 m × 5.8 m) must be selected. The flow used in the calculations is then selected as the flow required by the listing for the selected coverage.

The sprinkler listing is the source for positioning requirements when installing residential sprinklers (see A.8.4.5.1). The term positioning includes spacing of the sprinklers and placement of the sprinklers' deflectors in relation to the ceiling. Positioning does not include the location of the sprinklers. Location refers to the spaces where sprinklers must be installed, such as in a bedroom, in a hallway, in kitchens, or in concealed spaces. Location of residential sprinklers is strictly within the jurisdiction of NFPA 13.

Where corridors serve dwelling unit areas and other adjoining spaces, residential sprinklers would not be permitted within the corridor.

◀ **FAQ**
Is it the intent of 8.4.5 to allow residential sprinklers to be installed in corridors adjoining dwelling units that serve adjoining spaces other than dwelling units and their incidental service areas?

8.4.5.2 Residential sprinklers shall be used only in wet systems unless specifically listed for use in dry systems or preaction systems.

Paragraph 8.4.5.2 requires that residential sprinklers be used in wet pipe systems only. The performance of a residential sprinkler, which is primarily intended to be a life safety device, depends on the prompt operation provided by the combination of a fast-response operating element and the location and spacing restrictions placed on these sprinklers. In wet pipe systems, the piping is filled with water under pressure so water is applied with minimal delay. Dry pipe systems are associated with a delay in water delivery time. Because a larger fire is anticipated due to such a delay, residential sprinklers may not perform as intended if installed on a dry pipe system.

At this time, no listed residential sprinklers are acceptable for use in dry pipe or preaction sprinkler systems.

◀ **FAQ**
Are there any residential sprinklers listed for dry pipe or preaction sprinkler systems?

8.4.5.3 Where residential sprinklers are installed in a compartment as defined in 3.3.6, all sprinklers within the compartment shall be of the fast-response type that meets the criteria of 3.6.1(a)(1).

Sprinklers installed in a compartment are discussed in 8.4.5.3. When mixing sprinklers that are not of the same make, caution is needed to avoid the possibility of reverse operating order or spot operation of sprinklers. It is important that all residential sprinklers be of similar thermal sensitivity when they are installed in a compartment. The use of bulb-type and solder-type sprinklers or residential and other types of sprinklers is acceptable as long as all of the sprinklers in the compartment are fast response as defined in 3.6.1(a)(1).

8.4.6 Early Suppression Fast-Response (ESFR) Sprinklers.

8.4.6.1 ESFR sprinklers shall be used only in wet pipe systems unless specifically listed for use in dry systems where specifically listed for such service.

ESFR sprinklers, which are addressed in 8.4.6.1, use fast-response operating elements and are designed to respond very quickly to a fire. The design criteria specified in Chapter 12 are based on the assumption that a fire will not exceed a certain size when the sprinkler operates. Because fires in the spaces typically protected with ESFR sprinklers can grow extremely fast with large increases in heat release rates over a short period of time, the quickness with which water is applied is critical. Delayed application of water causes the fire to continue to grow, reaching a size at which the sprinkler system may no longer be able to suppress the fire. Once the fire has exceeded a critical size, many more sprinklers can be expected to operate and overtax the water supply.

FAQ ▶
Why are ESFR sprinklers only permitted in wet pipe systerms?

Calculations have shown that the time delays inherent in delivering water to sprinklers in both dry pipe and preaction systems cause many more ESFR sprinklers to operate than are contemplated by NFPA 13. Therefore, ESFR sprinklers are not allowed in dry pipe systems and will not be allowed until they are specifically tested and listed for such application.

8.4.6.2 ESFR sprinklers shall be installed only in buildings where roof or ceiling slope above the sprinklers does not exceed a pitch of two in 12 (a rise of two units in a run of 12 units, a roof slope of 16.7 percent).

Roof slope requirements, which are stated in 8.4.6.2, consider the effect of slope on sprinkler operating patterns. Sloped roofs tend to cause a skewed distribution of heat from a fire burning beneath the roof. With steep roof slopes, heat is likely to travel up the slope away from the sprinklers closest to the fire. This heat travel pattern delays operation of sprinklers near the fire and activates those sprinklers further from the fire, thus preventing early fire suppression.

 8.4.6.3* ESFR sprinklers shall be permitted for use in buildings with unobstructed or obstructed construction. Where depths of the solid structural members (beams, stem, etc.) exceed 12 in., ESFR sprinklers shall be installed in each channel formed by the solid structural members. Minimum sprinkler spacing and area of coverage shall comply with the requirements of 8.12.2 and 8.12.3.

 A.8.4.6.3 Storage in single-story or multistory buildings can be permitted, provided the maximum ceiling/roof height as specified in Table 8.12.2.2.1 is satisfied for each storage area.

Some types of obstructed construction, which are discussed in 8.4.6.3, can form long narrow pockets that can channel the heat away from sprinklers. ESFR sprinklers are designed to operate quickly and the channeling of heat would delay the operation of an ESFR sprinkler, if a sprinkler was not located in every channel, allowing the fire to grow larger than anticipated before the sprinkler operates. Sprinklers are required in each channel and must be located so that the minimum spacing requirements of 8.12.2 and 8.12.3 are maintained.

8.4.6.4 Draft Curtains.

8.4.6.4.1 Where ESFR sprinkler systems are installed adjacent to sprinkler systems with standard response sprinklers, a draft curtain of noncombustible construction and at least 2 ft (0.6 m) in depth shall be required to separate the two areas.

8.4.6.4.2 A clear aisle of at least 4 ft (1.2 m) centered below the draft curtain shall be maintained for separation.

Draft curtains are covered in 8.4.6.4.1 and 8.4.6.4.2. Where an ESFR sprinkler system is located adjacent to a standard response sprinkler system without any separation, it is possible for ESFR sprinklers to operate before the standard response sprinklers when the fire originates below the system using standard response sprinklers. The best way to prevent this situation is to separate the two systems by a wall. NFPA 13 recognizes that this type of separation is not always possible. In these cases, a draft curtain and an aisle can be used to separate the two systems. An aisle is needed to eliminate the potential for a fire to start under or near the draft curtain, operating sprinklers on both sides.

◄ FAQ
Why are draft curtains and clear aisles required where an ESFR system is adjacent to standard response sprinklers?

8.4.6.5 Temperature Ratings. Sprinkler temperature ratings for ESFR sprinklers shall be ordinary unless 8.3.2 requires intermediate- or high-temperature ratings.

8.4.7 Large Drop Sprinklers.

8.4.7.1 Large drop sprinklers shall be permitted to be used in wet, dry, or preaction systems.

The fires that have been used in testing large drop sprinklers, which are discussed in 8.4.7.1, (power law fires or t^2 fires) grow in an exponential manner. Therefore, a substantial escalation in heat release rates and thermal velocities would be expected in relatively short time periods. Testing large drop sprinklers installed on dry pipe and preaction systems has shown that fire control can be achieved if modifications to the number of design sprinklers and the minimum operating pressures are considered. Chapter 12 requirements for large drop applications reflect the design changes necessary when using large drop sprinklers on a dry pipe system. All of the supplemental provisions placed on preaction and dry pipe systems in Chapter 7 remain applicable when large drop sprinklers are used on these types of systems.

8.4.7.2* Galvanized Pipe.

A.8.4.7.2 The purpose of this requirement is to avoid scale accumulation.

8.4.7.2.1 Where steel pipe is used in preaction and dry pipe systems, piping materials shall be limited to internally galvanized steel.

8.4.7.2.2 Nongalvanized fittings shall be permitted.

Nongalvanized fittings are permitted by 8.4.7.2.2. The use of internally galvanized steel piping materials applies only where large drop sprinklers are used. Dry pipe systems using other types of sprinklers are not limited to a particular piping material but must comply with the requirements of Sections 6.3 and 6.4.

◄ FAQ
Does NFPA 13 require the use of internally galvanized steel pipe for all dry pipe and preaction sprinkler systems?

8.4.7.3 Temperature Ratings.
8.4.7.3.1 Unless the requirements of 8.4.7.3.2, 8.4.7.3.3, or 8.4.7.3.4 are met, sprinkler temperature ratings shall be the same as those indicated in Table 8.3.2.5(a) and Table 8.3.2.5(b) or those used in large-scale fire testing to determine the protection requirements for the hazard involved.

8.4.7.3.2 Sprinklers of intermediate- and high-temperature ratings shall be installed in specific locations as required by 8.3.2.

8.4.7.3.3 In storage occupancies, ordinary, intermediate, or high temperature–rated sprinklers shall be used for wet pipe systems.

8.4.7.3.4 In storage occupancies, high temperature–rated sprinklers shall be used for dry pipe systems.

8.4.8 QRES. (Reserved)

Subsection 8.4.8 is reserved for the quick-response early suppression (QRES) sprinkler, which still might be developed. Like other sprinklers, QRES devices will require specific requirements for their placement and temperature ratings. If the development of the QRES program is pursued, provisions for these and other parameters are likely to be added to NFPA 13.

8.4.9 Special Sprinklers.

8.4.9.1* Special sprinklers that are intended for the protection of specific hazards or construction features shall be permitted where such devices have been evaluated and listed for performance under the following conditions:

(1) Fire tests related to the intended hazard
(2) Distribution of the spray pattern with respect to wetting of floors and walls
(3) Distribution of the spray pattern with respect to obstructions
(4) Evaluation of the thermal sensitivity of the sprinkler
(5) Performance under horizontal or sloped ceilings
(6) Area of design

A.8.4.9.1 Tests of standard sprinklers by approved laboratories have traditionally encompassed a fire test using a 350-lb (160-kg) wood crib and water distribution tests in which water is collected in pans from several arrangements of sprinklers to evaluate distribution under non-fire conditions.

Tests of special sprinklers are customized to evaluation responsiveness, distribution, and other unique characteristics of the sprinkler to control or suppress a fire. Depending on the intended use, these tests may include variables such as the following:

(1) The location of the fire relative to the sprinklers (i.e., below one sprinkler, between two or between four sprinklers)
(2) Fire conditions that encompass a variety of fire growth rates representative of anticipated conditions of use
(3) Tests where multiple sprinklers are expected to operate
(4) Adverse conditions of use (i.e., pipe shadows or other obstructions to discharge)
(5) Effect of a fire plume on water sprinkler discharge

The listing of new sprinkler technology for storage protection should include large scale fire testing using a commodity or commodities representative of those intended to be protected and should consider at least the following variables:

(1) Ignition under one, between two, and between four sprinklers
(2) Range of clearances between the sprinkler and the commodity
(3) Test(s) at or near the minimum pressures specified for the sprinkler

Special sprinklers, which are discussed in 8.4.9.1, are intended to protect specific hazards or construction features. Special sprinklers must be listed, and their performance must be evaluated. The evaluation criteria includes fire tests related to the specific hazard, spray pattern distribution with respect to both the wetting of walls and floors and to obstructions, thermal sensitivity of the operating element, and the performance of the sprinkler under horizontal or sloped ceilings. The testing results are used to ensure adequate performance and identify special design and installation criteria to be included as part of the listing.

8.4.9.2 Special sprinklers shall maintain the following characteristics:

(1) Orifice size shall be in accordance with 6.2.3.
(2) Temperature ratings shall be in accordance with Table 6.2.5.1.
(3) The protection area of coverage shall not exceed 400 ft^2 (36 m^2) for light hazard and ordinary hazard occupancies.
(4) The protection area of coverage shall not exceed 196 ft^2 (17 m^2) for extra hazard and high-piled storage occupancies.

While a good deal of latitude is given to special sprinklers, the orifice size and temperature rating must be in compliance with the provisions of Chapter 6, and the maximum area of coverage cannot exceed 400 ft² (36 m²) for light and ordinary hazard occupancies and 196 ft² (17 m²) for extra hazard occupancies and high-piled storage. These requirements, which are found in 8.4.9.2, apply because of concerns for interchangeability and overall system reliability.

◀ **FAQ**
Are there any limits placed on special sprinklers?

8.5 Position, Location, Spacing, and Use of Sprinklers

Proper positioning and spacing of sprinklers, which are covered in Section 8.5, are important to ensure that sprinklers operate promptly and that obstructions to sprinkler distribution patterns do not adversely affect the performance of the sprinkler.

8.5.1 General.

8.5.1.1 Sprinklers shall be located, spaced, and positioned in accordance with the requirements of Section 8.5.

8.5.1.2 Sprinklers shall be positioned to provide protection of the area consistent with the overall objectives of this standard by controlling the positioning and allowable area of coverage for each sprinkler.

8.5.1.3 The requirements of 8.5.2 through 8.5.7 shall apply to all sprinkler types unless modified by more restrictive rules in Sections 8.6 through 8.12.

The general requirements with which all sprinklers must comply are covered in Section 8.5. Section 8.5 addresses protection area per sprinkler, sprinkler spacing, deflector position, obstruction to discharge, and clearance to storage. This generic information provides limiting minimum or maximum dimensions and guidance on how to determine these measurements.

Sections 8.6 through 8.13 provide specific requirements for standard upright and pendent spray sprinklers, standard sidewall spray sprinklers, EC upright and pendent spray sprinklers, EC sidewall sprinklers, residential pendent and sidewall sprinklers, large drop sprinklers, ESFR sprinklers, and in-rack sprinklers.

8.5.2 Protection Areas per Sprinkler.

8.5.2.1 Determination of the Protection Area of Coverage.

8.5.2.1.1 The protection area of coverage per sprinkler (A_s) shall be determined as follows:

(1) Along branch lines as follows:
   (a) Determine distance between sprinklers (or to wall or obstruction in the case of the end sprinkler on the branch line) upstream and downstream.
   (b) Choose the larger of either twice the distance to the wall or the distance to the next sprinkler.
   (c) This dimension will be defined as S.

(2) Between branch lines as follows:
   (a) Determine perpendicular distance to the sprinkler on the adjacent branch line (or to a wall or obstruction in the case of the last branch line) on each side of the branch line on which the subject sprinkler is positioned.
   (b) Choose the larger of either twice the distance to the wall or obstruction or the distance to the next sprinkler.
   (c) This dimension will be defined as L.

8.5.2.1.2 The protection area of coverage of the sprinkler shall be established by multiplying the S dimension by the L dimension, as follows: $A_s = S \times L$

Exhibit 8.5 illustrates how to determine the S and L dimensions, which are discussed in 8.5.2.1.1 and 8.5.2.1.2, and Exhibit 8.6 provides a specific example. The maximum dimensions for S and L, which are the distance from a wall and the area of coverage per sprinkler, are specified for specific types of sprinklers. See Sections 8.6 through 8.12.

EXHIBIT 8.5 Determining the Area of Coverage for a Sprinkler.

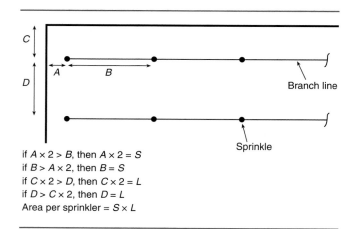

if $A \times 2 > B$, then $A \times 2 = S$
if $B > A \times 2$, then $B = S$
if $C \times 2 > D$, then $C \times 2 = L$
if $D > C \times 2$, then $D = L$
Area per sprinkler = $S \times L$

EXHIBIT 8.6 Example of How to Determine the Area of Coverage for a Specific Sprinkler.

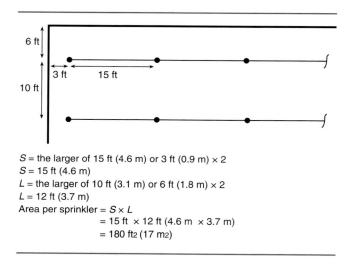

S = the larger of 15 ft (4.6 m) or 3 ft (0.9 m) $\times$ 2
S = 15 ft (4.6 m)
L = the larger of 10 ft (3.1 m) or 6 ft (1.8 m) $\times$ 2
L = 12 ft (3.7 m)
Area per sprinkler = $S \times L$
   = 15 ft $\times$ 12 ft (4.6 m $\times$ 3.7 m)
   = 180 ft2 (17 m2)

8.5.2.2 Maximum Protection Area of Coverage.

8.5.2.2.1 The maximum allowable protection area of coverage for a sprinkler (A_s) shall be in accordance with the value indicated in the section for each type or style of sprinkler.

8.5.2.2.2 The maximum area of coverage of any sprinkler shall not exceed 400 ft^2 (36 m^2).

The maximum allowable area of coverage for a specific sprinkler, which is discussed in 8.5.2.2.1 and 8.5.2.2.2, depends on the type of sprinkler being considered and the construction features and the occupancy hazard of the space in which the sprinkler is to be installed. The combustibility of the ceiling, the ceiling's effect on the flow of heat, and the ceiling's potential to obstruct the sprinkler's discharge pattern can affect overall sprinkler performance. Likewise, the actual distribution pattern—that is, the shape and throw—for a specific type of sprinkler also has an impact.

The maximum protection area of 400 ft² (36 m²) for any type of sprinkler limits the area that is permitted to be unprotected if the discharge from a single sprinkler is obstructed or if the sprinkler fails to operate. This maximum area of coverage is reduced for some sprinkler types as indicated in Sections 8.6 through 8.13.

◀ **FAQ**
Why has a limit of 400 ft² (36 m²) been established for any sprinkler?

8.5.3 Sprinkler Spacing.

8.5.3.1 Maximum Distance Between Sprinklers.

8.5.3.1.1 The maximum distance permitted between sprinklers shall be based on the center-line distance between sprinklers on the branch line or on adjacent branch lines.

8.5.3.1.2 The maximum distance shall be measured along the slope of the ceiling.

8.5.3.1.3 The maximum distance permitted between sprinklers shall comply with the value indicated in the applicable section for each type or style of sprinkler.

The spacing of sprinklers along branch lines depends on the maximum distance permitted between the sprinklers on branch lines and the maximum area of coverage permitted per sprinkler, as required in 8.5.3.1.1 through 8.5.3.1.3. To minimize the amount of piping used, branch lines are usually spaced as far apart as possible while maintaining even spacing within a ceiling bay or room. If the spacing of branch lines is uneven, the greatest distance between branch lines should be used to determine how far apart sprinklers can be spaced from each other along the branch lines.

The spacing of sprinklers is measured on the slope of the roof and the maximum distances and areas given in Sections 8.6 through 8.12 are applied to the distance measured along the slope. For curved surfaces, distance should be measured along the slope projected between the two sprinklers as indicated in Exhibit 8.7.

◀ **FAQ**
When defining the area of protection of a sprinkler installed under a sloped ceiling or roof, is the area of protection measured along the slope or the projected area on the floor?

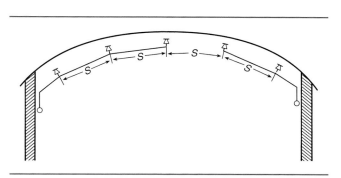

EXHIBIT 8.7 Sprinklers Installed Along a Curved Ceiling.

8.5.3.2 Maximum Distance from Walls.

8.5.3.2.1 The distance from sprinklers to walls shall not exceed one-half of the allowable maximum distance between sprinklers.

8.5.3.2.2 The distance from the wall to the sprinkler shall be measured perpendicular to the wall.

8.5.3.3 Minimum Distance from Walls.

8.5.3.3.1 The minimum distance permitted between a sprinkler and the wall shall comply with the value indicated in the applicable section for each type or style of sprinkler.

8.5.3.3.2 The distance from the wall to the sprinkler shall be measured perpendicular to the wall.

8.5.3.4 Minimum Distance Between Sprinklers.

8.5.3.4.1 A minimum distance shall be maintained between sprinklers to prevent operating sprinklers from wetting adjacent sprinklers and to prevent skipping of sprinklers.

8.5.3.4.2 The minimum distance permitted between sprinklers shall comply with the value indicated in the applicable section for each type or style of sprinkler.

8.5.4 Deflector Position.

8.5.4.1* Distance Below Ceilings. The distances between the sprinkler deflector and the ceiling above shall be selected based on the type of sprinkler and the type of construction.

Sprinkler distance below the ceiling is addressed in 8.5.4.1. In general, sprinklers should be located near the ceiling, because the ceiling is where heat from a fire typically collects. When the sprinkler is located further down from the ceiling, response time generally increases unless the sprinkler is located within the fire plume. Operation of sprinklers located very close to the ceiling can also be delayed if they are located in the dead-air space that develops under some ceilings. Obstructed construction requires that sprinklers be located further below the ceiling to allow the sprinkler discharge pattern to develop. This arrangement results in a slower sprinkler response time.

Ideally, for measurements affecting sprinkler sensitivity, the distance below the ceiling should be measured to the centerline of the thermal element rather than the deflector, because the relationship between the thermal element and the deflector varies with different sprinklers. In some cases, the centerline of the sprinkler's thermal element is not easily determined. Because the distance to the deflector is more readily attainable, NFPA 13 uses this method to measure the distance from the sprinkler to ceilings and obstructions. See Exhibit 8.8.

EXHIBIT 8.8 Sprinkler Deflector Location.

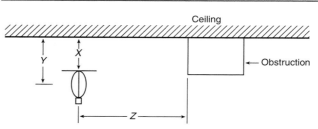

X = position of the deflector below the ceiling
Y = position of the center of the sprinkler link below the ceiling
Z = measurement from the near edge of the obstruction to the centerline of the sprinkler

A.8.5.4.1 Batt insulation creates an effective thermal barrier and can be considered the ceiling/roof deck when determining distances between deflector and ceiling. The insulation needs to be installed in each pocket (not just above the sprinkler) and attached to the ceiling/roof in such a manner that it will not fall out during a fire prior to sprinkler activation.

FAQ ▶
Can batt insulation be treated as a ceiling when determining sprinkler placement?

Paragraph A.8.5.4.1 identifies the conditions under which batt insulation can be treated as the ceiling for the purpose of determining sprinkler placement. The ceiling provides a means of heat collection to aid in the sprinkler's activation. The use of insulation as a thermal barrier is readily accepted by NFPA 13 as indicated by the requirements of 8.14.1.2 for the protection of concealed spaces. Therefore, heat from a fire starts to collect at the insulation rather than at the decking above the insulation. It is important to recognize that the thermal barrier is created by the insulation and not by the aluminum or other facing on the insulation.

8.5.4.2 Deflector Orientation. Deflectors of sprinklers shall be aligned parallel to ceilings, roofs, or the incline of stairs.

Deflector orientation is addressed in 8.5.4.2. Maintaining the deflector parallel to the ceiling results in minimum obstructions to discharge (it prevents the discharge from hitting a sloped ceiling) and a more effective discharge pattern.

8.5.5 Obstructions to Sprinkler Discharge.

Obstructions to sprinkler discharge are discussed in 8.5.5. In the 1991 edition, the sprinkler obstruction requirements were rewritten so that they no longer referred to specific construction features such as beams and bar joist webs. However, the revised method of categorizing obstructions as either horizontal or vertical was confusing.

For the 1996 edition, a new approach was introduced for dealing with obstructions to sprinkler discharge. Performance objectives were added, and the positioning rules were revised to specifically achieve these objectives. Subsection 8.5.5 provides general requirements, while Sections 8.6 through 8.13 provide requirements for specific types of sprinklers.

NFPA 13 addresses three general areas of concern with regard to obstructions. The first is the overall objective addressed by 8.5.5.1, which is to ensure that a sufficient amount of water from the sprinkler reaches the hazard.

This concern is largely addressed by using the 1991 edition's requirements for horizontal obstructions, which dealt largely with continuous obstructions such as beams, top chord members, and ducts that are tight to or very near the ceiling and in close proximity to the sprinkler.

The second concern, addressed by 8.5.5.2, deals with the obstruction to sprinkler discharge pattern development. This subsection addresses continuous and noncontinuous obstructions such as piping, light fixtures, truss webs, or building columns located within the first 18 in. (457 mm) of the sprinkler deflector. See Figure A.8.5.5.1. Obstructions located in this zone prevent the proper sprinkler discharge pattern from developing. As a result, sprinklers must be positioned so that they are located a certain distance away from the obstruction. The correct position is addressed within the section for each type of sprinkler. This requirement does not apply to continuous obstructions that are tight to the ceiling. Even though obstructions more than 18 in. (457 mm) below the sprinklers can prevent the proper discharge pattern from developing, the overall objective discussed in 8.5.5.1 provides for adequate sprinkler placement.

The third area of concern (see 8.5.5.3) deals with obstructions that prevent the sprinkler discharge from reaching the hazard. These obstructions typically consist of continuous and noncontinuous obstructions that interrupt the water spray pattern once it is below the 18-in. (457-mm) discharge pattern development zone. These types of obstructions can include overhead doors, ducts, or decks. When these obstructions exceed a certain dimension, sprinklers must be beneath them.

Another category of obstruction that is applicable to certain types of sprinklers includes those obstructions that are suspended from the ceiling, such as privacy curtains in a hospital, or floor-mounted obstructions that do not reach the ceiling, such as partitions in an office cubicle. In both cases, the sprinklers must be positioned so that a sufficient portion of the discharge pattern can extend over the obstruction.

While the first three objectives apply to all sprinklers, certain modifications are made to the objectives and positioning rules for specific types of sprinklers. See 8.6.5, 8.7.5, 8.8.5, 8.9.5, 8.10.5, 8.11.5, and 8.12.5.

8.5.5.1* Performance Objective. Sprinklers shall be located so as to minimize obstructions to discharge as defined in 8.5.5.2 and 8.5.5.3, or additional sprinklers shall be provided to ensure adequate coverage of the hazard. *(See Figure A.8.5.5.1.)*

A.8.5.5.1 See Figure A.8.5.5.1.   **A**

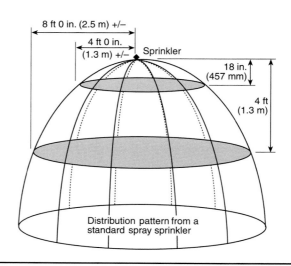

FIGURE A.8.5.5.1 *Obstructions to Sprinkler Discharge Pattern Development for Standard Upright or Pendent Spray Sprinklers.*

Locating sprinklers so as to minimize the impact of obstructions to the sprinkler discharge, as discussed in 8.5.5.1, is the preferred approach. The use of additional sprinklers to compensate for obstructions increases the water demand and the cost of the sprinkler system and may not provide the same level of protection that would be afforded if the effects of obstructions were minimized.

8.5.5.2* Obstructions to Sprinkler Discharge Pattern Development.

 A.8.5.5.2 Where of a depth that will obstruct the spray discharge pattern, girders, beams, or trusses forming narrow pockets of combustible construction along walls can require additional sprinklers.

FAQ ▶
What happened to the obstruction terms of *horizontal* and *vertical*?

Obstructions that affect sprinkler discharge pattern development, which are discussed in 8.5.5.2, are located within the sprinkler discharge pattern as shown in Figure A.8.5.5.1. The obstructions can be continuous, such as large beams; girders; top and bottom truss chord members; soffits; long horizontal light fixtures; heating, ventilation, and air-conditioning (HVAC) ductwork; and similar items, or can be smaller noncontinuous obstructions, such as building columns, bar joist and truss webs, and certain light fixtures. The terms *horizontal* and *vertical,* which were used in prior editions, are no longer used to refer to these types of obstructions.

NFPA 13 requires a minimum distance to be maintained between the sprinkler and smaller noncontinuous obstructions. A sprinkler must be positioned so that the discharge pattern is below the solid continuous obstructions.

8.5.5.2.1 Continuous or noncontinuous obstructions less than or equal to 18 in. (457 mm) below the sprinkler deflector that prevent the pattern from fully developing shall comply with 8.5.5.2.

The discharge pattern for most sprinklers is fully developed at about a 4-ft (1.2-m) distance below the sprinkler (see Figure A.8.5.5.1). However, avoiding all obstructions in this space is not practical, which is the reason for the requirement in 8.5.5.2.1. Most of the pattern development occurs within a zone beginning at the sprinkler deflector and extending 18 in. to 36 in. (457 mm to 914 mm) below the sprinkler. The obstructions to sprinkler discharge pattern development are a concern within this zone. The minimum distance of 18 in. (457 mm) is modified in subsequent sections for ESFR and large drop sprinklers, which require a larger space for pattern development.

8.5.5.2.2 Sprinklers shall be positioned in accordance with the minimum distances and special requirements of Sections 8.6 through 8.12 so that they are located sufficiently away from obstructions such as truss webs and chords, pipes, columns, and fixtures.

8.5.5.3* Obstructions that Prevent Sprinkler Discharge from Reaching the Hazard. Continuous or noncontinuous obstructions that interrupt the water discharge in a horizontal plane more than 18 in. (457 mm) below the sprinkler deflector in a manner to limit the distribution from reaching the protected hazard shall comply with 8.5.5.3.

A.8.5.5.3 Frequently, additional sprinkler equipment can be avoided by reducing the width of decks or galleries and providing proper clearances. Slatting of decks or walkways or the use of open grating as a substitute for automatic sprinklers thereunder is not acceptable. The use of cloth or paper dust tops for rooms forms obstruction to water distribution. If dust tops are used, the area below should be sprinklered.

Obstructions that prevent sprinkler discharge from reaching the hazard are discussed in 8.5.5.3. Once the sprinkler discharge pattern is developed, obstructions in the horizontal plane can prevent the sprinkler discharge from reaching the protected hazard. In some situations, the obstruction cannot be avoided, and additional sprinklers are necessary to compensate for areas under the obstruction that would not receive adequate coverage.

8.5.5.3.1 Sprinklers shall be installed under fixed obstructions over 4 ft (1.2 m) wide such as ducts, decks, open grate flooring, cutting tables, and overhead doors.

8.5.5.3.2 Sprinklers shall not be required under obstructions that are not fixed in place such as conference tables.

The size at which obstructions become too large to ignore is typically 4 ft (1.2 m). This width is reduced in Sections 8.11 and 8.12 for large drop and ESFR sprinklers. Paragraph 8.5.5.3.2 recognizes that some obstructions larger than 4 ft (1.2 m), such as the example of a conference table, are often moved and are not likely to have any significant combustibles located beneath them. In these cases, additional sprinklers do not need to be placed below the obstruction.

It also important to stress that overhead doors are considered obstructions (see 8.5.5.3.1). Although the overhead door is not considered an obstruction when in the closed position as indicated in Exhibit 8.9, the discharge from the sprinkler over the door will be obstructed when the door is in the open position. Sprinklers need to be positioned so that their discharge can adequately reach under the overhead door. The 1999 edition was revised to specifically allow the use of sidewall sprinklers for these applications. See 8.4.2(3).

◀ **FAQ**
Does NFPA 13 consider overhead doors obstructions?

8.5.5.3.3 Sprinklers installed under open gratings shall be of the intermediate level/rack storage type or otherwise shielded from the discharge of overhead sprinklers.

Sprinklers installed under open gratings are addressed in 8.5.5.3.3. Although open grating allows heat from a fire to pass through it and reach a sprinkler, the openings are not adequate to compensate for obstructions to the sprinkler spray pattern. Thus, supplemental sprinklers under the open grating deck become necessary. Gratings or slatted decks and walkways are frequently covered with goods in storage or by a light surface dust stop. Sprinklers are required under such gratings and walkways. Sprinklers located below the open grating must be provided with a water shield or be of the in-rack type to prevent water from operating sprinklers above from wetting the thermal element and delaying sprinkler operation.

◀ **FAQ**
Where open grating is utilized are additional sprinklers required below the open grating?

8.5.6* Clearance to Storage.

A.8.5.6 The fire protection system design should consider the maximum storage height. For new sprinkler installations, maximum storage height is the usable height at which commodities can be stored above the floor while the minimum required unobstructed space below sprinklers is maintained. Where evaluating existing situations, maximum storage height is the

EXHIBIT 8.9 Overhead Door Obstructs Sprinkler Discharge When in the Open Position.

maximum existing storage height if space between the sprinklers and storage is equal to or greater than that required.

Building heights where baled cotton is stored should allow for proper clearance between the pile height and sprinkler deflectors. Fire tests of high-piled storage have shown that sprinklers are generally more effective if located 1½ ft to 4½ ft (0.45 m to 1.4 m) above the storage height.

8.5.6.1 Unless the requirements of 8.5.6.2, 8.5.6.3, 8.5.6.4, or 8.5.6.5 are met, the clearance between the deflector and the top of storage shall be 18 in. (457 mm) or greater.

An 18-in. (457-mm) minimum clearance between a sprinkler deflector and the top of storage is the base requirement of 8.5.6.1 and provides for discharge pattern development and standardization between sprinklers. Paragraphs 8.5.6.2, 8.5.6.3, and 8.5.6.5 identify the conditions where a larger minimum clearance are required. In addition, a lesser clearance is not permitted as a base requirement for a sprinkler, but 8.5.6.4 allows clearances of less than 18 in. (457 mm) in specific situations when large-scale tests indicate that acceptable performance can be maintained at the reduced clearance. It is permissible to have more than the minimum clearance between the sprinklers and the top of storage; however high clearances can also affect sprinkler performance and may impact the design requirements.

8.5.6.2 Where other standards specify greater clearance to storage minimums, they shall be followed.

8.5.6.3 A minimum clearance to storage of 36 in. (0.91 m) shall be permitted for special sprinklers.

8.5.6.4 A minimum clearance to storage of less than 18 in. (457 mm) between the top of storage and ceiling sprinkler deflectors shall be permitted where proven by successful large-scale fire tests for the particular hazard.

8.5.6.5 The clearance from the top of storage to sprinkler deflectors shall be not less than 3 ft (0.9 m) where rubber tires are stored.

 8.5.7 Skylights. Sprinklers shall be permitted to be omitted from skylights and similar ceiling pockets not exceeding 32 ft² (3 m²) in area, regardless of hazard classification, that are separated by at least 10 ft (3 m) horizontally from any other skylight or unprotected ceiling pocket.

Skylights are discussed in 8.5.7. In past years the standard was silent on the omission of sprinklers from skylights and similar pockets; however past formal interpretations indicated that sprinkler protection was not required for 4 ft × 8 ft (1.2 m × 2.4 m) skylights. But these formal interpretations did not establish a permitted or acceptable depth of the skylight. There has always been a concern that unless a sprinkler was placed in deep skylights or similar pockets, heat would collect in the skylights and delay the operation of sprinklers.

Subsection 8.5.7 was added to allow the omission of sprinklers from skylights that do not exceed 32 ft^2 (3 m^2) in area and are separated from any adjacent unprotected ceiling pocket or skylight. A single small skylight should not have a significant impact on performance, and the requirement for 10 ft (3 m) separation between unprotected ceiling pockets and skylights insures that there will be a sprinkler in between skylights and prevent heat from collection in multiple adjacent skylights or pockets where sprinkler activation could be delayed (see Exhibit 8.10).

◄ FAQ
Do all skylights require sprinklers to be installed within the skylight?

EXHIBIT 8.10 *Separation Between Skylights.*

8.6 Standard Pendent and Upright Spray Sprinklers

8.6.1 General. All requirements of Section 8.5 shall apply to standard pendent and upright spray sprinklers except as modified in Section 8.6.

8.6.2 Protection Areas per Sprinkler (Standard Pendent and Upright Spray Sprinklers).

8.6.2.1 Determination of the Protection Area of Coverage.

8.6.2.1.1 Except as permitted by 8.6.2.1.2, the protection area of coverage per sprinkler (A_s) shall be determined in accordance with 8.5.2.1.

8.6.2.1.2 The requirements of 8.6.2.1.1 shall not apply in a small room as defined in 3.3.20; the protection area of coverage for each sprinkler in the small room shall be the area of the room divided by the number of sprinklers in the room.

Small rooms are discussed in 8.6.2.1.2. Note that the definition of small room (see 3.3.20) applies only to light hazard occupancies and also limits the type of ceiling construction and wall openings in addition to the 800 ft^2 (74.3 m^2) area limitation.

◄ FAQ
Can the requirements of 8.6.2.1.2 be applied in all occupancies?

8.6.2.2 Maximum Protection Area of Coverage.

8.6.2.2.1* The maximum allowable protection area of coverage for a sprinkler (A_s) shall be in accordance with the value indicated in Table 8.6.2.2.1(a) through Table 8.6.2.2.1(d).

FAQ ▶
Why are there additional requirements for sloped combustible ceilings in attic spaces?

Testing has shown that for sloped combustible ceilings in attic spaces of combustible joist or truss construction with slopes exceeding 4 in 12 that the fire tends to spread up the slope rapidly and involve the roof before sprinklers at the standard spacing allowed under flat roofs can control the fire. The ceiling fire then spreads above the sprinklers, eventually burning a hole in the roof. To improve sprinkler performance, two options are provided by Table 8.6.2.2.1(a): reduce the spacing of the sprinklers in the direction perpendicular to the slope, or increase the operating pressure of the sprinkler from 7 psi to 20 psi. The first option brings the sprinklers closer to the fire while utilizing the design pressure of 7 psi, and the second option improves the distribution and effectiveness of the sprinkler discharge pattern while utilizing the design pressure of 20 psi. For additional commentary on the protection of sloped combustible construction, see commentary on 8.6.4.1.4

 A.8.6.2.2.1 When the spacing between sprinklers perpendicular to the slope exceeds 8 ft, it is necessary to increase the minimum density or sprinkler operating pressure as noted in Table 8.6.2.2.1(a) and in 8.6.4.1.4. Time to sprinkler activation and water distribution can be affected within combustible concealed spaces with sloped roofs or ceilings in these combustible concealed spaces especially where wood joist rafters or wood truss construction is used. To reduce the probability of fires in these combustible concealed spaces involving the combustible roof or ceiling construction above standard spray sprinklers, more stringent spacing and installation guidelines apply.

8.6.2.2.2 In any case, the maximum area of coverage of a sprinkler shall not exceed 225 ft^2 (21 m^2).

Maximum protection area of coverage is covered in 8.6.2.2.1 and 8.6.2.2.2. In previous editions of NFPA 13, the protection area per sprinkler was a function of occupancy hazard classification and specific ceiling construction type. This arrangement created difficulties when a

TABLE 8.6.2.2.1(a) *Protection Areas and Maximum Spacing (Standard Spray Upright/Standard Spray Pendent) for Light Hazard*

Construction Type	System Type	Protection Area		Spacing (maximum)	
		ft^2	m^2	ft	m
Noncombustible obstructed and unobstructed and combustible unobstructed with members 3 ft or more on center	Pipe schedule	200	18.6	15	4.6
Noncombustible obstructed and unobstructed and combustible unobstructed with members 3 ft or more on center	Hydraulically calculated	225	20.9	15	4.6
Combustible obstructed with members 3 ft or more on center	All	168	15.6	15	4.6
Combustible obstructed or unobstructed with members less than 3 ft on center	All	130	12.1	15	4.6
Unoccupied attics having combustible wood joist or wood truss construction with members less than 3 ft on center with slopes having a pitch of 4 in 12 or greater	All	120	11.1	8* × 15 (minimum psi) 10* × 12 (minimum 20 psi)	2.4* × 4.6 (minimum 0.48 bar) 3* × 3.7 (minimum 1.34 bar)

*The smaller dimension shall be measured perpendicular to the slope.

TABLE 8.6.2.2.1(b) *Protection Areas and Maximum Spacing (Standard Spray Upright/ Standard Spray Pendent) for Ordinary Hazard*

Construction Type	System Type	Protection Area		Spacing (maximum)	
		ft²	m²	ft	m
All	All	130	12.1	15	4.6

TABLE 8.6.2.2.1(c) *Protection Areas and Maximum Spacing (Standard Spray Upright/ Standard Spray Pendent) for Extra Hazard*

Construction Type	System Type	Protection Area		Spacing (maximum)	
		ft²	m²	ft	m
All	Pipe schedule	90	8.4	12 [In buildings with storage bays 25 ft (7.6 m) wide, 12 ft 6 in. (3.8 m) shall be permitted]	3.7
All	Hydraulically calculated with density ≥0.25	100	9.3	12 [In buildings with storage bays 25 ft (7.6 m) wide, 12 ft 6 in. (3.8 m) shall be permitted]	3.7
All	Hydraulically calculated with density <0.25	130	12.1	15	4.6

TABLE 8.6.2.2.1(d) *Protection Areas and Maximum Spacing (Standard Spray Upright/ Standard Spray Pendent) for High-Piled Storage*

Construction Type	System Type	Protection Area		Spacing (maximum)	
		ft²	m²	ft	m
All	Hydraulically calculated with density ≥0.25	100	9.3	12 [In buildings with storage bays 25 ft (7.6 m) wide, 12 ft 6 in. (3.8 m) shall be permitted]	3.7
All	Hydraulically calculated with density <0.25	130	12.1	15	4.6

type of ceiling construction was not specifically discussed in the standard. Additionally, no guidance was provided for certain combinations of construction type and occupancy hazard. The construction classification approach currently employed—that is, obstructed and unobstructed—minimizes that difficulty by dealing with only with those constructions features that can affect sprinkler performance.

For light hazard occupancies, NFPA 13 recognizes that more efficient and effective designs can result from the application of hydraulic calculation techniques. Therefore, for unobstructed construction, an increase in protection area to 225 ft² (21 m²) per sprinkler is allowed.

FAQ ▶

Why is the maximum protection area reduced to 130 ft² for combustible construction with members less than 3 ft on center?

NFPA 13 also recognizes that combustible construction can increase the associated fire hazards. Many types of combustible obstructed construction, including wood joist, pre-engineered wood I-beams, and lightweight wood construction, such as trusses, can have certain characteristics such as numerous small pockets, a tendency to obstruct heat flow, a greater likelihood for obstructing sprinkler discharge, and increased susceptibility to fire damage. The protection area per sprinkler is reduced to 130 ft² (12.1 m²) where the distance between structural members is less than 3 ft (0.91 m) apart for these particular types of combustible ceiling construction. Effective sprinkler protection for the areas under these types of combustible ceiling construction is difficult, but not impossible, to provide.

The placement of sprinklers under combustible obstructed construction requires more attention, because obstructed construction by its very nature increases the possibility of sprinkler discharge pattern disruption, and the combustible materials can increase the overall fire hazard. If a fire is obstructed from sprinkler discharge and cannot be quickly controlled, the ceiling construction might become part of the fuel package. Once the combustible construction above the sprinkler is involved in the fire, controlling or suppressing the fire with sprinklers is very difficult, if not impossible.

Extra hazard occupancies contain large fuel loads that have the potential for developing into fires with very fast and high rates of heat release. Decreasing allowable areas of coverage to 90 ft² (8.4 m²) for pipe schedule systems and 100 ft² (9.3 m²) for hydraulically designed systems is intended to compensate for the larger, faster developing fires that are typical of extra hazard occupancies. For hydraulically designed systems below densities of 0.25 gpm/ft² (10.2 mm/min), areas of coverage per sprinkler are permitted to be extended to 130 ft² (12.1 m²).

For high-piled storage, tests conducted on various commodities can indicate that smaller protection areas per sprinkler are required. Any such criteria identified as part of the design criteria outlined in Chapter 12 of this standard or other appropriate NFPA standards need to be followed.

Table 8.6.2.2.1(c) also recognizes that in buildings containing extra hazard occupancies or high-piled storage with 25-ft (7.6-m) wide ceiling bays, maximum sprinkler spacing of 12 ft 6 in. (3.8 m) can be employed without compromising the system design integrity. In addition, 15-ft (4.6-m) sprinkler spacing is still acceptable in extra hazard occupancies and high-piled storage for relatively low discharge densities of less than 0.25 gpm/ft² (10.2 mm/min).

8.6.3 Sprinkler Spacing (Standard Pendent and Upright Spray Sprinklers).

8.6.3.1 Maximum Distance Between Sprinklers. The maximum distance permitted between sprinklers shall comply with Table 8.6.2.2.1(a) through Table 8.6.2.2.1(d).

8.6.3.2 Maximum Distance from Walls.

8.6.3.2.1 The distance from sprinklers to walls shall not exceed one-half of the allowable distance between sprinklers as indicated in Table 8.6.2.2.1(a) through Table 8.6.2.2.1(d).

8.6.3.2.2 The distance from the wall to the sprinkler shall be measured perpendicular to the wall.

The examples illustrated in Exhibits 8.11 and 8.12 demonstrate the requirements for positioning a sprinkler from a wall, which are discussed in 8.6.3.2.1 and 8.6.3.2.2. If the distance from a branch line to a wall exceeds one-half of the distance between the branch lines, then twice the distance between the branch line closest to the wall and the wall should be used in verifying if the distance between sprinklers on branch lines is in accordance with NFPA 13. More specifically, if the distance from the branch line to the wall is 7 ft (2.1 m), and the distance between branch lines is 13 ft (4.0 m), then twice the distance from the branch line to the wall would be 14 ft (4.3 m). The 14-ft (4.3-m) dimension needs to be used to determine the appropriate distance between sprinklers on the branch lines for the first branch line parallel to the wall. Other lines could use the 13-ft or 14-ft (4.0-m or 4.3-m) dimension, depending on whether symmetry was desired. If an ordinary hazard occupancy system with a protection area of 130 ft^2 (12 m^2) per sprinkler were being considered, the maximum distance between sprinklers on the branch lines could be as follows:

$$130 \text{ ft}^2 (12.1 \text{ m}^2) \div 14 \text{ ft} (4.3 \text{ m}) = 9.3 \text{ ft} (2.8 \text{ m})$$

8.6.3.2.3* The requirements of 8.6.3.2.1 shall not apply where walls are angled or irregular, and the maximum horizontal distance between a sprinkler and any point of floor area protected by that sprinkler shall not exceed 0.75 times the allowable distance permitted between sprinklers, provided the maximum perpendicular distance is not exceeded.

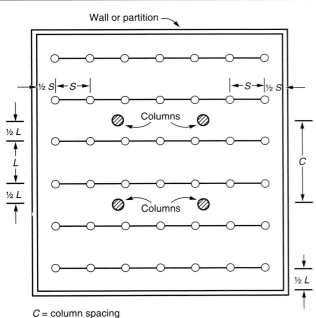

EXHIBIT 8.11 Positioning of Standard Spray Sprinkler Under a Flat Slab Concrete Ceiling in an Ordinary Hazard Occupancy.

C = column spacing
L = distance between branch lines, limit 15 ft
S = distance between sprinklers on branch lines, limit 15 ft

Examples

C	L	S (maximum)	C	L	S (maximum)
21 ft 8 in.	10 ft 10 in.	12 ft 0 in.	21 ft 6 in.	10 ft 9 in.	12 ft 1 in.
24 ft 2 in.	12 ft 1 in.	10 ft 9 in.			

For SI units, 1 in. = 25.4 mm; 1 ft = 0.3048 m; 1 ft^2 = 0.0929 m^2.

EXHIBIT 8.12 Positioning of Standard Spray Sprinkler Under a Ceiling Consisting of Continuous Smooth Bays with Beams Supported on Columns in an Ordinary Hazard Occupancy.

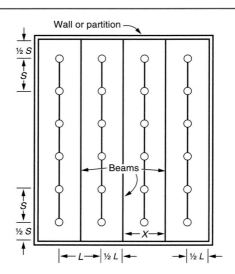

L = distance between branch lines, limit 15 ft
S = distance between sprinklers on branch lines, limit 15 ft
X = width of bay

Examples

X	L	S (maximum)	X	L	S (maximum)
10 ft 10 in.	10 ft 10 in.	12 ft 0 in.	10 ft 9 in.	10 ft 9 in.	12 ft 1 in.
12 ft 1 in.	12 ft 1 in.	10 ft 9 in.			

For SI units, 1 in. = 25.4 mm; 1 ft = 0.3048 m; 1 ft² = 0.0929 m².

Angled and irregular walls are discussed in 8.6.3.2.3. Angled and other irregular walls and corners with less than 90-degree angles can cause situations where additional sprinklers are required to protect small spaces within a larger area. A change first introduced in the 1996 edition allowed the maximum distance from a sprinkler to a corner or wall to be slightly increased, eliminating the need to install an additional sprinkler in these small spaces. For example, with a light hazard occupancy, the distance to the corner in Figure A.8.6.3.2.3 could be increased to 11.25 ft (3.4 m). Another common situation occurs when a window is recessed from the interior wall. This section allows the sprinkler to be further away from the window as long as the allowable distance from the wall is not exceeded.

A   **A.8.6.3.2.3** See Figure A.8.6.3.2.3.

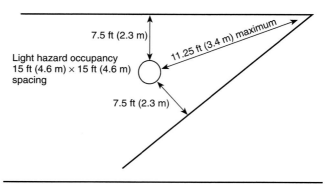

7.5 ft (2.3 m)

11.25 ft (3.4 m) maximum

Light hazard occupancy
15 ft (4.6 m) × 15 ft (4.6 m)
spacing

7.5 ft (2.3 m)

FIGURE A.8.6.3.2.3 Maximum Distance from Walls.

8.6.3.2.4* The requirements of 8.6.3.2.1 shall not apply within small rooms as defined in 3.3.20, sprinklers shall be permitted to be located not more than 9 ft (2.7 m) from any single wall, and sprinkler spacing limitations of 8.6.3 and area limitations of Table 8.6.2.2.1(a) shall not be exceeded.

The requirements of 8.6.3.2.4 only pertain to small rooms (see definition of *small room* in 3.3.20) in light hazard occupancies as defined in Section 5.2.

    To accommodate ceiling patterns, lighting fixtures, diffusers, and so forth, sprinklers are permitted to be moved a maximum of 1½ ft (0.5 m) in one direction beyond the usual requirements so that the maximum distance from a single wall is 9 ft (2.7 m), eliminating the need for adding additional sprinklers. This requirement assumes that only those sprinklers in the room will operate, resulting in a higher available operating pressure and, thus, greater discharge from each sprinkler and an improved spray pattern. See Figures A.8.6.3.2.4(a) through (d) for examples of the small room provision.

A.8.6.3.2.4 An example of sprinklers in small rooms for hydraulically designed and pipe schedule systems is shown in Figure A.8.6.3.2.4(a), and examples for hydraulically designed systems only are shown in Figure A.8.6.3.2.4(b), Figure A.8.6.3.2.4(c), and Figure A.8.6.3.2.4(d).

8.6.3.2.5 Under curved surfaces, the horizontal distance shall be measured at the floor level from the wall, or the intersection of the curved surface and the floor to the nearest sprinkler shall not be greater than one-half the allowable distance between sprinklers.

8.6.3.3 Minimum Distances from Walls. Sprinklers shall be located a minimum of 4 in. (102 mm) from a wall.

Dead-air spaces in corners would increase a sprinkler's operation time when installed near the corner. The 4-in. (102-mm) minimum location from a wall required by 8.6.3.3 ensures that the sprinkler will operate properly. *NFPA 72®*, *National Fire Alarm Code®*, provides more discussion on this phenomenon.

◀ **FAQ**
Can the requirements of 8.6.3.2.4 be applied in all occupancies?

Why are standard pendent and upright spray sprinklers required to be installed at least 4 in. from a wall?
◀ **FAQ**

FIGURE A.8.6.3.2.4(a) Small Room Provision—One Sprinkler.

FIGURE A.8.6.3.2.4(b) Small Room Provision—Two Sprinklers Centered Between Sidewalls.

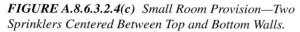

FIGURE A.8.6.3.2.4(c) Small Room Provision—Two Sprinklers Centered Between Top and Bottom Walls.

FIGURE A.8.6.3.2.4(d) Small Room Provision— Four Sprinklers.

8.6.3.4 Minimum Distances Between Sprinklers.

8.6.3.4.1 Unless the requirements of 8.6.3.4.2, 8.6.3.4.3, or 8.6.3.4.4 are met, sprinklers shall be spaced not less than 6 ft (1.8 m) on center.

8.6.3.4.2 Sprinklers shall be permitted to be placed less than 6 ft (1.8 m) on center where the following conditions are satisfied:

(1) Baffles shall be installed and located midway between sprinklers and arranged to protect the actuating elements.
(2) Baffles shall be of noncombustible or limited-combustible material that will stay in place before and during sprinkler operation.
(3) Baffles shall be not less than 8 in. (203 mm) wide and 6 in. (152 mm) high.
(4) The tops of baffles shall extend between 2 in. and 3 in. (51 mm and 76 mm) above the deflectors of upright sprinklers.
(5) The bottoms of baffles shall extend downward to a level at least even with the deflectors of pendent sprinklers.

FAQ ▶
Why are baffles required between closely spaced sprinklers?

Baffles, which are discussed in 8.6.3.4.2, minimize the possibility that discharge from one sprinkler will strike an adjacent sprinkler's actuating elements and delay or prevent the operation of the adjacent sprinklers. Because recessed and concealed sprinklers have their operating elements at or above the ceiling, they are less likely to be affected by the operation of adjacent sprinklers. However, NFPA 13 does not provide any exception that would allow recessed or concealed sprinklers to be located closer than 6 ft (1.8 m) apart.

8.6.3.4.3 In-rack sprinklers shall be permitted to be placed less than 6 ft (1.8 m) on center.

Paragraph 8.6.3.4.3 pertains to sprinklers located within storage racks. In-rack sprinklers are not required to be separated by baffles when installed closer than 6 ft (1.8 m) apart, because they were tested for these configurations. Because in-rack sprinklers are located in or adjacent to the fire and not at the ceiling where the heat will collect, the lower sprinklers normally operate first and are not usually subjected to this phenomenon.

8.6.3.4.4 Old-style sprinklers protecting fur storage vaults shall be permitted to be placed less than 6 ft (1.8 m) on center.

8.6.4 Deflector Position (Standard Pendent and Upright Spray Sprinklers).

8.6.4.1 Distance Below Ceilings.

The requirements for the position of sprinklers with respect to the floor or ceiling are established in 8.6.4.1. In all cases, a minimum of 1 in. (25.4 mm) of clearance is required to allow for the replacement of upright sprinklers. When applying the rules for positioning sprinklers, the dimensions are measured to the sprinkler deflector.

8.6.4.1.1 Unobstructed Construction.

8.6.4.1.1.1 Under unobstructed construction, the distance between the sprinkler deflector and the ceiling shall be a minimum of 1 in. (25.4 mm) and a maximum of 12 in. (305 mm) throughout the area of coverage of the sprinkler.

The 2002 edition modified the text of 8.6.4.1.1.1 to further clarify the measurement of the deflector distance. As stated in 8.6.4.1.1.1, it is the intent that the 1 in. to 12 in. limit be applied to the entire area of coverage of the sprinkler.

Additional text was also added in 8.6.4.1.1.3 to address ceilings having vertical changes in elevation. See commentary on 8.6.4.1.1.3.

◀ **FAQ**
Are the requirements of 8.6.4.1.1.1 applicable to the area directly above the sprinkler deflector or are they applicable to the entire area of coverage for the sprinkler?

8.6.4.1.1.2 The requirements of 8.6.4.1.1.1 shall not apply where ceiling-type sprinklers (concealed, recessed, and flush types) have the operating element above the ceiling and the deflector located nearer to the ceiling where installed in accordance with their listing.

Exhibit 3.27 shows a concealed sprinkler. This type of sprinkler would have the deflector positioned at a point even with or slightly above the ceiling. Concealed sprinklers are specifically evaluated under the condition stated in 8.6.4.1.1.2.

8.6.4.1.1.3 The requirements of 8.6.4.1.1.1 shall not apply for light and ordinary hazard occupancies with ceilings of noncombustible or limited combustible construction. Where there is a vertical change in ceiling elevation within the area of coverage of the sprinkler creating a distance of more than 36 in. between the upper ceiling and the sprinkler deflector, a vertical plane extending down from the ceiling at the change in elevation shall be considered a wall for the purpose of sprinkler spacing. Where the distance between the upper ceiling and the sprinkler deflector is less than or equal to 36 in., the sprinklers shall be permitted to be spaced as though the ceiling was flat provided the obstruction rules and ceiling pocket rules are observed. *(See Figure 8.6.4.1.1.3.)*

Many buildings use irregular ceilings, which are discussed in 8.6.4.1.1.3, as a design feature. These might include soffits around the perimeter, pockets purely for decorative purposes, stepped ceilings, and beams in the center to break the space up. Conference facilities at hotels are a good example of where this type of construction is used. These facilities may also have temporary partitions that can be opened and closed to separate a space into two or more separate rooms. Often these ceiling height changes are limited, while in other cases pockets or elevation changes can be quite varied. The placement of sprinklers can be challenging in these spaces if all of the rules in NFPA 13 are followed. Additional guidance for pockets and ceiling height changes was introduced in the 2002 edition of the standard and allows for protection of these spaces without the use of all the sprinklers that might be required under the previous rules. [See Exhibit 8.21 and commentary following 8.6.7.2(7).]

In simple terms, if the change in ceiling elevation exceeds 36 in. (0.9 m), the change in elevation is treated like a wall and sprinklers are spaced accordingly. If the change is less than 36 in. (0.9 m), then the ceiling is assumed to be flat (as long as the upper sprinkler is spaced so that it can throw underneath the lower ceiling), and the sprinklers are spaced accordingly. If the change in elevation is close enough to the sprinkler located at the ceiling that the sprinkler cannot develop its pattern, then the elevation change is treated like an obstruction and additional sprinklers must be added accordingly. See Figure 8.6.4.1.1.3. It is important to note that sprinklers are required within the upper ceiling area unless the requirements for unprotected ceiling pockets in 8.6.7 can be met.

◀ **FAQ**
How should changes in ceiling elevation be treated?

x 36 in. (0.91 m)
s = Maximum allowable distance
     between sprinklers

x > 36 in. (0.91 m)
s = Maximum allowable distance
     between sprinklers

FIGURE 8.6.4.1.1.3 *Vertical Changes in Ceiling Elevations.*

8.6.4.1.2 Obstructed Construction. Under obstructed construction, the sprinkler deflector shall be located in accordance with one of the following arrangements:

(1) Installed with the deflectors within the horizontal planes of 1 in. to 6 in. (25.4 mm to 152 mm) below the structural members and a maximum distance of 22 in. (559 mm) below the ceiling/roof deck

The position of sprinklers under obstructed construction, which is discussed in 8.6.4.1.2, varies widely. A basic series of requirements is set to allow the deflector to be positioned in a number of ways, such as below the structural member in some circumstances, beside the members, in between all the members, or, for concrete joist construction, entirely below the members.

Past substantive changes in the standard have permitted the sprinkler deflector to be as much as 22 in. (559 mm) below the ceiling for obstructed construction. A 22-in. (559-mm) maximum deflector position for other than concrete tee construction is set in 8.6.4.1.2(1). Positioning the sprinklers more than 22 in. (559 mm) below the ceiling negatively impacts sprinkler activation.

Exhibit 8.13 illustrates the placement of upright sprinklers underneath obstructed construction consisting of I-beams in accordance with the base rule of 8.6.4.1.2. If the I-beams

EXHIBIT 8.13 *Placement of Standard Spray Upright Sprinklers Underneath Obstructed Construction.*

had a depth of 10 in. (254 mm), then the sprinkler could be placed 1 in. to 6 in. (25.4 mm to 152 mm) below the bottom of the I-beam but no more than 11 in. to 16 in. (280 mm to 410 mm) below the ceiling. If the I-beam had a depth of 18 in. (0.46 m), another rule influences sprinkler placement. Because the sprinkler cannot be placed more than 22 in. (559 mm) from the ceiling, the sprinkler placement is limited to 1 in. to 4 in. (25.4 mm to 101.6 mm) below the I-beam and 19 in. to 22 in. (482.6 mm to 559 mm) below the ceiling. If the I-beams have a depth of 22 in. (559 mm) or more, then the sprinklers will need to be positioned in accordance with either 8.6.4.1.2(1) or 8.6.4.1.2(2).

Exhibit 8.14 shows the placement of sprinklers under solid wood joist construction in which the joists have a depth of 10 in. (254 mm). The sprinkler could be placed up to 6 in. (152 mm) below the joists, positioning it 16 in. (406 mm) from the ceiling or roof deck. Because sprinklers cannot be positioned more than 1 in. to 6 in. (25.4 mm to 152 mm) below the structural members, the maximum permitted dimension of 22 in. (559 mm) from the ceiling cannot be applied.

◀ **FAQ**
For all types of obstructed construction is it acceptable to locate all sprinklers 22 in. from the ceiling or roof deck?

(2) Installed with the deflectors at or above the bottom of the structural member to a maximum of 22 in. (559 mm) below the ceiling/roof deck where the sprinkler is installed in conformance with 8.6.5.1.2

Paragraph 8.6.4.1.2(1) allows sprinkler deflectors to be positioned at or above the bottom of the structural member, provided the distance from the ceiling or roof deck to the deflectors does not exceed 22 in. (559 mm) and the sprinklers are positioned in accordance with the obstruction rules of 8.6.5.1.2. Exhibit 8.15 depicts one such arrangement and illustrates that the sprinkler is positioned within 22 in. (559 mm) of the ceiling so as to not negatively impact sprinkler activation and so that the sprinkler discharge will adequately clear the structural members. This rule is typically employed where sprinklers are not installed in each bay of ob-

EXHIBIT 8.14 *Placement of Standard Spray Upright Sprinklers Underneath Solid Wood Joist Construction.*

Distance from ceiling/roof deck cannot exceed 22 in. and deflectors must be within 1 in. to 6 in. of the structural member

Wood joist

Floor slab

10 in.

2 in.

6 in. maximum for a 10-in. deep member

For SI units: 1 in. = 25.4 mm.

EXHIBIT 8.15 *Placement of Standard Spray Upright Sprinklers Underneath Obstructed Construction with the Sprinkler Deflector Positioned Above the Bottom of the Structural Member.*

structed construction. Paragraph 8.6.4.1.2(3) applies where sprinklers need to be installed in each bay of obstructed construction.

(3) Installed in each bay of obstructed construction, with the deflectors located a minimum of 1 in. (25.4 mm) and a maximum of 12 in. (305 mm) below the ceiling

Where the depths of the structural members are of such a dimension that compliance with the obstruction rules of Table 8.6.5.1.2 is not possible, sprinklers would need to be installed in each bay, and the requirements of 8.6.4.1.2(3) apply.

FAQ ▶
Where sprinklers are installed in each bay of obstructed construction, are they permitted to be up to 22 in. (559 mm) below the ceiling?

The standard permits the sprinklers to be located 1 in. to 12 in. (25.4 mm to 305 mm) below the ceiling, as they are for unobstructed construction, but they can be located up to 22 in. (559 mm) below the ceiling. The closer the sprinkler is to the ceiling, the faster its response to a fire. Where sprinklers are installed in each bay, the sprinklers should be spaced so that they are positioned no more than their allowable spacing from the near side of the structural members. Exhibit 8.16 shows an arrangement of upright sprinklers located in each bay of obstructed construction.

EXHIBIT 8.16 *Placement of Standard Spray Upright Sprinklers in Each Bay of Obstructed Construction.*

Are the requirements of 8.6.4.1.2(4) applicable when installing sprinklers below composite wood joist construction?

(4) Installed with the deflectors within the horizontal planes 1 in. to 6 in. below composite wood joists to a maximum distance of 22 in. below the ceiling/roof deck only where joist channels are fire-stopped to the full depth of the joists with material equivalent to the web construction so that individual channel areas do not exceed 300 ft² (27.9 m²)

FAQ ▶

Paragraph 8.6.4.1.2(4) identifies the only conditions under which sprinklers can be placed under composite wood joist construction. This requirement was revised for the 1999 edition to clarify that the distance between the sprinkler deflector and the ceiling cannot exceed 22 in. (559 mm) and that the maximum distance between the sprinkler deflector and the bottom of the joist cannot exceed 6 in. (152 mm).

(5)* Installed with deflectors of sprinklers under concrete tee construction with stems spaced less than 7½ ft (2.3 m) but more than 3 ft (0.9 m) on centers, regardless of the depth of the tee, located at or above a horizontal plane 1 in. (25.4 mm) below the bottom of the stems of the tees and shall comply with Table 8.6.5.1.2

Paragraph 8.6.4.1.2(5) applies only to specific types of concrete tee construction. The sprinkler is to be located as high as possible, taking into account the obstruction that could be created by the leg of the concrete tee. The allowance for this special condition is based on sensitivity tests conducted by the sprinkler industry. Concrete has a comparatively high threshold to withstand heat from fire. The concrete also has the capacity to act as a heat sink, collecting heat from the fire and creating a ceiling effect. This reaction ensures timely operation of the sprinkler.

A.8.6.4.1.2(5) For concrete joists spaced less than 3 ft (0.91 m) on center, the rules for obstructed construction shown in 8.6.4.1.2 apply. *[See Figure A.8.6.4.1.2(5).]*

◀ **FAQ**
When can the requirements of 8.6.4.1.2(5) be applied and the sprinkler deflector distance exceed 22 in. from the ceiling or roof deck?

FIGURE A.8.6.4.1.2(5) Typical Concrete Joist Construction.

8.6.4.1.3 Peaked Roofs and Ceilings.

8.6.4.1.3.1 Unless the requirements of 8.6.4.1.3.2 or 8.6.4.1.3.3 are met, sprinklers under or near the peak of a roof or ceiling shall have deflectors located not more than 3 ft (0.9 m) vertically down from the peak as indicated in Figure 8.6.4.1.3.1(a) and Figure 8.6.4.1.3.1(b).

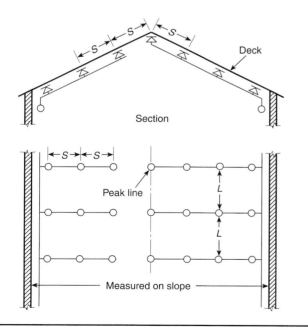

FIGURE 8.6.4.1.3.1(a) Sprinklers Under Pitched Roofs with Sprinkler Directly Under Peak; Branch Lines Run Up the Slope.

FIGURE 8.6.4.1.3.1(b) Sprinklers at Pitched Roofs; Branch Lines Run Up the Slope.

8.6.4.1.3.2* Under saw-toothed roofs, sprinklers at the highest elevation shall not exceed a distance of 3 ft (0.9 m) measured down the slope from the peak.

 A.8.6.4.1.3.2 Saw-toothed roofs have regularly spaced monitors of saw tooth shape, with the nearly vertical side glazed and usually arranged for venting. Sprinkler placement is limited to a maximum of 3 ft (0.91 m) down the slope from the peak because of the effect of venting on sprinkler sensitivity.

8.6.4.1.3.3 Under a steeply pitched surface, the distance from the peak to the deflectors shall be permitted to be increased to maintain a horizontal clearance of not less than 2 ft (0.6 m) from other structural members as indicated in Figure 8.6.4.1.3.3.

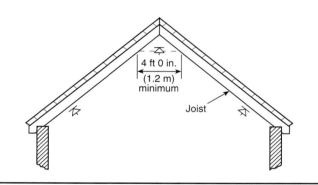

FIGURE 8.6.4.1.3.3 Horizontal Clearance for Sprinklers at Peak of Pitched Roof.

Peaked roofs and ceilings are covered in 8.6.4.1.3.1 through 8.6.4.1.3.3. Sprinklers must be within 3 ft (0.9 m) vertically of the peak but must also meet the position requirements of 8.6.4.1. The 3-ft (0.9-m) limitation addresses the concern that heat from a fire tends to collect at the peak. Locating sprinklers too far below the peak can delay their activation time. If the roof is steeply pitched, raising the sprinkler to improve responsiveness compromises the sprinkler spray pattern. A minimum 2-ft (0.6-m) horizontal clearance is required in this case.

 8.6.4.1.4 Sprinklers Under a Roof or Ceiling in Combustible Concealed Spaces of Wood Joist or Wood Truss Construction with Members 3 ft or Less on Center and a Slope Having a Pitch of Four in 12 or Greater. *(See Figure 8.6.4.1.4.)*

FAQ ▶
Why were the new requirements for sloped combustible concealed spaces added?

As noted in the commentary to 8.6.2.2.1, fire testing has demonstrated the reduced effectiveness of spray sprinklers in some steeply sloped (slope of 4 in 12 or greater) combustible concealed spaces. In addition to the sprinkler spacing and operating requirements of that section, three additional requirements were added to improve performance as shown in 8.6.4.1.4.1, 8.6.4.1.4.2, and 8.6.4.1.4.3.

 8.6.4.1.4.1 Sprinklers under a roof or ceiling in combustible concealed spaces of wood joist or wood truss construction with members 3 ft or less on center and a slope having a pitch of four in 12 or greater shall be quick response.

FAQ ▶
Why are quick-response sprinklers required?

Quick-response sprinklers, which are discussed in 8.6.4.1.4.1, are required to optimize operation time and performance with the goal of attacking the fire as quickly as possible while it remains small, and before the combustible ceiling construction becomes significantly involved, allowing the fire to spread above the sprinklers.

 8.6.4.1.4.2 Sprinklers under a roof or ceiling in combustible concealed spaces of wood joist or wood truss construction with members 3 ft or less on center and a slope having a pitch of

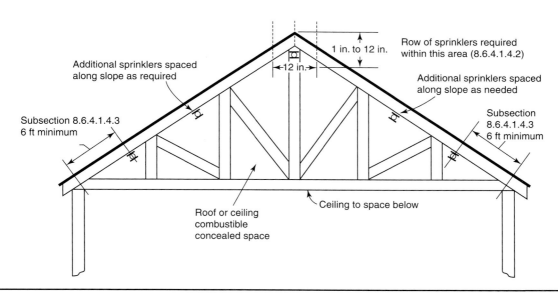

FIGURE 8.6.4.1.4 *Sprinklers Under a Roof or Ceiling in Combustible Concealed Spaces of Wood Joist or Wood Truss Construction with Members 3 ft or Less on Center and a Slope Having a Pitch of Four in 12 or Greater.*

four in 12 or greater shall be installed so that a row of sprinklers is installed within 12 in. horizontally of the peak.

A line of sprinklers is required within 12 in. (305 mm) horizontally of the peak, as stated in 8.6.4.1.4.2. The heat traveling up the slope will collect at the peak, and by locating a sprinkler there, the intent is that the sprinkler will open early in the development of the fire and help to limit the travel of the heat along the peak away from the fire.

8.6.4.1.4.3 Sprinklers under a roof or ceiling in combustible concealed spaces of wood joist or wood truss construction with members 3 ft or less on center and a slope having a pitch of four in 12 or greater shall be installed so that the sprinklers installed along the eave are located not less than 6 ft from the outer line of the concealed space.

Sprinklers are also required by 8.6.4.1.4.3 to be installed within 6 ft of the inside edge of the eave line so that if the fire starts along the eave, there will be a sprinkler close to the fire. The sprinklers located near the eave will also provide protection for a fire entering the concealed space from along the eave.

8.6.4.1.4.4 Nominal K-4.2 orifice sprinklers shall be permitted for use at the 20 psi minimum pressure option for wet pipe systems and dry pipe systems where piping is corrosion resistant or internally galvanized.

Paragraph 8.6.4.1.4.4 allows for the use of small orifice sprinklers having a nominal K-factor of 4.2 where the 20 psi design option from Table 8.6.2.2.1(a) is utilized and a wet pipe sprinkler system is installed. The use of small orifice sprinklers allows for the benefits of the 20-psi design pressure while permitting the reduced flow created by K-4.2 sprinklers. Since small orifice sprinklers are more easily obstructed internally, the additional requirement for piping to be corrosion resistant or internally galvanized was added.

8.6.4.1.5 Double Joist Obstructions.

8.6.4.1.5.1 Unless the requirements of 8.6.4.1.5.2 are met, where there are two sets of joists under a roof or ceiling, and there is no flooring over the lower set, sprinklers shall be installed

◀ **FAQ**
Why is a row of sprinklers required so close to the peak?

◀ **FAQ**
Why is a row of sprinklers required no closer than 6 ft from the outer line of the concealed space?

◀ **FAQ**
Why is the use of small orifice sprinklers permitted?

above and below the lower set of joists where there is a clearance of 6 in. (152 mm) or more between the top of the lower joist and the bottom of the upper joist as indicated in Figure 8.6.4.1.5.1.

FIGURE 8.6.4.1.5.1 *Arrangement of Sprinklers Under Two Sets of Open Joists—No Sheathing on Lower Joists.*

8.6.4.1.5.2 Sprinklers shall be permitted to be omitted from below the lower set of joists where at least 18 in. (0.46 m) is maintained between the sprinkler deflector and the top of the lower joist.

FAQ ▶
Do the requirements of 8.6.4.1.5 apply to wood truss construction?

Note that 8.6.4.1.5.2 only applies to joist construction such as solid sawn wood joists or composite wood joists and does not apply to wood truss constructions. When spacing sprinklers within wood truss construction, sprinklers should be spaced from the end of the truss.

8.6.4.2* Deflector Orientation.

 A.8.6.4.2 On sprinkler lines larger than 2 in. (51 mm), consideration should be given to the distribution interference caused by the pipe, which can be minimized by installing sprinklers on riser nipples or installing sprinklers in the pendent position.

8.6.4.2.1 Unless the requirements of 8.6.4.2.2, 8.6.4.2.3, or 8.6.4.2.4 are met, deflectors of sprinklers shall be aligned parallel to ceilings, roofs, or the incline of stairs.

8.6.4.2.2 Where sprinklers are installed in the peak below a sloped ceiling or roof surface, the sprinkler shall be installed with the deflector horizontal.

 8.6.4.2.3 Pitched roofs having slopes less than 2 in. per foot (16.7 percent) are considered level in the application of 8.6.4.2, and sprinklers shall be permitted to be installed with deflectors horizontal.

8.6.4.2.4 Pitched roofs having slopes not exceeding a pitch of one in six (a rise of two units in a run of 12 units, a roof slope of 16.7 percent) are considered level in the application of this rule, and sprinklers shall be permitted to be installed with deflectors horizontal.

8.6.5 Obstructions to Sprinkler Discharge (Standard Pendent and Upright Spray Sprinklers).

8.6.5.1 Performance Objective.

8.6.5.1.1 Sprinklers shall be located so as to minimize obstructions to discharge as defined in 8.6.5.2 and 8.6.5.3, or additional sprinklers shall be provided to ensure adequate coverage of the hazard.

8.6.5.1.2 Sprinklers shall be arranged to comply with one of the following arrangements:

(1) Subsection 8.5.5.2, Table 8.6.5.1.2, and Figure 8.6.5.1.2(a).

TABLE 8.6.5.1.2 *Positioning of Sprinklers to Avoid Obstructions to Discharge (SSU/SSP)*

Distance from Sprinklers to Side of Obstruction (A)	Maximum Allowable Distance of Deflector above Bottom of Obstruction (in.) (B)
Less than 1 ft	0
1 ft to less than 1 ft 6 in.	2½
1 ft 6 in. to less than 2 ft	3½
2 ft to less than 2 ft 6 in.	5½
2 ft 6 in. to less than 3 ft	7½
3 ft to less than 3 ft 6 in.	9½
3 ft 6 in. to less than 4 ft	12
4 ft to less than 4 ft 6 in.	14
4 ft 6 in. to less than 5 ft	16½
5 ft and greater	18

For SI units, 1 in. = 25.4 mm; 1 ft = 0.3048 m.

Note: For (A) and (B), refer to Figure 8.6.5.1.2(a).

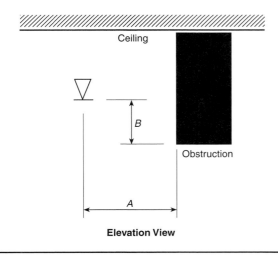

Elevation View

FIGURE 8.6.5.1.2(a) *Positioning of Sprinklers to Avoid Obstructions to Discharge (SSU/SSP).*

In past editions, the provision addressed by 8.6.5.1.2 was commonly referred to as the Beam Rule for standard spray sprinklers. The dimensions specified in Table 8.6.5.1.2 outline the discharge pattern of the sprinkler and define how far away from a building element a sprinkler must be positioned to allow the sprinkler discharge to extend underneath the building element rather than to hit it. After reviewing the discharge patterns for sprinklers at pressures from 15 psi to 100 psi (1 bar to 7 bar), Table 8.6.5.1.2 was adjusted in 1996 to better reflect the patterns of typical standard spray upright and pendent sprinklers.

(2) Sprinklers shall be permitted to be spaced on opposite sides of obstructions not exceeding 4 ft (1.2 m) in width provided the distance from the centerline of the obstruction to the sprinklers does not exceed one-half the allowable distance permitted between sprinklers.

When applying 8.6.5.1.2(2), the maximum spacing permitted between branch lines and between sprinklers on branch lines must still be followed. Therefore, the distance between sprinklers on opposite sides of the obstruction is measured from the centerline of the obstruction. The maximum allowable distances above the obstruction (see Table 8.6.5.1.2) can be exceeded if the trajectory and resultant discharge pattern of a particular sprinkler are verified by test.

(3) Obstructions located against the wall and that are not over 30 in. (762 mm) in width shall be permitted to be protected in accordance with Figure 8.6.5.1.2(b).

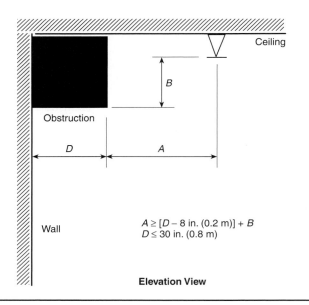

$$A \geq [D - 8 \text{ in. } (0.2 \text{ m})] + B$$
$$D \leq 30 \text{ in. } (0.8 \text{ m})$$

Elevation View

FIGURE 8.6.5.1.2(b) *Obstructions Against Walls (SSU/SSP).*

Paragraph 8.6.5.1.2(3) and Figure 8.6.5.1.2(b) identify the conditions under which sprinklers are not required underneath soffits and other similar building features located against a wall. In other words, this section identifies when soffits do not present an obstruction to sprinkler discharge. If the obstruction is not over 30 in. (762 mm) in width and if the sprinklers are positioned in front of the obstruction as shown in the figure, then additional sprinklers under the soffit can be omitted.

FAQ ▶
Do the requirements of 8.6.5.1.2(3) apply to building elements other than soffits?

This paragraph also applies to building elements other than soffits located against the wall, such as cable trays, ductwork, cabinets, or similar small projections attached to a wall.

8.6.5.2 Obstructions to Sprinkler Discharge Pattern Development.

8.6.5.2.1 General.

Obstruction to sprinkler discharge pattern development is covered in 8.6.5.2.1. When installing sprinklers in unobstructed construction containing noncontinuous obstructions, such as building columns, bar joists, or some truss configurations, adequate horizontal and vertical clearance from the obstruction are critical to maintain proper sprinkler discharge patterns. This clearance is especially true where the obstructions are structural members that affect each line of sprinklers. Bar joists, trusses, and similar construction types do not impede heat flow, but they are capable of obstructing the sprinkler's spray pattern once it is in operation. Exhibit 8.17 shows a standard spray upright sprinkler positioned near bar joist construction. The sprinkler in Exhibit 8.17 needs to be positioned an adequate distance from the horizontal and vertical members of the bar joist.

EXHIBIT 8.17 Standard Spray Upright Sprinkler Positioned Near a Bar Joist Construction.

8.6.5.2.1.1 Continuous or noncontinuous obstructions less than or equal to 18 in. (457 mm) below the sprinkler deflector that prevent the pattern from fully developing shall comply with 8.6.5.2.

8.6.5.2.1.2 Regardless of the rules of 8.6.5.2, solid continuous obstructions shall meet the applicable requirements of 8.6.5.1.2.

Large solid continuous obstructions, which are discussed in 8.6.5.2.1.2, were previously referred to as horizontal obstructions. These obstructions, such as deep beams or a large duct mounted on or very near the ceiling, have a significant impact on discharge patterns and must be located above the sprinkler discharge pattern in accordance with 8.6.5.1.2. Smaller continuous obstructions, such as pipes and bottom members of trusses, and noncontinuous obstructions, such as the web members of bar joists located within 18 in. (457 mm) below the sprinkler, should be in compliance with the requirements of 8.6.5.2.1.

8.6.5.2.1.3* Unless the requirements of 8.6.5.2.1.4 through 8.6.5.2.1.10 are met, sprinklers shall be positioned away from obstructions a minimum distance of three times the maximum dimension of the obstruction (e.g., structural members, pipe, columns, and fixtures). The maximum clear distance required shall be 24 in. (609 mm) in accordance with Figure 8.6.5.2.1.3.

A.8.6.5.2.1.3 The rules of 8.6.5.2.1.3 (known as the "Three Times Rule") have been written to apply to obstructions where the sprinkler can be expected to get water to both sides of the obstruction without allowing a significant dry shadow on the other side of the obstruction. This works for small noncontinuous obstructions and for continuous obstructions where the sprinkler can throw water over and under the obstruction, such as the bottom chord of an open truss or joist. For solid continuous obstructions, such as a beam, the Three Times Rule is ineffective since the sprinkler cannot throw water over and under the obstruction. Sufficient water must be thrown under the obstruction to adequately cover the floor area on the other side of the obstruction. To ensure this, compliance with the rules of 8.6.5.1.2 is necessary.

FIGURE 8.6.5.2.1.3 *Minimum Distance from Obstruction (SSU/SSP).*

8.6.5.2.1.4* For light and ordinary hazard occupancies, structural members only shall be considered when applying the requirements of 8.6.5.2.1.3.

 A.8.6.5.2.1.4 It is the intent of this section to exempt nonstructural elements in light and ordinary hazard occupancies from the obstruction criteria commonly called the "Three Times Rule." However, the other obstruction rules including the "Beam Rule" (8.6.5.1.2) and the "Wide Obstruction Rule" (8.6.5.3.3) still apply. If an obstruction is so close to a sprinkler that water cannot spray on both sides, it is effectively a continuous obstruction as far as the sprinkler is concerned and the Beam Rule should be applied.

It is not the intent of this section to permit the use of fixtures and architectural features or treatments to conceal, obscure, or otherwise obstruct sprinkler discharge. The exception should be applied in accordance with the performance objectives in 8.6.5.1.

The impact of an obstruction on sprinkler performance depends on many factors. One factor is the severity of the hazard being protected. Historically, NFPA 13 considered building structural elements and other large building elements, such as ducts, as being potential obstructions. In 1991, the standard was revised to consider other types of smaller building elements, such as piping and light fixtures, that could also obstruct sprinkler discharge patterns.

Beginning with the 1999 edition, NFPA 13 (see 8.6.5.2.1.4) acknowledged the difficulty in considering all nonstructural building elements as potential obstructions when designing the system. Additionally, NFPA 13 took into account the fact that more obstructions can be tolerated in light and ordinary hazard occupancies when spray sprinklers are used. However, nonstructural building elements must be considered when designing sprinkler systems in extra hazard and storage occupancies.

Structural members that are obstructions in light and ordinary hazard occupancies must still be considered because they are easier to locate on building plans than lights and pipes, and because they tend to be continuous, thereby affecting more than one sprinkler in a symmetrical arrangement.

The 2002 edition further clarified the intent of 8.6.5.2.1.4 by adding additional language to the annex. This additional language was added to clarify that the paragraph does not permit the use of nonstructural elements, including fixtures, and architectural features or treatments to conceal, obscure, or otherwise obstruct the sprinkler discharge. While the intent of 8.6.5.2.1.4 is to permit non-structural elements to not meet the "Three Times Rule," the requirements of 8.6.5.1.2 and 8.6.5.3.3 still apply and must be met.

8.6.5.2.1.5 Sprinklers shall be permitted to be spaced on opposite sides of the obstruction where the distance from the centerline of the obstruction to the sprinklers does not exceed one-half the allowable distance between sprinklers.

8.6.5.2.1.6 Sprinklers shall be permitted to be located one-half the distance between the obstructions where the obstruction consists of open trusses 20 in. (0.51 m) or greater apart [24 in. (0.61 m) on center], provided that all truss members are not greater than 4 in. (102 mm) (nominal) in width.

Many, but not all, of the obstruction problems are addressed in 8.6.5.2.1.

When open truss members are closely spaced, it is virtually impossible to locate the sprinkler far enough away from all truss elements that could cause an obstruction. Paragraph 8.6.5.2.1.6 addresses this specific problem by permitting the installation of sprinklers in between the members without requiring adherence to the Three Times Rule as long as the joists are spaced 24 in. (0.61 m) or more apart. Exhibit 8.18 illustrates such an arrangement.

◀ **FAQ**
Are the requirements of 8.6.5.2.1.3 (Three Times Rule) applicable when utilizing the requirements of 8.6.5.2.1.6?

8.6.5.2.1.7 Sprinklers shall be permitted to be installed on the centerline of a truss or bar joist or directly above a beam provided that the truss chord or beam dimension is not more than 8 in. (203 mm) and the sprinkler deflector is located at least 6 in. (152 mm) above the structural member and where the sprinkler is positioned at a distance three times greater than the maximum dimension of the web members away from the web members.

EXHIBIT 8.18 *Location of Sprinklers in Open Truss Construction.*

FAQ ▶

Are the requirements of 8.6.5.2.1.3 (Three Times Rule) applicable when utilizing the requirements of 8.6.5.2.1.7?

Paragraph 8.6.5.2.1.7 identifies the conditions under which standard spray upright and pendent sprinklers can be located directly over the centerline of the bottom chord of an open truss, bar joist, or beam without compliance with the Three Times Rule. Under the conditions specified by 8.6.5.2.1.7 and illustrated in Exhibit 8.19, the bottom chord and beams do not present a significant obstruction to sprinkler discharge. However, the vertical and diagonal truss and web members must comply with the Three Times Rule.

8.6.5.2.1.8 The requirements of 8.6.5.2.1.3 shall not apply to the piping to which an upright sprinkler is directly attached less than 3 in. (76 mm) in diameter.

8.6.5.2.1.9 The requirements of 8.6.5.2.1.3 shall not apply to the piping to which pendent sprinklers are directly attached.

The pipe on which a sprinkler is located is not considered a major obstruction unless the piping is 3 in. (76 mm) or larger (see 8.6.5.2.1.9). Upright sprinklers on large branch lines or mains must be placed on riser nipples or offset from the branch line to eliminate the obstruction that is created directly below the sprinkler. The elevation of the sprinkler eliminates problems that can occur when a fire is located directly below a sprinkler or directly under the branch line between two sprinklers. The obstruction can prevent the discharge from reaching the fire and can also eliminate dead-air spots that might delay sprinkler actuation, such as when an upright sprinkler is located directly on a 6-in. (152-mm) pipe.

EXHIBIT 8.19 Sprinkler Placed Over the Centerline of the Bottom Chord of a Wood Truss in Accordance with 8.6.5.2.1.7.

Elevation View

Section A–A

EXHIBIT 8.20 *Upright Sprinkler Installation.*

8.6.5.2.1.10 The requirements of 8.6.5.2.1.3 shall not apply to sprinklers positioned with respect to obstructions in accordance with 8.6.5.1.2.

Obstructions are addressed in 8.6.5.2.1.10. Other rules apply in addition to the obstruction rules of 8.6.5. The sprinkler's frame arm must be parallel to the branch line (see 8.3.1.3), and the distance between the centerline of an upright sprinkler and a hanger is required to be a minimum of 3 in. (76 mm) (see 9.2.3.3). Exhibit 8.20 shows an upright sprinkler attached directly to a branch line. The sprinkler is free of obstructions from structural ceiling elements, the branch line is less than 3 in. (76 mm) in diameter, the frame arm is parallel to the branch line, and the hanger is located at least 3 in. (76 mm) from the centerline of the sprinkler. However, verification that the sprinkler is properly positioned from the ceiling in accordance with 8.6.4 is needed, depending on whether the ceiling construction is obstructed or unobstructed.

8.6.5.2.2* Suspended or Floor-Mounted Vertical Obstructions. The distance from sprinklers to privacy curtains, free standing partitions, room dividers, and similar obstructions in light hazard occupancies shall be in accordance with Table 8.6.5.2.2 and Figure 8.6.5.2.2.

A.8.6.5.2.2 The use of mesh can affect the discharge pattern of the sprinkler. Top mesh can be used when it has a minimum vertical distance of 18 in. below the sprinkler deflector with mesh openings having a minimum percent opening of 70 percent or larger.

The distances specified in Table 8.6.5.2.2 were derived from NBSIR 80–2097, *Full-Scale Fire Tests with Automatic Sprinklers in a Patient Room.*

TABLE 8.6.5.2.2 *Suspended or Floor-Mounted Obstructions in Light Hazard Occupancies Only (SSU/SSP)*

Horizontal Distance (A)	Minimum Vertical Distance below Deflector (in.) (B)
6 in. or less	3
More than 6 in. to 9 in.	4
More than 9 in. to 12 in.	6
More than 12 in. to 15 in.	8
More than 15 in. to 18 in.	9½
More than 18 in to 24 in.	12½
More than 24 in. to 30 in.	15½
More than 30 in.	18

For SI units, 1 in. = 25.4 mm.

Note: For *(A)* and *(B)*, refer to Figure 8.6.5.2.2.

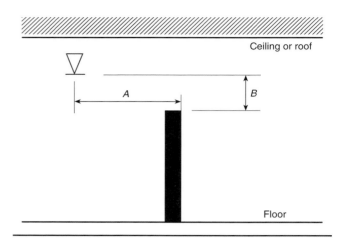

FIGURE 8.6.5.2.2 *Suspended or Floor-Mounted Obstructions in Light Hazard Occupancies Only (SSU/SSP).*

FAQ ▶
Can the requirements of 8.6.5.2.2 and Figure 8.6.5.2.2 be utilized in all occupancies?

The distance requirements of 8.6.5.2.2 and Figure 8.6.5.2.2 should not be applied beyond light hazard occupancies because the testing only evaluated sprinkler performance in a light hazard environment. The allowances of 8.6.5.2.2 have been misapplied, and to further clarify that the allowances of 8.6.5.2.2 apply to light hazard occupancies only, the 2002 edition has modified the titles of Table 8.6.5.2.2 and Figure 8.6.5.2.2 to include "in light hazard occupancies only."

8.6.5.3* Obstructions that Prevent Sprinkler Discharge from Reaching the Hazard.

 A.8.6.5.3 See A.8.5.5.3.

8.6.5.3.1 Continuous or noncontinuous obstructions that interrupt the water discharge in a horizontal plane more than 18 in. (457 mm) below the sprinkler deflector in a manner to limit the distribution from reaching the protected hazard shall comply with 8.6.5.3.

Once the sprinkler spray pattern has developed, small obstructions have a limited impact on sprinkler performance. However, larger obstructions located 18 in. (457 mm) or more below the sprinkler deflector, which are discussed in 8.6.5.3.1, prevent the sprinkler discharge from reaching combustibles located below them. This information identifies when additional upright or pendent sprinklers are required to compensate for these types of obstructions.

8.6.5.3.2 The requirements of 8.6.5.3 shall also apply to obstructions 18 in. or less below the sprinkler for light and ordinary hazard occupancies.

Because only structural members within 18 in. (457 mm) of the sprinkler are now considered by 8.6.5.2 for light and ordinary hazard occupancies, 8.6.5.3.2 was added. This paragraph requires that any continuous or noncontinuous obstructions wider than 4 ft (1.2 m) and located within 18 in. (457 mm) of the sprinkler deflector in light and ordinary hazard occupancies meet the requirements of 8.6.5.3.3 and 8.6.5.3.5.

8.6.5.3.3 Sprinklers shall be installed under fixed obstructions over 4 ft (1.2 m) wide such as ducts, decks, open grate flooring, cutting tables, and overhead doors.

8.6.5.3.4 Sprinklers shall not be required below obstructions that are not fixed in place, such as conference tables.

8.6.5.3.5 Sprinklers installed under open gratings shall be of the intermediate level/rack storage type or otherwise shielded from the discharge of overhead sprinklers.

As noted in 8.5.5.3.3, open gratings are often covered by storage or dust stops and require sprinklers below them. As stated in 8.6.5.3.5, sprinklers must be of the in-rack type or be provided with shields to prevent wetting of the thermal element by sprinkler discharge from above, which would delay the operation of the sprinkler.

8.6.6* Clearance to Storage (Standard Pendent and Upright Spray Sprinklers).

A.8.6.6 The 18-in. (457-mm) dimension is not intended to limit the height of shelving on a wall or shelving against a wall in accordance with 8.6.6. Where shelving is installed on a wall and is not directly below sprinklers, the shelves, including storage thereon, can extend above the level of a plane located 18 in. (457 mm) below ceiling sprinkler deflectors. Shelving, and any storage thereon, directly below the sprinklers cannot extend above a plane located 18 in. (457 mm) below the ceiling sprinkler deflectors.

Clearance to storage is covered in 8.6.6. The discharge pattern of upright and pendent spray sprinklers takes a parabolic shape as indicated in Figure A.8.5.5.1. To ensure the distribution of water over the area that the sprinkler was designed to protect, the spray pattern must encounter minimal obstructions. Rack storage fire tests, other tests with solid-piled storage, and field experience have shown that standard spray sprinklers are effective with a minimum 18-in. (457-mm) clearance.

Sprinklers installed near wall-mounted shelves or piled storage against a wall are not intended to be governed by the requirements of 8.6.6.1. The clear space beneath the sprinkler is needed for the spray pattern to fully develop to allow proper wetting of the floor and not the wall.

Paragraph 8.6.6.2 identifies the need to observe the clearance provisions that can be needed for special sprinklers or special design features. One example concerns the design provisions for miscellaneous storage found in Chapter 12 for Group A plastics. The design criteria for Group A plastics varies as the clearance increases.

◄ **FAQ**
Do the requirements of 8.6.6.1 apply to shelving against or installed on the wall?

8.6.6.1 The clearance between the deflector and the top of storage shall be 18 in. (457 mm) or greater.

8.6.6.2 Where other standards specify greater clearance to storage minimums, they shall be followed.

8.6.7 Ceiling Pockets.

8.6.7.1 Sprinklers shall be required in all ceiling pockets.

8.6.7.2 The requirements of 8.6.7.1 shall not apply where all of the following are met:

(1) The total volume of the unprotected ceiling pocket does not exceed 1000 ft^3.
(2) The depth of the unprotected pocket does not exceed 36 in.
(3) The entire floor under the unprotected ceiling pocket is protected by the sprinklers at the lower ceiling elevation.
(4) Each unprotected ceiling pocket is separated from any adjacent unprotected ceiling pocket by a minimum 10 ft horizontal distance.
(5) The unprotected ceiling pocket is constructed of noncombustible or limited combustible construction.
(6) Skylights not exceeding 32 ft^2 shall be permitted to have a plastic cover.
(7) Quick response sprinklers are utilized throughout the compartment.

Ceiling pockets are covered in 8.6.7.1 and 8.6.7.2 (see Exhibit 8.21). In past years the standard assumed that sprinklers would be located in all ceiling pockets, with the exception of small [4 ft × 8 ft (1.2 m × 2.4 m)] skylights. There has always been a concern that unless a sprinkler was placed in each pocket, heat would collect in the pocket and delay the operation of sprinklers. Some fire modeling was done to estimate the impact ceiling pockets would have

EXHIBIT 8.21 *Unprotected Ceiling Pockets.*

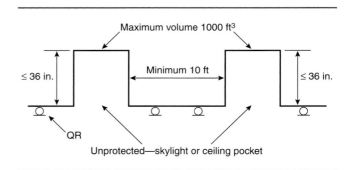

on sprinkler response at the lower ceiling elevation and to determine what type of pockets could be left unsprinklered. After reviewing the modeling results and field experience, new rules have been added to the 2002 edition to address these situations. To ensure adequate protection of the space, the following requirements were developed by the committee:

1. The volume of the pocket must be limited to no more than 1000 ft^3 [see 8.6.7.2(1)] and the depth of the pocket must be limited to a 36 in. [see 8.6.7.2(2)].
2. The entire floor area must be covered by the sprinkler discharge of the sprinklers at the lower ceiling [see 8.6.7.2(3)] and quick-response sprinklers must be used throughout the space [8.6.7.2(7)].
3. The pocket must be of noncombustible or limited combustible construction [see 8.6.7.2(5)] with the allowance for small skylights (less than or equal to 32 ft^2), which are allowed to have a plastic cover [see 8.6.7.2(6)]
4. Finally, to ensure that there is no impact from heat collecting from adjacent unprotected ceiling pockets or skylights, a 10 ft (3 m) separation must be maintained between unprotected ceiling pockets and skylights [see 8.6.7.2(4)].

 For additional information on the effect of ceiling pockets on sprinkler activation, see AFSA report "Evaluating the Impact of Ceiling Pockets on Sprinkler Activation."

8.7 Sidewall Standard Spray Sprinklers

Rules for horizontal sidewall, pendent sidewall, and upright sidewall sprinklers are covered by Section 8.7. EC sidewall sprinklers are covered in Section 8.9. In addition to the provisions of Section 8.7, sidewall sprinklers must also comply with all of the general requirements in Section 8.5.

8.7.1 General. All requirements of Section 8.5 shall apply to sidewall standard spray sprinklers except as modified in Section 8.7.

8.7.2 Protection Areas per Sprinkler (Standard Sidewall Spray Sprinklers).

8.7.2.1 Determination of the Protection Area of Coverage.

8.7.2.1.1 The protection area of coverage per sprinkler (A_s) shall be determined as follows:

(1) Along the wall as follows:
  (a) Determine the distance between sprinklers along the wall (or to the end wall or obstruction in the case of the end sprinkler on the branch line) upstream and downstream.
  (b) Choose the larger of either twice the distance to the end wall or the distance to the next sprinkler.
  (c) This dimension will be defined as *S*.

(2) Across the room as follows:

(a) Determine the distance from the sprinkler to the wall opposite the sprinklers or to the midpoint of the room where sprinklers are installed on two opposite walls *(see 8.7.3.1.5 and 8.7.3.1.6).*

(b) This dimension will be defined as *L.*

8.7.2.1.2 The protection area of the sprinkler shall be established by multiplying the *S* dimension by the *L* dimension, as follows: $A_s = S \times L$

8.7.2.2 Maximum Protection Area of Coverage.

8.7.2.2.1 The maximum allowable protection area of coverage for a sprinkler (A_s) shall be in accordance with the value indicated in Table 8.7.2.2.1.

TABLE 8.7.2.2.1 *Protection Areas and Maximum Spacing (Standard Sidewall Spray Sprinkler)*

	Light Hazard		Ordinary Hazard	
	Combustible Finish	*Noncombustible or Limited-Combustible Finish*	*Combustible Finish*	*Noncombustible or Limited-Combustible Finish*
Maximum distance along the wall *(S)*	14 ft	14 ft	10 ft	10 ft
Maximum room width *(L)*	12 ft	14 ft	10 ft	10 ft
Maximum protection area	120 ft^2	196 ft^2	80 ft^2	100 ft^2

For SI units, 1 ft = 0.3048 m; 1 ft^2 = 0.0929 m^2.

8.7.2.2.2 In any case, the maximum area of coverage of a sprinkler shall not exceed 196 ft^2 (18.2 m^2).

Maximum protection areas are covered in 8.7.2.2.1 and 8.7.2.2.2. Protection areas for sidewall sprinklers differ from those of standard spray upright and pendent sprinklers. Because of the characteristic horizontal or sideways travel of the sprinkler discharge, the water spray pattern of sidewall sprinklers has a greater tendency of being obstructed or otherwise impacted by furniture and other objects near the floor. The discharge of standard spray sprinklers is not normally as adversely affected by furniture and other objects on the floor. In addition, the discharge patterns of sidewall spray sprinklers are less uniform than those of standard spray sprinklers.

Table 8.7.2.2.1 indicates the maximum allowable protection areas. Table 8.7.2.2.1 also indicates sprinkler protection areas that are not affected by the building construction above the ceiling. The sprinkler system is intended to control the fire below the ceiling if properly designed and installed. Therefore, NFPA 13 only considers the combustibility of the exposed surfaces when determining the maximum allowable distance between sprinklers and the maximum sprinkler protection area. Section 8.14 identifies the concealed spaces above ceilings that are not required to be protected with sprinklers.

◀ **FAQ**
Why are standard sidewall spray sprinklers limited to a maximum of 196 ft^2 (18.2 m^2)?

8.7.3 Sprinkler Spacing (Standard Sidewall Spray Sprinklers).

8.7.3.1 Maximum Distance Between Sprinklers.

8.7.3.1.1 The maximum distance permitted between sidewall spray sprinklers shall be based on the centerline distance between sprinklers on the branch line.

8.7.3.1.2 The maximum distance between sidewall spray sprinklers or to a wall shall be measured along the slope of the ceiling.

8.7.3.1.3 Where sidewall spray sprinklers are installed along the length of a single wall of rooms or bays, they shall be spaced in accordance with the maximum spacing provisions of Table 8.7.2.2.1.

8.7.3.1.4 Sidewall spray sprinklers shall not be installed back-to-back without being separated by a continuous lintel or soffit.

FAQ ▶
Why are lintels or soffits required for back-to-back installations?

The use of a lintel or soffit, as required by 8.7.3.1.4, is necessary to ensure that the sprinkler closest to the fire operates and to minimize the possibility of sprinklers on both sides of the lintel operating unnecessarily. The baffle also serves to prevent the discharge pattern of the operating sprinkler from impinging on the operating element of an adjacent sprinkler. The baffle is an important feature, because sidewall sprinklers are actually designed to discharge a portion of their spray pattern behind the sprinkler.

8.7.3.1.5 Where sidewall spray sprinklers are installed on two opposite walls or sides of bays, the maximum width of the room or bay shall be permitted to be up to 24 ft (7.32 m) for light hazard occupancy or 20 ft (6.1 m) for ordinary hazard occupancy, with spacing as required by Table 8.7.2.2.1.

Due to the spacing limitations of sidewall sprinklers, only certain size rooms can be effectively protected. Paragraph 8.7.3.1.5 permits sidewall sprinklers to be used in larger rooms under certain conditions, including a maximum room width dimension and the use of two lines of sprinklers on opposite walls. The maximum room width allowed for light hazard occupancies when standard sidewall sprinklers are located on opposite walls was reduced from 30 ft (9.1 m) to 24 ft (7.32 m) beginning with the 1996 edition. EC sidewall sprinklers provide better coverage for wide rooms and should be used for rooms over 24 ft (7.32 m) wide.

8.7.3.1.6 Sidewall spray sprinklers shall be permitted to be installed on opposing or adjacent walls provided no sprinkler is located within the maximum protection area of another sprinkler.

Testing has determined the minimum required distance to prevent cold soldering from an adjacent sidewall sprinkler when both sprinklers are located along the same wall. However, no testing has been done to determine the minimum distance when sprinklers are located on opposite or adjacent walls (see 8.7.3.1.6). Placing sidewall sprinklers outside the protection area of the adjacent sprinklers is probably conservative but eliminates the potential for the discharge from one sprinkler wetting the thermal element of another.

8.7.3.2 Maximum Distance from Walls. The distance from sprinklers to the end walls shall not exceed one-half of the allowable distance permitted between sprinklers as indicated in Table 8.7.2.2.1.

8.7.3.3 Minimum Distance from Walls.

8.7.3.3.1 Sprinklers shall be located a minimum of 4 in. (102 mm) from an end wall.

8.7.3.3.2 The distance from the wall to the sprinkler shall be measured perpendicular to the wall.

Minimum distance from walls is covered in 8.7.3.3.1 and 8.7.3.3.2. The dead-air space described in the commentary to 8.6.3.3 can also have a detrimental effect on sidewall sprinklers. Exhibit 8.22 shows the correct placement of a sidewall sprinkler adjacent to an end wall.

8.7.3.4 Minimum Distance Between Sprinklers. Sprinklers shall be spaced not less than 6 ft (1.8 m) on center.

8.7.4 Deflector Position from Ceilings and Walls (Standard Sidewall Spray Sprinklers).

8.7.4.1 Distance Below Ceilings and from Walls.

EXHIBIT 8.22 *Sidewall Sprinkler Adjacent to an End Wall.*

8.7.4.1.1 Ceilings.

8.7.4.1.1.1 Unless the requirements of 8.7.4.1.1.2 are met, sidewall sprinkler deflectors shall be located not more than 6 in. (152 mm) or less than 4 in. (102 mm) from ceilings.

8.7.4.1.1.2 Horizontal sidewall sprinklers shall be permitted to be located in a zone 6 in. to 12 in. (152 mm to 305 mm) or 12 in. to 18 in. (305 mm to 457 mm) below noncombustible and limited-combustible ceilings where listed for such use.

Sidewall sprinklers should not be located in the dead-air space at the junction of the ceiling and the wall (see 8.7.4.1.1.2). The desirable sprinkler location is 4 in. to 6 in. (102 mm to 152 mm) from the ceiling to optimize performance. As the sprinkler is lowered to more than 6 in. (152 mm) from the ceiling, it is likely to take longer to operate. In addition, the ceiling has an impact on the discharge of a sidewall sprinkler, causing the spray pattern to change as the sprinkler is lowered. The sprinkler may be lowered as much as 18 in. (457 mm) when specifically tested and listed for such use.

8.7.4.1.2 Walls.

8.7.4.1.2.1 Vertical sidewall sprinkler deflectors shall be located not more than 6 in. (152 mm) or less than 4 in. (102 mm) from the wall they are projecting from.

8.7.4.1.2.2 Horizontal sidewall sprinkler deflectors shall be located no more than 6 in. (152 mm) and are permitted to be located with their deflectors less than 4 in. (102 mm) from the wall on which they are mounted.

The requirement in 8.7.4.1.2.2 allows horizontal sidewall sprinklers to be installed less than 4 sin. (102 mm) from the wall to which they are mounted. This requirement is similar to the requirement in 8.6.4.1.1.2 for flush and concealed pendent sprinklers with respect to the position relative to the ceiling and allows the sprinkler to be mounted on the surface of a wall or soffit.

8.7.4.1.3 Lintels and Soffits.

8.7.4.1.3.1 Sidewall sprinklers shall only be installed along walls, lintels, or soffits where the distance from the ceiling to the bottom of the lintel or soffit is at least 2 in. (51 mm) greater than the distances from the ceiling to sidewall sprinkler deflectors.

8.7.4.1.3.2 Where soffits used for the installation of sidewall sprinklers exceed 8 in. (203 smm) in width or projection from the wall, additional sprinklers shall be installed below the soffit.

Lintels and soffits are covered in 8.7.4.1.3.1 and 8.7.4.1.3.2. The evaluation of a sidewall sprinkler includes testing of its ability to project water to the back wall area of a soffit and wall. This ability decreases as the depth of the soffit becomes greater; thus, the 8-in. (203-mm) maximum soffit is viewed as a maximum practical width. See Exhibit 8.23. When installing sidewall sprinklers in a back-to-back configuration as described in 8.7.3.1.4, the width of the soffit should not exceed 16 in. (406 mm).

EXHIBIT 8.23 *Sidewall Sprinkler Along a Soffit.*

$x \geq 2$ in. (51 mm) + y
y (see 5-7.4.1.1)
$z \leq 8$ in. (203 mm) (see 8.7.4.1.4)

Elevation

8.7.4.2 Deflector Orientation.

8.7.4.2.1 Deflectors of sprinklers shall be aligned parallel to ceilings or roofs.

 8.7.4.2.2 Sidewall sprinklers, where installed under a sloped ceiling with a slope exceeding 2 in 12, shall be located at the high point of the slope and positioned to discharge downward along the slope.

FAQ ▶
Where sidewall sprinklers are installed under a sloped ceiling, is it acceptable to install the sprinkler at the low point of the slope?

As stated in 8.7.4.2.2, when the ceiling is sloped, the sprinkler must be located on the high point of the slope, which is where heat from the fire collects. If sprinklers were located on any of the other three walls, a delay in sprinkler operation would occur.

By definition, a horizontal ceiling is one where the slope is less than 2 in 12. If the ceiling has a slope that is not flat, but is less than 2 in 12, it is not necessary to place the sprinklers at the high point, but the sprinkler deflectors must be parallel to the ceiling as required by 8.7.4.2.1 to allow the discharge pattern to develop without hitting the ceiling.

8.7.5 Obstructions to Sprinkler Discharge (Standard Sidewall Spray Sprinklers).

8.7.5.1 Performance Objective.

Performance objectives are covered in 8.7.5.1. Sidewall sprinklers are intended to be used in unobstructed construction for light hazard under smooth, horizontal, or sloped flat ceilings and for ordinary hazard occupancies under smooth flat ceilings where specifically listed for ordinary hazard occupancies and to protect areas under overhead doors [see 8.4.2(3)]. The sprinklers are very sensitive to obstructions, such as fluorescent light fixtures or beams located near or along the ceiling, that would impair the horizontal throw of water needed to provide proper coverage. However, obstructions cannot be avoided in all cases, and provisions are given for locating sidewall sprinklers so as to reduce the effect of obstructions.

8.7.5.1.1 Sprinklers shall be located so as to minimize obstructions to discharge as defined in 8.5.5.2 and 8.5.5.3, or additional sprinklers shall be provided to ensure adequate coverage of the hazard.

8.7.5.1.2 Sidewall sprinklers shall be installed no closer than 4 ft (1.2 m) from light fixtures or similar obstructions.

8.7.5.1.3 The distance between light fixtures or similar obstructions located more than 4 ft (1.2 m) from the sprinkler shall be in conformity with Table 8.7.5.1.3 and Figure 8.7.5.1.3.

TABLE 8.7.5.1.3 *Positioning of Sprinklers to Avoid Obstructions (Standard Sidewall Spray Sprinklers)*

Distance from Sidewall Sprinkler to Side of Obstruction (A)	Maximum Allowable Distance of Deflector above Bottom of Obstruction (in.) (B)
Less than 4 ft	Not allowed
4 ft to less than 5 ft	1
5 ft to less than 5 ft 6 in.	2
5 ft 6 in. to less than 6 ft	3
6 ft to less than 6 ft 6 in.	4
6 ft 6 in. to less than 7 ft	6
7 ft to less than 7 ft 6 in.	7
7 ft 6 in. to less than 8 ft	9
8 ft to less than 8 ft 6 in.	11
8 ft 6 in. or greater	14

For SI units, 1 in. = 25.4 mm; 1 ft = 0.3048 m.

Note: For *(A)* and *(B)*, refer to Figure 8.7.5.1.3.

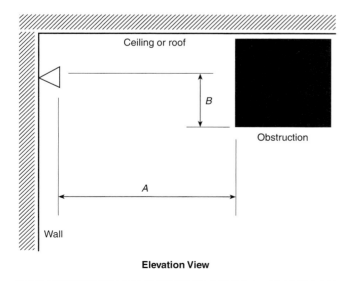

Elevation View

FIGURE 8.7.5.1.3 *Positioning of Sprinklers to Avoid Obstructions (Standard Sidewall Spray Sprinklers).*

Paragraph 8.7.5.1.3 is analogous to the provisions for solid continuous obstructions for upright and pendent spray sprinklers (see 8.6.5.1.2) and is intended to ensure the sprinkler discharge falls below the obstruction. Table 8.7.5.1.3 is based on the discharge pattern falling away from the ceiling in a descending trajectory pattern. The farther the ceiling obstruction is from the wall, the higher the deflector can be positioned with respect to the ceiling. The 2002 edition clarifies that the sprinkler must be located at least 4 ft (1.2 m) from an obstruction to allow the patterns to develop.

8.7.5.1.4 Obstructions projecting from the same wall as the one on which the sidewall sprinkler is mounted shall be in accordance with Table 8.7.5.1.4 and Figure 8.7.5.1.4.

TABLE 8.7.5.1.4 *Positioning of Sprinklers to Avoid Obstructions Along the Wall (Standard Sidewall Spray Sprinklers)*

Distance from Sidewall Sprinkler to Side of Obstruction (A)	*Maximum Allowable Distance of Deflector above Bottom of Obstruction (in.)* (B)
Less than 6 in.	1
6 in. to less than 1 ft	2
1 ft to less than 1 ft 6 in.	3
1 ft 6 in. to less than 2 ft	4½
2 ft to less than 2 ft 6 in.	5¾
2 ft 6 in. to less than 3 ft	7
3 ft to less than 3 ft 6 in.	8
3 ft 6 in. to less than 4 ft	9¼
4 ft to less than 4 ft 6 in.	10
4 ft 6 in. to less than 5 ft	11½
5 ft to less than 5 ft 6 in.	12¾
5 ft 6 in. to less than 6 ft	14
6 ft to less than 6 ft 6 in.	15
6 ft 6 in. to less than 7 ft	16¼
7 ft to less than 7 ft 6 in.	17½

For SI units, 1 in. = 25.4 mm; 1 ft = 0.3048 m.

Note: For *(A)* and *(B),* refer to Figure 8.7.5.1.4.

Sidewall sprinkler spray distribution is adversely affected by obstructions projecting out from the same wall on which the sprinkler is mounted, which is the reason for the requirement in 8.7.5.1.4. The effect is similar to the problems caused by a beam parallel to the wall on which the sprinkler is mounted (see 8.7.5.1.3). The obstruction prevents the sprinkler discharge from reaching the hazard on the other side of the obstruction. Because the sprinkler throw along the wall on which it is mounted is shorter than the throw outward, the sprinkler can be located closer to the obstruction.

8.7.5.2 Obstructions to Sprinkler Discharge Pattern Development.

Sidewall sprinklers, like upright and pendent sprinklers, must be located to avoid obstructions that affect the discharge pattern development or prevent the discharge from reaching the protected hazard. Paragraphs 8.7.5.2 through 8.7.5.3 on obstructions are similar in content to those for upright and pendent sprinklers in 8.6.5.2 through 8.6.5.3. Rather than assume that these types of obstructions do not exist, these requirements were added to NFPA 13 to address what to do when these obstructions are encountered. Other types of sprinklers such as upright or pendent should be used if the obstruction cannot be relocated or if the sidewall sprinkler cannot be repositioned along the wall to avoid the obstruction.

Elevation View

FIGURE 8.7.5.1.4 *Positioning of Sprinklers to Avoid Obstructions Along the Wall (Standard Sidewall Spray Sprinklers)*

8.7.5.2.1 General.

8.7.5.2.1.1 Continuous or noncontinuous obstructions less than or equal to 18 in. (457 mm) below the sprinkler deflector that prevent the pattern from fully developing shall comply with this section.

8.7.5.2.1.2 Regardless of the rules of this section, solid continuous obstructions shall meet the requirements of 8.7.5.1.2 and 8.7.5.1.3.

8.7.5.2.1.3* Unless the requirements of 8.7.5.2.1.4 or 8.7.5.2.1.5 are met, sprinklers shall be positioned away from obstructions a minimum distance of three times the maximum dimension of the obstruction (e.g., truss webs and chords, pipe, columns, and fixtures). The maximum clear distance required shall be 24 in. (609 mm) and shall be positioned in accordance with Figure 8.7.5.2.1.3 where obstructions are present.

A.8.7.5.2.1.3 The rules of 8.7.5.2.1.3 (known as the "Three Times Rule") have been written to apply to obstructions where the sprinkler can be expected to get water to both sides of the obstruction without allowing a significant dry shadow on the other side of the obstruction.

Plan View of Column   **Elevation View of Pipe Conduit or Light Fixture**

$A \geq 3C$ or $3D$
$A \leq 24$ in. (0.61 m)
(Use dimension C or D, whichever is greater)

FIGURE 8.7.5.2.1.3 *Minimum Distance from Obstruction (Standard Sidewall Spray Sprinkler).*

This works for small noncontinuous obstructions and for continuous obstructions where the sprinkler can throw water over and under the obstruction, such as the bottom chord of an open truss or joist. For solid continuous obstructions, such as a beam, the Three Times Rule is ineffective since the sprinkler cannot throw water over and under the obstruction. Sufficient water must be thrown under the obstruction to adequately cover the floor area on the other side of the obstruction. To ensure this, compliance with the rules of 8.7.5.1.2 is necessary.

8.7.5.2.1.4 The requirements of 8.7.5.2.1.3 shall not apply to the piping to which sidewall sprinklers are directly attached.

8.7.5.2.1.5 The requirements of 8.7.5.2.1.3 shall not apply where sprinklers are positioned with respect to obstructions in accordance with 8.7.5.1.2, 8.7.5.1.3, and 8.7.5.1.4.

8.7.5.2.2 Suspended or Floor-Mounted Vertical Obstructions. The distance from sprinklers to privacy curtains, free-standing partitions, room dividers, and similar obstructions in light hazard occupancies shall be in accordance with Table 8.7.5.2.2 and Figure 8.7.5.2.2.

TABLE 8.7.5.2.2 *Suspended or Floor-Mounted Obstructions (Standard Sidewall Spray Sprinklers)*

Horizontal Distance (A)	*Minimum Vertical Distance below Deflector (in.)* (B)
6 in. or less	3
More than 6 in. to 9 in.	4
More than 9 in. to 12 in.	6
More than 12 in. to 15 in.	8
More than 15 in. to 18 in.	9½
More than 18 in. to 24 in.	12½
More than 24 in. to 30 in.	15½
More than 30 in.	18

For SI units, 1 in. = 25.4 mm.

Note: For *(A)* and *(B)*, refer to Figure 8.7.5.2.2.

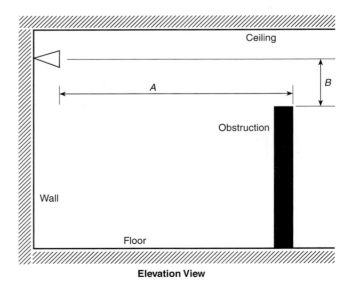

Elevation View

FIGURE 8.7.5.2.2 *Suspended or Floor-Mounted Obstructions (Standard Sidewall Spray Sprinklers).*

The distances specified in Table 8.7.5.2.2 were derived from NBSIR 80–2097.

The distance requirements of 8.7.5.2.2 and Figure 8.7.5.2.2 should not be applied beyond light hazard occupancies because the testing only evaluated sprinkler performance in a light hazard environment. The allowances of 8.7.5.2.2 have been misapplied, and to further clarify that the allowances of 8.7.5.2.2 apply to light hazard occupancies only, the 2002 edition has modified the titles of Table 8.7.5.2.2 and Figure 8.7.5.2.2 to include "in light hazard occupancies only."

◀ FAQ
Can the requirements
of 8.7.5.2.2 and
Figure 8.7.5.2.2 be utilized
in all occupancies?

8.7.5.3* Obstructions that Prevent Sprinkler Discharge from Reaching the Hazard.

A.8.7.5.3 See A.8.5.5.3.

A

8.7.5.3.1 Continuous or noncontinuous obstructions that interrupt the water discharge in a horizontal plane more than 18 in. (457 mm) below the sprinkler deflector in a manner to limit the distribution from reaching the protected hazard shall comply with this section.

8.7.5.3.2 Sprinklers shall be installed under fixed obstructions over 4 ft (1.2 m) wide such as ducts, decks, open grate flooring, cutting tables, and overhead doors.

8.7.5.3.3 Sprinklers shall not be required under obstructions that are not fixed in place such as conference tables.

8.7.6 Clearance to Storage (Standard Sidewall Spray Sprinklers). The clearance between the deflector and the top of storage shall be 18 in. (457 mm) or greater.

8.8 Extended Coverage Upright and Pendent Spray Sprinklers

Extended coverage upright and pendent spray sprinklers are covered in Section 8.8. In recent years, the number of extended coverage (EC) sprinklers has increased dramatically. Most manufacturers have models suitable for ordinary and light hazard occupancies. EC sprinklers have also become available for extra hazard occupancies and areas of high-piled storage. Many of the provisions in Section 8.8 are similar to those found in Section 8.6. The main difference is that EC sprinklers have larger protection areas and flatter distribution patterns than do standard spray pendent and upright sprinklers and, therefore, require greater separation distances from obstructions. Unless the rationale for the EC sprinkler requirements differs from those for standard upright and pendent sprinklers, commentary regarding related items in Section 8.6 is not repeated in Section 8.8 commentary.

8.8.1 General. All requirements of Section 8.5 shall apply to extended coverage upright and pendent sprinklers except as modified in Section 8.8.

8.8.2 Protection Areas per Sprinkler (Extended Coverage Upright and Pendent Spray Sprinklers).

8.8.2.1* Determination of the Protection Area of Coverage.

A.8.8.2.1 The protection area for extended coverage upright and pendent sprinklers is defined in the listing of the sprinkler as a maximum square area. Listing information is presented in even 2-ft (0.6-m) increments up to 20 ft (6.1 m). When a sprinkler is selected for an application, its area of coverage must be equal to or greater than both the length and width of the hazard area. For example, if the hazard to be protected is a room 13½ ft (4.1 m) wide and 17½ ft (5.3 m) long as indicated in Figure A.8.8.2.1, a sprinkler that is listed to protect an area of 18 ft × 18 ft (5.5 m × 5.5 m) must be selected. The flow used in the calculations is then selected as the flow required by the listing for the selected coverage.

FIGURE A.8.8.2.1 *Determination of Protection Area of Coverage for Extended Coverage Upright and Pendent Sprinklers.*

8.8.2.1.1 The protection area of coverage (A_s) for extended coverage sprinklers shall be not less than that prescribed by the listing.

8.8.2.1.2 Listing dimensions shall be even-numbered square protection areas as shown in Table 8.8.2.1.2.

FAQ ▶
Why are extended coverage sprinklers limited to square protection areas?

Restrictions are placed on the allowable spacing of upright and pendent EC sprinklers to promote interchangeability. As stated in 8.8.2.1.2, the protection area must be uniform—that is, a square pattern—so that the sprinkler can be installed without regard to the orientation of the frame arms. Limiting the spacing to even-numbered increments allows a variety of protection areas and promotes interchangeability among models from different manufacturers.

EC sprinklers are not allowed under combustible obstructed construction. Testing has shown that extending the sprinkler spacing under this type of construction allows the fire to ignite the ceiling, increasing the fire challenge and the potential for system failure.

TABLE 8.8.2.1.2 *Protection Areas and Maximum Spacing (Extended Coverage Upright and Pendent Spray Sprinklers)*

Construction Type	Light Hazard		Ordinary Hazard		Extra Hazard		High-Piled Storage	
	Protection Area (ft²)	Spacing (ft)	Protection Area (ft²)	Spacing (ft)	Protection Area (ft²)	Spacing (ft)	Protection Area (ft²)	Spacing (ft)
Unobstructed	400	20	400	20	—	—	—	—
	324	18	324	18	—	—	—	—
	256	16	256	16	—	—	—	—
	—	—	196	14	196	14	196	14
	—	—	144	12	144	12	144	12
Obstructed noncombustible	400	20	400	20	—	—	—	—
(when specifically listed	324	18	324	18	—	—	—	—
for such use)	256	16	256	16	—	—	—	—
	—	—	196	14	196	14	196	14
	—	—	144	12	144	12	144	12
Obstructed combustible	N/A	N/A	N/A	N/A	N/A	N/A	N/A	N/A

For SI units, 1 ft = 0.3048 m; 1 ft² = 0.0929 m².

8.8.2.1.3 Determination of the protection area of coverage and sprinkler spacing for sprinklers listed for extended coverage extra hazard or high-piled storage shall be permitted to be spaced in accordance with the requirements of 8.5.2 and 8.5.3 and shall not exceed 14 ft (4.3 m) maximum spacing and 196 ft^2 (18.2 m^2) maximum area per sprinkler.

Due to the fact that extended coverage sprinklers used in extra hazard and storage occupancies are limited by 8.8.2.1.3 to a maximum of 14 ft between sprinklers (a minimal increase considering the 12 ft allowed for upright and pendant sprinklers), and the fact that pressure is not as much of a factor in obtaining the extended spacing, the protection area for these sprinklers does not have to be a square pattern. The protection area for these sprinklers is calculated in the same manner as standard upright and pendant sprinklers.

◀ FAQ
Why are extended coverage sprinklers listed for extra hazard or high-piled storage permitted to be used per the requirements of 8.5.2 and 8.5.3?

8.8.2.2 Maximum Protection Area of Coverage.

8.8.2.2.1 The maximum allowable area of coverage for a sprinkler (A_s) shall be in accordance with the value indicated in Table 8.8.2.1.2.

8.8.2.2.2 In any case, the maximum area of coverage of a sprinkler shall not exceed 400 ft^2 (37.1 m^2).

The maximum protection area of coverage is addressed in 8.8.2.2.1 and 8.8.2.2.2. The maximum area of coverage for an EC sprinkler limits the area that would be unprotected should a sprinkler be severely obstructed or fail to operate. The limit of 196 ft^2 (18.2 m^2) for extra hazard and high-piled storage considers that fires in these occupancies develop much more rapidly than fires in light and ordinary hazard occupancies and can overtax adjacent sprinklers should one sprinkler not operate as anticipated.

8.8.3 Sprinkler Spacing (Extended Coverage Upright and Pendent Spray Sprinklers).

8.8.3.1 Maximum Distance Between Sprinklers.

8.8.3.1.1 The maximum distance permitted between sprinklers shall be based on the centerline distance between sprinklers on the branch line or on adjacent branch lines.

8.8.3.1.2 The maximum distance shall be measured along the slope of the ceiling.

8.8.3.1.3 The maximum distance permitted between sprinklers shall comply with Table 8.8.2.1.2.

8.8.3.2 Maximum Distance from Walls.

8.8.3.2.1 The distance from sprinklers to walls shall not exceed one-half of the allowable distance permitted between sprinklers as indicated in Table 8.8.2.1.2.

8.8.3.2.2 The distance from the wall to the sprinkler shall be measured perpendicular to the wall.

8.8.3.2.3 Where walls are angled or irregular, the maximum horizontal distance between a sprinkler and any point of floor area protected by that sprinkler shall not exceed 0.75 times the allowable distance permitted between sprinklers.

8.8.3.3 Minimum Distance from Walls. Sprinklers shall be located a minimum of 4 in. (102 mm) from a wall unless listed for distances less than 4 in. (102 mm).

8.8.3.4 Minimum Distance Between Sprinklers.

8.8.3.4.1 Unless the requirements of 8.8.3.4.2 are met, sprinklers shall be spaced not less than 8 ft (2.4 m) on center.

8.8.3.4.2 Sprinklers shall be permitted to be placed less than 8 ft (2.4 m) on center where the following conditions are satisfied:

(1) Baffles shall be installed and located midway between sprinklers and arranged to protect the actuating elements.
(2) Baffles shall be of noncombustible or limited-combustible material that will stay in place before and during sprinkler operation.
(3) Baffles shall be not less than 8 in. (203 mm) wide and 6 in. (152 mm) high.
(4) The tops of baffles shall extend between 2 in. and 3 in. (51 mm and 76 mm) above the deflectors of upright sprinklers.
(5) The bottoms of baffles shall extend downward to a level at least even with the deflectors of pendent sprinklers.

8.8.4 Deflector Position (Extended Coverage Upright and Pendent Spray Sprinklers).

8.8.4.1 Distance Below Ceilings.

8.8.4.1.1 Unobstructed Construction.

 8.8.4.1.1.1 Under unobstructed construction, the distance between the sprinkler deflector and the ceiling shall be a minimum of 1 in. (25.4 mm) and a maximum of 12 in. (305 mm) throughout the area of coverage of the sprinkler.

FAQ ▶
Are the requirements of 8.8.4.1.1.1 applicable to the area directly above the sprinkler deflector or are they applicable to the entire area of coverage for the sprinkler?

The 2002 edition modified the text of 8.8.4.1.1.1 to further clarify the measurement of the deflector distance. As stated in 8.6.4.1.1.1, it is the intent that the 1 in. to 12 in. limit be applied to the entire area of coverage of the sprinkler.

Additional text was also added in 8.8.4.1.1.3 to address ceilings having vertical changes in elevation. See commentary on 8.6.4.1.1.3.

8.8.4.1.1.2 The requirements of 8.8.4.1.1.1 shall not apply where ceiling-type sprinklers (concealed, recessed, and flush types) have the operating element above the ceiling and the deflector located nearer to the ceiling where installed in accordance with their listing.

8.8.4.1.1.3 The requirements of 8.8.4.1.1.1 shall not apply where sprinklers are listed for use under other ceiling construction features or for different distances where they shall be permitted to be installed in accordance with their listing.

 8.8.4.1.1.4 The requirements of 8.8.4.1.1.1 shall not apply for light and ordinary hazard occupancies with ceilings of noncombustible or limited combustible construction. Where there is a vertical change in ceiling elevation within the area of coverage of the sprinkler creating a distance of more than 36 in. between the upper ceiling and the sprinkler deflector, a vertical plane extending down from the ceiling at the change in elevation shall be considered a wall for the purpose of sprinkler spacing. Where the distance between the upper ceiling and the sprinkler deflector is less than or equal to 36 in., the sprinklers shall be permitted to be spaced as though the ceiling was flat provided the obstruction rules and ceiling pocket rules are observed. *(See Figure 8.8.4.1.1.4.)*

Many buildings use irregular ceilings, which are discussed in 8.8.4.1.1.4, as a design feature. These irregular ceilings might include soffits around the perimeter, pockets purely for decorative purposes, stepped ceilings, and beams in the center to break the space up. Conference facilities at hotels are a good example of where this type of construction is used. These facilities may also have temporary partitions that can be opened and closed to separate a space into two or more separate rooms. Often these ceiling height changes are limited, while in other cases pockets or elevation changes can be quite varied. The placement of sprinklers can be challenging in these spaces if all of the rules in NFPA 13 are followed.

x 36 in. (0.91 m)
s = Maximum allowable distance
between sprinklers

Maximum ½ *s*

Maximum ½ *s*

Vertical plane treated as wall
for sprinkler spacing

x > 36 in. (0.91 m)
s = Maximum allowable distance
between sprinklers

FIGURE 8.8.4.1.1.4 *Vertical Changes in
Ceiling Elevations.*

Additional guidance for pockets and ceiling height changes was introduced in the 2002 edition of the standard and allows for protection of these spaces without the use of all the sprinklers that might be required under the previous rules. In simple terms, if the change in ceiling elevation exceeds 36 in. (0.9 m), the change in elevation is treated like a wall and sprinklers are spaced accordingly. If the change is less than 36 in. (0.9 m), then the ceiling is assumed to be flat (as long as the upper sprinkler is spaced so that it can throw underneath the lower ceiling) and the sprinklers are spaced accordingly. If the change in elevation is close enough to the sprinkler located at the ceiling that the sprinkler cannot develop its pattern, then the elevation change is treated like an obstruction and additional sprinklers must be added accordingly. See Figure 8.8.4.1.1.4. It is important to note that sprinklers are required within the upper ceiling area unless the requirements for unprotected ceiling pockets in 8.8.7 can be met.

◄ FAQ
How should changes in ceiling elevation be treated?

8.8.4.1.2 Obstructed Construction. Under obstructed construction, the sprinkler deflector shall be located in accordance with one of the following arrangements:

(1) Installed with the deflectors within the horizontal planes of 1 in. to 6 in. (25.4 mm to 152 mm) below the structural members and a maximum distance of 22 in. (559 mm) below the ceiling/roof deck.

(2) Installed with the deflectors at or above the bottom of the structural member to a maximum of 22 in. (559 mm) below the ceiling/roof deck where the sprinkler is installed in conformance with 8.8.5.1.2.

(3) Installed in each bay of obstructed construction, with the deflectors located a minimum of 1 in. (25.4 mm) and a maximum of 12 in. (305 mm) below the ceiling.
(4) Where sprinklers are listed for use under other ceiling construction features or for different distances, they shall be permitted to be installed in accordance with their listing.

8.8.4.1.3* Peaked Roofs and Ceilings. Sprinklers under or near the peak of a roof or ceiling shall have deflectors located not more than 3 ft (0.9 m) vertically down from the peak in accordance with Figure 8.6.4.1.3.1(a) and Figure 8.6.4.1.3.1(b).

 A.8.8.4.1.3 Saw-toothed roofs have regularly spaced monitors of saw tooth shape, with the nearly vertical side glazed and usually arranged for venting. Sprinkler placement is limited to a maximum of 3 ft (0.91 m) down the slope from the peak because of the effect of venting on sprinkler sensitivity.

Peaked roofs and ceilings are discussed in 8.8.4.1.3. The installation of EC sprinklers under peaked roofs rarely occurs due to the limitations on ceiling slope outlined in 8.4.3. When EC sprinklers are specifically listed for slopes of up to 4 in./ft, 8.4.3(4) may come into play if the maximum allowable sprinkler spacing is used.

8.8.4.2 Deflector Orientation. Deflectors of sprinklers shall be aligned parallel to ceilings or roofs.

8.8.5 Obstructions to Sprinkler Discharge (Extended Coverage Upright and Pendent Spray Sprinklers).

Obstructions to sprinkler discharge are covered in 8.8.5. The provisions covering the location and placement of EC sprinklers are similar to those for standard spray sprinklers. Because their spray pattern is flatter and their throw is longer than standard spray sprinklers, EC sprinklers must be placed further away from obstructions than standard spray sprinklers. In addition, all obstructions must be considered, regardless of the occupancy hazard. The obstruction of the bottom chord must be considered even when the sprinkler is located in the centerline of a joist or truss. Also see commentary to Section 8.6.

8.8.5.1 Performance Objective.

8.8.5.1.1 Sprinklers shall be located so as to minimize obstructions to discharge as defined in 8.8.5.2 and 8.8.5.3, or additional sprinklers shall be provided to ensure adequate coverage of the hazard.

8.8.5.1.2 Sprinklers shall be arranged to comply with one of the following arrangements:

(1) Sprinklers shall be in accordance with 8.5.5.2, Table 8.8.5.1.2, and Figure 8.8.5.1.2(a).
(2) Sprinklers shall be permitted to be spaced on opposite sides of obstructions not exceeding 4 ft (1.2 m) in width provided the distance from the centerline of the obstruction to the sprinklers does not exceed one-half the allowable distance permitted between sprinklers.
(3) Obstructions located against the wall and that are not over 30 in. (762 mm) in width shall be permitted to be protected in accordance with Figure 8.8.5.1.2(b).

8.8.5.2 Obstructions to Sprinkler Discharge Pattern Development.

8.8.5.2.1 General.

8.8.5.2.1.1 Continuous or noncontinuous obstructions less than or equal to 18 in. (457 mm) below the sprinkler deflector that prevent the pattern from fully developing shall comply with 8.8.5.2.

8.8.5.2.1.2 Regardless of the rules of this section, solid continuous obstructions shall meet the applicable requirements of 8.8.5.1.2.

TABLE 8.8.5.1.2 *Position of Sprinklers to Avoid Obstructions to Discharge (Extended Coverage Upright and Pendent Spray Sprinklers)*

Distance from Sprinklers to Side of Obstruction (**A**)	Maximum Allowable Distance of Deflector above Bottom of Obstruction (in.) (**B**)
Less than 1 ft	0
1 ft to less than 1 ft 6 in.	0
1 ft 6 in. to less than 2 ft	1
2 ft to less than 2 ft 6 in.	1
2 ft 6 in. to less than 3 ft	1
3 ft to less than 3 ft 6 in.	3
3 ft 6 in. to less than 4 ft	3
4 ft to less than 4 ft 6 in.	5
4 ft 6 in. to less than 5 ft	7
5 ft to less than 5 ft 6 in.	7
5 ft 6 in. to less than 6 ft	7
6 ft to less than 6 ft 6 in.	9
6 ft 6 in. to less than 7 ft	11
7 ft and greater	14

For SI units, 1 in. = 25.4 mm; 1 ft = 0.3048 m.

Note: For *(A)* and *(B)*, refer to Figure 8.8.5.1.2(a).

8.8.5.2.1.3* Unless the requirements of 8.8.5.2.1.4 through 8.8.5.2.1.9 are met, sprinklers shall be positioned away from obstructions a minimum distance of four times the maximum dimension of the obstruction (e.g., truss webs and chords, pipe, columns, and fixtures). The maximum clear distance required shall be 36 in. (0.91 m) in accordance with Figure 8.8.5.2.1.3.

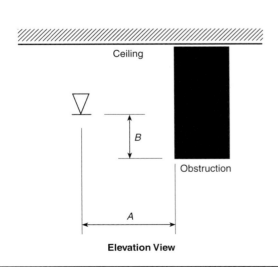

FIGURE 8.8.5.1.2(a) *Position of Sprinklers to Avoid Obstructions to Discharge (Extended Coverage Upright and Pendent Spray Sprinklers).*

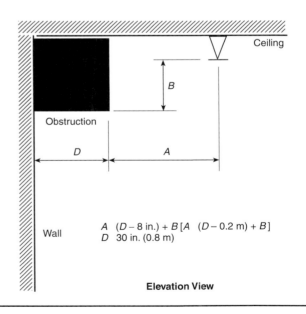

FIGURE 8.8.5.1.2(b) *Obstructions Against Walls (Extended Coverage Upright and Pendent Spray Sprinklers).*

Plan View of Column   Elevation View of Truss

A   4C or 4D
A   36 in. (0.91 m)
(Use dimension C or D, whichever is greater)

FIGURE 8.8.5.2.1.3 *Minimum Distance from Obstruction (Extended Coverage Upright and Pendent Spray Sprinklers).*

 A.8.8.5.2.1.3 The rules of 8.8.5.2.1.3 (known as the "Four Times Rule") have been written to apply to obstructions where the sprinkler can be expected to get water to both sides of the obstruction without allowing a significant dry shadow on the other side of the obstruction. This works for small noncontinuous obstructions and for continuous obstructions where the sprinkler can throw water over and under the obstruction, such as the bottom chord of an open truss or joist. For solid continuous obstructions, such as a beam, the Four Times Rule is ineffective since the sprinkler cannot throw water over and under the obstruction. Sufficient water must be thrown under the obstruction to adequately cover the floor area on the other side of the obstruction. To ensure this, compliance with the rules of 8.8.5.1.2 is necessary.

8.8.5.2.1.4 Sprinklers shall be permitted to be spaced on opposite sides of the obstruction where the distance from the centerline of the obstruction to the sprinklers does not exceed one-half the allowable distance between sprinklers.

8.8.5.2.1.5 Sprinklers shall be permitted to be located one-half the distance between the obstructions where the obstruction consists of open trusses 20 in. (0.51 m) or greater apart [24 in. (0.61 m) on center], provided that all truss members are not greater than 4 in. (102 mm) (nominal) in width and web members do not exceed 1 in. (25.4 mm) in width.

8.8.5.2.1.6 Sprinklers shall be permitted to be installed on the centerline of a truss or bar joist or directly above a beam provided that the truss chord or beam dimension is not more than 8 in. (203 mm) and the sprinkler deflector is located at least 6 in. (152 mm) above the structural member and where the sprinkler is positioned at a distance four times greater than the maximum dimension of the web members away from the web members.

8.8.5.2.1.7 The requirements of 8.8.5.2.1.3 shall not apply to the piping to which an upright sprinkler is directly attached less than 3 in. (75 mm) in diameter.

8.8.5.2.1.8 The requirements of 8.8.5.2.1.3 shall not apply to the piping to which pendent sprinklers are directly attached.

8.8.5.2.1.9 The requirements of 8.8.5.2.1.3 shall not apply to sprinklers positioned with respect to obstructions in accordance with 8.8.5.1.2.

8.8.5.2.2 Suspended or Floor-Mounted Vertical Obstructions. The distance from sprinklers to privacy curtains, free-standing partitions, room dividers, and similar obstructions in light hazard occupancies shall be in accordance with Table 8.8.5.2.2 and Figure 8.8.5.2.2.

TABLE 8.8.5.2.2 *Suspended or Floor-Mounted Obstructions (Extended Coverage Upright and Pendent Spray Sprinklers)*

Horizontal Distance (A)	Minimum Vertical Distance below Deflector (in.) (B)
6 in. or less	3
More than 6 in. to 9 in.	4
More than 9 in. to 12 in.	6
More than 12 in. to 15 in.	8
More than 15 in. to 18 in.	9½
More than 18 in. to 24 in.	12½
More than 24 in. to 30 in.	15½
More than 30 in.	18

For SI units, 1 in. = 25.4 mm.

Note: For *(A)* and *(B)*, refer to Figure 8.8.5.2.2.

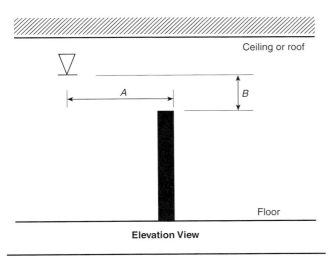

Elevation View

FIGURE 8.8.5.2.2 *Suspended or Floor-Mounted Obstructions (Extended Coverage Upright and Pendent Spray Sprinklers).*

8.8.5.3* Obstructions that Prevent Sprinkler Discharge from Reaching the Hazard.

A.8.8.5.3 See A.8.5.5.3.

8.8.5.3.1 Continuous or noncontinuous obstructions that interrupt the water discharge in a horizontal plane more than 18 in. (457 mm) below the sprinkler deflector in a manner to limit the distribution from reaching the protected hazard shall comply with 8.8.5.3.

8.8.5.3.2 Sprinklers shall be installed under fixed obstructions over 4 ft (1.2 m) wide such as ducts, decks, open grate flooring, cutting tables, and overhead doors.

8.8.5.3.3 Sprinklers shall not be required under obstructions that are not fixed in place such as conference tables.

8.8.5.3.4 Sprinklers installed under open gratings shall be of the intermediate level/rack storage type or otherwise shielded from the discharge of overhead sprinklers.

8.8.6 Clearance to Storage (Extended Coverage Upright and Pendent Spray Sprinklers).

8.8.6.1 The clearance between the deflector and the top of storage shall be 18 in. (457 mm) or greater.

8.8.6.2 Where other standards specify greater clearance to storage minimums, they shall be followed.

 8.8.7 Ceiling Pockets.

8.8.7.1 Sprinklers shall be required in all ceiling pockets.

8.8.7.2 The requirements of 8.8.7.1 shall not apply where all of the following are met:

(1) The total volume of the unprotected ceiling pocket does not exceed 1000 ft^3.
(2) The depth of the unprotected pocket does not exceed 36 in.
(3) The entire floor under the unprotected ceiling pocket is protected by the sprinklers at the lower ceiling elevation.
(4) Each unprotected ceiling pocket is separated from any adjacent unprotected ceiling pocket by a minimum 10 ft horizontal distance.
(5) The unprotected ceiling pocket is constructed of noncombustible or limited combustible construction.
(6) Skylights not exceeding 32 ft^2 shall be permitted to have a plastic cover.
(7) Quick response sprinklers are utilized throughout the compartment.

Ceiling pockets are covered in 8.8.7.1 and 8.8.7.2. In past years the standard assumed that sprinklers would be located in all ceiling pockets, with the exception of small [4 ft × 8 ft (1.2 m × 2.4 m)] skylights. There has always been a concern that unless a sprinkler was placed in each pocket, heat would collect in the pocket and delay the operation of sprinklers. Some fire modeling was done to estimate the impact ceiling pockets would have on sprinkler response at the lower ceiling elevation and to determine what type of pockets could be left unsprinklered. After reviewing the modeling results and field experience, new rules have been added to the 2002 edition to address these situations. To ensure adequate protection of the space, the following requirements were developed by the committee:

1. The volume of the pocket must be limited to no more than 1000 ft^3 [see 8.8.7.2(1)] and the depth of the pocket must be limited to 36 in. [see 8.8.7.2(2)].
2. The entire floor area must be covered by the sprinkler discharge of the sprinklers at the lower ceiling [see 8.8.7.2(3)] and quick-response sprinklers must be used throughout the space [8.8.7.2(7)].
3. The pocket must be of noncombustible or limited combustible construction [see 8.8.7.2(5)] with the allowance for small skylights (less than or equal to 32 ft^2), which are allowed to have a plastic cover [see 8.8.7.2(6)].
4. Finally, to ensure that there is no impact from heat collecting from adjacent unprotected ceiling pockets or skylights, a 10 ft (3 m) separation must be maintained between unprotected ceiling pockets and skylights [see 8.8.7.2(4)].

 For additional information on the effect of ceiling pockets on sprinkler activation, see AFSA report "Evaluating the Impact of Ceiling Pockets on Sprinkler Activation."

8.9 Extended Coverage Sidewall Spray Sprinklers

Most of the provisions in Section 8.9 are similar to those found in Section 8.7. The main difference is that EC sidewall sprinklers have larger protection areas and flatter distribution patterns than standard spray sidewall sprinklers and, therefore, require greater separation distances from obstructions. Unless the rationale for the EC sprinkler requirements differs from those for standard sidewall sprinklers, commentary regarding related items in Section 8.7 is not repeated in Section 8.9 commentary.

8.9.1 General. All requirements of Section 8.5 shall apply to extended coverage sidewall spray sprinklers except as modified in Section 8.9.

8.9.2 Protection Areas per Sprinkler (Extended Coverage Sidewall Spray Sprinklers).

8.9.2.1* Determination of the Protection Area of Coverage.

A.8.9.2.1 The protection area for extended coverage sidewall spray sprinklers is defined in the listing of the sprinkler as a maximum square or rectangular area. Listing information is presented in even 2-ft (0.65-m) increments up to 28 ft (9 m) for extended coverage sidewall spray sprinklers. When a sprinkler is selected for an application, its area of coverage must be equal to or greater than both the length and width of the hazard area. For example, if the hazard to be protected is a room 14½ ft (4.4 m) wide and 20 ft (6.3 m) long as indicated in Figure A.8.9.2.1, a sprinkler that is listed to protect an area of 16 ft × 22 ft (4.9 m × 6.7 m) must be selected. The flow used in the calculations is then selected as the flow required by the listing for the selected coverage.

FIGURE A.8.9.2.1 *Determination of Protection Area of Coverage for Extended Coverage Sidewall Sprinklers.*

8.9.2.1.1 The protection area of coverage per sprinkler (A_s) for extended coverage sidewall sprinklers shall be not less than that prescribed by the listing.

8.9.2.1.2 Listing dimensions shall be in 2 ft (0.61 m) increments up to 28 ft (8.5 m).

Restrictions are placed on the allowable spacing of EC sidewall sprinklers to maintain a degree of order and to promote interchangeability. Limiting the spacing to even-numbered increments (see 8.9.2.1.2) allows a variety of protection areas and promotes interchangeability between models from different manufacturers.

8.9.2.2 Maximum Protection Area of Coverage.

8.9.2.2.1 The maximum allowable protection area of coverage for a sprinkler (A_s) shall be in accordance with the value indicated in Table 8.9.2.2.1.

TABLE 8.9.2.2.1 *Protection Area and Maximum Spacing for Extended Coverage Sidewall Sprinklers*

| | Light Hazard | | | | Ordinary Hazard | | | |
| | Protection Area | | Spacing | | Protection Area | | Spacing | |
Construction Type	ft²	m²	ft	m	ft²	m²	ft	m
Unobstructed, smooth, flat	400	37.2	28	8.5	400	37.2	24	7.3

8.9.2.2.2 In any case, the maximum area of coverage of a sprinkler shall not exceed 400 ft² (37.1 m²).

8.9.3 Sprinkler Spacing (Extended Coverage Sidewall Spray Sprinklers).

8.9.3.1 Maximum Distance Between Sprinklers.

8.9.3.1.1 The maximum distance permitted between sprinklers shall be based on the center-line distance between sprinklers on the branch line along the wall.

8.9.3.1.2 Where sprinklers are installed along the length of a single wall of rooms or bays they shall be spaced in accordance with the maximum spacing provisions of Table 8.9.2.2.1.

8.9.3.1.3 Sidewall sprinklers shall not be installed back-to-back without being separated by a continuous lintel, soffit, or baffle.

8.9.3.1.4 Sidewall sprinklers shall be permitted to be installed on opposing or adjacent walls provided no sprinkler is located within the maximum protection area of another sprinkler.

8.9.3.2 Maximum Distance from Walls. The distance from sprinklers to the end walls shall not exceed one-half of the allowable distance permitted between sprinklers as indicated in Table 8.9.2.2.1.

8.9.3.3 Minimum Distance from Walls.

8.9.3.3.1 Sprinklers shall be located a minimum of 4 in. (102 mm) from an end wall.

8.9.3.3.2 The distance from the wall to the sprinkler shall be measured perpendicular to the wall.

8.9.3.4 Minimum Distance Between Sprinklers. No sprinklers shall be located within the maximum protection area of any other sprinkler.

8.9.4 Deflector Position from Ceilings and Walls (Extended Coverage Sidewall Spray Sprinklers).

8.9.4.1 Distance Below Ceilings and from Walls to Which Sprinklers are Mounted.

8.9.4.1.1 Ceilings.

8.9.4.1.1.1 Unless the requirements of 8.9.4.1.1.2 are met, sidewall sprinkler deflectors shall be located not more than 6 in. (152 mm) nor less than 4 in. (102 mm) from ceilings.

8.9.4.1.1.2 Horizontal sidewall sprinklers shall be permitted to be located in a zone 6 in. to 12 in. (152 mm to 305 mm) or 12 in. to 18 in. (305 mm to 457 mm) below noncombustible or limited-combustible ceilings where listed for such use.

8.9.4.1.2 Walls.

8.9.4.1.2.1 Sidewall sprinkler deflectors shall be located not more than 6 in. (152 mm) or less than 4 in. (102 mm) from walls on which they are mounted.

8.9.4.1.2.2 Horizontal sidewall sprinklers shall be permitted to be located with their deflectors less than 4 in. (102 mm) from the wall on which they are mounted.

8.9.4.1.3 Lintels and Soffits.

8.9.4.1.3.1 Sidewall sprinklers shall only be installed along walls, lintels, or soffits where the distance from the ceiling to the bottom of the lintel or soffit is at least 2 in. (51 mm) greater than the distances from the ceiling to sidewall sprinkler deflectors.

8.9.4.1.3.2 Where soffits used for the installation of sidewall sprinklers exceed 8 in. (203 mm) in width or projection from the wall, additional sprinklers shall be installed below the soffit.

8.9.4.2 Deflector Orientation.

8.9.4.2.1 Deflectors of sprinklers shall be aligned parallel to ceilings or roofs.

8.9.4.2.2 Sidewall sprinklers, where installed under a sloped ceiling with a slope exceeding 2 in 12, shall be located at the high point of the slope and positioned to discharge downward along the slope.

As stated in 8.9.4.2.2, when the ceiling is sloped, the sprinkler must be located on the high point of the slope, which is where heat from the fire collects. If sprinklers were located on any of the other three walls, a delay in sprinkler operation would occur.

By definition, a horizontal ceiling is one where the slope is less than 2 in 12. If the ceiling has a slope that is not flat but is less than 2 in 12, it is not necessary to place the sprinklers at the high point, but the sprinkler deflectors must be parallel to the ceiling as required by 8.9.4.2.1 to allow the discharge pattern to develop without hitting the ceiling.

◀ **FAQ**
Where sidewall sprinklers are installed under a sloped ceiling, is it acceptable to install the sprinkler at the low point of the slope?

8.9.4.2.3 Sidewall sprinklers specifically listed for other ceiling configurations shall be permitted to be installed in accordance with the listing requirements.

The requirements of 8.9.4.2.3 were added to the 1999 edition because listings have been achieved for sidewall sprinklers located along the sloping wall of a sloped ceiling room.

8.9.5 Obstructions to Sprinkler Discharge (Extended Coverage Sidewall Spray Sprinklers).

8.9.5.1 Performance Objective.

8.9.5.1.1 Sprinklers shall be located so as to minimize obstructions to discharge as defined in 8.5.5.2 and 8.5.5.3, or additional sprinklers shall be provided to ensure adequate coverage of the hazard.

8.9.5.1.2 Sidewall sprinklers shall be installed no closer than 8 ft (2.4 m) from light fixtures or similar obstructions.

8.9.5.1.3 The distance between light fixtures or similar obstructions located more than 8 ft (2.4 m) from the sprinkler shall be in conformity with Table 8.9.5.1.3 and Figure 8.9.5.1.3.

8.9.5.2 Obstructions to Sprinkler Discharge Pattern Development.

8.9.5.2.1 General.

TABLE 8.9.5.1.3 *Positioning of Sprinklers to Avoid Obstructions (Extended Coverage Sidewall Sprinklers)*

Distance from Sidewall Sprinkler to Side of Obstruction (A)	Maximum Allowable Distance of Deflector above Bottom of Obstruction (in.) (B)
Less than 8 ft	Not allowed
8 ft to less than 10 ft	1
10 ft to less than 11 ft	2
11 ft to less than 12 ft	3
12 ft to less than 13 ft	4
13 ft to less than 14 ft	6
14 ft to less than 15 ft	7
15 ft to less than 16 ft	9
16 ft to less than 17 ft	11
17 ft or greater	14

For SI units, 1 in. = 25.4 mm; 1 ft = 0.3048 m.

Note: For *(A)* and *(B),* refer to Figure 8.9.5.1.3.

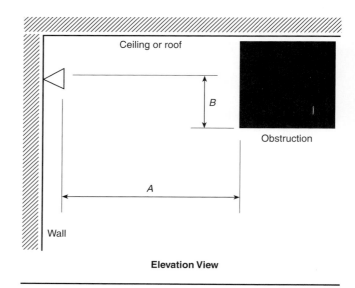

Elevation View

FIGURE 8.9.5.1.3 *Positioning of Sprinklers to Avoid Obstructions (Extended Coverage Sidewall Sprinklers).*

8.9.5.2.1.1 Continuous or noncontinuous obstructions less than or equal to 18 in. (457 mm) below the sprinkler deflector that prevent the pattern from fully developing shall comply with this section.

8.9.5.2.1.2 Regardless of the rules of this section, solid continuous obstructions shall meet the requirements of 8.9.5.1.2 and 8.9.5.1.3.

8.9.5.2.1.3* Unless the requirements of 8.9.5.2.1.4 or 8.9.5.2.1.5 are met, sprinklers shall be positioned away from obstructions a minimum distance of four times the maximum dimension of the obstruction (e.g., truss webs and chords, pipe, columns, and fixtures). The maximum clear distance required shall be 36 in. (0.91 m) from the sprinkler.

A.8.9.5.2.1.3 The rules of 8.9.5.2.1.3 (known as the "Four Times Rule") have been written to apply to obstructions where the sprinkler can be expected to get water to both sides of the obstruction without allowing a significant dry shadow on the other side of the obstruction. This works for small noncontinuous obstructions and for continuous obstructions where the sprinkler can throw water over and under the obstruction, such as the bottom chord of an open truss or joist. For solid continuous obstructions, such as a beam, the Four Times Rule is ineffective since the sprinkler cannot throw water over and under the obstruction. Sufficient water must be thrown under the obstruction to adequately cover the floor area on the other side of the obstruction. To ensure this, compliance with the rules of 8.9.5.1.2 is necessary.

8.9.5.2.1.4 Sidewall sprinklers shall be positioned in accordance with Figure 8.9.5.2.1.4 when obstructions are present.

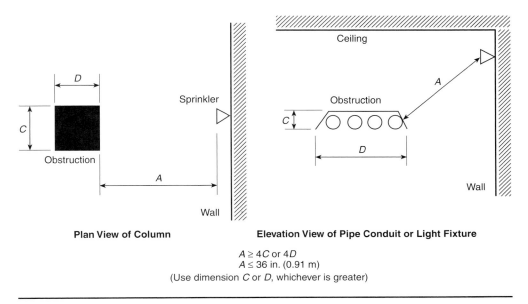

FIGURE 8.9.5.2.1.4 *Minimum Distance from Obstruction (Extended Coverage Sidewall).*

8.9.5.2.1.5 The requirements of 8.9.5.2.1.3 and 8.9.5.2.1.4 shall not apply where sprinklers are positioned with respect to obstructions in accordance with 8.9.5.1.2 and 8.9.5.1.3.

8.9.5.2.2 Suspended or Floor-Mounted Vertical Obstructions. The distance from sprinklers to privacy curtains, free-standing partitions, room dividers, and similar obstructions in light hazard occupancies shall be in accordance with Table 8.9.5.2.2 and Figure 8.9.5.2.2.

8.9.5.3* **Obstructions that Prevent Sprinkler Discharge from Reaching the Hazard.**

A.8.9.5.3 See A.8.5.5.3.

8.9.5.3.1 Continuous or noncontinuous obstructions that interrupt the water discharge in a horizontal plane more than 18 in. (457 mm) below the sprinkler deflector in a manner to limit the distribution from reaching the protected hazard shall comply with this section.

8.9.5.3.2 Sprinklers shall be installed under fixed obstructions over 4 ft (1.2 m) wide such as ducts, decks, open grate flooring, cutting tables, and overhead doors.

8.9.5.3.3 Sprinklers shall not be required under obstructions that are not fixed in place such as conference tables.

TABLE 8.9.5.2.2 *Suspended or Floor-Mounted Obstructions (Extended Coverage Sidewall Sprinklers)*

Horizontal Distance (A)	Minimum Allowable Distance below Deflector (in.) (B)
6 in. or less	3
More than 6 in. to 9 in.	4
More than 9 in. to 12 in.	6
More than 12 in. to 15 in.	8
More than 15 in. to 18 in.	9½
More than 18 in. to 24 in.	12½
More than 24 in. to 30 in.	15½
More than 30 in.	18

For SI units, 1 in. = 25.4 mm.

Note: For *(A)* and *(B)*, refer to Figure 8.9.5.2.2.

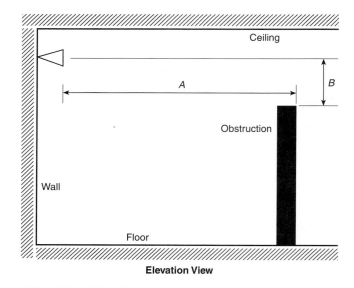

Elevation View

FIGURE 8.9.5.2.2 *Suspended or Floor-Mounted Obstructions (Extended Coverage Sidewall Sprinklers).*

8.10 Residential Sprinklers

Previous editions of NFPA 13 referred the user to NFPA 13D and NFPA 13R for location and positioning requirements of residential sprinklers and to the rules for extended coverage sprinklers for obstruction rules. To minimize the potential for confusion, Section 8.10 now contains guidance for residential sprinklers. No changes in intent have been made. As always, the manufacturer's requirements must also be followed. Since the rules here are similar to those in Sections 8.8 and 8.9, commentary from related items is not repeated in the Section 8.10 commentary.

8.10.1 Reserved

8.10.2 Areas of coverage shall be in accordance with the manufacturer's listing.

8.10.3 Distances Between Sprinklers.

8.10.3.1 Maximum distances between sprinklers shall be in accordance with the manufacturer's listing.

8.10.3.2 The distance between the sprinkler and the wall shall not exceed half the maximum allowable distance between sprinklers per the manufacturer's listing.

8.10.3.3 The minimum distance between sprinklers within a compartment shall be 8 ft, unless the listing of the sprinkler requires a greater distance.

8.10.4 Distance Below Ceilings.

8.10.4.1 Pendent and upright sprinklers shall be positioned so that the deflectors are 1 in. to 4 in. from the ceiling unless the listing allows a greater distance.

8.10.4.2 Sidewall sprinklers shall be positioned so that the deflectors are within 4 in. to 6 in. from the ceiling unless the listing allows greater distances.

8.10.5 Residential sprinkler installed in conformance with this standard shall follow the sprinkler obstruction rules of 8.10.6 or 8.10.7 as appropriate for their installation orientation (upright, pendent, or sidewall) and the obstruction criteria specified in the manufacturer's installation instructions.

8.10.6 Obstructions to Sprinkler Discharge (Residential Upright and Pendent Spray Sprinklers).

The obstruction rules for residential upright and pendent spray sprinklers are the same requirements as for extended coverage upright and pendent spray sprinklers and have been duplicated in 8.10.6 to provide the needed design criteria for residential upright and pendent spray sprinklers. For additional information, see the commentary for Section 8.8.

8.10.6.1 Performance Objective.

8.10.6.1.1 Sprinklers shall be located so as to minimize obstructions to discharge as defined in 8.10.6.2 and 8.10.6.3, or additional sprinklers shall be provided to ensure adequate coverage of the hazard.

8.10.6.1.2 Sprinklers shall be arranged to comply with one of the following arrangements:

(1) Sprinklers shall be in accordance with 8.5.5.2, Table 8.10.6.1.2, and Figure 8.10.6.1.2(a).
(2) Sprinklers shall be permitted to be spaced on opposite sides of obstructions not exceeding 4 ft (1.2 m) in width provided the distance from the centerline of the obstruction to the sprinklers does not exceed one-half the allowable distance permitted between sprinklers.
(3) Obstructions located against the wall and that are not over 30 in. (762 mm) in width shall be permitted to be protected in accordance with Figure 8.10.6.1.2(b).

8.10.6.2 Obstructions to Sprinkler Discharge Pattern Development.

8.10.6.2.1 General.

8.10.6.2.1.1 Continuous or noncontinuous obstructions less than or equal to 18 in. (457 mm) below the sprinkler deflector that prevent the pattern from fully developing shall comply with 8.10.6.2.

TABLE 8.10.6.1.2 *Position of Sprinklers to Avoid Obstructions to Discharge (Residential Upright and Pendent Spray Sprinklers)*

Distance from Sprinklers to Side of Obstruction (A)	Maximum Allowable Distance of Deflector above Bottom of Obstruction (in.) (B)
Less than 1 ft	0
1 ft to less than 1 ft 6 in.	0
1 ft 6 in. to less than 2 ft	1
2 ft to less than 2 ft 6 in.	1
2 ft 6 in. to less than 3 ft	1
3 ft to less than 3 ft 6 in.	3
3 ft 6 in. to less than 4 ft	3
4 ft to less than 4 ft 6 in.	5
4 ft 6 in. to less than 5 ft	7
5 ft to less than 5 ft 6 in.	7
5 ft 6 in. to less than 6 ft	7
6 ft to less than 6 ft 6 in.	9
6 ft 6 in. to less than 7 ft	11
7 ft and greater	14

For SI units, 1 in. = 25.4 mm; 1 ft = 0.3048 m.
Note: For *(A)* and *(B),* refer to Figure 8.10.6.1.2(a).

8.10.6.2.1.2 Regardless of the rules of this section, solid continuous obstructions shall meet the applicable requirements of 8.10.6.1.2.

8.10.6.2.1.3* Unless the requirements of 8.10.6.2.1.4 through 8.10.6.2.1.9 are met, sprinklers shall be positioned away from obstructions a minimum distance of four times the maximum

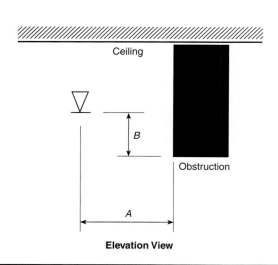

FIGURE 8.10.6.1.2(a) *Position of Sprinklers to Avoid Obstructions to Discharge (Residential Upright and Pendent Spray Sprinklers).*

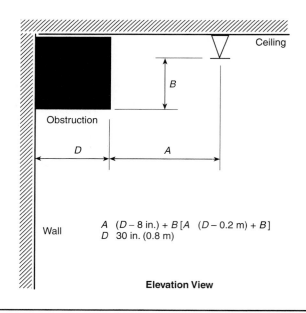

FIGURE 8.10.6.1.2(b) *Obstructions Against Walls (Residential Upright and Pendent Spray Sprinklers).*

dimension of the obstruction (e.g., truss webs and chords, pipe, columns, and fixtures). The maximum clear distance required shall be 36 in. (0.91 m) in accordance with Figure 8.10.6.2.1.3.

Plan View of Column   **Elevation View of Truss**

A   4C or 4D
A   36 in. (0.91 m)
(Use dimension C or D, whichever is greater)

FIGURE 8.10.6.2.1.3 *Minimum Distance from Obstruction (Residential Upright and Pendent Spray Sprinklers).*

A.8.10.6.2.1.3 The rules of 8.10.6.2.1.3 (known as the "Four Times Rule") have been written to apply to obstructions where the sprinkler can be expected to get water to both sides of the obstruction without allowing a significant dry shadow on the other side of the obstruction. This works for small noncontinuous obstructions and for continuous obstructions where the sprinkler can throw water over and under the obstruction, such as the bottom chord of an open truss or joist. For solid continuous obstructions, such as a beam, the Four Times Rulne is ineffective since the sprinkler cannot throw water over and under the obstruction. Sufficient water must be thrown under the obstruction to adequately cover the floor area on the other side of the obstruction. To ensure this, compliance with the rules of 8.10.6.1.2 is necessary.

8.10.6.2.1.4 Sprinklers shall be permitted to be spaced on opposite sides of the obstruction where the distance from the centerline of the obstruction to the sprinklers does not exceed one-half the allowable distance between sprinklers.

8.10.6.2.1.5 Sprinklers shall be permitted to be located one-half the distance between the obstructions where the obstruction consists of open trusses 20 in. (0.51 m) or greater apart [24 in. (0.61 m) on center], provided that all truss members are not greater than 4 in. (102 mm) (nominal) in width and web members do not exceed 1 in. (25.4 mm) in width.

8.10.6.2.1.6 Sprinklers shall be permitted to be installed on the centerline of a truss or bar joist or directly above a beam provided that the truss chord or beam dimension is not more than 8 in. (203 mm) and the sprinkler deflector is located at least 6 in. (152 mm) above the structural member and where the sprinkler is positioned at a distance four times greater than the maximum dimension of the web members away from the web members.

8.10.6.2.1.7 The requirements of 8.10.6.2.1.3 shall not apply to the piping to which an upright sprinkler is directly attached less than 3 in. (75 mm) in diameter.

8.10.6.2.1.8 The requirements of 8.10.6.2.1.3 shall not apply to the piping to which pendent sprinklers are directly attached.

8.10.6.2.1.9 The requirements of 8.10.6.2.1.3 shall not apply to sprinklers positioned with respect to obstructions in accordance with 8.10.6.1.2.

8.10.6.2.2 Suspended or Floor-Mounted Vertical Obstructions. The distance from sprinklers to privacy curtains, free-standing partitions, room dividers, and similar obstructions in light hazard occupancies shall be in accordance with Table 8.10.6.2.2 and Figure 8.10.6.2.2.

TABLE 8.10.6.2.2 *Suspended or Floor-Mounted Obstructions (Residential Upright and Pendent Spray Sprinklers)*

Horizontal Distance (A)	Minimum Vertical Distance below Deflector (in.) (B)
6 in. or less	3
More than 6 in. to 9 in.	4
More than 9 in. to 12 in.	6
More than 12 in. to 15 in.	8
More than 15 in. to 18 in.	9½
More than 18 in. to 24 in.	12½
More than 24 in. to 30 in.	15½
More than 30 in.	18

For SI units, 1 in. = 25.4 mm.
Note: For *(A)* and *(B),* refer to Figure 8.10.6.2.2.

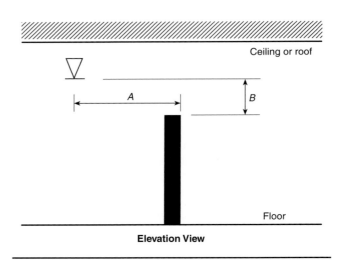

Elevation View

FIGURE 8.10.6.2.2 *Suspended or Floor-Mounted Obstructions (Residential Upright and Pendent Spray Sprinklers).*

8.10.6.3* Obstructions that Prevent Sprinkler Discharge from Reaching the Hazard.

A.8.10.6.3 See A.8.5.5.3.

8.10.6.3.1 Continuous or noncontinuous obstructions that interrupt the water discharge in a horizontal plane more than 18 in. (457 mm) below the sprinkler deflector in a manner to limit the distribution from reaching the protected hazard shall comply with 8.10.6.3.

8.10.6.3.2 Sprinklers shall be installed under fixed obstructions over 4 ft (1.2 m) wide such as ducts, decks, open grate flooring, cutting tables, and overhead doors.

8.10.6.3.3 Sprinklers shall not be required under obstructions that are not fixed in place such as conference tables.

8.10.6.3.4 Sprinklers installed under open gratings shall be of the intermediate level/rack storage type or otherwise shielded from the discharge of overhead sprinklers.

8.10.7 Obstructions to Sprinkler Discharge (Residential Sidewall Spray Sprinklers).

The obstruction rules for residential side wall spray sprinklers are the same requirements as for extended coverage sidewall spray sprinklers and have been duplicated in 8.10.7 to provide the needed design criteria for residential sidewall spray sprinklers. For additional information, see the commentary for Section 8.9.

8.10.7.1 Performance Objective.

8.10.7.1.1 Sprinklers shall be located so as to minimize obstructions to discharge as defined in 8.5.5.2 and 8.5.5.3, or additional sprinklers shall be provided to ensure adequate coverage of the hazard.

8.10.7.1.2 Sidewall sprinklers shall be installed no closer than 8 ft (2.4 m) from light fixtures or similar obstructions.

8.10.7.1.3 The distance between light fixtures or similar obstructions located more than 8 ft (2.4 m) from the sprinkler shall be in conformity with Table 8.10.7.1.3 and Figure 8.10.7.1.3.

TABLE 8.10.7.1.3 *Positioning of Sprinklers to Avoid Obstructions (Residential Sidewall Sprinklers)*

Distance from Sidewall Sprinkler to Side of Obstruction (A)	Maximum Allowable Distance of Deflector above Bottom of Obstruction (in.) (B)
Less than 8 ft	Not Allowed
8 ft to less than 10 ft	1
10 ft to less than 11 ft	2
11 ft to less than 12 ft	3
12 ft to less than 13 ft	4
13 ft to less than 14 ft	6
14 ft to less than 15 ft	7
15 ft to less than 16 ft	9
16 ft to less than 17 ft	11
17 ft or greater	14

For SI units, 1 in. = 25.4 mm; 1 ft = 0.3048 m.
Note: For *(A)* and *(B),* refer to Figure 8.10.7.1.3.

8.10.7.2 Obstructions to Sprinkler Discharge Pattern Development.

8.10.7.2.1 General.

8.10.7.2.1.1 Continuous or noncontinuous obstructions less than or equal to 18 in. (457 mm) below the sprinkler deflector that prevent the pattern from fully developing shall comply with this section.

8.10.7.2.1.2 Regardless of the rules of this section, solid continuous obstructions shall meet the requirements of 8.10.7.1.2 and 8.10.7.1.3.

8.10.7.2.1.3* Unless the requirements of 8.10.7.2.1.4 or 8.10.7.2.1.5 are met, sprinklers shall be positioned away from obstructions a minimum distance of four times the maximum dimension

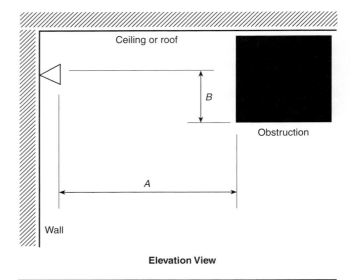

FIGURE 8.10.7.1.3 *Positioning of Sprinklers to Avoid Obstructions (Residential Sidewall Sprinklers).*

of the obstruction. The maximum clear distance required shall be 36 in. (0.91 m) from the sprinkler (e.g., truss webs and chords, pipe, columns, and fixtures).

 A.8.10.7.2.1.3 The rules of 8.10.7.2.1.3 (known as the "Four Times Rule") have been written to apply to obstructions where the sprinkler can be expected to get water to both sides of the obstruction without allowing a significant dry shadow on the other side of the obstruction. This works for small noncontinuous obstructions and for continuous obstructions where the sprinkler can throw water over and under the obstruction, such as the bottom chord of an open truss or joist. For solid continuous obstructions, such as a beam, the Four Times Rule is ineffective since the sprinkler cannot throw water over and under the obstruction. Sufficient water

$A \geq 4C$ or $4D$
$A \leq 36$ in. (0.91 m)
(Use dimension C or D, whichever is greater)

FIGURE 8.10.7.2.1.4 *Minimum Distance from Obstruction (Residential Sidewall).*

TABLE 8.10.7.2.2 *Suspended or Floor-Mounted Obstructions (Residential Sidewall Sprinklers)*

Horizontal Distance (A)	Minimum Allowable Distance below Deflector (in.) (B)
6 in. or less	3
More than 6 in. to 9 in.	4
More than 9 in. to 12 in.	6
More than 12 in. to 15 in.	8
More than 15 in. to 18 in.	9½
More than 18 in. to 24 in.	12½
More than 24 in. to 30 in.	15½
More than 30 in.	18

For SI units, 1 in. = 25.4 mm.

Note: For *(A)* and *(B)*, refer to Figure 8.10.7.2.2.

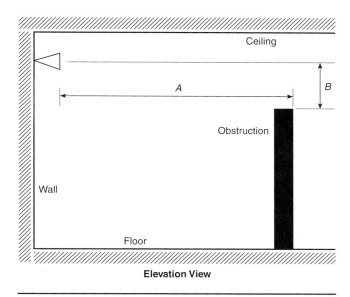

Elevation View

FIGURE 8.10.7.2.2 *Suspended or Floor-Mounted Obstructions (Residential Sidewall Sprinklers).*

must be thrown under the obstruction to adequately cover the floor area on the other side of the obstruction. To ensure this, compliance with the rules of 8.10.6.1.2 is necessary.

8.10.7.2.1.4 Sidewall sprinklers shall be positioned in accordance with Figure 8.10.7.2.1.4 when obstructions are present.

8.10.7.2.1.5 The requirements of 8.10.7.2.1.3 and 8.10.7.2.1.4 shall not apply where sprinklers are positioned with respect to obstructions in accordance with 8.10.7.1.2 and 8.10.7.1.3.

8.10.7.2.2 Suspended or Floor-Mounted Vertical Obstructions. The distance from sprinklers to privacy curtains, free-standing partitions, room dividers, and similar obstructions in light hazard occupancies shall be in accordance with Table 8.10.7.2.2 and Figure 8.10.7.2.2.

8.10.7.3* Obstructions that Prevent Sprinkler Discharge from Reaching the Hazard.

A.8.10.7.3 See A.8.5.5.3.

A

8.10.7.3.1 Continuous or noncontinuous obstructions that interrupt the water discharge in a horizontal plane more than 18 in. (457 mm) below the sprinkler deflector in a manner to limit the distribution from reaching the protected hazard shall comply with this section.

8.10.7.3.2 Sprinklers shall be installed under fixed obstructions over 4 ft (1.2 m) wide such as ducts, decks, open grate flooring, cutting tables, and overhead doors.

8.10.7.3.3 Sprinklers shall not be required under obstructions that are not fixed in place such as conference tables.

8.11 Large Drop Sprinklers in All Applications and Other Specific Application Sprinklers Used for Storage Protection.

Many of the installation requirements found in Section 8.11 for large drop sprinklers are similar to those found in Section 8.6. Unless the rationale for large drop requirements differs from those for standard upright and pendent sprinklers, commentary from related items in Section 8.6 is not repeated in Section 8.11 commentary.

8.11.1 General. All requirements of Section 8.5 shall apply to large drop sprinklers except as modified in Section 8.11.

8.11.2* Protection Areas per Sprinkler (Large Drop Sprinklers).

A.8.11.2 Tests involving areas of coverage over 100 ft^2 (9.3 m^2) for large drop sprinklers are limited in number, and use of areas of coverage over 100 ft^2 (9.3 m^2) should be carefully considered.

8.11.2.1 Determination of the Protection Area of Coverage. The protection area of coverage per sprinkler (A_s) shall be determined in accordance with 8.5.2.1.

8.11.2.2 Maximum Protection Area of Coverage.

8.11.2.2.1 The maximum allowable protection area of coverage for a sprinkler (A_s) shall be in accordance with the value indicated in Table 8.11.2.2.1.

TABLE 8.11.2.2.1 Protection Areas and Maximum Spacing for Large Drop Sprinklers

Construction Type	Protection Area		Maximum Spacing	
	ft^2	*m^2*	*ft*	*m*
Noncombustible unobstructed	130	12.1	12	3.7
Noncombustible obstructed	130	12.1	12	3.7
Combustible unobstructed	130	12.1	12	3.7
Combustible obstructed	100	9.3	10	3.1
Rack storage applications	100	9.3	10	3.1

8.11.2.2.2 In any case, the maximum area of coverage of any sprinkler shall not exceed 130 ft^2 (12.9 m^2).

Maximum area of coverage is discussed in 8.11.2.2.1 and 8.11.2.2.2. Tests involving areas of coverage over 100 ft^2 (9.3 m^2) for large drop sprinklers are limited in number. Limiting the area of coverage for large drop sprinklers to 100 ft^2 (9.3 m^2) for all constructions types is common practice. Careful consideration should be given when designing large drop sprinkler installations with protection areas exceeding 100 ft^2 (9.3 m^2).

8.11.2.3 Minimum Protection Area of Coverage. The minimum allowable protection area of coverage for a sprinkler (A_s) shall be not less than 80 ft^2 (7.4 m^2).

The minimum protection area for large drop sprinklers, which is discussed in 8.11.2.3, is limited to 80 ft^2 (7.4 m^2) to prevent "skipping." Skipping occurs when the sprinklers do not operate in a normal pattern and when sprinklers some distance from the fire operate before those sprinklers closest to the fire. Air movement and general cooling of temperatures at the ceiling cause the skipping phenomenon. When skipping occurs, the fire continues to grow, resulting in a larger, more difficult fire to control. Limiting the sprinkler protection area, as well as the minimum distance between sprinklers set forth in 8.11.3.4, minimizes the possibility of skipping.

◀ **FAQ**
Why are large drop sprinklers limited to a minimum protection area of 80 ft^2 (7.4 m^2)?

8.11.3 Sprinkler Spacing (Large Drop Sprinklers).

Spacing requirements for large drop sprinklers, which are given in 8.11.3, were determined by testing at various sprinkler spacings and discharge pressures on the basis of the following parameters:

1. Do not exceed the maximum allowable distance between sprinklers to ensure sufficient overlapping of sprinkler discharge patterns for adequate penetration of the fire plume.
2. Maintain sufficient separation of sprinklers to prevent sprinkler skipping.
3. Maintain sufficient cooling at ceiling level.

The importance of satisfying these three parameters cannot be overstated. These criteria are so closely intertwined that evaluating one without considering the effect on the others is difficult. Certain combinations of spacing dimensions, when used with the discharge pressures and fire hazards contemplated in 8.11.3, result in skipping, loss of sprinkler water penetration, and excessively high ceiling temperatures. If any of these adverse conditions occur, the adequacy of the sprinkler protection can be seriously compromised.

8.11.3.1* Maximum Distance Between Sprinklers.

A.8.11.3.1 It is important that sprinklers in the immediate vicinity of the fire center not skip, and this requirement imposes certain restrictions on the spacing.

8.11.3.1.1 Under unobstructed and obstructed noncombustible construction and unobstructed combustible construction, the distance between sprinklers shall be limited to not more than 12 ft (3.7 m) between sprinklers, as shown in Table 8.11.2.2.1.

8.11.3.1.2 Under obstructed combustible construction, the maximum distance shall be limited to 10 ft (3 m).

8.11.3.2 Maximum Distance from Walls. The distance from sprinklers to walls shall not exceed one-half of the allowable distance permitted between sprinklers as indicated in Table 8.11.2.2.1.

8.11.3.3 Minimum Distance from Walls. Sprinklers shall be located a minimum of 4 in. (102 mm) from a wall.

8.11.3.4 Minimum Distance Between Sprinklers. Sprinklers shall be spaced not less than 8 ft (2.4 m) on center.

8.11.4 Deflector Position (Large Drop Sprinklers).

8.11.4.1* Distance Below Ceilings.

A.8.11.4.1 If all other factors are held constant, the operating time of the first sprinkler will vary exponentially with the distance between the ceiling and deflector. At distances greater than 7 in. (178 mm), for other than open wood joist construction, the delayed operating time will permit the fire to gain headway, with the result that substantially more sprinklers operate. At distances less than 7 in. (178 mm), other effects occur. Changes in distribution, penetration, and cooling nullify the advantage gained by faster operation. The net result again is increased fire damage accompanied by an increase in the number of sprinklers operated. The optimum clearance between deflectors and ceiling is, therefore, 7 in. (178 mm). For open wood joist construction, the optimum clearance between deflectors and the bottom of joists is 3½ in. (89 mm).

8.11.4.1.1 Unobstructed Construction. Under unobstructed construction, the distance between the sprinkler deflector and the ceiling shall be a minimum of 6 in. (152 mm) and a maximum of 8 in. (203 mm).

8.11.4.1.2 Obstructed Construction. Under obstructed construction, the sprinkler deflector shall be located in accordance with one of the following arrangements:

(1) Installed with the deflectors located a minimum of 6 in. (152 mm) and a maximum of 12 in. (305 mm) from the ceiling.
(2) Installed with the deflectors within the horizontal planes 1 in. to 6 in. below wood joist or composite wood joist construction, to a maximum distance of 22 in. (559 mm) below the ceiling/roof or deck.
(3) Installed with deflectors of sprinklers under concrete tee construction with stems spaces less than 7½ ft (2.3 m) but more than 3 ft (0.9 m) on centers, regardless of the depth of the tee, located at or above a horizontal plane 1 in. (25.4 mm) below the bottom of the stems of the tees and shall comply with Table 8.11.5.1.2.

The requirement in 8.11.4.1.2(3), which has been a long-standing provision for standard spray sprinklers, is included in the standard because a large drop sprinkler is a standard response sprinkler with operating features similar to those of standard spray sprinklers. Therefore, the positioning rules pertaining to sprinkler activation should remain uniform.

8.11.4.2 Deflector Orientation. Deflectors of sprinklers shall be aligned parallel to ceilings or roofs.

8.11.5* Obstructions to Sprinkler Discharge (Large Drop Sprinklers).

 A.8.11.5 To a great extent, large drop sprinklers rely on direct attack to gain rapid control of both the burning fuel and ceiling temperatures. Therefore, interference with the discharge pattern and obstructions to the distribution should be avoided.

Obstructions to sprinkler discharge for large drop sprinklers is covered in 8.11.5. Large drop sprinklers are more sensitive to obstructions than standard spray pendent and upright sprinklers. Large drop sprinklers "attack" the fire source and rely less on prewetting of combustibles than do standard spray pendent and upright sprinklers. The discharge from large drop sprinklers contains larger water droplets. These droplets have greater momentum, which allows them to penetrate the fire plumes typically generated by the kinds of fires experienced in warehouse and storage operations. Any obstructions that interrupt the discharge reduce the amount of water that reaches the seat of the fire, limiting the sprinkler's effectiveness and allowing the fire to grow larger and become more difficult to control. As a result, the obstruction provisions for large drop sprinklers are more restrictive than for standard spray pendent and upright sprinklers.

8.11.5.1 Performance Objective.

8.11.5.1.1 Sprinklers shall be located so as to minimize obstructions to discharge as defined in 8.5.5.2 and 8.5.5.3, or additional sprinklers shall be provided to ensure adequate coverage of the hazard.

8.11.5.1.2 Sprinklers shall be arranged to comply with 8.5.5.2, Table 8.11.5.1.2, and Figure 8.11.5.1.2.

8.11.5.1.3 The requirements of 8.11.5.1.2 shall not apply, where sprinklers are positioned on opposite sides of the obstruction.

TABLE 8.11.5.1.2 *Positioning of Sprinklers to Avoid Obstructions to Discharge (Large Drop Sprinkler)*

Distance from Sprinkler to Side of Obstruction (A)	Maximum Allowable Distance of Deflector above Bottom of Obstruction (in.) (B)
Less than 1 ft	0
1 ft to less than 1 ft 6 in.	1½
1 ft 6 in. to less than 2 ft	3
2 ft to less than 2 ft 6 in.	5½
2 ft 6 in. to less than 3 ft	8
3 ft to less than 3 ft 6 in.	10
3 ft 6 in. to less than 4 ft	12
4 ft to less than 4 ft 6 in.	15
4 ft 6 in. to less than 5 ft	18
5 ft to less than 5 ft 6 in.	22
5 ft 6 in. to less than 6 ft	26
6 ft	31

For SI units, 1 in. = 25.4 mm; 1 ft = 0.3048 m.

Note: For *(A)* and *(B)*, refer to Figure 8.11.5.1.2.

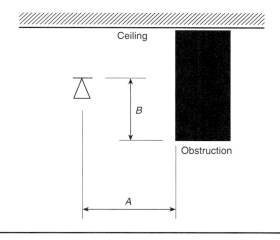

FIGURE 8.11.5.1.2 *Positioning of Sprinklers to Avoid Obstructions to Discharge (Large Drop Sprinkler).*

Paragraph 8.11.5.1.3 was added to the 1999 edition to formally permit the installation of large drop sprinklers on opposite sides of an obstruction.

8.11.5.2 Obstructions to Sprinkler Discharge Pattern Development.

8.11.5.2.1 General.

8.11.5.2.1.1 Continuous or noncontinuous obstructions less than or equal to 36 in. (914 mm) below the sprinkler deflector that prevent the pattern from fully developing shall comply with 8.11.5.2.

8.11.5.2.1.2 Regardless of the rules of this section, solid continuous obstructions shall meet the requirements of 8.11.5.1.2 or 8.11.5.1.3.

Solid continuous obstructions are discussed in 8.11.5.2.1.2. The discharge pattern of a large drop sprinkler is more narrow than that of a standard spray pendent and upright sprinkler. To allow the discharge pattern to develop and the sprinkler patterns to overlap, a 36-in. (914-mm) zone below the sprinkler must be evaluated for potential obstructions to discharge pattern development.

8.11.5.2.1.3* Unless the requirements of 8.11.5.1.2 or 8.11.5.1.3 are met, for obstructions 8 in. (203 mm) or less in width, as shown in Figure 8.11.5.2.1.3, sprinklers shall be positioned such that they are located at least a distance three times greater than the maximum dimension of the obstruction from the sprinkler (e.g., webs and chord members, pipe, columns, and fixtures).

$A \geq 3C$ or $3D$
(Use dimension C or D, whichever is greater)

FIGURE 8.11.5.2.1.3 *Minimum Distance from Obstruction (Large Drop Sprinkler).*

A.8.11.5.2.1.3 The rules of 8.11.5.2.1.3 (known as the "Three Times Rule") have been written to apply to obstructions where the sprinkler can be expected to get water to both sides of the obstruction without allowing a significant dry shadow on the other side of the obstruction. This works for small noncontinuous obstructions and for continuous obstructions where the sprinkler can throw water over and under the obstruction, such as the bottom chord of an open truss or joist. For solid continuous obstructions, such as a beam, the Three Times Rule is ineffective since the sprinkler cannot throw water over and under the obstruction. Sufficient water must be thrown under the obstruction to adequately cover the floor area on the other side of the obstruction. To ensure this, compliance with the rules of 8.11.5.1.2 is necessary.

8.11.5.2.2 Branch Lines. Sprinklers shall be positioned with respect to branch lines in accordance with one of the following:

(1) Sprinklers shall be permitted to be attached directly to branch lines less than 2 in. (51 mm) in diameter.
(2) Sprinklers shall be permitted to be offset horizontally a minimum of 12 in. (305 mm) from the pipe.
(3) Sprinklers shall be permitted to be supplied by a riser nipple to elevate the sprinkler deflector a minimum of 13 in. (330 mm) from the centerline of 2½-in. (64-mm) pipe.
(4) Sprinklers shall be permitted to be supplied by a riser nipple to elevate the sprinkler deflector a minimum of 15 in. (380 mm) from the centerline of 3-in. (76-mm) pipe.

Branch lines are discussed in 8.11.5.2.2. When an upright sprinkler is installed directly on the branch line, the branch line becomes an obstruction. As the branch line pipe size is increased, the "pipe shadow," or area below the sprinkler that is affected, increases. Because large drop sprinklers attack the fire, this obstruction can have a significant impact if the fire is located directly below the sprinkler and is a concern when the branch line piping is larger than 2 in. (51 mm).

Many systems require larger piping to meet the hydraulic design requirements of the large drop sprinkler. Raising the sprinkler on a riser nipple reduces the angle of obstruction by limiting the area affected by the obstruction to no more than would be created by a smaller branch line.

Another approach to the problem is taken in 8.11.5.2.2(2). If the sprinkler is offset at least 12 in. (305 mm), the discharge from the sprinkler can flow under the branch line. This position eliminates the obstruction or limits the impact of the obstruction caused by the branch line so that it does not pose a significant problem.

8.11.5.3* Obstructions that Prevent Sprinkler Discharge from Reaching the Hazard.

A.8.11.5.3 See A.8.5.5.3.

A

8.11.5.3.1 Continuous or noncontinuous obstructions that interrupt the water discharge in a horizontal plane below the sprinkler deflector in a manner to limit the distribution from reaching the protected hazard shall comply with 8.11.5.3.

8.11.5.3.2 Sprinklers shall be positioned with respect to fluorescent lighting fixtures, ducts, and obstructions more than 24 in. (610 mm) wide and located entirely below the sprinklers so that the minimum horizontal distance from the near side of the obstruction to the center of the sprinkler is not less than the value specified in Table 8.11.5.3.2 and Figure 8.11.5.3.2.

TABLE 8.11.5.3.2 Obstruction Entirely Below the Sprinkler (Large Drop Sprinkler)

Distance of Deflector above Bottom of Obstruction (B)	Minimum Distance to Side of Obstruction (ft) (A)
Less than 6 in.	1½
6 in. to less than 12 in.	3
12 in. to less than 18 in.	4
18 in. to less than 24 in.	5
24 in. to less than 30 in.	5½
30 in. less than 36 in.	6

For SI units, 1 in. = 25.4 mm; 1 ft = 0.3048 m.

Note: For *(A)* and *(B)*, refer to Figure 8.11.5.3.2.

Because large drop sprinklers are more sensitive to obstructions, any obstruction more than 24 in. (610 mm) wide and less than 24 in. (610 mm) below the sprinkler must be located so that the sprinkler discharge pattern falls under it, as stated in 8.11.5.3.2. The intent is to minimize obstruction to the lateral distribution from individual sprinklers.

8.11.5.3.3 Sprinklers installed under open gratings shall be shielded from the discharge of overhead sprinklers.

8.11.5.3.4 Where the bottom of the obstruction is located 24 in. (610 mm) or more below the sprinkler deflectors, the following shall occur:

(1) Sprinklers shall be positioned so that the obstruction is centered between adjacent sprinklers in accordance with Figure 8.11.5.3.4.

(2) The obstruction width shall meet the following requirements:

FIGURE 8.11.5.3.2 *Obstruction Entirely Below the Sprinkler (Large Drop Sprinkler).*

    (a) The obstruction shall be limited to a maximum width of 24 in. (610 mm) in accordance with Figure 8.11.5.3.4.
    (b) Where the obstruction is greater than 24 in. (610 mm) wide, one or more lines of sprinklers shall be installed below the obstruction.

(3) The obstruction extension shall meet the following requirements:

    (a) The obstruction shall not extend more than 12 in. (305 mm) to either side of the midpoint between sprinklers in accordance with Figure 8.11.5.3.4.
    (b) Where the extensions of the obstruction exceed 12 in. (305 mm), one or more lines of sprinklers shall be installed below the obstruction.

(4) At least 18 in. (457 mm) clearance shall be maintained between the top of storage and the bottom of the obstruction in accordance with Figure 8.11.5.3.4.

At distances more than 24 in. (610 mm) below the sprinklers, obstructions interfere with the distribution from more than one sprinkler due to characteristics of the sprinkler's discharge pattern (see Figure 8.11.5.3.4). The provisions in 8.11.5.3.4 provide for sufficient overlap of discharge patterns from adjacent sprinklers, which ensures that adequate water distribution is available to penetrate the fire plume.

8.11.5.3.5 In the special case of an obstruction running parallel to and directly below a branch line, the following shall occur:

(1) The sprinkler shall be located at least 36 in. (914 mm) above the top of the obstruction in accordance with Figure 8.11.5.3.5.
(2) The obstruction shall be limited to a maximum width of 12 in. (305 mm) in accordance with Figure 8.11.5.3.5.
(3) The obstruction shall be limited to a maximum extension of 6 in. (152 mm) to either side of the centerline of the branch line in accordance with Figure 8.11.5.3.5.

The obstruction to distribution as expected under the conditions specified in 8.11.5.3.5 would not be significantly greater than that which would occur due to pipe shadow. It is important to follow all of these obstruction provisions, because relatively minor obstructions can reduce the effectiveness of a large drop sprinkler. The use of large drop sprinklers can provide a more effective means of protecting high-challenge storage fire hazards, often without the use of in-rack sprinklers. However, large drop sprinklers are obstruction sensitive and require special attention to be paid to the details of these installation requirements.

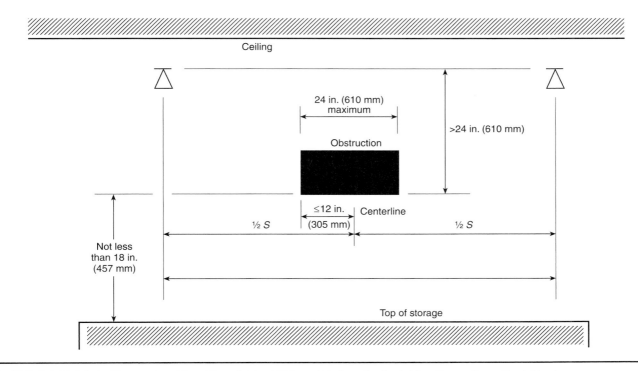

FIGURE 8.11.5.3.4 Obstruction More Than 24 in. (610 mm) Below the Sprinkler (Large Drop Sprinkler).

FIGURE 8.11.5.3.5 Obstruction More Than 36 in. (914 mm) Below the Sprinkler (Large Drop Sprinkler).

8.11.6 Clearance to Storage (Large Drop Sprinklers). The clearance between the deflector and the top of storage shall be 36 in. (914 mm) or greater.

At clearances of less than 36 in. (914 mm), large drop sprinklers installed within the allowable spacing guidelines do not provide sufficient overlapping of sprinkler discharge patterns between adjacent sprinklers, which is the reason for the requirement in 8.11.6.

Why do large drop sprinklers require 36 in. (914 mm) of clearance to the top of storage?
◄ FAQ

8.12 Early Suppression Fast-Response Sprinklers

8.12.1 General. All requirements of Section 8.5 shall apply except as modified in Section 8.12.

Early suppression fast-response (ESFR) sprinklers are covered in Section 8.12. The spacing and location requirements of ESFR sprinklers are designed to ensure that the sprinklers operate while the fire size is sufficiently small so that the fire can be suppressed. ESFR sprinklers are also designed to minimize the impact of obstructions so that the sprinkler discharge can reach the seat of the fire. Spacing requirements are determined on the basis of the following parameters:

FAQ ▶
What is the basis for ESFR
spacing requirements?

    1. Maintain sufficient actual delivered density (see commentary on 3.6.2.1) for various sprinkler spacings and clearances between sprinklers and the top of storage. (Scenarios consisting of a fire ignition source centered among four sprinklers, centered between two sprinklers, and located directly under one sprinkler are evaluated to ensure that early fire suppression will be achieved. Ideally, an unshielded fire should be completely extinguished. In the worst case, where the seat of the fire is shielded from direct sprinkler discharge, the fire's heat release rate should be severely diminished with the likelihood of the fire rekindling or spreading nearly nonexistent.)
    2. Maintain sufficient separation of sprinklers to prevent skipping.
    3. Maintain sufficient cooling at ceiling level.

8.12.2 Protection Areas per Sprinkler (Early Suppression Fast-Response Sprinklers).

8.12.2.1 Determination of the Protection Area of Coverage. The protection area of coverage per sprinkler (A_S) shall be determined in accordance with 8.5.2.1.

8.12.2.2 Maximum Protection Area of Coverage.

8.12.2.2.1 The maximum allowable protection area of coverage for a sprinkler (A_S) shall be in accordance with the value indicated in Table 8.12.2.2.1.

TABLE 8.12.2.2.1 *Protection Areas and Maximum Spacing of ESFR Sprinklers*

| | Ceiling/Roof Heights up to 30 ft (9.1 m) | | | | Ceiling/Roof Heights over 30 ft (9.1 m) | | | |
| | *Protection Area* | | *Spacing* | | *Protection Area* | | *Spacing* | |
Construction Type	*ft²*	*m²*	*ft*	*m*	*ft²*	*m²*	*ft*	*m*
Noncombustible unobstructed	100	9.3	12	3.7	100	9.3	10	3.1
Noncombustible obstructed	100	9.3	12	3.7	100	9.3	10	3.1
Combustible unobstructed	100	9.3	12	3.7	100	9.3	10	3.1
Combustible obstructed	N/A		N/A		N/A		N/A	

Table 8.12.2.2.1 indicates that ESFR sprinklers cannot be used under obstructed combustible construction. However, 8.4.6.3 allows ESFR sprinklers in this construction category as long as sprinklers are installed in each channel if the members exceed 12 in. in depth. ESFR has been used under beam and girder and also panel construction. The 2002 edition changes to 8.4.6.3 will allow its use in other types of combustible obstructed construction.

8.12.2.2.2 Unless the requirements of 8.12.2.2.3 are met, the maximum area of coverage of any sprinkler shall not exceed 100 ft² (9.3 m²).

 8.12.2.2.3* It shall be permitted to deviate from the maximum sprinkler spacing to eliminate obstructions created by trusses and bar joists by moving a sprinkler along the branch line a maximum of 1 ft (0.31 m) from its allowable spacing provided coverage for that sprinkler does not exceed 110 ft² (10.2 m²) per sprinkler where all of the following conditions are met:

(1) The average actual floor area protected by the moved sprinkler and the adjacent sprinklers does not exceed 100 ft² (9.3 m²).
(2) Adjacent branch lines shall maintain the same pattern.
(3) In no case shall the distance between sprinklers exceed 12 ft (3.7 m).

A.8.12.2.2.3 See Figure A.8.12.2.2.3.

FIGURE A.8.12.2.2.3 *ESFR Sprinkler Spacing Within Trusses and Bar Joists.*

ESFR sprinklers must be located a minimum distance from the nearest edge of any bottom chord of a bar joist or truss, as indicated in 8.12.5.2 and 8.12.5.3. If the spacing of sprinklers is not an even multiple of the chord spacing, then the standard sprinkler spacing will not meet this requirement. Paragraphs 8.12.2.2.3 and 8.12.2.2.4 allow sprinklers to be moved 1 ft (0.31 m) to eliminate the obstruction caused by the bottom chord as long as the pattern is repeated and the protection area restrictions outlined in 8.12.2.2.3 are met.

8.12.2.2.4 Where branch lines are parallel to trusses and bar joists it shall be permitted to deviate from the maximum sprinkler spacing to eliminate obstructions created by trusses and bar joists by moving a single branch line a maximum of 1 ft (0.31 m) from its allowable spacing provided coverage for the sprinklers on that branch line and the sprinklers on the branch line it is moving away from does not exceed 110 ft² per sprinkler where all of the following conditions are met:

(1) The average actual floor area protected by the sprinklers on the moved branch line and the sprinklers on the adjacent branch lines does not exceed 100 ft² per sprinkler.
(2) In no case shall the distance between sprinklers exceed 12 ft (3.7 m).
(3) It shall not be permitted to move a branch line where there are moved sprinklers on a branch line that exceed the maximum sprinkler spacing.

Similar to the requirements of 8.12.2.2.3, 8.12.2.2.4 allows an entire branch line to be moved a maximum of 1 ft (0.31 m) provided the requirements of 8.12.2.2.4 are met.

8.12.2.3 Minimum Protection Area of Coverage. The minimum allowable protection area of coverage for a sprinkler (A_s) shall be not less than 80 ft^2 (7.4 m^2).

FAQ ▶
Why are ESFR sprinklers limited to a minimum protection area of 80 ft^2 (7.4 m^2)?

The protection area for ESFR sprinklers is limited to 80 ft^2 (7.4 m^2) by 8.12.2.3 to prevent the possibility of skipping. (See commentary following 8.11.2.3 for an explanation of skipping.) Limiting the minimum distance between sprinklers as required in 8.12.3.4 also minimizes the potential for skipping.

The direct relationship between the spacing and the skipping of ESFR sprinklers is not known. With ESFR sprinkler installations, the first few sprinklers should suppress the fire and limit the potential for skipping. However, no tests have been conducted using ESFR sprinklers with less than 80-ft^2 (7.4-m^2) protection areas. If skipping should occur, the likely result is an overtaxing of the ESFR design and a failure of the sprinklers to suppress the fire.

8.12.3 Sprinkler Spacing (Early Suppression Fast-Response Sprinklers).

 8.12.3.1 Maximum Distance Between Sprinklers. The maximum distance between sprinklers shall be in accordance with the following:

(1) Where the storage height is less than or equal to 25 ft (7.6 m) and the ceiling height is less than or equal to 30 ft (9.1 m), the distance between sprinklers shall be limited to not more than 12 ft (3.7 m) between sprinklers as shown in Table 8.12.2.2.1.

(2) Unless the requirements of 8.12.3.1(3) are met, where the storage height exceeds 25 ft (7.6 m) and ceiling height exceeds 30 ft (9.1 m), the distance between sprinklers shall be limited to not more than 10 ft (3 m) between sprinklers.

(3)* Regardless of the storage or ceiling height arrangement, it shall be permitted to deviate from the maximum sprinkler spacing to eliminate obstructions created by trusses and bar joists by moving a sprinkler along the branch line a maximum of 1 ft (0.31 m) from its allowable spacing provided coverage for that sprinkler does not exceed 110 ft^2 (10.2 m^2) where all of the following conditions are met:

    (a) The average actual floor area protected by the moved sprinkler and the adjacent sprinklers shall not exceed 100 ft^2 (9.3 m^2).

    (b) Adjacent branch lines shall maintain the same pattern.

    (c) In no case shall the distance between sprinklers exceed 12 ft (3.7 m).

 A.8.12.3.1(3) See Figure A.8.12.2.2.3.

ESFR sprinklers must be spaced so that patterns have sufficient overlap. As the storage height increases, so does the strength of the fire plume. As indicated by 8.12.3.1(1), additional pattern overlap for storage heights over 25 ft (7.6 m) and ceiling heights over 30 ft (9.1 m) is required for suppression.

Paragraph 8.12.3.1 allows a sprinkler or a line of sprinklers to be moved an additional 1 ft (0.31 m) to eliminate the obstruction caused by the bottom chord as long as spacing and protection restrictions are followed.

Paragraphs 8.12.3.1(3) and 8.12.3.1(4) are similar to 8.12.2.2.3 and 8.12.2.2.4 concerning protection area limitations and provide the needed allowance for the spacing rules to permit the 1-ft (0.31-m) deviation.

 (4) Where branch lines are parallel to trusses and bar joists it shall be permitted to deviate from the maximum sprinkler spacing to eliminate obstructions created by trusses and bar joists by moving a single branch line a maximum of 1 ft (0.31 m) from its allowable spacing provided coverage for the sprinklers on that branch line and the sprinklers on the branch line it is moving away from does not exceed 110 ft^2 per sprinkler where all of the following conditions are met:

    (a) The average actual floor area protected by the sprinklers on the moved branch line and the sprinklers on the adjacent branch lines shall not exceed 100 ft^2 per sprinkler.

    (b) In no case shall the distance between sprinklers exceed 12 ft (3.7 m).

(c) It shall not be permitted to move a branch line where there are moved sprinklers on a branch line that exceed the maximum sprinkler spacing.

8.12.3.2 Maximum Distance from Walls. The distance from sprinklers to walls shall not exceed one-half of the allowable distance permitted between sprinklers as indicated in Table 8.12.2.2.1.

8.12.3.3 Minimum Distance from Walls. Sprinklers shall be located a minimum of 4 in. (102 mm) from a wall.

8.12.3.4 Minimum Distance Between Sprinklers. Sprinklers shall be spaced not less than 8 ft (2.4 m) on center.

8.12.4 Deflector Position (Early Suppression Fast-Response Sprinklers).

8.12.4.1 Distance Below Ceilings.

Distance below ceilings is covered in 8.12.4.1. The requirements for deflector positioning are based on the use of upright- or pendent-type sprinklers. Positioning the sprinklers below the ceiling at distances greater than that permitted results in a delayed sprinkler response and allows the fire to grow larger in size. When the sprinklers do finally activate, the fire is likely to be of a size that does not allow early suppression.

The testing for pendent ESFR sprinklers with a nominal K-factor of 25.2 demonstrated that a distance of 18 in. (457 mm) could be tolerated. Similarly, for upright ESFR sprinklers, the rules are based on test conditions. All of the testing for the K-11.2 upright sprinklers was done with the sprinkler deflector placed 4 in. (102 mm) from the ceiling. Consequently, the impact of any delayed activation that would accompany increased sprinkler-to-ceiling distances is not known. For a K-14 upright ESFR sprinkler, the rules are similar to a standard upright sprinkler.

8.12.4.1.1 Pendent sprinklers with a nominal K-factor of 14 shall be positioned so that deflectors are a maximum 14 in. (356 mm) and a minimum 6 in. (152 mm) below the ceiling.

8.12.4.1.2 Pendent sprinklers with a nominal K-factor of 25.2 shall be positioned so that deflectors are a maximum 18 in. (457 mm) and a minimum 6 in. (152 mm) below the ceiling.

8.12.4.1.3 Upright sprinklers with a nominal K-factor of 11.2 shall be positioned so that the deflector is 3 in. to 5 in. (76 mm to 127 mm) below the ceiling.

8.12.4.1.4 Upright sprinklers with a nominal K-factor of 14 shall be positioned so that the deflector is 3 in. to 12 in. (76 mm to 304 mm) below the ceiling.

8.12.4.1.5 With obstructed construction, the branch lines shall be permitted to be installed across the beams, but sprinklers shall be located in the bays and not under the beams.

8.12.4.2 Deflector Orientation. Deflectors of sprinklers shall be aligned parallel to ceilings or roofs.

8.12.5 Obstructions to Sprinkler Discharge (Early Suppression Fast-Response Sprinklers).

The effects of sprinkler discharge pattern interruption due to an obstruction must be minimized using the provisions contained in 8.12.5. Shadow areas in a high-piled storage occupancy provide enough of a fuel supply to a growing fire that the effect is not considered minimal. Thus, great care in positioning ESFR sprinklers with respect to lights, structural members, and similar obstructions must be exercised. Many obstructions that can be tolerated for other types of sprinklers are unacceptable where ESFR sprinklers are used.

If possible, ESFR sprinklers should be positioned or obstructions should be relocated so that any obstructions are above the discharge pattern of the sprinklers. All large continuous obstructions, including beams and ductwork, must be located so as to adhere to Table 8.12.5.1.1.

Smaller isolated obstructions, such as light fixtures, can be handled by following the requirements in 8.12.5.2. Continuous obstructions affecting the discharge pattern of more than one sprinkler can have a significant impact on sprinkler performance and must be located so as to comply with 8.11.5.3. Overall, these provisions are much more restrictive than those for other types of sprinklers but are necessary for successful performance of the ESFR sprinkler system.

8.12.5.1 Obstructions at or Near the Ceiling.

8.12.5.1.1 Sprinklers shall be arranged to comply with Table 8.12.5.1.1 and Figure 8.12.5.1.1 for obstructions at the ceiling such as beams, ducts, lights, and top chords of trusses and bar joists.

TABLE 8.12.5.1.1 *Positioning of Sprinklers to Avoid Obstructions to Discharge (ESFR Sprinkler)*

Distance from Sprinkler to Side of Obstruction (A)	*Maximum Allowable Distance of Deflector above Bottom of Obstruction (in.)* (B)
Less than 1 ft	0
1 ft to less than 1 ft 6 in.	1½
1 ft 6 in. to less than 2 ft	3
2 ft to less than 2 ft 6 in.	5½
2 ft 6 in. to less than 3 ft	8
3 ft to less than 3 ft 6 in.	10
3 ft 6 in. to less than 4 ft	12
4 ft to less than 4 ft 6 in.	15
4 ft 6 in. to less than 5 ft	18
5 ft to less than 5 ft 6 in.	22
5 ft 6 in. to less than 6 ft	26
6 ft	31

For SI units, 1 in. = 25.4 mm; 1 ft = 0.3048 m.

Note: For *(A)* and *(B)*, refer to Figure 8.12.5.1.1.

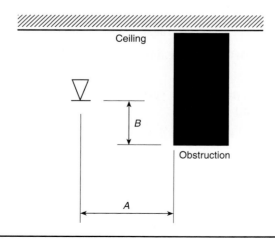

FIGURE 8.12.5.1.1 *Positioning of Sprinklers to Avoid Obstructions to Discharge (ESFR Sprinkler).*

8.12.5.1.2 The requirements of 8.12.5.1.1 shall not apply where sprinklers are spaced on opposite sides of obstructions less than 24 in. wide provided the distance from the centerline on the obstructions to the sprinklers does not exceed one-half the allowable distance between sprinklers.

8.12.5.1.3 Sprinklers with a special obstruction allowance shall be installed according to their listing.

8.12.5.2* Isolated Obstructions Below the Elevation of Sprinklers. Sprinklers shall be arranged with respect to obstructions in accordance with one of the following:

(1) Sprinklers shall be installed below isolated noncontinuous obstructions that restrict only one sprinkler and are located below the elevation of sprinklers such as light fixtures and unit heaters.
(2) Additional sprinklers shall not be required where the obstruction is 2 ft (0.6 m) or less in width and the sprinkler is located horizontally 1 ft (0.3 m) or greater from the nearest edge of the obstruction.
(3) Additional sprinklers shall not be required where sprinklers are positioned with respect to the bottom of obstructions in accordance with 8.12.5.1.
(4) Additional sprinklers shall not be required where the obstruction is 2 in. (51 mm) or less in width and is located a minimum of 2 ft (0.6 m) below the elevation of the sprinkler deflector or is positioned a minimum of 1 ft (0.3 m) horizontally from the sprinkler.
(5) Sprinklers with a special obstruction allowance shall be installed according to their listing.

A.8.12.5.2 Isolated obstructions that block adjacent sprinklers in a similar manner should be treated as a continuous obstruction.

8.12.5.3 Continuous Obstructions Below the Sprinklers.

8.12.5.3.1 General Continuous Obstructions. Sprinklers shall be arranged with respect to obstructions in accordance with one of the following:

(1) Sprinklers shall be installed below continuous obstructions or they shall be arranged to comply with Table 8.12.5.1.1 for horizontal obstructions entirely below the elevation of sprinklers that restrict sprinkler discharge pattern for two or more adjacent sprinklers such as ducts, lights, pipes, and conveyors.
(2) Additional sprinklers shall not be required where the obstruction is 2 in. (51 mm) or less in width and is located a minimum of 2 ft (0.6 m) below the elevation of the sprinkler deflector or is positioned a minimum of 1 ft (0.3 m) horizontally from the sprinkler.
(3) Additional sprinklers shall not be required where the obstruction is 1 ft (0.3 m) or less in width and located a minimum of 1 ft (0.3 m) horizontally from the sprinkler.
(4) Additional sprinklers shall not be required where the obstruction is 2 ft (0.6 m) or less in width and located a minimum of 2 ft (0.6 m) horizontally from the sprinkler.
(5) Ceiling sprinklers shall not be required to comply with Table 8.12.5.1.1 where a row of sprinklers is installed under the obstruction.

8.12.5.3.2 Upright Sprinklers.

8.12.5.3.2.1 Upright sprinklers shall be installed on sprigs arranged so that the deflector is a minimum of 7 in. (178 mm) above the top of the sprinkler pipe.

8.12.5.3.2.2 K-11.2 upright sprinklers shall be permitted to be installed on sprigs arranged so that the deflector is a minimum of 7 in. (178 mm) above the top of the sprinkler pipe.

8.12.5.3.3 Bottom Chords of Bar Joists or Open Trusses. ESFR sprinklers shall be positioned a minimum of 1 ft (0.3 m) horizontally from the nearest edge to any bottom chord of a bar joist or open truss.

8.12.5.3.4 Open Gratings. Sprinklers installed under open gratings shall be of the intermediate level/rack storage type or otherwise shielded from the discharge of overhead sprinklers.

 8.12.5.3.5 Overhead Doors. Quick response spray sprinklers shall be permitted to be utilized under overhead doors.

 8.12.5.3.6 Special Obstruction Allowance. Sprinklers with a special obstruction allowance shall be installed according to their listing.

8.12.6 Clearance to Storage (Early Suppression Fast-Response Sprinklers). The clearance between the deflector and the top of storage shall be 36 in. (914 mm) or greater.

FAQ ▶
Why do ESFR sprinklers require 36 in. (914 mm) of clearance to the top of storage?

At clearances of less than 36 in. (914 mm), ESFR sprinklers installed within the allowable spacing guidelines cannot provide sufficient overlapping of adjacent sprinkler discharge patterns, which is the reason for the requirement in 8.12.6.

8.13 In-Rack Sprinklers

A number of conditions in Chapter 12 require the installation of in-rack sprinklers to protect miscellaneous storage. Numerous protection schemes in Chapter 12 also depend on in-rack sprinklers. Section 8.13 identifies the installation criteria for in-rack sprinklers. Specific spacing and location criteria provided in Chapter 12 for in-rack sprinklers take precedence over the requirements in Section 8.13, which provides general requirements for in-rack installation.

8.13.1 System Size. The area protected by a single system of sprinklers in racks shall not exceed 40,000 ft² (3716 m²) of floor area occupied by the racks, including aisles, regardless of the number of levels of in-rack sprinklers.

8.13.2 Type of In-Rack Sprinklers.

8.13.2.1 Sprinklers in racks shall be ordinary-temperature standard-response or quick-response classification with a nominal K-factor of 5.6 or 8.0, pendent or upright.

Type of in-rack sprinklers is discussed in 8.13.2.1. Theoretically, the use of quick-response in-rack sprinklers can speed up sprinkler operation, resulting in the application of water to a smaller fire, thereby improving sprinkler performance. Because the in-rack sprinkler does not activate until it is immersed in the fire plume—that is, at very high temperatures—the difference between the size of the fire when a quick-response in-rack sprinkler opens and the size of a fire when a standard response in-rack sprinkler opens, however, is negligible. Therefore, the design requirements when using quick-response in-rack sprinklers remain the same as the design requirements when using standard response in-rack sprinklers.

8.13.2.2 Sprinklers with intermediate- and high-temperature ratings shall be used near heat sources as required by 8.3.2.

8.13.3 In-Rack Sprinkler Water Shields.

Water shields are discussed in 8.13.3. Where there is more than one level of in-rack sprinklers and horizontal barriers are not used, water shields over the lower level in-rack sprinklers are required to minimize the likelihood of discharge from upper level in-rack sprinklers cold soldering the lower level in-rack sprinklers. As an exception to water shields, listed intermediate level/rack storage sprinklers are permitted. Exhibit 8.24 shows an in-rack sprinkler equipped with a water shield and a guard.

8.13.3.1 In-Rack Sprinkler Water Shields for Storage of Class I through IV Commodities. Water shields shall be provided directly above in-rack sprinklers, or listed intermediate level/rack storage sprinklers shall be used where there is more than one level, if not shielded by horizontal barriers. *(See Section C.3.)*

EXHIBIT 8.24 In-Rack Sprinkler Equipped with a Listed Water Shield and Guard.

8.13.3.2 In-Rack Sprinkler Water Shields for Plastic Storage. Where in-rack sprinklers are not shielded by horizontal barriers, water shields shall be provided above the sprinklers, or listed intermediate level/rack storage sprinklers shall be used.

8.13.4 Location, Position, and Spacing of In-Rack Sprinklers. See Section 12.3.

Location, position, and spacing of in-rack sprinklers are addressed in 8.13.4.7 In-rack sprinklers usually operate because they are located within the developing fire plume. Water distribution is not as critical because the pattern does not need to penetrate the fire plume. Obstructions to the sprinkler discharge patterns are much less critical, and, therefore, the general requirements for obstructions do not apply to in-rack sprinklers.

8.13.5 Obstructions to In-Rack Sprinkler Discharge. In-rack sprinklers shall not be required to meet the obstruction criteria and clearance from storage requirements of Section 8.5.

8.14 Special Situations

As indicated in 8.1.1(1), sprinklers are required throughout the premises. Under certain conditions, however, the omission of sprinklers in certain areas and spaces within a building is permitted. Section 8.14 identifies these spaces and conditions.

8.14.1 Concealed Spaces.

8.14.1.1 Concealed Spaces Requiring Sprinkler Protection. All concealed spaces enclosed wholly or partly by exposed combustible construction shall be protected by sprinklers except in concealed spaces where sprinklers are not required to be installed by 8.14.1.2.1 through 8.14.1.2.15.

Concealed spaces requiring sprinkler protection are covered in 8.14.1.1. Concealed spaces, unless protected, can provide an unabated passage for firespread throughout a building. Paragraph 8.14.1 applies to those portions of a building that have construction or finish materials of a combustible nature, are used for the storage of combustible materials, and can contain combustibles associated with building system features such as computer wiring or large quantities of nonmetallic piping.

Any of these scenarios could be found in a concealed space. It is important to recognize that concealed spaces are not exclusively limited to areas above ceilings but can also be found in walls and in spaces beneath the floor. For example, a raised floor in a computer room is a concealed space. If none of the three prescribed conditions exists, the space is defined as a concealed, noncombustible space with respect to combustible objects and requires no additional sprinkler protection.

Some minor quantities of combustible materials, such as communication wiring, can be present in some concealed spaces but should not typically be viewed as requiring sprinklers (see 8.14.1.1). The threshold value at which sprinklers become necessary in the concealed space is not defined. For example, the usual amounts of data or telephone wiring found above a ceiling would not typically constitute a threat. If bundles of unsheathed computer wiring are installed above the ceiling or beneath the floor in a manner where fire propagation in all directions is likely, then the concealed space should be treated the same as a combustible space, thereby requiring appropriate sprinkler protection. If some other protection measure is provided, such as a CO_2 system, then the concealed space is considered to be protected, and sprinklers are not required.

8.14.1.2* Concealed Spaces Not Requiring Sprinkler Protection.

A.8.14.1.2 Subsections 8.14.1.2.3, 8.14.1.2.4, and 8.14.1.2.5 do not require sprinkler protection because it is not physically practical to install sprinklers in the types of concealed spaces discussed in these three exceptions. To reduce the possibility of uncontrolled fire spread, consideration should be given in these unsprinklered concealed space situations to using 8.14.1.2.7, 8.14.1.2.10, and 8.14.1.2.12.

The subparagraphs of 8.14.1.2 indicate conditions where sprinklers are not required in spaces that would normally require sprinklers. Sometimes the building is modified to meet one of these exceptions to avoid installing sprinklers in the space. Not all of these exceptions provide an equivalent level of fire safety, because some of the exceptions simply recognize that the installation of sprinklers in the space is not physically practical. This difference in level of fire safety is especially true of 8.14.1.2.3, 8.14.1.2.4, and 8.14.1.2.5, which primarily exist to cover situations where sprinklers are retrofitted into existing buildings.

8.14.1.2.1 Noncombustible and limited combustible concealed spaces with no combustible loading having no access shall not require sprinkler protection. The space shall be considered a concealed space even with small openings such as those used as return air for a plenum.

8.14.1.2.2 Noncombustible and limited combustible concealed spaces with limited access and not permitting occupancy or storage of combustibles shall not require sprinkler protection. The space shall be considered a concealed space even with small openings such as those used as return air for a plenum.

Paragraphs 8.14.1.2.1 and 8.14.1.2.2 were added to the 2002 edition to address an area where exceptions were not clearly stated in previous editions. These new paragraphs permit the omission of sprinklers from noncombustible or limited combustible concealed spaces having no combustible loading and limited or no access. These spaces are permitted to have small openings such as those used for return air plenums and still be considered a concealed space.

8.14.1.2.3 Concealed spaces formed by studs or joists with less than 6 in. (152 mm) between the inside or near edges of the studs or joists shall not require sprinkler protection. *(See Figure 8.6.4.1.5.1.)*

8.14.1.2.4 Concealed spaces formed by bar joists with less than 6 in. (152 mm) between the roof or floor deck and ceiling shall not require sprinkler protection.

8.14.1.2.5 Concealed spaces formed by ceilings attached directly to or within 6 in. (152 mm) of wood joist construction shall not require sprinkler protection.

Paragraph 8.14.1.2.5 applies to sheathed joist construction or similar narrow spaces formed by attachment of a ceiling to or within 6 in. (152 mm) of joists. This exception is intended to apply only to joists with no openings in the members and up to a nominal depth of 14 in. (356 mm).

8.14.1.2.6* Concealed spaces formed by ceilings attached to composite wood joist construction either directly or onto metal channels not exceeding 1 in. in depth, provided the joist channels are firestopped into volumes each not exceeding 160 ft^3 (4.53 m^3) using materials equivalent to the web construction and at least 3½ in. of batt insulation is installed at the bottom of the joist channels when the ceiling is attached utilizing metal channels, shall not require sprinkler protection.

A.8.14.1.2.6 See Figure A.8.14.1.2.6.

Subfloor

Gypsum board
Resilient channel
Batt insulation

FIGURE A.8.14.1.2.6 *Combustible Concealed Space Cross Section.*

8.14.1.2.7 Concealed spaces entirely filled with noncombustible insulation shall not require sprinkler protection.

In some cases, filling an unsprinklered combustible concealed space with noncombustible insulation, as indicated by 8.14.1.2.7, might be more economically advantageous than installing sprinklers.

8.14.1.2.8 Concealed spaces within wood joist construction and composite wood joist construction having noncombustible insulation filling the space from the ceiling up to the bottom edge of the joist of the roof or floor deck, provided that in composite wood joist construction the joist channels are firestopped into volumes each not exceeding 160 ft^3 (4.53 m^3) to the full depth of the joist with material equivalent to the web construction, shall not require sprinkler protection.

8.14.1.2.9 Concealed spaces over isolated small rooms not exceeding 55 ft^2 (4.6 m^2) in area shall not require sprinkler protection.

8.14.1.2.10 Concealed spaces where rigid materials are used and the exposed surfaces have a flame spread rating of 25 or less and the materials have been demonstrated not to propagate fire in the form in which they are installed shall not require sprinkler protection.

The requirements of 8.14.1.2.10 permit the use of limited-combustible materials as a substitute for sprinkler protection. When considering these materials, it is important to verify that the testing used to determine the material's combustibility was conducted with the material arranged in the position in which it will be installed. Changes in the orientation or arrangement of the material can significantly change the flamespread characteristics and the combustibility of the material. Additionally, the materials are required to be rigid because experience indicates that nonrigid materials do not demonstrate the same characteristics during a fire.

8.14.1.2.11 Concealed spaces in which the exposed materials are constructed entirely of fire-retardant treated wood as defined by NFPA 703, *Standard for Fire Retardant Impregnated Wood and Fire Retardant Coatings for Building Materials,* shall not require sprinkler protection.

 8.14.1.2.12 Noncombustible concealed spaces having exposed combustible insulation where the heat content of the facing and substrate of the insulation material does not exceed 1000 Btu/ft^2 (11,356 kJ/m^2) shall not require sprinkler protection.

Paragraph 8.14.1.2.12 allows the use of paper-coated insulation material in a space that is otherwise defined as a noncombustible space.

8.14.1.2.13 Concealed spaces below insulation that is laid directly on top of or within the ceiling joists in an otherwise sprinklered attic shall not require sprinkler protection.

Paragraph 8.14.1.2.13 indicates that sprinklers are not required in the space between the insulation in an attic and the ceiling sheathing. The sprinklers in the attic are anticipated to provide sufficient protection.

 8.14.1.2.14 Vertical pipe chases under 10 ft^2 (0.93 m^2), where provided that in multifloor buildings the chases are fire stopped at each floor using materials equivalent to the floor construction, and where such pipe chases shall contain no sources of ignition, piping shall be noncombustible, and pipe penetrations at each floor shall be properly sealed and shall not require sprinkler protection.

Paragraph 8.14.1.2.14 is included in the standard due to the impracticality of installing sprinklers in the small spaces that are usually behind the walls of bathrooms and kitchens in residential facilities. This requirement supports the premise that sprinklers can only be omitted in concealed spaces where the installation of sprinklers is absolutely impractical, such as those spaces identified by 8.14.1.2.3, 8.14.1.2.4, and 8.14.1.2.5 or where combustibles or ignition sources will not be present.

 8.14.1.2.15 Exterior columns under 10 ft^2 in area formed by studs or wood joist, supporting exterior canopies that are fully protected with a sprinkler system, shall not require sprinkler protection.

8.14.1.3 Concealed Space Design Requirements. Sprinklers in concealed spaces having no access for storage or other use shall be installed in accordance with the requirements for light hazard occupancy.

The sprinkler requirement in 8.14.1.3 applies to a concealed combustible space that requires sprinkler protection because of 8.14.1.1. The reference to light hazard occupancy is for the purpose of selecting a density or the appropriate pipe schedule table (if allowed in Chapter 11). The type of construction must be evaluated to determine what area of coverage is needed for the sprinklers.

The intention of 8.14.1.3 is not to require sprinklers in a concealed noncombustible space that contains mechanical equipment made of noncombustible materials. Nor is the intent to require sprinklers simply because an access panel is installed to gain entry to the equipment. The existence of an access panel to a concealed space could lead to the space being used for storage or other purposes. However, if the size or arrangement of the access is such that the space cannot or will not be utilized and the combustibility is limited to the combustible construction, sprinklers can then be installed according to the requirements for a light hazard occupancy.

If sprinklers are installed in a concealed space following the rules of light hazard occupancies, then they are required to be quick-response sprinklers.

8.14.1.4 Heat Producing Devices with Composite Wood Joist Construction. Where heat-producing devices such as furnaces or process equipment are located in the joist channels above a ceiling attached directly to the underside of composite wood joist construction that would not otherwise require sprinkler protection of the spaces, the joist channel containing the heat-producing devices shall be sprinklered by installing sprinklers in each joist channel, on each side, adjacent to the heat-producing device.

8.14.1.5 Localized Protection of Exposed Combustible Construction or Exposed Combustibles. In concealed spaces having exposed combustible construction, or containing exposed combustibles, in localized areas, the combustibles shall be protected as follows:

(1) If the exposed combustibles are in the vertical partitions or walls around all or a portion of the enclosure, a single row of sprinklers spaced not over 12 ft (3.7 m) apart nor more than 6 ft (1.8 m) from the inside of the partition shall be permitted to protect the surface. The first and last sprinklers in such a row shall not be over 5 ft (1.5 m) from the ends of the partitions.

(2) If the exposed combustibles are in the horizontal plane, the area of the combustibles shall be permitted to be protected with sprinklers on a light hazard spacing. Additional sprinklers shall be installed no more than 6 ft (1.8 m) outside the outline of the area and not more than 12 ft (3.7 m) on center along the outline. When the outline returns to a wall or other obstruction, the last sprinkler shall not be more than 6 ft (1.8 m) from the wall or obstruction.

Two situations where isolated combustibles are in an otherwise noncombustible concealed space are covered in 8.14.1.4 and 8.14.1.5. Sprinklers are provided to protect the combustible material and limit the potential for firespread. Where numerous areas contain combustibles, consideration should be given to providing sprinklers throughout the space.

8.14.1.6* Sprinklers used in horizontal combustible concealed spaces (with a slope not exceeding 2 in 12) having a combustible upper surface where the assembly or supporting members channel heat and where the depth of the space is less than 36 in. from deck to deck or with double wood joist construction with a maximum of 36 in. between the top of the bottom joist and the bottom of the upper joist shall be listed for such use.

A.8.14.1.6 Surfaces should be considered to channel heat when the surface or supporting members are greater than 2 in. in depth.

Testing of open web truss and solid wood joist construction in relatively shallow comb concealed sprinklers shows that standard spray sprinklers are ineffective at fire control above ceilings or below floors (see 8.14.1.6). The shallow space inhibits discharge pattern development and also increases the probability that a small fire will involve the upper combustible members above the sprinkler, significantly increasing the fire challenge. Sprinklers specifically listed to protect these spaces are available. Once the height of the space exceeds 36 in. (0.9 m), standard sprinklers can be utilized.

8.14.2 Vertical Shafts.

8.14.2.1 General. Unless the requirements of 8.14.2.1.1 or 8.14.2.1.2 are met, one sprinkler shall be installed at the top of shafts.

8.14.2.1.1 Noncombustible or limited-combustible, nonaccessible vertical duct shafts shall not require sprinkler protection.

◄ FAQ
Where sprinklers are installed in combustible concealed spaces utilizing the requirements of light hazard occupancies, are quick-response sprinklers required?

8.14.2.1.2 Noncombustible or limited-combustible, nonaccessible vertical electrical or mechanical shafts shall not require sprinkler protection.

Sprinklers are to be provided at the top of all shafts used for stairs or other shafts open to more than one floor. Previously, the requirement in 8.14.2.1.2 applied to elevator shafts, which is no longer the case. Elevator shafts now have a distinct set of requirements in 8.14.5 that addresses the needs of the elevator industry. Concealed combustible shafts must be sprinklered. Concealed shafts of noncombustible or limited-combustible construction and contents in a suitably rated enclosure do not require sprinklers.

8.14.2.2* Shafts with Combustible Surfaces.

 A.8.14.2.2 Where practicable, sprinklers should be staggered at the alternate floor levels, particularly where only one sprinkler is installed at each floor level.

8.14.2.2.1 Where vertical shafts have combustible surfaces, one sprinkler shall be installed at each alternate floor level.

8.14.2.2.2 Where a shaft having combustible surfaces is trapped, an additional sprinkler shall be installed at the top of each trapped section.

Shafts with combustible surfaces are covered in 8.14.2.2.1 and 8.14.2.2.2. The additional sprinklers for shafts with combustible sides must be placed to effectively wet the combustible surfaces. Where the shaft changes direction to form a trapped section, sprinklers are required at the top of each trapped section.

8.14.2.3 Accessible Shafts with Noncombustible Surfaces. Where accessible vertical shafts have noncombustible surfaces, one sprinkler shall be installed near the bottom.

Where shafts are accessible, trash and other material can potentially collect at the bottom of the shaft. In these cases, 8.14.2.3 requires a sprinkler at the bottom of the shaft even if the shaft is of noncombustible construction.

8.14.3 Stairways.

8.14.3.1 Combustible Construction. Sprinklers shall be installed beneath all stairways of combustible construction.

8.14.3.2 Noncombustible Construction.

8.14.3.2.1 In noncombustible stair shafts with noncombustible stairs, sprinklers shall be installed at the top of the shaft and under the first landing above the bottom of the shaft.

 8.14.3.2.2 Where noncombustible stair shafts are divided by walls or doors, sprinklers shall be provided on each side of the separation.

8.14.3.2.3 Sprinklers shall be installed beneath landings or stairways where the area beneath is used for storage.

FAQ ▶
Why are sprinklers required in noncombustible stair shafts at the top of the shaft and under the first landing above the bottom of the shaft?

The storage of materials in stairwells obstructs the egress route and is usually prohibited. When storage does occur, it is often at the top landing or under the first landing. As a result, 8.14.3.2.3 requires sprinklers at these locations and at any other area in the stair shaft where storage can occur.

8.14.3.3* Stairs Serving Two or More Fire Divisions. Sprinklers shall be installed in the stair shaft at each floor landing where two or more doors open from that landing into separate fire divisions.

 A.8.14.3.3 See Figure A.8.14.3.3(a) and Figure A.8.14.3.3(b). Sprinklers would be required in the case shown in Figure A.8.14.3.3(a) but not in the case shown in Figure A.8.14.3.3(b).

FIGURE A.8.14.3.3(a) *Noncombustible Stair Shaft Serving Two Fire Sections.*

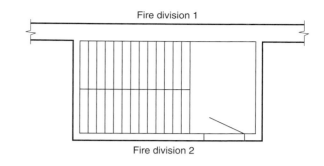

FIGURE A.8.14.3.3(b) *Noncombustible Stair Shaft Serving One Fire Section.*

Sprinklers are required at each floor landing where a noncombustible stair shaft serves two fire-separated buildings or two fire sections of one building as shown in Figure A.8.14.3.3(a) or where the stair landing serves as a horizontal exit. If the stair serves only one fire section, then sprinklers are required only at the roof and under the lowest landing. See Figures A.8.14.3.3(a) and A.8.14.3.3(b).

8.14.4* Vertical Openings.

A.8.14.4 Where sprinklers in the normal ceiling pattern are closer than 6 ft (1.8 m) from the water curtain, it might be preferable to locate the water curtain sprinklers in recessed baffle pockets. *(See Figure A.8.14.4.)*

FIGURE A.8.14.4 *Sprinklers Around Escalators.*

8.14.4.1 General. Unless the requirements of 8.14.4.4 or 8.14.4.5 are met, where moving stairways, staircases, or similar floor openings are unenclosed, the floor openings involved shall be protected by closely spaced sprinklers in combination with draft stops in accordance with 8.14.4.2 and 8.14.4.3.

Vertical openings are discussed in 8.14.4.1. By placing sprinklers close to a ceiling opening, the floor area under the opening can be protected. (Small openings are discussed in 8.14.2, and larger openings are addressed in 8.14.4.)

FAQ ▶
Why are closely spaced sprinklers and draft stops required around openings not meeting the requirements of 8.14.4.4?

Subsection 8.14.4 is limited to openings that do not meet the definition of an atrium. These smaller openings tend to behave much the same as a chimney, allowing rapid vertical movement of the hot gases from the fire. This phenomenon is practically nonexistent in larger openings. Closely spaced sprinklers in conjunction with draft stops are an effective method of gaining control of the fire in these smaller sized openings and in preventing sprinklers from operating on the upper levels by cooling the convective air stream.

Some of these openings, such as escalator openings in department stores, tend to have displays of combustible material directly adjacent to the opening, and the sprinklers prevent the propagation of the fire to the upper story.

8.14.4.2 Draft Stops. Draft stops shall meet all of the following:

(1) The draft stops shall be located immediately adjacent to the opening.
(2) The draft stops shall be at least 18 in. (457 mm) deep.
(3) The draft stops shall be of noncombustible or limited-combustible material that will stay in place before and during sprinkler operation.

8.14.4.3 Sprinklers.

8.14.4.3.1 Sprinklers shall be spaced not more than 6 ft (1.8 m) apart and placed 6 in. to 12 in. (152 mm to 305 mm) from the draft stop on the side away from the opening.

8.14.4.3.2 Where sprinklers are closer than 6 ft (1.8 m), cross baffles shall be provided in accordance with 8.6.3.4.2.

When the features of the opening warrant sprinklers are spaced at intervals of less than 6 ft (1.8 m), as described in 8.14.4.3.2, the installation of baffles between adjacent sprinklers prevents the occurrence of the cold solder effect. The use of such devices is discussed in the commentary to 8.6.3.4 for standard spray sprinklers.

Sprinklers used to achieve the protection outlined in 8.14.4 can be the open or automatic type. Privately conducted tests using closed sprinklers have indicated their effectiveness. The use of deluge-type water curtains has become quite rare since the early 1960s. Accidental discharge of deluge-type water curtains results in considerable water damage as well as potential injury to persons on escalators when such false actuation occurs.

8.14.4.4 Large Openings. Closely spaced sprinklers and draft stops are not required around large openings such as those found in shopping malls, atrium buildings, and similar structures where all adjoining levels and spaces are protected by automatic sprinklers in accordance with this standard and where the openings have all horizontal dimensions between opposite edges of 20 ft (6 m) or greater and an area of 1000 ft^2 (93 m^2) or greater.

8.14.4.5 Convenience Openings in Individual Dwelling Units. Draft stops and closely spaced sprinklers are not required for convenience openings within individual dwelling units that meet all of the following criteria:

(1) Such openings shall connect a maximum of two adjacent stories (pierce one floor only).
(2)* Such openings shall be separated from unprotected vertical openings serving other floors by a barrier with a fire resistance rating equal to that required for enclosure of floor openings by NFPA *101*®, *Life Safety Code*®.

Openings are routinely provided between the floors of dwelling units, and 8.14.4.5 addresses these arrangements. These openings do not need to be protected if they connect only two floors, are separated from other vertical openings by fire barriers, are not corridors, and are not required for egress by NFPA *101*. A typical example of this situation would be a stairway in a two-level apartment located in a high-rise building.

A.8.14.4.5(2) Subsection 8.2.5.4 of the 2000 edition of NFPA *101,® Life Safety Code®* requires a 2-hour separation for enclosures connecting four stories or more in new construction, a 1-hour separation for other enclosures in new construction, and a 30-minute separation for existing buildings. Special rules for residential construction exist in Chapters 26 through 31 of NFPA *101.*

(3) Such openings shall be separate from corridors.

(4) Such openings shall not serve as a required means of egress, although they can serve as a required means of escape.

8.14.5 Elevator Hoistways and Machine Rooms.

Elevator hoistways and machine rooms are covered in 8.14.5. Codes that cover elevator design, such as ASME A17.1, *Safety Code for Elevators and Escalators,* do not permit water discharge in elevator shafts until electrical power to the elevator cab has been shut down. This situation necessitates some special arrangement, such as a preaction system, to make sure that water does not flow in the elevator shaft until power shutdown has occurred. The additional cost of a special installation and the benefits returned for the protection must be weighed against the small number of fires in elevator shafts.

Several papers on this topic were presented at a symposium in February 1991 in Baltimore, MD [ASME Proceedings 1991] Subjects presented at this symposium ranged from elevator safety in general to the potential problems associated with premature discharge of water onto elevator control elements. Following this symposium, representatives from the building code organizations and the American Society of Mechanical Engineers (ASME) worked to resolve the problem of providing proper fire protection without sacrificing any of the inherent safety features of the sprinkler system or elevator and its associated equipment. The result of this cooperation was the development of 8.14.5 to specifically address the installation of sprinklers in elevator shafts and equipment rooms.

This is an area that is constantly changing and some changes have been proposed to ASME A17.1 that may require modification of these requirements in the future. Also, in some jurisdictions there is a movement to eliminate the sprinklers and automatic shutdown so that the fire service can continue to use the elevator as long as possible when fighting fires in a high-rise building. Any modifications to these rules to permit the omission of sprinklers by local officials needs to be carefully considered due to the possibility of uncontrolled fire growth within elevator machine rooms combined with simultaneous fire department dependence on those elevators. Additional concern surrounds the fire department's assumption when responding to a fire incident within an elevator machine room that these spaces within the building are fully sprinklered.

8.14.5.1* Sidewall spray sprinklers shall be installed at the bottom of each elevator hoistway not more than 2 ft (0.61 m) above the floor of the pit.

A.8.14.5.1 The sprinklers in the pit are intended to protect against fires caused by debris, which can accumulate over time. Ideally, the sprinklers should be located near the side of the pit below the elevator doors, where most debris accumulates. However, care should be taken that the sprinkler location does not interfere with the elevator toe guard, which extends below the face of the door opening.

ASME A17.1, *Safety Code for Elevators and Escalators,* allows the sprinklers within 2 ft (0.65 m) of the bottom of the pit to be exempted from the special arrangements of inhibiting waterflow until elevator recall has occurred.

Refuse and residual hydraulic fluids tend to collect at the bottom of shafts. A properly located sprinkler, as required by 8.14.5.1, can control a fire of such material. Conventional requirements regarding the placement of the deflector and clear space below the sprinkler cannot always be adhered to in this area. These issues are not critical, however, because the sprinkler would be physically close to any point where a fire could originate, still allowing the sprinkler to control the fire.

FAQ ▶
Where sprinklers are installed at the bottom of the elevator shaft, is water discharge required to be delayed until power shutdown has occurred?

Because the sprinkler at the bottom of the shaft cannot discharge onto the elevator or other operating components of the elevator, ASME A17.1 no longer requires that the sprinkler discharge at the bottom of the shaft be delayed until power shutdown has occurred. The sprinkler at the bottom of the shaft, where installed, is allowed to be part of the normal building sprinkler system and is not required to be part of the special system used to protect the rest of the elevator equipment.

8.14.5.2 The sprinkler required at the bottom of the elevator hoistway by 8.14.5.1 shall not be required for enclosed, noncombustible elevator shafts that do not contain combustible hydraulic fluids.

8.14.5.3* Automatic sprinklers in elevator machine rooms or at the tops of hoistways shall be of ordinary- or intermediate-temperature rating.

A.8.14.5.3 ASME A17.1, *Safety Code for Elevators and Escalators,* requires the shutdown of power to the elevator upon or prior to the application of water in elevator machine rooms or hoistways. This shutdown can be accomplished by a detection system with sufficient sensitivity that operates prior to the activation of the sprinklers *(see also NFPA 72®, National Fire Alarm Code®)*. As an alternative, the system can be arranged using devices or sprinklers capable of effecting power shutdown immediately upon sprinkler activation, such as a waterflow switch without a time delay. This alternative arrangement is intended to interrupt power before significant sprinkler discharge.

8.14.5.4* Upright or pendent spray sprinklers shall be installed at the top of elevator hoistways.

A.8.14.5.4 Passenger elevator cars that have been constructed in accordance with ASME A17.1, *Safety Code for Elevators and Escalators,* Rule 204.2a (under A17.1a-1985 and later editions of the code) have limited combustibility. Materials exposed to the interior of the car and the hoistway, in their end-use composition, are limited to a flame spread rating of 0 to 75 and a smoke development rating of 0 to 450.

8.14.5.5 The sprinkler required at the top of the elevator hoistway by 8.14.5.4 shall not be required where the hoistway for passenger elevators is noncombustible and the car enclosure materials meet the requirements of ASME A17.1, *Safety Code for Elevators and Escalators.*

8.14.6 Spaces Under Ground Floors, Exterior Docks, and Platforms.

8.14.6.1 Unless the requirements of 8.14.6.2 are met, sprinklers shall be installed in spaces under all combustible ground floors, exterior docks, and platforms.

8.14.6.2 Sprinklers shall be permitted to be omitted from spaces under ground floors, exterior docks, and platforms where all of the following conditions prevail:

(1) The space is not accessible for storage purposes and is protected against accumulation of wind-borne debris.
(2) The space contains no equipment such as conveyors or fuel-fired heating units.
(3) The floor over the space is of tight construction.
(4) No combustible or flammable liquids or materials that under fire conditions would convert into combustible or flammable liquids are processed, handled, or stored on the floor above the space.

Paragraph 8.14.6.2 is another exception to the general requirement that all combustible spaces must be sprinklered. It recognizes the possibility of maintenance problems, such as lack of access and danger of freezing with piping under a floor. The conditions intend to eliminate sources of ignition from the concealed space and prevent combustibles from being stored or trash from accumulating, thereby limiting combustibles to the floor materials only.

8.14.7* Exterior Roofs or Canopies.

A.8.14.7 Small loading docks, covered platforms, ducts, or similar small unheated areas can be protected by dry-pendent sprinklers extending through the wall from wet sprinkler piping in an adjacent heated area. Where protecting covered platforms, loading docks, and similar areas, a dry-pendent sprinkler should extend down at a 45-degree angle. The width of the area to be protected should not exceed 7½ ft (2.3 m). Sprinklers should be spaced not over 12 ft (3.7 m) apart. *(See Figure A.8.14.7.)*

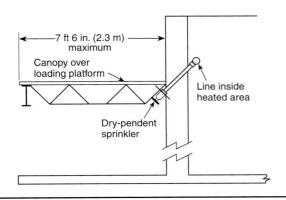

FIGURE A.8.14.7 Dry-Pendent Sprinklers for Protection of Covered Platforms, Loading Docks, and Similar Areas.

8.14.7.1* Unless the requirements of 8.14.7.2 or 8.14.7.3 are met, sprinklers shall be installed under exterior roofs or canopies exceeding 4 ft (1.2 m) in width.

A.8.14.7.1 Balconies, decks, and similar projections from the building should be treated as exterior roofs and canopies when applying the criteria of 8.14.7.1.

Exterior canopies exceeding 4 ft (1.2 m) in width must be sprinklered if they are of combustible construction, as stated in 8.14.7.1, regardless of whether or not combustible goods are stored or handled underneath them.

Canopies less than 4 ft (1.2 m) in width do not need to be sprinklered regardless of construction type provided no combustibles are stored beneath them.

8.14.7.2 Sprinklers shall be permitted to be omitted where the canopy or roof is of noncombustible or limited combustible construction.

As stated in 8.14.7.2, sprinklers can be omitted if the canopy construction assembly is comprised totally of noncombustible or limited combustible materials and the area underneath is essentially restricted to pedestrian use. The reference to noncombustible and limited combustible construction applies to the entire canopy assembly and not just the exposed surface.

The roof canopy typically found on strip shopping malls, in which the area under the canopy is limited to pedestrians, is one example of this condition. Automobiles stopping briefly to pick up or drop off passengers are not considered storage. Areas located at drive-in bank windows or *porte cocheres* at motels and hotels normally do not require sprinklers. However, the area under the exterior ceiling shown in Exhibit 8.25 requires sprinkler protection. The space is used primarily for parking vehicles, and the remainder of the building is sprinklered.

Figure A.8.14.7 shows one method of protecting areas under roofs or canopies up to 7½ ft (2.3 m) wide. Sprinklers are required under all such coverings where combustible goods are stored or handled.

◄ **FAQ**
Does the requirement of 8.14.7.1 require sprinklers under exterior roofs or canopies of combustible construction that exceed 4 ft in width where no combustibles are stored or handled under the roof or canopy?

◄ **FAQ**
Does the requirement of 8.14.7.2 require that the exterior roof or canopy be surfaced with noncombustible or limited combustible materials, or is the entire canopy required to be constructed of noncombustible or limited combustible materials?

EXHIBIT 8.25 *Parking Area Under an Exterior Ceiling That Is Required to Be Sprinklered.*

8.14.7.3 Sprinklers shall be permitted to be omitted from exterior exit corridors when the exterior walls of the corridor are at least 50 percent open and when the corridor is entirely of noncombustible construction.

As stated in 8.14.7.3, exit corridors wider than 4 ft (such as might be found on the outside of a motel or similar structure) will not normally contain combustibles and do not require sprinklers, providing that the corridor is entirely constructed of noncombustible materials and the exterior walls are 50 percent open so that there is access for fire fighting should a fire occur.

8.14.7.4* Sprinklers shall be installed under roofs or canopies over areas where combustibles are stored and handled.

 A.8.14.7.4 Short-term transient storage, such as that for delivered packages, and the presence of planters, newspaper machines, and so forth, should not be considered storage or handling of combustibles.

8.14.8 Dwelling Units.

The risk associated with not providing sprinkler protection in the spaces described in 8.14.8 is considered acceptable, because the incidence of fires, property damage, and fatalities that occur in these spaces is relatively small. A specific limit, however, is imposed on the size of the space, its location, and the type of occupancy in which it is located.

8.14.8.1 Bathrooms.

Bathrooms are discussed in 8.14.8.1. The 2002 edition added Annex A material to clarify what constitutes a bathroom (see A.3.3.3). For example, a bathroom could contain a toilet and a tub but no sink and an adjacent room that contains a sink could also be considered a bathroom.

 8.14.8.1.1 Unless sprinklers are required by 8.14.8.1.2 or 8.14.8.1.3, sprinklers shall not be required in bathrooms that are located within dwelling units, that do not exceed 55 ft² (5.1 m²) in area, and that have walls and ceilings of noncombustible or limited-combustible materials with a 15-minute thermal barrier rating including the walls and ceilings behind fixtures.

 8.14.8.1.2 Sprinklers shall be required in bathrooms of nursing homes, as defined in NFPA *101, Life Safety Code.*

 The 2002 edition modified the requirements of 8.14.8.1.2 to indicate that nursing homes are as defined in NFPA *101*. By referencing NFPA *101*'s definition, there is a clear definition of what is considered a nursing home.

8.14.8.1.3 Sprinklers shall be required in bathrooms opening directly onto public corridors or exitways.

8.14.8.2* Closets and Pantries. Sprinklers are not required in clothes closets, linen closets, and pantries within dwelling units in hotels and motels where the area of the space does not exceed 24 ft² (2.2 m²), the least dimension does not exceed 3 ft (0.9 m), and the walls and ceilings are surfaced with noncombustible or limited-combustible materials.

A.8.14.8.2 Portable wardrobe units, such as those typically used in nursing homes and mounted to the wall, do not require sprinklers to be installed in them. Although the units are attached to the finished structure, this standard views those units as pieces of furniture rather than as a part of the structure; thus, sprinklers are not required.

The provision in 8.14.8.2, which permits sprinklers to be omitted in closets, is limited to clothes, linen, and pantry-type closets in hotel and motel guest rooms. This provision does not extend to any other types of dwelling units, such as apartments, nursing homes, dormitories, condominiums, or other residential properties that are not defined as a hotel or motel. Closets in hotels and motels are not expected to contain the types and quantities of combustibles typically found in the closets of residences.

◄ **FAQ**
Are sprinklers permitted to be omitted from closets within all dwelling units?

8.14.9 Library Stack Rooms. Sprinklers shall be installed in accordance with one of the following:

(1) Sprinklers shall be permitted to be installed without regard to aisles where there is 18 in. (457 mm) or more clearance between sprinkler deflectors and tops of racks.
(2) Where the 18 in. (457 mm) clearance between sprinkler deflectors and tops of racks cannot be maintained, sprinklers shall be installed in every aisle and at every tier of stacks with distance between sprinklers along aisles not to exceed 12 ft (3.7 m) in accordance with Figure 8.14.9(a).
(3) Where the 18 in. (457 mm) clearance between sprinkler deflectors and tops of racks cannot be maintained and where vertical shelf dividers are incomplete and allow water distribution to adjacent aisles, sprinklers shall be permitted to be omitted in alternate aisles on each tier, and where ventilation openings are also provided in tier floors, sprinklers shall be staggered vertically in accordance with Figure 8.14.9(b).

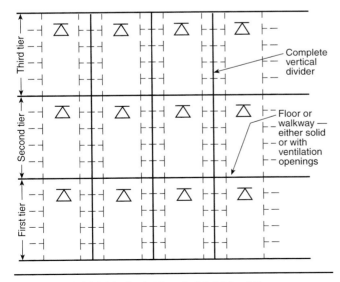

FIGURE 8.14.9(a) Sprinklers in Multitier Library Bookstacks with Complete Vertical Dividers.

FIGURE 8.14.9(b) Sprinklers in Multitier Library Bookstacks with Incomplete Vertical Dividers.

Library stack rooms, which are discussed in 8.14.9, are generally thought of as high-density book storage on shelves and, in some ways, can be thought of as a type of rack storage. To overcome the obstruction caused by the bookshelves, sprinklers are installed at every tier and aisle unless adequate clearance can be maintained.

Paragraph 8.14.9(3) departs somewhat from the typical sprinkler clearance requirements, because 8.14.9 assumes that the 18 in. (457 mm) of clear space below the sprinkler deflector will not be maintained. In order to compensate for this closer sprinkler placement, sprinklers are required in each aisle unless the 18-in. (457-mm) clear space is available.

FAQ ▶
Do the library stack room rules apply to high-density mobile shelving?

Although not explicitly covered by NFPA 13, the same logic with respect to high-density mobile shelving can be applied when the 18-in. (457-mm) clear space is not provided. If a determination can be made concerning the various combinations of aisles, then a row of sprinklers can be placed along the centerline to compensate for the lack of clearance. This approach frequently results in the need to install baffles, because the line spacing decreases to less than 6 ft (1.8 m) apart.

Additionally, the rules of 8.14.9 can be applied to the storage of medical records as indicated by FI 13-99-2.

Formal Interpretation

Reference: 8.14.9

F.I. No.: 13-99-2

Background: Section 8-5.6 states that the clearance between the sprinkler deflector and the top of storage shall be 18 in. (457 mm) or greater. Section 8.14.9 provides guidance on sprinkler protection of library stacks. This guidance allows floor to ceiling bookshelves and requires sprinklers to be installed in every aisle with a distance between sprinklers along aisles not to exceed 12 ft (3.6 m).

Question: Is it acceptable to apply the principles of NFPA 13, 8.14.9 to the storage of Medical Records on fixed open bookshelves, thereby allowing the tops of the bookshelves used for this purpose to come within less than 18 inches of the horizontal plane of the sprinkler deflector with sprinklers installed in every aisle?

Answer: Yes.

Issue Edition: 1999

Reference: 5-13.10

Issue Date: January 3, 2002

Effective Date: January 23, 2002

8.14.10 Electrical Equipment.

8.14.10.1 Unless the requirements of 8.14.10.3 are met, sprinkler protection shall be required in electrical equipment rooms.

8.14.10.2 Hoods or shields installed to protect important electrical equipment from sprinkler discharge shall be noncombustible.

8.14.10.3 Sprinklers shall not be required in electrical equipment rooms where all of the following conditions are met:

(1) The room is dedicated to electrical equipment only.
(2) Only dry-type electrical equipment is used.
(3) Equipment is installed in a 2-hour fire-rated enclosure including protection for penetrations.
(4) No combustible storage is permitted to be stored in the room.

Sprinkler protection in electrical equipment rooms is required by 8.1.1(1) and 8.14.10.1. Water shields of noncombustible material can be used to prevent direct contact between the electrical equipment and the discharging water.

Although sprinkler systems have been successfully installed in rooms containing electrical equipment for 100 years with no documented instances of a problem, NFPA 13 identifies certain conditions that, if followed, will permit sprinklers to be omitted from electrical equipment rooms (see 8.14.10.3). The conditions identified are relatively easy to determine; however, building owners need to police the areas. The building owner must control access to all such electrical equipment rooms to reduce the likelihood that storage of any type occurs in these spaces.

8.14.11* Industrial Ovens and Furnaces.

A.8.14.11 The combustible materials present inside industrial ovens and furnaces can be protected by automatic sprinklers. Wet sprinkler systems are preferred. However, water-filled piping exposed to heat within an oven or furnace can incur deposition and buildup of minerals within the pipe. If the oven or furnace could be exposed to freezing temperatures, dry-pendent sprinklers are an alternative to wet pipe systems. Another option is to use a dry pipe system.

The preferred arrangement for piping is outside of the oven; the sprinkler should be installed in the pendent position. The sprinkler temperature rating should be at least 50°F (28°C) greater than the high-temperature limit setting of the oven or applicable zone. As a minimum, the sprinkler system inside the oven or furnace should be designed to provide 15 psi (1 bar) with all sprinklers operating inside the oven/furnace. Sprinkler spacing on each branch line should not exceed 12 ft (3.7 m).

8.14.12* Open-Grid Ceilings. Open-grid ceilings shall only be installed beneath sprinklers where one of the following is met:

(1) Open-grid ceilings in which the openings are ¼ in. (6.4 mm) or larger in the least dimension, where the thickness or depth of the material does not exceed the least dimension of the opening, and where such openings constitute 70 percent of the area of the ceiling material. The spacing of the sprinklers over the open-grid ceiling shall then comply with the following:

   (a) In light hazard occupancies where sprinkler spacing (either spray or old-style sprinklers) is less than 10 ft × 10 ft (3 m × 3 m), a minimum clearance of at least 18 in. (457 mm) shall be provided between the sprinkler deflectors and the upper surface of the open-grid ceiling. Where spacing is greater than 10 ft × 10 ft (3 m × 3 m) but less than 10 ft × 12 ft (3 × 3.7 m), a clearance of at least 24 in. (610 mm) shall be provided from spray sprinklers and at least 36 in. (914 mm) from old-style sprinklers. Where spacing is greater than 10 ft × 12 ft (3 m × 3.7 m), a clearance of at least 48 in. (1219 mm) shall be provided.

   (b) In ordinary hazard occupancies, open-grid ceilings shall be permitted to be installed beneath spray sprinklers only. Where sprinkler spacing is less than 10 ft × 10 ft (3 m × 3 m), a minimum clearance of at least 24 in. (610 mm) shall be provided between the sprinkler deflectors and the upper surface of the open-grid ceiling. Where spacing is greater than 10 ft × 10 ft (3 m × 3 m), a clearance of at least 36 in. (914 mm) shall be provided.

(2) Other types of open-grid ceilings shall be permitted to be installed beneath sprinklers where they are listed for such service and are installed in accordance with instructions contained in each package of ceiling material.

A.8.14.12 The installation of open-grid egg crate, louver, or honeycomb ceilings beneath sprinklers restricts the sideways travel of the sprinkler discharge and can change the character of discharge.

The requirements in 8.14.12 for clearance between the sprinkler deflectors and the top of the grid ceiling ensure that sprinkler discharge is not too severely impaired. The grid ceiling can obstruct the discharge pattern to some degree. In addition to the height above the grid ceiling, other obstructions, such as pipes or ducts, must also be considered.

8.14.13 Drop-Out Ceilings.

8.14.13.1 Drop-out ceilings shall be permitted to be installed beneath sprinklers where ceilings are listed for that service and are installed in accordance with their listings.

8.14.13.2 Special sprinklers shall not be installed above drop-out ceilings unless specifically listed for this purpose.

Drop-out ceilings, which are covered in 8.14.13.1 and 8.14.13.2, are designed to shrink and fall when heated by a fire, permitting the activation of the sprinkler located above. Only ceiling panels that are listed and tested for this use are acceptable. The use of opaque ceilings, which make it difficult to determine if the tile has been painted or if material is stored above the ceiling, should be discouraged.

Quick-response and some EC sprinklers installed above drop-out ceiling panels can operate before all the ceiling panels drop out. Because both types of sprinklers have fast-acting heat-responsive elements, they should not be used above ceiling panels unless the panels have been specifically investigated for use with sprinklers containing fast-response elements.

FAQ ▶
Why are special sprinklers prohibited above drop-out ceilings, unless specifically listed?

8.14.13.3 Drop-out ceilings shall not be considered ceilings within the context of this standard.

Because the drop-out ceiling falls in the early stages of a fire, the ceiling does not need to be considered with respect to the positioning of sprinklers (see 8.14.13.3). The permanent ceiling/deck above the drop-out ceiling should be used as the point of reference for deflector placement.

8.14.13.4* Piping installed above drop-out ceilings shall not be considered concealed piping.

A.8.14.13.4 Drop-out ceilings do not provide the required protection for soft-soldered copper joints or other piping that requires protection.

8.14.13.5* Sprinklers shall not be installed beneath drop-out ceilings.

A.8.14.13.5 The ceiling tiles might drop before sprinkler operation. Delayed operation might occur because heat must then bank down from the deck above before sprinklers will operate.

Sprinklers must not be installed beneath drop-out ceilings, as required by 8.14.13.5, because the danger exists for the falling drop-out ceiling tiles to catch on a sprinkler located below the ceiling and interfere with that sprinkler's proper operation or distribution pattern.

8.14.14 Old-Style Sprinklers.

8.14.14.1 Unless required by 8.14.14.2 or 8.14.14.3, old-style sprinklers shall not be used in a new installation.

8.14.14.2* Old-style sprinklers shall be installed in fur storage vaults.

A.8.14.14.2 For tests of sprinkler performance in fur vaults see "Fact Finding Report on Automatic Sprinkler Protection for Fur Storage Vaults" of Underwriters Laboratories Inc., dated November 25, 1947.

Sprinklers should be listed old-style with orifice sizes selected to provide a flow rate as close as possible to, but not less than, 20 gpm (76 L/min) per sprinkler, for four sprinklers, based on the water pressure available.

Sprinklers in fur storage vaults should be located centrally over the aisles between racks and should be spaced not over 5 ft (1.5 m) apart along the aisles.

Where sprinklers are spaced 5 ft (1.5 m) apart along the sprinkler branch lines, pipe sizes should be in accordance with the following schedule:

1 in. (25.4 mm)—4 sprinklers

1 ¼ in. (31.8 mm)—6 sprinklers

1 ½ in. (38.1 mm)—10 sprinklers

2 in. (51 mm)—20 sprinklers

2 ½ in. (63.5 mm)—40 sprinklers

3 in. (76.2 mm)—80 sprinklers

Paragraph 8.14.14.2 identifies the only conditions under which NFPA 13 still requires the use of old-style sprinklers. Full-scale testing conducted in 1947 on fur storage vaults found that the optimum system design required the operation of four old-style sprinklers. The test results are reported in "Fact Finding Report on Automatic Sprinkler Protection for Fire Storage Vaults." Because no further testing was conducted for this storage configuration, the Technical Committee on Sprinkler System Installation Criteria has no basis for modifying this requirement. The pipe schedule identified in A.8.14.14.2 applies to piping running in the same direction as the aisles.

8.14.14.3 Use of old-style sprinklers shall be permitted where construction features or other special situations require unique water distribution.

Care should be taken when using old-style sprinklers, as permitted by 8.14.14.3, to protect unusual construction features, especially when a heavy fire-loading situation exists or the sprinklers are also protecting storage arrangements with designs that were originally tested with spray sprinklers.

8.14.15 Stages.

8.14.15.1 Sprinklers shall be installed under the roof at the ceiling, in spaces under the stage either containing combustible materials or constructed of combustible materials, and in all adjacent spaces and dressing rooms, storerooms, and workshops.

8.14.15.2 Where proscenium opening protection is required, a deluge system shall be provided with open sprinklers located not more than 3 ft (0.9 m) away from the stage side of the proscenium arch and spaced up to a maximum of 6 ft (1.8 m) on center. *(See Chapter 11 for design criteria.)*

The sprinkler requirements for proscenium opening protection are addressed in 8.14.15.2. Building codes and NFPA *101* describe a series of protection schemes to properly protect these openings. One method of protecting these openings is with a deluge-type system.

The primary purpose of the sprinklers is to protect the audience from a fire on the stage. When a curtain is provided, the sprinklers should be on the stage side of the curtain between the curtain and the fire, so that they wet the curtain when they operate.

8.14.16 Provision for Flushing Systems.

8.14.16.1 All sprinkler systems shall be arranged for flushing.

8.14.16.2 Readily removable fittings shall be provided at the end of all cross mains.

8.14.16.3 All cross mains shall terminate in 1¼ in. (31.8 mm) or larger pipe.

8.14.16.4 All branch lines on gridded systems shall be arranged to facilitate flushing.

 Branch lines in gridded systems are covered in 8.14.16.4. The readily removable fitting at the end of each cross main is not limited with regard to maximum pipe size. Branch lines in gridded systems must be installed in such a manner that the piping can be readily disconnected. Further requirements are provided in NFPA 25.

The system should provide for flushing, particularly where the water system is from a nonpotable water supply, such as a pond, stream, or lake, or where the system was changed from a wet system to a dry system or vice versa. In either of these cases, foreign material that blocks the system's individual sprinklers can be introduced. It is necessary to provide for flushing and removal of this foreign material.

8.14.17 Stair Towers. Stairs, towers, or other construction with incomplete floors, if piped on independent risers, shall be treated as one area with reference to pipe sizes.

A fire in a stair or tower, which is discussed in 8.14.17, can open a large percentage of sprinklers in the area. An independent riser supplying a stair or tower must be sized to supply all the sprinklers.

8.14.18 Return Bends.

8.14.18.1 Unless the requirements of 8.14.18.3 or 8.14.18.4 are met, return bends shall be used where pendent sprinklers are supplied from a raw water source, a mill pond, or open-top reservoirs.

8.14.18.2 Return bends shall be connected to the top of branch lines in order to avoid accumulation of sediment in the drop nipples in accordance with Figure 8.14.18.2.

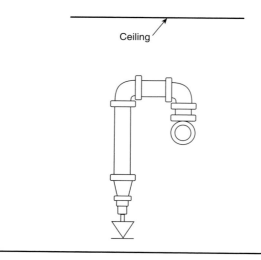

Ceiling

FIGURE 8.14.18.2 Return Bend Arrangement.

8.14.18.3 Return bends shall not be required for deluge systems.

8.14.18.4 Return bends shall not be required where dry-pendent sprinklers are used.

The purpose of return bends, which are covered in 8.14.18.1 through 8.14.18.4, is to prevent collection of sediment in drop nipples. Return bends should not be taken directly off the bottom of branch lines in wet pipe sprinkler systems, particularly where the systems are supplied from water sources that could contain excessive sediment. Return bends are not necessary on wet pipe systems that use a potable water supply. In this regard, water supplied from a swimming pool is not considered a raw source requiring return bends.

Return bends are also useful where centering of sprinklers in ceiling tile or exact positioning of sprinklers is desirable from an aesthetic or architectural viewpoint. The use of a return bend is shown in Exhibit 8.26. When standard pendent sprinklers, rather than dry pendent sprinklers, are installed on preaction and dry pipe systems, return bends are required per 7.2.2(3), 7.3.2.4(3), and 7.4.1.4(3). Return bends are required due to the possibility of scale buildup obstructing the sprinkler orifice.

8.14.19 Piping to Sprinklers Below Ceilings.

8.14.19.1* In new installations expected to supply sprinklers below a ceiling, minimum 1-in. (25.4-mm) outlets shall be provided.

A.8.14.19.1 Outlets meeting the requirements of this standard should be provided in anticipation of the final finished area.

8.14.19.2 The 1-in. (25.4-mm) outlets required by 8.14.19.1 shall be permitted to utilize hexagonal bushings to accommodate temporary sprinklers and shall be removed with the temporary sprinklers when the permanent ceiling sprinklers are installed.

Piping to sprinklers below ceilings is discussed in 8.14.19.1 and 8.14.19.2. When a system is to be temporarily installed in an exposed manner and a false ceiling will eventually be added, the outlets for sprinklers on the pipes are to be 1 in. (25.4 mm) and reduced to the thread size of the sprinklers. A common example of the need to install temporary sprinklers is in an office building with some unfinished floors that are not yet occupied. The initial installation can involve upright sprinklers. If these sprinklers are installed in 1-in. (25.4-mm) outlets using bushings, the proper fitting will be available for the final sprinkler installation when the false ceiling is installed and the office space is finished.

8.14.19.3 Revamping of Pipe Schedule Systems.

8.14.19.3.1 When pipe schedule systems are revamped, a nipple not exceeding 4 in. (102 mm) in length shall be permitted to be installed in the branch line fitting.

8.14.19.3.2 All piping other than the nipple permitted in 8.14.19.3.1 and 8.14.19.3.3 shall be a minimum of 1 in. (25.4 mm) in diameter in accordance with Figure 8.14.19.3.2.

EXHIBIT 8.26 *Return Bend Used for Pendent Sprinkler Positioning.*

FIGURE 8.14.19.3.2 *Nipple and Reducing Elbow Supplying Sprinkler Below Ceiling.*

8.14.19.3.3 When it is necessary to pipe two new ceiling sprinklers from an existing outlet in an overhead system, the use of a nipple not exceeding 4 in. (102 mm) in length and of the same pipe thread size as the existing outlet shall be permitted, provided that a hydraulic calculation verifies that the design flow rate will be achieved in accordance with Figure 8.14.19.3.3.

FIGURE 8.14.19.3.3 *Sprinklers in Concealed Space and Below Ceiling.*

Changing the existing line fitting is not required when revamping existing pipe schedule systems. Because a sprinkler retained in the concealed space and a sprinkler below the ceiling are in separate areas, both can be supplied by a single connection. (See Figure 8.14.19.3.3.)

Paragraph 8.14.19.3.3 is critical when work on an existing pipe schedule system is contemplated. Without this requirement, the in-place line tee would have to be removed, replaced with a 1-in. (25.4-mm) tee, and reassembled. The requirement permits an existing tee with a ½-in. (12.7-mm) or ¾-in. (19-mm) outlet to remain in place to supply sprinklers below a newly installed ceiling. This arrangement must be verified with hydraulic calculations when two sprinklers are to be installed beneath the ceiling from the existing line tee.

8.14.19.3.4 The use of pipe nipples less than 1 in. (25.4 mm) in diameter shall not be permitted in areas subject to earthquakes.

Paragraph 8.14.19.3.4 addresses pipe nipples in areas subject to earthquakes. Piping with diameters less than 1 in. (25.4 mm) is likely to fail during an earthquake, especially when supplying sprinklers below a ceiling. To prevent the failures, a minimum 1-in. (25.4-mm) fitting and pipe is required.

◀ **FAQ**
Why are pipe nipples less than 1 in. (25.4 mm) prohibited in areas subject to earthquakes?

8.14.19.4 Revamping of Hydraulic Design Systems.

8.14.19.4.1 When hydraulically designed systems are revamped, any existing bushing shall be removed and a nipple not exceeding 4 in. (102 mm) in length shall be permitted to be installed in the branch line fitting.

8.14.19.4.2 Calculations shall be provided to verify that the system design flow rate will be achieved.

Calculations for hydraulic design systems are discussed in 8.14.19.4.2. When a hydraulically designed system is modified, new calculations must be provided to verify that the arrangement can provide the necessary flow and pressure. The calculation must be made in the case of one or two sprinklers being supplied from the existing line fitting.

◀ **FAQ**
Are new hydraulic calculations required when revamping hydraulical designed systems?

8.14.19.4.3 When it is necessary to pipe two new ceiling sprinklers from an existing outlet in an overhead system, any bushings shall be removed and the use of a nipple not exceeding 4 in. (102 mm) in length and of the same pipe thread size as the existing outlet shall be permitted, provided that a hydraulic calculation verifies that the design flow rate will be achieved.

8.14.19.4.4 The use of pipe nipples less than 1 in. (25.4 mm) in diameter is not permitted in areas subject to earthquakes.

8.14.20 Dry Pipe Underground.

8.14.20.1 Where necessary to place pipe that will be under air pressure underground, the pipe shall be protected against corrosion.

8.14.20.2 Unprotected cast-iron or ductile-iron pipe shall be permitted where joined with a gasketed joint listed for air service underground.

Corrosion that forms on the exterior of cast-iron or ductile-iron pipe insulates that pipe from further corrosion. Such pipe is normally used to transport water, which is less likely to leak than air. When this type of pipe is subject to air pressure, the gasketed joints must be specifically listed for use under air pressure, as required by 8.14.20.2, to prevent leakage.

8.14.21* System Subdivision. Where individual floor/zone control valves are not provided, a flanged joint or mechanical coupling shall be used at the riser at each floor for connections to piping serving floor areas in excess of 5000 ft^2 (465 m^2).

A.8.14.21 See Figure A.8.14.21.

A

System subdivision is discussed in 8.14.21. When a system protects multiple floors, each floor should be able to be isolated so that the entire system is not impaired when a repair or modification needs to be made on a given floor. Floor or zone control valves that are part of a floor control assembly such as the one shown in Exhibit 8.27 are normally used for this purpose and are the preferred method, although NFPA 13 does not require them. All NFPA 13 requires is a flanged joint or mechanical coupling, which enables the piping to be disconnected and a blank or cap to be inserted, allowing the remainder of the system to remain in service while repairs or modifications are being made on one floor.

FIGURE A.8.14.21 *One Arrangement of Flanged Joint at Sprinkler Riser.*

EXHIBIT 8.27 *Floor Control Assembly.*

8.14.22 Spaces Above Ceilings.

 8.14.22.1 Where spaces have ceilings that are lower than the rest of the area, the space above this lower ceiling shall be sprinklered unless it complies with the rules of 8.14.1.2 for allowable unsprinklered concealed spaces.

8.14.22.2 Where the space above a drop ceiling is sprinklered, the sprinkler system shall conform to the rules of 12.1.13.

FAQ ▶
Where an office space is located within a storage or manufacturing facility which results in an open area above the office space that is not utilized, is the sprinkler protection from the warehouse or manufacturing area required to be extended above the office area?

Spaces above ceilings are covered in 8.14.22.1 and 8.14.22.2. NFPA 13 considers sprinkler protection throughout the building. When sprinklers are provided in a space (for example, a warehouse or manufacturing facility) and an office or other area with a drop ceiling occupies a portion of the space, the ceiling above the space must be sprinklered. The sprinkler design above the space should be the same as the remaining ceiling sprinklers in the storage area. The only exception is a case in which the wall around the space with the lower ceiling extends all the way to the roof and creates a concealed space that does not require sprinklers (see 8.14.1).

8.15 Piping Installation

The methods and procedures necessary for the proper installation of pipe and associated appurtenances are addressed in Section 8.15. Essentially, Section 8.15 describes the proper methods for assembling pipe, fittings, and associated equipment.

8.15.1 Valves.

8.15.1.1* Control Valves.

A.8.15.1.1 See Figure A.8.15.1.1.

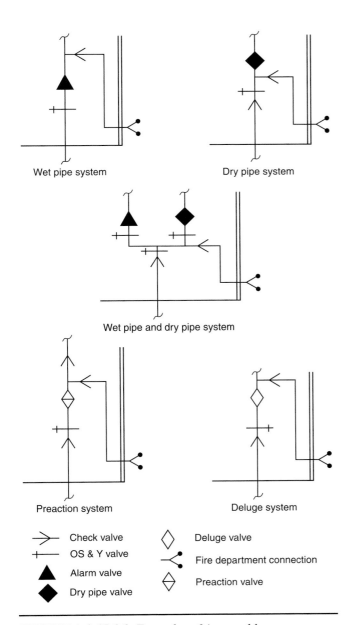

FIGURE A.8.15.1.1 Examples of Acceptable Valve Arrangements.

8.15.1.1.1* General.

A.8.15.1.1.1 A water supply connection should not extend into a building or through a building wall unless such connection is under the control of an outside listed indicating valve or an inside listed indicating valve located near the outside wall of the building.

All valves controlling water supplies for sprinkler systems or portions thereof, including floor control valves, should be accessible to authorized persons during emergencies. Permanent ladders, clamped treads on risers, chain-operated hand wheels, or other accepted means should be provided where necessary.

Outside control valves are suggested in the following order of preference:

(1) Listed indicating valves at each connection into the building at least 40 ft (12.2 m) from buildings if space permits
(2) Control valves installed in a cutoff stair tower or valve room accessible from outside
(3) Valves located in risers with indicating posts arranged for outside operation.
(4) Key-operated valves in each connection into the building

8.15.1.1.1.1 Each sprinkler system shall be provided with a listed indicating valve in an accessible location, so located as to control all automatic sources of water supply.

8.15.1.1.1.2 At least one listed indicating valve shall be installed in each source of water supply.

Each source of water supply, with the exception of the fire department connection, is to be equipped with an indicating control valve to isolate each source of water supply, as stated in 8.15.1.1.2. Exhibit 8.28 illustrates the application of the requirements of 8.15.1.1.2 for a sprinkler system loop on each floor of a high-rise building that is supplied by two risers. Each riser must be capable of being isolated.

Exhibit 8.28 illustrates an example of a valve arrangement for a high-rise building with two risers supplying both sprinklers and 2 ½-in. hose outlets with a connection from each of the risers to a sprinkler loop main on each floor, where each connection from the riser to the loop contains an indicating-type pressure regulating control valve, waterflow switch, and OS&Y control valve.

EXHIBIT 8.28 Valve Arrangement.

8.15.1.1.1.3 The requirements of 8.15.1.1.1.2 shall not apply to the fire department connection, and there shall be no shutoff valve in the fire department connection.

Exhibit 8.29 illustrates a wet pipe sprinkler system riser with a fire department connection. The fire department connection does not have a control valve in accordance with 8.15.1.1.1.3.

8.15.1.1.2* Supervision.

Vane-type
waterflow
detector

Tee
connection

System water
gauge

Standard
check valve

Main drain
valve

Supply water
gauge and
valve

Check
valve

Fire
department
connection

Drain
outlet

Automatic
drip valve

Tamper switch

Control
valve

EXHIBIT 8.29 Straight Pipe
Riser.

A.8.15.1.1.2 The management is responsible for the supervision of valves controlling water
supply for fire protection and should exert every effort to see that the valves are maintained in
the normally open position. This effort includes special precautions to ensure that protection
is promptly restored by completely opening valves that are necessarily closed during repairs
or alterations. The precautions apply equally to valves controlling sprinklers and other fixed
water-based fire suppression systems, hydrants, tanks, standpipes, pumps, street connections,
and sectional valves.

Either one or a combination of the methods of valve supervision described in the following list is considered essential to ensure that the valves controlling fire protection systems are
in the normally open position. The methods described are intended as an aid to the person responsible for developing a systematic method of determining that the valves controlling sprinkler systems and other fire protection devices are open.

Continual vigilance is necessary if valves are to be kept in the open position. Responsible
day and night employees should be familiar with the location of all valves and their proper use.

The authority having jurisdiction should be consulted as to the type of valve supervision
required. Contracts for equipment should specify that all details are to be subject to the approval of the authority having jurisdiction.

(1) *Central Station Supervisory Service.* Central station supervisory service systems involve
    complete, constant, and automatic supervision of valves by electrically operated devices
    and circuits continually under test and operating through an approved outside central sta-
    tion, in compliance with *NFPA 72, National Fire Alarm Code.* It is understood that only
    such portions of *NFPA 72* that relate to valve supervision should apply.

(2) *Proprietary Supervisory Service Systems.* Proprietary supervisory service systems include
    systems where the operation of a valve produces some form of signal and record at a com-
    mon point by electrically operated devices and circuits continually under test and operating
    through a central supervising station at the property protected, all in compliance with the
    standards for the installation, maintenance, and use of local protective, auxiliary protective,

remote station protective, and proprietary signaling systems. It is understood that only portions of the standards that relate to valve supervision should apply.

The standard method of locking, sealing, and tagging valves to prevent, so far as possible, their unnecessary closing, to obtain notification of such closing, and to aid in restoring the valve to normal condition is a satisfactory alternate to valve supervision. The authority having jurisdiction should be consulted as to details for specific cases.

Where electrical supervision is not provided, locks or seals should be provided on all valves and should be of a type acceptable to the authority having jurisdiction.

Seals can be marked to indicate the organization under whose jurisdiction the sealing is conducted. All seals should be attached to the valve in such a manner that the valves cannot be operated without breaking the seals. Seals should be of a character to prevent injury in handling and to prevent reassembly when broken. When seals are used, valves should be inspected weekly. The authority having jurisdiction can require a valve tag to be used in conjunction with the sealing.

A padlock, with a chain where necessary, is especially desirable to prevent unauthorized closing of valves in areas where valves are subject to tampering. When such locks are employed, valves should be inspected monthly.

If valves are locked, any distribution of keys should be restricted to only those directly responsible for the fire protection system. Multiple valves should not be locked together; they should be individually locked.

The individual performing the inspections should determine that each valve is in the normal position, properly locked or sealed, and so note on an appropriate record form while still at the valve. The authority having jurisdiction should be consulted for assistance in preparing a suitable report form for this activity.

Identification signs should be provided at each valve to indicate its function and what it controls.

The position of the spindle of OS&Y valves or the target on the indicator valves cannot be accepted as conclusive proof that the valve is fully open. The opening of the valve should be followed by a test to determine that the operating parts have functioned properly.

The test consists of opening the main drain valve and permitting free flow of water until the gauge reading becomes stationary. If the pressure drop is excessive for the water supply involved, the cause should be determined immediately and the proper remedies taken. When sectional valves or other special conditions are encountered, other methods of testing should be used.

If it becomes necessary to break a seal for emergency reasons, the valve, following the emergency, should be opened by the person responsible for the fire protection of the plant, or his or her designated representative, and this person should apply a seal at the time of the valve opening. This seal should be maintained in place until such time as the authority having jurisdiction can replace it with one of its own.

Seals or locks should not be applied to valves reopened after closure until such time as the inspection procedure is carried out.

Where water is shut off to the sprinkler or other fixed water-based fire suppression systems, a guard or other qualified person should be placed on duty and required to continuously patrol the affected sections of the premises until such time as protection is restored.

During specific critical situations, a person should be stationed at the valve so that the valve can be reopened promptly if necessary. It is the intent of this section that the person remain within sight of the valve and have no other duties beyond this responsibility. This procedure is considered imperative when fire protection is shut off immediately following a fire.

An inspection of all other fire protection equipment should be made prior to shutting off water in order to make sure it is in operative condition.

In case of changes to fire protection equipment, all possible work should be done in advance of shutting off the water so that final connections can be made quickly and protection restored promptly. Many times it will be found that by careful planning open outlets can be plugged and protection restored on a portion of the equipment while the alterations are being made.

Where changes are being made in underground piping, all possible piping should be laid before shutting off the water for final connections. Where possible, temporary feed lines, such as temporary piping for reconnection of risers by hose lines, and so forth, should be used to afford maximum protection. The plant, public fire department, and other authorities having jurisdiction should be notified of all impairments to fire protection equipment.

8.15.1.1.2.1 Valves on connections to water supplies, sectional control and isolation valves, and other valves in supply pipes to sprinklers and other fixed water-based fire suppression systems shall be supervised by one of the following methods:

(1) Central station, proprietary, or remote station signaling service
(2) Local signaling service that will cause the sounding of an audible signal at a constantly attended point
(3) Valves locked in the correct position
(4) Valves located within fenced enclosures under the control of the owner, sealed in the open position, and inspected weekly as part of an approved procedure

The four methods of supervision listed in 8.15.1.1.2.1 help to ensure that a common mode of sprinkler system failure is minimized. Approximately one-third of system failures are attributable to closed or partially closed sprinkler system control valves [Rohr 1998]. The means of supervision are listed in descending order of preference.

Central station, proprietary, or remote station supervision methods are preferred over the other methods listed. Supervisory signals received at such alarm facilities are usually forwarded to trouble or maintenance crews responsible for the protected property. This method also allows for much quicker notification of the fire department. Early knowledge that a control valve has been closed for any reason can change the fire department response and firefighting tactics. The use of electrical supervision has not, however, been mandated due to the cost of such a system, particularly in existing, large, sprawling facilities. Exhibit 8.30 shows an outside stem and yoke (OS&Y) valve supervised both electronically with a tamper switch and manually with a lock and chain.

EXHIBIT 8.30 OS&Y Valve.

8.15.1.1.2.2 Floor control valves in high-rise buildings and valves controlling flow to sprinklers in circulating closed loop systems shall comply with 8.15.1.1.2.1(1) or 8.15.1.1.2.1(2).

8.15.1.1.2.3 The requirements of 8.15.1.1.2.1 shall not apply to underground gate valves with roadway boxes.

8.15.1.1.2.4 Where control valves are installed overhead, they shall be positioned so that the indicating feature is visible from the floor below.

One example of the requirement in 8.15.1.1.2.4 would be the use of an OS&Y valve installed as a sectional control valve in a rack storage system. The valve should be installed so that the stem is in a horizontal position when viewed from the floor.

8.15.1.1.3 Check Valves.

8.15.1.1.3.1 Where there is more than one source of water supply, a check valve shall be installed in each connection.

 8.15.1.1.3.2 A listed backflow prevention device shall be considered a check valve, and an additional check valve shall not be required.

FAQ ▶
Why does each source of water supply require a check valve?

Each source of water supply must have a check valve to isolate the supplies from each other (see 8.15.1.1.3.2). In a fire situation, water flows from the highest pressure source. For example, consider a system supplied by a gravity tank, a city connection, and a fire department connection. The gravity tank has the highest pressure source. Initial flow would be from the gravity tank. If the tank's pressure dropped below that of the city connection, the tank's check valve would close and the supply would come from the city. When the fire department connected onto the system, the check valves in both automatic supplies would close and the supply would come through the fire department pumps via the fire department connection.

8.15.1.1.3.3 Where cushion tanks are used with automatic fire pumps, no check valve is required in the cushion tank connection.

Cushion tanks are discussed in 8.15.1.1.3.3. A cushion tank, when installed, is a part of the fire pump supply. The cushion tank is subject to the pump's check valve.

8.15.1.1.3.4 Check valves shall be installed in a vertical or horizontal position in accordance with their listing.

8.15.1.1.3.5* Where a single wet pipe sprinkler system is equipped with a fire department connection, the alarm valve is considered a check valve, and an additional check valve shall not be required.

 A.8.15.1.1.3.5 Where a system having only one dry pipe valve is supplied with city water and a fire department connection, it will be satisfactory to install the main check valve in the water supply connection immediately inside of the building. In instances where there is no outside control valve, the system indicating valve should be placed at the service flange, on the supply side of all fittings.

An alarm valve is a check valve designed to activate waterflow alarms (see 8.15.1.1.3.5). Another check valve would be redundant and would increase the friction loss characteristics of the system, because an alarm check valve has the same checking ability as a gravity check valve. Exhibit 8.31 shows a wet pipe system employing an alarm valve that also functions as the check valve for the water supply source.

8.15.1.1.4* Control Valves with Check Valves.

 A.8.15.1.1.4 See Figure A.8.15.1.1.4. For additional information on controlling valves, see NFPA 22, *Standard for Water Tanks for Private Fire Protection.*

The intent in 8.15.1.1.4 of requiring control valves on both sides of a check valve is to isolate the check valve for maintenance or repair while permitting the system to remain in service. If the system has only one automatic supply, an indicating, or gate, valve on the system side of

EXHIBIT 8.31 Wet Pipe
System.

the check valve is not required. An alarm valve is a specialized device, and control valves are not required on the system side of alarm check valves.

8.15.1.1.4.1 In a connection serving as one source of supply, listed indicating valves or post-indicator valves shall be installed on both sides of all check valves required in 8.15.1.1.3.

8.15.1.1.4.2 The requirements of 8.15.1.1.4.1 shall not apply to the check valve located in the fire department connection piping, and there shall be no control valves in the fire department connection piping.

FIGURE A.8.15.1.1.4 Pit for Gate Valve, Check Valve, and
Fire Department Connection.

8.15.1.1.4.3 The requirements of 8.15.1.1.4.1 shall not apply, where the city connection serves as the only automatic source of supply to a wet pipe sprinkler system, a control valve is not required on the system side of the check valve or the alarm check valve.

8.15.1.1.5* Gravity Tanks.

A.8.15.1.1.5 For additional information on controlling valves, see NFPA 22, *Standard for Water Tanks for Private Fire Protection.*

8.15.1.1.5.1 Where a gravity tank is located on a tower in the yard, the control valve on the tank side of the check valve shall be an outside screw and yoke or listed indicating valve; the other shall be either an outside screw and yoke, a listed indicating valve, or a listed valve having a post-type indicator.

8.15.1.1.5.2 Where a gravity tank is located on a building, both control valves shall be outside screw and yoke or listed indicating valves, and all fittings inside the building except the drain tee and heater connections shall be under the control of a listed valve.

8.15.1.1.6* Pumps. When a pump is located in a combustible pump house or exposed to danger from fire or falling walls, or when a tank discharges into a private fire service main fed by another supply, either the check valve in the connection shall be located in a pit or the control valve shall be of the post-indicator type located a safe distance outside buildings.

A.8.15.1.1.6 Check valves on tank or pump connections, when located underground, can be placed inside of buildings and at a safe distance from the tank riser or pump, except in cases where the building is entirely of one fire area, when it is ordinarily considered satisfactory to locate the check valve overhead in the lowest level.

The intent of 8.15.1.1.6 is to ensure that the control valves for the fire pump discharge piping remain accessible during a fire. Fire pumps should not be located where they will be subject to falling walls or impaired during an emergency.

8.15.1.1.7* Control Valve Accessibility. All control valves shall be located where readily accessible and free of obstructions.

A.8.15.1.1.7 It might be necessary to provide valves located in pits with an indicator post extending above grade or other means so that the valve can be operated without entering the pit.

8.15.1.1.8 Control Valve Identification. Identification signs shall be provided at each valve to indicate its function and what it controls.

8.15.1.2 Pressure-Reducing Valves.

8.15.1.2.1 In portions of systems where all components are not listed for pressure greater than 175 psi (12.1 bar) and the potential exists for normal (nonfire condition) water pressure in excess of 175 psi (12.1 bar), a listed pressure-reducing valve shall be installed and set for an outlet pressure not exceeding 165 psi (2.4 bar) at the maximum inlet pressure.

Pressure-reducing and pressure control valves, which are discussed in 8.15.1.2.1, allow a predetermined quantity of water to pass through the system at some established pressure. These devices can be installed in a system riser that supports the entire system or at individual feed mains that supply a floor. The installation of these devices requires special knowledge. All provisions contained in the listing criteria as well as the manufacturer's instructions must be followed. These valves also require routine flow testing. Provisions for such testing should be provided as part of the initial design. When the pressure on the system exceeds 165 psi, the valve will open and relieve pressure on the system. The relief valve is arranged so that waterflow due to excess pressure will drain through the system's main drain.

8.15.1.2.2 Pressure gauges shall be installed on the inlet and outlet sides of each pressure-reducing valve.

8.15.1.2.3* A relief valve of not less than ½ in. (13 mm) in size shall be provided on the discharge side of the pressure-reducing valve set to operate at a pressure not exceeding 175 psi (12.1 bar).

A.8.15.1.2.3 Where the relief valve operation would result in water being discharged onto interior walking or working surfaces, consideration should be given to piping the discharge from the valve to a drain connection or other safe location.

8.15.1.2.4 A listed indicating valve shall be provided on the inlet side of each pressure-reducing valve, unless the pressure-reducing valve meets the listing requirements for use as an indicating valve.

8.15.1.2.5 Means shall be provided downstream of all pressure-reducing valves for flow tests at sprinkler system demand.

The requirement in 8.15.1.2.5 for a means of flow testing downstream of all pressure-reducing valves facilitates their testing. NFPA 25 currently requires that these devices be tested every 5 years. In high-rise buildings, where pressure-reducing valves are typically used, a drain riser is normally provided and should now be sized to accommodate the testing of full sprinkler flow demand.

8.15.1.3* Post-Indicator Valves.

A.8.15.1.3 Outside control valves are suggested in the following order of preference:

(1) Listed indicating valves at each connection into the building at least 40 ft (12.2 m) from buildings if space permits
(2) Control valves installed in a cutoff stair tower or valve room accessible from outside
(3) Valves located in risers with indicating posts arranged for outside operation
(4) Key-operated valves in each connection into the building

Post-indicator valves should be located not less than 40 ft (12.2 m) from buildings. When post-indicator valves cannot be placed at this distance, they are permitted to be located closer, or wall post-indicator valves can be used, provided they are set in locations by blank walls where the possibility of injury by falling walls is unlikely and from which people are not likely to be driven by smoke or heat. Usually, in crowded plant yards, they can be placed beside low buildings, near brick stair towers, or at angles formed by substantial brick walls that are not likely to fall.

8.15.1.3.1 Post-indicator valves shall be set so that the top of the post will be 36 in. (0.9 m) above the final grade.

8.15.1.3.2 Post-indicator valves shall be properly protected against mechanical damage where needed.

Post-indicator valves, which are discussed in 8.15.1.3.1 and 8.15.1.3.2, should be located where they are not subject to mechanical damage. When post-indicator valves are located along roadways, near loading docks, or in other areas where they could be hit by vehicular traffic or otherwise damaged, they should be protected. One method is to provide concrete-filled pipes or other barriers for protection as indicated in Exhibit 8.32. Note that the conduit on the post-indicator valve, which is part of the means of valve supervision, is damaged and needs to be repaired. This condition would be in violation of NFPA 25. In addition to the post-indicator valve, Exhibit 8.32 also includes the outlet for the system main drain, the fire pump test header, and a fire department connection. Exhibit 8.33 illustrates a wall post-indicator valve, which can also be used.

EXHIBIT 8.32 *Post-Indicator Valve with Means of Supervision Damaged.*

8.15.1.4 Valves in Pits.

8.15.1.4.1 General. Where it is impractical to provide a post-indicator valve, valves shall be permitted to be placed in pits with permission of the authority having jurisdiction.

Valves in pits are discussed in 8.15.1.4.1. Whenever possible, valves that can be operated above grade should be used. Valve pits are considered confined spaces and can be a safety hazard. Valves in the pit may need to be arranged so they can be actuated remotely via an extension handle, allowing the valve to be operated in an emergency without the need to enter the pit.

8.15.1.4.2* Valve Pit Construction.

A.8.15.1.4.2 A valve wrench with a long handle should be provided at a convenient location on the premises.

8.15.1.4.2.1 When used, valve pits shall be of adequate size and readily accessible for inspection, operation, testing, maintenance, and removal of equipment contained therein.

8.15.1.4.2.2 Valve pits shall be constructed and arranged to properly protect the installed equipment from movement of earth, freezing, and accumulation of water.

8.15.1.4.2.3 Poured-in-place or precast concrete, with or without reinforcement, or brick (all depending upon soil conditions and size of pit) shall be appropriate materials for construction of valve pits.

8.15.1.4.2.4 Other approved materials shall be permitted to be used for valve pit construction.

8.15.1.4.2.5 Where the water table is low and the soil is porous, crushed stone or gravel shall be permitted to be used for the floor of the pit. [*See Figure A.8.16.2(b) for a suggested arrangement.*]

8.15.1.4.2.6 Valve pits located at or near the base of the riser of an elevated tank shall be designed in accordance with Chapter 9 of NFPA 22, *Standard for Water Tanks for Private Fire Protection.*

Wall PIV
(wall post-indicator valve)

EXHIBIT 8.33 *Wall Post-Indicator Valve.*

8.15.1.4.3 Valve Pit Marking. The location of the valve shall be clearly marked, and the cover of the pit shall be kept free of obstructions.

In cold climates, the pit's cover can be covered with snow or ice, making the pit inaccessible and the cover difficult to find. To maintain pit accessibility, the locations must be clearly marked and snow or ice promptly removed, as required by 8.15.1.4.3.

8.15.1.5 Sectional Valves.

8.15.1.5.1 Large private fire service main systems shall have sectional controlling valves at appropriate points in order to permit sectionalizing the system in the event of a break or for the making of repairs or extensions.

Sectional valves are discussed in 8.15.1.5.1. Placing a sectional control valve between every four to six pieces of fire protection equipment, such as a sprinkler system or hydrant, is common practice. The reason for this spacing is so that only a small section of the underground main must be isolated when making repairs or system modifications.

8.15.1.5.2 A valve shall be provided on each bank where a main crosses water and outside the building foundation(s) where the main or section of main runs under a building.

8.15.1.6* In-Rack Sprinkler System Control Valves.

A.8.15.1.6 In-rack sprinklers and ceiling sprinklers selected for protection should be controlled by at least two separate indicating valves and drains. In higher rack arrangements, consideration should be given to providing more than one in-rack control valve in order to limit the extent of any single impairment.

The control valves discussed in 8.15.1.6 are intended to allow isolation of the in-rack system from the ceiling system as indicated in Exhibit 8.34. In-rack sprinklers are susceptible to damage due to their location. These valves are required to permit the ceiling system to remain in service while an in-rack sprinkler is replaced. Additionally, when the ceiling system is out of service, the valves are to be arranged so that the in-rack system remains operational.

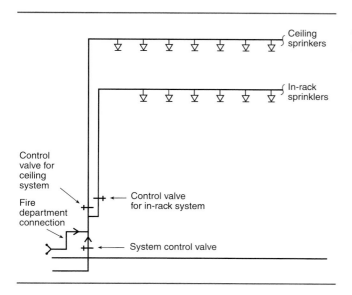

EXHIBIT 8.34 *Separately Controlled Ceiling and In-Rack Sprinklers.*

8.15.1.6.1 Unless the requirements of 8.15.1.6.2 or 8.15.1.6.3 are met, where sprinklers are installed in racks, separate indicating control valves and drains shall be provided and arranged so that ceiling and in-rack sprinklers can be controlled independently.

8.15.1.6.2 Installation of 20 or fewer in-rack sprinklers supplied by any one ceiling sprinkler system shall not require a separate indicating control valve.

Paragraph 8.15.1.6.2 allows an in-rack sprinkler system consisting of up to 20 sprinklers to be supplied from the overhead system without a separate control valve (see Exhibit 8.35). The 20-sprinkler limit is the total number of in-rack sprinklers supplied from a given system riser.

EXHIBIT 8.35 *In-Rack Sprinklers Supplied Directly from Ceiling System without a Separate Control Valve.*

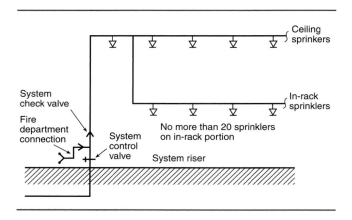

8.15.1.6.3 The separate indicating valves shall be permitted to be arranged as sectional control valves where the racks occupy only a portion of the area protected by the ceiling sprinklers.

Paragraph 8.15.1.6.3 allows the control valves used to isolate the overhead system from the in-rack system to be arranged as sectional valves so that portions rather than the entire overhead system can be isolated. This requirement applies only where the in-rack system occupies a portion of the area protected by the overhead system. Exhibit 8.36 provides an example of this arrangement, and Exhibit 8.37 shows a sectional valve arrangement for an in-rack system.

8.15.2 Drainage.

The requirements in the paragraphs that follow 8.15.2 regarding drains are necessary to facilitate system maintenance, repair, modifications, and additions. When systems are to be taken out of service for any reason, properly sized and arranged drains help minimize the amount of

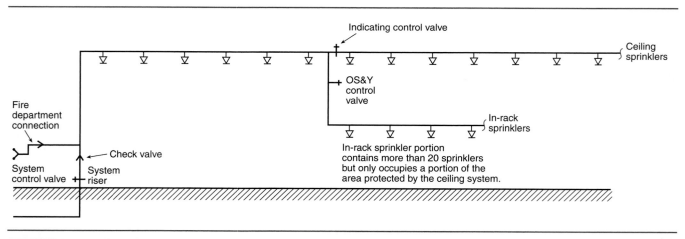

EXHIBIT 8.36 *In-Rack Sprinklers Occupying Only a Portion of the Area Protected by Ceiling Sprinklers.*

time the system is out of service. For dry pipe and preaction systems protecting cold environments, immediate drainage of any water that has entered the system is critical. Properly sized drains and the requirements in 8.15.2.3 for installing the pipe at a specific pitch serve this purpose. Additionally, after a system is involved in a fire and the fire is extinguished, the system needs to be shut down and drained so that the sprinklers that operated can be replaced.

Some of these drain features are also used to check the status of the water supply. NFPA 25 provides guidance on the main drain test, which is accomplished using the drain connections discussed in 8.15.2.4.

8.15.2.1* General. All sprinkler pipe and fittings shall be so installed that the system can be drained.

A.8.15.2.1 All piping should be arranged where practicable to drain to the main drain valve.

Drainage is addressed in 8.15.2.1. Ideally, the entire system should be arranged so that all water can be drained through the main drain. If this cannot be accomplished, auxiliary drainage facilities per 8.15.2.5 and sectional drainage in accordance with 8.15.2.4.3 need to be sized and arranged with consideration for the type of system and the volume of trapped piping.

8.15.2.2 Wet Pipe Systems.

8.15.2.2.1 On wet pipe systems, sprinkler pipes shall be permitted to be installed level.

In pipe schedule systems, the reduction in pipe size from the supply to the branch lines has the effect of a slight pitch when the piping is installed level (see 8.15.2.2.1). This effect is due to the slope of the reducing fittings necessitated by the reduction in pipe size.

8.15.2.2.2 Trapped piping shall be drained in accordance with 8.15.2.5.

8.15.2.3 Dry Pipe and Preaction Systems. Piping shall be pitched to drain as stated in 8.15.2.3.1 through 8.15.2.3.4.

8.15.2.3.1 Dry Pipe Systems in Non-Refrigerated Areas. In dry pipe systems branch lines shall be pitched at least half ½ in. per 10 ft (4 mm/m) and mains shall be pitched at least ¼ in. per 10 ft (2 mm/m).

8.15.2.3.2 Preaction Systems Subject to Freezing. In preaction systems where a portion of the piping is subject to freezing, branch lines shall be pitched at least ½ in. per 10 ft (4 mm/m) and mains shall be pitched at least ¼ in. per 10 ft (2 mm/m).

Because dry pipe systems and preaction systems are usually installed in areas subject to freezing (see 8.15.2.3.2), proper drainage is critical due to the potential freezing of a pipe network after a system trip. Water trapped in the pipe network can begin to freeze in a matter of minutes in systems installed in structures that maintain temperatures at or below 0°F (−18°C).

8.15.2.3.3 Preaction Systems Not Subject to Freezing. Preaction systems located entirely in areas not subject to freezing shall not be required to be pitched.

8.15.2.3.4 Dry Pipe and Preaction Systems in Refrigerated Areas. Branch lines shall be pitched at least ½ in. per 10 ft (4 mm/m), and mains shall be pitched at least ½ in. per 10 ft (4 mm/m) in refrigerated areas.

8.15.2.4* System, Main Drain, or Sectional Drain Connections. See Figure 8.15.2.4.

A.8.15.2.4 Figure A.8.15.2.4 is an example of an unacceptable arrangement, because it will not give a true residual reading, it will indicate an excessive pressure drop.

Paragraphs 8.15.2.4 through 8.15.2.5.3.4 describe the facilities needed to drain any portion of a system in an efficient manner without undue risk of water damage. The arrangement of main, sectional, and auxiliary drains expedites the manner in which a system can be taken out of service for maintenance or repairs.

EXHIBIT 8.37 *Sectional Control Valve for In-Rack Sprinklers.*

FIGURE 8.15.2.4 *Drain Connection for System Riser.*

FIGURE A.8.15.2.4 *Unacceptable Pressure Gauge Location.*

8.15.2.4.1 Provisions shall be made to properly drain all parts of the system.

8.15.2.4.2 Drain connections for systems supply risers and mains shall be sized as shown in Table 8.15.2.4.2.

TABLE 8.15.2.4.2 *Drain Size*

Riser or Main Size	Size of Drain Connection
Up to 2 in.	¾ in. or larger
2½ in., 3 in., 3½ in.	1¼ in. or larger
4 in. and larger	2 in. only

For SI units, 1 in. = 25.4 mm.

8.15.2.4.3 Where an interior sectional or floor control valve(s) is provided, it shall be provided with a drain connection having a minimum size as shown in Table 8.15.2.4.2 to drain that portion of the system controlled by the sectional valve.

8.15.2.4.4 Drains shall discharge outside or to a drain connection. *[See Figure A.8.16.4.2(b).]*

8.15.2.4.5 For those drains serving pressure-reducing valves, the drain, drain connection, and all other downstream drain piping shall be sized to permit a flow of at least the greatest system demand supplied by the pressure-reducing valve.

Piping controlled by sectional valves represents a significant segment of the sprinkler system. Sectional or floor control valves serve the same function for that portion of the system as the main drain does for the entire system. The use of express drains in high-rise buildings is one method of disposing of water from upper floors.

   With regard to 8.15.2.4.5, NFPA 25 requires annual flow testing of pressure-regulating devices. To facilitate flow testing, the drain connection serving such devices must be capable of handling the system flow rate and pressure for the area served by that pressure-reducing valve.

8.15.2.4.6 The test connections required by 8.16.4.1 shall be permitted to be used as main drain connections.

8.15.2.4.7 Where drain connections for floor control valves are tied into a common drain riser, the drain riser shall be one pipe size larger than the largest size drain connection tying into it.

8.15.2.5 Auxiliary Drains.

Auxiliary drains, which are covered in 8.15.2.5, are necessary for trapped piping. The type of auxiliary drain, its size, and its arrangement depend on the type of system and the volume of trapped piping.

8.15.2.5.1 Auxiliary drains shall be provided where a change in piping direction prevents drainage of system piping through the main drain valve.

8.15.2.5.2 Auxiliary Drains for Wet Pipe Systems and Preaction Systems in Areas Not Subject to Freezing.

8.15.2.5.2.1* Where the capacity of isolated trapped sections of pipe is 50 gal (189 L) or more, the auxiliary drain shall consist of a valve not smaller than 1 in. (25.4 mm), piped to an accessible location.

A.8.15.2.5.2.1 An example of an accessible location would be a valve located approximately 7 ft (2 m) above the floor level to which a hose could be connected to discharge the water in an acceptable manner.

8.15.2.5.2.2 Where the capacity of isolated trapped sections of pipe is more than 5 gal (18.9 L) and less than 50 gal (189 L), the auxiliary drain shall consist of a valve ¾ in. (19 mm) or larger and a plug or a nipple and cap.

A drain valve is required by 8.15.2.5.2.2 when the trapped section exceeds 5 gal (18.9 L). A drain valve allows the trapped piping to be emptied in a reasonable amount of time. The valve outlet also permits the trapped portion to be drained without creating a nuisance water spill. Exhibit 8.38 shows an auxiliary drain consisting of a valve and a plug.

EXHIBIT 8.38 Auxiliary Drain Consisting of a Valve and a Plug.

8.15.2.5.2.3 Where the capacity of trapped sections of pipes in wet systems is less than 5 gal (18.9 L), one of the following arrangements shall be provided:

(1) An auxiliary drain shall consist of a nipple and cap or plug not less than ½ in. (12 mm) in size.

(2) An auxiliary drain shall not be required for trapped sections less than 5 gal (18.9 L) where the system piping can be drained by removing a single pendent sprinkler.

(3) Where flexible couplings or other easily separated connections are used, the nipple and cap or plug shall be permitted to be omitted.

The drainage of trapped piping sections in wet pipe systems is not typically a common event. Therefore, a nipple and cap or a plug, as required by 8.15.2.5.2.3, is adequate when the volume of the trapped section is 5 gal (18.9 L) or less. This small quantity of water can be emptied into a bucket. A nipple and cap are preferable to a plug because of the comparative ease with which they can be removed. For easier removal, the plug should be brass.

Paragraph 8.15.2.5.2.3(2) recognizes that the small volume of water trapped in one pendent sprinkler can be drained as readily through the sprinkler connection as through a plug. Requiring a drain is unrealistic where pendent sprinklers are installed below a ceiling and are supplied directly from branch lines concealed above the ceiling. Paragraph 8.15.2.5.2.3(3) recognizes that many of the fittings currently used can be separated easily and can be used to drain small trapped portions of a wet system with little inconvenience.

8.15.2.5.2.4 Tie-in drains shall not be required on wet pipe systems and preaction systems protecting non-freezing environments.

Tie-in drains, which are addressed in 8.15.2.5.2.4, are cross connections of the ends of trapped branch lines that are piped to a single drain valve. These drains are not required on wet pipe systems and preaction systems protecting non-freezing environments, because such piping is not drained at the same frequency as systems protecting cold environments.

8.15.2.5.3 Auxiliary Drains for Dry Pipe Systems and Preaction Systems in Areas Subject to Freezing.

8.15.2.5.3.1 Where the capacity of trapped sections of pipe is less than 5 gal (18.9 L), the auxiliary drain shall consist of a valve not smaller than ½ in. (12 mm) and a plug or a nipple and cap.

Because dry pipe systems and some preaction systems are installed in areas subject to freezing, small trapped sections of piping of 5 gal (18.9 L) or less must be provided with drain valves, as stated in 8.15.2.5.3.1. Water that has entered the system, either because the dry pipe valve tripped or from condensation of moisture from the pressurized air in the system, must be easily drained to prevent freezing. An auxiliary drain is not required when pendent sprinklers in a heated area are supplied by piping that is also in a heated area.

8.15.2.5.3.2 Auxiliary drains are not for pipe drops supplying dry-pendent sprinklers installed in accordance with 7.2.2.

8.15.2.5.3.3 Where the capacity of isolated trapped sections of system piping is more than 5 gal (18.9 L), the auxiliary drain shall consist of two 1-in. (25.4-mm) valves and one 2-in. × 12-in. (51-mm × 305-mm) condensate nipple or equivalent, accessibly located in accordance with Figure 8.15.2.5.3.3.

The condensate nipple illustrated in Figure 8.15.2.5.3.3 or its equivalent is required for each section of trapped piping with more than 5 gal (18.9 L) capacity in a dry pipe system and a preaction system protecting cold environments. The condensate nipple is capable of collecting and removing moisture from the system while minimizing the potential for excessive loss of air pressure and possible unplanned operation of a dry pipe valve. The upper valve is normally open, allowing moisture to enter the chamber, while the lower valve is closed and sealed to avoid leaks. To drain the chamber, the upper valve is closed to temporarily isolate it from the system, and the lower valve is opened to remove the accumulated condensate. If inside and outside temperatures are extreme, isolating the exterior drain pipe from the interior

Dry system
auxiliary
drain

1-in. (25.4-mm) valve

2-in. (51-mm) × 12-in. (305-mm)
nipple or equivalent

1-in. (25.4-mm) valve

1-in. (25.4-mm) nipple and cap or plug

FIGURE 8.15.2.5.3.3 *Dry System Auxiliary Drain.*

drain pipe with a threaded fitting can be desirable. This separation can have the effect of limiting moisture buildup by checking the transfer of a high exterior ambient temperature to the cooler interior temperature of the drain pipe. Also see the commentary to 8.15.2.5.3.4.

8.15.2.5.3.4 Tie-in drains shall be provided for multiple adjacent trapped branch pipes and shall be only 1 in. (25.4 mm). Tie-in drain lines shall be pitched a minimum of ½ in. per 10 ft (4 mm/m).

When two or more adjacent branch lines are trapped in a dry pipe or preaction system, the ends of the branch lines must be piped together and run to a low-point drain at least 1 in. (25.4 mm) in size, as stated in 8.15.2.5.3.4. The drain needs to be equipped with a valve and nipple and cap or a plug to facilitate moisture removal from the system.

Properly pitching tie-in drains and removing condensate from drains prior to freezing weather is extremely important. Typically, tie-in drains consist of smaller-sized piping connected to a rather large volume of piping, and, with these smaller drains, freeze-ups are possible.

Tie-in drains on multiple adjacent branch lines should be avoided if possible, because the use of tie-in drains in effect creates a gridded system. Gridded dry pipe systems and gridded double interlock preaction systems are prohibited by 7.2.3.5 and 7.3.2.5. In these types of systems, all of the air in the piping must be evacuated before a steady flow of water is discharged from the operated sprinklers. A gridded pipe arrangement is very likely to result in excessive time delays before effective sprinkler discharge occurs. Tie-in drains are considered necessary to allow rapid drainage of systems protecting cold environments. The restriction that tie-in drains be limited to 1 in. (25.4 mm) should help minimize any delays.

8.15.2.6 Discharge of Drain Valves.

8.15.2.6.1* Direct interconnections shall not be made between sprinkler drains and sewers.

A.8.15.2.6.1 Where possible, the main sprinkler riser drain should discharge outside the building at a point free from the possibility of causing water damage. Where it is not possible to discharge outside the building wall, the drain should be piped to a sump, which in turn should discharge by gravity or be pumped to a waste water drain or sewer. The main sprinkler riser drain connection should be of a size sufficient to carry off water from the fully open drain valve while it is discharging under normal water system pressures. Where this is not possible, a supplementary drain of equal size should be provided for test purposes with free discharge, located at or above grade.

8.15.2.6.2 The drain discharge shall conform to any health or water department regulations.

The restriction on the connection of sprinkler drains and sewers in 8.15.2.6.1 is intended to prevent any harmful element from first entering the sprinkler system by way of the drain connection and then the public water system by way of the sprinkler system. An air gap is the method usually employed to avoid a direct connection and potential backflow. Exhibit 8.39 shows the main drain discharging to atmosphere.

EXHIBIT 8.39 System Main Drain Discharging to Atmosphere.

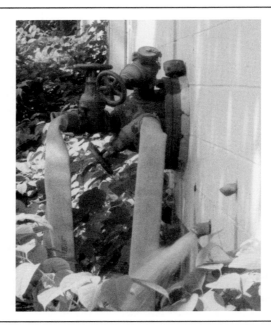

The valve between the sprinkler system and the drain connection and the check valve between the sprinkler system and the public water supply, as required by 8.15.2.6.2, provide sufficient protection against contamination. This additional regulation prohibiting direct interconnections is considered necessary to further enhance protection of the potable water.

The drain connections on risers must be capable of handling the water discharged under normal system pressure. In some situations, such as in high-rise buildings where the drain lines can be long, making the drain riser one size larger than the largest drain connection (see 8.15.2.4.7), may not be sufficient to prevent overpressurization of the normally atmospheric drain line from a high-pressure system.

8.15.2.6.3 Where drain pipes are buried underground, approved corrosion-resistant pipe shall be used.

8.15.2.6.4 Drain pipes shall not terminate in blind spaces under the building.

The drain discharge must be piped in a manner that allows the operator to ascertain that the drain is not obstructed and that it is not causing water damage (see 8.15.2.6.4).

8.15.2.6.5 Where exposed to the atmosphere, drain pipes shall be fitted with a turned-down elbow.

The turned-down elbow discussed in 8.15.2.6.5 discourages the use of the drain piping as a refuse receptacle and minimizes the possibility of damage to property or of passersby getting wet.

8.15.2.6.6 Drain pipes shall be arranged to avoid exposing any part of the sprinkler system to freezing conditions.

Freezing conditions are discussed in 8.15.2.6.6. When systems are installed where the exterior ambient temperatures are subject to freezing, at least 4 ft (1.2 m) of the drain line beyond the valve should be installed in a warm room. The recommended 4 ft (1.2 m) of pipe beyond the valve provides a frost break that prevents water in the system from freezing due to cold air from outside. Additionally, all moisture needs to be removed from trapped, unheated areas in dry pipe and preaction systems. (See NFPA 25.)

8.15.3 Protection of Piping.

8.15.3.1 Protection of Piping Against Freezing.

8.15.3.1.1 Unless the requirements of 8.15.3.1.2 are met, where portions of systems are subject to freezing and temperatures cannot reliably be maintained at or above 40°F (4°C), sprinklers shall be installed as a dry pipe or preaction system.

8.15.3.1.2 Small unheated areas are permitted to be protected by antifreeze systems or by other systems specifically listed for this purpose.

A wet pipe system should always be the first choice when selecting a system as required by 8.15.3.1.2. Dry pipe systems should be considered when the minimum temperature of 40°F (4°C) cannot be maintained. The use of a dry pipe system for any unheated area should be limited to that area, and a separate wet pipe system should be used for the heated portions of a building. Dry pipe systems tend to have slower operating times, increased corrosion rates on the internal portions of the pipe, and greater maintenance requirements than wet pipe systems.

Paragraph 8.15.3.1.2 permits an alternative to dry pipe systems such as antifreeze or other listed means of freeze protection.

8.15.3.1.3* Where aboveground water-filled supply pipes, risers, system risers, or feed mains pass through open areas, cold rooms, passageways, or other areas exposed to freezing temperatures, the pipe shall be protected against freezing by insulating coverings, frostproof casings, or other reliable means capable of maintaining a minimum temperature between 40°F (4°C) and 120°F (48.9°C).

A.8.15.3.1.3 Branch lines have been intentionally left out of this paragraph as it is an unacceptable practice to heat trace and insulate branch lines.

Other means of freeze protection referred to in 8.15.3.1.3 include steam coils, heat tracing, or circulating hot water tubing that has been specifically investigated and listed for use with sprinkler systems. With any of those alternative approaches, caution must be used to verify that temperatures do not exceed the maximum ambient temperature allowed for the sprinkler's temperature rating. Excessive temperatures can be conducted through the piping and lead to unwanted sprinkler operation. In addition, the need for insulation in conjunction with an alternative approach system must also be evaluated. At least one electrical heating system is on the market that can be used to comply with this requirement.

It should be noted that branch lines have intentionally been left out of 8.15.3.1.3 as it is an unacceptable practice to heat trace and insulate branch lines.

◀ FAQ
Is it permitted by 8.15.3.1.3 to heat trace and insulate branch lines?

8.15.3.2 Protection of Piping Against Corrosion.

8.15.3.2.1* Where corrosive conditions are known to exist due to moisture or fumes from corrosive chemicals or both, special types of fittings, pipes, and hangers that resist corrosion shall be used, or a protective coating shall be applied to all unprotected exposed surfaces of the sprinkler system.

A.8.15.3.2.1 Types of locations where corrosive conditions can exist include bleacheries, dye houses, metal plating processes, animal pens, and certain chemical plants.

If corrosive conditions are not of great intensity and humidity is not abnormally high, good results can be obtained by a protective coating of red lead and varnish or by a good grade of commercial acid-resisting paint. The paint manufacturer's instructions should be followed in the preparation of the surface and in the method of application.

Where moisture conditions are severe but corrosive conditions are not of great intensity, copper tube or galvanized steel pipe, fittings, and hangers might be suitable. The exposed threads of steel pipe should be painted.

In instances where the piping is not readily accessible and where the exposure to corrosive fumes is severe, either a protective coating of high quality can be employed or some form of corrosion-resistant material used.

Piping installed in ocean-front facilities can also be subject to higher than normal rates of corrosion.

The protective paints and coatings referenced in 8.15.3.2.1 are not applied to the automatic sprinklers. Automatic sprinklers must be provided with corrosion-resistant coatings applied by the manufacturer in accordance with 6.2.6.1.

8.15.3.2.2 Where water supplies are known to have unusual corrosive properties and threaded or cut-groove steel pipe is to be used, wall thickness shall be in accordance with Schedule 30 [in sizes 8 in. (200 mm) or larger] or Schedule 40 [in sizes less than 8 in. (200 mm)].

Caution must be exercised when considering the inclusion of corrosion-control additives to sprinkler systems, and the authority having jurisdiction should be consulted (see 8.15.3.2.2). A remote possibility of contaminating the domestic supply through backflow exists. Some additives can solidify when exposed to air, causing obstruction to water flow. Such chemicals have been used for poor quality water or as a corrosion inhibitor for the circulating closed-loop systems discussed in 7.6.1.

Although corrosion protection for exposed surfaces is independent of wall thickness and acceptable pipe-joining methods, the use of threaded thin-wall pipe must be avoided where subject internally to water having unusual corrosive properties. The thinner wall between the inside diameter of the pipe and the root diameter of the threads cannot withstand the same amount of corrosion and introduces a failure point for the piping system. If threaded pipe is used, it should be Schedule 30 or heavier for pipe sizes 8 in. (200 mm) or larger and Schedule 40 for pipe sizes less than 8 in. (200 mm). The use of welded or roll-grooved Schedule 10 pipe would also be satisfactory.

8.15.3.2.3 Where corrosive conditions exist or piping is exposed to the weather, corrosion-resistant types of pipe, fittings, and hangers or protective corrosion-resistant coatings shall be used.

8.15.3.2.4 Where steel pipe is used underground, the pipe shall be protected against corrosion.

8.15.3.3 Protection of Piping in Hazardous Areas.

8.15.3.3.1 Private service main aboveground piping shall not pass through hazardous areas and shall be located so that it is protected from mechanical and fire damage.

8.15.3.3.2 Private service main aboveground piping shall be permitted to be located in hazardous areas protected by an automatic sprinkler system.

Private fire service main piping discussed in 8.15.3.3.2 should be located outside of buildings and buried. In some cases, running piping within the building may be necessary. The piping must not be exposed to hazardous areas because it would be subject to damage and not be able to provide water to other areas that may need protection. If automatic sprinkler protection designed for the hazard involved is provided, the potential for main damage is minimized.

 8.15.4 Protection of Risers Subject to Mechanical Damage. Sprinkler risers subject to mechanical damage shall be protected by steel posts, concrete barriers, or other approved means.

8.16 System Attachments

8.16.1* Sprinkler Alarms/Waterflow Alarms.

A.8.16.1 Central station, auxiliary, remote station, or proprietary protective signaling systems are a highly desirable supplement to local alarms, especially from a safety to life standpoint. *(See 8.16.1.6.)*

Approved identification signs, as shown in Figure A.8.16.1, should be provided for outside alarm devices. The sign should be located near the device in a conspicuous position and should be worded as follows:

SPRINKLER FIRE ALARM—WHEN BELL RINGS
CALL FIRE DEPARTMENT OR POLICE.

FIGURE A.8.16.1 *Identification Sign.*

8.16.1.1 Local Waterflow Alarms. Local waterflow alarms shall be provided on all sprinkler systems having more than 20 sprinklers.

Paragraph 8.16.1.1 of NFPA 13 requires an audible waterflow alarm on the premises for all systems that have more than 20 sprinklers. The systems are not required to have supplemental alarm systems. The standard does require alarm supervision of valves controlling sprinkler systems with non—fire protection connections and recommends, but does not require, such supervision in other instances.

The sprinkler alarms are waterflow alarms and are not building evacuation alarms. However, in some applications building owners can choose to react to waterflow alarms as evacuation alarms. The purpose for which the alarm is intended should be considered in the overall design of both actuating mechanisms and audible alarm devices.

◀ **FAQ**
Is it the intent of 8.16.1.1 that the required waterflow alarm serve as a building evacuation alarm?

8.16.1.2 Retarding Devices.

8.16.1.2.1 On each alarm check valve used under conditions of variable water pressure, a retarding device shall be installed.

8.16.1.2.2 Valves shall be provided in the connections to retarding devices to permit repair or removal without shutting off sprinklers; these valves shall be so arranged that they can be locked or sealed in the open position.

Retarding devices are covered in 8.16.1.2.1 and 8.16.1.2.2. Retarding chambers (see Exhibit 8.40) are required when alarm devices connected to alarm valves would otherwise be subject to nuisance operation caused by surges from variable pressure supplies, such as city water or fire pumps. When the supply is a constant pressure source, such as a gravity tank or pressure tank, retarding chambers may not be necessary.

8.16.1.3 Alarm Bypass Test Connections.

Alarm bypass test connections are covered in 8.16.1.3. Local waterflow alarms should be tested at least quarterly. (See NFPA 25.) The required bypass from the water side of the system allows these tests to be conducted without tripping the system. Tripping the system in areas subject to freezing requires more care, as it could cause the system to freeze.

8.16.1.3.1 Alarm, dry pipe, preaction, and deluge valves shall be fitted with an alarm bypass test connection for an electric alarm switch, water motor gong, or both.

8.16.1.3.2 The alarm bypass test connection for alarm, dry pipe, preaction, and deluge valves shall be made on the water supply side of the system and provided with a control valve and drain for the alarm piping.

8.16.1.3.3 The alarm bypass test connection for alarm valves at the riser shall be permitted to be made on the system side of an alarm valve.

8.16.1.3.4 A check valve shall be installed in the pipe connection from the intermediate chamber of a dry pipe valve.

8.16.1.4 Indicating Control Valves.

8.16.1.4.1 An indicating control valve shall be installed in the connection to pressure-type contactors or water motor-operated alarm devices.

8.16.1.4.2 Such valves shall be sealed, locked, or electrically supervised in the open position.

8.16.1.4.3 The control valve for the retarding chamber on alarm check valves shall be accepted as complying with the requirements of 8.16.1.4.

The control valve discussed in 8.16.1.4.3 is to be located in the piping between the connection from the alarm valve, dry pipe valve, preaction valve, or deluge valve and the local waterflow alarm device(s). This piping is normally subject to only atmospheric air pressure, and lacking an indicating-type valve, no visual means exists to ascertain if the valve was open and if water could reach the alarm actuators. Exhibit 8.40 identifies the bypass test connection along with the control valve.

8.16.1.5* Attachments—Mechanically Operated.

A.8.16.1.5 Water motor-operated devices should be located as near as practicable to the alarm valve, dry pipe valve, or other waterflow detecting device. The total length of the pipe to these devices should not exceed 75 ft (22.9 m), nor should the water motor-operated device be located over 20 ft (6.1 m) above the alarm device or dry pipe valve.

8.16.1.5.1 For all types of sprinkler systems employing water motor-operated alarms, a listed ¾-in. (19-mm) strainer shall be installed at the alarm outlet of the waterflow detecting device.

8.16.1.5.2 Where a retarding chamber is used in connection with an alarm valve, the strainer shall be located at the outlet of the retarding chamber unless the retarding chamber is provided with an approved integral strainer in its outlet.

See commentary following 6.9.3.4 and Exhibit 8.40. The strainer and the pipe of corrosion-resistant material are required to protect against obstruction of the small orifice through which water enters the water motor (see 8.16.1.5.2).

8.16.1.6* Alarm Attachments—High-Rise Buildings. When a fire must be fought internally due to the height of a building, the following additional alarm apparatus shall be provided:

(1) Where each sprinkler system on each floor is equipped with a separate waterflow device, it shall be connected to an alarm system in such a manner that operation of one sprinkler will actuate the alarm system, and the location of the operated flow device shall be indi-

Alarm pressure switch

Water motor alarm

Riser

Strainer

System side gauge

Water

2 in. main drain valve

Retarding chamber

Main water clapper

③

2 in. main drain

Supply side gauge

Water

②

Alarm test shutoff valve to retard chamber, pressure switch, and water motor alarm valve to be supervised in accordance with 8.15.1.1.2

To drain

①

Main water control valve

Water supply pipe

Note: Valves 1 and 2 are normally open and Valve 3 is normally closed. Close Valve 2 to silence alarm.

EXHIBIT 8.40 *Wet Alarm Valve with Alarm Test Shutoff Valve.*

cated on an annunciator and/or register. The annunciator or register shall be located at grade level at the normal point of fire department access, at a constantly attended building security control center, or at both locations.

(2) Where the location within the protected buildings where supervisory or alarm signals are received is not under constant supervision by qualified personnel in the employ of the owner, a connection shall be provided to transmit a signal to a remote central station.

(3) A distinct trouble signal shall be provided to indicate a condition that will impair the satisfactory operation of the sprinkler system.

A.8.16.1.6 Monitoring should include but not be limited to control valves, building temperatures, fire pump power supplies and running conditions, and water tank levels and temperatures. Pressure supervision should also be provided on pressure tanks.

Check valves can be required to prevent false waterflow signals on floors where sprinklers have not activated—for example, floor systems interconnected to two supply risers.

Alarm attachments in high-rise buildings are discussed in 8.16.1.6. To improve the reliability of an automatic sprinkler system in a high-rise building, supervision of any portion of the system that could impair its operation is required. A sprinkler waterflow alarm annunciated by floor is not required because some systems can take on configurations that would not lend themselves to this type of zoning. On the other hand, where sprinkler waterflow alarms are provided on each floor, they are intended to be annunciated at a point to allow rapid identification of the fire location by the fire department on arrival.

The overall reliability of the system is further improved by requiring remote monitoring of supervisory signals in the numerous cases where 24-hour surveillance of on-site supervisory equipment is not provided.

8.16.1.7* Alarm Service.

 A.8.16.1.7 For further information, see *NFPA 72, National Fire Alarm Code.*

8.16.1.7.1 A central station, auxiliary, remote station, or proprietary sprinkler waterflow alarm shall be provided for sprinkler systems protecting storage in accordance with Section 12.3.

8.16.1.7.2 A local waterflow alarm shall be permitted where recorded guard service is provided.

8.16.1.8 Sprinkler Waterflow Alarm for In-Rack Sprinklers. See Section C.4.

8.16.2* Fire Department Connections.

 A.8.16.2 The fire department connection should be located not less than 18 in. (457 mm) and not more than 4 ft (1.2 m) above the level of the adjacent grade or access level.

Typical fire department connections are shown in Figure A.8.16.2(a) and Figure A.8.16.2(b). See NFPA 13E, *Recommended Practice for Fire Department Operations in Properties Protected by Sprinkler and Standpipe Systems.*

8.16.2.1* Unless the requirements of 8.16.2.2 are met, a fire department connection shall be provided as described in 8.16.2 in accordance with Figure 8.16.2.1.

 A.8.16.2.1 Fire department connections should be located and arranged so that hose lines can be readily and conveniently attached without interference from nearby objects including

FIGURE A.8.16.2(a) *Fire Department Connection.*

Plan (no scale)

Section (no scale)

Notes:

1. Various backflow prevention regulations accept different devices at the connection between public water mains and private fire service mains.

2. The device shown in the pit could be any or a combination of the following:

(a) Gravity check valve

(b) Detector check vlave

(c) Double check valve assembly

(d) Reduced pressure zone (RPZ) device

(e) Vacuum breaker

3. Some backflow prevention regulations prohibit these devices from being installed in a pit.

4. In all cases, the device(s) in the pit should be approved or listed as necessary. The requirements of the local or municipal water department should be reviewed prior to design or installation of the connection.

5. Pressure drop should be considered prior to the installation of any backflow prevention devices.

FIGURE A.8.16.2(b) *Typical City Water Pit—Valve Arrangement.*

1 in. to 3 in. (25.4 mm to 76.2 mm) waterproof mastic

Fire department connection

Header in valve room

Check valve

Automatic drip

FIGURE 8.16.2.1 *Fire Department Connections.*

buildings, fences, posts, or other fire department connections. Where a hydrant is not available, other water supply sources such as a natural body of water, a tank, or reservoir should be utilized. The water authority should be consulted when a nonpotable water supply is proposed as a suction source for the fire department.

8.16.2.2 The following systems shall not require a fire department connection:

(1) Buildings located in remote areas that are inaccessible for fire department support
(2) Large-capacity deluge systems exceeding the pumping capacity of the fire department
(3) Single-story buildings not exceeding 2000 ft² (186 m²) in area

FAQ ▶
Why are some systems not required to have a fire department connection?

Paragraphs 8.16.2.2(1), 8.16.2.2(2), and 8.16.2.2(3) are examples of situations in which a fire department connection is not practical. Paragraphs 8.16.2.2(1) and 8.16.2.2(2) are conditions in which the connection would be of little or no benefit; thus, the decision not to provide the connection is an economical one. Paragraph 8.16.2.2(3) addresses a situation in which fire department access is readily available to all sides and areas of the structure; thus, the connection is likely to provide only a minimal benefit.

8.16.2.3 Size. The size of the pipe for the fire department connection shall be in accordance with one of the following:

(1) Pipe size shall be a minimum of 4 in. (102 mm) for fire engine connections
(2) Pipe size shall be a minimum of 6 in. (152 mm) for fire boat connections
(3) For hydraulically calculated systems, the fire department connection shall be permitted to be less than 4 in. (102 mm) and no less than the size of system riser, where serving one system riser
(4) A single-outlet fire department connection shall be acceptable where piped to a 3-in. (76 mm) or smaller riser

8.16.2.4* Arrangement. See Figure 8.16.2.1.

A.8.16.2.4 The check valve should be located to maximize accessibility and minimize freezing potential.

Arrangement of fire department connections is addressed in 8.16.2.4. Each separate water supply connection for sprinkler systems, whether automatic or manual, should be made on the system side of a check valve. Only in this way can pressure differentials between municipal, fire pump, pressure tank, or fire department connections effectively supply the sprinklers. The highest pressure supply comes in first until its capacity is reached. As capacity is exceeded, the pressure drops until the next highest pressure supply comes in. The check valve prevents the higher pressure supply from backing up or circulating into lower pressure supplies. (See 8.15.1.1.3.2 and its associated commentary, and for examples, see Exhibits 8.41 and 8.42.)

Sprinklers shown in Exhibits 8.41 and 8.42 are normally supplied by a public main with a static pressure of 50 psi (3.4 bar). On arrival at a fire in this building, the fire officer would order a pumper to connect to the hydrant across the street and to pump at 150 psi (10.3 bar) into the yard fire department connection, adding supplementary pressure to the sprinkler system. If the connection were not on the system side of a check valve, the pumped water would circulate back into the same main to the suction side of the pumper, and no supplementary pressure could be added.

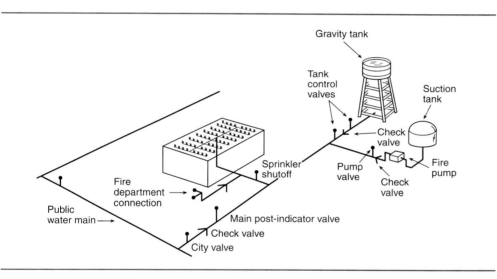

EXHIBIT 8.41 *Alternative Water Supplies to Sprinkler System.*

EXHIBIT 8.42 *Fire Department Water Supply Connections to Sprinkler System.*

8.16.2.4.1* The fire department connection shall be on the system side of the water supply check valve.

A.8.16.2.4.1 The fire department connection should be connected to the system riser. For single systems it is an acceptable arrangement to attach the fire department connection to any point in the system provided the pipe size meets the requirements of 8.16.2.3.

See Exhibit 8.29, which illustrates the proper arrangement for a fire department connection on a wet pipe system (see 8.16.2.4.1).

8.16.2.4.2 For single systems, the fire department connection shall be installed as follows:

(1) Wet system—on the system side of system control, check, and alarm valves *(see Figure A.8.15.1.1)*
(2) Dry system—between the system control valve and the dry pipe valve
(3) Preaction system—between the preaction valve and the check valve on the system side of the preaction valve
(4) Deluge system—on the system side of the deluge valve

8.16.2.4.3 For multiple systems, the fire department connection shall be connected between the supply control valves and the system control valves.

8.16.2.4.4 The requirements of 8.16.2.4.2 and 8.16.2.4.3 shall not apply where the fire department connection is connected to the underground piping.

8.16.2.4.5 Where a fire department connection services only a portion of a building, a sign shall be attached indicating the portions of the building served.

Confusion can occur when there are multiple fire department connections or where the fire department connection serves only a portion of a building, as discussed in 8.16.2.4.5. If the fire department cannot determine which fire department connection to use, the proper connection or any connection at all may not be used. On other occasions, the fire department may pump into a fire department connection that does not serve the fire area. To avoid these types of problems, NFPA 13 requires that the fire department connection serve all of the sprinkler systems when multiple systems exist (see 8.16.2.4.3) and that connections that serve only a portion of the building be marked with the area they serve.

8.16.2.4.6 Fire department connections shall be on the street side of buildings and shall be located and arranged so that hose lines can be readily and conveniently attached to the inlets without interference from any nearby objects including buildings, fences, posts, or other fire department connections.

8.16.2.4.7 Signs.

8.16.2.4.7.1 Each fire department connection to sprinkler systems shall be designated by a sign having raised or engraved letters at least 1 in. (25.4 mm) in height on plate or fitting reading service design—for example, AUTOSPKR., OPEN SPKR., AND STANDPIPE.

8.16.2.4.7.2 A sign shall also indicate the pressure required at the inlets to deliver the greatest system demand.

8.16.2.4.7.3 The sign required in 8.16.2.4.7.2 shall not be required where the system demand pressure is less than 150 psi (10.3 bar).

FAQ ▶
Why is the fire department connection required on the sprinkler system side of the discharge check valve for fire pump installations?

According to 8.16.2.4.1 through 8.16.2.4.3, the fire department connection is made on the system side of a check valve. For installation on systems with fire pumps, the fire department connection needs to be made on the sprinkler system side of the discharge check valve for the fire pump. Full efficiency and reliability cannot be obtained for a suction-side connection because of losses through the pump and valves and because of the inability to supplement the system if the discharge-side control valves are closed. Pumping into the suction side of a fire pump or booster pump increases the discharge pressure of the pump, frequently beyond the pressure limits of the system. The fire department connection should be made on the system side of a pump and on the system side—that is, the discharge side—of the pump's discharge check valve and control valves.

The information provided on the sign at the fire department connection, as discussed in 8.16.2.4.7.1 through 8.16.2.4.7.3, is directed at the engineer on the fire department pumper. Since fire department procedures normally require the pump operator to provide 150 psi (10.3 bar) at the connection, the sign is required to indicate that some pressure beyond 150 psi (10.3 bar) is necessary. (See NFPA 13E, *Recommended Practice for Fire Department Operations in Properties Protected by Sprinkler and Standpipe Systems.*)

8.16.2.4.8 Fire department connections shall not be connected on the suction side of fire pumps.

8.16.2.4.9 Fire department connections shall be properly supported.

8.16.2.5 Valves.

8.16.2.5.1 A listed check valve shall be installed in each fire department connection.

8.16.2.5.2 There shall be no shutoff valve in the fire department connection piping.

The installation of a shutoff valve on both sides of a check valve to facilitate repair is usually considered good practice. The check valve in the fire department connection is considered to be an exception to general good practice, and no shutoff valve is permitted by 8.16.2.5.2 at that point in the fire department connection. Control valves in a fire department connection serve no useful purpose and only provide a point of system failure. See Exhibit 8.29.

8.16.2.6 Drainage. The piping between the check valve and the outside hose coupling shall be equipped with an approved automatic drip in areas subject to freezing.

Drainage is discussed in 8.16.2.6. In the event that the check valve in the siamese connection leaks, the purpose of the automatic drip is to drain this water to a safe location and to maintain the piping between the check valve and the hose couplings free of water. Without the automatic drip, any collected water could freeze and prevent the fire department from pumping into the system under fire conditions. This automatic drip also facilitates any maintenance of the fire department connection piping, because this portion of the pipe is already free of water. Exhibits 8.26 and 8.43 show an automatic drip valve used on the fire department connections. The drain should be located at the lowest point of the fire department connection piping to allow complete drainage.

EXHIBIT 8.43
Fire Department Connection with an Automatic Drain Valve Located on the Outside of the Building.

8.16.3 Gauges.

8.16.3.1 A pressure gauge with a connection not smaller than ¼ in. (6.4 mm) shall be installed at the system main drain, at each main drain associated with a floor control valve, and on the inlet and outlet side of each pressure reducing valve.

8.16.3.2 Each gauge connection shall be equipped with a shutoff valve and provisions for draining.

8.16.3.3 The required pressure gauges shall be listed and shall have a maximum limit not less than twice the normal system working pressure at the point where installed.

8.16.3.4 Gauges shall be installed to permit removal and shall be located where they will not be subject to freezing.

8.16.4 System Connections.

Paragraph 8.15.2.4 should be referenced to determine the relation between the test connections noted in the subparagraphs of 8.16.4 and the drain sizes previously discussed. A single drain normally serves both functions.

8.16.4.1* Main Drain Test Connections.

A.8.16.4.1 See Figure A.8.16.4.1.

FIGURE A.8.16.4.1 *Water Supply Connection with Test Connection.*

FAQ ▶
What purpose does the main drain test connection serve?

FAQ ▶
Can water supply tests be conducted through the main drain test connection?

FAQ ▶
Why are main drain tests conducted?

Main drain test connections are covered in 8.16.4.1. Test connections or drain pipes are used to drain the system and to help evaluate the water supply. Test connections and drain pipes are used to drain systems when repairs are necessary or when dry pipe valves have tripped. They are also used to help confirm that the proper water supply is available at the system riser and on the system side of all check valves, control valves, and underground piping.

Test connections or drain pipes are normally smaller than all other water supply piping. Therefore, they are not capable of large-scale flow tests and should not be used as a means of evaluating the available water supply. Waterflow tests conducted through the main drain test do not provide an accurate reading of the water supply. One reason for an inaccurate reading is the unknown friction loss values of check valves under low flow conditions.

Two-in. (51-mm) main drain tests, as they are commonly called, normally consist of opening the 2-in. (51-mm) main drain wide until the pressure stabilizes. Records are kept of these tests to detect possible deterioration of water supplies or to detect valves in the overall water supply system that may have been closed. The 2-in. (51-mm) drain test on new systems necessitates the establishment of a benchmark when the system is first approved during the acceptance tests.

See NFPA 25 for additional information on conducting 2-in. (51-mm) drain tests. See Exhibits 8.29, 8.32, and 8.39

8.16.4.1.1 Main drain test connections shall be provided at locations that will permit flow tests of water supplies and connections.

8.16.4.1.2 They shall be so installed that the valve can be opened wide for a sufficient time to assure a proper test without causing water damage.

8.16.4.1.3 Main drain connections shall be sized in accordance with 8.15.2.4 and 8.15.2.6.

8.16.4.2* Wet Pipe Systems.

A.8.16.4.2 This test connection should be in the upper story, and the connection preferably should be piped from the end of the most remote branch line. The discharge should be at a point where it can be readily observed. In locations where it is not practical to terminate the test connection outside the building, the test connection is permitted to terminate into a drain capable of accepting full flow under system pressure. In this event, the test connection should be made using an approved sight test connection containing a smooth bore corrosion-resistant orifice giving a flow equivalent to one sprinkler simulating the least flow from an individual sprinkler in the system. *[See Figure A.8.16.4.2(a) and Figure A.8.16.4.2(b).]* The test valve should be located at an accessible point and preferably not over 7 ft (2.1 m) above the floor. The control valve on the test connection should be located at a point not exposed to freezing.

8.16.4.2.1 An alarm test connection not less than 1 in. (25.4 mm) in diameter, terminating in a smooth bore corrosion-resistant orifice, giving a flow equivalent to one sprinkler of a type having the smallest orifice installed on the particular system, shall be provided to test each waterflow alarm device for each system.

8.16.4.2.2 The test connection valve shall be readily accessible.

8.16.4.2.3 The discharge shall be to the outside, to a drain connection capable of accepting full flow under system pressure, or to another location where water damage will not result.

Elevation

Note: Not less than 4 ft (1.2 m) of exposed test pipe in warm room beyond valve where pipe extends through wall to outside.

FIGURE A.8.16.4.2(a) System Test Connection on Wet Pipe System.

FIGURE A.8.16.4.2(b) Floor Control Valve.

Wet pipe systems are covered in 8.16.4.2.1 through 8.16.4.2.3. The primary function of the wet pipe system inspector's test is to verify the operation of the waterflow alarm device(s)—for example, water-motor gong, pressure switch, or flow switch—at a flow equivalent to that of one operating sprinkler.

The intent of 8.16.4.2 is to require inspector's test connections in a manner that provides for the testing of all waterflow alarm devices. Both an electrically operated alarm and a water-motor alarm supplied from an alarm valve may be tested through a single test connection.

FAQ ▶

For a wet pipe sprinkler system, is the inspector's test connection required to be at the end of the most remote branch line?

Ideally the inspector's test connection is located at the end of the most remote branch line in the upper story. Such a location is not, however, required. For a wet pipe system, the exclusive purpose of the inspector's test is to verify operation of the alarm attachment, which is the reason that the test connection is not mandated at the remote portion of the system. The test connection is only required to be located downstream of the alarm device. Exhibit 8.44 shows a test connection located in the fire pump room near the sprinkler system alarm valve.

8.16.4.3* Dry Pipe Systems.

A **A.8.16.4.3** See Figure A.8.16.4.3.

Note: To minimize condensation of water in the drop to the test connection, provide a nipple-up off of the branch line.

FIGURE A.8.16.4.3 *System Test Connection on Dry Pipe System.*

8.16.4.3.1 A trip test connection not less than 1 in. (25.4 mm) in diameter, terminating in a smooth bore corrosion-resistant orifice, to provide a flow equivalent to one sprinkler of a type installed on the particular system, shall be installed.

8.16.4.3.2 The trip test connection shall be located on the end of the most distant sprinkler pipe in the upper story and shall be equipped with a readily accessible shutoff valve and plug not less than 1 in. (25.4 mm), at least one of which shall be brass.

8.16.4.3.3 In lieu of a plug, a nipple and cap shall be acceptable.

EXHIBIT 8.44 *Inspector's Test Connection for a Wet Pipe System.*

Dry pipe systems are covered in 8.16.4.3.1 through 8.16.4.3.3. The dry pipe system inspector's test connection is used to measure the approximate time from the opening of the most distant sprinkler in the system until water flows from that sprinkler. For that reason, the test connection must be located at the end of the farthest line in the top story of the protected occupancy. The valve must be sealed with a plug or nipple and cap when not in use to avoid leakage of air and to avoid accidental tripping of the dry pipe valve.

The installation of the test valve on the drop pipe is permitted for the purpose of accessibility. In this case, the connection should be made to the top of the branch line to minimize condensation buildup. Moisture should be drained periodically as is done with low-point drains in areas subject to freezing. Manufacturer's instructions should be followed to avoid accidental operation of dry pipe valves equipped with quick-opening devices.

◀ FAQ
For dry pipe systems why does 8.16.4.3 require the inspector's test connection to be located at the most distant sprinkler pipe in the upper story?

8.16.4.4 Preaction Systems.

8.16.4.4.1 A test connection shall be provided on a preaction system using supervisory air.

8.16.4.4.2 The connection used to control the level of priming water shall be considered adequate to test the operation of the alarms monitoring the supervisory air pressure.

8.16.4.5 Deluge Systems. A test connection is not required on a deluge system.

8.16.4.6* Backflow Devices.

A.8.16.4.6 Where backflow prevention devices are installed, they should be in an accessible location to provide for service and maintenance.

8.16.4.6.1* Backflow Prevention Valves. Means shall be provided downstream of all backflow prevention valves for flow tests at system demand.

A.8.16.4.6.1 The full flow test of the backflow prevention valve can be performed with a test header or other connection downstream of the valve. A bypass around the check valve in the fire department connector line with a control valve in the normally closed position can be an acceptable arrangement. When flow to a visible drain cannot be accomplished, closed loop flow can be acceptable if a flow meter or site glass is incorporated into the system to ensure flow. When a backflow prevention device is retroactively installed on a pipe schedule system, the revised hydraulic calculation still follows the pipe schedule method of 11.2.2 with the inclusion of friction loss for the device.

8.16.4.6.2 Retroactive Installation. When backflow prevention devices are to be retroactively installed on existing systems, a thorough hydraulic analysis, including revised hydraulic calculations, new fire flow data, and all necessary system modifications to accommodate the additional friction loss, shall be completed as a part of the installation.

A hydraulic analysis is required by 8.16.4.6.2 to determine and properly account for the impact of a retroactively installed backflow prevention device on the performance of an existing sprinkler system. Existing pipe schedule systems are not required to be recalculated in accordance with the hydraulic calculation methods of Chapter 11 when a backflow prevention device is retroactively installed. However, pipe schedule systems are required to meet certain pressure and flow requirements in accordance with Chapter 11. As with a hydraulically calculated sprinkler system, the water supply must be verified to still meet the demand of the pipe schedule system after the installation of a backflow prevention device. A backflow prevention device is shown in Exhibit 8.45.

8.16.5 Hose Connections.

8.16.5.1 Small (1½-in.) Hose Connections. See Section C.5.

8.16.5.1.1* Where required by Chapter 12, small (1½ in.) hose lines shall be available to reach all portions of the storage area.

EXHIBIT 8.45 Backflow
Prevention Device.

 Storage fires normally require the use of small hose lines, which are discussed in 8.16.5.1.1, for complete extinguishment of fires within boxes or other areas that can be shielded from the sprinklers at the ceiling. These hose connections can be supplied from separate or adjacent systems or outside hydrants so that the ceiling sprinklers can be shut off during the clean-up operation. These hose connections are not intended to serve as standpipes in accordance with NFPA 14, *Standard for the Installation of Standpipe, Private Hydrant, and Hose Systems.* Exhibit 8.46 shows a hose connection equipped with a hose line in a storage facility.

A.8.16.5.1.1 In areas used to store baled cotton, due consideration to access aisle configuration should be given with maximum hose lengths not exceeding 100 ft (30.1 m). Additionally, in these areas, where a separate piping system is used to supply hose lines it should be in accordance with NFPA 14, *Standard for the Installation of Standpipe, Private Hydrant, and Hose Systems.*

EXHIBIT 8.46 Sprinkler
System Equipped with a
Hose Connection.

Hose connections of 1½ in. (38 mm) are restricted to wet pipe systems (see A.8.16.5.1.1). The maintenance problems due to loss of air pressure through the hose valves in other types of systems would outweigh their value. These types of connections are convenience connections for first-aid fire-fighting conditions. These connections are not standpipe connections. Thus, the flows noted in Chapter 11 and Chapter 12 are all that need to be accounted for in this type of connection.

Hose connections of 1½ in. (38 mm) supplied from sprinkler systems have been successful in fire extinguishment and fire control for many years. The requirements for Class II standpipe systems in NFPA 14 do not apply to hose connections attached to sprinkler systems.

The pressure at the outlet is restricted to 100 psi (6.9 bar) due to the danger to the operator in using a hose subject to high pressure in either static or underflow conditions. Therefore, the maximum allowable pressure at the hose outlet under both conditions is 100 psi (6.9 bar).

8.16.5.1.2 The hose connections shall not be required to meet the requirements of Class II hose systems defined by NFPA 14, *Standard for the Installation of Standpipe, Private Hydrant, and Hose Systems.*

8.16.5.1.3 Hose connections shall be supplied from one of the following:

(1) Outside hydrants
(2) A separate piping system for small hose stations
(3) Valved hose connections on sprinkler risers where such connections are made upstream of all sprinkler control valves
(4) Adjacent sprinkler systems
(5) In rack storage areas, the ceiling sprinkler system in the same area (as long as in-rack sprinklers are provided in the same area and are separately controlled)

8.16.5.1.4* Hose used for fire purposes only shall be permitted to be connected to wet sprinkler systems only, subject to the following restrictions:

(1) Hose station's supply pipes connected to shall not be connected to any pipe smaller than 2½ in. (64 mm).
(2) The requirements of 8.16.5.1.4 shall not apply to hydraulically designed loops and grids, where the minimum size pipe between the hose station's supply pipe and the source shall be permitted to be 2 in. (51 mm).
(3) For piping serving a single hose station, pipe shall be a minimum of 1 in. (25.4 mm) for horizontal runs up to 20 ft (6.1 m), a minimum of 1¼ in. (33 mm) for the entire run for runs between 20 ft and 80 ft (6.1 m and 24.4 m), and a minimum of 1½ in. (38 mm) for the entire run for runs greater than 80 ft (24.4 m). For piping serving multiple hose stations, runs shall be a minimum of 1½ in. (38 mm) throughout.
(4) Piping shall be at least 1 in. (25 mm) for vertical runs.
(5) When the pressure at any hose station outlet exceeds 100 psi (6.9 bar), an approved device shall be installed at the outlet to reduce the pressure at the outlet to 100 psi (6.9 bar).

A.8.16.5.1.4 This standard covers 1½-in. (38-mm) hose connections for use in storage occupancies and other locations where standpipe systems are not required. Where Class II standpipe systems are required, see the appropriate provisions of NFPA 14, *Standard for the Installation of Standpipe, Private Hydrant, and Hose Systems,* with respect to hose stations and water supply for hose connections from sprinkler systems.

8.16.5.2* Hose Connections for Fire Department Use.

A.8.16.5.2 Combined automatic sprinkler and standpipe risers should not be interconnected by sprinkler system piping.

8.16.5.2.1 In buildings of light or ordinary hazard occupancy, 2½-in. (64-mm) hose valves for fire department use shall be permitted to be attached to wet pipe sprinkler system risers.

8.16.5.2.2 The following restrictions shall apply:

(1) Sprinklers shall be under separate floor control valves.
(2) The minimum size of the riser shall be 4 in. (102 mm) unless hydraulic calculations indicate that a smaller size riser will satisfy sprinkler and hose stream demands.
(3) Each combined sprinkler and standpipe riser shall be equipped with a riser control valve to permit isolating a riser without interrupting the supply to other risers from the same source of supply.

Hose connections for fire department use are covered in 8.16.5.2.1 and 8.16.5.2.2. Hose connections of 2½ in. (64 mm) are allowed to be attached to wet pipe sprinkler systems only. These connections can be used for final extinguishment of the fire or to cool residual heat. Requirements for calculating the water supply under these circumstances are provided in 11.2.3.1.8(8). These connections are also not to be treated as standpipe hose connections. If standpipes are installed and the standpipe system risers also supply the sprinklers, then all provisions of NFPA 14, including the water supply and pressure provisions, need to be followed. When either one of the hose connections described in 8.16.5 is provided, the flow rates need only be added to the sprinkler system at the design pressure available at the point of connection to the sprinkler system pipe.

When risers are used to supply combination sprinkler and standpipe systems, guidance is needed to avoid confusion where systems in remotely located areas are controlled by more than one valve. No appreciable improvement in reliability is realized by interconnection. In addition, if the risers are cross connected and the hydraulic calculations account for this feature, the sprinkler system might not perform as intended if one of the risers is removed from service.

SUMMARY

Chapter 8 covers the installation details, such as positioning, and location of system components, such as sprinklers and valves. The requirements in this chapter identify the location and positioning rules for system components and consider the impact of building construction and equipment on satisfactory sprinkler system performance.

REFERENCES CITED IN COMMENTARY

National Fire Protection Association, 1 Batterymarch Park, P.O. Box 9101, Quincy, MA 02269-9101

NFPA 13D, *Standard for the Installation of Sprinkler Systems in One- and Two-Family Dwellings and Manufactured Homes,* 2002 edition

NFPA 13E, *Recommended Practice for Fire Department Operations in Properties Protected by Sprinkler and Standpipe Systems,* 2000 edition

NFPA 13R, *Standard for the Installation of Sprinkler Systems in Residential Occupancies up to and Including Four Stories in Height,* 2002 edition

NFPA 14, *Standard for the Installation of Standpipe, Private Hydrant, and Hose Systems,* 2000 edition

NFPA 25, *Standard for the Inspection, Testing, and Maintenance of Water-Based Fire Protection Systems,* 2002 edition

NFPA 72®, *National Fire Alarm Code®,* 2002 edition

NFPA 101®, *Life Safety Code®,* 2000 edition

NFPA 409, *Standard on Aircraft Hangars,* 2001 edition

Rohr, K. D. "U.S. Experience with Sprinklers: Who Has Them? How Well Do They Work?," Quincy, MA: National Fire Protection Association Fire Analysis and Research Division, 1998

American Society of Mechanical Engineers, Three Park Avenue, New York, NY 10016-5990

ASME A17.1, *Safety Code for Elevators and Escalators,* 2000 edition

Proceedings of the Symposium on Elevators and Fire, American Society of Mechanical Engineers, Three Park Avenue, New York, NY 10016-5990, February 1991

American Fire Sprinkler Association, 9696 Sillman Street, Suite 300, Dallas, TX 75243

"Evaluating the Impact of Ceiling Pockets in Sprinkler Activation" (available at *www.sprinklernet.org*)

National Institute of Standards and Technology, Gaithersburg, MD 20899

NBSIR 80–2097, *Full-Scale Fire Tests with Automatic Sprinklers in a Patient Room,* 1980

Underwriters Laboratories Inc., 333 Pfingsten Road, Northbrook, IL 60062

UL 1626, *Residential Sprinklers for Fire Protection Service,* 2nd edition, 1994 "Fact Finding Report on Automatic Sprinkler Protection for Fire Storage Vaults," November 25, 1947

CHAPTER 9

Hanging, Bracing, and Restraint of System Piping

Chapter 9 addresses the structural issues related to installation of fire protection piping systems. Section 9.1 contains regulations for acceptable types of hangers, Section 9.2 covers hanger installation, and Section 9.3 addresses protection of piping where subject to earthquakes. The Technical Committee on Hanging and Bracing has attempted to make this chapter suitable for reference by other fire protection system documents. For example, NFPA 13 earthquake protection criteria have been referenced by other water-based fire protection system standards that use similar piping materials and configurations, such as NFPA 14, *Standard for the Installation of Standpipe, Private Hydrant, and Hose Systems,* and NFPA 15, *Standard for Water Spray Fixed Systems for Fire Protection.*

The hanger requirements in this standard generally contemplate support from overhead structural members. In some cases, however, floor support of piping is appropriate. NFPA 15 contains rules governing sizing of pipe stands used to support fire protection piping in the absence of a building structure or where floor support is required.

9.1 Hangers

9.1.1* General.

A.9.1.1 See Figure A.9.1.1.

Hangers, which are discussed in 9.1.1, can consist of one individual component such as a U-hook or up to three separate components as indicated in Exhibit 9.1. The first component is a building-attached component that attaches to the building structure. In Exhibit 9.1, the building-attached component includes a C-clamp attached to an I-beam. Fasteners used to attach the building-attached component to the building structure are considered part of the hanger and must meet the applicable requirements of NFPA 13.

The second possible component includes the pipe attachment component and consists of the portion of the hanger assembly that is attached to the sprinkler piping. Exhibit 9.1 shows the use of an adjustable swivel ring as the pipe attachment component.

The third possible component includes the connecting piece that joins the building attachment component with the pipe attachment component. An all-thread rod is used for this purpose in Exhibit 9.1.

9.1.1.1 Unless the requirements of 9.1.1.2 are met, types of hangers shall be in accordance with the requirements of Section 9.1.

9.1.1.2 Hangers certified by a registered professional engineer to include all of the following shall be an acceptable alternative to the requirements of Section 9.1:

(1) Hangers shall be designed to support five times the weight of the water-filled pipe plus 250 lb (114 kg) at each point of piping support.

FIGURE A.9.1.1 Common Types of Acceptable Hangers.

EXHIBIT 9.1 Hanger Assembly Consisting of a C-Clamp, an All-Thread Rod, and an Adjustable Swivel Ring.

(2) These points of support shall be adequate to support the system.
(3) The spacing between hangers shall not exceed the value given for the type of pipe as indicated in Table 9.2.2.1.
(4) Hanger components shall be ferrous.
(5) Detailed calculations shall be submitted, when required by the reviewing authority, showing stresses developed in hangers, piping, and fittings and safety factors allowed.

Paragraph 9.1.1.2 permits a performance-based approach in place of the normal rules of 9.1.1 to accommodate unusual applications or situations. The performance-based approach requires the services of a professional engineer to certify that the five conditions specified in 9.1.1.2(1) through 9.1.1.2(5) are satisfied. The safety factor of five times the weight of the water-filled pipe plus 250 lb (114 kg) is traditional for fire protection piping and includes the assumed weight of a sprinkler fitter with associated work equipment who could grasp the pipe to prevent falling from a ladder or platform. This performance-based alternative is not intended to substitute for using listed hangers but rather to allow for the use of other methods where listed hangers cannot be used for a particular building arrangement. See also commentary to 9.2.1.3.1.

The 250-lb (114-kg) load is specified to be applied at the point of piping support in recognition of the fact that some types of piping will not support the additional load at a point mid-span between hangers.

9.1.1.3 Where water-based fire protection systems are required to be protected against damage from earthquakes, hangers shall also meet the requirements of 9.3.7.

Hangers can experience forces other than those resulting from gravity in areas subject to earthquakes. As discussed in 9.1.1.3, additional measures as required in 9.3.7 are needed for certain hanger arrangements to guard against the effect of these forces.

9.1.1.4 Listing.

9.1.1.4.1 Unless permitted by 9.1.1.4.2 or 9.1.1.4.3, the components of hanger assemblies that directly attach to the pipe or to the building structure shall be listed.

9.1.1.4.2 Mild steel hangers formed from rods shall be permitted to be not listed.

9.1.1.4.3 Fasteners as specifically identified in 9.1.5 shall be permitted to be not listed.

9.1.1.4.4 Other fasteners shall be permitted as part of the hanger assembly that has been tested, listed, and installed in accordance with the listing requirements.

Listing requirements are covered in 9.1.1.4.1 through 9.1.1.4.4. Hanger assembly components that attach to the pipe or to the building structure must be listed.

FAQ ▶
Are the mild steel rods utilized in hangers required to be listed?

Mild steel rod hangers are not required to be listed according to 9.1.1.4.2 since it has been demonstrated through standard practice that rods in the sizes required in Table 9.1.2.1 can support, at maximum permitted spacing, five times the weight of water-filled Schedule 40 pipe plus 250 lb (114 kg) applied as a temporary point load. U-bolts and eye rods are also considered types of mild steel hangers formed from rods and meet the conditions of 9.1.1.4.4.

The requirements of 9.1.1.4.3 specifically allow for screws and bolts identified in NFPA 13 to not be considered to be part of the hanger assembly requiring listing. Other fastener assemblies not specifically identified in 9.1.5 must be listed.

9.1.1.5 Component Material.

9.1.1.5.1 Unless permitted by 9.1.1.5.2 or 9.1.1.5.3, hangers and their components shall be ferrous.

9.1.1.5.2 Nonferrous components that have been proven by fire tests to be adequate for the hazard application, that are listed for this purpose, and that are in compliance with the other requirements of this section shall be acceptable.

9.1.1.5.3 Holes through solid structural members shall be permitted to serve as hangers for the support of system piping provided such holes are permitted by applicable building codes and the spacing and support provisions for hangers of this standard are satisfied.

FAQ ▶
Do the requirements of 9.1.1.5.3 allow for the use of holes in structural members to be utilized for the support of sprinkler piping?

Paragraph 9.1.1.5.3 recognizes that holes through structural members are occasionally used for piping support but requires that structural strength considerations be given priority. To avoid weakening a beam or joist, most codes prohibit the cutting of a hole in the top or bottom third of the depth and anywhere within twice the depth from either end support.

9.1.1.6* Trapeze Hangers.

Trapeze hangers are discussed in 9.1.1.6. A trapeze hanger generally consists of a length of steel pipe or an angle iron that serves as a trapeze bar between the building structural members, along with other conventional hanger components. Conventional hangers are used to support the sprinkler system piping from the trapeze and can also be used to support the trapeze from the adjacent structural members. In any event, the hanger requirements of NFPA 13 apply to the hangers used to support the sprinkler pipe from the trapeze and any hangers used to support the trapeze from the building structure.

The selection of the minimum size of pipe or angle that can serve as the bar of the trapeze is made on the basis of required section modulus. The section modulus relates to the ability of a structural member, including a length of pipe or angle used as a trapeze, to withstand flexure. The top numbers in Table 9.1.1.6.1(b) provide the required section modulus for support of Schedule 10 steel pipe, and the lower numbers show the required section modulus for support of the heavier Schedule 40 steel pipe. Table 9.1.1.6.1(a) provides the available section moduli for various diameters of Schedule 10 pipe, Schedule 40 pipe, and shapes of angles commonly used as trapeze bars. The section modulus for each member is denoted as Z in the following example.

The following example illustrates the intended use of Tables 9.1.1.6.1(a) and 9.1.1.6.1(b).

EXAMPLE 9.1

An installation involves the support of 4-in. (102-mm) Schedule 10 pipe. The span, generally the horizontal distance between the building structural members that support the trapeze bar, is 6 ft (1.8 m). (See Exhibit 9.2.) The trapeze consists of an angle iron.

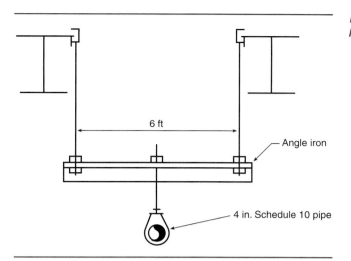

EXHIBIT 9.2 Trapeze
Installation.

6 ft

Angle iron

4 in. Schedule 10 pipe

EXAMPLE 9.1

Trapeze Installation

Determine acceptable size of trapeze.

Solution: From Table 9.1.1.6.1(b), the required section modulus is 0.51 in.³. From Table 9.1.1.6.1(a), an angle iron with dimensions of 3 in. × 2 in. × ¼ in. (Z = 0.54 in.³) provides a section modulus of 0.54 in.³ Any other angle (or pipe) with a section modulus higher than 0.51 in.³ would also be acceptable. In accordance with 9.1.1.6.3, the longer leg of the angle would be installed in the vertical position. If Schedule 10 pipe were used as the trapeze, it would require a nominal diameter of 2 1/2 in. (Z = 0.69 in.³). If Schedule 40 pipe were used, it would require a nominal diameter of 2 in. (Z = 0.56 in.³). Other steel shapes that meet or exceed the predetermined Z of 0.51 in.³ are also acceptable in accordance with 9.1.1.6.2.

A.9.1.1.6 Table 9.1.1.6.1(b) assumes that the load from 15 ft (5 m) of water-filled pipe, plus 250 lb (114 kg), is located at the midpoint of the span of the trapeze member, with a maximum allowable bending stress of 15 ksi (111 kg). If the load is applied at other than the midpoint, for the purpose of sizing the trapeze member, an equivalent length of trapeze can be used, derived from the following formula:

$$L = \frac{4ab}{a + B}$$

where:

L = equivalent length

a = distance from one support to the load

b = distance from the other support to the load

Where multiple mains are to be supported or multiple trapeze hangers are provided in parallel, the required or available section modulus can be added.

9.1.1.6.1 For trapeze hangers, the minimum size of steel angle or pipe span between purlins or joists shall be such that the available section modulus of the trapeze member from Table 9.1.1.6.1(a) equals or exceeds the section modulus required in Table 9.1.1.6.1(b).

TABLE 9.1.1.6.1(a) *Available Section Moduli of Common Trapeze Hangers (in.^{3})*

Pipe (in.)	Modulus	Angles	Modulus
Schedule 10			
1	0.12	1½ × 1½ × ³⁄₁₆	0.10
1¼	0.19	2 × 2 × ⅛	0.13
1½	0.26	2 × 1½ × ³⁄₁₆	0.18
2	0.42	2 × 2 × ³⁄₁₆	0.19
2½	0.69	2 × 2 × ¼	0.25
3	1.04	2½ × 1½ × ³⁄₁₆	0.28
3½	1.38	2½ × 2 × ³⁄₁₆	0.29
4	1.76	2 × 2 × ⁵⁄₁₆	0.30
5	3.03	2½ × 2½ × ³⁄₁₆	0.30
6	4.35	2 × 2 × ⅜	0.35
		2½ × 2½ × ¼	0.39
		3 × 2 × ³⁄₁₆	0.41
Schedule 40			
1	0.13	3 × 2½ × ³⁄₁₆	0.43
1¼	0.23	3 × 3 × ³⁄₁₆	0.44
1½	0.33	2½ × 2½ × ⁵⁄₁₆	0.48
2	0.56	3 × 2 × ¼	0.54
2½	1.06	2½ × 2 × ⅜	0.55
3	1.72	2½ × 2½ × ⅜	0.57
3½	2.39	3 × 3 × ¼	0.58
4	3.21	3 × 3 × ⁵⁄₁₆	0.71
5	5.45	2½ × 2½ × ½	0.72
6	8.50	3½ × 2½ × ¼	0.75
		3 × 2½ × ⅜	0.81
		3 × 3 × ⅜	0.83
		3½ × 2½ × ⁵⁄₁₆	0.93
		3 × 3 × ⁷⁄₁₆	0.95
		4 × 4 × ¼	1.05
		3 × 3 × ½	1.07
		4 × 3 × ⁵⁄₁₆	1.23
		4 × 4 × ⁵⁄₁₆	1.29
		4 × 3 × ⅜	1.46
		4 × 4 × ⅜	1.52
		5 × 3½ × ⁵⁄₁₆	1.94
		4 × 4 × ½	1.97
		4 × 4 × ⅝	2.40
		4 × 4 × ¾	2.81
		6 × 4 × ⅜	3.32
		6 × 4 × ½	4.33
		6 × 4 × ¾	6.25
		6 × 6 × 1	8.57

For SI units, 1 in. = 25.4 mm; 1 ft = 0.3048 m.

TABLE 9.1.1.6.1(b) *Section Modulus Required for Trapeze Members (in.^{3})*

Span of Trapeze	**Nominal Diameter of Pipe Being Supported**											
	1 in.	*1¼ in.*	*1½ in.*	*2 in.*	*2½ in.*	*3 in.*	*3½ in.*	*4 in.*	*5 in.*	*6 in.*	*8 in.*	*10 in.*
1 ft 6 in.	0.08	0.09	0.09	0.09	0.10	0.11	0.12	0.13	0.15	0.18	0.24	0.32
	0.08	0.09	0.09	0.10	0.11	0.12	0.13	0.15	0.18	0.22	0.30	0.41
2 ft 0 in.	0.11	0.12	0.12	0.13	0.13	0.15	0.16	0.17	0.20	0.24	0.32	0.43
	0.11	0.12	0.12	0.13	0.15	0.16	0.18	0.20	0.24	0.29	0.40	0.55
2 ft 6 in.	0.14	0.14	0.15	0.16	0.17	0.18	0.20	0.21	0.25	0.30	0.40	0.54
	0.14	0.15	0.15	0.16	0.18	0.21	0.22	0.25	0.30	0.36	0.50	0.68
3 ft 0 in.	0.17	0.17	0.18	0.19	0.20	0.22	0.24	0.26	0.31	0.36	0.48	0.65
	0.17	0.18	0.18	0.20	0.22	0.25	0.27	0.30	0.36	0.43	0.60	0.82
4 ft 0 in.	0.22	0.23	0.24	0.25	0.27	0.29	0.32	0.34	0.41	0.48	0.64	0.87
	0.22	0.24	0.24	0.26	0.29	0.33	0.36	0.40	0.48	0.58	0.80	1.09
5 ft 0 in.	0.28	0.29	0.30	0.31	0.34	0.37	0.40	0.43	0.51	0.59	0.80	1.08
	0.28	0.29	0.30	0.33	0.37	0.41	0.45	0.49	0.60	0.72	1.00	1.37
6 ft 0 in.	0.33	0.35	0.36	0.38	0.41	0.44	0.48	0.51	0.61	0.71	0.97	1.30
	0.34	0.35	0.36	0.39	0.44	0.49	0.54	0.59	0.72	0.87	1.20	1.64
7 ft 0 in.	0.39	0.40	0.41	0.44	0.47	0.52	0.55	0.60	0.71	0.83	1.13	1.52
	0.39	0.41	0.43	0.46	0.51	0.58	0.63	0.69	0.84	1.01	1.41	1.92
8 ft 0 in.	0.44	0.46	0.47	0.50	0.54	0.59	0.63	0.68	0.81	0.95	1.29	1.73
	0.45	0.47	0.49	0.52	0.59	0.66	0.72	0.79	0.96	1.16	1.61	2.19
9 ft 0 in.	0.50	0.52	0.53	0.56	0.61	0.66	0.71	0.77	0.92	1.07	1.45	1.95
	0.50	0.53	0.55	0.59	0.66	0.74	0.81	0.89	1.08	1.30	1.81	2.46
10 ft 0 in.	0.56	0.58	0.59	0.63	0.68	0.74	0.79	0.85	1.02	1.19	1.61	2.17
	0.56	0.59	0.61	0.65	0.74	0.82	0.90	0.99	1.20	1.44	2.01	2.74

For SI units, 1 in. = 25.4 mm; 1 ft = 0.3048 m.

Notes:

1. Top values are for Schedule 10 pipe; bottom values are for Schedule 40 pipe.

2. The table is based on a maximum allowable bending stress of 15 ksi and a midspan concentrated load from 15 ft (4.6 m) of water-filled pipe, plus 250 lb (114 kg).

A trapeze hanger, as indicated in 9.1.1.6.1, must be capable of supporting the weight of the water-filled piping plus 250 lb (114 kg). Other types of hangers are generally required to be able to support five times the weight of the water-filled piping plus 250 lb (114 kg). The safety factor of five is used in the traditional listing requirements for hangers and is also found in the performance-based criteria of 9.1.1.2(1). The requirement for trapeze hangers matches the requirement for the building structure found in 9.2.1.3.1 since the trapeze hanger can be considered an extension of the building structure needed to provide points of hanging for system piping.

The following formula merits some explanation:

$$L = \frac{4ab}{a + B}$$

The section moduli given in Table 9.1.1.6.1(b) are based on the assumption that the pipe to be supported will be located in the exact center of the span and, thus, will put maximum stress on the trapeze bar. The nearer the load is to one side of the span, the less stress it exerts. If the load is sufficiently off center, a trapeze bar of smaller size may possibly be used to support it.

In Example 9.1, to determine acceptable trapeze members, assume that the 4-in. (102-mm) Schedule 10 pipe is to be located 1 ft (0.3 m) from one end of the span. Using the following formula, the equivalent span was determined to be 3.33 ft (10.2 m). Because Table

9.1.1.6.1(b) provides the required section modulus for 1-ft (0.3-m) increments of trapeze length, the equivalent span was rounded up to 4 ft (1.2 m).

$$L = \frac{(4)(1\,\text{ft})(5\,\text{ft})}{1\,\text{ft} + 5\,\text{ft}} = \frac{20\,\text{ft}^2}{6\,\text{ft}} = 3.33\,\text{ft}$$

Referring to Table 9.1.1.6.1(b), the section modulus needed for 4-in. (102-mm) Schedule 10 pipe with a 4-ft (1.22-m) span is 0.34. As Table 9.1.1.6.1(a) indicates, the trapeze bar could be either 2-in. (50-mm) Schedule 10 or Schedule 40 pipe or a 2-in. × 2-in. × ⅜-in. angle iron.

9.1.1.6.2 Any other sizes or shapes giving equal or greater section modulus shall be acceptable.

Where materials other than steel are proposed for use as trapeze members, an engineering analysis must be completed to determine the material's capability (see 9.1.1.6.2). Comparable beam strength and appropriate fire endurance characteristics are required.

NFPA 13 does not specifically allow the use of wood trapeze members, and 9.1.5.5 prohibits the use of nails as fasteners. However, it should be recognized that the building designer always has the option of allowing a modification of the building structure to provide a built-in trapeze. The manner in which extensions are made to the building structure must be acceptable to the responsible design professional.

9.1.1.6.3 All angles shall be used with the longer leg vertical.

9.1.1.6.4 The trapeze member shall be secured to prevent slippage.

FAQ ▶
Is it acceptable to allow trapeze members to be placed with the structural members as a means of securement?

Securing of the trapeze member is covered in 9.1.1.6.4. It is not acceptable to simply place a trapeze member between bar joists or other successive structural members and hang from it. The trapeze must be secured to the structure using bolts or other fasteners that meet the requirements of this chapter.

9.1.1.6.5 Where a pipe is suspended from a pipe trapeze of a diameter less than the diameter of the pipe being supported, ring, strap, or clevis hangers of the size corresponding to the suspended pipe shall be used on both ends.

The phrase "on both ends" in the last sentence of 9.1.1.6.5 refers to the top and bottom ends of the rod supporting the main. The phrase does not mean both ends of the trapeze. The top hanger ring, strap, or clevis is being used in a position that is opposite its normal use, and it must have strength appropriate to the larger pipe size. Ideally, the ring or strap can be shaped to accommodate the smaller pipe size. Otherwise the potential exists for the ring or strap to elongate over time with the load, which could result in a change of pitch of the piping.

9.1.1.6.6 The size of hanger rods and fasteners required to support the steel angle iron or pipe indicated in Table 9.1.1.6.1(a) shall comply with 9.1.4.

Paragraph 9.1.1.6.6 refers to the size of hanger rods and fasteners. Each of the rods used to support the trapeze needs to be sized according to the size of the trapeze pipe in accordance with Table 9.1.2.1. Although these rods are not sized for the larger pipe being supported, the lower safety factors relating to trapeze hangers and the shared load between two points of support are generally adequate. In the case of a very large pipe supported by a small diameter trapeze, or where the supported pipe is located such that the load will be predominately carried by one side of the trapeze member, additional analysis is warranted. Where sizing of the rods is of concern, the rod size can be selected based upon the large supported pipe size.

9.1.1.6.7 Holes for bolts shall not exceed ¹⁄₁₆ in. greater than the diameter of the bolt.

9.1.1.6.8 Bolts shall be provided with a flat washer and nut.

9.1.1.7* **Support of Non-System Components.** Sprinkler piping or hangers shall not be used to support non-system components.

EXHIBIT 9.3 *Sprinkler Pipe Inappropriately Used to Support Electrical Conduit.*

A.9.1.1.7 The rules covering the hanging of sprinkler piping take into consideration the weight of water-filled pipe plus a safety factor. No allowance has been made for the hanging of nonsystem components from sprinkler piping. NFPA 13 provides the option to support sprinkler piping from other sprinkler piping where the requirements of 9.1.1.2 are met.

In many cases, sprinkler pipe and even the sprinklers become convenient, accessible, and tempting hangers for signs and decorations. Such use of sprinkler system components is strictly prohibited by 9.1.1.7.

The detectors and wiring associated with a preaction or deluge systems are permitted to be supported by the pipe and hangers because they are system components. However, detection systems not associated with the sprinkler system cannot be attached to the pipe.

The arrangement shown in Exhibit 9.3, in which the electrical conduit is draped over and supported by the sprinkler piping, violates the requirement in 9.1.1.7.

 A

◄ **FAQ**
Do the requirements of 9.1.1.7 prohibit the hanging of detection wiring associated with preaction or deluge systems on sprinkler pipe and hangers?

9.1.2 Hanger Rods.

9.1.2.1 Unless the requirements of 9.1.2.2 are met, hanger rod size shall be the same as that approved for use with the hanger assembly, and the size of rods shall not be less than that given in Table 9.1.2.1.

TABLE 9.1.2.1 *Hanger Rod Sizes*

	Diameter of Rod	
Pipe Size	*in.*	*mm*
Up to and including 4 in.	⅜	9.5
5 in., 6 in., and 8 in.	½	12.7
10 in. and 12 in.	⅝	15.9

Table 9.1.2.1 indicates the smallest rod sizes that can be used as part of a hanger assembly. Paragraph 9.1.2.2 allows for smaller diameters if proven satisfactory through testing and listing.

9.1.2.2 Rods of smaller diameters than indicated in Table 9.1.2.1 shall be permitted where the hanger assembly has been tested and listed by a testing laboratory and installed within the limits of pipe sizes expressed in individual listings.

9.1.2.3 U-Hooks. The size of the rod material of U-hooks shall not be less than that given in Table 9.1.2.3.

TABLE 9.1.2.3 *U-Hook Rod Sizes*

	Hook Material Diameter	
Pipe Size	in.	mm
Up to 2 in.	⁵⁄₁₆	7.9
2½ in. to 6 in.	⅜	9.5
8 in.	½	12.7

9.1.2.4 Eye Rods.

9.1.2.4.1 The size of the rod material for eye rods shall not be less than specified in Table 9.1.2.4.1.

TABLE 9.1.2.4.1 *Eye Rod Sizes*

	Diameter of Rod			
	With Bent Eye		With Welded Eye	
Pipe Size	in.	mm	in.	mm
Up to 4 in.	⅜	9.5	⅜	9.5
5 in. to 6 in.	½	12.7	½	12.7
8 in.	¾	19.1	½	12.7

9.1.2.4.2 Eye rods shall be secured with lock washers to prevent lateral motion.

9.1.2.4.3 Where eye rods are fastened to wood structural members, the eye rod shall be backed with a large flat washer bearing directly against the structural member, in addition to the lock washer.

9.1.2.5 Threaded Sections of Rods. Threaded sections of rods shall not be formed or bent.

FAQ ▶
Why do the requirements of 9.1.2.5 prohibit the bending of threaded sections of rods?

Bending the threaded section of hanger rods, which is prohibited in 9.1.2.5, could result in cracks at the thread root. Such cracks affect the structural ability of the member and can lead to failure of the rod. This requirement also applies to the rod once it is installed. Cracks can also result if the rod is arranged in such a manner that it has a lateral load applied to it. In other words, the rod must be in a true vertical position once it is connected between the building structure and the pipe. Exhibit 9.4 illustrates an unacceptable condition, because the threaded portion of the hanger rod is bent.

Also note that the bag placed over the sprinkler to protect the sprinkler from paint overspray has not been removed.

Some hangers listed for attachment to the building structure are available that can accommodate angles from vertical, allowing the rod to remain unbent.

9.1.3 Fasteners in Concrete.

9.1.3.1 Unless prohibited by 9.1.3.2 or 9.1.3.3, the use of listed inserts set in concrete and listed expansion shields to support hangers shall be permitted for mains and branch lines.

9.1.3.2 Expansion shields shall not be used in cinder concrete, except for branch lines where the expansion shields are alternated with through-bolts or hangers attached to beams.

9.1.3.3 Expansion shields shall not be used in ceilings of gypsum or other similar soft material.

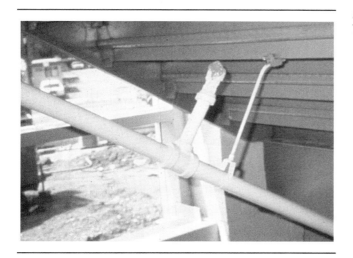

EXHIBIT 9.4 Bent Section of Threaded Hanger Rod.

Expansion shields are discussed in 9.1.3.3. The effectiveness of expansion shields depends on the gripping power of the material with which they are used. Expansion shields pull out of soft materials such as gypsum.

9.1.3.4 Unless the requirements of 9.1.3.5 are met, expansion shields shall be installed in a horizontal position in the sides of concrete beams.

Expansion shields installed in a horizontal position, which is required by 9.1.3.4, are more secure because the associated hanger assembly is not subject to a direct downward pulling force as indicated in Exhibit 9.5. However, under the conditions specified in 9.1.3.5, expansion shields can be installed in a vertical position for certain sizes of pipe (see Exhibit 9.6).

9.1.3.5 Expansion shields shall be permitted to be installed in the vertical position under the following conditions:

(1) When used in concrete having gravel or crushed stone aggregate to support pipes 4 in. (102 mm) or less in diameter
(2) When expansion shields are alternated with hangers connected directly to the structural members, such as trusses and girders, or to the sides of concrete beams [to support pipe 5 in. (127 mm) or larger]
(3) When expansion shields are spaced not over 10 ft (3 m) apart [to support pipe 4 in. (102 m) or larger]

9.1.3.6 Holes for expansion shields in the side of beams shall be above the centerline of the beam or above the bottom reinforcement steel rods.

Shields must be located where they provide maximum strength. If a reinforcing rod is contacted when drilling for a shield, a new hole above the bottom reinforcing rod must be made to the required depth (see 9.1.3.6).

9.1.3.7 Holes for expansion shields used in the vertical position shall be drilled to provide uniform contact with the shield over its entire circumference.

9.1.3.8 The depth of the expansion shield hole shall not be less than specified for the type of shield used.

9.1.3.9 Powder-Driven Studs.

9.1.3.9.1 Powder-driven studs, welding studs, and the tools used for installing these devices shall be listed.

EXHIBIT 9.5 Hanger Assembly Attached to Concrete That Uses an Expansion Shield in the Horizontal Position.

EXHIBIT 9.6 Hanger Assembly Attached to Concrete Decking That Uses Expansion Shields in the Vertical Position.

TABLE 9.1.3.10.1 *Minimum Bolt Size for Concrete*

	Size of Bolt	
Pipe Size	*in.*	*mm*
Up to and including 4 in.	⅜	9.5
5 in. to 8 in.	½	12.7
10 in.	⅝	15.9
12 in.	¾	19.1

Powder-driven studs are discussed in 9.1.3.9.1. The limitations placed on powder-actuated tools and stud welders vary depending on the individual tool. Limitations of each device and the components of its installation unit are specified in its individual listing.

9.1.3.9.2 Pipe size, installation position, and construction material into which they are installed shall be in accordance with individual listings.

9.1.3.9.3* Representative samples of concrete into which studs are to be driven shall be tested to determine that the studs will hold a minimum load of 750 lb (341 kg) for 2-in. (51 mm) or smaller pipe, 1000 lb (454 kg) for 2 ½-in., 3-in., or 3 ½-in. (64-mm, 76-mm, or 89-mm) pipe, and 1200 lb (545 kg) for 4-in. or 5-in. (102-mm or 127-mm) pipe.

A.9.1.3.9.3 The ability of concrete to hold the studs varies widely according to type of aggregate, quality of concrete, and proper installation.

The concrete in the facility where the system is being installed must be tested to ascertain that powder-driven studs do not have less than the indicated holding power (see 9.1.3.9.3). The strength of the concrete varies depending on the type of cement and aggregate used and the needed cure time for the concrete. The safety factor imposed in 9.2.1.3.1 must be increased as specified in 9.1.3.9.3 when powder-driven studs are installed in concrete, but no additional safety factors need to be prescribed. The loads required in 9.1.3.9.3 are test loads, not working loads. Working loads are those recognized in the listing of the studs and the NFPA 13 requirements.

9.1.3.9.4 Increaser couplings shall be attached directly to the powder-driven studs.

Listings commonly permit studs with a smaller diameter than that required by Table 9.1.2.1 for rods. Hanger rods that comply with the dimensions given in the table must be connected directly to the studs with increaser couplings, which are discussed in 9.1.3.9.4.

9.1.3.10 Minimum Bolt Size for Concrete.

9.1.3.10.1 The size of a bolt used with a hanger and installed through concrete shall not be less than specified in Table 9.1.3.10.1.

9.1.3.10.2 Holes for bolts shall not exceed ⅟₁₆ in. (1.6 mm) greater than the diameter of the bolt.

9.1.3.10.3 Bolts shall be provided with a flat washer and nut.

9.1.4 Fasteners in Steel.

9.1.4.1* Powder-driven studs, welding studs, and the tools used for installing these devices shall be listed.

A.9.1.4.1 Powder-driven studs should not be used in steel of less than ³⁄₁₆ in. (4.8 mm) total thickness.

The limitations placed on powder-actuated tools and stud welders vary depending on the individual tool. Limitations of each device and the components of its installation unit are specified in its individual listing, which is required by 9.1.4.1.

9.1.4.2 Pipe size, installation position, and construction material into which they are installed shall be in accordance with individual listings.

9.1.4.3 Increaser couplings shall be attached directly to the powder-driven studs or welding studs.

Listings commonly permit studs with a smaller diameter than that required by Table 9.1.2.1 for rods. Hanger rods that comply with the dimensions given in the table must be connected directly to the studs with increaser couplings, as stated in 9.1.4.3.

9.1.4.4 Welding studs or other hanger parts shall not be attached by welding to steel less than U.S. Standard, 12 gauge.

U.S. Standard, 12 gauge, which is required by 9.1.4.4, is 0.081 in. (2.06 mm) thick. Steel thinner than this lacks the necessary strength for welding.

9.1.4.5 Minimum Bolt Size for Steel.

9.1.4.5.1 The size of a bolt used with a hanger and installed through steel shall not be less than specified in Table 9.1.4.5.1.

TABLE 9.1.4.5.1 *Minimum Bolt Size for Steel*

	Size of Bolt	
Pipe Size	*in.*	*mm*
Up to and including 4 in.	⅜	9.5
5 in. to 8 in.	½	12.7
10 in.	⅝	15.9
12 in.	¾	19.1

9.1.4.5.2 Holes for bolts shall not exceed ¹⁄₁₆ in. (1.6 mm) greater than the diameter of the bolt.

9.1.4.5.3 Bolts shall be provided with a flat washer and nut.

9.1.5 Fasteners in Wood.

9.1.5.1 Drive Screws.

9.1.5.1.1 Drive screws shall be used only in a horizontal position as in the side of a beam and only for 2-in. pipe or smaller.

9.1.5.1.2 Drive screws shall only be used in conjunction with hangers that require two points of attachments.

Hangers that require two points of attachments are the only ones under which drive screws can be used, as stated in 9.1.5.1.2. Table 9.1.5.2.1 limits the use of drive screws to U-hooks supporting pipe with diameters of 2 in. (50 mm) or less. The acceptable level of performance with drive screws is restricted to those cases where the weight requirements are relatively small and where two drive screws are installed horizontally. However, specially listed hanger assemblies with two points of attachment intended to be used with drive screws are available. See Figures A.9.1.1 and A.9.2.3.4.3(b) for illustrations of a drive screw and a U-hook.

9.1.5.2 Ceiling Flanges and U-hooks with Screws.

9.1.5.2.1 Unless the requirements of 9.1.5.2.2 or 9.1.5.2.3 are met, for ceiling flanges and U-hooks, screw dimensions shall not be less than those given in Table 9.1.5.2.1.

TABLE 9.1.5.2.1 *Screw Dimensions for Ceiling Flanges and U-Hooks*

Pipe Size	*Two Screw Ceiling Flanges*
Up to 2 in.	Wood screw No. 18 × 1½ in. or Lag screw ⁵⁄₁₆ in. × 1½ in.

Pipe Size	*Three Screw Ceiling Flanges*
Up to 2 in.	Wood screw No. 18 × 1½ in.
2½ in., 3 in., 3½ in.	Lag screw ⅜ in. × 2 in.
4 in., 5 in., 6 in.	Lag screw ½ in. × 2 in.
8 in.	Lag screw ⅝ in. × 2 in.

Pipe Size	*Four Screw Ceiling Flanges*
Up to 2 in.	Wood screw No. 18 × 1½ in.
2½ in., 3 in., 3½ in.	Lag screw ⅜ in. × 1½ in.
4 in., 5 in., 6 in.	Lag screw ½ in. × 2 in.
8 in.	Lag screw ⅝ in. × 2 in.

Pipe Size	*U-Hooks*
Up to 2 in.	Drive screw No. 16 × 2 in.
2½ in., 3 in., 3½ in.	Lag screw ⅜ in. × 2½ in.
4 in., 5 in., 6 in.	Lag screw ½ in. × 3 in.
8 in.	Lag screw ⅝ in. × 3 in.

For SI units, 1 in. = 25.4 mm.

The types of screws that can be used to fasten ceiling flanges and U-hooks to the building structure are identified in 9.1.5.2.1. Where ceiling flanges are used, the screws are installed in a vertical position. For U-hook applications, the screws are installed in a horizontal position [see Figure A.9.2.3.4.3(b)]. As indicated in Table 9.1.5.2.1, only lag screws and wood screws are to be used to fasten ceiling flanges to the building structure. Other types of screws are not permitted. Drive screws, which are intended to be installed with a hammer, do not have the holding capacity of wood screws and lag screws. Drive screws can only be installed horizontally in conjunction with U-hooks to support 2-in. (50-mm) or smaller pipe.

The screw dimensions in Table 9.1.5.2.1 are intended for use with hangers spaced in accordance with Table 9.2.2.1 for steel pipe. Paragraph 9.1.5.2.3 recognizes that it is not always possible to use screws with the lengths specified in the table and allows for use of shorter screws with closer hanger spacing.

9.1.5.2.2 When the thickness of planking and thickness of flange do not permit the use of screws 2 in. (51 mm) long, screws 1¾ in. (44 mm) long shall be permitted with hangers spaced not over 10 ft (3 m) apart.

9.1.5.2.3 When the thickness of beams or joists does not permit the use of screws 2½ in. (64 mm) long, screws 2½ in. (51 mm) long shall be permitted with hangers spaced not over 10 ft (3 m) apart.

9.1.5.3 Bolt or Lag Screw.

9.1.5.3.1 Unless the requirements of 9.1.5.3.2 are met, the size of bolt or lag screw used with a hanger and installed on the side of the beam shall not be less than specified in Table 9.1.5.3.1.

TABLE 9.1.5.3.1 *Minimum Bolt or Lag Screw Sizes for Side of Beam Installation*

| | Size of Bolt or Lag Screw | | Length of Lag Screw Used with Wood Beams | |
Pipe Size	in.	mm	in.	mm
Up to and including 2 in.	3/8	9.5	2½	64
2½ in. to 6 in. (inclusive)	½	12.7	3	76
8 in.	5/8	15.9	3	76

The minimum sizes of lag screws and bolts that can be used to fasten hanger components other than U-hooks to the sides of beams are identified in 9.1.5.3.1.

9.1.5.3.2 Where the thickness of beams or joists does not permit the use of screws 2½ in. (64 mm) long, screws 2 in. (51 mm) long shall be permitted with hangers spaced not over 10 ft (3 m) apart.

9.1.5.3.3 All holes for lag screws shall be pre-drilled 1/8 in. (3.2 mm) less in diameter than the maximum root diameter of the lag screw thread.

Pre-drilling holes 1/8 in. (3.2 mm) smaller than the root diameter of the lag screw thread, as required by 9.1.5.3.3, combines ease of installation with the assurance of the needed gripping capacity of the lag screw into the wood.

9.1.5.3.4 Holes for bolts shall not exceed 1/16 in. (1.6 mm) greater than the diameter of the bolt.

9.1.5.3.5 Bolts shall be provided with a flat washer and nut.

9.1.5.4 Wood Screws. Wood screws shall be installed with a screwdriver.

Wood screws are required by 9.1.5.4 to be installed with a screwdriver. Wood screws and wood lag bolts can only provide the proper holding strength when installed using the proper tools. Hammering these devices in place can reduce their holding power and result in unacceptable installations.

9.1.5.5 Nails. Nails shall not be acceptable for fastening hangers.

9.1.5.6 Screws in Side of Timber or Joists.

9.1.5.6.1 Screws in the side of a timber or joist shall be not less than 2½ in. (64 mm) from the lower edge where supporting branch lines and not less than 3 in. (76 mm) where supporting main lines.

9.1.5.6.2 The requirements of 9.1.5.6.1 shall not apply to 2-in. (51-mm) or thicker nailing strips resting on top of steel beams.

9.1.5.7 Coach Screw Rods.

9.1.5.7.1 Minimum Coach Screw Rod Size. The size of coach screw rods shall not be less than the requirements of Table 9.1.5.7.1.

◄ **FAQ**
Why do the requirements of 9.1.5.3.3 require that holes be pre-drilled 1/8 in. (3.2 mm) smaller than the root diameter of the lag screw?

TABLE 9.1.5.7.1 *Minimum Coach Screw Rod Size*

| | Diameter of Rod | | Minimum Penetration |
Pipe Size	in.	mm	
Up to 4 in.	3/8	9.5	3 in.
Larger than 4 in.	Not permitted	Not permitted	Not permitted

9.1.5.7.2 The minimum plank thickness and the minimum width of the lower face of beams or joists in which coach screw rods are used shall be not less than that specified in Table 9.1.5.7.2.

TABLE 9.1.5.7.2 *Minimum Plank Thicknesses and Beam or Joist Widths*

	Nominal Plank Thickness		Nominal Width of Beam or Joist Face	
Pipe Size	*in.*	*mm*	*in.*	*mm*
Up to 2 in.	3	76	2	51
2½ in. to 3½ in.	4	102	2	51
4 in. and 5 in.	4	102	3	76
6 in.	4	102	4	102

The reference to nominal wood dimensions in Table 9.1.5.7.2 recognizes that nominal members such as 2 × 6 joists can only have an actual thickness of 1½ in. (38 mm). Exhibit 9.7 illustrates the installation of a coach screw rod in the bottom of a beam or joist. Once the coach screw rod is installed, the hanger is attached to it. Exhibit 9.8 illustrates the installation of coach screw rods in wood ceiling planking.

 9.1.5.7.3 Coach screw rods shall not be used for support of pipes larger than 4 in. in diameter.

9.1.5.7.4 All holes for coach screw rods shall be predrilled ⅛ in. (3.2 mm) less in diameter than the maximum root diameter of the wood screw thread.

FAQ ▶
Why do the requirements of 9.1.5.7.4 require that holes be pre-drilled ⅛ in. (3.2 mm) smaller than the root diameter of the lag screw?

Predrilling holes ⅛ in. (3.2 mm) smaller than the root diameter of the coach screw thread, which is required by 9.1.5.7.4, combines ease of installation with assurance of the needed gripping power.

EXHIBIT 9.7 *Installation of a Coach Screw Rod in the Bottom of a Beam or Joist.*

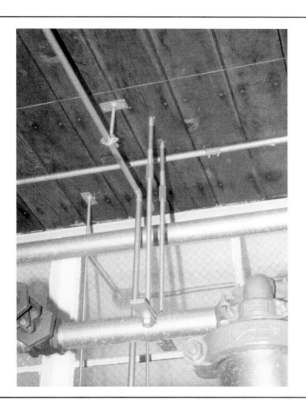

EXHIBIT 9.8 *Installation of Coach Screw Rods in Wood Ceiling Planking.*

9.2 Installation of Pipe Hangers

9.2.1 General.

9.2.1.1 Ceiling Sheathing.

9.2.1.1.1 Unless the requirements of 9.2.1.1.2 are met, sprinkler piping shall be supported independently of the ceiling sheathing.

9.2.1.1.2 Toggle hangers shall be permitted only for the support of pipe 1½ in. (38 mm) or smaller in size under ceilings of hollow tile or metal lath and plaster.

Toggle hangers, which are discussed in 9.2.1.1.2, are not permitted for use with gypsum wallboard or other less substantial types of ceiling materials, including metal deck roofs. Sprinkler piping must be supported from the building structure, with the exception of 1½-in. (38-mm) or smaller piping, which can be supported under ceilings of hollow tile or metal lath and plaster with toggle hangers, as shown in Exhibit 9.9.

9.2.1.2 Storage Racks. Where sprinkler piping is installed in storage racks, piping shall be supported from the storage rack structure or building in accordance with all applicable provisions of Sections 9.2 and 9.3.

9.2.1.3* Building Structure.

A.9.2.1.3 The method used to attach the hanger to the structure and the load placed on the hanger should take into account any limits imposed by the structure. Design manual information for pre-engineered structures or other specialty construction materials should be consulted, if appropriate.

 FAQ
Are toggle hangers permitted to be utilized in gypsum wallboard ceilings?

EXHIBIT 9.9 *Toggle Hanger for the Support of 1½ in. (38 mm) or Smaller Pipe.*

Spring clip
ceiling plate

System mains hung to a single beam, truss, or purlin can affect the structural integrity of the building by introducing excessive loads not anticipated in the building design. Also, special conditions such as collateral and concentrated load limits, type or method of attachment to the structural components, or location of attachment to the structural components might need to be observed when hanging system piping in pre-engineered metal buildings or buildings using other specialty structural components such as composite wood joists or combination wood and tubular metal joists.

9.2.1.3.1 Sprinkler piping shall be substantially supported from the building structure, which must support the added load of the water-filled pipe plus a minimum of 250 lb (114 kg) applied at the point of hanging.

Each individual point where the hanger is attached to the structure must be able to support the weight of the water-filled pipe plus 250 lb (114 kg), as stated in 9.2.1.3.1. This requirement does not intend to add 250 lb (114 kg) concurrently for each hanger when determining the minimum strength of the building structure. As mentioned in the commentary to 9.1.1, the 250-lb (114-kg) load represents the assumed weight of a sprinkler pipe fitter with associated work equipment who grasps the pipe during a mishap. It is a temporary point load applied at any hanger.

The safety factor for the structure is slightly different than the safety factor for the hanger, because it includes only one times, not five times, the weight of the water-filled pipe. The hangers are held to a higher minimum requirement.

9.2.1.3.2 Trapeze hangers shall be used where necessary to transfer loads to appropriate structural members.

9.2.1.4 Metal Deck.

Metal deck is discussed in 9.2.1.4. The allowance to attach to decking material applies only to very small diameter pipe using through bolts. With the exception of 9.2.1.4 and that for toggle hangers in 9.2.1.1.2, hanger attachment must be made to the building structure or to racks in the case of in-rack sprinklers.

9.2.1.4.1 Branch line hangers under metal deck shall be permitted only for the support of pipe 1 in. (25.4 mm) or smaller in size, by drilling or punching vertical members and using through bolts.

9.2.1.4.2 The distance from the bottom of the bolt hole to the bottom of the vertical member shall be not less than in. (9.5 mm).

9.2.1.5 Where sprinkler piping is installed below ductwork, piping shall be supported from the building structure or from the ductwork supports, provided such supports are capable of handling both the load of the ductwork and the load specified in 9.2.1.3.1.

As stated in 9.2.1.5, if the ductwork supports are not capable of supporting both the ductwork load and the weight of the water-filled pipe plus 250 lb (114 kg), then either the ductwork supports must be increased in size or another method of support must be used. Additionally, where the ductwork is to be supported by the building structure rather than the ductwork supports, the sprinkler piping hanger assembly is not to penetrate the ductwork, as shown in Exhibit 9.10.

◀ FAQ
Can sprinkler piping be supported from duct work supports?

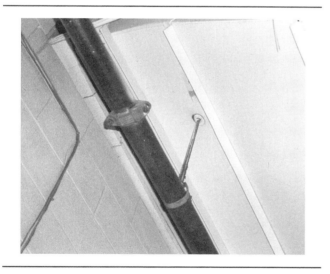

EXHIBIT 9.10 *Hanger Assembly Improperly Penetrating Ductwork.*

9.2.2* Maximum Distance between Hangers.

A.9.2.2 Where copper tube is to be installed in moist areas or other environments conducive to galvanic corrosion, copper hangers or ferrous hangers with an insulating material should be used.

9.2.2.1 The maximum distance between hangers shall not exceed that specified in Table 9.2.2.1.

The values given in Table 9.2.2.1 are based on the use of materials and component sizes given in Section 9.1. When pipe hangers are designed in accordance with 9.1.1.2, the values given in Table 9.2.2.1 cannot be modified.

TABLE 9.2.2.1 *Maximum Distance Between Hangers (ft-in.)*

	Nominal Pipe Size (in.)											
	¾	*1*	*1¼*	*1½*	*2*	*2½*	*3*	*3½*	*4*	*5*	*6*	*8*
Steel pipe except threaded lightwall	N/A	12–0	12–0	15–0	15–0	15–0	15–0	15–0	15–0	15–0	15–0	15–0
Threaded lightwall steel pipe	N/A	12–0	12–0	12–0	12–0	12–0	12–0	N/A	N/A	N/A	N/A	N/A
Copper tube	8–0	8–0	10–0	10–0	12–0	12–0	12–0	15–0	15–0	15–0	15–0	15–0
CPVC	5–6	6–0	6–6	7–0	8–0	9–0	10–0	N/A	N/A	N/A	N/A	N/A
Polybutylene (IPS)	N/A	3–9	4–7	5–0	5–11	N/A	N/A	N/A	N/A	N/A	N/A	N/A
Polybutylene (CTS)	2–11	3–4	3–11	4–5	5–5	N/A	N/A	N/A	N/A	N/A	N/A	N/A
Ductile iron pipe	N/A	N/A	N/A	N/A	N/A	N/A	15–0	N/A	15–0	N/A	15–0	15–0

For SI units, 1 in. = 25.4 mm; 1 ft = 0.3048 m.

Note: IPS iron—pipe size; CTS—copper tube size.

Because of the lack of material between the inside diameter and the root diameter of the thread, hangers must be spaced closer for threaded thin-wall pipe.

9.2.2.2 The maximum distance between hangers for listed nonmetallic pipe shall be modified as specified in the individual product listings.

Maximum distance between hangers is discussed in 9.2.2.1 and 9.2.2.2. Because of the unique characteristics of some types of fittings, certain manufacturers recommend hanger spacings less than the maximums given in Table 9.2.2.1. In such circumstances, the manufacturer's recommendations should be followed.

9.2.3 Location of Hangers on Branch Lines.

9.2.3.1 Subsection 9.2.3 shall apply to the support of steel pipe or copper tube as specified in 6.3.1 and subject to the provisions of 9.2.2.

9.2.3.2 Minimum Number of Hangers.

9.2.3.2.1 Unless the requirements of 9.2.3.2.2 or 9.2.3.2.3 are met, there shall be not less than one hanger for each section of pipe.

9.2.3.2.2* Where sprinklers are spaced less than 6 ft (1.8 m) apart, hangers spaced up to a maximum of 12 ft (3.7 m) shall be permitted.

A **A.9.2.3.2.2** See Figure A.9.2.3.2.2.

FIGURE A.9.2.3.2.2 *Distance Between Hangers.*

Unless unique characteristics of the fitting make it appropriate to provide support near each fitting, spacing hangers up to 12 ft (3.7 m) apart, as permitted by 9.2.3.2.2, is expected to adequately support the branch line piping when sprinklers are less than 6 ft (1.8 m) apart. This rule can also be applied when multiple pipe fittings are installed at dimensions not exceeding 6 ft (1.8 m) from one another.

9.2.3.2.3 Starter lengths less than 6 ft (1.8 m) shall not require a hanger, unless on the end line of a sidefeed system or where an intermediate cross main hanger has been omitted.

9.2.3.3 Clearance to Hangers. The distance between a hanger and the centerline of an upright sprinkler shall not be less than 3 in. (76 mm).

Clearance to hangers is discussed in 9.2.3.3. Guidance for deflector positioning with respect to the hanger is intended to ensure that the hanger does not become an obstruction to discharge. If hangers, sway braces, or other pipe supports have an obstructing dimension in excess of ½ in. (12.7 mm), the obstruction rules in Chapter 8 for the appropriate type of sprinkler should be followed.

◀ **FAQ**
Why are upright sprinklers required to be at least 3 in. (76 mm) away from hangers?

9.2.3.4* Unsupported Lengths.

A.9.2.3.4 Sprinkler piping should be adequately secured to restrict the movement of piping upon sprinkler operation. The reaction forces caused by the flow of water through the sprinkler could result in displacement of the sprinkler, thereby adversely affecting sprinkler discharge. Listed CPVC pipe and listed polybutylene pipe have specific requirements for piping support to include additional pipe bracing of sprinklers. See Figure A.9.2.3.4.

FIGURE A.9.2.3.4 *Distance from Sprinkler to Hanger.*

As Figure A.9.2.3.4 illustrates, extending the branch line to the next structural member prevents an excessive cantilever of the piping. The 36-in. (0.91-m) overhang limitation also applies to ¾-in. (19-mm) copper pipe.

9.2.3.4.1 The unsupported length between the end sprinkler and the last hanger on the line shall not be greater than 36 in. (0.9 m) for 1-in. pipe, 48 in. (1.2 m) for 1¼-in. pipe, and 60 in. (1.5 m) for 1½-in. or larger pipe.

9.2.3.4.2 Where the limits of 9.2.3.4.1 are exceeded, the pipe shall be extended beyond the end sprinkler and shall be supported by an additional hanger.

9.2.3.4.3* Unsupported Length with Maximum Pressure Exceeding 100 psi.

A.9.2.3.4.3 See Figure A.9.2.3.4.3(a) and Figure A.9.2.3.4.3(b).

Data have shown that unrestrained pendent sprinklers operating at high pressures can create a thrust force that lifts the branch line piping. At the end sprinkler and at armovers, the amount of thrust can be sufficient to lift a pendent sprinkler out of the ceiling tile and up into the concealed space.

Figure A.9.2.3.4.3(a) illustrates the intent of 9.2.3.4.3. Figure A.9.2.3.4.3(b) provides examples of acceptable types of hangers for end of line sprinklers or armover sprinklers.

9.2.3.4.3.1 When the maximum static or flowing pressure, whichever is greater at the sprinkler, applied other than through the fire department connection, exceeds 100 psi (6.9 bar) and a branch line above a ceiling supplies sprinklers in a pendent position below the ceiling, the hanger assembly supporting the pipe supplying an end sprinkler in a pendent position shall be of a type that prevents upward movement of the pipe.

9.2.3.4.3.2 The unsupported length between the end sprinkler in a pendent position or drop nipple and the last hanger on the branch line shall not be greater than 12 in. (305 mm) for steel pipe or 6 in. (152 mm) for copper pipe.

9.2.3.4.3.3 When the limit of 9.2.3.4.3.2 is exceeded, the pipe shall be extended beyond the end sprinkler and supported by an additional hanger.

9.2.3.4.3.4 The hanger closest to the sprinkler shall be of a type that prevents upward movement of the piping.

9.2.3.5* **Unsupported Armover Length.**

 A.9.2.3.5 See Figure A.9.2.3.5.

9.2.3.5.1 The cumulative horizontal length of an unsupported armover to a sprinkler, sprinkler drop, or sprig-up shall not exceed 24 in. (610 mm) for steel pipe or 12 in. (305 mm) for copper tube.

9.2.3.5.2* **Unsupported Armover Length with Maximum Pressures Exceeding 100 psi.**

FIGURE A.9.2.3.4.3(a) *Distance from Sprinkler to Hanger Where Maximum Pressure Exceeds 100 psi (6.9 bar) and a Branch Line Above a Ceiling Supplies Pendent Sprinklers Below the Ceiling.*

Short strap   U-hook

(Pipe tight to structure)

Wraparound
U-hook

Pipe size	D dimension
1 in.	⅛ in.
1¼ in.	⅛ in.
1½ in.	⅛ in.
2 in.	¼ in.
2½ in.	¼ in.

Clevis hanger

Adjustable swivel
ring — rod tight
to pipe

Adjustable swivel
ring with surge
suppressor

Clip-on wraparound U-hook devices

FIGURE A.9.2.3.4.3(b) *Examples of Acceptable Hangers for End-of-Line (or Armover) Pendent Sprinklers.*

A.9.2.3.5.2 See Figure A.9.2.3.5.2.

Exhibit 9.11 illustrates an unsupported armover for an upright sprinkler (see 9.2.3.5.2). Special listed fittings that tend to rotate unless restrained either incorporate a mechanism to make rotation impossible or have, as part of their listing, a requirement for a hanger on any armover regardless of length. Incorporation of these requirements maintains system effectiveness even at high operating pressures.

FIGURE A.9.2.3.5 *Maximum Length for Unsupported Armover.*

FIGURE A.9.2.3.5.2 *Maximum Length of Unsupported Armover Where the Maximum Pressure Exceeds 100 psi (6.9 bar) and a Branch Line Above a Ceiling Supplies Pendent Sprinklers Below the Ceiling.*

9.2.3.5.2.1 Where the maximum static or flowing pressure, whichever is greater at the sprinkler, applied other than through the fire department connection, exceeds 100 psi (6.9 bar) and a branch line above a ceiling supplies sprinklers in a pendent position below the ceiling, the cumulative horizontal length of an unsupported armover to a sprinkler or sprinkler drop shall not exceed 12 in. (305 mm) for steel pipe and 6 in. (152 mm) for copper tube.

9.2.3.5.2.2 The hanger closest to the sprinkler shall be of a type that prevents upward movement of the piping.

9.2.3.6 Wall-mounted sidewall sprinklers shall be restrained to prevent movement.

9.2.4 Location of Hangers on Mains.

9.2.4.1 Unless the requirements of 9.2.4.2, 9.2.4.3, 9.2.4.4, or 9.2.4.5 are met, hangers for mains shall be in accordance with 9.2.2 or between each branch line, whichever is the lesser dimension.

9.2.4.2 For cross mains in steel pipe systems in bays having two branch lines, the intermediate hanger shall be permitted to be omitted provided that a hanger attached to a purlin is in-

EXHIBIT 9.11 *Unsupported Armover to an Upright Sprinkler.*

stalled on each branch line located as near to the cross main as the location of the purlin permits. The remaining branch line hangers shall be installed in accordance with 9.2.3.

9.2.4.3 For cross mains in steel pipe systems only in bays having three branch lines, either side or center feed, one (only) intermediate hanger shall be permitted to be omitted provided that a hanger attached to a purlin is installed on each branch line located as near to the cross main as the location of the purlin permits. The remaining branch line hangers shall be installed in accordance with 9.2.3.

9.2.4.4 For cross mains in steel pipe systems only in bays having four or more branch lines, either side or center feed, two intermediate hangers shall be permitted to be omitted provided the maximum distance between hangers does not exceed the distances specified in 9.2.2 and a hanger attached to a purlin on each branch line is located as near to the cross main as the purlin permits.

As indicated in 9.2.4.4, cross mains of materials other than steel must have at least one hanger between every two branch lines. With steel pipe cross mains, a hanger can be installed between every two branch lines or, alternatively, on each branch line as near as possible to the cross main while omitting one intermediate cross main hanger in each bay. This approach can reduce or eliminate the need for trapeze hangers.

The option to omit the intermediate cross main hanger applies to the last piece of cross main only if the main is extended to the next framing member and a hanger is also installed at that point.

9.2.4.5 At the end of the main, intermediate trapeze hangers shall be installed unless the main is extended to the next framing member with a hanger installed at this point, in which event an intermediate hanger shall be permitted to be omitted in accordance with 9.2.4.2, 9.2.4.3, and 9.2.4.4.

9.2.5 Support of Risers.

9.2.5.1 Risers shall be supported by pipe clamps or by hangers located on the horizontal connections within 24 in. of the centerline of the riser.

Support of risers is addressed in 9.2.5.1. Typically, risers are supported by a friction-type clamp that rests on or is secured to the floor slab. However, risers can also be supported using riser clamps that are fastened to the building structure (see Exhibit 9.12) or through the use of hangers that support the horizontal piping at the top of the riser.

EXHIBIT 9.12 *Riser Supported with a Pipe Clamp Fastened to the Building Structure.*

9.2.5.2 Pipe clamps supporting risers by means of set screws shall not be used.

To adequately support a riser, the full surface of a clamp must bear against the surface of the pipe, as shown in Exhibit 9.12 (see 9.2.5.2).

9.2.5.3 Multistory Buildings.

9.2.5.3.1 In multistory buildings, riser supports shall be provided at the lowest level, at each alternate level above, above and below offsets, and at the top of the riser.

9.2.5.3.2 Supports above the lowest level shall also restrain the pipe to prevent movement by an upward thrust where flexible fittings are used.

Multistory buildings are discussed in 9.2.5.3.1 and 9.2.5.3.2. Flexible couplings and fittings allow limited axial movement. In the case of risers in multistory buildings, the axial expansion resulting from system pressurization can be significant unless the movement from upward thrust is prevented.

Risers with horizontal offsets can be supported at both the top and bottom in accordance with 9.2.5.1. A horizontal offset exceeding 6 ft (1.8 m) in length is required to be supported with its own hanger in accordance with other provisions of NFPA 13.

9.2.5.3.3 Where risers are supported from the ground, the ground support shall constitute the first level of riser support.

9.2.5.3.4 Where risers are offset or do not rise from the ground, the first ceiling level above the offset shall constitute the first level of riser support.

 9.2.5.4 Distance between supports for risers shall not exceed 25 ft (7.6 m).

A maximum distance between supports, as required by 9.2.5.4, is necessary to distribute the load.

9.3 Protection of Piping Against Damage Where Subject to Earthquakes

Section 9.3 describes how to protect sprinkler systems against earthquake damage but not geographically where to provide such protection.

FAQ ▶
Does NFPA 13 establish where protection against earthquakes is required?

The decision to require protection of sprinkler systems or other mechanical systems against earthquake forces is generally stated within building codes or is determined by other authorities having jurisdiction. The decision is based on the past seismic activity of an area and its potential for future earthquakes.

Earthquake design criteria for sprinkler systems have been included in NFPA 13 since 1947. The performance of sprinkler systems in earthquakes has generally been quite good. Following the San Fernando, CA, earthquake in 1971 (6.7 moment magnitude), the Pacific Fire Rating Bureau surveyed 973 sprinklered buildings and reported that "if a sprinklered building fared well, so did the sprinkler system." Studies of fire sprinkler performance in more recent earthquakes, such as the Loma Prieta, CA, earthquake of 1989 (6.9 moment magnitude) and the Northridge, CA, earthquake of 1994 (6.7 moment magnitude), have reinforced this observation. Knowledge gained from past earthquakes, however, has led to modifications of the requirements of NFPA 13 over the years. The modifications have been aimed at avoiding significant damage to the sprinkler systems and permitting sprinkler systems to remain functional following an earthquake.

The protection criteria do not specifically address water supply components such as pumps and tanks, because installation of these components is outside the scope of NFPA 13. Nevertheless, pumps and tanks should be braced against horizontal accelerations in a fashion similar to system piping. The fastener load criteria of this standard can be applied.

9.3.1* General.

A.9.3.1 Sprinkler systems are protected against earthquake damage by means of the following:

(1) Stresses that would develop in the piping due to differential building movement are minimized through the use of flexible joints or clearances.
(2) Bracing is used to keep the piping fairly rigid when supported from a building component expected to move as a unit, such as a ceiling.

Areas known to have a potential for earthquakes have been identified in building code and insurance maps. Examples of two such maps are shown in Figure A.9.3.1(a) and Figure A.9.3.1(b).

The earthquake protection criteria discussed in 9.3.1 involve requirements aimed at avoiding piping stress through the use of flexible fittings and clearances and requirements to maintain system alignment and to prevent the development of damage-inducing momentum through the use of sway bracing.

The maps in Figures A.9.3.1(a) and A.9.3.1(b) are provided for example purposes only and are not intended to specify where earthquake protection features are appropriate.

In general, if the building is specially designed to resist earthquakes, the sprinkler system should also be protected. However, some codes exempt sprinkler and other mechanical systems from protection criteria in low-risk seismic zones. Using Figure A.9.3.1(b) as an example, some model building codes do not require protection of the sprinkler system in Zone 0, and Zone 1 would require protection only for systems located in essential facilities such as hospitals, police stations, communication buildings, and buildings that would release hazardous contents if damaged.

◀ **FAQ**
Do the maps in Figures A.9.3.1(a) and A.9.3.1(b) determine where earthquake protection is required?

9.3.1.1 Where water-based fire protection systems are required to be protected against damage from earthquakes, the requirements of Section 9.3 shall apply, unless the requirements of 9.3.1.2 are met.

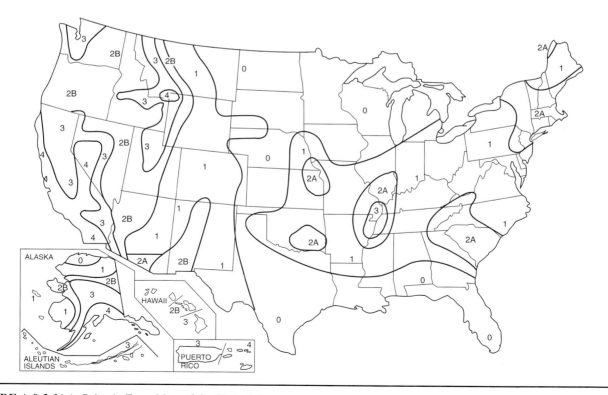

FIGURE A.9.3.1(a) Seismic Zone Map of the United States.

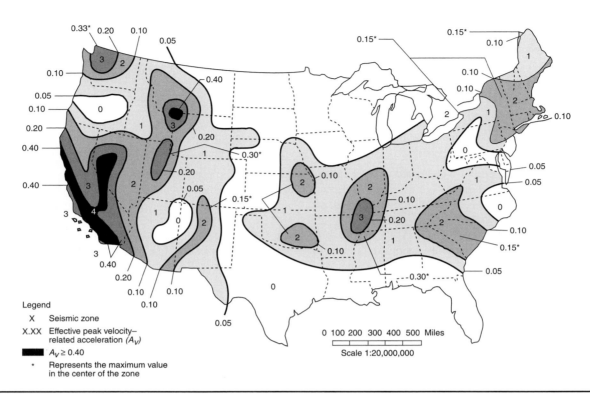

Legend

X   Seismic zone

X.XX   Effective peak velocity–
         related acceleration (A_v)

■■■■ $A_v \geq 0.40$

*   Represents the maximum value
         in the center of the zone

0 100 200 300 400 500 Miles

Scale 1:20,000,000

FIGURE A.9.3.1(b) *Map of Seismic Zones and Effective Peak Velocity-Related Acceleration (A_v)*
for the Contiguous 48 States; Linear Interpolation Between Contours is Acceptable.

9.3.1.2 Alternative methods of providing earthquake protection of sprinkler systems based on a seismic analysis certified by a registered professional engineer such that system performance will be at least equal to that of the building structure under expected seismic forces shall be permitted.

Paragraph 9.3.1.2 permits a performance-based alternative to the rules of Section 9.3 in the form of a seismic analysis certified by a registered professional engineer. This allows a waiver of NFPA 13 criteria for special building designs, such as those buildings equipped with base isolation systems to prevent the transfer of earthquake accelerations to the building and its mechanical systems.

9.3.2* Couplings.

A.9.3.2 Strains on sprinkler piping can be greatly lessened and, in many cases, damage prevented by increasing the flexibility between major parts of the sprinkler system. One part of the piping should never be held rigidly and another part allowed to move freely without provision for relieving the strain. Flexibility can be provided by using listed flexible couplings, by joining grooved end pipe at critical points, and by allowing clearances at walls and floors.

Tank or pump risers should be treated the same as sprinkler risers for their portion within a building. The discharge pipe of tanks on buildings should have a control valve above the roof line so any pipe break within the building can be controlled.

Piping 2 in. (51 mm) or smaller in size is pliable enough so that flexible couplings are not usually necessary. "Rigid-type" couplings that permit less than 1 degree of angular movement at the grooved connections are not considered to be flexible couplings. *[See Figure A.9.3.2(a) and Figure A.9.3.2(b).]*

FIGURE A.9.3.2(a) *Riser Details.*

FIGURE A.9.3.2(b) *Detail at Short Riser.*

Couplings are discussed in 9.3.2. Flexible listed pipe couplings are defined in 3.5.4 as couplings or fittings that allow axial displacement, rotation, and at least 1 degree of angular movement of the pipe without inducing harm on the pipe. Couplings or fittings that do not permit such movement are considered "rigid-type" mechanical couplings. The manufacturer is obligated to declare any particular mechanical fitting as being flexible or rigid, and this characteristic can be verified by the listing agency.

Flexible couplings are required within the system at critical points to minimize stresses on the piping. Flexible special listed pipe should be considered to satisfy the requirements for flexible couplings only if equivalent levels of flexibility can be achieved without harm to the pipe. See Exhibit 9.13.

EXHIBIT 9.13 *Flexible Pipe Coupling.*

Although Figure A.9.3.2(a) shows risers connected only to roof framing, it is sometimes necessary to support risers from a wall, including bracing for the top of the riser. This is usually the case when very lightweight roof structures are used. In such cases, bracing to the wall should be below the upper flexible coupling on the riser. In this manner, the piping is not held rigidly to building components that may move differentially (wall and roof structure) during an earthquake.

9.3.2.1 Listed flexible pipe couplings joining grooved end pipe shall be provided as flexure joints to allow individual sections of piping 2½ in. (64 mm) or larger to move differentially with the individual sections of the building to which it is attached.

9.3.2.2 Couplings shall be arranged to coincide with structural separations within a building.

9.3.2.3 Systems having more flexible couplings than required by this section shall be provided with additional sway bracing as required in 9.3.5.3.6. The flexible couplings shall be installed as follows:

(1) Within 24 in. (610 mm) of the top and bottom of all risers, unless the following provisions are met:

    (a) In risers less than 3 ft (0.9 m) in length, flexible couplings are permitted to be omitted.
    (b) In risers 3 ft to 7 ft (0.9 m to 2.1 m) in length, one flexible coupling is adequate.

(2)* Within 12 in. (305 mm) above and within 24 in. below the floor in multistory buildings. When the flexible coupling below the floor is above the tie-in main to the main supplying that floor, a flexible coupling shall be provided on the vertical portion of the tie-in piping.

A **A.9.3.2.3(2)** The flexible coupling should be at the same elevation as the flexible coupling on the main riser. *[See Figure A.9.3.2.3(2).]*

FIGURE A.9.3.2.3(2) *Flexible Coupling on Main Riser and Branch Line Riser.*

Since the 1994 edition, two flexible couplings per floor are required on the riser of a multistory building as indicated in 9.3.2.3(2). The couplings are intended to provide a minimum of 2 degrees of angular displacement per story without damaging the riser. One flexible coupling is to be located within 12 in. (305 mm) above the floor. The other coupling is to be located just below the point of connection of the riser to the main supplying the system on that floor, but within 24 in. (610 mm) of the ceiling. In the 1999 edition, the requirement was modified, and Figure A.9.3.2.3(2) was added. This change requires an additional coupling on the piping serving the floor main if it is taken off the riser below the top flexible coupling. With regard to 9.3.2.3(5), where racks are freestanding—that is, independent of the building structure—their movement relative to the ceiling can be considerably more than can be accommodated by a single flexible coupling. In cases where ceiling sprinkler piping drops to the top of a freestanding rack, a swing joint comprised of multiple flexible elbows may be needed. Earthquake experts have suggested that differential lateral movement of 5 percent of the rack height can be expected.

Drops to a single sprinkler are not required to be equipped with a flexible coupling because of the concern regarding the difficulty of sprinkler installation and replacement [see 9.3.2.3(6)]. The rotation inherent in a flexible coupling can prevent the development of the torque necessary to properly install the sprinkler.

(3) On both sides of concrete or masonry walls within 1 ft of the wall surface, unless clearance is provided in accordance with 9.3.4.

(4)* Within 24 in. (610 mm) of building expansion joints.

A.9.3.2.3(4) A building expansion joint is usually a bituminous fiber strip used to separate blocks or units of concrete to prevent cracking due to expansion as a result of temperature changes. Where building expansion joints are used, the flexible coupling is required on one side of the joint by 9.3.2.3(4).

For seismic separation joints, considerably more flexibility is needed, particularly for piping above the first floor. Figure A.9.3.3 shows a method of providing additional flexibility through the use of swing joints.

(5) Within 24 in. (610 mm) of the top and bottom of drops to hose lines, rack sprinklers, and mezzanines, regardless of pipe size.

(6) Within 24 in. (610 mm) of the top of drops exceeding 15 ft (4.6 m) in length to portions of systems supplying more than one sprinkler, regardless of pipe size.

(7) Above and below any intermediate points of support for a riser or other vertical pipe.

9.3.3* Seismic Separation Assembly.
Seismic separation assemblies with flexible fittings shall be installed where sprinkler piping, regardless of size, crosses building seismic separation joints above ground level.

A.9.3.3 Plan and elevation views of a seismic separation assembly assembled with flexible elbows are shown in Figure A.9.3.3.

A seismic separation assembly is considered to be an assembly of fittings, pipe, and couplings or an assembly of pipe and couplings that permits movement in all directions. The extent of permitted movement should be sufficient to accommodate calculated differential motions during earthquakes. In lieu of calculations, permitted movement can be made at least twice the actual separations, at right angles to the separation as well as parallel to it.

The seismic separation assembly (see Figure A.9.3.3) provides sufficient flexibility to accommodate the substantial relative motion that can be expected at building seismic separation joints. In many cases, providing each building section with its own riser can be more economical.

The seismic separation assembly is not required on piping located below ground level.

The seismic separation assembly is required for all piping that crosses seismic joints above ground level, including branch lines, without regard for pipe size.

Several listed devices (piping assemblies) are now available that can be used as seismic separation assemblies where they provide the intended flexibility. This means that they must be designed to allow full closure of the seismic separation, opening of the seismic separation to twice its original width, and offsets in both the vertical and horizontal planes equal to the width of the

Do the requirements of 9.3.3 apply to piping installed in areas below ground level?
◀ **FAQ**
◀ **FAQ**
Do the requirements of 9.3.3 apply to all piping crossing seismic joints regardless of size, including branch lines?

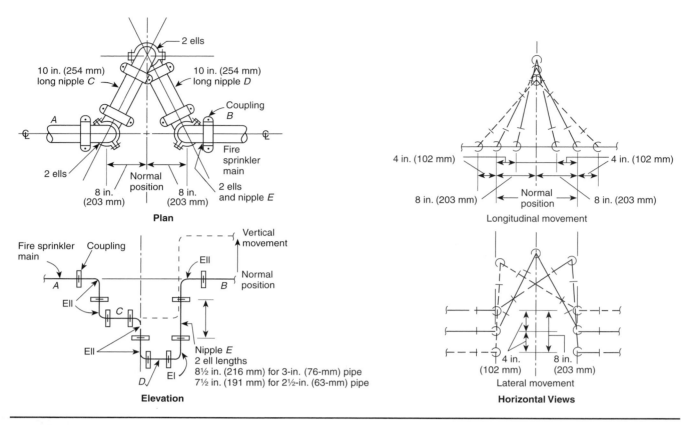

FIGURE A.9.3.3 *Seismic Separation Assembly. Shown are an 8-in. (203-mm) Separation Crossed by Pipes up to 4 in. (102 mm) in Nominal Diameter. For Other Separation Distances and Pipe Sizes, Lengths and Distances Should Be Modified Proportionally.*

seismic separation. There is no requirement that a listed device be used for this purpose, but the piping configuration to be used as a seismic separation assembly must be approved by the authority having jurisdiction.

There are no special requirements relating to the exact location of the seismic separation assembly, but the performance basis of the required movement necessitates that it be located in close proximity to the seismic separation. The seismic separation assembly may be provided with hangers or supports, but such supports should be breakaway or otherwise light enough so as not to prevent the intended movement of the assembly in the event of an earthquake.

Piping on both sides of the seismic separation assembly must be braced in accordance with the requirements of the standard, since no bracing capability is carried across the seismic separation assembly.

9.3.4* Clearance.

 A.9.3.4 While clearances are necessary around the sprinkler piping to prevent breakage due to building movement, suitable provision should also be made to prevent passage of water, smoke, or fire.

Drains, fire department connections, and other auxiliary piping connected to risers should not be cemented into walls or floors; similarly, pipes that pass horizontally through walls or foundations should not be cemented solidly or strains will accumulate at such points.

Where risers or lengths of pipe extend through suspended ceilings, they should not be fastened to the ceiling framing members.

Clearance is discussed in 9.3.4. Clearances have traditionally been used to prevent damage to piping passing through walls, floors, platforms, and foundations, but recent trends have been toward the use of flexible couplings or fittings. When such couplings or fittings are located within 1 ft (0.31 m) of both sides of such structural elements, clearance can be eliminated in accordance with 9.3.4.5.

◄ **FAQ**
Can clearance be eliminated with the use of flexible couplings?

9.3.4.1 Clearance shall be provided around all piping extending through walls, floors, platforms, and foundations, including drains, fire department connections, and other auxiliary piping.

As stated in 9.3.4.6, clearance is not required around pipes passing through successive floor joists or closely spaced beams expected to move as a unit, such as a part of a ceiling/roof deck. Clearance must be provided around pipes passing through beams that are considered primary structural members (see 9.3.4.1). Large openings can reduce the strength of structural members, and openings in beams should generally be located only in the center one-third of their depth and not close to either end of their span.

9.3.4.2 Unless the requirements of 9.3.4.3, 9.3.4.4, or 9.3.4.5 are met, where pipe passes through holes in platforms, foundations, walls, or floors, the holes shall be sized such that the diameter of the holes is nominally 2 in. (51 mm) larger than the pipe for 1-in. (25.4-mm) nominal to 3½-in. (89-mm) nominal and 4-in. (102-mm) larger than the pipe for pipe 4 in. (102 mm) nominal and larger. Clearance from structural members not penetrated or used collectively or independently to support the pipe shall be at least 2 in. (51 mm).

The clearance around the pipe discussed in 9.3.4.2 does not need to be annular—that is, the pipe does not need to be placed in the exact center of the opening. This is also true where holes through primary structural members substitute for hangers as permitted in 9.1.1.5.3.

◄ **FAQ**
Is it the intent of NFPA 13 to require the pipe to be centered within the opening?

9.3.4.3 Where clearance is provided by a pipe sleeve, a nominal diameter 2 in. (51 mm) larger than the nominal diameter of the pipe is acceptable for pipe sizes 1 in. (25.4 mm) through 3½ in. (89 mm), and the clearance provided by a pipe sleeve of nominal diameter 4 in. (102 mm) larger than the nominal diameter of the pipe is acceptable for pipe sizes 4 in. (102 mm) and larger.

9.3.4.4 No clearance is required for piping passing through gypsum board or equally frangible construction that is not required to have a fire resistance rating.

Generally there is no concern where sprinkler piping penetrates frangible construction, which is discussed in 9.3.4.4, since it is not expected that the piping would be damaged by differential movement. However, where the frangible construction is part of a rated enclosure, such as an exit stair, clearance must be provided to prevent compromising the required fire integrity of the enclosure following an earthquake. Additionally, the clearance needs to be filled with flexible material that maintains the integrity of the fire resistance rating. An alternative would be to provide flexible couplings on both sides of the penetration in accordance with 9.3.4.5.

◄ **FAQ**
Why is clearance required where the construction is required to have a fire resistance rating?

9.3.4.5 No clearance is required if flexible couplings are located within 1 ft (0.31 m) of each side of a wall, floor, platform, or foundation.

As with walls, flexible couplings located within 1 ft (0.31 m) on each side of beams may be substituted for the required clearances, as stated in 9.3.4.5.

9.3.4.6 No clearance is required where horizontal piping passes perpendicularly through successive studs or joists that form a wall or floor/ceiling assembly.

9.3.4.7 No clearance is required where nonmetallic pipe has been demonstrated to have inherent flexibility equal to or greater than the minimum provided by flexible couplings located within 1 ft (0.3 m) of each side of a wall, floor, platform, or foundation.

9.3.4.8 Where required, the clearance shall be filled with a flexible material such as mastic.

 Most building codes now require the annular space around piping penetrations through fire-rated assemblies, other than sprinkler penetrations of ceiling membranes, to be filled with an appropriate material, as stated in 9.3.4.8. Listed penetration sealants are available that are tested in accordance with ASTM E 814, *Test Methods for Fire Tests of Through-Penetration Fire Stops,* and that are flexible as installed.

9.3.4.9 Clearance from structural members not penetrated or used, collectively or independently, to support the piping shall be at least 2 in. (51 mm).

FAQ ▶

Why do the requirements of 9.3.4.9 require at least 2 in. (50 mm) of clearance from structural members not penetrated or utilized for support?

The requirement in 9.3.4.9 for minimum 2-in. (50-mm) clearance from structural members not penetrated or used for support prevents the possibility that system components would be damaged by being pushed against rigid structural members in the event of differential movement within the building. In other words, a main supported from the roof structure would be required to be suspended at least 2 in. (50 mm) laterally from the side of a building column.

9.3.5* Sway Bracing.

 A.9.3.5 Figure A.9.3.5(a) and Figure A.9.3.5(b) are examples of forms used to aid in the preparation of bracing calculations.

Sway bracing, which is covered in 9.3.5, is provided to prevent excessive movement of system piping. Shifting of large pipe as a result of earthquake motion has led to the pull-out of hangers and fracture of fittings. With some exceptions as specifically stated, bracing is required for the following:

1. The top of the system riser
2. All feed and cross mains, regardless of size
3. Branch lines 2½ in. (64 mm) in diameter and larger (lateral bracing only)

Branch line piping 2 in. (51 mm) in diameter and smaller is considered capable of considerable movement without damage. A lesser degree of support than bracing is referred to as restraint and is separately addressed in 9.3.6.

NFPA 13 contains requirements for both lateral (perpendicular to the piping) and longitudinal (parallel to the piping) horizontal braces. A lateral sway brace is shown in Exhibit 9.14, and a longitudinal brace is shown in Exhibit 9.15. The normal maximum spacing of lateral braces [40 ft (12.2 m)] is based on the strength of the piping as a beam under the uniform load of its expected horizontal "weight." Longitudinal braces are required at a maximum spacing of 80 ft (24.4 m).

Lateral and longitudinal braces are "two-way" braces—that is, they prevent piping from moving back and forth in a single direction. The sway braces illustrated in Exhibits 9.14 and 9.15 are two-way braces. "Four-way" bracing, as shown in Exhibit 9.16, requires the simultaneous effect of lateral and longitudinal bracing.

As with system hangers, sway braces must be attached directly to the building structure. Fasteners and structural elements at the points of connection must be adequate to handle the expected loads.

The forces applied to piping during an earthquake can be vertical as well as horizontal, but vertical uplift forces are generally expected to be offset by gravity, and vertical downward forces are expected to be handled within the normal safety factors of system hangers. Where high horizontal force factors are combined with low brace angles from vertical, 9.3.5.7 requires the use of supplemental supports to resist net upward vertical reactions.

9.3.5.1 General.

9.3.5.1.1 The system piping shall be braced to resist both lateral and longitudinal horizontal seismic loads and to prevent vertical motion resulting from seismic loads.

Seismic Bracing Calculations

Sheet _____ of _____

Project: _____   Contractor: _____

Address: _____   Address: _____

_____   _____

Telephone: _____

Fax: _____

Brace Information

Length of brace: _____

Diameter of brace: _____

Type of brace: _____

Angle of brace: _____

Least radius of gyration:* _____

L/R value:* _____

Maximum horizontal load: _____

Fastener Information

Orientation of connecting surface: _____

Fastener:

Type: _____

Diameter: _____

Length (in wood): _____

Maximum load: _____

Seismic Brace Attachments

Structure attachment fitting or tension-only bracing system:

Make: _____   Model: _____

Listed load rating: _____   Adjusted load rating per 9.3.5.10.3: _____

Sway brace (pipe attachment) fitting:

Make: _____   Model: _____

Listed load rating: _____   Adjusted load rating per 9.3.5.10.3: _____

Seismic Brace Assembly Detail
(Provide detail on plans)

Brace identification no.
(to be used on plans) _____

☐ Lateral brace   ☐ Longitudinal brace

Sprinkler System Load Calculation [F_p = ____W_p (default is 0.5)]

Diameter	Type	Length (ft)	Total (ft)	Weight per ft	Total Weight
				lb/ft	lb
				lb/ft	lb
				lb/ft	lb
				lb/ft	lb
				lb/ft	lb
				Total weight	lb
				$F_p \times 1.15$	lb

* Excludes tension-only bracing systems

FIGURE A.9.3.5(a) Seismic Bracing Calculation Form.

Seismic Bracing Calculations

Sheet _____ of _____

Project:	Acme Warehouse	Contractor:	Smith Sprinkler Company
Address:	321 First Street	Address:	123 Main Street
	Any City, Any State		Any City, Any State
		Telephone:	(555) 555-1234
		Fax:	(555) 555-4321

Brace Information

Length of brace:	6 ft 8 in.
Diameter of brace:	1 in.
Type of brace:	Schedule 40
Angle of brace:	30° to 45°
Least radius of gyration:*	0.42
L/R value:*	200
Maximum horizontal load:	1767 lb

Fastener Information

Orientation of connecting surface: _____ "D"

Fastener:

Type:	Through bolt
Diameter:	5/8 in.
Length (in wood):	3 5/8 in.
Maximum load:	491 lb

Seismic Brace Attachments

Structure attachment fitting or tension-only bracing system:

Make: ____Acme____ Model: ____123____

Listed load rating: _1000_ Adjusted load rating per 9.3.5.10.3: _500_

Sway brace (pipe attachment) fitting:

Make: ____Acme____ Model: ____321____

Listed load rating: _1200_ Adjusted load rating per 9.3.5.10.3: _600_

Seismic Brace Assembly Detail
(Provide detail on plans)

5/8 in. x 6 in. through bolt with nut and washer

Acme 123

1/2 beam depth minimum

30° minimum

4 in. x 12 in. beam

1 in. Schedule 40

Acme 321

Brace identification no. (to be used on plans) ____SB-1____

[X] Lateral brace   [ ] Longitudinal brace

Sprinkler System Load Calculation [$F_p =$ ____ W_p (default is 0.5)]

Diameter	Type	Length (ft)	Total (ft)	Weight per ft		W_p	Total Weight	
1 in.	Sch 40	15 ft + 25 ft + 8 ft + 22 ft	70 ft	2.05	lb/ft	0.5	71.74	lb
1¼ in.	Sch 40	25 ft + 33 ft + 18 ft	76 ft	2.93	lb/ft	0.5	111.34	lb
1½ in.	Sch 40	8 ft + 8 ft + 10 ft + 10 ft	36 ft	3.61	lb/ft	0.5	64.98	lb
2 in.	Sch 40	20 ft	20 ft	5.13	lb/ft	0.5	51.3	lb
4 in.	Sch 10	20 ft	20 ft	11.78	lb/ft	0.5	119.5	lb
				Total weight			416.87	lb
				$F_p \times 1.15$			480	lb

* Excludes tension-only bracing systems

FIGURE A.9.3.5(b) *Sample Seismic Bracing Calculation.*

EXHIBIT 9.14 *Lateral Sway Brace Attached to Wood.*

EXHIBIT 9.15 *Longitudinal Sway Brace Attached Steel Bar Joist. (Courtesy of Tolco)*

EXHIBIT 9.16 *Four-Way Brace. (Courtesy of AFCON)*

9.3.5.1.2 The structural components to which bracing is attached shall be determined to be capable of carrying the added applied seismic loads.

9.3.5.2 Sway Bracing.

9.3.5.2.1 Sway braces shall be designed to withstand forces in tension and compression, unless the requirements of 9.3.5.2.2 are met.

9.3.5.2.2* Tension-only bracing systems shall be permitted for use where listed for this service and where installed in accordance with their listing limitations, including installation instructions.

A.9.3.5.2.2 The investigation of tension-only bracing using materials, connection methods, or both, other than those described in Table 9.3.5.8.9(a), Table 9.3.5.8.9(b), and Table 9.3.5.8.9(c), should involve consideration of the following:

(1) Corrosion resistance.
(2) Prestretching to eliminate permanent construction stretch and to obtain a verifiable modulus of elasticity.
(3) Color coding or other verifiable marking of each different size cable for field verification.
(4) The capacity of all components of the brace assemblies, including the field connections, to maintain the manufacturer's minimum certified break strength.
(5) Manufacturer's published design data sheets/manual showing product design guidelines, including connection details, load calculation procedures for sizing of braces, and the maximum recommended horizontal load-carrying capacity of the brace assemblies including the associated fasteners as described in Figure 9.3.5.9.1. The maximum allowable horizontal loads shall not exceed the manufacturer's minimum certified break strength of the brace assemblies, excluding fasteners, after taking a safety factor of 1.5 and then adjusting for the brace angle.
(6) Brace product shipments accompanied by the manufacturer's certification of the minimum break strength and prestretching and installation instructions.
(7) The manufacturer's literature, including any special tools or precautions required to ensure proper installation.
(8) A means to prevent vertical motion due to seismic forces when required.

Table A.9.3.5.2.2 identifies some specially listed tension-only bracing systems.

As with nonmetallic pipe, tension-only bracing systems are acceptable for use by NFPA 13 only if specially investigated and listed for this service and installed in conformance with all

TABLE A.9.3.5.2.2 *Specially Listed Tension-Only Seismic Bracing*

Materials and Dimensions	*Standard*
Manual for Structural Application of Steel Cables	ASCE 19-96
Wire Rope Users Manual of the Wire Rope Technical Board	ASCE 19-96
Mechanical Strength Requirements	ASTM A 603
Breaking Strength Failure Testing	ASTM E 8

requirements of the listing (see 9.3.5.2.2). Tension-only bracing systems are not to be confused with the wire restraint method permitted by 9.3.6.1(3). A tension-only bracing system is illustrated in Exhibit 9.17.

EXHIBIT 9.17 *Tension-Only Bracing System.*

9.3.5.3 Lateral Sway Bracing.

9.3.5.3.1 Lateral sway bracing spaced at a maximum interval of 40 ft (12.2 m) on center shall be provided on all feed and cross mains regardless of size and all branch lines and other piping with a diameter of 2½ in. (63.5 mm) and larger.

FAQ ▶
Why is lateral sway bracing only required for branch lines that exceed 2½ in. (63.5 mm)?

Lateral sway bracing is discussed in 9.3.5.3.1. For branch line and other piping smaller than 2½ in. (63.5 mm), bracing is not required. Branch lines of 2 in. (51 mm) in diameter and smaller are considered to have sufficient flexibility to avoid damage under their own momentum. Mains, however, can also carry the loads of adjacent branch lines and must be braced regardless of size.

9.3.5.3.2 The distance between the last brace and the end of the pipe shall not exceed 20 ft (6.1 m).

9.3.5.3.3 The requirements of 9.3.5.3.1 and 9.3.5.3.2 shall not apply where building primary structural members exceed 40 ft (12.2 m) on center, lateral braces shall be permitted to be spaced up to 50 ft (15.2 m) on center, and the distance between the last brace and the end of the pipe shall be permitted to be extended to 25 ft (7.6 m).

9.3.5.3.4 The last length of pipe at the end of a feed or cross main shall be provided with a lateral brace.

9.3.5.3.5 Lateral braces shall be allowed to act as longitudinal braces if they are within 24 in. (610 mm) of the centerline of the piping braced longitudinally for lines that are 2½ in. (63.5 mm) and greater in diameter.

9.3.5.3.6 Where flexible couplings are installed on mains other than as required in 9.3.2, a lateral brace shall be provided within 24 in. (610 mm) of every other coupling, but not more than 40 ft (12.2 m) on center.

The intent of 9.3.5.3.6 is to prevent excessive movement of the mains, possibly resulting in "bellows" or "accordion" effects. Bracing is not required near every flexible coupling but near every other such coupling. This additional bracing is not required where rigid-type mechanical couplings are used. Rigid-type mechanical couplings are those not meeting the definition of *flexible listed pipe coupling* in 3.5.4.

The requirement 9.3.5.3.6 applies only to horizontal mains and branch lines required to be braced as mains. It does not apply to other branch lines or to vertical piping such as risers.

9.3.5.3.7 The requirements of 9.3.5.3 shall not apply to pipes individually supported by rods less than 6 in. (152 mm) long measured between the top of the pipe and the point of attachment to the building structure.

Lateral sway bracing may be omitted for pipes supported by rods less than 6 in. (152 mm) in length, which is permitted by 9.3.5.3.7. Short hangers are expected to limit movement that could result in damage-inducing momentum. The types of hangers used should be able to withstand horizontal earthquake loads and should not be brittle or otherwise highly susceptible to fatigue failure.

In general, the 6-in. (152-mm) length is measured between the points of support of the rod at the building structure and the pipe ring or clamp. Oversized pipe rings are not permitted as a means of extending the allowable distance between the structure and the pipe under this exception. A hole in a beam that is used to support the pipe gives the same intended result as 9.3.5.3.7 and allows for the omission of lateral sway bracing.

◀ **FAQ**
How should the 6-in. (152-mm) length be measured?

9.3.5.3.8 The requirements of 9.3.5.3 shall not apply where U-type hooks of the wraparound type or those U-type hooks arranged to keep the pipe tight to the underside of the structural element shall be permitted to be used to satisfy the requirements for lateral sway bracing, provided the legs are bent out at least 30 degrees from the vertical and the maximum length of each leg and the rod size satisfies the conditions of Table 9.3.5.8.9(a), Table 9.3.5.8.9(b), and Table 9.3.5.8.9(c).

9.3.5.4 Longitudinal Sway Bracing.

9.3.5.4.1 Longitudinal sway bracing spaced at a maximum of 80 ft (24.4 m) on center shall be provided for feed and cross mains.

Although the 1994 edition of NFPA 13 permitted omission of longitudinal sway bracing for mains supported by rods less than 6 in. (152 mm) in length, experience in the 1994 Northridge, CA, earthquake showed that such omission is inappropriate, and, therefore, longitudinal sway bracing for mains supported by rods less than 6 in. (152 mm) in length is required by 9.3.5.4.1.

◀ **FAQ**
Why was the exception for longitudinal sway bracing for mains supported with rods less than 6 in. (152 mm) eliminated?

9.3.5.4.2 Longitudinal braces shall be permitted to serve as lateral braces where they are installed within 24 in. (610 mm) of the piping that is braced laterally.

9.3.5.4.3 The distance between the last brace and the end of the pipe shall not exceed 40 ft (12.2 m).

9.3.5.5 Risers.

9.3.5.5.1* Tops of risers exceeding 3 ft (1 m) in length shall be provided with a four-way brace.

A.9.3.5.5.1 The four-way brace provided at the riser can also provide longitudinal and lateral bracing for adjacent mains.

 9.3.5.5.2 Distance between four-way braces for risers shall not exceed 25 ft (7.6 m).

9.3.5.5.3 Four-way bracing shall not be required where risers penetrate intermediate floors in multistory buildings where the clearance does not exceed the limits of 9.3.4.

Limited clearance around a riser extending through a substantial floor or roof restricts movement and provides the equivalent of bracing (see 9.3.5.5.3). For risers that extend above a roof to serve a standpipe outlet, the bracing can be located at the underside of the roof or can be provided by the clearance through the roof structure in this manner.

9.3.5.6* Horizontal Force Factors.

 A.9.3.5.6 *Location of Sway Bracing.* Two-way braces are either longitudinal or lateral depending on their orientation with the axis of the piping. *[See Figure A.9.3.5.6(a), Figure A.9.3.5.6(b), Figure A.9.3.5.6(c), and Figure A.9.3.5.6(d).]* The simplest form of two-way brace is a piece of steel pipe or angle. Because the brace must act in both compression and tension, it is necessary to size the brace to prevent buckling.

An important aspect of sway bracing is its location. In Building 1 of Figure A.9.3.5.6(a), the relatively heavy main will pull on the branch lines when shaking occurs. If the branch lines are held rigidly to the roof or floor above, the fittings can fracture due to the induced stresses.

Bracing should be on the main as indicated at Location B. With shaking in the direction of the arrows, the light branch lines will be held at the fittings. Where necessary, a lateral brace or other restraint should be installed to prevent a branch line from striking against building components or equipment.

A four-way brace is indicated at Location A. This keeps the riser and main lined up and also prevents the main from shifting.

In Building 1, the branch lines are flexible in a direction parallel to the main, regardless of building movement. The heavy main cannot shift under the roof or floor, and it also steadies the branch lines. While the main is braced, the flexible couplings on the riser allow the sprinkler system to move with the floor or roof above, relative to the floor below.

Figure A.9.3.5.6(b), Figure A.9.3.5.6(c), and Figure A.9.3.5.6(d) show typical locations of sway bracing.

For all threaded connections, sight holes or other means should be provided to permit indication that sufficient thread is engaged.

To properly size and space braces, it is necessary to employ the following steps:

(1) Based on the distance of mains from the structural members that will support the braces, choose brace shapes and sizes from Table 9.3.5.8.9(a), Table 9.3.5.8.9(b), and Table 9.3.5.8.9(c) such that the maximum slenderness ratios, l/r, do not exceed 300. The angle of the braces from the vertical should be at least 30 degrees and preferably 45 degrees or more.

(2) Tentatively space lateral braces at 40-ft (12-m) maximum distances along mains and tentatively space longitudinal braces at 80-ft (24-m) maximum distances along mains. Lateral braces should meet the piping at right angles, and longitudinal braces should be aligned with the piping.

(3) Determine the total load tentatively applied to each brace in accordance with the examples shown in Figure A.9.3.5.6(e) and the following:

(a) For the loads on lateral braces on cross mains, add one-half the weight of the branch to one-half the weight of the portion of the cross main within the zone of influence of the brace. *[See examples 1, 3, 6, and 7 in Figure A.9.3.5.6(e).]*

(b) For the loads on longitudinal braces on cross mains, consider only one-half the weight of the cross mains and feed mains within the zone of influence. Branch lines need not be included. *[See examples 2, 4, 5, 7, and 8 in Figure A.9.3.5.6(e).]* For the

FIGURE A.9.3.5.6(a) *Earthquake Protection for Sprinkler Piping.*

A Four-way brace at riser
B Lateral brace
C Lateral brace
D Short drop [Figure A.9.3.2(b)]
E Couplings at wall penetration
F Longitudinal brace

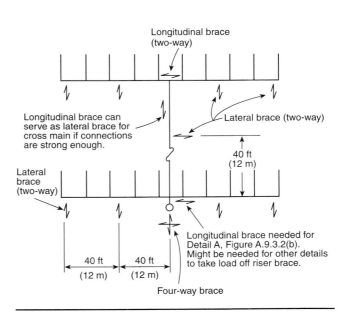

FIGURE A.9.3.5.6(b) *Typical Location of Bracing on a Tree System.*

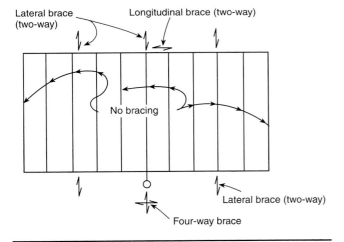

FIGURE A.9.3.5.6(c) *Typical Location of Bracing on a Gridded System.*

FIGURE A.9.3.5.6(d) *Typical Location of Bracing on a Looped System.*

four-way bracing at the top of the riser, half the weight of the riser should be assigned to both of the lateral and longitudinal loads as they are separately considered.

(c) For the four-way brace at the riser, add the longitudinal and lateral loads within the zone of influence of the brace *[see examples 2, 3, and 5 in Figure A.9.3.5.6(e)]*. For the four-way bracing at the top of the riser, half the weight of the riser should be assigned to both the lateral and longitudinal loads as they are separately considered.

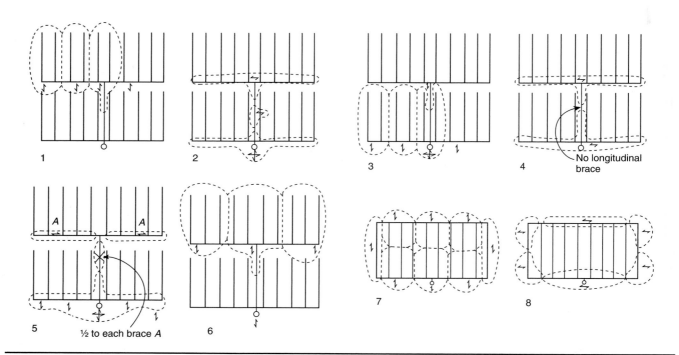

FIGURE A.9.3.5.6(e) *Examples of Load Distribution to Bracing.*

(4) If the total expected loads are less than the maximums permitted in Table 9.3.5.8.9(a), Table 9.3.5.8.9(b), and Table 9.3.5.8.9(c) for the particular brace and orientation, go on to step (5). If not, add additional braces to reduce the zones of influence of overloaded braces.

(5) Check that fasteners connecting the braces to structural supporting members are adequate to support the expected loads on the braces in accordance with Table 9.3.5.8.9(a), Table 9.3.5.8.9(b), and Table 9.3.5.8.9(c). If not, again add additional braces or additional means of support.

  Use the information on weights of water-filled piping contained within Table A.9.3.5.6. The factor of 1.15 is intended to approximate the additional weight of all the valves, fittings, and other devices attached to the system.

Prior to the 1999 edition, two methods were permitted by NFPA 13 for determining the loads to be carried by earthquake braces:

1. The assigned load method
2. The "zone of influence" method

The assigned load method was based on a table of assigned loads according to the size of the main. The table was developed based on conservative worst-case assumptions relative to the loads contributed by branch lines. In almost all cases, loads could be reduced through the use of the zone of influence option, in which loads are assigned based on the particular configuration of the piping. Use of the zone of influence method is now required.

Under the zone of influence method, both branch lines and mains are considered to contribute to the loads on lateral braces, but only mains are considered to contribute to the loads

TABLE A.9.3.5.6 *Piping Weights for Determining Horizontal Load*

Nominal Dimensions	Weight of Water-Filled Pipe		Nominal Dimensions	Weight of Water-Filled Pipe	
	lb/ft	kg/m		lb/ft	kg/m
Schedule 40 Pipe (in.)			Schedule 10 Pipe (in.)		
1	2.05	3.05	1	1.81	2.69
1¼	2.93	4.36	1¼	2.52	3.75
1½	3.61	5.37	1½	3.04	4.52
2	5.13	7.63	2	4.22	6.28
2½	7.89	11.74	2½	5.89	8.77
3	10.82	16.10	3	7.94	11.82
3½	13.48	20.06	3½	9.78	14.55
4	16.40	24.41	4	11.78	17.53
5	23.47	34.93	5	17.30	25.75
6	31.69	47.16	6	23.03	34.27
8*	47.70	70.99	8	40.08	59.65

*Schedule 30.

in longitudinal braces. The longitudinal braces are not expected to be impacted by branch line loads, because these forces are not uniformly transferred during earthquake motion. For each brace, the combined weights of the contributory water-filled piping are multiplied by the appropriate percentage of gravity used as the horizontal force factor (default of 0.5) to determine the total load. For braces that serve as a lateral brace for one main and as a longitudinal brace for a perpendicular main, the loads must be added since these forces would be applied simultaneously to the brace.

Figures A.9.3.5.6(a) through A.9.3.5.6(e) show typical locations of sway bracing on various configurations of systems. Figure A.9.3.5.6(c) has no lateral bracing on the outside lines because the outside lines are typical branch lines of the grid—that is, not oversized—and, therefore, are not considered mains.

9.3.5.6.1 Unless the requirements of 9.3.5.6.2 are met, the horizontal loads for braces shall be determined by analysis based on a horizontal force of $F_p = 0.5\ W_p$, where F_p is the horizontal force factor and W_p is 1.15 times the weight of the water-filled piping.

Horizontal force factors are discussed in 9.3.5.6.1. NFPA 13 earthquake protection criteria have traditionally been based on an assumed horizontal acceleration of 0.5 g ($A_h = 0.5$ g). This acceleration results in a horizontal force factor of 0.5 W_p or a horizontal force equivalent to half the weight of the water-filled piping. This acceleration was judged to be suitably conservative for even highly active earthquake areas, and it was not considered economically justified to fine-tune system bracing loads to accommodate lower expected earthquake forces in some localities. The 0.5 g value continues to serve as the default value for bracing criteria. However, since the 1994 edition, NFPA 13 has permitted the use of other force factors to accommodate code requirements that specify the use of higher or lower horizontal acceleration values. Use of alternative force factors is becoming common for the following two reasons:

◄ **FAQ**
What is the basis for the assumed horizontal acceleration of 0.5 g contained in NFPA 13?

1. Recent earthquakes in California have demonstrated horizontal accelerations in excess of 0.5 g.
2. Earthquake protection of sprinkler systems is now mandated in many areas where expected accelerations can be less than 0.5 g.

Where earthquake protection of the system is required but other horizontal acceleration factors are not specified to the satisfaction of the authority having jurisdiction, the $A_h = 0.5$ g default value should continue to be used.

9.3.5.6.2 Where the use of horizontal force factors other than the horizontal force factor required by 9.3.5.6.1 is required or permitted by the authority having jurisdiction, they shall take precedence.

9.3.5.6.3 For lateral braces, the load shall include all branch lines and mains, unless the branch lines are provided with longitudinal bracing, within the zone of influence of the brace.

9.3.5.6.4 For longitudinal braces, the load shall include all mains within the zone of influence of the brace.

9.3.5.7 Horizontal Force Factors. Where the horizontal force factors used exceed 0.5 W_p and the brace angle is less than 45 degrees from vertical or where the horizontal force factor exceeds 1.0 W_p and the brace angle is less than 60 degrees from vertical, the braces shall be arranged to resist the net vertical reaction produced by the horizontal load.

First introduced in the 1996 edition, 9.3.5.7 addresses the need to protect against upward vertical movement of the pipe as a result of a strong horizontal load in combination with a limited brace angle from vertical. Previous editions did not specifically address such vertical movement. When needed, this additional support could take the form of hanger rods located in close proximity [within 24 in. (610 mm)] of braces and reinforced against buckling by use of pipe sheathing or other means.

9.3.5.8* Horizontal Loads.

A.9.3.5.8 Sway brace members should be continuous. Where necessary, splices in sway bracing members should be designed and constructed to insure that brace integrity is maintained.

9.3.5.8.1 Sway bracing shall be tight.

9.3.5.8.2 For individual braces, the slenderness ratio *(l/r)* shall not exceed 300 where *l* is the length of the brace and *r* is the least radius of gyration.

FAQ ▶
What is the slenderness ratio (*l/r*)?

The slenderness ratio of a brace *(l/r)*, which is discussed in 9.3.5.8.2, is determined by dividing the length of the brace *(l)* by its least radius of gyration *(l/r)*. The least radius of gyration is a mathematical abstraction related to the ability of a shape to resist buckling. When determining the least radius of gyration of a shape that is nonsymmetrical along its axis, the least stable axis must be considered, because that is where buckling is expected to occur.

The slenderness ratio is limited to a maximum of 300 because most braces are expected to act as long columns when they are resisting horizontal and vertical loads in compression. Long columns can help absorb some of the energy of an earthquake, but excessive length reduces the column's ability to resist buckling and invites fatigue failure over time. Prior to the 1994 edition of NFPA 13, the maximum slenderness ratio was limited to 200.

Tables 9.3.5.8.9(a), 9.3.5.8.9(b), and 9.3.5.8.9(c) indicate the formulas used to determine the least radius of gyration for common brace shapes and the maximum lengths of braces that qualify for slenderness ratios of 100, 200, and 300 respectively.

9.3.5.8.3 Where threaded pipe is used as part of a sway brace assembly, it shall not be less than Schedule 30.

9.3.5.8.4 All parts and fittings of a brace shall lie in a straight line to avoid eccentric loadings on fittings and fasteners.

9.3.5.8.5 For longitudinal braces only, the brace shall be permitted to be connected to a tab welded to the pipe in conformance with 6.5.2.

9.3.5.8.6 For individual braces, the slenderness ratio, l/r, shall not exceed 300 where l is the length of the brace and r is the least radius of gyration.

9.3.5.8.7 For tension-only braces, two tension-only brace components opposing each other must be installed at each lateral or longitudinal brace location.

9.3.5.8.8 For all braces, whether or not listed, the maximum allowable horizontal load shall be based on the weakest component of the brace with safety factors.

9.3.5.8.9 The loads determined in 9.3.5.6 shall not exceed the lesser of the maximum allowable loads provided in Table 9.3.5.8.9(a), Table 9.3.5.8.9(b), and Table 9.3.5.8.9(c) or the manufacturer's certified maximum allowable horizontal loads for 30- to 44-degree, 45- to 59-degree, 60- to 89-degree, and 90-degree brace angles.

The load values in Tables 9.3.5.8.9(a), 9.3.5.8.9(b), and 9.3.5.8.9(c) are calculated based on determining critical loads for buckling in columns in accordance with Euler's formula. Euler's formula is as follows:

$$P = \frac{AE\pi^2}{l/r^2}$$

where:

P = maximum axial load

A = cross-sectional area of brace

E = modulus of elasticity for steel equal to 29,000,000 psi (1,998,100 bar)

l/r = slenderness ratio

The following illustrates how the maximum horizontal load is determined for 1 in. (25 mm) Schedule 40 steel pipe. The cross-sectional area of the pipe is calculated using the following formula and Table A.6.3.2:

$$A = x(d^2{}_0 - d^2{}_i)$$
$$4 = 0.494 \text{ in.}^2$$

where:

d_o = outside diameter

d_i = inside diameter

The maximum axial load is found as follows:

$$p = \frac{0.494 \text{ in. } (29,000,000 \text{ psi}).x}{300} = 1571 \text{ lb}$$

The three values for maximum horizontal load that appear in Tables 9.3.5.8.9(a), 9.3.5.8.9(b), and 9.3.5.8.9(c) were determined by multiplying this maximum axial load by the sine of the angle made with the vertical plane. The determination is based on the worst-case angle within each range of angles. This adjustment is needed because the axial load in the brace is higher than the horizontal load when the brace is at some angle from the horizontal. For the 1-in.

TABLE 9.3.5.8.9(a) *Maximum Horizontal Loads for Sway Braces with* l/r=100

Shape and Size	Least Radius of Gyration	Maximum Length for:	Maximum Horizontal Load (lb)		
			30° to 44° Angle from Vertical	45° to 59° Angle from Vertical	60° to 90° Angle from Vertical
Pipe (Schedule 40)	$\dfrac{\sqrt{r_0^2 + r_i^2}}{2}$	l/r=100			
1 in.	0.42	3 ft 6 in.	7,068	9,996	12,242
1¼ in.	0.54	4 ft 6 in.	9,567	13,530	16,570
1½ in.	0.623	5 ft 2 in.	11,441	16,181	19,817
2 in.	0.787	6 ft 6 in.	15,377	21,746	26,634
Rods	$= \dfrac{r}{2}$	l/r=100			
⅜ in.	0.094	0 ft 9 in.	1,580	2,234	2,737
½ in.	0.125	1 ft 0 in.	2,809	3,972	4,865
⅝ in.	0.156	1 ft 3 in.	4,390	6,209	7,605
¾ in.	0.188	1 ft 6 in.	6,322	8,941	10,951
⅞ in.	0.219	1 ft 9 in.	8,675	12,169	14,904

TABLE 9.3.5.8.9(b) *Maximum Horizontal Loads for Sway Braces with* l/r=200

Shape and Size	Least Radius of Gyration	Maximum Length for:	Maximum Horizontal Load (lb)		
			30° to 44° Angle from Vertical	45° to 59° Angle from Vertical	60° to 90° Angle from Vertical
Pipe (Schedule 40)	$\dfrac{\sqrt{r_0^2 + r_i^2}}{2}$	l/r =200			
1 in.	0.42	7 ft 0 in.	1,767	2,500	3,061
1¼ in.	0.54	9 ft 0 in.	2,392	3,385	4,145
1½ in.	0.623	10 ft 4 in.	2,858	4,043	4,955
2 in.	0.787	13 ft 1 in.	3,828	5,414	6,630
Angles		l/r = 200			
1½ × 1½ × ¾ in.	0.292	4 ft 10 in.	2,461	3,481	4,263
2 × 2 × ¼ in.	0.391	6 ft 6 in.	3,356	4,746	5,813
2½ × 2 × ¼ in.	0.424	7 ft 0 in.	3,792	5,363	6,569
2½ × 2½ × ¼ in.	0.491	8 ft 2 in.	4,257	6,021	7,374
3 × 2½ × ¼ in.	0.528	8 ft 10 in.	4,687	6,628	8,118
3 × 3 × ¼ in.	0.592	9 ft 10 in.	5,152	7,286	8,923
Rods	$= \dfrac{r}{2}$	l/r = 200			
⅜ in.	0.094	1 ft 6 in.	395	559	685
½ in.	0.125	2 ft 6 in.	702	993	1,217
⅝ in.	0.156	2 ft 7 in.	1,087	1,537	1,883
¾ in.	0.188	3 ft 1 in.	1,580	2,235	2,737
⅞ in.	0.219	3 ft 7 in.	2,151	3,043	3,726
Flats	$= 0.29h$ (where h is smaller of two side dimensions)	l/r = 200			
1½ × ¼ in.	0.0725	1 ft 2 in.	1,118	1,581	1,936
2 × ¼ in.	0.0725	1 ft 2 in.	1,789	2,530	3,098
2 × ⅜ in.	0.109	1 ft 9 in.	2,683	3,795	4,648

TABLE 9.3.5.8.9(c) *Maximum Horizontal Loads for Sway Braces with* l/r=300

Shape and Size	Least Radius of Gyration	Maximum Length for:	Maximum Horizontal Load (lb)		
			30° to 44° Angle from Vertical	45° to 59° Angle from Vertical	60° to 90° Angle from Vertical
Pipe (Schedule 40)	$\sqrt{\dfrac{r_0^2 + r_i^2}{2}}$	l/r = 300			
1 in.	0.42	10 ft 6 in.	786	1,111	1,360
1¼ in.	0.54	13 ft 6 in.	1,063	1,503	1,841
1½ in.	0.623	15 ft 7 in.	1,272	1,798	2,202
2 in.	0.787	19 ft 8 in.	1,666	2,355	2,885
Rods	$= \dfrac{r}{2}$	l/r = 300			
⅜ in.	0.094	2 ft 4 in.	176	248	304
½ in.	0.125	3 ft 1 in.	312	441	540
⅝ in.	0.156	3 ft 11 in.	488	690	845
¾ in.	0.219	5 ft 6 in.	956	1,352	1,656

Schedule 40 steel pipe with a *(l/r)* ratio of 300 (maximum length of 10 ft, 6 in.), the maximum horizontal load at each angle is as follows:

$$1571 \text{ lb } (\sin 30°) = 1571(0.5) = 786 \text{ lb}$$

$$1571 \text{ lb } (\sin 45°) = 1571(0.707) = 1111 \text{ lb}$$

$$1571 \text{ lb } (\sin 60°) = 1571(0.867) = 1360 \text{ lb}$$

Therefore, maximum allowable loads for each type of brace in the tables are stated as a function of the angle of the brace from vertical. The allowable loads increase as the brace moves toward a horizontal position, where it can most efficiently handle lateral loads.

For shorter braces, Tables 9.3.5.8.9(a) and 9.3.5.8.9(b) can be used to allow greater loads on brace members. For example, if the 1-in. Schedule 40 pipe used in the example is no longer than 3 ft 6 in. between its points of support at the sway brace (pipe attachment) fitting and the structure attachment fitting, Table 9.3.5.8.9(a) can be used and the maximum allowable loads based on angle of the brace from vertical increase to the following:

$$14,136 \text{ lb } (\sin 30°) = 14,136(0.5) = 7068 \text{ lb}$$

$$14,136 \text{ lb } (\sin 45°) = 14,136(0.707) = 9996 \text{ lb}$$

$$14,136 \text{ lb } (\sin 60°) = 14,136(0.867) = 12,242 \text{ lb}$$

It should be recognized, however, that the allowable loads for brace members may be much higher than the allowable loads for listed brace fittings and fasteners. The strength of the brace assembly is based on the "weakest link" of the brace, the sway brace (pipe attachment) fitting, the structure attachment fitting, and the fastener.

Exhibit 9.18 illustrates an unacceptable and an acceptable lateral bracing arrangement. The arrangement on the left in Exhibit 9.18 is unacceptable because the hanger ring is not snug and the brace is not perpendicular to the pipe. The bracing is required to be tight. In addition, the bracing on all parts and fittings of the brace are to lie in a straight line to avoid an eccentric loading on fittings and fasteners. For longitudinal braces, the brace will obviously

EXHIBIT 9.18
*An Unacceptable
Connection to Brace Pipe
(on the Left) and an
Acceptable Connection to
Brace Pipe (on the Right).*

meet the pipe strap at an angle from vertical but should be aligned with the centerline of the pipe.

9.3.5.8.10 These certified allowable horizontal loads must include a minimum safety factor of 1.5 against the ultimate break strength of the brace components and then be further reduced according to the brace angles.

The 1.5 safety factor stated in 9.3.5.8.10 is intended as guidance to the listing organizations when addressing special listed brace assemblies and components. Appropriate safety factors have already been included for the types of braces included within the tables.

9.3.5.8.11 Other pipe schedules and materials not specifically included in Table 9.3.5.8.9(a), Table 9.3.5.8.9(b), and Table 9.3.5.8.9(c) shall be permitted to be used if certified by a registered professional engineer to support the loads determined in accordance with the above criteria. Calculations shall be submitted where required by the authority having jurisdiction.

9.3.5.9* Fasteners.

 A.9.3.5.9 The criteria in Table 9.3.5.8.9(a), Table 9.3.5.8.9(b), and Table 9.3.5.8.9(c) are based upon the use of a shield-type expansion anchor. Use of other anchors in concrete should be in accordance with the listing provisions of the anchor.

Current fasteners for anchoring to concrete are referred to as expansion anchors. Expansion anchors come in two types. Deformation-controlled anchors are set by driving a plug into the expansion port in the anchor or driving the anchor over a plug that expands the end of the anchor into the concrete. Torque-controlled expansion anchors are set by applying a torque to the anchor, usually to a nut, which causes the expansion sleeves to be pressed against the wall of the drilled hole.

Consideration should be given with respect to the position near the edge of the concrete and to the type of bolts used in conjunction with the anchors.

Fasteners are discussed in 9.3.5.9. For connections to wood components, the fastener load values within Figure 9.3.5.9.1 are based on tests conducted by the Forest Products Laboratory in Madison, WI. However, the values are increased 80 percent to adapt to anchorage design, the yield point of lag screws and bolts subject to a force of at least 45,000 psi (3103 bar), and basic stress of wood subject to a force of 1300 psi (90 bar) parallel to the grain and 275 psi (19 bar) perpendicular to the grain. For lag screws, depth of penetration, including shank, is assumed to be at least eight diameters. For through-bolts in wood, the allowable load increases with the bolt length up to a point, because more area is available for bearing. From that point, the allowable load decreases with the increasing length due to bending in the bolt.

The allowable loads on unfinished steel bolts (see ASTM A 307, *Standard Specification for Carbon Steel Bolts and Studs*) are based on AISC N690, *Specification for the Design Fabrication and Erection of Structural Steel for Buildings,* and are increased 33⅓ percent for earthquake loading.

For lag screws, expansion shields, and steel bolts, the maximum fastener loads are adjusted based on the brace angle with the structural base. The adjustments are based on a combination of shear and pull-out strength assuming the worst possible angle within the ranges that are shown in Figure 9.3.5.9.1, Examples A through I. The loads are further adjusted to account for the difference in axial loading of the brace as compared to the horizontal load as in Tables 9.3.5.8.9(a), 9.3.5.8.9(b), and 9.3.5.8.9(c). With a through-bolt, pull-out is considered to be resisted by the washer on the far side, and only shear loads are considered.

Paragraph 9.3.5.9.6 allows for the use of fastening methods other than those specified by NFPA 13 to be used to fasten sway bracing provided the other methods have been evaluated by a registered professional engineer.

9.3.5.9.1 For individual fasteners, the loads determined in 9.3.5.6 shall not exceed the allowable loads provided in Figure 9.3.5.9.1.

9.3.5.9.2 The type of fasteners used to secure the bracing assembly to the structure shall be limited to those shown in Figure 9.3.5.9.1.

9.3.5.9.3 For connections to wood, through-bolts with washers on each end shall be used, unless the requirements of 9.3.5.9.4 are met.

9.3.5.9.4 Where it is not practical to install through bolts due to the thickness of the member or inaccessibility, lag screws shall be permitted. Holes shall be pre-drilled ⅛ in. (3.2 mm) smaller than the maximum root diameter of the lag screw.

9.3.5.9.5 Holes for through bolts shall be ¹⁄₁₆ in. (1.6 mm) greater than the diameter of the bolt.

9.3.5.9.6 The requirements of 9.3.5.9 shall not apply to other fastening methods, which shall be acceptable for use if certified by a registered professional engineer to support the loads determined in accordance with the criteria in 9.3.5.9. Calculations shall be submitted where required by the authority having jurisdiction.

9.3.5.10 Assemblies.

9.3.5.10.1 Sway bracing assemblies shall be listed for a maximum load rating, unless the requirements of 9.3.5.10.2 are met.

9.3.5.10.2 Where sway bracing utilizing pipe, angles, flats, or rods as shown in Table 9.3.5.8.9(a), Table 9.3.5.8.9(b), and Table 9.3.5.8.9(c) is used, the components do not require listing. Bracing fittings and connections used with those specific materials shall be listed.

Sway brace components other than pipes, angles, flats, and rods must be listed, as stated in 9.3.5.10.2. These components include the brace fittings that attach to the pipe and to the building structure. Listings of the brace components include a maximum horizontal load. The listed loads are to be reduced in accordance with Table 9.3.5.10.3 for braces configured at less than 90 degrees from vertical. This reduction is consistent with the reductions built into Tables 9.3.5.8.9(a), 9.3.5.8.9(b), and 9.3.5.8.9(c) and Figure 9.3.5.9.1 for brace members and fasteners. The listing requirement ensures that the fitting does not compromise the integrity of the brace assembly.

The most common cause of earthquake bracing failure is the overloading of fasteners at the point of connection to the building structure. Brace fitting manufacturers generally make available special brackets that allow multiple fasteners to be used to connect the end of the brace to the building structure. These brackets can distribute the load, which helps to reduce

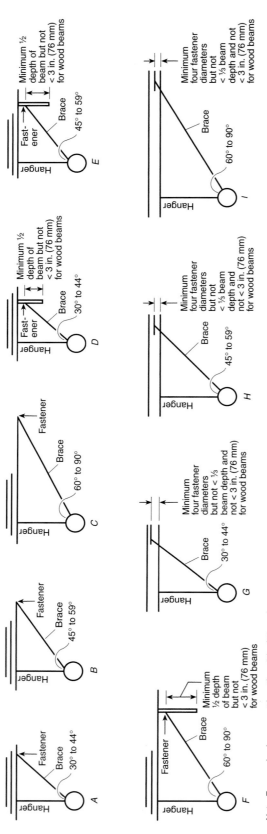

Note: Loads (given in pounds) are keyed to vertical angles of braces and orientation of connecting surface. These values are based on concentric loadings of the fastener. Use figures to determine proper reference within table. For angles between those shown, use most restrictive case. Braces should not be attached to light structure members.

Note: For wooden beams not less than 3 in. (76 mm).

Lag Screws and Lag Bolts in Wood (Load Perpendicular to Grain — Holes Predrilled Using Good Practice)

Shank Diameter of Lag (in.)

		3/8									1/2									5/8									7/8							
		A	B	C	D	E	F	G	H	I	A	B	C	D	E	F	G	H	I	A	B	C	D	E	F	G	H	I	A	B	C	D	E	F	G	H	I
Length under head (in.)	3	304	325	292	168	325	526	230	324	400	366	—	—	—	—	632	—	—	—	410	—	—	—	—	716	—	—	—	487	—	—	—	—	843	—	—	—
	4	392	354	317	183	354	678	250	352	435	473	509	456	264	509	818	360	507	626	538	—	—	—	—	929	—	—	—	548	—	—	—	—	1122	—	—	—
	5	476	375	336	194	375	824	265	373	461	582	545	488	282	545	1008	385	542	670	687	728	653	277	728	1154	515	725	896	813	—	—	—	—	1407	—	—	—
	6	564	382	342	196	382	976	270	380	470	689	559	501	288	559	1192	395	556	687	791	778	697	403	778	1360	550	775	957	971	—	—	—	—	1630	—	—	—
	8	—	—	—	—	—	—	—	—	—	905	573	513	296	573	1586	405	570	704	1044	806	723	416	806	1807	570	803	991	1297	1365	1223	685	1365	2244	965	1359	1678

For SI units, 1 in. = 25.4 mm; 1 ft = 0.3048 m; 1 lb = 0.45 kg.

FIGURE 9.3.5.9.1 Maximum Loads for Various Types of Structure and Maximum Loads for Various Types of Fasteners to Structure.

Through Bolts in Wood (Load Perpendicular to Grain)

Diameter of Bolt (in.)

Length of Bolt in Timber (in.)	3/8						1/2						5/8						7/8					
	ABCE	D	F	G	H	I	ABCE	D	F	G	H	I	ABCE	D	F	G	H	I	ABCE	D	F	G	H	I
1½	300	173	519	150	211	261	340	197	589	170	239	296	390	225	675	195	275	339	470	272	614	235	331	409
2	370	214	641	185	261	322	420	243	727	210	296	365	470	272	814	235	331	409	580	335	1004	290	408	504
2½	460	266	796	230	324	400	550	318	952	275	387	478	620	358	1074	310	437	539	760	439	1316	380	535	661
3	480	277	831	240	338	417	630	364	1091	315	444	548	710	410	1229	355	500	617	870	503	1506	435	613	757
3⅝	460	268	797	230	324	400	720	416	1247	360	507	626	850	491	1472	425	599	739	1050	607	1818	525	739	913
5½	—	—	—	—	—	—	680	393	1177	340	479	591	1020	590	1766	510	718	887	1580	913	2736	790	1113	1374

For SI units, 1 in. = 25.4 mm; 1 lb = 0.45 kg.

Expansion Shields in Concrete

Diameter of Bolt (in.)

Min. Depth of Hole (in.)	3/8									1/2									5/8									7/8								
	A	B	C	D	E	F	G	H	I	A	B	C	D	E	F	G	H	I	A	B	C	D	E	F	G	H	I	A	B	C	D	E	F	G	H	I
2½	498	962	1173	678	668	860	925	1303	1609	—	—	—	—	—	—	1638	2306	2848	—	—	—	—	—	—	2080	2930	3617	—	—	—	—	—	—	2470	4113	5078
3¼	—	—	—	—	—	—	925	1303	1609	923	1782	2076	1200	1782	1597	1638	2306	2848	—	—	—	—	—	—	2080	2930	3617	—	—	—	—	—	—	2970	4113	5078
3¾	—	—	—	—	—	—	925	1303	1609	—	—	—	—	—	—	1638	2306	2848	1480	2857	2637	1524	2857	2581	2080	2930	3617	—	—	—	—	—	—	2970	4113	5078
4½	—	—	—	—	—	—	925	1303	1609	—	—	—	—	—	—	1638	2306	2848	—	—	—	—	—	—	2080	2930	3617	3070	4130	3702	2139	4130	5312	2970	4113	5078

For SI units, 1 in. = 25.4 mm; 1 lb = 0.45 kg.

Connections to Steel (Values Assume Bolt Perpendicular to Mounting Surface)

Diameter of Unfinished Steel Bolt (in.)

1/4									3/8									1/2									5/8								
A	B	C	D	E	F	G	H	I	A	B	C	D	E	F	G	H	I	A	B	C	D	E	F	G	H	I	A	B	C	D	E	F	G	H	I
400	500	600	300	500	650	325	458	565	900	1200	1400	800	1200	1550	735	1035	1278	1600	2050	2550	1450	2050	2850	1300	1830	2260	2500	3300	3950	2250	3300	4400	2045	2880	3557

For SI units, 1 in. = 25.4 mm; 1 ft = 0.3048 m; 1 lb = 0.45 kg.

FIGURE 9.3.5.9.1 Continued.

the load on each fastener to levels allowed by Figure 9.3.5.9.1. If the load cannot be reduced in this manner, additional braces should be added to reduce the load on each brace.

9.3.5.10.3 The loads shall be reduced as shown in Table 9.3.5.10.3 for loads that are less than 90 degrees from vertical.

TABLE 9.3.5.10.3 *Allowable Horizontal Load on Brace Assemblies Based on the Weakest Component of the Brace Assembly*

Brace Angle	Allowable Horizontal Load
30–44 degrees from vertical	Listed load rating divided by 2.000
45–59 degrees from vertical	Listed load rating divided by 1.414
60–89 degrees from vertical	Listed load rating divided by 1.155
90 degrees from vertical	Listed load rating

9.3.5.11 Attachments.

9.3.5.11.1 Bracing shall be attached directly to feed and cross mains.

Bracing of feed and cross mains through the branch lines is not permitted by 9.3.5.11.1.

9.3.5.11.2 Each run of pipe between changes in direction shall be provided with both lateral and longitudinal bracing, unless the requirements of 9.3.5.11.3 are met.

9.3.5.11.3 Pipe runs less than 12 ft (3.6 m) in length shall be permitted to be supported by the braces on adjacent runs of pipe.

Short runs of main do not require bracing by 9.3.5.11.3 if their loads can be assumed by adjacent piping runs.

9.3.5.12 Braces to Buildings with Differential Movement. A length of pipe shall not be braced to sections of the building that will move differentially.

The requirement in 9.3.5.12 also applies to rigidly connected portions of systems, because they are also susceptible to damage from differential movement. In the 1994 Northridge, CA, earthquake, for example, fracture of a large threaded elbow took place near the intersection of a wall and the roof of a mercantile occupancy. One section of piping extending from the elbow was secured to the wall, and the other section was secured to the roof. Following the earthquake, a flexible fitting in the form of a roll-groove elbow was used to repair the main, incorporating two flexible couplings to handle future differential movement.

9.3.6 Restraint of Branch Lines.

Restraint of branch lines is discussed in 9.3.6. Restraint is considered a way of holding piping components in place but to a lesser degree than bracing. Most of the restraint requirements were added to NFPA 13 based on the performance of sprinkler systems in the 1989 Loma Prieta, CA, earthquake, and were reinforced by the 1994 Northridge, CA, earthquake. These earthquakes demonstrated that strong vertical movement of unrestrained branch lines pulled sprinklers upward then back down through the ceilings. Where lateral movement took place simultaneously, the operating mechanisms of flush-type sprinklers were susceptible to damage as the sprinklers broke through ceiling tiles. Ordinary gypsum board ceilings were found to shear concealed sprinklers where considerable lateral branch line movement took place. In evaluating the potential for damage to sprinklers, consideration should be given to the degree of lateral or upward movement permitted by the particular hanging arrangement. Exhibit 9.19 shows restraint of a branch line using a wraparound U-hook.

EXHIBIT 9.19 *Restraint of Branch Line with a Wraparound U-Hook. (Courtesy of Tolco)*

9.3.6.1* Restraint is considered a lesser degree of resisting loads than bracing and shall be provided by use of one of the following:

(1) A listed sway brace assembly
(2) A wraparound U-hook satisfying the requirements of 9.3.5.3.8
(3) No. 12, 440-lb (200-kg) wire installed at least 45 degrees from the vertical plane and anchored on both sides of the pipe
(4) Other approved means

A.9.3.6.1 Wires used for piping restraints should be attached to the branch line with two tight turns around the pipe and fastened with four tight turns within 1½ in. (38 mm), and should be attached to the structure in accordance with the details shown in Figure A.9.3.6.1(a) through Figure A.9.3.6.1(d) or other approved method.

Restraint for branch lines, which is discussed in 9.3.6.1, must be in the lateral as well as the vertical direction. Simple clips used to provide vertical restraint to meet the requirements of 9.2.3.4.3.1 and 9.2.3.5.2.1 can provide adequate restraint if used in combination with a substantial ceiling that provides lateral restraint. The necessary restraint can also be provided by additional hangers brought at an angle, wraparound U-hooks, lateral earthquake braces, or the wire restraint method detailed in A.9.3.6.1.

9.3.6.2 Wire used for restraint shall be located within 2 ft (610 mm) of a hanger. The hanger closest to a wire restraint shall be of a type that resists upward movement of a branch line.

9.3.6.3 The end sprinkler on a line shall be restrained against excessive vertical and lateral movement.

A wraparound U-hook or other restraint at the end of each branch line, as required by 9.3.6.3, prevents the piping from whipping or bouncing out of hangers, which is a possibility even with conventional U-hooks.

Why does 9.3.6.3 require the end sprinkler on a line to be restrained against excessive vertical and lateral movement?
◄ **FAQ**

9.3.6.4* Where upward or lateral movement of the system piping would result in damage to the sprinkler through impact against the building structure, equipment, or finish materials, branch lines shall be restrained at intervals not exceeding 30 ft (9 m).

Detail A — Splayed seismic restraint wire attachment   **Detail B**

FIGURE A.9.3.6.1(a) Wire Attachment to Cast-in-Place Concrete.

Note: See Figure A.9.3.6.1(a), Detail B.

Detail A — At steel beams

Notes:
1. Splay wires parallel to joist. Splay wires cannot be perpendicular to joist.
2. See Figure A.9.3.6.1(a), Detail A.

Detail B — At open web steel joist

Note: If self-tapping screws are used with concrete fill, set screws before placing concrete.

Detail C — At steel roof deck

FIGURE A.9.3.6.1(b) *Acceptable Details—Wire Connections to Steel Framing.*

 A.9.3.6.4 The restraining wire should be provided as close as possible to the hanger.

Restraint is required by 9.3.6.4 at 30-ft (9-m) intervals for branch lines if branch line movement could result in damage to the sprinklers from contact with structural members, mechanical equipment, or finish materials such as rigid ceilings. While lay-in acoustical tile would not be considered a rigid ceiling, gypsum board or metal ceilings would, because they can damage most sprinklers. Pendent sprinklers with deep escutcheons would not be expected to be susceptible to damage in any case due to the fact that the interface with the ceiling would consist of the penetration of a 1-in. (25.4-mm) drop.

9.3.6.5* Sprig-ups 4 ft (1.2 m) or longer shall be restrained against lateral movement.

FIGURE A.9.3.6.1(c) *Acceptable Details—Wire Connections to Steel Decking with Fill.*

A.9.3.6.5 Such restraint can be provided by using the restraining wire discussed in 9.3.6.1.

Sprig-ups are addressed in 9.3.6.5. A vertical sprig, or a sprig-up, is considered the opposite of a pipe drop. A vertical sprig is a pipe rising from the branch line to serve an individual upright sprinkler. They are susceptible to rotation during relatively minor seismic events. The requirement for restraint of sprigs was originally instituted for sprigs more than 8 ft (2.4 m) in length but was changed in the 1996 edition to apply to sprigs exceeding 4 ft (1.2 m) in length. The change was based on observations of rotated sprigs following the Northridge, CA, earthquake. The additional stability gained from this requirement results in time and money saved because sprigs do not have to be manually repositioned after the event. The restraint provisions of 9.3.6.5 do not apply to drops to individual sprinklers, because gravity acts to pull them back to center.

A

◀ **FAQ**
Why are sprigs greater than 4 ft (1.2 m) required to be restrained?

9.3.7 Hangers and Fasteners Subject to Earthquakes.

9.3.7.1 C-type clamps (including beam and large flange clamps) used to attach hangers to the building structure in areas subject to earthquakes shall be equipped with a restraining strap.

Three 1½-in. (38-mm) × 9 galvanized staples or three stronghold "J" nails at each wire loop

1 in. (25.4 mm) minimum

Restraint wire

Detail A — Wood joist or rafter

¼-in. (6.3-mm) diameter screw eye with full thread embedment [1¼ in. (32 mm) minimum]

Top half of joist

Joist or rafter

Restraint wire

Detail B — At wood joist or rafter

Three 1½-in. (38-mm) × 9 galvanized staples or three stronghold "J" nails at each wire loop

2 (50 mm) × blkg. w/2-16d common nails ea. end

Restraint wire

Detail C — At wood joist or block

For restraint wires — fully embed screw eye threads in direction of wire

¼-in. (6.3-mm) diameter drilled hole

2 in. (50 mm) minimum

Restraint wire

Saddle tie (see Detail G)

Detail D — To bottom of joist

Web member

Bottom chord

Saddle tie (see Detail G)

Restraint wire

Detail E — Restraint wire parallel to wood truss

Do not insert screw eyes into side of laminated veneer lumber flange.

Restraint wire

Detail F — Laminated veneer lumber upper flange

1½ in. (38 mm)

Dimension greater than ½ in. (12 mm)

Restraint wires — four tight turns

Detail G — Typical saddle tie

Note: Do not insert screw eyes parallel to laminations (see Detail F). (Details can also be used at top chord.)

¼-in. (6.3-mm) diameter screw eye with 1¼-in. (32-mm) minimum penetration

Restraint wire

1 in. (25.4 mm) minimum

Detail H — Laminated veneer lumber lower flange

FIGURE A.9.3.6.1(d) *Acceptable Details—Wire Connections to Wood Framing.*

Beginning with the 1996 edition, restraining straps were required on all C-type clamps used for system hangers in areas subject to earthquakes (see 9.3.7.1). Previously, NFPA 13 permitted any other means the authority having jurisdiction determined acceptable to prevent C-type clamps from sliding off beam flanges during earthquake movement. Specific criteria for the restraining strap are provided in 9.3.7.2. Exhibits 9.20 and 9.21 illustrate the use of C-clamps with restraining straps.

9.3.7.2 The restraining strap shall be listed for use with a C-type clamp or shall be a steel strap of not less than 16 gauge thickness and not less than 1 in. (25.4 mm) wide for pipe diameters 8 in. (203 mm) or less and 14 gauge thickness and not less than 1¼ in. (31.7 mm) wide for pipe diameters greater than 8 in. (203 mm).

9.3.7.3 The restraining strap shall wrap around the beam flange not less than 1 in. (25.4 mm).

9.3.7.4 A lock nut on a C-type clamp shall not be used as a method of restraint.

9.3.7.5 A lip on a "C" or "Z" purlin shall not be used as a method of restraint.

9.3.7.6 Where purlins or beams do not provide an adequate lip to be secured by a restraining strap, the strap shall be through-bolted or secured by a self-tapping screw.

9.3.7.7 C-type clamps (including beam and large flange clamps), with or without restraining straps, shall not be used to attach braces to the building structure.

9.3.7.8 Powder-driven fasteners shall not be used to attach braces to the building structure, unless they are specifically listed for service in resisting lateral loads in areas subject to earthquakes.

Reports of powder-driven fasteners pulling out during earthquakes have led to the prohibition of their use in attaching braces, unless the fasteners are specifically listed for such use, as stated in 9.3.7.8. As of the time of publication of the 2002 edition of NFPA 13, no such listings were available.

9.3.7.9 In areas where the horizontal force factor exceeds 0.50 W_p powder-driven studs shall be permitted to attach hangers to the building structure where they are specifically listed for use in areas subject to earthquakes.

Powder-driven fasteners are prohibited by 9.3.7.9 as a means of attaching system hangers in strong motion earthquake areas, defined as those in which the authority having jurisdiction designates a horizontal force factor in excess of 0.50 W_p (more than one-half the weight of the water-filled pipe), unless the fasteners have been specifically investigated and listed for such

EXHIBIT 9.20 Application of a C-Clamp with a Restraining Strap on an I-Beam. (Courtesy of AFCON)

EXHIBIT 9.21 C-Clamp with a Restraining Strap.

loads. As of the time of publication of the 2002 edition of NFPA 13, no such listings were available.

SUMMARY

Chapter 9 addresses the structural issues related to installation of fire protection piping systems. Section 9.1 contains regulations for acceptable types of hangers, Section 9.2 covers hanger installation, and Section 9.3 addresses protection of piping where subject to earthquakes.

REFERENCES CITED IN COMMENTARY

National Fire Protection Association, 1 Batterymarch Park, P.O. Box 9101, Quincy, MA 02269-9101

NFPA 14, *Standard for the Installation of Standpipe, Private Hydrant, and Hose Systems,* 2000 edition

NFPA 15, *Standard for Water Spray Fixed Systems for Fire Protection,* 2001 edition

American Institute of Steel Construction, 1 East Wacker Drive, Suite 3100, Chicago, IL 60601

AISC N690, *Specification for the Design Fabrication and Erection of Structural Steel for Buildings,* 1984 edition

American Society for Testing and Materials, 100 Barr Harbor Drive, West Conshohocken, PA 19428-2959

ASTM A 307, *Standard Specification for Carbon Steel Bolts and Studs,* 1997 edition

ASTM E 814, *Test Methods for Fire Tests of Through-Penetration Fire Stops,* 1988 edition

Underground Piping

Chapter 10 has been added to NFPA 13 for the 2002 edition to consolidate all of the requirements for underground piping including piping materials, fittings, joining of pipe and fittings, depth of cover, protection against freezing, protection against damage, requirements for laying pipe, joint restraint, backfilling, and testing and acceptance. The provisions of Chapter 10 also appear as Chapter 10 in the 2002 edition of NFPA 24, *Standard for the Installation of Private Fire Service Mains and Their Appurtenances*. The wording of the two chapters is identical, including all section numbers, tables, and figures. This duplication allows better coordination between the two standards and uniformity in the requirements for underground piping serving water-based fire protection systems.

◀ **FAQ**
Are the underground requirements in NFPA 13 the same as in NFPA 24?

10.1* Piping Materials

A.10.1 The term *underground* is intended to mean direct buried piping. For example, piping installed in trenches and tunnels but exposed should be treated as aboveground piping.

Loop systems for yard piping are recommended for increased reliability and improved hydraulics. Loop systems should be sectionalized by placing valves at branches and at strategic locations to minimize the extent of impairments.

10.1.1* Listing. Piping shall be listed for fire protection service or shall comply with the standards in Table 10.1.1.

A.10.1.1 Copper tubing (Type K) with brazed joints conforming to Table 10.1.1 and Table 10.2.1(a) is acceptable for underground service. Listing and labeling information, along with applicable publications for reference, follows:

(1) *Listing and Labeling.* Testing laboratories list or label the following:

    (a) Cast-iron and ductile iron pipe (cement-lined and unlined, coated and uncoated)

    (b) Asbestos-cement pipe and couplings

    (c) Steel pipe

    (d) Copper pipe

    (e) Fiberglass filament-wound epoxy pipe and couplings

    (f) Polyethylene pipe

    (g) Polyvinyl chloride (PVC) pipe and couplings

    (h) Underwriters Laboratories Inc. lists, under re-examination service, reinforced concrete pipe (cylinder pipe, nonprestressed and prestressed).

(2) *Pipe Standards.* The various types of pipe are usually manufactured to one of the following standards:

    (a) ASTM C296, *Standard Specification for Asbestos-Cement Pressure Pipe*

    (b) AWWA C151, *Ductile Iron Pipe, Centrifugally Cast for Water*

TABLE 10.1.1 *Manufacturing Standards for Underground Pipe*

Materials and Dimensions	*Standard*
Ductile Iron	
Cement Mortar Lining for Ductile Iron Pipe and Fittings for Water	AWWA C104
Polyethylene Encasement for Ductile Iron Pipe Systems	AWWA C105
Ductile Iron and Gray Iron Fittings, 3-in. Through 48-in., for Water and Other Liquids	AWWA C110
Rubber-Gasket Joints for Ductile Iron Pressure Pipe and Fittings	AWWA C111
Flanged Ductile Iron Pipe with Ductile Iron or Gray Iron Threaded Flanges	AWWA C115
Thickness Design of Ductile Iron Pipe	AWWA C150
Ductile Iron Pipe, Centrifugally Cast for Water	AWWA C151
Standard for the Installation of Ductile Iron Water Mains and Their Appurtenances	AWWA C600
Steel	
Steel Water Pipe 6 in. and Larger	AWWA C200
Coal-Tar Protective Coatings and Linings for Steel Water Pipelines Enamel and Tape—Hot Applied	AWWA C203
Cement-Mortar Protective Lining and Coating for Steel Water Pipe 4 in. and Larger—Shop Applied	AWWA C205
Field Welding of Steel Water Pipe	AWWA C206
Steel Pipe Flanges for Waterworks Service—Sizes 4 in. Through 144 in.	AWWA C207
Dimensions for Fabricated Steel Water Pipe Fittings	AWWA C208
A Guide for Steel Pipe Design and Installation	AWWA M11
Concrete	
Reinforced Concrete Pressure Pipe, Steel-Cylinder Type, for Water and Other Liquids	AWWA C300
Prestressed Concrete Pressure Pipe, Steel-Cylinder Type, for Water and Other Liquids	AWWA C301
Reinforced Concrete Pressure Pipe, Non-Cylinder Type, for Water and Other Liquids	AWWA C302
Reinforced Concrete Pressure Pipe, Steel-Cylinder Type, Pretensioned, for Water and Other Liquids	AWWA C303
Asbestos-Cement Distribution Pipe, 4 in. Through 16 in., for Water and Other Liquids	AWWA C400
Standard Practice for Selection of Asbestos-Cement Water Pipe	AWWA C401
Cement-Mortar Lining of Water Pipe Lines 4 in. and Larger—in Place	AWWA C602
Standard for the Installation of Asbestos-Cement Water Pipe	AWWA C603
Plastic	
Polyvinyl Chloride (PVC) Pressure Pipe, 4 in. Through 12 in., for Water and Other Liquids	AWWA C900
Copper	
Specification for Seamless Copper Tube	ASTM B 75
Specification for Seamless Copper Water Tube	ASTM B 88
Requirements for Wrought Seamless Copper and Copper-Alloy Tube	ASTM B 251

(c) AWWA C300, *Reinforced Concrete Pressure Pipe, Steel-Cylinder Type, for Water and Other Liquids*

(d) AWWA C301, *Prestressed Concrete Pressure Pipe, Steel-Cylinder Type, for Water and Other Liquids*

(e) AWWA C302, *Reinforced Concrete Pressure Pipe, Non-Cylinder Type, for Water and Other Liquids*

(f) AWWA C303, *Reinforced Concrete Pressure Pipe, Steel-Cylinder Type, Pretensioned, for Water and Other Liquids*

(g) AWWA C400, *Standard for Asbestos-Cement Distribution Pipe, 4 in. Through 16 in., for Water and Other Liquids*

(h) AWWA C900, *Polyvinyl Chloride (PVC) Pressure Pipe, 4 in. Through 12 in., for Water and Other Liquids*

Underground pipe must be listed for fire protection service or must comply with the American Water Works Association (AWWA) standards specified in Table 10.1.1; however many piping products that are manufactured in accordance with the AWWA standards are nevertheless also listed for fire protection service.

Although several of these standards deal with steel pipe, flanges, welding, and installation, steel pipe is currently prohibited from use in underground fire protection service except for fire department connections or unless specially listed for this service. (See 10.1.2 and 10.1.3.)

Although the only plastic pipe included in Table 10.1.1 is polyvinyl chloride (PVC) pipe manufactured in accordance with AWWA C900, *Polyvinyl Chloride (PVC) Pressure Pipe, 4 in. Through 12 in. (100 mm Through 300 mm), for Water and Other Liquids,* with diameters up to 12 in. (300 mm), listings are available for PVC with nominal diameters up to 30 in. (750 mm). Listings are also available for chlorinated polyvinyl chloride (CPVC) in the ¾ in. (20 mm) to 3 in. (75 mm) size, and for fiberglass-wound epoxy pipe in sizes 2 in. through 16 in. (50 mm through 400 mm) nominal diameter.

An often overlooked materials issue is that most nonmetallic underground piping brought up through the floor of a building is vulnerable to fire exposure and spills of corrosive liquids. Transition should be made to metallic pipe to avoid problems, and this transition is essentially required by the listing of the nonmetallic pipe, since such use is no longer underground. For more information on the transition of the underground to the aboveground piping see 15.1.6.1.2.

10.1.2 Steel Pipe. Steel piping shall not be used for general underground service unless specifically listed for such service.

Steel pipe is addressed in 10.1.2. Past experience and loss data indicate that a high potential for failure of buried steel pipe exists even where the pipe is externally coated and wrapped and internally galvanized. The integrity of the coating, wrapping, and galvanizing can be easily compromised in many underground applications. Accordingly, steel pipe can no longer be installed for general underground service unless it is specially listed for this purpose. At this time no such listings are available.

10.1.3 Steel Pipe Used with Fire Department Connections. Where externally coated and wrapped and internally galvanized, steel pipe shall be permitted to be used between the check valve and the outside hose coupling for the fire department connection.

Steel pipe can be used for piping to a fire department connection, as discussed in 10.1.3, because the fire department connection is an auxiliary rather than a primary water supply for the sprinkler system. Both coating and wrapping are required when internally galvanized steel pipe may be used between an exterior fire department connection and the check valve where it connects to the system. Coating is also required for clamps, tie rods, and all bolted joint accessories. (See 10.3.6.2 and 10.8.3.5.)

AWWA C203, *Coal-Tar Protective Coatings and Linings for Steel Water Pipelines Enamel and Tape—Hot Applied,* is a referenced standard for coating materials in Table 10.1.1, but other bituminous (coal-tar) coatings are available in the marketplace.

AWWA C105, *Polyethylene Encasement for Ductile Iron Pipe Systems,* another of the referenced standards in Table 10.1.1, provides useful installation guidance where wrapping is required. The standard basically requires that high-density polyethylene tubes or sheets with a minimum nominal thickness of 0.004 in. (0.1 mm) or low-density polyethylene tubes or sheets with a minimum nominal thickness of 0.008 in. (0.2 mm) be used for the wrapping.

◄ FAQ
Do the requirements of 10.1.1 require that all piping utilized underground be listed for fire protection service?

◄ FAQ
Several of the AWWA standards referenced in Table 10.1.1 address steel pipe. Does this indicate that steel pipe is permitted for general underground use if it meets the applicable AWWA standards in Table 10.1.1?

◄ FAQ
Where plastic pipe is utilized underground, is it acceptable to transition to steel pipe aboveground?

◄ FAQ
Can steel pipe be utilized for general underground fire protection applications?

◄ FAQ
Can steel pipe be used for fire department connection piping?

The minimum width to be used is based on the nominal pipe diameter as shown in Commentary Table 10.1.

COMMENTARY TABLE 10.1 *Minimum Width of High-Density Polyethylene Flat Tubes and Sheets*

Nominal Pipe Diameter		Minimum Width of Flat Tube		Minimum Width of Sheet	
in.	*mm*	*in.*	*mm*	*in.*	*mm*
3	75	14	350	28	700
4	100	14	350	28	700
6	150	16	400	32	800
8	200	20	500	40	1000
10	250	24	600	48	1200
12	300	27	670	54	1350
14	350	30	750	60	1500

The polyethylene is not intended to create an airtight or watertight enclosure, but to prevent contact between the pipe and surrounding backfill/bedding material. Slack must be provided to prevent stretching the polyethylene where it bridges irregular surfaces such as bolted joints, anticipating backfilling operations. Cuts, tears, and punctures must be repaired. Overlaps must be a minimum of 1 ft (0.3 m) and must be secured using tape, string, or tie straps. Overlaps to pipe areas not wrapped must extend a minimum of 3 ft (1.0 m) and be circumferentially taped. Where piping is installed below the water table or in areas affected by tidal flooding, the wrapping must be circumferentially taped every 2 ft (0.6 m).

10.1.4* Pipe Type and Class. The type and class of pipe for a particular underground installation shall be determined through consideration of the following factors:

(1) Fire resistance of the pipe
(2) Maximum system working pressure
(3) Depth at which the pipe is to be installed
(4) Soil conditions
(5) Corrosion
(6) Susceptibility of pipe to other external loads, including earth loads, installation beneath buildings, and traffic or vehicle loads

 A.10.1.4 The following pipe design manuals can be used as guides:

(1) AWWA C150, *Thickness Design of Ductile Iron Pipe*
(2) AWWA C401, *Standard Practice for the Selection of Asbestos-Cement Water Pipe*
(3) AWWA M41, *Ductile Iron Pipe and Fittings*
(4) *Concrete Pipe Handbook,* American Concrete Pipe Association

10.1.5 Working Pressure. Pipe shall be designed to withstand a system working pressure of not less than 150 psi (10.3 bar).

10.1.6* Lining of Buried Pipe.

 A.10.1.6 The following standards apply to the application of coating and linings:

(1) AWWA C104, *Cement Mortar Lining For Ductile Iron Pipe and Fittings for Water*
(2) AWWA C105, *Polyethylene Encasement for Ductile Iron Pipe Systems*

(3) AWWA C203, *Coal-Tar Protective Coatings and Linings for Steel Water Pipelines Enamel and Tape—Hot Applied*

(4) AWWA C205, *Cement-Mortar Protective Lining and Coating for Steel Water Pipe 4 in. and Larger—Shop Applied*

(5) AWWA C602, *Cement-Mortar Lining of Water Pipe Lines 4 in. and Larger—in Place*

Lining of buried pipe is discussed in 10.1.6. Nominal diameters of available listed lined ferrous metal pipe range from 3 in. (75 mm) to 24 in. (600 mm). Ductile-iron pipe is generally cement-mortar lined in accordance with AWWA C104, *Cement Mortar Lining for Ductile Iron Pipe and Fittings for Water.* Cement-mortar linings were first used with cast iron pipe in 1922 and help prevent tuberculation of ferrous pipe through the creation of a high pH at the pipe wall as well as by providing a physical barrier to the water. The minimum thickness of the lining is 1/16 in. (1.6 mm) for pipe sizes 3 in. to 12 in. (75 mm to 300 mm) in nominal diameter, and greater for larger diameter pipe.

Care should be taken in hydraulic calculations of underground piping since manufacturers generally do not include the thickness of linings when providing information on internal diameters of their piping products. Therefore, when calculating underground lined piping, it is imperative that the actual internal diameter be utilized throughout the calculations.

◄ **FAQ**
When calculating lined underground piping should the actual internal diameter be used?

10.1.6.1 Unless the requirements of 10.1.6.2 are met, all ferrous metal pipe shall be lined in accordance with the applicable standards in Table 10.1.1.

10.1.6.2 Steel pipe utilized in fire department connections and protected in accordance with the requirements of 10.1.3 shall not be additionally required to be lined.

10.2 Fittings

10.2.1 Standard Fittings. Fittings shall meet the standards in Table 10.2.1(a) or shall be in accordance with 10.2.2. In addition to the standards in Table 10.2.1(a), CPVC fittings shall also be in accordance with 10.2.2 and with the portions of the ASTM standards specified in Table 10.2.1(b) that apply to fire protection service.

TABLE 10.2.1(a) *Fittings Materials and Dimensions*

Materials and Dimensions	**Standard**
Cast Iron	
Cast Iron Threaded Fittings, Class 125 and 250	ASME B16.4
Cast Iron Pipe Flanges and Flanged Fittings	ASME B16.1
Malleable Iron	
Malleable Iron Threaded Fittings, Class 150 and 300	ASME B16.3
Steel	
Factory-Made Wrought Steel Buttweld Fittings	ASME B16.9
Buttwelding Ends for Pipe, Valves, Flanges, and Fittings	ASME B16.25
Specification for Piping Fittings of Wrought Carbon Steel and Alloy Steel for Moderate and Elevated Temperatures	ASTM A 234
Steel Pipe Flanges and Flanged Fittings	ASME B16.5
Forged Steel Fittings, Socket Welded and Threaded	ASME B16.11
Copper	
Wrought Copper and Bronze Solder Joint Pressure Fittings	ASME B16.22
Cast Bronze Solder Joint Pressure Fittings	ASME B16.18

TABLE 10.2.1(b) *Specially Listed Fittings Materials and Dimensions*

Materials and Dimensions	Standard
Chlorinated Polyvinyl Chloride (CPVC) Specification for Schedule 80 CPVC Threaded Fittings	ASTM F 437
Specification for Schedule 40 CPVC Socket-Type Fittings	ASTM F 438
Specification for Schedule 80 CPVC Socket-Type Fittings	ASTM F 439

10.2.2 Special Listed Fittings. Other types of fittings investigated for suitability in automatic sprinkler installations and listed for this service including, but not limited to, polybutylene, CPVC, and steel differing from that provided in Table 10.2.1(a), and shall be permitted when installed in accordance with their listing limitations, including installation instructions.

10.2.3 Pressure Limits. Listed fittings shall be permitted for system pressures as specified in their listings, but not less than 150 psi (10 bar).

10.2.4* Buried Joints. Joints shall be approved.

 A.10.2.4 The following standards apply to joints used with the various types of pipe:

(1) ASME B16.1, *Cast-Iron Pipe Flanges and Flanged Fittings*
(2) AWWA C111, *Rubber-Gasket Joints for Ductile Iron Pressure Pipe and Fittings*
(3) AWWA C115, *Flanged Ductile Iron Pipe with Ductile Iron or Gray Iron Threaded Flanges*
(4) AWWA C206, *Field Welding of Steel Water Pipe*
(5) AWWA C606, *Grooved and Shouldered Joints*

10.2.5* Buried Fittings. Fittings shall be of an approved type with joints and pressure class ratings compatible with the pipe used.

 A.10.2.5 Fittings generally used are cast iron with joints made to the specifications of the manufacturer of the particular type of pipe *(see the standards listed in A.10.2.4)*. Steel fittings also have some applications. The following standards apply to fittings:

(1) ASME B16.1, *Cast-Iron Pipe Flanges and Flanged Fittings*
(2) AWWA C110, *Ductile Iron and Gray Iron Fittings, 3-in. Through 48-in., for Water and Other Liquids*
(3) AWWA C153, *Ductile Iron Compact Fittings, 3 in. through 24 in. and 54 in. through 64 in. for Water Service*
(4) AWWA C208, *Dimensions for Fabricated Steel Water Pipe Fittings*

10.3 Joining of Pipe and Fittings

 Section 10.3 covers joining of pipe and fittings. Although 10.2.4 and 10.2.5 simply require that buried joints be approved and that buried fittings be of an approved type, acceptable joining methods for listed piping are generally controlled as part of the pipe listing. Both ductile iron and PVC pipe are generally joined by bell and spigot ends in conjunction with rubber gaskets or by listed mechanical joints. A simple rubber-gasket joint is termed a "push-on joint," in which a single rubber-ring gasket is fitted into the recess of a bell end of a length of pipe and is compressed by the plain end of the entering pipe, forming a seal. The gasket and the annular recess are specially shaped to lock the gasket in place against displacement. AWWA C111, *Rubber Gasket Joints for Ductile Iron Pressure Pipe and Fittings*, one of the

standards referenced in Table 10.1.1, requires that lubricants used in conjunction with push-on joints be labeled with the trade name or trademark and the pipe manufacturer's name to ensure compatibility with gasket material.

10.3.1 Threaded Pipe and Fittings. All threaded steel pipe and fittings shall have threads cut in accordance with ASME B1.20.1, *Pipe Threads, General Purpose (Inch).*

10.3.2 Welded Pipe and Fittings. Welding methods that comply with the applicable requirements of AWS B2.1, *Specification for Welding Procedure and Performance Qualification,* shall be permitted as means of joining steel piping.

10.3.3 Groove Joining Methods. Pipes joined with grooved fittings shall be joined by a listed combination of fittings, gaskets, and grooves.

10.3.4 Brazed and Pressure Fitting Methods. Joints for the connection of copper tube shall be brazed or joined using pressure fittings as specified in Table 10.2.1(a).

10.3.5 Other Joining Methods. Other joining methods listed for this service shall be permitted where installed in accordance with their listing limitations.

10.3.6 Pipe Joint Assembly.

10.3.6.1 Joints shall be assembled by persons familiar with the particular materials being used and in accordance with the manufacturer's instructions and specifications.

10.3.6.2 All bolted joint accessories shall be cleaned and thoroughly coated with asphalt or other corrosion-retarding material after installation.

10.4 Depth of Cover

Depth of cover over pipes is discussed in Section 10.4. Buried piping must be located below the frost line to prevent freezing during the winter months. The piping must also be located deep enough to be protected from other surface loads that could cause mechanical damage. Piping located under driveways, roads, and railroad tracks must be buried deeper to prevent undue loads on the sprinkler piping.

10.4.1* The depth of cover over water pipes shall be determined by the maximum depth of frost penetration in the locality where the pipe is laid.

A.10.4.1 The following documents apply to the installation of pipe and fittings:

(1) AWWA C603, *Standard for the Installation of Asbestos-Cement Water Pipe*
(2) AWWA C600, *Standard for the Installation of Ductile-Iron Water Mains and Their Appurtenances*
(3) AWWA M11, *A Guide for Steel Pipe Design and Installation*
(4) AWWA M41, *Ductile Iron Pipe and Fittings*
(5) *Concrete Pipe Handbook,* American Concrete Pipe Association
(6) *Handbook of PVC Pipe,* Uni-Bell Plastic Pipe Association
(7) *Installation Guide for Ductile Iron Pipe,* Ductile Iron Pipe Research Association
(8) *Thrust Restraint Design for Ductile Iron Pipe,* Ductile Iron Pipe Research Association

As there is normally no circulation of water in private fire mains, they require greater depth of covering than do public mains. Greater depth is required in a loose gravelly soil (or in rock) than in compact soil containing large quantities of clay. The recommended depth of cover above the top of underground yard mains is shown in Figure A.10.4.1.

10.4.2 The top of the pipe shall be buried not less than 1 ft (0.3 m) below the frost line for the locality.

10.4.3 In those locations where frost is not a factor, the depth of cover shall be not less than 2½ ft (0.8 m) to prevent mechanical damage.

10.4.4 Pipe under driveways shall be buried a minimum of 3 ft (0.9 m).

10.4.5 Pipe under railroad tracks shall be buried at a minimum of 4 ft (1.2 m).

10.4.6 The depth of cover shall be measured from the top of the pipe to finished grade, and due consideration shall always be given to future or final grade and nature of soil.

10.5 Protection Against Freezing

 10.5.1* Where it is impracticable to bury pipe, pipe shall be permitted to be laid above-ground, provided the pipe is protected against freezing and mechanical damage.

FIGURE A.10.4.1 *Recommended Depth of Cover (in feet) Above Top of Underground Yard Mains.*

A.10.5.1 In determining the need to protect aboveground piping from freezing, the lowest mean temperature should be considered as shown in Figure A.10.5.1.

10.5.2 Pipe shall be buried below the frost line where entering streams and other bodies of water.

10.5.3 Where pipe is laid in water raceways or shallow streams, care shall be taken that there will be sufficient depth of running water between the pipe and the frost line during all seasons of frost; a safer method is to bury the pipe 1 ft (0.3048 m) or more under the bed of the waterway.

10.5.4 Pipe shall be located at a distance from stream banks and embankment walls that prevents danger of freezing through the side of the bank.

10.6 Protection Against Damage

10.6.1 Pipe shall not be run under buildings.

Piping located under buildings is extremely difficult to repair, which is one of the reasons that 10.6.1 prohibits the installation of pipe under buildings. When buildings are built over existing underground piping, the piping should be rerouted around the new building. When piping under buildings requires repair, operations in the building must be curtailed, equipment may need to be moved, and the floor must be excavated. Leaks in the buried piping underneath the building can go undetected for long periods, and they can also undermine the building support. The location of system valves in the center of a building also places the system controls in the center of the building, which may not be desirable during a fire event.

◀ **FAQ**
Why do the requirements of 10.6.1 prohibit the installation of pipe under buildings?

10.6.2 When pipe must be run under buildings, special precautions shall be taken, including the following:

(1) Arching the foundation walls over the pipe
(2) Running pipe in covered trenches
(3) Providing valves to isolate sections of pipe under buildings

Subsection 10.6.2 outlines some of the measures that can be taken to minimize the exposure to damage but not completely eliminate it. Where the main penetrates the foundation wall, arching of the foundation wall over the main or other means of ensuring system and structural integrity needs to be provided.

10.6.3 Fire service mains shall be permitted to enter the building adjacent to the foundation.

Paragraph 10.6.3 permits the fire main to run underneath the building's footing or to penetrate the foundation wall if the main rises immediately inside the building adjacent to the exterior wall.

10.6.4 Where adjacent structures or physical conditions make it impractical to locate risers immediately inside an exterior wall, such risers shall be permitted to be located as close as practical to exterior walls to minimize underground piping under the building.

Where it is not practical to locate risers adjacent to exterior walls, 10.6.4 nevertheless requires pipe runs to be minimized, and the fire main under the building that connects to the system riser needs to be accessible through trench plates or other means of access in accordance with the requirements of 10.6.2.

10.6.5 Where a riser is close to building foundations, underground fittings of proper design and type shall be used to avoid pipe joints being located in or under the foundations.

FIGURE A.10.5.1 *Isothermal Lines—Lowest One-Day Mean Temperature.*

Compiled from United States Weather Bureau records.
SI units: °C = 5/9 (°F − 32); 1 mi = 1.609 km.

10.6.6 Mains shall be subjected to an evaluation of the following specific loading conditions and protected, if necessary:

(1) Mains running under railroads carrying heavy cargo
(2) Mains running under large piles of heavy commodities
(3) Mains located in areas that subject the main to heavy shock and vibrations

10.6.7* When it is necessary to join metal pipe with pipe of dissimilar metal, the joint shall be insulated against the passage of an electric current using an approved method.

A.10.6.7 Gray cast iron is not considered galvanically dissimilar to ductile iron. Rubber gasket joints (unrestrained push-on or mechanical joints) are not considered connected electrically. Metal thickness should not be considered a protection against corrosive environments. In the case of cast-iron or ductile iron pipe for soil evaluation and external protection systems, see Appendix A of AWWA C105, *Polyethylene Encasement for Ductile Iron Pipe Systems.*

10.6.8 In no case shall pipe specified in 10.6.7 be used for grounding of electrical services.

The use of underground fire protection piping for electrical grounding increases the potential for stray currents and increased galvanic corrosion, which is why this use is prohibited by 10.6.8. Grounding to piping containing nonconductive joints is especially dangerous since it may not provide the expected ground. In no case should the underground piping be used as a grounding electrode for electrical systems. Electrical equipment should be grounded in accordance with NFPA 70, *National Electrical Code*®.

◀ **FAQ**
Why do the requirements of 10.6.8 prohibit the use of underground piping for grounding of electrical services?

10.7 Requirement for Laying Pipe

The precautions that must be taken to minimize damage to underground piping, eliminate stresses, and ensure a long service life are outlined in Section 10.7.

In the United States, the federal Occupational Safety and Health Administration (OSHA) has a number of requirements relating to safety issues involved in underground piping installation. These OSHA regulations can be found in standards 29 CFR 1926, Subpart P, Appendix F on excavations and 29 CFR 1910.146, Appendix A on confined spaces.

For trenching operations involving excavations exceeding 5 ft (1.5 m) in depth, sloping, shoring, or shielding is required unless the excavation is entirely in stable rock. Additional soil classification is needed to select options, or, in the absence of soil classification, sloping of the excavation wall must be performed with the slope limited to 1½ horizontal to 1 vertical, which is a maximum 34 degrees from horizontal.

Confined spaces regulations can be invoked when valves on underground piping are located in pits. For this reason, valves are usually brought above ground in areas where freezing is not a concern, and special prefabricated heated enclosures (see Exhibit 10.1) are now marketed to allow aboveground valve installations in other areas as well.

10.7.1 Pipes, valves, hydrants, and fittings shall be inspected for damage when received and shall be inspected prior to installation.

10.7.2 The torquing of bolted joints shall be checked.

10.7.3 Pipe, valves, hydrants, and fittings shall be clean inside.

10.7.4 When work is stopped, the open ends of pipe, valves, hydrants, and fittings shall be plugged to prevent stones and foreign materials from entering.

Precautions must be taken to prevent rocks and other foreign materials from entering piping during installation, as stated in 10.7.4. These materials can be carried into fire protection system

EXHIBIT 10.1 Heated Enclosure. (Courtesy of AquaSHIELD)

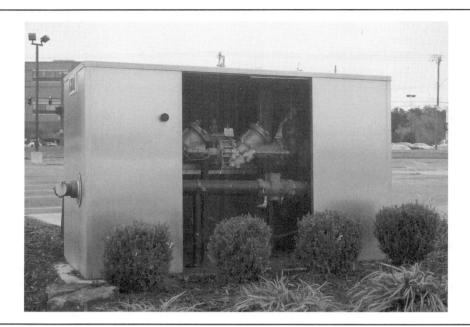

piping and cause blockages and system failure during an emergency. Care in installation is necessary but does not eliminate the need to flush the piping as part of the acceptance testing.

10.7.5 All pipe, fittings, valves, and hydrants shall be carefully lowered into the trench using appropriate equipment and carefully examined for cracks or other defects while suspended above the trench.

10.7.6 Plain ends shall be inspected for signs of damage prior to installation.

10.7.7 Under no circumstances shall water main materials be dropped or dumped.

10.7.8 Pipe shall not be rolled or skidded against other pipe materials.

10.7.9 Pipes shall bear throughout their full length and shall not be supported by the bell ends only or by blocks.

10.7.10 If ground is soft, or of a quicksand nature, special provisions shall be made for supporting pipe.

10.7.11 Valves and fittings used with nonmetallic pipe shall be properly supported and restrained in accordance with the manufacturer's specifications.

10.8 Joint Restraint

The rules of Section 10.8 address the need to provide thrust blocks only at turns in piping, because the soil surrounding underground pipe is generally satisfactory to hold the piping in place along straight runs.

10.8.1 General.

10.8.1.1* All tees, plugs, caps, bends, reducers, valves, and hydrant branches shall be restrained against movement by using thrust blocks in accordance with 10.8.2 or restrained joint systems in accordance with 10.8.3.

A.10.8.1.1 It is a fundamental design principle of fluid mechanics that dynamic and static pressures, acting at changes in size or direction of a pipe, produce unbalanced thrust forces at locations such as bends, tees, wyes, dead ends, and reducer offsets. This design principle includes consideration of lateral soil pressure and pipe/soil friction, variables that can be reliably determined using current soil engineering knowledge. Refer to A.10.1.1 for a list of references for use in calculating and determining joint restraint systems.

Except for the case of welded joints and approved special restrained joints, such as is provided by approved mechanical joint retainer glands or locked mechanical and push-on joints, the usual joints for underground pipe are expected to be held in place by the soil in which the pipe is buried. Gasketed push-on and mechanical joints without special locking devices have limited ability to resist separation due to movement of the pipe.

10.8.1.2 Piping with fused, threaded, grooved or welded joints shall not require additional restraining, provided that such joints can pass the hydrostatic test of 10.10.2.2 without shifting of piping or leakage in excess of permitted amounts.

10.8.1.3 Steep Grades. On steep grades, mains shall be additionally restrained to prevent slipping.

10.8.1.3.1 Pipe shall be restrained at the bottom of a hill and at any turns (lateral or vertical).

10.8.1.3.2 The restraint specified in 10.8.1.3.1 shall be to natural rock or to suitable piers built on the downhill side of the bell.

10.8.1.3.3 Bell ends shall be installed facing uphill.

10.8.1.3.4 Straight runs on hills shall be restrained as determined by the design engineer.

10.8.2* Thrust Blocks.

Thrust blocks are covered in 10.8.2. Exhibit 10.2 illustrates a typical thrust block arrangement.

EXHIBIT 10.2 *Typical Thrust Block Arrangement. (Courtesy of Los Angeles Department of Water and Power)*

A.10.8.2 Thrust Blocks. Concrete thrust blocks are one of the most common methods of restraint now in use, provided that stable soil conditions prevail and space requirements permit placement. Successful blocking is dependent upon factors such as location, availability and placement of concrete, and possibility of disturbance by future excavations.

Resistance is provided by transferring the thrust force to the soil through the larger bearing area of the block such that the resultant pressure against the soil does not exceed the horizontal bearing strength of the soil. The design of thrust blocks consists of determining the appropriate bearing area of the block for a particular set of conditions. The parameters involved in the design include pipe size, design pressure, angle of the bend (or configuration of the fitting involved), and the horizontal bearing strength of the soil.

Table A.10.8.2(a) gives the nominal thrust at fittings for various sizes of ductile iron and PVC piping. Figure A.10.8.2(a) shows an example of how thrust forces act on a piping bend. Figure A.10.8.2(b) shows an example of a typical connection to a fire protection systems riser.

Thrust blocks are generally categorized into two groups—bearing and gravity blocks. Figure A.10.8.2(c) depicts a typical bearing thrust block on a horizontal bend.

The following are general criteria for bearing block design:

(1) The bearing surface should, where possible, be placed against undisturbed soil.
(2) Where it is not possible to place the bearing surface against undisturbed soil, the fill between the bearing surface and undisturbed soil must be compacted to at least 90 percent Standard Proctor density.
(3) Block height *(h)* should be equal to or less than one-half the total depth to the bottom of the block *(H_t)* but not less than the pipe diameter *(D)*.
(4) Block height *(h)* should be chosen such that the calculated block width *(b)* varies between one and two times the height.

 The required block area *(A_b)* is as follows:

$$A_b = (h)(b) = \frac{T(S_f)}{S_b}$$

where:

A_b = required block area

h = block height

TABLE A.10.8.2(a) *Thrust at Fittings at 100 psi (6.9 bar) Water Pressure for Ductile Iron and PVC Pipe*

Nominal Pipe Diameter (in.)	Total Pounds					
	Dead End	90-Degree Bend	45-Degree Bend	22½-Degree Bend	11¼-Degree Bend	5⅛-Degree Bend
4	1,810	2,559	1,385	706	355	162
6	3,739	5,288	2,862	1,459	733	334
8	6,433	9,097	4,923	2,510	1,261	575
10	9,677	13,685	7,406	3,776	1,897	865
12	13,685	19,353	10,474	5,340	2,683	1,224
14	18,385	26,001	14,072	7,174	3,604	1,644
16	23,779	33,628	18,199	9,278	4,661	2,126
18	29,865	42,235	22,858	11,653	5,855	2,670
20	36,644	51,822	28,046	14,298	7,183	3,277
24	52,279	73,934	40,013	20,398	10,249	4,675
30	80,425	113,738	61,554	31,380	15,766	7,191
36	115,209	162,931	88,177	44,952	22,585	10,302
42	155,528	219,950	119,036	60,684	30,489	13,907
48	202,683	286,637	155,127	79,083	39,733	18,124

Notes:

1. For SI units, 1 lb. = 0.454 kg.

2. To determine thrust at pressure other than 100 psi (6.9 bar), multiply the thrust obtained in the table by the ratio of the pressure to 100 psi (6.9 bar). For example, the thrust on a 12-in., 90-degree bend at 125 psi (8.6 bar) is 19,353 × 125/100 = 24,191 lb.

$T_x = PA\,(1 - \cos\theta)$

$T_y = PA\sin\theta$

$T = 2\,PA\sin\dfrac{\theta}{2}$

$\Delta = \left(90 - \dfrac{\theta}{2}\right)$

T Thrust force resulting from change in direction of flow

T_x Component of the thrust force acting parallel to the original direction of flow

T_y Component of the thrust force acting perpendicular to the original direction of flow

P Water pressure

A Cross-sectional area of the pipe interior

V Velocity in direction of flow

FIGURE A.10.8.2(a) *Thrust Forces Acting on a Bend.*

FIGURE A.10.8.2(b) *Typical Connection to a Fire Protection System Riser.*

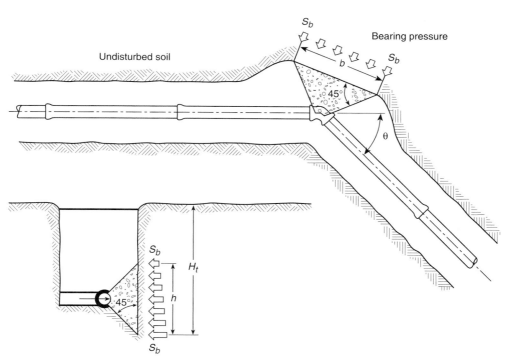

T Thrust force resulting from the change in direction of flow

S_b Horizontal bearing strength of the soil

FIGURE A.10.8.2(c) *Bearing Thrust Block.*

b = calculated block width

T = thrust force

S_f = safety factor

S_b = bearing strength

Figure A.10.8.2(b) shows an underground stub-up with rods holding the base of the flange and spigot piece within the bell opening of the last length of bell and spigot piping at the base of the riser. Such rods and clamps are not always necessary if other measures are taken to ensure that sufficient restraint is provided in accordance with Section 10.8.

 Then, for a horizontal bend, the following formula is used:

$$b = \frac{2(S_f)(A)\sin(\theta/2)}{(h)(S_b)}$$

where:

S_f = safety factor (usually 1.5 for thrust block design)

P = water pressure

A = cross sectional area of the pipe interior

h = block height

S_b = horizontal bearing strength of the soil

A similar approach can be used to design bearing blocks to resist the thrust forces at locations such as tees and dead ends. Typical values for conservative horizontal bearing strengths of various soil types are listed in Table A.10.8.2(b).

TABLE A.10.8.2(b) *Horizontal Bearing Strengths*

Soil	Bearing Strength, S_b		Soil	Bearing Strength, S_b	
	lb/ft²	*kN/m²*		*lb/ft²*	*kN/m²*
Muck	0	0	Sand	4000	191.5
Soft clay	1000	47.9	Sandy clay	6000	287.3
Silt	1500	71.8	Hard clay	9000	430.9
Sandy silt	3000	143.6			

Notes:

1. Although the bearing strength values in this table have been used successfully in the design of thrust blocks and are considered to be conservative, their accuracy is totally dependent on accurate soil identification and evaluation. The ultimate responsibility for selecting the proper bearing strength of a particular soil type must rest with the design engineer.

2. Gravity thrust blocks can be used to resist thrust at vertical down bends. In a gravity thrust block, the weight of the block is the force providing equilibrium with the thrust force. The design problem is then to calculate the required volume of the thrust block of a known density. The vertical component of the thrust force in Figure A.10.8.2(d) is balanced by the weight of the block.

In lieu of the values for soil bearing strength shown in Table A.10.8.2(b), a designer might choose to use calculated Rankine passive pressure (P_p) or other determination of soil bearing strength based on actual soil properties.

The soil bearing strength value to be used for sizing thrust blocks is the horizontal bearing strength, which is shown in Table A.10.8.2(b). Vertical bearing strength values are often determined for purposes of structural support but are not necessarily the same.

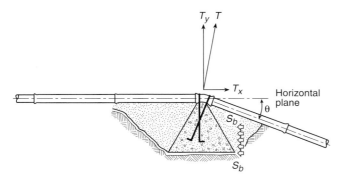

T   Thrust force resulting from the change of direction of flow
T_x Horizontal component of the thrust force
T_y Vertical component of the thrust force
S_b Horizontal bearing strength of the soil

FIGURE A.10.8.2(d) *Gravity Thrust Block.*

It can be easily be shown that $T_y = PA$ sin. The required volume of the block is as follows:

$$V_g = \frac{S_f PA \sin\theta}{W_m}$$

where:

S_f = safety factor

P = water pressure

A = cross sectional area of the pipe interior

W_m = density of the block material

In a case such as the one shown, the horizontal component of thrust force is calculated as follows:

$$T_x = PA(1 - \cos\theta)$$

where:

P = water pressure

A = cross sectional area of the pipe interior

The horizontal component of thrust force must be resisted by the bearing of the right side of the block against the soil. Analysis of this aspect will follow the same principles as the previous section on bearing blocks.

10.8.2.1 Thrust blocks shall be considered satisfactory where soil is suitable for their use.

10.8.2.2 Thrust blocks shall be of a concrete mix not leaner than one part cement, two and one-half parts sand, and five parts stone.

10.8.2.3 Thrust blocks shall be placed between undisturbed earth and the fitting to be restrained and shall be capable of such bearing to ensure adequate resistance to the thrust to be encountered.

10.8.2.4 Wherever possible, thrust blocks shall be placed so that the joints are accessible for repair.

10.8.3 Restrained Joint Systems. Fire mains utilizing restrained joint systems shall include the following:

(1) Locking mechanical or push-on joints
(2) Mechanical joints utilizing setscrew retainer glands
(3) Bolted flange joints
(4) Heat-fused or welded joints
(5) Pipe clamps and tie rods
(6) Other approved methods or devices

 Restrained joint systems are discussed in 10.8.3. Flange adapter fittings and other mechanical joints do not necessarily provide joint restraint. For example, flange adapter fittings are listed by Underwriters Laboratories as "fittings, retainer type" in UL 194, *Gasketed Joints for Ductile-Iron Pipe and Fittings for Fire Protection Service.* UL 194 further categorizes such fittings as either "gasketed joints with self-restraining feature" or "gasketed joints without self-restraining feature." The latter includes gasketed joints consisting of merely a pipe or fitting bell and a spigot end without a feature for joint restraint. Under the provisions of UL 194, all gasketed joints are provided with a pressure test at twice the rated working pressure with samples deflected to the maximum angle specified by the manufacturer. Joints for which the manufacturer claims a self-restraining feature are not provided with external restraint during the test. The manufacturer's literature should specify whether external restraint is required.

An example of a restrained joint system is shown in Exhibit 10.3.

10.8.3.1 Sizing Clamps, Rods, Bolts, and Washers.

10.8.3.1.1 Clamps.

10.8.3.1.1.1 Clamps shall have the following dimensions:

(1) ½ in. × 2 in. (12.7 mm × 50.8 mm) for pipe 4 in. to 6 in.
(2) ⅝ in. × 2½ in. (15.9 mm × 63.5 mm) for pipe 8 in. to 10 in.
(3) ⅝ in. × 3 in. (15.9 mm × 76.2 mm) for 12-in. pipe

10.8.3.1.1.2 The diameter of a bolt hole shall be ¹⁄₁₆ in. (1.6 mm) larger than that of the corresponding bolts.

10.8.3.1.2 Rods.

10.8.3.1.2.1 Rods shall be not less than ⅝ in. (15.9 mm) in diameter.

10.8.3.1.2.2 Table 10.8.3.1.2.2 provides numbers of various diameter rods that shall be used for a given pipe size.

EXHIBIT 10.3 *Example of a Restrained Joint System.*

TABLE 10.8.3.1.2.2 *Rod Number—Diameter Combinations*

Nominal Pipe Size (in.)	⅝ in. (15.9 mm)	¾ in. (19.1 mm)	⅞ in. (22.2 mm)	1 in. (25.4 mm)
4	2	—	—	—
6	2	—	—	—
8	3	2	—	—
10	4	3	2	—
12	6	4	3	2
14	8	5	4	3
16	10	7	5	4

Note: This table has been derived using pressure of 225 psi (15.5 bar) and design stress of 25,000 psi (172.4 MPa).

FIGURE 10.8.3.2.3 *Restraint Straps for Tees.*

10.8.3.1.2.3 When using bolting rods, the diameter of mechanical joint bolts shall limit the diameter of rods to ¾ in. (19.1 mm).

10.8.3.1.2.4 Threaded sections of rods shall not be formed or bent.

10.8.3.1.2.5 Where using clamps, rods shall be used in pairs for each clamp.

10.8.3.1.2.6 Assemblies in which a restraint is made by means of two clamps canted on the barrel of the pipe shall be permitted to use one rod per clamp if approved for the specific installation by the authority having jurisdiction.

10.8.3.1.2.7 Where using combinations of rods in numbers greater than two, the rods shall be symmetrically spaced.

10.8.3.1.3 Clamp Bolts. Clamp bolts shall have the following diameters:

(1) ⅝ in. (15.9 mm) for pipe 4 in., 6 in., and 8 in.
(2) ¾ in. (19.1 mm) for pipe 10 in.
(3) ⅞ in. (22.2 mm) for 12-in. pipe

10.8.3.1.4 Washers.

10.8.3.1.4.1 Washers shall be permitted to be cast iron or steel and round or square.

10.8.3.1.4.2 Cast-iron washers shall have the following dimensions:

(1) ⅝ in. × 3 in. (15.9 mm × 76.2 mm) for 4-in., 6-in., 8-in., and 10-in. pipe
(2) ¾ in. × 3½ in. (19.1 mm × 88.9 mm) for 12-in. pipe

10.8.3.1.4.3 Steel washers shall have the following dimensions:

(1) ½ in. × 3 in. (12.7 mm × 76.2 mm) for 4-in., 6-in., 8-in., and 10-in. pipe
(2) ½ in. × 3½ in. (12.7 mm × 88.9 mm) for 12-in. pipe

10.8.3.1.4.4 The diameter of holes shall be ⅛ in. (3.2 mm) larger than that of rods.

10.8.3.2 Sizes of Restraint Straps for Tees.

10.8.3.2.1 Restraint straps for tees shall have the following dimensions:

(1) ⅝ in. (15.9 mm) thick and 2½ in. (63.5 mm) wide for 4-in., 6-in., 8-in., and 10-in. pipe
(2) ⅝ in. (15.9 mm) thick and 3 in. (76.2 mm) wide for 12-in. pipe

10.8.3.2.2 The diameter of rod holes shall be ¹/₁₆ in. (1.6 mm) larger than that of rods.

10.8.3.2.3 Figure 10.8.3.2.3 and Table 10.8.3.2.3 shall be used in sizing the restraint straps for both mechanical and push-on joint tee fittings.

10.8.3.3 Sizes of Plug Strap for Bell End of Pipe.

10.8.3.3.1 Strap shall be ¾ in. (19.1 mm) thick and 2½ in. (63.5 mm) wide.

10.8.3.3.2 The strap length shall be the same as dimension *A* for tee straps as shown in Figure 10.8.3.2.3.

10.8.3.3.3 The distance between the centers of rod holes shall be the same as dimension *B* for tee straps as shown in Figure 10.8.3.2.3.

10.8.3.4 Material. Clamps, rods, rod couplings or turnbuckles, bolts, washers, restraint straps, and plug straps shall be of a material that has physical and chemical characteristics that indicate its deterioration under stress can be predicted with reliability.

10.8.3.5* Corrosion Resistance. After installation, rods, nuts, bolts, washers, clamps, and other restraining devices shall be cleaned and thoroughly coated with a bituminous or other acceptable corrosion-retarding material.

A.10.8.3.5 Examples of materials and the standards covering these materials are as follows:

(1) Clamps, steel *(see Note)*
(2) Rods, steel *(see Note)*
(3) Bolts, steel (ASTM A 307, *Standard Specification for Carbon Steel Bolts and Studs*)
(4) Washers, steel *(see Note);* cast iron (Class A cast iron as defined by ASTM A 126, *Standard Specification for Gray Iron Casting for Valves, Flanges and Pipe Fittings*)
(5) Anchor straps and plug straps, steel *(see Note)*
(6) Rod couplings or turnbuckles, malleable iron (ASTM A 197, *Standard Specification for Cupola Malleable Iron*)

Steel of modified range merchant quality as defined in U.S. Federal Standard No. 66C, *Standard for Steel Chemical Composition and Harden Ability,* April 18, 1967, change notice No. 2, April 16, 1970, as promulgated by the U.S. Federal Government General Services Administration.

The materials specified in A.10.8.3.5(1) through (6) do not preclude the use of other materials that will also satisfy the requirements of this section.

10.9 Backfilling

10.9.1 Backfill shall be tamped in layers or puddled under and around pipes to prevent settlement or lateral movement and shall contain no ashes, cinders, refuse, organic matter, or other corrosive materials.

Backfill is discussed in 10.9.1. Improper backfill is a major cause of underground piping failures. Proper consolidation of backfill can prevent voids that eventually place stress on the piping and joints.

Underground piping should be laid on a firm bed of earth for its entire length with the earth scooped out at the bells. Clean earth or screened gravel should be tamped under, around, and above the pipe to a level of 1 ft above. The excavation should then be backfilled to grade, compacting the fill in layers of 2 ft or less, unless otherwise directed by the project soils engineer.

TABLE 10.8.3.2.3 Restraint Straps for Tees

Nominal Pipe Size (in.)	A		B		C		D	
	in.	*mm*	*in.*	*mm*	*in.*	*mm*	*in.*	*mm*
4	12½	318	10⅛	257	2½	64	1¾	44
6	14½	368	12⅛	308	3⁹⁄₁₆	90	2¹³⁄₁₆	71
8	16¾	425	14⅜	365	4²¹⁄₃₂	118	3²⁹⁄₃₂	99
10	19¹⁄₁₆	484	16¹¹⁄₁₆	424	5¾	146	5	127
12	22⁵⁄₁₆	567	19³⁄₁₆	487	6¾	171	5⅞	149

Puddling, which involves the use of water to help consolidate soil around and below the piping, is occasionally used to assist the backfill compaction effort.

10.9.2 Rocks shall not be placed in trenches.

Subsection 10.9.2 requires that rocks not be placed in trenches. Clean fill cushions the pipe and distributes the load to the surrounding earth. The presence of cinders, refuse, and other organic matter can create points of accelerated corrosion that can reduce the life of underground piping.

10.9.3 Frozen earth shall not be used for backfilling.

10.9.4 In trenches cut through rock, tamped backfill shall be used for at least 6 in. (150 mm) under and around the pipe and for at least 2 ft (0.6 m) above the pipe.

10.10 Testing and Acceptance

10.10.1 Approval of Underground Piping. The installing contractor shall do the following:

(1) Notifying the authority having jurisdiction and the owner's representative of the time and date testing is to be performed
(2) Performing all required acceptance tests
(3) Completing and signing the contractor's material and test certificate(s) shown in Figure 10.10.1.

10.10.2 Acceptance Requirements.

10.10.2.1* Flushing of Piping.

A.10.10.2.1 Underground mains and lead-in connections to system risers should be flushed through hydrants at dead ends of the system or through accessible aboveground flushing outlets allowing the water to run until clear. Figure A.10.10.2.1 shows acceptable examples of flushing the system. If water is supplied from more than one source or from a looped system, divisional valves should be closed to produce a high-velocity flow through each single line. The flows specified in Table 10.10.2.1.3 will produce a velocity of at least 10 ft/sec (3 m/sec), which is necessary for cleaning the pipe and for lifting foreign material to an aboveground flushing outlet.

10.10.2.1.1 Underground piping, from the water supply to the system riser, and lead-in connections to system riser shall be completely flushed before connection is made to downstream fire protection system piping.

10.10.2.1.2 The flushing operation shall be continued for a sufficient time to ensure thorough cleaning.

10.10.2.1.3 The minimum rate of flow shall be not less than one of the following:

(1) Hydraulically calculated water demand rate of the system, including any hose requirements
(2) Flow necessary to provide a velocity of 10 ft/sec (3.1 m/sec) in accordance with Table 10.10.2.1.3
(3) Maximum flow rate available to the system under fire conditions

The minimum rate of flow for flushing of piping is discussed in 10.10.2.1.3. A supply of water producing velocities of 10 ft/sec (3.1 m/sec) may not be available under all circumstances.

Contractor's Material and Test Certificate for Underground Piping

PROCEDURE

Upon completion of work, inspection and tests shall be made by the contractor's representative and witnessed by an owner's representative. All defects shall be corrected and system left in service before contractor's personnel finally leave the job.

A certificate shall be filled out and signed by both representatives. Copies shall be prepared for approving authorities, owners, and contractor. It is understood the owner's representative's signature in no way prejudices any claim against contractor for faulty material, poor workmanship, or failure to comply with approving authority's requirements or local ordinances.

Property name	Date
Property	

Plans	Accepted by approving authorities (names)		
	Address		
	Installation conforms to accepted plans	☐ Yes	☐ No
	Equipment used is approved If no, state deviations	☐ Yes	☐ No
Instructions	Has person in charge of fire equipment been instructed as to location of control valves and care and maintenance of this new equipment? If no, explain	☐ Yes	☐ No
	Have copies of appropriate instructions and care and maintenance charts been left on premises? If no, explain	☐ Yes	☐ No
Location	Supplies buildings		

Underground pipes and joints	Pipe types and class	Type joint	
	Pipe conforms to _____ standard	☐ Yes	☐ No
	Fittings conform to _____ standard If no, explain	☐ Yes	☐ No
	Joints needed anchorage clamped, strapped, or blocked in accordance with _____ standard If no, explain	☐ Yes	☐ No

Test description	**Flushing:** Flow the required rate until water is clear as indicated by no collection of foreign material in burlap bags at outlets such as hydrants and blow-offs. Flush at flows not less than 390 gpm (1476 L/min) for 4-in. pipe, 880 gpm (3331 L/min) for 6-in. pipe, 1560 gpm (5905 L/min) for 8-in. pipe, 2440 gpm (9235 L/min) for 10-in. pipe, and 3520 gpm (13,323 L/min) for 12-in. pipe. When supply cannot produce stipulated flow rates, obtain maximum available. **Hydrostatic:** Hydrostatic tests shall be made at not less than 200 psi (13.8 bar) for 2 hours or 50 psi (3.4 bar) above static pressure in excess of 150 psi (10.3 bar) for 2 hours. **Leakage:** New pipe laid with rubber gasketed joints shall, if the workmanship is satisfactory, have little or no leakage at the joints. The amount of leakage at the joints shall not exceed 2 quarts per hour (1.89 L/hr) per 100 joints irrespective of pipe diameter. The leakage shall be distributed over all joints. If such leakage occurs at a few joints, the installation shall be considered unsatisfactory and necessary repairs made. The amount of allowable leakage specified above can be increased by 1 fluid ounce per inch valve diameter per hr. (30 mL/25 mm/hr) for each metal seated valve isolating the test section. If dry barrel hydrants are tested with the main valve open so the hydrants are under pressure, an additional 5 ounces per minute (150 mL/min) leakage is permitted for each hydrant.

Flushing tests	New underground piping flushed according to _____ standard by (company) If no, explain	☐ Yes ☐ No
	How flushing flow was obtained ☐ Public water ☐ Tank or reservoir ☐ Fire pump	Through what type opening ☐ Hydrant butt ☐ Open pipe
	Lead-ins flushed according to _____ standard by (company) If no, explain	☐ Yes ☐ No
	How flushing flow was obtained ☐ Public water ☐ Tank or reservoir ☐ Fire pump	Through what type opening ☐ Y connection to flange and spigot ☐ Open pipe

FIGURE 10.10.1 *Sample of Contractor's Material and Test Certificate for Underground Piping.*

Hydrostatic test	All new underground piping hydrostatically tested at _____ psi for _____ hours		Joints covered ☐ Yes ☐ No
Leakage test	Total amount of leakage measured _____ gallons _____ hours		
	Allowable leakage _____ gallons _____ hours		
Hydrants	Number installed	Type and make	All operate satisfactorily ☐ Yes ☐ No
Control valves	Water control valves left wide open If no, state reason		☐ Yes ☐ No
	Hose threads of fire department connections and hydrants interchangeable with those of fire department answering alarm		☐ Yes ☐ No
Remarks	Date left in service		
Signatures	Name of installing contractor		
	Tests witnessed by		
	For property owner (signed)	Title	Date
	For installing contractor (signed)	Title	Date
Additional explanation and notes			

FIGURE 10.10.1 *Continued*

If the velocity is not available, then the system's anticipated actual demand should be simulated to clear any foreign matter that may be obstructing the underground piping.

Stones, gravel, blocks of wood, bottles, work tools, work clothes, and other objects have been found in piping when flushing procedures were performed. Objects in underground piping that are quite remote from a sprinkler installation and that would otherwise remain stationary can sometimes be carried into sprinkler system piping when sprinkler systems operate. Sprinkler systems can draw greater flows than most domestic or process uses. Fire department pumpers taking suction from hydrants for pumping into sprinkler systems and normal fire-fighting operations further increase flow rates and velocities and can dislodge other materials in the piping network, forcing them into sprinkler system piping.

Because of the inherent nature of sprinkler system design in which pipe sizes usually decrease beginning at the point of connection to the underground piping, objects that move from the underground piping into the sprinkler system can become lodged at a point in the system where they may obstruct the passage of water. Exhibit 10.4 illustrates an object that was carried from the underground piping into the sprinkler system. When the dry pipe valve was reset, the object was discovered.

Previous studies by FM Global concluded that the size of particles that will move upward in piped water streams can be determined if the specific gravity of the particle and the velocity of the water stream are known. For example, granite that is 2 in. (51 mm) in diameter will

◄ **FAQ**
Why is flushing of the underground piping required?

FIGURE A.10.10.2.1 *Methods of Flushing Water Supply Connections.*

move upward in piping if the water stream velocity is 5.64 ft/sec (1.72 m/sec). In the 1991 edition of NFPA 13, the flow rates were increased to reflect velocities of 10 ft/sec (3.1 m/sec) because this number is more in line with requirements of other accepted standards. The velocity of 10 ft/sec (3.1 m/sec) is also in agreement with the flushing requirements of NFPA 15, *Standard for Water Spray Fixed Systems for Fire Protection.*

EXHIBIT 10.4 *Object Trapped in a Dry Pipe Sprinkler System.*

TABLE 10.10.2.1.3 *Flow Required to Produce a Velocity of 10 ft/sec (3 m/sec) in Pipes*

Pipe Size		Flow Rate	
in.	*mm*	*gpm*	*L/min*
4	102	390	1,476
6	152	880	3,331
8	203	1,560	5,905
10	254	2,440	9,235
12	305	3,520	13,323

In the field, actual flushing is normally done without measuring the flow rate. Flushing is normally accomplished at the maximum flow rate available from the water supply as allowed by 10.10.2.1.3(3).

10.10.2.2 Hydrostatic Test.

The trench must be backfilled prior to hydrostatic testing, which is discussed in 10.10.2.2, to prevent movement of underground piping. The backfilling can take place between joints if it is desired to observe the joints for leakage and if the backfill depth is sufficient to prevent movement. As an alternative, the joints can also be covered, but the contractor remains responsible for locating and correcting excessive leakage. The latter is usually preferred where a delay is expected in scheduling the hydrostatic test, since it is not desirable to leave trenches open for any length of time from a safety standpoint.

A 2-hour hydrostatic test is required at not less than 200 psi (13.8 bar), but at least 50 psi (3.4 bar) above the maximum expected static pressure. The piping between an exterior fire department connection and the check valve in the connection's inlet pipe must also be hydrostatically tested. All thrust blocks should be hardened before testing.

It is recommended that the underground piping be filled with water for a 24-hour period prior to the hydrostatic test to stabilize the system. It is also recommended that the test pressure be held for 1 hour, the pressure then be decreased to zero to look for signs of leakage, and then re-pressurized for the second hour.

10.10.2.2.1* All piping and attached appurtenances subjected to system working pressure shall be hydrostatically tested at 200 psi (13.8 bar) or 50 psi (3.5 bar) in excess of the system working pressure, whichever is greater, and shall maintain that pressure without loss for 2 hours.

A.10.10.2.2.1 A sprinkler system has for its water supply a connection to a public water service main. A 100-psi (6.9-bar) rated pump is installed in the connection. With a maximum normal public water supply of 70 psi (4.8 bar) at the low elevation point of the individual system or portion of the system being tested and a 120-psi (8.3-bar) pump (churn) pressure, the hydrostatic test pressure is 70 psi + 120 psi + 50 psi or 240 psi (16.5 bar).

To reduce the possibility of serious water damage in case of a break, pressure can be maintained by a small pump, the main controlling gate meanwhile being kept shut during the test.

Polybutylene pipe will undergo expansion during initial pressurization. In this case, a reduction in gauge pressure might not necessarily indicate a leak. The pressure reduction should not exceed the manufacturer's specifications and listing criteria.

When systems having rigid thermoplastic piping such as CPVC are pressure tested, the sprinkler system should be filled with water. The air should be bled from the highest and farthest sprinklers. Compressed air or compressed gas should never be used to test systems with rigid thermoplastic pipe.

A recommended test procedure is as follows: The water pressure is to be increased in 50-psi (3.4-bar) increments until the test pressure described in 10.10.2.2.1 is attained. After each increase in pressure, observations are to be made of the stability of the joints. These observations are to include such items as protrusion or extrusion of the gasket, leakage, or other factors likely to affect the continued use of a pipe in service. During the test, the pressure is not to be increased by the next increment until the joint has become stable. This applies particularly to movement of the gasket. After the pressure has been increased to the required maximum value and held for 1 hour, the pressure is to be decreased to 0 psi while observations are made for leakage. The pressure is again to be slowly increased to the value specified in 10.10.2.2.1 and held for 1 more hour while observations are made for leakage and the leakage measurement is made.

The use of noncombustible compressed gas to increase the pressure in a water filled system is an acceptable test procedure.

10.10.2.2.2 Loss shall be determined by a drop in gauge pressure or visual leakage.

10.10.2.2.3 The test pressure shall be read from a gauge located at the low elevation point of the system or portion being tested.

10.10.2.2.4 The permitted amount of underground piping leakage shall be as follows:

(1)* The amount of leakage at the joints shall not exceed 2 qt/hr (1.89 L/hr) per 100 gaskets or joints, irrespective of pipe diameter.

A.10.10.2.2.4(1) New pipe laid with rubber gasketed joints should, if the workmanship is satisfactory, have no leakage at the joints. Unsatisfactory amounts of leakage usually result from twisted, pinched, or cut gaskets. However, some leakage might result from small amounts of grit or small imperfections in the surfaces of the pipe joints.

(2)* The amount of allowable leakage specified in 10.10.2.2.4(1) shall be permitted to be increased by 1 fl oz (30 ml) per inch valve diameter per hour for each metal-seated valve isolating the test section.

A.10.10.2.2.4(2) The use of a blind flange or skillet is preferred for use when hydrostatically testing segments of new work. Metal seated valves are susceptible to developing slight imperfections during transport, installation, and operation and thus can be likely to leak more than 1 fl oz (30 ml) per inch of valve diameter per hour. For this reason, the blind flange should be used when hydrostatically testing.

(3) If dry barrel hydrants are tested with the main valve open so the hydrants are under pressure, an additional 5 fl oz/min (150 ml/min) of leakage shall be permitted for each hydrant.

(4) The amount of leakage in buried piping shall be measured at the specified test pressure by pumping from a calibrated container.

SUMMARY

Chapter 10 consolidates all of the requirements for underground piping and includes piping materials, fittings, joining of pipe and fittings, depth of cover, protection against freezing, protection against damage, requirements for laying pipe, joint restraint, backfilling, and testing and acceptance. The inclusion of Chapter 10 in NFPA 13 and NFPA 24 ensures that the requirement for underground piping is consistent throughout all fire protection applications.

REFERENCES CITED IN COMMENTARY

National Fire Protection Association, 1 Batterymarch Park, P.O. Box 9101, Quincy, MA 02269-9101

NFPA 70, *National Electrical Code®*, 2002 edition

American Water Works Association, 6666 West Quincy Avenue, Denver, CO 80235

AWWA C104, *Cement Mortar Lining for Ductile Iron Pipe and Fittings for Water,* 1995 edition
AWWA C105, *Polyethylene Encasement for Ductile Iron Pipe Systems,* 1999 edition
AWWA C111, *Rubber Gasket Joints for Ductile Iron Pressure Pipe and Fittings,* 2000 edition
AWWA C203, *Coal-Tar Protective Coatings and Linings for Steel Water Pipelines Enamel and Tape—Hot Applied,* 1997 edition
AWWA C900, *Polyvinyl Chloride (PVC) Pressure Pipe, 4 in. Through 12 in. (100 mm Through 300 mm), for Water and Other Liquids,* 1997 edition

Underwriters Laboratories Inc., 333 Pfingsten Road, Northbrook, IL 60062

UL 194, *Gasketed Joints for Ductile-Iron Pipe and Fittings for Fire Protection Service,* 1996 edition

U.S. Government Printing Office, Washington, DC 20402

Title 29, Code of Federal Regulations, Part 1926, Subpart P
Title 29, Code of Federal Regulations, Part 1910.146, Appendix A

Design Approaches

Chapter 11 sets forth the minimum requirements concerning the amount of water—that is, sprinkler system discharge criteria—needed under the occupancy hazard approach to effectively control or suppress a fire. In the 1999 edition of NFPA 13 this chapter included requirements for storage occupancies and special hazards addressed by other NFPA documents. In this edition of NFPA 13, the requirements for storage occupancies, including requirements for miscellaneous storage, miscellaneous Group A plastics, miscellaneous tire storage, and miscellaneous rolled paper storage, and storage of Class I through IV commodities stored up to 12 ft (3.7 m) in height have been consolidated in Chapter 12. In addition, the special hazards discharge criteria addressed by other NFPA documents has been extracted or referenced in a new Chapter 13.

Chapter 11 recognizes occupancy hazards in combination with the density/area method as the traditional, more common design approach to determining water demand for sprinkler systems (see Section 11.2). In addition, an approach for residential sprinklers has been successfully developed and is also addressed (see 11.2.3.5).

11.1 General

11.1.1 Water demand requirements shall be determined from the following:

(1) Occupancy hazard fire control approach
(2) Storage design approaches of Chapter 12
(3) Special design approaches of Chapter 13

11.1.2 For buildings with two or more adjacent occupancies that are not physically separated by a barrier or partition capable of delaying heat from a fire in one area from fusing sprinklers in the adjacent area, the required sprinkler protection for the more demanding occupancy shall extend 15 ft (4.6 m) beyond its perimeter.

It is not unusual for buildings to have various fire hazards within them resulting in different occupancy or commodity classifications. Because the discharge criteria for all fire hazards are not the same, the intent of the requirement in 11.1.2 is to ensure that all fire hazards are adequately protected.

11.2 Occupancy Hazard Fire Control Approach

11.2.1 Occupancy Classifications.

11.2.1.1 Occupancy classifications for this standard relate to sprinkler installations and their water supplies only.

11.2.1.2 Occupancy classifications shall not be used as a general classification of occupancy hazards.

11.2.1.3 Occupancies or portions of occupancies shall be classified according to the quantity and combustibility of contents, the expected rates of heat release, the total potential for energy release, the heights of stockpiles, and the presence of flammable and combustible liquids, using the definitions contained in Sections 5.2 through 5.5. Classifications are as follows:

(1) Light hazard
(2) Ordinary hazard (Groups 1 and 2)
(3) Extra hazard (Groups 1 and 2)
(4) Special occupancy hazard *(see Chapter 13)*

Paragraph 11.2.1.3 is the only section that specifically identifies that a facility can contain multiple types of fire hazards or occupancies. Each hazard can be protected with the appropriate discharge criteria, or the most demanding criteria can be used throughout the facility. Prior to the 1991 edition of NFPA 13, the ordinary hazard classification was divided into three groups. In 1991, the former ordinary hazard (Group 2) and ordinary hazard (Group 3) classifications were essentially merged into a single ordinary hazard (Group 2) classification. The impact of this change was considered minimal because the level of protection provided by the associated design densities was essentially the same. In this edition of NFPA 13, discharge criteria for special occupancy hazards are specifically identified in Chapter 13. Exhibit 11.1 compares the previous density/area curves with those now in use. The solid lines in Exhibit 11.1 represent curves based on the 1989 edition of NFPA 13, and the dotted lines represent curves based on this 2002 edition.

11.2.2 Water Demand Requirements—Pipe Schedule Method.

The pipe schedule method, which is discussed in 11.2.2, is the older means of determining the sprinkler system water demand under the occupancy hazard fire control approach.

FAQ ▶
Why has the use of pipe schedule systems been restricted?

   The pipe schedule method is still an acceptable method in many cases, although its application is not that common. The hydraulic method typically results in more economical systems. The use of pipe schedule systems was restricted to avoid their use under marginal conditions of water supply pressure and flow.

11.2.2.1 Table 11.2.2.1 shall be used in determining the minimum water supply requirements for light and ordinary hazard occupancies protected by systems with pipe sized according to the pipe schedules of Section 14.5.

EXHIBIT 11.1 *Comparison of Density/Area Curves.*

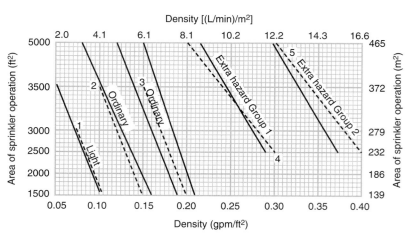

For SI units, 1 ft² = 0.092 m²; 1 gpm/ft² = 40.746 (L/min)/m².

TABLE 11.2.2.1 Water Supply Requirements for Pipe Schedule Sprinkler Systems

Occupancy Classification	Minimum Residual Pressure Required (psi)	Acceptable Flow at Base of Riser (Including Hose Stream Allowance) (gpm)	Duration (minutes)
Light hazard	15	500–750	30–60
Ordinary hazard	20	850–1500	60–90

Note: For SI units, 1 gpm = 3.785 L/min; 1 psi = 0.0689 bar.

11.2.2.2 Pressure and flow requirements for extra hazard occupancies shall be based on the hydraulic calculation methods of 11.2.3.

11.2.2.3 Unless the requirements of 11.2.2.5 are met the pipe schedule method shall be permitted only for new installations of 5000 ft² (465 m²) or less or for additions or modifications to existing pipe schedule systems sized according to the pipe schedules of Section 14.5.

11.2.2.4 Table 11.2.2.1 shall be used in determining the minimum water supply requirements.

11.2.2.5 The pipe schedule method shall be permitted for use in systems exceeding 5000 ft² (465 m²) where the flows required in Table 11.2.2.1 are available at a minimum residual pressure of 50 psi (3.4 bar) at the highest elevation of sprinkler.

11.2.2.6 The pipe schedule method shall be permitted for additions or modifications to existing extra hazard pipe schedule systems.

Existing pipe schedule systems, which are discussed in 11.2.2.1 through 11.2.2.6, must comply with the provisions of Section 14.5 if they are to be expanded.

Many mistakenly believe that pipe schedule systems are restricted to small buildings of less than 5000 ft² (465 m²). The size of the building only affects the required residual pressure (see Table 11.2.2.1), not whether the pipe schedule method can be used.

In 1991, NFPA 13 prohibited the use of the pipe schedule method for new extra hazard occupancies. However, 11.2.2.6 permits the use of pipe schedule systems for additions and modifications to existing extra hazard systems.

◄ **FAQ**
Can the pipe schedule method be utilized for buildings larger than 5000 ft² (465 m²)?

11.2.2.7 The lower duration value of Table 11.2.2.1 shall be acceptable only where remote station or central station waterflow alarm service is provided.

The lower duration value is permitted where remote or central station waterflow alarm service is provided, as stated in 11.2.2.7. It is expected that the fire department or fire brigade will be made aware of the fire more quickly than if only a local alarm were employed. Although remote or central station alarm monitoring does not have any impact on sprinkler system performance, it does allow the fire service to arrive at the scene sooner, when the fire is smaller, to initiate its fire attack.

◄ **FAQ**
When can the lower duration values of Table 11.2.2.1 be utilized?

11.2.2.8* Residual Pressure.

A.11.2.2.8 The additional pressure that is needed at the level of the water supply to account for sprinkler elevation is 0.433 psi/ft (0.098 bar/m) of elevation above the water supply.

The residual pressure requirement, which is discussed in 11.2.2.8, is to be applied at the elevation of the highest sprinkler. The process of calculating the available pressure starts at the connection to the water supply, which is typically at the street but can be at the base of the riser. The available residual pressure of the water supply at the acceptable flow identified in Table 11.2.2.1 must meet or exceed the minimum residual pressure required, which is also

FAQ ▶
What is the pressure loss
associated with elevation?

FAQ ▶
Why is the friction loss from
backflow devices required
to be accounted for?

identified in Table 11.2.2.1. For installations larger than 5000 ft² (465 m²), the 50 psi (3.4 bar) required by 11.2.2.5 supersedes Table 11.2.2.1.

Elevation pressure [see 14.4.4.5(1)] is the product of the elevation in feet (meters) multiplied by 0.433 psi/ft (0.096 bar/m).

This requirement for elevation pressure demonstrates that some calculation is now necessary with pipe schedule systems. Traditional pipe schedule approaches required no additional hydraulic calculations.

The installation of backflow prevention devices on pipe schedule systems is quite common. Because of the high friction losses associated with backflow devices, the effect of backflow devices on system performance must be considered. The friction loss for the backflow device must be obtained from the device manufacturer and be based on the acceptable flow identified in Table 11.2.2.1. Also see commentary to 8.16.4.6.2.

11.2.2.8.1 The residual pressure requirement of Table 11.2.2.1 shall be met at the elevation of the highest sprinkler.

 11.2.2.8.2 When backflow prevention valves are installed on pipe schedule systems, the friction losses of the device shall be accounted for when determining acceptable residual pressure at the top level of sprinklers. The friction loss of this device [in psi (bar)] shall be added to the elevation loss and the residual pressure at the top row of sprinklers to determine the total pressure needed at the water supply.

11.2.2.9 The lower flow figure of Table 11.2.2.1 shall be permitted only where the building is of noncombustible construction or the potential areas of fire are limited by building size or compartmentation such that no open areas exceed 3000 ft² (279 m²) for light hazard or 4000 ft² (372 m²) for ordinary hazard.

11.2.3 Water Demand Requirements—Hydraulic Calculation Methods.

Hydraulic calculation methods are covered in 11.2.3. The following two hydraulic calculation approaches are permitted for determining the water demand for hydraulically calculated systems under the occupancy hazard fire control approach:

1. The density/area method
2. The room design method

Even though 11.2.3 does not address the sprinkler discharge criteria for storage application (see Chapter 12), it does provide hose stream demands for general and rack storage.

11.2.3.1 General.

11.2.3.1.1* The minimum water supply requirements for a hydraulically designed occupancy hazard fire control sprinkler system shall be determined by adding the hose stream demand from Table 11.2.3.1.1 to the water supply for sprinklers determined in 11.2.3.1.5.

TABLE 11.2.3.1.1 *Hose Stream Demand and Water Supply Duration Requirements for Hydraulically Calculated Systems*

Occupancy	*Inside Hose (gpm)*	*Total Combined Inside and Outside Hose (gpm)*	*Duration (minutes)*
Light hazard	0, 50, or 100	100	30
Ordinary hazard	0, 50, or 100	250	60–90
Extra hazard	0, 50, or 100	500	90–120

For SI units, 1 gpm = 3.785 L/min.

A.11.2.3.1.1 Appropriate area/density, other design criteria, and water supply requirements should be based on scientifically based engineering analyses that can include submitted fire testing, calculations, or results from appropriate computational models.

Recommended water supplies anticipate successful sprinkler operation. Because of the small but still significant number of uncontrolled fires in sprinklered properties, which have various causes, there should be an adequate water supply available for fire department use.

The discharge criteria for the specific special occupancy hazards identified in Chapter 13 might differ from the requirements of Table 11.2.3.1.1. For example, NFPA 415, *Standard on Airport Terminal Buildings, Fueling Ramp Drainage, and Loading Walkways,* classifies passenger handling areas as ordinary hazard (Group 1) occupancies. Therefore, the discharge criteria for the sprinklers would be in accordance with the ordinary hazard (Group 1) density/area curve in Figure 11.2.3.1.5. However, NFPA 415 requires a hose stream demand of 500 gpm (1893 L/min), which exceeds the 250-gpm (946-L/min) hose stream allowance required by Table 11.2.3.1.1 for ordinary hazard occupancies.

11.2.3.1.2 The minimum water supply shall be available for the minimum duration specified in Table 11.2.3.1.1.

11.2.3.1.3 An allowance for inside and outside hose shall not be required where tanks supply sprinklers only.

11.2.3.1.4 Where pumps taking suction from a private fire service main supply sprinklers only, the pump need not be sized to accommodate inside and outside hose. Such hose allowance shall be considered in evaluating the available water supplies.

11.2.3.1.5 Density/Area Curves. The water supply for sprinklers only shall be determined either from the density/area curves of Figure 11.2.3.1.5 in accordance with the method of 11.2.3.2 or be based upon the room design method in accordance with 11.2.3.3, at the discretion of the designer.

The sprinkler discharge criteria discussed in 11.2.3.1.5 are permitted to be determined through hydraulic calculations in accordance with the density/area method of 11.2.3.2, or the room design method of 11.2.3.3, or the special design methods of 11.2.3.4. The special design methods mainly apply to building service chutes and spaces protected by a single line of sprinklers such as a corridor.

FIGURE 11.2.3.1.5 *Density/Area Curves.*

11.2.3.1.6 Special Areas. For special areas under consideration, as described in 11.2.3.4, separate hydraulic calculations shall be required in addition to those required by 11.2.3.2 or 11.2.3.3.

 11.2.3.1.7* Systems with Multiple Hazard Classifications. For systems with multiple hazard classifications, the hose stream demand shall be in accordance with one of the following:

(1) Add the hose demand for the highest hazard classification within the system, or
(2) Add the hose demand for each individual hazard classification to the calculations for the design area for that hazard, or
(3) For systems with multiple hazard classifications where the higher classification only lies within single rooms less than or equal to 400 ft² in area with no such rooms adjacent, add the hose demand for the principal occupancy for the remainder of the system.

 A.11.2.3.1.7 When a light hazard occupancy, such as a school, contains separate ordinary hazard storage rooms no more than 400 ft², the hose stream demand would be that required for a light hazard occupancy.

11.2.3.1.8 Restrictions. Regardless of which of the two methods is used, the following restrictions shall apply:

(1) For areas of sprinkler operation less than 1500 ft² (139 m²) used for light and ordinary hazard occupancies, the density for 1500 ft² (139 m²) shall be used.
(2) For areas of sprinkler operation less than 2500 ft² (232 m²) for extra hazard occupancies, the density for 2500 ft² (232 m²) shall be used.
(3)* For buildings having unsprinklered combustible concealed spaces, as described in 8.14.1.2 and 8.14.6, the minimum area of sprinkler operation shall be 3000 ft² (279 m²).

 A.11.2.3.1.8(3) This section is included to compensate for possible delay in operation of sprinklers from fires in combustible concealed spaces found in wood frame, brick veneer, and ordinary construction.

The sprinkler system is expected to control the fire when the proper discharge density is applied, assuming the system is properly designed, installed, and maintained. Although a sprinkler system can control or suppress a fire with fewer sprinklers than are required in the design area, restrictions for minimum design areas in accordance with 11.2.3.1.8(1) and 11.2.3.1.8(2) provide a safety factor. A number of factors such as ventilation and ceiling configuration can lead to an inconsistent sprinkler operating sequence—that is, skipping of sprinklers. A shielded fire can also require the use of most or all sprinklers in the design area.

FAQ ▶
Do the requirements of
11.2.3.1.8(3) apply when
the room design method
is utilized?

The 3000-ft² (279-m²) requirement of 11.2.3.1.8(3) also applies to the room design method and supersedes limiting the remote area based only on room size.

This requirement has been further clarified by 11.2.3.2.7.2 whereby the 3000 ft² (279 m²) is applied after all other area modifications have been made.

The intention of 11.2.3.1.8(3) is not to permit the omission of sprinklers from concealed combustible spaces but rather to compensate for the anticipated delay of sprinkler operation for a fire originating in an unprotected, concealed combustible space. As noted, 8.14.1.2 describes the conditions under which sprinklers do not have to be installed in concealed spaces.

(4) The following unsprinklered combustible concealed spaces shall not require a minimum area of sprinkler operation of 3000 ft² (279 m²):

(a) Combustible concealed spaces filled entirely with noncombustible insulation.
 (b)*Light or ordinary hazard occupancies where noncombustible or limited combustible ceilings are directly attached to the bottom of solid wood joists so as to create enclosed joist spaces 160 ft³ (4.5 m³) or less in volume, including space below insulation that is laid directly on top or within the ceiling joists in an otherwise sprinklered attic.

A.11.2.3.1.8(4)(b) Composite wood joists are not considered solid wood joists for the purposes of this section. Their web members are too thin and easily penetrated to adequately compartment a fire in an unsprinklered space. Application of this item is not affected by the depth of the joist channel except in determining the volume.

    (c)*Concealed spaces where the exposed surfaces have a flame spread rating of 25 or less and the materials have been demonstrated to not propagate fire in the form in which they are installed in the space.

A.11.2.3.1.8(4)(c) This exception is intended to apply only when the exposed materials in the space are limited combustible materials or fire retardant–treated wood as defined in NFPA 703, *Standard for Fire Retardant Impregnated Wood and Fire Retardant Coatings for Building Materials.*

    (d) Concealed spaces over isolated small rooms not exceeding 55 ft² (5.1 m²) in area.

    (e) Vertical pipe chases under 10 ft² (0.93 m²), provided that in multifloor buildings the chases are firestopped at each floor using materials equivalent to the floor construction. Such pipe chases shall contain no sources of ignition, piping shall be noncombustible, and pipe penetrations at each floor shall be properly sealed.

Paragraphs 11.2.3.1.8(4)(a) through 11.2.3.1.8(4)(e) clarify that the 3000-ft² (279-m²) design area does not apply where an unsprinklered concealed space that is entirely filled with noncombustible insulation is enclosed with limited-combustible construction materials or is of a certain volume.

    Also, if residential sprinklers are used in a dwelling unit and an unprotected, combustible concealed space exists, the area limitations of 11.2.3.1.8(3) do not apply because the discharge criteria for residential sprinklers are not based on the density/area method.

◀ **FAQ**
Do the requirements of 11.2.3.1.8(3) apply when residential sprinklers are utilized in the dwelling units?

(5) Water demand of sprinklers installed in racks or water curtains shall be added to the ceiling sprinkler water demand at the point of connection. Demands shall be balanced to the higher pressure. *(See Chapter 8.)*

(6) Water demand of sprinklers installed in concealed spaces or under obstructions such as ducts and cutting tables need not be added to ceiling demand.

Sprinklers both at the ceiling and under an obstruction or in a concealed space as identified in 11.2.3.1.8(6) are not anticipated to operate during a fire when using the density/area method. This provision also applies to those situations in which a sprinkler is installed under a temporary obstruction such as an overhead garage door.

(7) Where inside hose stations are planned or are required, the following shall apply:

    (a) A total water allowance of 50 gpm (189 L/min) for a single hose station installation shall be added to the sprinkler requirements.

    (b) A total water allowance of 100 gpm (378 L/min) for a multiple hose station installation shall be added to the sprinkler requirements.

    (c) The water allowance shall be added in 50-gpm (189-L/min) increments beginning at the most remote hose station, with each increment added at the pressure required by the sprinkler system design at that point.

The size and type of hose connections contemplated by 11.2.3.1.8(7) are basically limited to those necessary for first-aid fire fighting or final extinguishment. Even though more than two such hose stations could be connected to the system, operation of more than two stations simultaneously during an incident is considered unlikely. Thus, only a maximum of two hose stations, simultaneously operating, are to be included in the total water supply. The demand of only one hose station is permitted to be included where only one hose station is needed. Table 11.2.3.1.1 highlights this point because the inside hose demand is presented as either 0 gpm, 50 gpm, or 100 gpm. Accounting for this potential use of water permits the sprinkler system to operate as intended while at the same time allowing some form of manual first-aid fire fighting. Hose connection requirements are identified in 8.16.5.

◀ **FAQ**
Why are only two hose stations required in facilities with multiple hose stations?

The hose connections contemplated in 11.2.3.1.8(7) are not standpipe connections as defined by NFPA 14, *Standard for the Installation of Standpipe, Private Hydrant, and Hose Systems.* NFPA 14 provides specific requirements for Class II standpipe systems that are intended for building occupant use. These requirements are considerably more demanding in terms of flow and pressure for the standpipe system than the values given in NFPA 13. NFPA 14 requires that Class II standpipes provide 100 gpm (378 L/min) at 65 psi (4.5 bar). The distinction between hose connections and standpipes is important. NFPA 13 provides requirements for convenience connections, and NFPA 14 provides requirements for standpipe system connections. Although both have 1½-in. (40-mm) outlets, Class II standpipe outlets have 1½-in. (40-mm) inlets, and hose connections to sprinkler systems typically have 1-in. (25.4-mm) inlets.

FAQ ▶
How should the inside hose station discussed in 11.2.3.1.8(7) be added to the hydraulic calculations?

For all practical purposes, the inside hose connections to sprinkler systems should be viewed as large sprinklers with no pressure requirements of their own but that are to flow the required amount of water at the pressure available at the hose outlet. The required flow at the hose outlets is to be carried through the calculations back to the system riser.

(8) When hose valves for fire department use are attached to wet pipe sprinkler system risers in accordance with 8.16.5.2 the following shall apply:

  (a) The water supply shall not be required to be added to standpipe demand as determined from NFPA 14, *Standard for the Installation of Standpipe, Private Hydrant, and Hose Systems.*

  (b) Where the combined sprinkler system demand and hose stream allowance of Table 11.2.3.1.1 exceeds the requirements of NFPA 14, *Standard for the Installation of Standpipe, Private Hydrant, and Hose Systems,* this higher demand shall be used.

For a completely sprinklered building using a combined sprinkler and standpipe riser, the pressure and flow demand for the standpipe system can, in most cases, exceed the demand of the sprinkler system. This results in exclusive adherence to NFPA 14 for determination of total water demand. In those instances where the sprinkler system demand is determined to be more demanding than the standpipe demand, the sprinkler system demand is to be used, as stated in 11.2.3.1.8(8)(b).

  (c) For partially sprinklered buildings, the sprinkler demand, not including hose stream allowance, as indicated in Table 11.2.3.1.1 shall be added to the requirements given in NFPA 14, *Standard for the Installation of Standpipe, Private Hydrant, and Hose Systems.*

If a building is only partially sprinklered, which is strongly discouraged by 8.1.1, the sprinkler demand from NFPA 13 and hose demand from NFPA 14 must be added to determine the discharge criteria for the combined system, as stated in 11.2.3.1.8(8)(c). This combined demand is necessary because fires can originate in the nonsprinklered area and grow to the point that they activate nearby sprinklers while still requiring full standpipe water supplies to be available for manual suppression.

(9) Water allowance for outside hose shall be added to the sprinkler and inside hose requirement at the connection to the city water main or a yard hydrant, whichever is closer to the system riser.

With regard to 11.2.3.1.8(9), if no inside hose connections are provided, the outside hose requirement is the value in the third column from the left in Table 11.2.3.1.1. This relatively small quantity of water is apportioned to the fire department to allow for final and complete extinguishment of the fire. The flow rate established in Table 11.2.3.1.1 can be added into the hydraulic calculations at the connection to the city water main or yard hydrant at the prevailing system pressure. The outside hose stream water typically receives its pressure from the fire department apparatus.

(10) The lower duration values in Table 11.2.3.1.1 shall be permitted where remote station or central station waterflow alarm service is provided.

The lower durations indicated by 11.2.3.1.8(10) are permitted where remote or central station waterflow alarm service is provided. This reduction is permitted because it is expected that the fire department or fire brigade will be made aware of the fire much sooner than if only a local alarm were employed. Although remote or central station alarm monitoring does not have any impact on sprinkler system performance, it does allow the fire service to arrive at the scene more quickly to initiate its fire attack. Because systems designed in accordance with the density/area method are to control the fire until the fire department arrives, the earlier the fire department arrives, the smaller the amount of time needed for the sprinkler system to control the fire.

◀ FAQ
When are the lower durations of Table 11.2.3.1.1 permitted?

(11) Where pumps, gravity tanks, or pressure tanks supply sprinklers only, requirements for inside and outside hose need not be considered in determining the size of such pumps or tanks.

With regard to 11.2.3.1.8(11), where pumps or tanks supply sprinklers only, the hose stream requirements need not be added when sizing the pump or tank. For example, if the pump or tank supplies a system that is required to be equipped with small hose stations, the demand of the hose stations needs to be included when sizing the pump or tank.

(12) For all occupancies consisting of combustible wood joist or wood truss construction with members spaced less than 3 ft on center used with slopes with a pitch at or exceeding 4 in 12 (4/12) using standard spray sprinklers, sprinklers shall be quick response having pressures in accordance with the requirements of Table 8.6.2.2.1(a).

For additional information on the protection of combustible wood joist or wood truss construction with members spaced less than 3 ft on center and used with slopes greater than or equal to 4 in 12, which is discussed in 11.2.3.1.8(12), see commentary on Table 8.6.2.2.1(a) and 8.6.4.1.4.

11.2.3.1.9 Total system water supply requirements shall be determined in accordance with the hydraulic calculation procedures of Section 14.4.

11.2.3.2 Density/Area Method.

11.2.3.2.1 Water Supply.

11.2.3.2.1.1* The water supply requirement for sprinklers only shall be calculated from the density/area curves of Figure 11.2.3.1.5 or from Chapter 13 where density/area criteria are specified for special occupancy hazards.

A.11.2.3.2.1.1 The situation frequently arises where a small area of a higher hazard is surrounded by a lesser hazard. For example, consider a 600-ft^2 area consisting of 10-ft high on-floor storage of cartoned solid plastic commodities surrounded by a plaster injection molding operation in a 15-ft high building. In accordance with Chapter 12, the density required for the plastic storage must meet the requirements for extra hazard (Group 1) occupancies. The injection molding operation should be considered an ordinary hazard (Group 2) occupancy. In accordance with Chapter 11, the corresponding discharge densities should be 0.3 gpm/ft^2 over 2500 ft^2 for the storage and 0.2 gpm/ft^2 over 1500 ft^2 for the remainder of the area. (Also see Chapter 11 for the required minimum areas of operation.)

If the storage area is not separated from the surrounding area by a wall or partition *(see 11.1.2),* then the size of the operating area is determined by the higher hazard storage.

For example, the operating area is 2500 ft^2. The system must be able to provide the 0.3-gpm/ft^2 density over the storage area and 15 ft beyond. If part of the remote area is outside the 600 ft^2 plus the 15-ft overlap, then only 0.2 gpm/ft^2 is needed for that portion.

If the storage is separated from the surrounding area by a floor-to-ceiling/roof partition that is capable of preventing heat from a fire on one side from fusing sprinklers on the other side, then the size of the operating area is determined by the occupancy of the surrounding area. In this example, the design area is 1500 ft^2. A 0.30-gpm/ft^2 density is needed within the separated area with 0.20 gpm/ft^2 in the remainder of the remote area.

11.2.3.2.1.2 When using Figure 11.2.3.1.5, the calculations shall satisfy any single point on the appropriate density/area curve.

11.2.3.2.1.3 When using Figure 11.2.3.1.5, it shall not be necessary to meet all points on the selected curve.

Why would a design point be selected from the lower points of the density/area curves of Figure 11.2.3.1.5?

FAQ ▶

Design of a sprinkler system in accordance with the density/area method requires that only a single point be met on a density/area curve, which is discussed in 11.2.3.2.1.3. This requirement applies to the curves in Figure 11.2.3.1.5.

Selecting a point on the low end—that is, smaller operating area—of a density/area curve can result in a somewhat higher density but a lower total water demand. The higher density also requires a higher pressure but is generally considered superior in terms of fire control and is expected to confine the fire to a smaller area, reducing the total number of operating sprinklers.

FAQ ▶
Why would a design point be selected from the higher points of the density/area curves of Figure 11.2.3.1.5?

Selection of a point on the high end—that is, larger operating area—of the curve allows for a lower density, and, therefore, lower pressure, but a higher total water demand for the system, as well as a larger fire. Therefore, more sprinklers would be expected to operate.

The area of operation shown on the vertical axis of Figure 11.2.3.1.5 is independent of the building's size. Selection of a density/area combination can limit the number of sprinklers expected to operate to the area selected from the density/area curve.

11.2.3.2.2 Sprinklers.

11.2.3.2.2.1 The densities and areas provided in Figure 11.2.3.1.5 are for use only with spray sprinklers.

Why does 11.2.3.2.2.2 prohibit the use of quick-response sprinklers from extra hazard occupancies?
FAQ ▶

11.2.3.2.2.2* Quick-response sprinklers shall not be permitted for use in extra hazard occupancies.

Paragraph 11.2.3.2.2.2 imposes a limit on the use of quick-response sprinklers in extra hazard occupancies due to a lack of extensive full-scale testing.

A **A.11.2.3.2.2.2** It is not the intent of this exception to restrict the use of quick-response sprinklers in extra hazard occupancies but rather to indicate that the areas and densities shown in might not be appropriate for use with quick-response sprinklers in those environments due to a concern with water supplies.

11.2.3.2.2.3 Sidewall spray sprinklers shall be permitted for use in light hazard occupancies and where specifically listed for use in ordinary hazard Group 1 and 2 occupancies.

Because of their mode of operation, sidewall sprinklers must be specifically listed for ordinary hazard occupancies in accordance with 11.2.3.2.2.3 if intended for such use.

11.2.3.2.2.4 For extended coverage sprinklers, the minimum design area shall be that corresponding to the maximum density for the hazard in Figure 11.2.3.1.5 or the area protected by five sprinklers, whichever is greater.

11.2.3.2.2.5 Extended coverage sprinklers shall be listed with and designed for the minimum flow corresponding to the density for the smallest area of operation for the hazard as specified in Figure 11.2.3.1.5.

Paragraph 11.2.3.2.2.4 clarifies that extended coverage (EC) sprinklers have a minimum design area, namely the area that comprises not less than five sprinklers or 1500 ft^2 (135 m^2).

FAQ ▶
Where extended coverage sprinklers protect an area of 20 ft x 20 ft (6.1 m × 6.1 m) each, what would be the minimum design area?

For an EC sprinkler listed for use in light hazard occupancies and a protection area per sprinkler of 20 ft × 20 ft (6.1 m × 6.1 m), the design area would be a 2000-ft^2 (186-m^2) area—that is, 400 ft^2 (36 m^2) per sprinkler multiplied by five sprinklers.

If an EC sprinkler was listed with a protection area of 16 ft × 16 ft (5 m × 5 m), the design area would be based on a 1500-ft^2 (139-m^2) area of operation. In this case, the sprinkler is listed to cover 256 ft^2 (23 m^2). Multiplying the minimum five-sprinkler design area by 256 ft^2

(23 m^2) results in an area of operation of 1280 ft^2 (115 m^2). The requirements of 11.2.3.2.2.4 require the larger of the 1500-ft^2 (139-m^2) area from the density/area curve or the five-sprinkler design area.

11.2.3.2.3 Quick-Response Sprinklers.

11.2.3.2.3.1 Where listed quick-response sprinklers, including extended coverage quick-response sprinklers, are used throughout a system or portion of a system having the same hydraulic design basis, the system area of operation shall be permitted to be reduced without revising the density as indicated in Figure 11.2.3.2.3.1 when all of the following conditions are satisfied:

(1) Wet pipe system
(2) Light hazard or ordinary hazard occupancy
(3) 20-ft (6.1-m) maximum ceiling height
(4) There are no unprotected ceiling pockets as allowed by 8.6.7 and 8.8.7 exceeding 32 ft^2

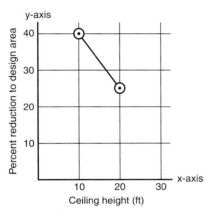

Note: $y = \dfrac{-3x}{2} + 55$

For ceiling height ≥ 10 ft and ≤ 20 ft, $y = \dfrac{-3x}{2} + 55$
For ceiling height < 10 ft, $y = 40$
For ceiling height > 20, $y = 0$
For SI units, 1 ft = 0.31 m.

FIGURE 11.2.3.2.3.1 *Design Area Reduction for Quick-Response Sprinklers.*

11.2.3.2.3.2 The number of sprinklers in the design area shall never be less than five.

11.2.3.2.3.3 Where quick-response sprinklers are used on a sloped ceiling, the maximum ceiling height shall be used for determining the percent reduction in design area.

11.2.3.2.3.4 Where quick-response sprinklers are installed, all sprinklers within a compartment shall be of the quick-response type.

11.2.3.2.3.5 Where circumstances require the use of other than ordinary temperature–rated sprinklers, standard-response sprinklers shall be permitted to be used.

Quick-response sprinklers are covered in 11.2.3.2.3.1 through 11.2.3.2.3.5. The reduction in design area for quick-response sprinklers ranges from a maximum of 40 percent for ceiling heights of 10 ft (3 m) and less to 25 percent for ceiling heights of 20 ft (6.1 m). The design area reduction is based on comparative tests of quick-response and standard response spray sprinklers which demonstrated that the earlier water is applied, the smaller the size of the fire. The smaller fire size in turn results in the operation of fewer sprinklers.

The Technical Committee on Sprinkler System Discharge Criteria recognized that the time of sprinkler activation is the result of a number of factors in addition to sprinkler thermal sensitivity. These factors include temperature rating of sprinklers, spacing of sprinklers, distance of the sprinklers below the ceiling, ceiling height, and the fire itself. With the exception of ceiling height, however, most of these factors are controlled within specified ranges by NFPA 13 provisions for a particular occupancy class. The reduction in operating area provides a valid credit for the increased effectiveness of quick-response sprinklers with regard to ceiling heights.

The reduction for sloped ceilings is based on the maximum ceiling height within the space.

The use of quick-response sprinklers is not required throughout the entire building. It is recognized that different portions of the building, or of a single floor, can have a different design basis. The portion of the building for which the pipe size is based on a reduced remote area must use quick-response sprinklers.

11.2.3.2.4 Sloped Ceilings in Non-Storage Applications. The system area of operation shall be increased by 30 percent without revising the density when the following types of sprinklers are used on sloped ceilings with a pitch exceeding one in six (a rise of two units in a run of 12 units, a roof slope of 16.7 percent) in non-storage applications:

(1) Spray sprinklers, including extended coverage sprinklers listed in accordance with 8.4.3(4), and quick-response sprinklers
(2) Large drop sprinklers

Sloped ceilings are discussed in 11.2.3.2.4. The design area increase of 30 percent for sloped ceilings with a pitch exceeding 2 in. in 12 in. (50.8 mm in 304.8 mm) (16.7 percent) is based on the test work and modeling conducted at FM Global. In those tests, slopes greater than 16.7 percent resulted in erratic sprinkler operating patterns that could adversely affect operating sprinklers outside of the design area. Heat from the fire is likely to accumulate near the peak of the slope and to activate sprinklers that are some distance from the fire. Paragraph 11.2.3.2.4 compensates for the fact that more sprinklers are expected to operate under steeply pitched surfaces. The modifier applies to all sprinklers allowed under a sloped ceiling, including quick-response sprinklers.

The 30-percent area increase does not apply to those types of sprinklers that utilize methods other than the density/area method to determine their discharge criteria, such as residential sprinklers, or to those types of sprinklers that are limited to slopes of 2 in. in 12 in. (50.8 mm in 304.8 mm), such as extended coverage and ESFR sprinklers. (See Section 8.4.)

The design area increase is intended to apply only to continuously sloped ceilings or roofs such as those in large attic spaces. The increase is not intended to apply to saw tooth roofs or other similar situations in which the extent of the slope is small relative to the sprinkler design area.

11.2.3.2.5 Dry Pipe and Double Interlock Preaction Systems. For dry pipe systems and double interlock preaction systems, the area of sprinkler operation shall be increased by 30 percent without revising the density.

Dry pipe and double interlock precaution systems are discussed in 11.2.3.2.5. The delivery of water to operated sprinklers in dry pipe and double interlock preaction sprinkler systems takes longer than it does for wet pipe systems and non-interlock or single interlock preaction systems. Because of this delay, system size in terms of volume is limited (see 7.3.2.2). To compensate for this delay, a 30 percent increase in the design area is mandated. This increase is necessary because more sprinklers in the fire area are expected to operate while the pipe is be-

FAQ ▶
For areas having sloping ceilings, what ceiling height is required to be utilized by 11.2.3.2.3?

FAQ ▶
To utilize the requirements of 11.2.3.2.3, are quick-response sprinklers required throughout the entire building?

FAQ ▶
Why is the 30 percent increase required for slopes exceeding 2 in. in 12 in.?

ing charged with water, and the fire will be larger when water reaches the operating sprinklers. The 30 percent increase is applied as follows.

If the density and area for an ordinary hazard (Group 2) occupancy are selected at 0.20 gpm/ft² [8.1 (L/min)/m²] and 1500 ft² (139 m²) (see Figure 11.2.3.1.5), this density would be adjusted for a dry pipe system as follows:

$$(30 \text{ percent} \times 1500 \text{ ft}^2) + 1500 \text{ ft}^2 = 1950 \text{ ft}^2 \ (182 \text{ m}^2)$$

The density of 0.20 gpm/ft² [8.1 (L/min)/m²] remains unchanged.

The 30 percent area increase rule does not apply to preaction systems other than to double interlock systems. Even though the pipe has no water in it, the delay in operation of non-interlock and single interlock systems is minimal because the detection device typically responds to the fire sooner than the sprinkler. (See the commentary to 7.3.2.1.)

11.2.3.2.6 High-Temperature Sprinklers. Where high-temperature sprinklers are used for extra hazard occupancies, the area of sprinkler operation shall be permitted to be reduced by 25 percent without revising the density, but not to less than 2000 ft² (186 m²).

High-temperature sprinklers are discussed in 11.2.3.2.6. Fire tests for extra hazard occupancies using sprinklers with nominal K-factors of 5.6 and 8.0 indicate that fewer high-temperature sprinklers operate when compared to ordinary temperature–rated sprinklers. Use of high-temperature sprinklers for light and ordinary hazard applications is restricted to those conditions defined in 8.3.2.

11.2.3.2.7* Multiple Adjustments.

A.11.2.3.2.7 *Example 1.* A dry pipe sprinkler system (OH₂) in a building with a ceiling slope exceeding two in 12 in. (16.6 percent slope). The initial area must be increased 30 percent for the dry pipe system and the resulting area an additional 30 percent for the roof slope. If the point 0.2 gpm/ft² (8.2 mm/min) over 1500 ft² (139 m²) is chosen from, the 1500-ft² (139-m²) area is increased 450 ft² (42 m²) to 1950 ft² (181 m²), which is then further increased 585 ft² (54 m²). The final discharge criterion is then 0.2 gpm/ft² (8.2 mm/min) over 2535 ft² (236 m²).

Example 2. A wet pipe sprinkler system (light hazard) in a building with a 16 ft 8 in. ceiling and a slope exceeding two in 12 in. (16.6 percent slope) employs quick-response sprinklers qualifying for a 30 percent reduction as permitted by 11.2.3.2.3. The initial area must be increased 30 percent for the ceiling slope and the resulting area decreased 30 percent for quick-response sprinklers. It does not matter if the reduction is applied first. If a discharge density of 0.1 gpm/ft² (4.1 mm/min) over 1500 ft² (139 m²) is chosen from, the 1500 ft² (139 m²) is increased 450 ft² (42 m²), resulting in 1950 ft² (181 m²), which is then decreased 585 ft² (54 m²). The final design is 0.1 gpm/ft² (4.1 mm/min) over 1365 ft² (126.8 m²).

11.2.3.2.7.1 Where multiple adjustments to the area of operation are required to be made in accordance with 11.2.3.2.4, 11.2.3.2.5, 11.2.3.2.6, or 11.2.3.2.7, these adjustments shall be compounded based on the area of operation originally selected from Figure 11.2.3.1.5.

11.2.3.2.7.2 If the building has unsprinklered combustible concealed spaces, the rules of 11.2.3.1.7 shall be applied after all other modifications have been made.

The order in which simultaneous modifications for dry pipe system quick-response sprinklers, sloped ceilings, or high-temperature sprinklers are applied to the area of system operation is not important, provided that the 3000-ft² (270-m²) minimum area limitation for unsprinklered concealed spaces in 11.2.3.1.8(3) is applied last, as stated in 11.2.3.2.7.2. Additionally, where simultaneous modifications are made, the adjustments must be compounded based on the initial operating area selected from the density/area curve of Figure 11.2.3.1.5.

11.2.3.3 Room Design Method.

11.2.3.3.1* The water supply requirements for sprinklers only shall be based upon the room that creates the greatest demand.

 A.11.2.3.3.1 This subsection allows for calculation of the sprinklers in the largest room, so long as the calculation produces the greatest hydraulic demand among selection of rooms and communicating spaces. For example, in a case where the largest room has four sprinklers and a smaller room has two sprinklers but communicates through unprotected openings with three other rooms, each having two sprinklers, the smaller room and group of communicating spaces should also be calculated.

Corridors are rooms and should be considered as such.

Walls can terminate at a substantial suspended ceiling and need not be extended to a rated floor slab above for this section to be applied.

The room design method, which is discussed in 11.2.3.3.1, has also been referred to as the largest room design method and applies to rooms of light hazard, ordinary hazard, and extra hazard occupancies. When opting for this approach, the designer must use the room that is also the most hydraulically demanding in terms of water supply and pressure. Enclosing walls of such a room must provide a fire resistance rating equal to the water supply duration requirements of Table 11.2.3.1.1 for the applicable occupancy hazard. If two values are given for an occupancy, the lower value can be used where remote station or central station waterflow alarm service is provided.

Any communicating openings into such a room are to be protected in the same manner as any opening in a fire-resistive partition, with the exception that any non-rated or rated self-closing or automatic doors satisfy the protection requirement for light hazard occupancies.

When use is made of the room design method, the various design area increases and decreases of 11.2.3.2 do not apply.

Are the automatic or self-closing doors required by 11.2.3.3.5 required to be rated fire doors for all occupancies?
FAQ ▶

FAQ ▶
Do the design area increases and decreases of 11.2.3.2 apply when the room design method is utilized?

11.2.3.3.2 The density selected shall be that from Figure 11.2.3.1.5 corresponding to the room size.

11.2.3.3.3 To utilize the room design method, all rooms shall be enclosed with walls having a fire-resistance rating equal to the water supply duration indicated in Table 11.2.3.1.1.

11.2.3.3.4 If the room is smaller than the smallest area shown in the applicable curve in Figure 11.2.3.1.5, the provisions of 11.2.3.1.8(1) and 11.2.3.1.8(2) shall apply.

11.2.3.3.5 Minimum protection of openings shall be as follows:

(1) Light hazard—Non-rated automatic or self-closing doors
(2) Light hazard with no opening protection—Where openings are not protected, calculations shall include the sprinklers in the room plus two sprinklers in the communicating space nearest each such unprotected opening unless the communicating space has only one sprinkler, in which case calculations shall be extended to the operation of that sprinkler. The selection of the room and communicating space sprinklers to be calculated shall be that which produces the greatest hydraulic demand.
(3) Ordinary and extra hazard—Automatic or self-closing doors with appropriate fire-resistance ratings for the enclosure

 11.2.3.3.6 Where the room design method is used and the area under consideration is a corridor protected by one row of sprinklers with protected openings in accordance with 11.2.3.3.5, the maximum number of sprinklers that needs to be calculated is five.

If a corridor is present, as discussed in 11.2.3.3.6, the designer has to calculate the largest room as well as the five sprinklers in the corridor to determine if the largest room or the corridor requires the higher water supply. If a corridor is not provided with self-closing or automatic doors, 11.2.3.3.6 recognizes that a seven-sprinkler design area is sufficient to control a fire in the corridor.

Due to the anticipated limited fuel load in the corridor, it is not necessary to add additional sprinklers from the communicating rooms to the seven-sprinkler design. It is necessary, however, to add the additional sprinklers required by 11.2.3.3.5(2) when evaluating the largest room and the communicating space is a corridor.

11.2.3.3.7 Where the area under consideration is a corridor protected by a single row of sprinklers in a light hazard occupancy, the design area shall include all sprinklers in the corridor to a maximum of five.

11.2.3.3.8 Where the area under consideration is a corridor protected by a single row of sprinklers and the openings are not protected, the design area shall include all sprinklers in the corridor to a maximum of seven.

11.2.3.4 Special Design Areas.

11.2.3.4.1 Where the design area consists of a building service chute supplied by a separate riser, the maximum number of sprinklers that needs to be calculated is three.

11.2.3.4.2* Where an area is to be protected by a single line of sprinklers, the design area shall include all sprinklers on the line up to a maximum of seven.

A.11.2.3.4.2 This section is intended to apply to all types of systems including dry pipe and preaction systems.

When protecting a long, narrow space with one line of sprinklers consisting of more than seven sprinklers, as discussed in 11.2.3.4.2, it is unlikely that all sprinklers in the space will activate unless the sprinkler system is overwhelmed.

11.2.3.5 Residential Sprinklers.

Residential sprinklers are covered in 11.2.3.5. The spaces in which residential sprinklers can be used within the scope of NFPA 13 are identified in 8.4.5. Because residential sprinklers were developed to protect against residential fire scenarios, they are permitted in residential portions (primarily dwelling units) of all buildings regardless of size or height. For example, NFPA 13 allows the use of residential sprinklers in high-rise apartment buildings.

In accordance with 11.2.3.5.4, nonresidential spaces (those primarily outside of the dwelling unit) must be protected with other types of sprinklers appropriate for the hazard.

NFPA 13R, *Standard for the Installation of Sprinkler Systems in Residential Occupancies up to and Including Four Stories in Height,* is available as an alternative to NFPA 13 for residential occupancies up to and including four stories in height. NFPA 13R does not address all types of residential facilities. Where sprinkler systems are being considered for single-family homes, NFPA 13D, *Standard for the Installation of Sprinkler Systems in One- and Two-Family Dwellings and Manufactured Homes,* should be used. NFPA provides three different design and installation standards for residential sprinklers. However, the differences in scope between NFPA 13, NFPA 13R, and NFPA 13D need to be understood, because the design and performance objectives of these documents are not identical.

11.2.3.5.1* The design area shall be the area that includes the four hydraulically most demanding sprinklers.

A.11.2.3.5.1 The protection area for residential sprinklers with extended coverage areas is defined in the listing of the sprinkler as a maximum square or rectangular area. Listing information is presented in even 2-ft (0.61-m) increments from 12 ft to 20 ft (3.6 m to 6.1 m) for residential sprinklers. When a sprinkler is selected for an application, its area of coverage must be equal to or greater than both the length and width of the hazard area. For example, if the hazard to be protected is a room 14 ft 6 in. (4.3 m) wide and 20 ft 8 in. (6.2 m) long, a sprinkler that is listed to protect an area of 16 ft × 22 ft (4.9 m × 6.8 m) must be selected. The flow used in the calculations is then selected as the flow required by the listing for the selected coverage. *(See Figure A.11.2.3.5.1.)*

FIGURE A.11.2.3.5.1 *Determination of Protection Area of Coverage for Residential Sprinklers.*

 11.2.3.5.2* Unless the requirements of 11.2.3.5.3 are met, the minimum required discharge from each of the four hydraulically most demanding sprinklers shall be the greater of the following:

(1) In accordance with minimum flow rates indicated in individual listings
(2) Calculated based on delivering a minimum of 0.1 gpm/ft^2 (4.1 mm/min) over the design area in accordance with the provisions of 8.5.2.1

 A.11.2.3.5.2 In Figure A.11.2.3.5.2, calculate the area indicated by the heavy outline and X. The circle indicates sprinklers.

Residential sprinklers are discussed in 11.2.3.5.1 and 11.2.3.5.2. NFPA 13D requires the sprinkler system design to be based on a maximum of two sprinklers operating. Two sprinklers are considered satisfactory for a one- or two-family dwelling, but the four-sprinkler design area required for an NFPA 13 system is intended to compensate for conditions that could occur in a larger residential occupancy, such as an apartment or hotel.

FAQ ▶
How does the four-sprinkler design basis of NFPA 13 differ from the four-sprinkler design basis of NFPA 13R?

Unlike the four-sprinkler design basis of NFPA 13R, the four-sprinkler design area in NFPA 13 must be determined without regard to compartment boundaries. The NFPA 13 residential design area consists of the four contiguous sprinklers that together produce the greatest demand, even if they are located in four individual adjacent compartments.

11.2.3.5.3 For modifications or additions to existing systems equipped with residential sprinklers, the listed discharge criteria less than 0.1 gpm/ft^2 (4.1 mm/min) shall be permitted to be used.

11.2.3.5.4 Where areas such as attics, basements, or other types of occupancies are outside of dwelling units but within the same structure, these areas shall be protected in accordance with the provisions of this standard, including appropriate design criteria of 11.2.3.

11.2.3.5.5 Hose stream demand and water supply duration requirements shall be in accordance with those for light hazard occupancies in Table 11.2.3.1.1.

11.2.3.6 Quick-Response Early Suppression (QRES) Sprinklers. (Reserved)

11.2.3.7 Exposure Protection.

11.2.3.7.1* Piping shall be hydraulically calculated in accordance with Section 14.4 to furnish a minimum of 7 psi (0.5 bar) at any sprinkler with all sprinklers facing the exposure operating.

 A.11.2.3.7.1 If the system is a deluge type, then all the sprinklers need to be calculated even if they are located on different building faces.

11.2.3.7.2 Where the water supply feeds other fire protection systems, it shall be capable of furnishing total demand for such systems as well as the exposure system demand.

11.2.3.8 Water Curtains.

11.2.3.8.1 Sprinklers in a water curtain such as described in 8.14.4 shall be hydraulically designed to provide a discharge of 3 gpm per lineal foot (37 L/min per lineal meter) of water curtain, with no sprinklers discharging less than 15 gpm (56.8 L/min).

11.2.3.8.2 For water curtains employing automatic sprinklers, the number of sprinklers calculated in this water curtain shall be the number in the length corresponding to the length parallel to the branch lines in the area determined by 14.4.4.1.1.

11.2.3.8.3 If a single fire can be expected to operate sprinklers within the water curtain and within the design area of a hydraulically calculated system, the water supply to the water curtain shall be added to the water demand of the hydraulic calculations and shall be balanced to the calculated area demand.

11.2.3.8.4 Hydraulic design calculations shall include a design area selected to include ceiling sprinklers adjacent to the water curtain.

11.2.3.9 Dry System Water Delivery.

Dry water system delivery is covered in 11.2.3.9. Paragraph 7.2.3.1 limits the capacity of a dry pipe sprinkler system controlled by one dry pipe valve to 750 gal (2839 L). The standard offers two methods of increasing the size of a system. The first method involves physically delivering water to a remote test connection within 60 seconds (see 7.2.3.2). The second method to the physical test in 7.2.3.2 is a mathematical calculation, which takes advantage of recent research into dry pipe sprinkler systems using various piping configurations and water supplies (see 7.2.3.3). This testing has lead to the development of listed calculation methods for predicating the trip and transit time of a dry pipe sprinkler system.

11.2.3.9.1 Calculations for dry system water delivery shall be based on the hazard shown in Table 11.2.3.9.1.

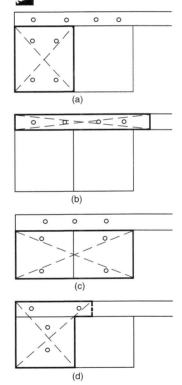

TABLE 11.2.3.9.1 *Dry System Water Delivery*

Hazard	Number of Most Remote Sprinklers Initially Open	Maximum Time of Water Delivery
Residential	1	15 seconds
Light	1	60 seconds
Ordinary I	2	50 seconds
Ordinary II	2	50 seconds
Extra I	4	45 seconds
Extra II	4	45 seconds
High piled	4	40 seconds

FIGURE A.11.2.3.5.2
Examples of Design Area for Dwelling Units.

Table 11.2.3.9.1 has been developed to represent the anticipated minimum number of most remote sprinklers initially open in the early stages of fire growth. Fires that have a higher heat release rate are expected to activate a greater number of sprinklers as shown in Table 11.2.3.9.1. A larger number of open sprinklers results in a more rapid transit time for water traveling from the dry pipe valve, through the piping network to the open sprinklers.

11.2.3.9.2 The calculation program and method shall be listed by a nationally recognized laboratory.

SUMMARY

Chapter 11 establishes the sprinkler system discharge criteria needed under the occupancy hazard approach to effectively control or suppress a fire. Chapter 11 recognizes occupancy hazard in combination with the density/area method as the traditional, more common design approach to determining water demand for sprinkler systems. In addition, an approach for residential sprinklers has been successfully developed and is also addressed.

 ## REFERENCES CITED IN COMMENTARY

National Fire Protection Association, 1 Batterymarch Park, P.O. Box 9101, Quincy, MA 02269-9101

NFPA 13D, *Standard for the Installation of Sprinkler Systems in One- and Two-Family Dwellings and Manufactured Homes,* 2002 edition

NFPA 13R, *Standard for the Installation of Sprinkler Systems in Residential Occupancies up to and Including Four Stories in Height,* 2002 edition

NFPA 14, *Standard for the Installation of Standpipe, Private Hydrant, and Hose Systems,* 2000 edition

NFPA 415, *Standard on Airport Terminal Buildings, Fueling Ramp Drainage, and Loading Walkways,* 2002 edition

Storage

Chapter 12 is a new chapter for the 2002 edition of NFPA 13. Chapter 12 contains all of the design criteria for protection storage, and the requirements have been consolidated into one chapter. Additionally, the storage requirements have been significantly updated and expanded throughout the chapter. Chapter 12 contains design criteria for the protection of storage occupancies. These occupancies contain a wide variety of stored materials defined in the commodity classifications of Class I through IV, plastics, rubber tires, baled cotton, rolled paper, and some other special commodities. All storage designs need to first follow Section 12.1 (General), followed by the design criteria specific to the type and arrangement of storage to be protected. The outline below is a quick reference to find the sections containing specific criteria for palletized, rack, rubber tire, baled cotton and roll paper storage, and special designs.

While Chapter 12 is a new chapter for 2002, major technical changes are indicated with the "new" icon.

12.1 General

The requirements of Section 12.1 shall apply to all storage arrangements and commodities unless modified by specific section in Chapter 12.

FAQ ▶
Do the rules of Section 12.1 apply to all storage arrangements?

It is important to note that all of the rules of Section 12.1 apply to all storage arrangements addressed by Chapter 12. The only allowance is where specific sections modify the requirements of Section 12.1. Section 12.1 also provides the design requirements for idle pallets, miscellaneous storage, and storage of Class I through Class IV commodities stored up to 12 ft in height.

12.1.1 Roof Vents and Draft Curtains. Sprinkler protection criteria are based on the assumption that roof vents and draft curtains are not being used. *(See Section C.6.)*

FAQ ▶
Why are the requirements of Chapter 12 based on no roof vents or draft curtains?

Most of the full-scale fire tests used as a basis for this chapter have been done without roof vents or draft curtains, which are discussed in 12.1.1. Testing sponsored by the National Fire Protection Research Foundation (NFPRF) has shown that draft curtains can alter the operating pattern of sprinklers. For further details see the Technical Reports of the International Fire Sprinkler/Smoke and Heat Vent/Draft Curtain Fire Test Project, published by the NFPRF. In some cases this can have a detrimental effect on the level of protection. If roof vents or draft curtains are used, experienced judgment and consideration to the effect on the sprinkler performance should be given in determining the final design criteria.

12.1.2 Building Height.

12.1.2.1 The maximum building height shall be measured to the underside of the roof deck or ceiling.

12.1.2.2 Early suppression fast-response (ESFR) sprinklers shall be used only in buildings equal to, or less than, the height of the building for which they have been listed.

Where utilizing ESFR sprinklers in a building having a sloped roof resulting in a ceiling height of 38 ft (11.6 m) at the edge of the building and a ceiling height of 42 ft (12.8 m) at the center, can I average the ceiling height for a protection height of 40 ft (12.2 m)?
FAQ ▶

The performance of ESFR technology is based on ceiling height (see 12.1.2.2). It is not acceptable, for example, to assume that an ESFR listed to a maximum ceiling height of 45 ft (13.7 m) can protect a 75 ft (22.9-m) high building with in-rack sprinklers protecting the first 30 ft (9.1 m) of storage—leaving the upper 45 ft (13.7 m) of protection to the ESFR. Currently, the maximum ceiling height that can be protected by ESFRs is 45 ft (13.7 m).

The protection criteria for ESFR sprinklers is based upon the actual maximum ceiling height. For this example, the building would be required to follow the ESFR criteria for the protection of a 45-ft (13.7-m) high building.

12.1.2.3 Large drop, control mode specific application and ESFR sprinklers shall be permitted to protect ordinary hazard, storage of Class I through Class IV commodities, plastic commodities, miscellaneous storage, and other storage as specified in Chapter 12 or by other NFPA standards.

FAQ ▶
Where there is a light manufacturing (ordinary hazard) area next to a rack storage area protected with ESFR sprinklers, is it acceptable to extend the ESFR protection over the manufacturing area in accordance with 12.1.2.3?

Many occupancies have storage areas that are adjacent to other non-storage areas of use such as production assembly areas. Typically, these areas are protected utilizing the density/area methods of Chapter 11. Large drop, control mode specific application, and ESFR sprinkler designs, which are discussed in 12.1.2.3, are based on minimum operating pressures combined with a minimum number of sprinklers. With these minimums, these sprinklers are not considered to be "density" based. The protection of ordinary hazard or miscellaneous storage based on its density requirement is generally considered to be less of a hazard and, therefore, it is acceptable that it be protected by large drop or ESFR sprinklers provided they are designed to their listed minimums.

Ordinary hazard areas are common to storage occupancies, are considered less of a fire challenge than the minimum design criteria for ESFR, and can be protected by ESFR sprinklers provided the listing requirements of the ESFR sprinklers are met.

12.1.3 Hose Connections. Small hose connections [1½ in. (38 mm)] shall be provided in accordance with 8.16.5 for first-aid fire-fighting and overhaul operations.

Hose connections are addressed in 12.1.3. Hose stations 1½ in. (38 mm) in size are considered indispensable for first-aid fire-fighting and final extinguishment (mop-up) operations in storage and warehouse facilities. The effectiveness of hose stations depends on the training of the plant fire brigade or plant emergency organization (PEO) with regard to fire-fighting tactics. Sounding the alarm, notifying the fire department, and evacuating all non-fire-fighting personnel are the initial steps before and during fire-fighting operations. Experience shows that many fires are extinguished in the early stages when trained plant personnel use interior hose stations. Experience also shows that maintenance of the hose and hose stations is critical. Most warehouse fires, if not extinguished in the early stages with the use of hose stations, are controlled but not entirely extinguished by a properly designed, installed, and maintained sprinkler system. Generally, interior hose stations are needed for final extinguishment (mop-up) during salvage and overhaul operations.

Hose connections are required in all occupancies with the exception of miscellaneous storage and Class I through Class IV storage up to 12 ft (3.7 m) in height.

◀ **FAQ**
Are hose connections required in all storage areas?

12.1.4* Wet Pipe Systems.

A.12.1.4 Wet systems are recommended for storage occupancies. Dry pipe systems should be permitted only where it is impractical to provide heat.

12.1.4.1 Sprinkler systems shall be wet pipe systems.

The requirement in 12.1.4.1 to utilize a wet pipe sprinkler system for the protection of storage occupancies is to ensure that water is applied immediately upon activation of the sprinklers. This immediate application of water provides control, prewetting, and or suppression during the early stages of fire growth.

12.1.4.2* In areas that are subject to freezing or where special conditions exist, dry-pipe systems and preaction systems shall be permitted to protect storage occupancies.

A.12.1.4.2 Wet systems are recommended for rack storage occupancies. Dry systems are permitted only where it is impractical to provide heat. Preaction systems should be considered for rack storage occupancies that are unheated, particularly where in-rack sprinklers are installed or for those occupancies that are highly susceptible to water damage.

For storage occupancies, dry-pipe or preaction systems should be avoided, unless absolutely necessary (see 12.1.4.2). The water delay, corrosion, and dependability of the valve maintenance associated with dry pipe and preaction systems are a concern for fast-developing fires. Where dry-pipe or preaction systems are utilized to protect storage occupancies, additional design requirements are needed to account for the delay in application of water.

12.1.4.3 ESFR sprinklers shall only be permitted to be wet pipe systems.

ESFR sprinklers are prohibited from use in dry-pipe or preaction systems, as stated in 12.1.4.3. However, ESFR sprinklers can be utilized in a wet system that utilizes an anti-freeze solution if the solution is listed for use with ESFR sprinklers. Unlike large drop sprinklers, no special provisions for the use of ESFR sprinklers are available in dry pipe or preaction systems. Initial water delivery is critical to the successful suppression properties of ESFR sprinklers. No delay of water is anticipated in the standard for ESFR.

12.1.5* Adjacent Occupancies. For buildings with two or more adjacent occupancies the following shall apply:

(1) Where areas are not physically separated by a barrier or partition capable of delaying heat from a fire in one area from fusing sprinklers in the adjacent area, the required sprinkler protection for the more demanding occupancy shall extend 15 ft (4.6 m) beyond its perimeter.
(2) The requirements of 12.1.5(1) shall not apply where the areas are separated by a barrier partition that is capable of preventing heat from a fire in the storage area from fusing sprinklers in the non-storage area.

A.12.1.5 Where high temperature–rated sprinklers are installed at the ceiling, high temperature–rated sprinklers also should extend beyond storage in accordance with Table A.12.1.5.

TABLE A.12.1.5 *Extension of Installation of High-Temperature Sprinklers over Storage*

Design Area for High Temperature–Rated Sprinklers		Distance Beyond Perimeter of High-Hazard Occupancy for High Temperature–Rated Sprinklers	
ft²	m²	ft	m
2000	185.8	30	9.14
3000	278.7	40	12.2
4000	371.6	45	13.72
5000	464.5	50	15.24
6000	557.4	55	16.76

It is not unusual for buildings to have various fire hazards within them resulting in different occupancy or commodity classifications. Because the discharge criteria for all fire hazards are not the same, the intent of the requirement in 12.1.5 is to ensure that all fire hazards are adequately protected. In storage fires, sprinklers operate well beyond the actual fire unless a barrier as described by 12.1.5(2) is present. Typically, the sprinkler operating area is 10 times or more the actual fire area. For a fire starting near the edge of the storage, sprinklers beyond the storage area will likely operate. The higher the storage and the more severe the commodity classification, the greater the likelihood that sprinklers further from the fire will operate. Where storage heights exceed 20 ft (6.1 m) for any commodity, especially Class IV and Group A plastics, extension of the designed sprinkler protection beyond 15 ft (4.6 m) should be considered.

12.1.6 Dry Pipe and Preaction Systems.

12.1.6.1 For dry pipe systems and preaction systems, the area of sprinkler operation shall be increased by 30 percent without revising the density.

12.1.6.2 Densities and areas shall be selected so that the final area of operation after the 30 percent increase is not greater than 6000 ft² (557.4 m²).

Dry pipe and preaction systems are covered in 12.1.6.1 and 12.1.6.2. Subsection 12.1.6 applies only to density/area control mode sprinklers. Large drop and control mode specific application sprinklers have their own dry system criteria found in their respective sections of Chapter 12.

Because no water immediately flows from the actuated sprinklers in a dry pipe or preaction system, the fire grows unimpeded for a period of time before the water actually arrives at the open sprinklers in a properly designed system. During this water transit time, sprinklers continue to operate, increasing the actual operating area.

FAQ ▶
Why is the 30 percent increase required for dry pipe and preaction systems?

A review of fire loss data by FM Global (formerly Factory Mutual Research Corporation) showed that about 30 percent more sprinklers operate with a dry pipe system than with a wet pipe system. Although the 30 percent penalty for dry pipe systems is not necessarily appropriate because of the many uncontrollable variables that affect the number of sprinkler operations in a dry pipe system, the 30 percent penalty was retained to allow for the likelihood that more sprinklers would operate in a dry pipe or preaction system than in a comparable wet pipe system. This increase is necessary because more sprinklers in the fire area are expected to operate while the pipe is being charged with water, and the fire will be larger when water reaches the operating sprinklers. As previously stated, the 30 percent increase does not apply to large drop or control mode specific application sprinklers. The relative design tables in this chapter specify the number of design sprinklers for dry system applications. Large drop or control mode specific application sprinklers can only be used in dry systems when allowed by the individual tables. ESFR sprinklers are not permitted in dry pipe or preaction systems.

12.1.6.3 The requirements of 12.1.6 shall not apply where it can be demonstrated that the detection system that activates the preaction system causes water to be discharged from sprinklers as quickly as the discharge from a wet pipe system.

If it can be demonstrated that a detection system in a preaction system is faster than the activation of the first sprinkler and can adequately deliver water to the sprinklers prior to their opening in a fire event, then the 30 percent increase does not apply, as discussed in 12.1.6.3.

12.1.7 Ceiling Slope. The sprinkler system criteria specified in this chapter are intended to apply to buildings with ceiling slopes not exceeding 2 in 12 (16.7 percent).

Ceiling slope is addressed in 12.1.7. All of the testing used to develop storage protection requirements was done under flat roofs. A ⅙-scale model of a full-scale test facility was used to investigate the effects of varying ceiling slopes. These investigations indicated that sprinkler operating patterns and sequences will not be adversely affected when slopes do not exceed 2 in 12 (16.7 percent). Where the slope exceeds 16.7 percent, the sprinkler operating area and sequence can be skewed. Unless the fire occurs directly under a row of sprinklers, sprinklers nearest the fire may not operate. Heat from the fire will collect at the peak and result in the operation of an excessive number of sprinklers and loss of fire control.

Design criteria for storage buildings having ceiling or roof slopes exceeding 2 in 12 (16.7 percent) is outside the scope of Chapter 12. For storage buildings that have sloped ceilings greater than 16.7 percent, consideration should be given to larger design areas combined with skewed operating patterns. A good example of this is the construction type commonly referred to as "Saw Tooth Roof" in which there are generally only two or three sprinklers running up the sloped section of roof greater than 16.7 percent. These sprinklers can be calculated as if all the sprinklers running up the slope will operate for the width of the hydraulic remote area. Experienced judgment will have to be used for small portions of the ceiling/roof that exceed 16.7 percent slope; large roof/ceiling slopes over 16.7 percent slope are outside the scope of this chapter.

◀ FAQ
What design criteria should be utilized for storage buildings that have ceiling or roof slopes greater than 2 in 12 (16.7 percent)?

12.1.8* Multiple Adjustments. Where multiple adjustments to the area of operation are required to be made, these adjustments shall be compounded based on the area of operation originally selected. If the building has unsprinklered combustible concealed spaces, the rules of 11.2.3.1.8 shall be applied after all other modifications have been made.

A.12.1.8 In a dry pipe system, the area increase of 30 percent should be compounded [e.g., 2000 ft^2 (186 m^2) (1.67 for low-temperature sprinklers and 1.3 for dry pipe systems) = 4343 ft^2 (403.5 m^2) total area]. Where dry pipe systems are used in existing installations, the areas of operation indicated by the tables should be increased by 30 percent.

12.1.9* Protection of Idle Pallets.

A.12.1.9 Idle pallet storage introduces a severe fire condition. Stacking idle pallets in piles is the best arrangement of combustibles to promote rapid spread of fire, heat release, and complete combustion. After pallets are used for a short time in warehouses, they dry out and edges become frayed and splintered. In this condition they are subject to easy ignition from a small ignition source. Again, high piling increases considerably both the challenge to sprinklers and the probability of involving a large number of pallets when fire occurs. Therefore, it is preferable to store pallets outdoors where possible.

A fire in stacks of idle plastic or wooden pallets is one of the greatest challenges to sprinklers. The undersides of the pallets create a dry area on which a fire can grow and expand to other dry or partially wet areas. This process of jumping to other dry, closely located, parallel, combustible surfaces continues until the fire bursts through the top of the stack. Once this happens, very little water is able to reach the base of the fire. The only practical method of stopping a fire in a large concentration of pallets with ceiling sprinklers is by means of prewetting. In high stacks, this cannot be done without abnormally high water supplies. The storage of empty wood pallets should not be permitted in an unsprinklered warehouse containing other storage.

12.1.9.1 Wood Pallets.

Wooden pallets, which are covered in 12.1.9.1, present a unique challenge for sprinkler protection. Idle pallets create an ideal configuration for efficient combustion by presenting many surfaces for burning and many openings to provide an almost unlimited source of air. At the same time, the configuration shields much of the burning surfaces from sprinkler discharge. In addition, pallets are subject to easy ignition due to their frayed, splintered edges and typical dried-out condition.

12.1.9.1.1* Pallets shall be permitted to be stored in the following arrangements:

(1) Stored outside
(2) Stored in a detached structure
(3) Stored indoors where arranged and protected in accordance with 12.1.9.1.2

 A.12.1.9.1.1 See Table A.12.1.9.1.1.

12.1.9.1.2* Pallets, where stored indoors, shall be protected as indicated in Table 12.1.9.1.2(a) using standard spray sprinklers, Table 12.1.9.1.2(b) using control mode specific application sprinklers, or Table 12.1.9.1.2(c) using ESFR sprinklers, unless the following conditions are met:

(1) Pallets shall be stored no higher than 6 ft (1.8 m).
(2) Each pallet pile of no more than four stacks shall be separated from other pallet piles by at least 8 ft (1.4 m) of clear space or 25 ft (7.6 m) of commodity.

TABLE A.12.1.9.1.1 *Recommended Clearance Between Outside Idle Pallet Storage and Building*

| Wall Construction | | Minimum Distance of Wall from Storage of | | | | | |
| | | Under 50 Pallets | | 50 to 200 Pallets | | Over 200 Pallets | |
Wall Type	Openings	ft	m	ft	m	ft	m
Masonry	None	0	0	0	0	0	0
	Wired glass with outside sprinklers and 1-hour doors	0	0	10	3.1	20	6.1
	Wired or plain glass with outside sprinklers and ¾-hour doors	10	3.1	20	6.1	30	9.1
Wood or metal with outside sprinklers		10	3.1	20	6.1	30	9.1
Wood, metal, or other		20	6.1	30	9.1	50	15.2

Notes:

1. Fire-resistive protection comparable to that of the wall also should be provided for combustible eaves lines, vent openings, and so forth.

2. Where pallets are stored close to a building, the height of storage should be restricted to prevent burning pallets from falling on the building.

3. Manual outside open sprinklers generally are not a reliable means of protection unless property is attended to at all times by plant emergency personnel.

4. Open sprinklers controlled by a deluge valve are preferred.

TABLE 12.1.9.1.2(a) *Control Mode Density-Area Protection of Indoor Storage of Idle Wood Pallets*

Type of Sprinkler	Location of Storage	Nominal K-Factor	Maximum Storage Height		Sprinkler Density		Areas of Operation				Hose Stream Demand		Water Supply Duration (hours)
							High Temperature		Ordinary Temperature				
			ft	m	gpm/ft²	mm/min	ft²	m²	ft²	m²	gpm	L/min	
Control mode density/area	On floor	K 8 or larger	Up to 6	Up to 1.8	0.2	8.2	2000	186	3000	279	500	1900	1½
		K 11.2 or larger	6 to 8	1.8 to 2.4	0.45	18.3	2500	232	4000	372	500	1900	1½
			8 to 12	2.4 to 3.7	0.6	24.5	3500	325	6000	557	500	1900	1½
			12 to 20	3.7 to 6.1	0.6	24.5	4500	418	—	—	500	1900	1½

TABLE 12.1.9.1.2(b) *Control Mode Specific Application Protection of Indoor Storage of Idle Wood Pallets*

Type of Sprinkler	Location of Storage	Nominal K-Factor	Maximum Storage Height		Maximum Ceiling/ Roof Height		Type of System	Number of Design Sprinklers by Minimum Pressure			Hose Stream Demand		Water Supply Duration (hours)
								25 psi (1.7 bar)	50 psi (3.4 bar)	75 psi (5.2 bar)			
			ft	m	ft	m					gpm	L/min	
Large drop	On floor	11.2	20	6.1	30	9.1	Wet	15	15	15	500	1900	1½
							Dry	25	25	25	500	1900	1½

TABLE 12.1.9.1.2(c) *ESFR Protection of Indoor Storage of Idle Wood Pallets*

Type of Sprinkler (Orientation)	Location of Storage	Nominal K-Factor	Maximum Storage Height		Maximum Ceiling/Roof Height		Minimum Operating Pressure	Hose Stream Demand		Water Supply Duration (hours)
			ft	m	ft	m	psi	gpm	L/min	
ESFR (pendent)	On floor or rack without solid shelves	14.0	25	7.6	30	9.1	50	250	946	1
			25	7.6	32	9.8	60			
			35	10.7	40	12.2	75			
		16.8	25	7.6	30	9.1	35			
			25	7.6	32	9.8	42			
			35	10.7	40	12.2	52			
ESFR (upright)	On floor only	14.0	20	6.1	30	9.1	50			
			20	6.1	35	10.7	75			

A.12.1.9.1.2 No additional protection is necessary, provided the requirements of 12.1.9.1.2 are met.

Where idle wood pallets are stored in accordance with the two conditions of 12.1.9.1.2, experience indicates that most sprinklered buildings will normally withstand the heat produced as long as the heat is not prolonged. Thus, some idle pallet storage without extra protection is considered acceptable. Exhibit 12.1 shows such an arrangement.

The two conditions identified in 12.1.9.1.2 are often difficult to enforce. Designing the sprinkler protection for the idle pallet storage heights anticipated is usually the preferred approach. If storage of idle pallets does not meet the conditions of 12.1.9.1.2, standard spray sprinklers in accordance with Table 12.1.9.1.2(a), large drop sprinklers and control mode specific application sprinklers in accordance with Table 12.1.9.1.2(b), or ESFR sprinklers in accordance with Table 12.1.9.1.2(c) need to be considered.

EXHIBIT 12.1 Idle Pallet Storage Arrangement That Meets the Conditions of 12.1.9.1.2.

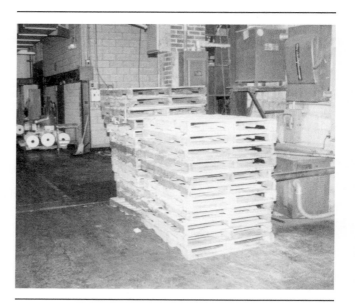

FAQ ▶
How can idle wood pallets be protected in racks?

12.1.9.1.3 Idle wood pallets shall not be stored in racks unless they are protected in accordance with the appropriate provisions of Table 12.1.9.1.2(c). *(See Section C.7.)*

Only ESFR sprinklers can be utilized to protect idle wood pallets stored in racks as indicated in Table 12.1.9.1.2(c) (see 12.1.9.1.3). No protection schemes using standard spray sprinklers at the ceiling along with in-rack sprinklers have been tested to confirm effective protection of idle wood pallet storage in racks.

12.1.9.2 Plastic Pallets.

For additional information on the effect of plastic pallets, which are discussed in 12.1.9.2, on the overall fire hazard and commodity classification, see the commentary following 5.6.2.7.

12.1.9.2.1 Plastic pallets shall be permitted to be stored in the following manners:

(1) Plastic pallets shall be permitted to be stored outside.
(2) Plastic pallets shall be permitted to be stored in a detached structure.
(3) Plastic pallets shall be permitted to be stored indoors where arranged and protected in accordance with the requirements of 12.1.9.2.2.
(4) Indoor storage of plastic pallets shall be permitted to be protected in accordance with the requirements of Table 12.1.9.2.1

TABLE 12.1.9.2.1 *ESFR Protection of Indoor Storage of Idle Plastic Pallets*

Type of Sprinkler (Orientation)	Location of Storage	Nominal K-Factor	Maximum Storage Height		Maximum Ceiling/Roof Height		Minimum Operating Pressure		Hose Stream Demand		Water Supply Duration (hours)
			ft	m	ft	m	psi	bar	gpm	L/min	
ESFR (pendent)	On floor or rack without solid shelves	14.0	25	7.6	30	9.1	50	3.4	250	946	1
			25	7.6	32	9.8	60	4.1			
			35	10.7	40	12.2	75	5.2			
		16.8	25	7.6	30	9.1	35	2.4			
			25	7.6	32	9.8	42	2.9			
			35	10.7	40	12.2	52	3.6			

(5) Indoor storage of plastic pallets shall be permitted to be protected in accordance with the following arrangement:

    (a) Maximum storage height of 10 ft
    (b) Maximum ceiling height of 30 ft
    (c) Sprinkler density 0.6 gpm/ft^2 over 2000 ft^2
    (d) Minimum sprinkler K-factor of 16.8

Testing has shown that control mode sprinklers with a nominal K-factor of 16.8 can adequately control a fire in plastic pallet storage up to 10 ft (3 m) in height. Therefore, 12.1.9.2.1(5)(d) does not require any additional protection such as a cutoff room.

(6) Indoor storage of non-wood pallets having a demonstrated fire hazard that is equal to or less than idle wood pallets and is listed for such equivalency shall be permitted to be protected in accordance with 12.1.9.1.2.

Pallets that meet the requirements of 12.1.9.2.1(6) must be listed as defined in this standard. A mark of the listing agency should identify the plastic pallet for its capability to burn at a rate less than or equal to wood pallets.

(7) When specific test data is available, the data shall take precedence in determining the required protection of idle plastic pallets.

There are many different kinds of plastic pallets (see Exhibit 12.2) and many unique storage arrangements. Since all possible arrangements and configurations cannot be addressed within NFPA 13, specific test data, where available, can be utilized in lieu of other sections of this standard, as stated in 12.1.9.2.1(7).

12.1.9.2.2 Plastic pallets where stored indoors shall be protected as follows:

(1) Where stored in cutoff rooms the following shall apply:

    (a) The cutoff rooms shall have at least one exterior wall.
    (b) The plastic pallet storage shall be separated from the remainder of the building by 3 hour–rated fire walls.
    (c) Sprinkler protection by one of the following:

        i. The storage shall be protected by sprinklers designed to deliver 0.6 gpm/ft^2 (24.5 mm/min) for the entire room or by high-expansion foam and sprinklers as indicated in 12.1.11.

*EXHIBIT 12.2
Non-Reinforced
Plastic Pallet.*

ii. K-14 ESFR upright sprinklers when the storage is on floor and the system is designed to supply all sprinklers in the room at 50 psi (3.4 bar) for a maximum of 30 ft (9.1 m) ceiling or 75 psi (5.2 bar) for a maximum 35 ft (10.7 m) ceiling.

(d) The storage shall be piled no higher than 12 ft (3.7 m).

(e) Any steel columns shall be protected by 1-hour fireproofing or a sidewall sprinkler directed to one side of the column at the top or at the 15-ft (4.6-m) level, whichever is lower. Flow from these sprinklers shall be permitted to be omitted from the sprinkler system demand for hydraulic calculations.

(2) Where stored without cutoffs from other storage the following shall apply:

(a) Plastic pallet storage shall be piled no higher than 4 ft (1.2 m).

(b) Sprinkler protection shall employ high temperature–rated sprinklers.

(c) Each pallet pile of no more than two stacks shall be separated from other pallet piles by at least 8 ft (2.4 m) of clear space or 25 ft (7.6 m) of stored commodity.

12.1.9.2.3 Idle plastic pallets shall only be stored in racks where protected in accordance with the requirements of Table 12.1.9.2.1.

Certain arrangements of idle plastic pallets stored in racks can be protected using ESFR sprinklers as required by Table 12.1.9.2.1 (see 12.1.9.2.3).

12.1.10 Miscellaneous Storage and Storage of Class I through IV up to 12 ft in Height.

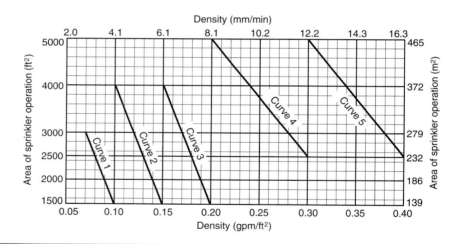

FIGURE 12.1.10 *Miscellaneous Storage and Commodity Classes I through IV Storage 12 ft (3.7 m) or Less in Height—Design Curves (see Table 12.1.10.1).*

12.1.10.1 Discharge Criteria.

 12.1.10.1.1 For protection of miscellaneous storage up to 12 ft (3.7 m) in height of Group A plastic, rubber tires, rolled paper, and storage of idle pallets up to 6 ft (1.4 m) in height, the discharge criteria in Table 12.1.10.1.1 and Figure 12.1.10 shall apply.

 12.1.10.1.2 For the protection of storage of Class I through IV commodities up to 12 ft (3.7 m) in height, the discharge criteria in Table 12.1.10.1.1 and Figure 12.1.10 shall apply.

Paragraphs 12.1.101.1 and 12.1.10.1.2 contain the design criteria for the protection of storage that meets the definition of miscellaneous storage and criteria for the protection of all Class I through Class IV storage up to 12 ft (3.7 m).

TABLE 12.1.10.1.1 *Discharge Criteria for Miscellaneous Storage and Commodity Classes I through IV Storage 12 ft (3.7 m) or Less in Height*[1]

Commodity		Type of Storage	Storage Height ft	Storage Height m	Maximum Ceiling Height ft	Maximum Ceiling Height m	Design Curve Figure 12.1.10	Note	Inside Hose (gpm)	Total Combined Inside and Outside Hose (gpm)	Duration (minutes)
Class I to IV											
Class I		Palletized, bin box, shelf, and rack	≤12	≤3.7	—	—	Curve 2		0, 50, or 100	250	90
Class II			≤10	≤3.05	—	—	Curve 2		0, 50, or 100	250	90
Class II			>10 to ≤12	>3.05 to ≤3.7	—	—	Curve 3		0, 50, or 100	250	90
Class III			≤12	≤3.7	—	—	Curve 3		0, 50, or 100	250	90
Class IV			≤10	≤3.05	—	—	Curve 3		0, 50, or 100	250	90
Class IV		Palletized, bin box, and shelf	>10 to ≤12	>3.05 to ≤3.7	—	—	Curve 3		0, 50, or 100	500	90
Class IV		Rack	>10 to ≤12	>3.05 to ≤3.7	—	—	Curve 4		0, 50, or 100	500	90
Miscellaneous Group A Plastic Storage											
Cartoned	Solid and expanded	Palletized, bin box, shelf, and rack	≤5	≤1.5	—	—	Curve 3		0, 50, or 100	500	90
			>5 to ≤10	>1.5 to ≤3.05	15	4.6	Curve 4		0, 50, or 100	500	120
			>5 to ≤10	>1.5 to ≤3.05	20	6.1	Curve 5		0, 50, or 100	500	120
			>10 to ≤12	>3.05 to ≤3.7	17	5.2	Curve 5		0, 50, or 100	500	120
			>10 to ≤12	>3.05 to ≤3.7	17	5.2	Curve 3	+1 level of in-rack	0, 50, or 100	500	120
		Palletized, bin box, and shelf	>10 to ≤12	>3.05 to ≤3.7	27	8.2	Curve 5		0, 50, or 100	500	120
		Rack	>10 to ≤12	>3.05 to ≤3.7	—	—	Curve 3	+1 level of in-rack	0, 50, or 100	500	120
Exposed	Solid and expanded	Palletized, bin box, shelf, and rack	≤5	≤1.5	—	—	Curve 3		0, 50, or 100	500	90
		Palletized, bin box, and shelf	>5 to ≤8	>1.5 to ≤2.4	—	—	Curve 5		0, 50, or 100	500	120
		Palletized, bin box, shelf, and rack	>5 to ≤10	>1.5 to ≤3.05	15	4.6	Curve 5		0, 50, or 100	500	120

(Continues)

TABLE 12.1.10.1.1 *Continued*

Commodity		Type of Storage	Storage Height ft	Storage Height m	Maximum Ceiling Height ft	Maximum Ceiling Height m	Design Curve Figure 12.1.10	Note	Inside Hose (gpm)	Total Combined Inside and Outside Hose (gpm)	Duration (minutes)
	Miscellaneous Group A Plastic Storage *(continued)*										
Exposed	Solid	Palletized, bin box, shelf, and rack	>5 to ≤10	>1.5 to ≤3.05	20	6.1	Curve 5		0, 50, or 100	500	120
	Expanded	Rack	>5 to ≤10	>1.5 to ≤3.05	20	6.1	Curve 3	+1 level of in-rack	0, 50, or 100	500	120
	Solid and expanded	Palletized, bin box, and shelf	>10 to ≤12	>3.05 to ≤3.7	17	5.2	Curve 5		0, 50, or 100	500	120
		Rack	>10 to ≤12	>3.05 to ≤3.7	17	5.2	Curve 5		0, 50, or 100	500	120
			>10 to ≤12	>3.05 to ≤3.7	17	5.2	Curve 3	+1 level of in-rack	0, 50, or 100	500	120
			>10 to ≤12	>3.05 to ≤3.7	—	—	Curve 3	+1 level of in-rack	0, 50, or 100	500	120
	Miscellaneous Tire Storage										
Tires		On floor, on side	>5 to ≤12	>1.5 to ≤3.7	—	—	Curve 4		0, 50, or 100	750	180
		On floor, on tread or on side	≤5	≤1.5	—	—	Curve 3		0, 50, or 100	750	180
		Single-, double-, or multiple-row racks on tread or on side	≤5	≤1.5	—	—	Curve 3		0, 50, or 100	750	180
		Single-row rack, portable, on tread or on side	>5 to ≤12	>1.5 to ≤3.7	—	—	Curve 4		0, 50, or 100	750	180
		Single-row rack, fixed, on tread or on side	>5 to ≤12	>1.5 to ≤3.7	—	—	Curve 4		0, 50, or 100	750	180
			>5 to ≤12	>1.5 to ≤3.7	—	—	Curve 3	+1 level of in-rack	0, 50, or 100	750	180

(Continues)

TABLE 12.1.10.1.1 *Continued*

Commodity	Type of Storage	Storage Height ft	Storage Height m	Maximum Ceiling Height ft	Maximum Ceiling Height m	Design Curve Figure 12.1.10	Note	Inside Hose (gpm)	Total Combined Inside and Outside Hose (gpm)	Duration (minutes)
						Miscellaneous Rolled Paper Storage				
Heavy and medium weight	On end	≤10	≤3.05	—	—	Curve 3		0, 50, or 100	500	120
Tissue and light weight	On end	≤10	≤3.05	—	—	Curve 4		0, 50, or 100	500	120
						Idle Pallet Storage				
Wooden pallets	Single-row rack, fixed	≤6	≤1.8	—	—	Curve 3		0, 50, or 100	500	90
Plastic pallets	Single-row rack, fixed	≤4	≤1.2	—	—	Curve 3		0, 50, or 100	500	90

Class I through Class IV storage does not have to meet the definition of miscellaneous storage to be protected by the requirements in 12.10.1. The only limiting factor for the protection of Class I through Class IV commodities is that the height of storage cannot exceed 12 ft (3.7 m).

It is important to understand that not all miscellaneous storage, such as rolled paper and idle pallets, can be stored as high as 12 ft (3.7 m). The miscellaneous storage of car or truck tires in facilities such as automobile service centers presents significant fire safety concerns. Burning tires tend to create very hot and smoky fires that are difficult to control and extinguish. Because of their structure, tires possess inherent flue spaces that allow for an unobstructed air supply during a fire. Additionally, fires burning on the interior surfaces of tires are often obstructed from sprinkler system discharge.

◄ **FAQ**
Do the requirements of 12.1.10 apply to all storage of Class I through Class IV commodities stored up to 12 ft (3.7 m) in height?

12.1.10.2 Hose Stream Demand and Water Supply Duration.

12.1.10.2.1 The hose stream demand and water supply duration for the protection of palletized, solid piled, bin box, shelf storage, or rack storage of Class I through IV commodities, miscellaneous storage of Group A plastics, and miscellaneous rack storage of Class I through IV commodities, up to 12 ft (3.7 m) in height shall be in accordance with the requirements of Table 12.1.10.1.1.

12.1.10.2.2 The hose stream demand and water supply duration for the protection of miscellaneous storage of rubber tires, rolled paper, and idle pallets shall be in accordance with the requirements of Table 12.1.10.1.1.

12.1.11 High-Expansion Foam Systems.

12.1.11.1 High-expansion foam systems that are installed in addition to automatic sprinklers shall be installed in accordance with NFPA 11A, *Standard for Medium- and High-Expansion Foam.*

12.1.11.2 High-expansion foam systems shall be automatic in operation.

12.1.11.3 A reduction in ceiling density to one-half that required for Class I through Class IV commodities, idle pallets, or plastics shall be permitted without revising the design area, but the density shall be no less than 0.15 gpm/ft^2 (6.1 mm/min).

Ceiling sprinklers are necessary when protecting storage with high-expansion foam, as discussed in 12.1.11.1 through 12.1.11.3. The sprinklers are needed to help maintain the structural integrity of the building columns and roof structure by keeping them relatively cool while the foam covers the fire. Sprinkler discharge breaks down the foam, which needs to be taken into account when designing the system. Very few tests have been conducted using high-expansion foam in conjunction with sprinkler protection. The ceiling density of one-half that required for sprinkler protection is based largely on experience and judgment.

12.1.11.4 High-expansion foam used to protect the idle pallet shall have a maximum fill time of 4 minutes.

12.1.12 In-Rack Sprinklers. In-rack sprinklers mandated by this standard shall meet the requirements of this section and the applicable storage protection and arrangement sections of this chapter.

12.1.12.1 Operating Pressure. In-rack sprinklers shall operate at a minimum of 15 psi (1 bar).

12.1.12.2 Water Demand. Where one level of in-rack sprinklers is installed for miscellaneous storage, water demand shall be based on simultaneous operation of the hydraulically most demanding four adjacent sprinklers.

FAQ ▶
When in-rack sprinklers are required for the protection of miscellaneous storage in accordance with Table 12.1.10.1.1, how many sprinklers must be added to the ceiling demand?

For miscellaneous storage, the maximum number of in-rack sprinklers that must be hydraulically calculated for one level of in-racks is four. Currently, Table 12.1.10.1.1 does not require more than one level of in-rack protection. Additional levels of in-rack sprinklers installed due to solid shelf criteria should not present any greater hazard; therefore, the four head hydraulic criteria in 12.1.12.2 should be acceptable for miscellaneous storage with solid shelves.

12.1.13* Storage Applications.

A.12.1.13 The reasons for using larger orifice sprinklers in storage situations are based on a number of fire tests in recent years that continue to show an advantage of the larger orifice (K-11.2 and K-16.8) sprinklers over the K-5.6 and even the K-8 orifice sprinklers. Following are four sets of fire test comparisons using constant densities. *[See Table A.12.1.13(a) and Table A.12.1.13(b)].*

(1) K-5.6 vs. K-11.2
   (a) Commodity—idle wood two-way pallets
   (b) 2 stacks × 3 stacks × 8 ft high
   (c) Ceiling height—30 ft
   (d) Density—constant 0.30 gpm/ft^2
   (e) Test #1–165°F rated, K-11.2 sprinklers
   (f) Test #2–165°F rated, K-5.6 sprinklers
   (g) Test #1 results—4 A.S. operated
   (h) Test #2 results—29 A.S. operated, less fire control and greater temperatures

(2) K-8.0 vs. K-11.2 vs. K-16.8
   (a) Commodity—idle wood four-way pallets
   (b) Two stacks × three stacks × 12 ft high
   (c) Ceiling height—30 ft
   (d) Density—constant 0.6 gpm/ft^2
   (e) Test #1–286°F rated, K-8 sprinklers
   (f) Test #2–165°F rated, K-11.2 sprinklers
   (g) Test #3–165°F rated, K-16.8 sprinklers
   (h) Test #1 results—10 A.S. operated, 658°C maximum steel temperature, fire spread to all sides

TABLE A.12.1.13(a) *Ceiling Type*

	Ceiling Type	Sprinkler Distance Below Ceiling (in.)	Time to Activation (seconds)	Size of Fire at Activation (Btu/s)
Fast-growing fire	Insulated deck	1	76	450
	Steel	1	97	580
	Wood	1	71	420
	Insulated deck	12	173	1880
	Steel	12	176	1930
	Wood	12	172	1900
Slow-growing fire	Insulated deck	1	281	220
	Steel	1	375	390
	Wood	1	268	200
	Insulated deck	12	476	630
	Steel	12	492	675
	Wood	12	473	620

TABLE A.12.1.13(b) *Ceiling Arrangement*

Situation	Fire	Time to Activate Sprinkler (seconds)	Fire Size at Time of Activation (Btu/s)
Ceiling with pocket	Fast	86 to 113	585
Sprinkler 12 in. below ceiling	Fast	172 to 176	1880 to 1900
Ceiling with pocket	Slow	288 to 395	490
Sprinkler 12 in. below ceiling	Slow	473 to 492	620 to 675

(i) Test #2 results—13 A.S. operated, 94°C maximum steel temperature, fire spread to three sides

(j) Test #3 results—6 A.S. operated, 54°C maximum steel temperature, fire spread (just reached) one side

(3) K-5.6 vs. K-16.8

    (a) Commodity—FMRC standard plastic commodity rack style 9 ft high

    (b) Ceiling height—30 ft

    (c) Density—0.45 gpm/ft^2

    (d) Test #1—K-5.6 orifice sprinklers

    (e) Test #2—K-16.8 orifice sprinklers

    (f) Test #1 results—29 A.S. operated, 14 pallet loads consumed

    (g) Test #2 results—5 A.S. operated, 2 pallet loads consumed

(4) K-8.0 vs. K-16.8

    (a) Commodity—FMRC standard plastic commodity rack stage 14 ft high

    (b) Ceiling height—25 ft

    (c) Density—0.60 gpm/ft^2

    (d) Test #1—K-8.0 sprinklers

    (e) Test #2—K-16.8 sprinklers

    (f) Test #1 results—29 A.S. operated, 25 pallet loads consumed

    (g) Test #2 results—7 A.S. operated, 4 pallet loads consumed

On an equal density basis the fire test comparisons show the advantage of the larger orifices. A possibly even bigger advantage can be seen when investigating the performance of larger orifice sprinklers in the real world condition of high initial operating pressures.

The volume of water discharged through the larger K-factor for the initial sprinklers has three significant effects.

(1) First, the increase in sheer volume flowing through the larger orifice enhances performance. For example, a 165 psi initial operating pressure would provide 102.8 gpm from a K-8, while the K-16.8 will discharge 215.8 gpm.

(2) Second, fire testing at high pressures (100+ psi) with K-5.6 and K-8 (when high fire updrafts occur) have shown less water penetration and more sprinkler skipping. When fire testing the K-11 and K-16.8 sprinklers at 100+ psi, more water penetration is evident and little or no sprinkler skipping has occurred.

(3) Third, with such high initial discharge rates among K-16.8 sprinklers, the friction loss in the supply pipes would be greater. This would result in lower initial pressures than a K-8 as well as being farther down the water supply curve with greater flows resulting in lower initial operating pressures.

Figure A.12.1.13 highlights the differences of the K-8 and K-16.8 initial operating pressures.

FIGURE A.12.1.13 *Available Pressure Comparison.*

The higher flow rate of the K-16.8 sprinkler results in greater friction losses in the initial operating heads as compared to the K-8. Combined with the lower pressure available on the water supply curve, the end result is a self-regulating orifice size allowing greater initial pressures without a negative impact.

Table A.12.1.13(c) summarizes the paper product testing.

The results: The tests indicated that even at a high temperature of 286°F, the K-8 sprinklers operating at higher pressures were not effective in controlling the fire. Conversely, the K-16.8 was able to control the fire at the lower temperature (155°F), by operating sooner, and at lower, self-regulating flowing pressures.

Conclusions: The larger K-factor of the K-16.8 is not affected by high initial operating pressures. In fact, the protection is enhanced, providing better fire protection.

TABLE A.12.1.13(c) *Paper Product Testing Results*

Test Date	3/25/98	3/18/98[a]	4/4/98	6/4/98[b]
Sprinklers	K-8	K-8	K-11	K-17-231
Temperature	286°F	286°F	165°F	155°F
Storage Type	4 tier pyramid	5 tier pyramid	4 tier pyramid	5 tier pyramid
Storage Height	16 ft	22 ft	16 ft	22 ft
Ceiling Height	30 ft	31 ft	30 ft	31 ft
Sprinkler Flow Pressure	22.6 psi	175 psi	11.9 psi	130 psi
Number of Operated Sprinklers	15	2	10	2
Peak Gas Temperature	—	868°F	—	424°F
Peak Steel Temperature	—	421°F	—	113°F
Fire Spread Across Aisle (30 in.)	N/A	Yes	N/A	No

[a]This test was run with a fire brigade response of 20:00 minutes.
[b]This test was run with a fire brigade response of 7:00 minutes.

The ability to use lower rated temperatures, such as 155°F in lieu of 286°F, shows that the performance of the initial operating sprinklers is effective in controlling the fire. Therefore, using high temperature heads to reduce the number of surrounding rings of sprinklers to open is not necessary when using the K-16.8 technology.

In short, the K-16.8 proved highly effective when subjected to high initial operating pressures.

12.1.13.1 For storage applications with densities of 0.20 gpm/ft^2 (8.2 mm/min) or less, standard response sprinklers with a K-factor of 5.6 or larger shall be permitted.

At the higher pressures that are likely to be available when the first few sprinklers operate, sprinklers with K-factors of 5.6 can produce smaller water droplets that are unable to penetrate the fire plume and attack the fire; therefore, for the protection of storage, they are limited to densities of 0.20 gpm/ft^2 (8.2 mm/min) or less (see 12.1.13.1).

12.1.13.2 For general storage applications, rack storage, rubber tire storage, roll paper storage, and baled cotton storage being protected with standard upright and pendent spray sprinklers with required densities of greater than 0.20 gpm/ft^2 (8.2 mm/min) to 0.34 gpm/ft^2 (13.9 mm/min), standard response sprinklers with a nominal K-factor of 8.0 or larger shall be used.

12.1.13.3 For general storage applications, rack storage, rubber tire storage, roll paper storage, and baled cotton storage being protected with standard upright and pendent spray sprinklers with required densities greater than 0.34 gpm/ft^2 (13.9 mm/min), standard response spray sprinklers with a K-factor of 11.2 or larger that are listed for storage applications shall be used.

Fire tests have shown that sprinklers with larger orifices—that is, K-factors of 11.2 or larger—perform better during storage fires with strong fire plumes than sprinklers with smaller orifices at the same design density (see 12.1.13.3). The lower water velocity through the sprinkler orifice generally results in larger water droplets that more readily penetrate the fire plume and allow more water to reach the fire's seat.

For nominal K-5.6 and K-8.0 sprinklers, high initial operating pressures of the first operating sprinklers has been shown to cause skipping of sprinkler activation sequence (skipping is an event where sprinklers further from the fire source operate before sprinklers closer to the source). Skipping is a result of strong fire plumes stopping penetration of small water droplets produced by high pressures through relatively small orifice sizes and carrying these droplets back to the ceiling. These droplets at the ceiling have the potential to wet adjacent sprinklers, causing them to not activate when required. The higher the density required, the stronger the fire plume that is expected, and the nominal K-11.2 or larger sprinklers do not demonstrate skipping and, therefore, are required for these higher densities.

12.1.13.4 The requirements of 12.1.13.2 and 12.1.13.3 shall not apply to modifications to existing storage application systems, using sprinklers with K-factors of 8.0 or less.

12.1.13.5 The use of quick-response spray sprinklers for storage applications shall be permitted when listed for such use.

Quick response spray sprinklers, which are discussed in 12.1.13.5, used as control mode density/area for storage protection have not yet demonstrated equivalence to standard response spray sprinklers. Factors such as obstructions to discharge and shielding have not been fully investigated in storage occupancies as to their effect on quick response sprinklers. Additionally, there are many design densities for control mode sprinklers; some are conservative and some are absolute minimums. Until complete validation tests are run, the density/area standard spray sprinklers for the protection of storage are limited to standard response unless they are specifically listed as quick response sprinklers for the protection of storage.

12.2 Fire Control Approach for the Protection of Commodities That are Stored Palletized, Solid Piled, Bin Boxes, or Shelf Storage

12.2.1 General.

12.2.1.1 This section shall apply to a broad range of combustibles, including plastics that are stored palletized, solid piled, bin boxes, or shelf storage using standard spray sprinklers.

12.2.1.2* The minimum water supply requirements for a hydraulically designed occupancy hazard fire control sprinkler system shall be determined by adding the hose stream demand from Table 12.2.1.2 to the water supply for sprinklers. This supply shall be available for the minimum duration specified in Table 12.2.1.2. *(See Section C.8.)*

 A.12.2.1.2 Appropriate area/density, other design criteria, and water supply requirements should be based on scientifically based engineering analyses that can include submitted fire testing, calculations, or results from appropriate computational models.

TABLE 12.2.1.2 Hose Stream Demand and Water Supply Duration Requirements

Commodity Classification	Storage Height		Inside Hose		Total Combined Inside and Outside Hose		Duration (minutes)
	ft	*m*	*gpm*	*L/min*	*gpm*	*L/min*	
Class I, II, and III	Over 12 up to 20	Over 3.7 up to 6.1	0, 50, or 100	0, 190, 380	500	1900	90
	Over 20 up to 30	Over 6.1 up to 9.1	0, 50, or 100	0, 190, 380	500	1900	120
Class IV	Over 12 up to 20	Over 3.7 up to 6.1	0, 50, or 100	0, 190, 380	500	1900	120
	Over 20 up to 30	Over 6.1 up to 9.1	0, 50, or 100	0, 190, 380	500	1900	150
Group A plastic	< 5	< 1.5	0, 50, or 100	0, 190, 380	500	1900	90
	Over 5 up to 20	Over 1.5 up to 6.1	0, 50, or 100	0, 190, 380	500	1900	120
	Over 20 up to 25	Over 6.1 up to 7.6	0, 50, or 100	0, 190, 380	500	1900	150

Recommended water supplies anticipate successful sprinkler operation. Because of the small but still significant number of uncontrolled fires in sprinklered properties, which have various causes, there should be an adequate water supply available for fire department use.

12.2.1.2.1 An allowance for inside and outside hose shall not be required where tanks supply sprinklers only.

12.2.1.2.2 Where pumps taking suction from a private fire service main supply sprinklers only, the pump need not be sized to accommodate inside and outside hose. Such hose allowance shall be considered in evaluating the available water supplies.

12.2.1.3 High-Expansion Foam Systems.

12.2.1.3.1 A reduction in ceiling density to one-half that required for Class I through Class IV commodities, idle pallets, or plastics shall be permitted without revising the design area, but the density shall be no less than 0.15 gpm/ft^2 (6.1 mm/min).

Ceiling sprinklers are necessary when protecting storage with high-expansion foam (see 12.2.1.3.1). The sprinklers are needed to help maintain the structural integrity of the building columns and roof structure by keeping them relatively cool while the foam covers the fire. Sprinkler discharge breaks down the foam, which needs to be taken into account when designing the system. Very few tests have been conducted using high-expansion foam in conjunction with sprinkler protection. The ceiling density of one-half that required for sprinkler protection is based largely on experience and judgment.

12.2.1.3.2 Detectors for high-expansion foam systems shall be listed and shall be installed at no more than one-half the listed spacing.

Quick detection of a fire in a warehouse protected by high-expansion foam is essential, which is the reason for the requirement in 12.2.1.3.2. The foam requires a period of time to cover the burning stock. The faster the foam is discharged onto the fire, the less the amount of damage that will occur. Reducing the detector spacing at the ceiling by one-half of what is typically required helps assure faster response of the foam system.

12.2.1.3.3 Detection systems, concentrate pumps, generators, and other system components that are essential to the operation of the system shall have an approved standby power source.

High-expansion foam systems also need electrical power to operate. Thus, a reliable standby power supply is needed, as stated in 12.2.1.3.3.

12.2.2 Protection Criteria for Palletized, Solid Piled, Bin Box, or Shelf Storage of Class I through IV Commodities.

Through experience and full-scale testing, the fire protection industry has determined that for Class I through Class IV commodities, the protection requirements in subsection 12.2.2 are more a function of the class of commodity stored rather than the manner in which the commodity is stored. For example, the protection of Class III commodities is the same regardless of whether the commodity is stored palletized, in a solid pile, in bin boxes, or in shelves. Protection criteria beyond certain storage heights are not provided in 12.2.2.

12.2.2.1* Control Mode Density-Area Sprinkler Protection Criteria for Palletized, Solid Piled, Bin Box, or Shelf Storage of Class I through IV Commodities.

A.12.2.2.1 The following procedure should be followed in determining the proper density and area as specified in Chapter 12:

(1) Determine the commodity class.
(2) Select the density and area of application.
(3) Adjust the required density for storage height.

(4) Increase the operating area by 30 percent where a dry pipe system is used.
(5) Satisfy the minimum densities and areas.

Example:

Storage—greeting cards in boxes in cartons on pallets
Height—22 ft (6.7 m)
Clearance—6 ft (1.8 m)
Sprinklers—ordinary temperature
System type—dry

(a) Classification—Class III
(b) Selection of density/area—0.225 gpm/ft² (9.2 mm/min) over 3000 ft² (279 m²)
(c) Adjustment for height of storage—1.15 × 0.225 gpm/ft³ = 0.259 gpm/ft² (10.553 mm/min), rounded up to 0.26 gpm/ft² (10.6 mm/min)
(d) Adjustment of area of operation for dry system—1.3 × 3000 ft² = 3900 ft² (363 m²)
(e) Confirmation that minimum densities and areas have been achieved

The minimum design density for a dry sprinkler system is 0.15 gpm/ft² over 2600 ft² (6.1 mm/min over 242 m²) for Class III.

The corresponding minimum density at 3000 ft² (279 m²) is 0.17 gpm/ft² (6.9 mm/min) (satisfied); 1.3 × 3000 ft² = 3900 ft² (363 m²), 0.17 gpm/ft² (6.9 mm/min) over 3900 ft² (363 m²).

The design density and area of application equals 0.26 gpm/ft² over 3900 ft² (10.6 mm/min over 363 m²).

12.2.2.1.1 Protection for Class I through Class IV commodities in the following configurations shall be provided in accordance with this chapter:

(1) Nonencapsulated commodities that are solid pile, palletized, or bin box storage up to 30 ft (9.1 m) in height
(2) Nonencapsulated commodities on shelf storage up to 15 ft (4.6 m) in height
(3)* Encapsulated commodities that are solid pile, palletized, bin box, or shelf storage up to 15 ft (4.6 m) in height

The only available test data on shelf storage is limited and was conducted at a storage height of 15 ft (4.6 m) (see 12.2.2.1.1). In actual practice, shelf storage is rarely higher than 15 ft (4.6 m). Shelf storage exceeding 15 ft (4.6 m) can be protected in accordance with the criteria for rack storage in Section 12.3. If the shelf storage is considered record storage as described in NFPA 232, *Standard for the Protection of Records,* it should be protected in accordance with the guidelines of that standard.

It is important to understand the limitations of 12.2.2.1 since there are many storage configurations that are outside its scope. An example of encapsulated storage above 15 ft (4.6 m) is prohibited from being protected by control mode density/area sprinklers. Other protection designs such as large drop, control mode specific application, and ESFR protection schemes should be considered.

A.12.2.2.1.1(3) Full-scale tests show no appreciable difference in the number of sprinklers that open for either nonencapsulated or encapsulated products up to 15 ft (4.6 m) high. Test data is not available for encapsulated products stored higher than 15 ft (4.6 m). However, in rack storage tests involving encapsulated storage 20 ft (6.1 m) high, increased protection was needed over that for nonencapsulated storage.

The protection specified contemplates a maximum of 10-ft (3-m) clearances from top of storage to sprinkler deflectors for storage heights of 15 ft (4.6 m) and higher.

12.2.2.1.2 The area and density for the hydraulically remote area and the water supply shall be determined as specified in 12.1.11 for storage 12 ft (3.7 m) or less and Section 12.2 for storage over 12 ft (3.7 m).

Paragraphs 12.2.2.1.1 and 12.2.2.1.2 clearly indicate that 12.2.2.1 is for the protection of Class I through IV storage above 12 ft. Storage 12 ft and below does not apply to paragraph 12.2.2.1 and should be protected in accordance with the requirements of subsection 12.1.10.

12.2.2.1.3 Hose connections shall not be required for the protection of Class I, II, III, and IV commodities stored 12 ft (3.7 m) or less in height.

Paragraph 12.2.2.1.3 acknowledges the omission of hose stations for certain storage arrangements and recognizes the cost of installing hose stations in any storage facility. Hose stations would still be beneficial, but the sprinkler system in combination with fire department response is considered adequate to guard against the associated fire risk. Whenever possible, hose stations should be considered in all storage facilities regardless of storage heights because their benefits generally outweigh their expense.

◄ FAQ
Are hose connections required for all storage?

12.2.2.1.4 Minimum System Discharge Requirements.

12.2.2.1.4.1 The design density shall not be less than 0.15 gpm/ft^2 (6.1 mm/min), and the design area shall not be less than 2000 ft^2 (186 m^2) for wet systems or 2600 ft^2 (242 m^2) for dry systems for any commodity, class, or group.

12.2.2.1.4.2 The sprinkler design density for any given area of operation for a Class III or Class IV commodity, calculated in accordance with 12.2.2, shall not be less than the density for the corresponding area of operation for ordinary hazard Group 2.

The requirements of 12.2.2.1.4.2 were added after miscellaneous storage of Class III and Class IV commodities was determined to need protection in accordance with the discharge criteria for ordinary hazard (Group 2) occupancies (see Curve 3 in Figure 12.1.10). Because miscellaneous storage is considered to present the least hazardous storage arrangement, the sprinkler protection of larger amounts of storage should not be any less than that required for miscellaneous storage.

12.2.2.1.5 Protection Criteria.

12.2.2.1.5.1 Where using ordinary temperature–rated sprinklers, a single point shall be selected from the appropriate commodity curve on Figure 12.2.2.1.5.1.

FIGURE 12.2.2.1.5.1 *Sprinkler System Design Curves, 20-ft (6.1-m) High Storage–Ordinary Temperature–Rated Sprinklers.*

The densities shown in Figure 12.2.2.1.5.1 were developed from full-scale fire tests. The area of operation is not less than 2000 ft² (186 m²) because control-mode density/area protection with standard sprinklers for the specified temperature cannot reliably limit sprinkler operating areas below 2000 ft² (186 m²), even with increased discharge densities.

When intermediate-temperature sprinklers are used, the design density should follow the criteria for ordinary-temperature sprinklers.

12.2.2.1.5.2 Where using high temperature–rated sprinklers, a single point shall be selected from the appropriate commodity curve on Figure 12.2.2.1.5.2.

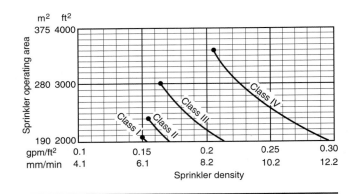

FIGURE 12.2.2.1.5.2 *Sprinkler System Design Curves, 20-ft (6.1-m) High Storage–High Temperature–Rated Sprinklers.*

When using sprinklers with K-factors of nominal 8.0 or 5.6, the use of high-temperature sprinklers has been shown to operate fewer sprinklers in full-scale fire tests (see 12.2.2.1.5.2). It should be noted that 12.2.2.1.7 allows all temperatures of sprinklers with K-factors of nominal 11.2 or greater to use the lower design densities for high-temperature sprinklers as shown in Figure 12.2.2.1.5.2 (see commentary on 12.2.2.1.7).

12.2.2.1.5.3 The densities selected in accordance with 12.2.2.1.5.1 or 12.2.2.1.5.2 shall be modified in accordance with Figure 12.2.2.1.5.3 without revising the design area.

FAQ ▶
Figure 12.2.2.1.5.1 and Figure 12.2.2.1.5.2 indicate that they are for storage 20 ft high. Can these figures be applied to storage heights either less than or greater than 20 ft?

The majority of testing that led to the development of the discharge criteria in Figures 12.2.2.1.5.1 and 12.2.2.1.5.2 is based on 20-ft (6.1-m) storage heights. Data from the tests in combination with field experience were extrapolated to produce discharge criteria for other storage heights. The values in Figure 12.2.2.1.5.3 have proven to be accurate when compared to actual fire events.

12.2.2.1.6 In the case of metal bin boxes with face areas not exceeding 16 ft² (1.5 m²) and metal closed shelves with face areas not exceeding 16 ft² (1.5 m²), the area of application shall be permitted to be reduced by 50 percent, provided the minimum requirements of 12.2.2.1.4 are met.

Paragraph 12.2.2.1.6 was developed from a series of test results which showed that the 50 percent reduction in area of sprinkler system operation for the protection of metal closed shelves and bin boxes is acceptable as long as the exposed storage on the face of the bin boxes or shelves is no greater than 16 ft² (1.5 m²).

12.2.2.1.7 Ordinary- and intermediate-temperature sprinklers with K-factors of 11.2 or larger, where listed for storage, shall be permitted to use the densities from the high temperature curves of Figure 12.2.2.1.5.2.

FIGURE 12.2.2.1.5.3 *Ceiling Sprinkler Density vs. Storage Height.*

Full-scale fire testing has shown that ordinary-temperature sprinklers with a nominal K-factor of 11.2 or greater perform to the lower density requirements of high-temperature sprinklers in Figure 12.2.2.1.5.2. Therefore, sprinklers having nominal K-factors of 11.2 or greater can utilize the lower design densities of Figure 12.2.2.1.5.2 regardless of the temperature rating of the sprinkler utilized, as stated in 12.2.2.1.7.

12.2.2.2 Large Drop Sprinklers and Specific Application Control Mode Sprinklers for Palletized or Solid Piled Storage of Class I through IV Commodities.

The large drop sprinkler, which is covered in 12.2.2.2, is a type of specific application control mode technology as defined in this standard. The names have remained separate due to the long history of the name "large drop" and its relation to the nominal K-factor of 11.2. Applications of large drop sprinklers and specific application control mode sprinklers are described in 12.2.2.2. Listing of large drop sprinklers and control mode specific application sprinklers takes into consideration the ability of the sprinkler discharge pattern to penetrate a high-velocity fire plume. Only listed large drop and specific application control mode sprinklers are to be used in accordance with the special design approach of 12.2.2.2.

12.2.2.2.1 Protection of palletized and solid-piled storage of Class I through Class IV commodities shall be in accordance with Table 12.2.2.2.1(a) and Table 12.2.2.2.1(b).

12.2.2.2.2 Protection shall be provided as specified in Table 12.2.2.2.1(a) and Table 12.2.2.2.1(b), or appropriate NFPA standards in terms of minimum operating pressure and the number of sprinklers to be included in the design area.

12.2.2.2.2.1 The minimum number of design sprinklers for ordinary hazard and miscellaneous storage in accordance with this standard shall be 15 for wet pipe systems and 25 for double interlock preaction systems and dry pipe systems.

The criteria of 12.2.2.2.2.1 are intended to apply primarily to the protection of ordinary hazard and miscellaneous storage using large drop and specific application control mode sprinklers.

12.2.2.2.2.2 For large drop sprinkler design purposes, 95 psi (6.6 bar) shall be the maximum discharge pressure at the hydraulically most remote sprinkler.

◀ **FAQ**
Why are ordinary-temperature sprinklers with K-factors of 11.2 or greater permitted to utilize the densities for high-temperature sprinklers?

TABLE 12.2.2.2.1(a) *Large-Drop Sprinkler Design Criteria for Palletized and Solid-Piled Storage of Class I through IV Commodities*

Storage Arrangement	Commodity Class	Nominal K-Factor	Maximum Storage Height		Maximum Ceiling/ Roof Height		Type of System	Number of Design Sprinklers/ Minimum Pressure		Hose Stream Demand		Water Supply Duration (hours)
			ft	m	ft	m		/psi	/bar	gpm	L/min	
Palletized	I, II, III	11.2	25	7.6	35	10.7	Wet	15/25	15/1.7	500	1900	2
							Dry	25/25	25/1.7	500	1900	2
	IV	11.2	20	6.1	30	9.1	Wet	20/25	20/1.7	500	1900	2
							Dry	N/A	N/A	N/A	N/A	N/A
		11.2	20	6.1	30	9.1	Wet	15/50	15/3.4	500	1900	2
							Dry	N/A	N/A	N/A	N/A	N/A
Solid Pile	I, II, III	11.2	20	6.1	30	9.1	Wet	15/25	15/1.7	500	1900	2
							Dry	25/25	25/1.7	N/A	N/A	N/A
	IV	11.2	20	6.1	30	9.1	Wet	15/50	15/3.4	500	1900	2
							Dry	N/A	N/A	N/A	N/A	N/A

TABLE 12.2.2.2.1(b) *Specific Application Control Mode (16.8 K-Factor) Sprinkler Design Criteria for Palletized and Solid-Piled Storage of Class I through IV Commodities*

Configuration	Commodity Class	Maximum Storage Height		Maximum Building Height		Type of System	Number of Design Sprinklers by Minimum Operating Pressure		Hose Stream Demand		Water Supply Duration (hours)
		ft	m	ft	m		10 psi (0.7 bar)	22 psi (1.5 bar)	gpm	L/min	
Palletized	I or II	25	7.6	30	9.1	Wet	15	—	500	1900	2
Palletized	III or IV	25	7.6	30	9.1	Wet	—	15	500	1900	2
Solid pile	I or II	25	7.6	30	9.1	Wet	15	—	500	1900	1½
Solid pile	III or IV	25	7.6	30	9.1	Wet	—	15	500	1900	1½

Discharge pressures in excess of 95 psi (6.6 bar) negatively impact the sprinkler's discharge pattern and droplet size, which is the reason for the requirement in 12.2.2.2.2.2.

12.2.2.2.2.3 Open Wood Joist Construction.

(A) Where large drop K-11.2 sprinklers are installed under open wood joist construction, their minimum operating pressure shall be 50 psi (3.4 bar).

(B) For large drop sprinklers, where each joist channel of open, wood joist construction is fully fire-stopped to its full depth at intervals not exceeding 20 ft (6.1 m), the lower pressures specified in Table 12.2.2.2.1(a) shall be permitted to be used.

12.2.2.2.2.4 For large drop sprinklers, the design area shall be a rectangular area having a dimension parallel to the branch lines at least 1.2 times the square root of the area protected by the number of sprinklers to be included in the design area. Any fractional sprinkler shall be included in the design area.

Starting with the 1996 edition, NFPA 13 provided more information about the shape of the design area where large drop and specific application control mode sprinklers are used (see 12.2.2.2.2.4). Although earlier editions implied that the design area was to be a rectangular shape having a dimension parallel to the branch lines of at least 1.2 times the square root of the area protected by the number of sprinklers, it was not explicitly stated.

12.2.2.2.2.5 Hose stream demand and water supply duration requirements shall be in accordance with Table 12.2.2.2.1(a) and Table 12.2.2.2.1(b).

12.2.2.2.2.6 Preaction Systems.

(A) For the purpose of using Table 12.2.2.2.1(a) and Table 12.2.2.2.1(b), preaction systems shall be classified as dry pipe systems.

Paragraph 12.2.2.2.2.6(A) requires that all preaction systems be treated as dry pipe sprinkler systems when applying the requirements of Table 12.2.2.2.1(a) and Table 12.2.2.2.1(b).

(B) Where it can be demonstrated that the detection system activating the preaction system will cause water to be at the sprinklers when they operate, preaction systems shall be permitted to be treated as wet pipe systems.

If it can be demonstrated that a detection system activating the preaction system will cause water to be at the sprinklers when they operate, the wet system design criteria can be used. Preaction systems that perform to 12.2.2.2.2.6(B) are not considered dry systems.

12.2.2.2.2.7 The nominal diameter of branch line pipes (including riser nipples) shall meet the following:

(1) Shall not be not less than 1¼ in. (32 mm) nor greater than 2 in. (51 mm).
(2) Starter pieces shall be permitted to be 2½ in. (64 mm).
(3) Where branch lines are larger than 2 in. (51 mm), the sprinkler shall be supplied by a riser nipple to elevate the sprinkler 13 in. (330 mm) for 2½ -in. (64-mm) pipe and 15 in. (380 mm) for 3-in. (76-mm) pipe. These dimensions are measured from the centerline of the pipe to the deflector. In lieu of this, sprinklers shall be permitted to be offset horizontally a minimum of 12 in. (305 mm).

The purpose of limiting the maximum diameter of branch lines or riser nipples, as required by 12.2.2.2.2.7, is to minimize the effect of pipe shadow below the sprinkler. Pipe shadow can result in significant shielded or dry areas with reduced water application and loss of sprinkler water penetration.

12.2.2.2.2.8 Building steel shall not require special protection where Table 12.2.2.2.1(a) and Table 12.2.2.2.1(b) are applied as appropriate for the storage configuration.

12.2.2.3 Early Suppression Fast-Response (ESFR) Sprinklers for Palletized or Solid Piled Storage of Class I through IV Commodities.

Applications of ESFR sprinklers are described in 12.2.2.3. The special design approach for ESFR sprinklers is based on fire suppression by the first operating ring of ESFR sprinklers.

12.2.2.3.1 Protection of palletized and solid pile storage of Classes I through IV shall be in accordance with Table 12.2.2.3.1.

ESFR protection criteria are provided in Table 12.2.2.3.1, which addresses protection of palletized and solid-piled storage. ESFR sprinklers are also permitted to be utilized for protec-

◄ **FAQ**
For large drop and specific application control mode sprinklers, are all types of preaction systems treated as dry pipe systems?

◄ **FAQ**
For large drop and specific application control mode sprinklers, are preaction systems always treated as dry pipe systems?

TABLE 12.2.2.3.1 *ESFR Protection of Palletized and Solid-Pile Storage of Class I through IV Commodities*

Commodity	Maximum Storage Height		Maximum Ceiling/ Roof Height		Nominal K-Factor	Orientation	Minimum Operating Pressure		Hose Stream Demand		Water Supply Duration (hours)
	ft	m	ft	m			psi	bar	gpm	L/min	
Class I, II, III, or IV, encapsulated (no open-top containers or solid shelves)	20	6.1	25	7.6	11.2	Upright	50	3.4	250	946	1
					14.0	Upright or pendent	50	3.4			
					16.8	Pendent	35	2.4			
					25.2	Pendent	15	1.0			
	25	7.6	30	9.1	14.0	Upright or pendent	50	3.4			
					16.8	Pendent	35	2.4			
					25.2	Pendent	15	1.0			
			32	9.8	14.0	Upright or pendent	60	4.1			
					16.8	Pendent	42	2.9			
	30	9.1	35	10.7	14.0	Upright or pendent	75	5.2			
					16.8	Pendent	52	3.6			
					25.2	Pendent	20	1.4			
	35	10.7	40	12.2	14.0	Pendent	75	5.2			
					16.8	Pendent	52	3.6			
					25.2	Pendent	25	1.7			
	35	10.7	45	13.7	25.2	Pendent	40	2.8			
	40	12.2	45	13.7	25.2	Pendent	40	2.8			

tion of ordinary hazard occupancies and miscellaneous storage. The criteria in Table 12.2.2.3.1 have been expanded to permit broader applications of ESFR sprinkler technology, based on large-scale test results reviewed by the Technical Committee on Sprinkler System Discharge Criteria. Design criteria for K-11.2, K-16.8, and K-25.2 ESFR sprinkler technology have been incorporated into the tables where test data supports such inclusion.

12.2.2.3.2 ESFR sprinkler systems shall be designed such that the minimum operating pressure is not less than that indicated in Table 12.2.2.3.1 commodity, storage height, and building height involved.

After selecting the commodity, the ceiling height for ESFR protection is the most important factor when selecting the minimum operating pressure (see 12.2.2.3.2). ESFR performance is highly dependent on the ceiling/roof height. This is why averaging of ceiling/roof height based for pitched roofs is not acceptable; the maximum ceiling/roof height over the storage area being protected must be selected.

Where the ceiling/roof height falls above the selected criteria, the design criteria for the next higher ceiling/roof height must be chosen with a maximum ceiling/roof height limit of 45 ft as established by Table 12.2.2.3.1.

Additionally, verification that the maximum storage height does not exceed the value for the ceiling/roof height selected in Table 12.2.2.3.1 is also necessary. It is important to verify that the storage height does not exceed the maximum storage height for the maximum ceiling/roof height design selected from Table 12.2.2.3.1. Lower storage heights that result in greater commodity clearances within a given design are acceptable provided the ESFR design criteria from Table 12.2.2.3.1 is based upon the maximum ceiling/roof height.

◀ FAQ
For ESFR applications where the ceiling/roof height falls between design criteria in Table 12.2.2.3.1, is it acceptable to interpolate the design criteria?

12.2.2.3.3 The design area shall consist of the most hydraulically demanding area of 12 sprinklers, consisting of four sprinklers on each of three branch lines. The design shall include a minimum of 960 ft^2 (89 m^2).

12.2.2.3.4 Where ESFR sprinklers are installed above and below obstructions, the discharge for up to two sprinklers for one of the levels shall be included with those of the other level in the hydraulic calculations.

Additional ESFR sprinklers installed below fixed obstructions as required by the obstruction rules in Chapter 8 must be included in the hydraulic calculations. Paragraph 12.2.2.3.4 requires that up to an additional two ESFR sprinklers that are located below obstructions be included with the 12 ESFR sprinkler calculations for a total of up to 14 ESFR sprinklers. This is a maximum of two additional ESFR sprinklers regardless of the number of ESFR sprinklers installed below obstructions in the remote area. Where only one additional ESFR sprinkler is needed to address an isolated obstruction, then only that one ESFR sprinkler would need to be added to the calculation. Care must be taken to identify the appropriate hydraulic remote area when such additional ESFR sprinklers are installed below fixed obstructions. The additional two ESFR sprinklers need only to be added to the 12 ESFR sprinkler demand directly above the obstruction when the combined number of sprinklers creates the hydraulically most demanding area.

◀ FAQ
Where additional ESFR sprinklers are added below obstructions, what is the total number of sprinklers that must be calculated?

12.2.2.4 Special Design for Palletized, Solid Piled, Bin Box, or Shelf Storage of Class I through IV Commodities. Bin box and shelf storage that is over 12 ft (3.7 m) but not in excess of the height limits of 12.2.2.1 and that is provided with walkways at vertical intervals of not over 12 ft (3.7 m) shall be protected with automatic sprinklers under the walkway(s). Protection shall be as follows:

(1) Ceiling design density shall be based on the total height of storage within the building.
(2) Automatic sprinklers under walkways shall be designed to maintain a minimum discharge pressure of 15 psi (1 bar) for the most hydraulically demanding six sprinklers on each level. Walkway sprinkler demand shall not be required to be added to the ceiling sprinkler demand. Sprinklers under walkways shall not be spaced more than 8 ft (2.4 m) apart horizontally.

With regard to 12.2.2.4.1(1), sprinklers should be designed to protect the worst-case combination of storage height and clearance. An operating pressure of at least 15 psi (1 bar) is necessary for sprinklers located underneath the walkway so that a sufficient amount of the sprinklers' discharge reaches into the bin boxes and storage shelves. The purpose of the sprinklers underneath the walkways is the following:

1. To reduce the likelihood of horizontal fire-spread under the walkway
2. To protect any storage in the walkway
3. To help control the fire in the shelves or bin boxes

Sprinklers under walkways should have water shields in accordance with A.6.2.8 to protect them from sprinkler discharge from above. Listed in-rack sprinklers also meet this requirement and could be utilized under the walkways. Unless the walkways are solid, sprinklers over the walkway will not operate until flames directly strike them or unless they are located directly over the fire. Covering the entire walkway with plywood or metal eliminates the delayed operation of the sprinklers and is a better alternative for protecting the under-walkway sprinkler from ceiling sprinkler discharge. Warehouse managers often cover walkways to prevent debris or product from falling through grated walkways and causing damage or injuries below. However, not every warehouse does this, so this situation should not be anticipated.

12.2.3 Protection Criteria for Palletized, Solid Piled, Bin Box, or Shelf Storage of Plastic and Rubber Commodities.

12.2.3.1* Control Mode Density-Area Sprinkler Protection Criteria for Palletized, Solid Piled, Bin Box, or Shelf Storage of Plastic and Rubber Commodities.

A.12.2.3.1 The densities and area of application have been developed from fire test data. Most of these tests were conducted with K-8 orifice sprinklers and 80-ft^2 or 100-ft^2 (7.4-m^2 or 9.3-m^2) sprinkler spacing. These and other tests have indicated that, with densities of 0.4 gpm/ft^2 (16.3 mm/min) and higher, better results are obtained with K-8 orifice and 70-ft^2 to 100-ft^2 (7.4-m^2 to 9.3-m^2) sprinkler spacing than where using K-5.6 orifice sprinklers at 50-ft^2 (4.6-m^2) spacing. A discharge pressure of 100 psi (6.9 bar) was used as a starting point on one of the fire tests. It was successful, but has a 1½-ft (0.5-m) clearance between the top of storage and ceiling sprinklers. A clearance of 10 ft (3 m) could have produced a different result due to the tendency of the higher pressure to atomize the water and the greater distance that the fine water droplets had to travel to the burning fuel.

Table A.12.2.3.1 explains and provides an example of the method and procedure to follow in using this standard to determine proper protection for Group A plastics.

TABLE A.12.2.3.1 Metric Conversion Factors for Examples

To Convert from	to	Multiply by
feet (ft)	meters (m)	0.3048
square feet (ft^2)	square meters (m^2)	0.0929
gallons/minute (gpm)	liters/second (L/sec)	0.0631
gallons per minute per square foot (gpm/ft^2)	millimeters per minute (same as liters per minute per square meter) (mm/min)	40.746

Example 1. Storage is expanded, cartoned, stable, 15 ft (4.6 m) high in a 20-ft (6.1-m) building.
   Answer 1. Column E—design density is 0.45 gpm/ft^2 (18.3 mm/min).
Example 2. Storage is nonexpanded, unstable, 15 ft (4.6 m) high in a 20-ft (6.1-m) building.
   Answer 2. Column A—design density is listed as 0.25 gpm/ft^2 (10.2 mm/min); however, it is also possible that the storage can be 12 ft (3.66 m) in this 20-ft (6.1-m) building, which would require a design density of 0.3 (12.2 mm/min). Unless the owner can guarantee that the storage will always be 15 ft (4.6 m), the design density = 0.3 gpm/ft^2 (12.2 mm/min).
Example 3. Storage is a nonexpanded, stable 15-ft (4.6-m) fixed-height unit load, one high, in an 18-ft (5.5-m) building.
   Answer 3. Column A—design density is 0.25 gpm/ft^2 (10.2 mm/min). Note that this design density does not increase to 0.3 gpm/ft^2 (12.2 mm/min) as in the previous example because of the use of a fixed-height unit load. The storage height will never be 12 ft (3.66 m). It will always be 15 ft (4.6 m).

Example 4. Storage is expanded, exposed, unstable, 20 ft (6.1 m) high in a 27-ft (8.2-m) building.

Answer 4. Column C—design density is 0.7 gpm/ft² (28.5 mm/min). Note that other lower storage heights should also be checked, but they reveal the same, or lower, densities [0.7 gpm/ft² and 0.6 gpm/ft² (28.5 mm/min and 24.5 mm/min)], so the design density remains at 0.7 gpm/ft² (28.5 mm/min).

Example 5. Storage is expanded, cartoned, unstable, 17 ft (5.2 m) high in 32-ft (9.75-m) building.

Answer 5. Column D—15-ft (4.6 m) storage in a 32-ft (9.75-m) building would be 0.55 gpm/ft² (22.4 mm/min); 20-ft (6.1-m) storage in a 32-ft (9.75-m) building would be 0.7 gpm/ft² (28.5 mm/min). Interpolation for 17-ft (5.2-m) storage is as follows:

$$0.7 - 0.55 = 0.15$$

$$\frac{0.15}{(20 - 15)} = 0.03$$

$$0.03 \times (17 - 15) = 0.06$$

$$0.55 + 0.06 = 0.61$$

Design density = 0.61 gpm/ft² (24.9 mm/min)

Example 6. Storage is expanded, exposed, stable, 22 ft (6.71 m) high in a 23½-ft (7.16-m) building.

Answer 6. Column B—could interpolate between 0.6 gpm/ft² and 0.75 gpm/ft² (24.5 mm/min and 30.6 mm/min); however, this would be a moot point since the density for 15-ft (4.6-m) storage in this 23½-ft (7.16-m) building would be 0.8 gpm/ft² (32.6 mm/min). Unless the owner can guarantee 22-ft (6.71-m) storage, the design density is 0.8 gpm/ft² (32.6 mm/min). If the owner can, in a manner acceptable to the authority having jurisdiction, guarantee 22-ft (6.71-m) storage, the interpolation would yield a design density of 0.66 gpm/ft² (26.9 mm/min).

Example 7. Storage is nonexpanded, stable, exposed, 13½ ft (4.1 m) high in a 15-ft (4.6-m) building.

Answer 7. Column E—12-ft (3.66-m) storage in a 15-ft (4.6-m) building would be extra hazard, Group 2 [0.4 gpm/ft² over 2500 ft² (16.3 mm/min over 230 m²)].

Storage 15 ft (4.6 m) high in a 15-ft (4.6-m) building would be 0.45 gpm/ft² (18.3 mm/ min). Interpolation for 13½-ft (4.1-m) storage is as follows:

$$0.45 - 0.4 = 0.05$$

$$\frac{0.15}{(15 - 12)} = 0.017$$

$$0.017 \times (13.5 - 12) = 0.026$$

$$0.4 + 0.026 = 0.426$$

Design density = 0.426 gpm/ft² (17.4 mm/min)

The majority of testing that led to the development of the discharge criteria in 12.2.3.1 is based on 20-ft (6.1-m) storage heights. Data from the tests in combination with field experience was extrapolated to produce discharge criteria for other storage heights. The values in 12.2.3.1 have proven to be accurate when compared to actual fire events. All palletized, solid piled, bin box, or shelf storage of Group A plastic that does not meet the definition of miscellaneous storage must be protected in accordance with the requirements of 12.2.3 regardless of height.

12.2.3.1.1* Plastics stored up to 25 ft (7.62 m) in height protected by spray sprinklers shall be in accordance with 12.2.3.1. The decision tree shown in Figure 12.2.3.1.1 shall be used to determine the protection in each specific situation.

Note: Cartons that contain Group A plastic material shall be permitted to be treated as Class IV commodities under the following conditions:

(a) There shall be multiple layers of corrugation or equivalent outer material that would significantly delay fire involvement of the Group A plastic

(b) The amount and arrangement of Group A plastic material within an ordinary carton would not be expected to significantly increase the fire hazard

FIGURE 12.2.3.1.1 *Decision Tree.*

A.12.2.3.1.1 Two direct comparisons between ordinary temperature– and high temperature–rated sprinklers are possible, as follows:

(1) With nonexpanded polyethylene 1-gal (3.8-L) bottles in corrugated cartons, a 3-ft (0.9-m) clearance, and the same density, approximately the same number of sprinklers operated (nine at high temperature versus seven at ordinary temperature).

(2) With exposed, expanded polystyrene meat trays, a 9.5-ft (1.9-m) clearance, and the same density, three times as many ordinary temperature–rated sprinklers operated as did high temperature–rated sprinklers (11 at high temperature versus 33 at ordinary temperature).

The cartoned plastics requirements of this standard are based to a great extent on test work that used a specific commodity—16-oz (0.473-L) polystyrene plastic jars individually separated by thin carton stock within a large corrugated carton [3½ ft² (0.32 m²)]. *[See Figure A.12.2.3.1.1(a).]*

Other Group A plastic commodities can be arranged in cartons so that they are separated by multiple thicknesses of carton material. In such arrangements, less plastic becomes involved in the fire at any one time. This could result in a less vigorous fire that can be controlled by Class IV commodity protection.

Other situations exist in which the plastics component is surrounded by several layers of less hazardous material and is therefore temporarily protected or insulated from a fire involving adjacent plastic products. Such conditions also could produce a less vigorous fire and be successfully handled by Class IV protection. *[See Figure A.12.2.3.1.1(b).]*

The decision to protect as a Class IV commodity, however, should be made only based on experienced judgment and only with an understanding of the consequences of underprotecting the storage segment.

The height limitation in 12.2.3.1.1 of 25 ft (7.6 m) is based on the fact that 25 ft (7.6 m) was the maximum height tested with control mode density/area sprinklers.

Figure 12.2.3.1.1 illustrates the differences in protection criteria for various types of plastic commodities (Groups A, B, and C). These three categories were developed using full-scale

FIGURE A.12.2.3.1.1(a) *Corrugated Carton Containing Individually Separated Plastic Jars.*

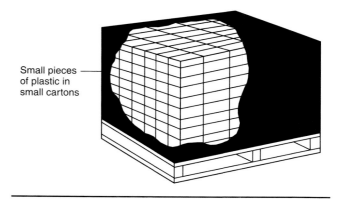

FIGURE A.12.2.3.1.1(b) *Corrugated Carton Containing Plastic Pieces Individually Separated by Carton Material.*

tests (as large as 30 ft × 30 ft × 25 ft high), small-scale sprinklered tests (usually 8 ft × 8 ft × 10 ft high), and "bench" tests to evaluate heat content and burning rate. After all the comparison tests were conducted, the three groups of plastic commodities were established.

The possible fire severity within any one of the broad categories of plastic is different. For example, polystyrene will normally burn much more severely (faster) than even the most highly plasticized polyvinyl chloride (PVC). However, the protection suggested by the decision tree should control a fire in the polystyrene product and do even a better job of controlling a fire in the highly plasticized PVC product.

The next level in the decision tree requires that Group A plastics be identified as either expanded, nonexpanded, or free-flowing. Expanded plastics have a cellular structure containing pockets of a blowing agent that is usually air but that could also be a flammable gas. Due the surface-to-air ratio inherent with expanded plastics, when they burn they do so much more rapidly than nonexpanded plastics. Virtually all expanded plastics are Group A plastics, and, therefore, most of the testing of expanded plastics has been conducted on Group A plastics. However, it should be anticipated that Groups B and C expanded plastics would burn much more rapidly than nonexpanded Groups B and C plastics.

The sprinkler protection for free-flowing plastics is based on commodity tests with resins in large corrugated cartons. Annex A describes randomly packed, small objects as another example of a free-flowing product, but they cannot be expected to flow freely if they melt at a low temperature. Also, randomly packed, small objects can catch on each other and not flow freely from the carton. If the product does not flow freely very early in the fire—that is, before or very soon after sprinklers operate—the fire's intensity will not be reduced. A rule of thumb is that a product can be expected to flow freely from a box in a fire if it will flow through the hole created by cutting off a 2-in. × 2-in. × 2-in. (50-mm × 50-mm × 50-mm) corner from the container's bottom.

The next level under expanded Group A plastics requires that the commodity be identified as being stored exposed or in cartons. In general, water from sprinklers and hose streams does not affect the burning of exposed plastic commodities to the same degree as if it the plastic were in cartons. Cartons absorb water, prewetting the commodities ahead of the fire and slowing or stopping the progress of the fire. Exhibit 12.3 shows a cartoned nonexpanded plastic. Exposed plastics do not absorb water but instead allow the sprinkler discharge to flow over the plastics, virtually eliminating any benefit of prewetting. As a result, greater sprinkler protection is required.

Pile stability is also a key factor in determining the proper protection of plastic commodities. The differences in the burning characteristics of unstable piles versus stable piles is de-

EXHIBIT 12.3 Cartoned
Nonexpanded Plastic.

scribed in 12.2.3.1.1. Fundamentally, a pile can be considered unstable only if it can be expected to collapse within the first few minutes of a fire. In actual practice, a pile is rarely unstable. Predicting when, if ever, a pile will collapse during a fire is virtually impossible. The concept of unstable piles was added because in some, but not all, tests of expanded polystyrene meat trays in polyethylene bags on pallets in which the ignition source was close to the outside of the pile, some stacks collapsed and the fire was more easily controlled. However, other tests with the same commodity produced different results. Because of a different ignition location, the tendency of the stacks to lean in a different way, or variable air movement in the building, the fire spread into the pile, no collapse occurred, and a more severe fire challenge resulted. Variables such as these are generally beyond the control of the property owner or occupant, and a sprinkler protection scheme designed to protect against unstable fires would in all likelihood be ineffective against a fire in stable piles.

12.2.3.1.2* Factors affecting protection requirements such as closed/open array, clearance between storage and sprinklers, and stable/unstable piles shall be applicable only to storage of Group A plastics. This decision tree also shall be used to determine protection for commodities that are not wholly Group A plastics but contain such quantities and arrangements of the same that they are deemed more hazardous than Class IV commodities.

A.12.2.3.1.2 There are few storage facilities in which the commodity mix or storage arrangement remains constant, and a designer should be aware that the introduction of different materials can change protection requirements considerably. Design should be based on higher densities and areas of application, and the various reductions allowed should be applied cautiously. For evaluation of existing situations, however, the allowances can be quite helpful.

In a closed array, the stacks of material are butted together in one direction, and there are 6-in. (152-mm) flues in the other direction (see 12.2.3.1.2). Fire tests of closed arrays burned less severely on the interior of the piles. The limited flues restricted the airflow into the flues, significantly reducing the burning rate. In an open array, the stacks of material are butted together in one direction, and there are 12-in. (304-mm) flues in the other direction. By contrast, fire tests had more than enough airflow to sustain a high burning rate. The larger flues of the open stacks allowed adequate oxygen to the fire, and the plastic burned unimpeded. No fire tests were conducted with the flue space greater than 6 in. (152 mm) but less than 12 in. (304 mm). Considering any flue space greater than 6 in. (152 mm), an open array is, therefore, a conservative approach.

The size of the flue space is hard to police, and it is rare that a true closed array would always be present. Closed array protection should only be used when there is complete confidence in warehouse management and employees to maintain the closed condition at all times. If the protection is designed for a closed array but open array conditions exist at the time of a fire, the sprinkler system would not be adequate and a major loss could occur. The closed array protection cannot control a fire in an open array.

12.2.3.1.3 Group B plastics and free-flowing Group A plastics shall be protected in the same manner as a Class IV commodity. See 12.2.2 for protection of these storage commodities with spray sprinklers.

Small- and bench-scale testing of Group B plastics and large-scale testing of free-flowing Group A plastics show that Class IV commodity protection is adequate for this storage (see 12.2.3.1.3).

12.2.3.1.4 Group C plastics shall be protected in the same manner as a Class III commodity. See 12.2.2 for protection of these storage commodities with spray sprinklers.

Bench-scale tests with Group C plastics and Class III commodities produced similar results to those described in the commentary to 12 2.3.1.3—they indicate that Class III protection is adequate for this storage (see 12.2.3.1.4).

12.2.3.1.5* Storage Conditions.

A.12.2.3.1.5 An evaluation for each field situation should be made to determine the worst applicable height-clearance relationship that can be expected to appear in a particular case. Fire tests have shown that considerably greater demands occur where clearance is 10 ft (3.1 m) as compared to 3 ft (0.9 m) and where a pile is stable as compared to an unstable pile. Since a system is designed for a particular clearance, the system could be inadequate when significant areas do not have piling to the design height and larger clearances exist between stock and sprinklers. This can also be true where the packaging or arrangement is changed so that stable piling is created where unstable piling existed. Recognition of these conditions is essential to avoid installation of protection that is inadequate or becomes inadequate because of changes.

No tests were conducted simulating a peaked roof configuration. However, it is expected that the principles of Chapter 12 still apply. The worst applicable height-clearance relationship that can be expected to occur should be found, and protection should be designed for it. If storage is all at the same height, the worst height-clearance relationship creating the greatest water demand would occur under the peak. If commodities are stored higher under the peak, the various height-clearance relationships should be tried and the one creating the greatest water demand used for designing protection.

12.2.3.1.5.1 The design of the sprinkler system shall be based on those conditions that routinely or periodically exist in a building that create the greatest water demand. These conditions include the following:

(1) Pile height
(2) Clearance
(3) Pile stability
(4) Array

12.2.3.1.5.2 Where the distance between roof/ceiling height and top of storage exceeds 20 ft (6.1 m), protection shall be provided for the storage height that would result in a 20-ft (6.1-m) distance between the roof/ceiling height and top of storage.

The clearance between the storage and the roof/ceiling, which is discussed in 12.2.3.1.5.2, is an important factor for control mode density/area protection as indicated in Table 12.2.3.1.6. High clearance affects sprinkler performance in two ways. First, as the clearance increases, the size of the fire before sprinklers operate also increases. Second, as the clearance increases, the fire plume that the sprinkler discharge must penetrate to reach the burning materials also increases. These two factors together significantly reduce the effectiveness of sprinklers. Implicit in storage protection requirements is that protection for a given storage height in a building of a given height must also be adequate to protect any lesser storage height in that building. This requirement becomes necessary because warehouses are never completely full, and storage heights can fluctuate widely over both the short and long term. Clearances greater than 20 ft (6.1 m) are beyond the scope of testing used to develop the protection requirements for control mode density/area sprinklers. Therefore, protection adequate for a storage height that results in a clearance of less than 20 ft (6.1 m) will be adequate for lesser storage heights, despite the fact that clearance exceeds 20 ft (6.1 m).

12.2.3.1.6* Design areas and densities for the appropriate storage configuration shall be selected from Table 12.2.3.1.6. The columns A, B, C, D, and E correspond to the protection required by the decision tree shown in Figure 12.2.3.1.1.

A.12.2.3.1.6 Test data is not available for all combinations of commodities, storage heights, and clearances. Some of the protection criteria in this standard are based on extrapolations of test data for other commodities and storage configurations, as well as available loss data.

For example, there is very limited test data for storage of expanded plastics higher than 20 ft (6.1 m). The protection criteria in this standard for expanded plastics higher than 20 ft (6.1 m) are extrapolated from test data for expanded plastics storage 20 ft (6.1 m) and less in height and test data for unexpanded plastics above 20 ft (6.1 m).

TABLE 12.2.3.1.6 *Design Densities for Palletized, Solid Piled, Bin Box, or Shelf Storage of Plastic and Rubber Commodities*

Storage Height		Roof/Ceiling Height		Density									
				A		B		C		D		E	
ft	m	ft	m	gpm/ft²	mm/min	gpm/ft²	mm/min	gpm/ft²	mm/min	gpm/ft²	mm/min	gpm/ft²	mm/min
≤5	1.52	up to 25	up to 7.62	Curve 3	Curve 3	Curve 3	Curve 3	Curve 3	Curve 3	Curve 3	Curve 3	Curve 3	Curve 3
≤12	3.66	up to 15	up to 4.57	0.2	8.2	Curve 5	Curve 5	0.3	12.2	Curve 4	Curve 4	Curve 5	Curve 5
		>15 to 20	>4.57 to 6.1	0.3	12.2	0.6	24.5	0.5	20.4	Curve 5	Curve 5	Curve 5	Curve 5
		>20 to 32	>6.1 to 9.75	0.4	16.3	0.8	32.6	0.6	24.5	0.45	18.3	0.7	28.5
15	4.5	up to 20	up to 6.1	0.25	10.2	0.5	20.4	0.4	16.3	0.3	12.2	0.45	18.3
		>20 to 25	>6.1 to 7.62	0.4	16.3	0.8	32.6	0.6	24.5	0.45	18.3	0.7	28.5
		>25 to 35	>7.62 to 10.67	0.45	18.3	0.9	36.7	0.7	28.5	0.55	22.4	0.85	34.6
20	6.1	up to 25	up to 7.62	0.3	12.2	0.6	24.5	0.45	18.3	0.35	14.3	0.55	22.4
		>25 to 30	>7.62 to 9.14	0.45	18.3	0.9	36.7	0.7	28.5	0.55	22.4	0.85	34.6
		>30 to 35	>9.14 to 10.67	0.6	24.5	1.2	48.9	0.85	34.6	0.7	28.5	1.1	44.8
25	7.62	up to 30	up to 9.14	0.4	16.3	0.75	30.6	0.55	22.4	0.45	18.3	0.7	28.5
		>30 to 35	>9.14 to 10.67	0.6	24.5	1.2	48.9	0.85	34.6	0.7	28.5	1.1	44.8

Notes:

1. Minimum clearance between sprinkler deflector and top of storage shall be maintained as required.

2. Column designations correspond to the configuration of plastics storage as follows:

   A: (1) Nonexpanded, unstable
      (2) Nonexpanded, stable, solid unit load
   B: Expanded, exposed, stable
   C: (1) Expanded, exposed, unstable
      (2) Nonexpanded, stable, cartoned

   D: Expanded, cartoned, unstable
      (1) Expanded, cartoned, stable
      (2) Nonexpanded, stable, exposed

3. Curve 3 = Density required by Figure 12.1.10 for Curve 3
   Curve 4 = Density required by Figure 12.1.10 for Curve 4
   Curve 5 = Density required by Figure 12.1.10 for Curve 5

4. Hose streams and durations shall be as follows: ≤ 5 ft 250 gpm and 90 minutes; >5 ft to ≤20 ft 500 gpm and 120 minutes, >20 ft to ≤25 ft 500 gpm and 150 minutes.

Further examples can be found in the protection criteria for clearances up to 15 ft (4.6 m). Test data is limited for clearances greater than 10 ft (3.1 m). It should be assumed that, if protection is adequate for a given storage height in a building of a given height, the same protection will protect storage of any lesser height in the same building. For example, protection adequate for 20-ft (6.1-m) storage in a 30-ft (9.1-m) building [10-ft (3.1-m) clearance] would also protect 15-ft (4.6-m) storage in a 30-ft (9.1-m) building [15-ft (4.6-m) clearance]. Therefore, the protection criteria in Table 12.2.3.1.6 for 15-ft (4.6-m) clearance are based on the protection criteria for storage 5 ft (1.5 m) higher than the indicated height with 10-ft (3.1-m) clearance.

Table 12.2.3.1.6 is based on tests that were conducted primarily with high temperature–rated, K-8 orifice sprinklers. Other tests have demonstrated that, where sprinklers are used with orifices greater than K-8, ordinary-temperature sprinklers are acceptable.

The use of sprinklers with a nominal K-factor of 11.2 to produce the densities in Table 12.2.3.1.6 will normally allow larger droplets, greater initial densities at lower pressures, and more efficient use of water affecting the fire, and the impact of large clearances is lessened.

12.2.3.1.7 For Table 12.2.3.1.6 the design areas shall be as follows:

(1) The area shall be a minimum of 2500 ft² (232 m²).
(2) Where Table 12.2.3.1.6 allows densities and areas to be selected in accordance with Figure 12.1.10, Curve 3, any density-area from Curve 3 shall be permitted.
(3) For closed arrays, the area shall be permitted to be reduced to 2000 ft² (186 m²).

12.2.3.1.8 Interpolation of densities between storage heights shall be permitted. Densities shall be based upon the 2500 ft² (232 m²) design area. The "up to" in the table is intended to aid in the interpolation of densities between storage heights. Interpolation of ceiling/roof heights shall not be permitted.

An example of interpolation of densities based on storage height, as described in 12.2.3.1.8, is as follows:

Given—Group A plastic (column E in Table 12.2.3.1.6) stored 18 ft (5.5/m) high in a 24-ft (7.3-m) building height. The density will be interpolated between 20 ft (6.1 m) and 15 ft (4.6 m) height of storage from the table as follows:

1. The density from Table 12.2.3.1.6 Column E for 20 ft (6.1 m) of storage for Group A plastic in a building with a height up to 25 ft (7.6 m) = 0.55 gpm/ft² (22.4 mm/min/m²)
2. The density from Table 12.2.3.1.6 Column E for 15 ft (4.6 m) of storage for Group A plastic in a building with a height between 20 ft (6.1 m) to 25 ft (7.6 m) = 0.70 gpm/ft² (28.5 mm/min/m²)

Note the density for 15 ft (4.6 m) is greater than 20 ft (6.1 m) of storage due to the clearance factor being greater for 15 ft (4.6 m) of storage.

3. The interpolated density is determined as follows:

   a. 15 ft (4.6 m) of storage   0.70 gpm/ft² (28.5 mm/min/m²)
       –20 ft (6.1 m) of storage   0.55 gpm/ft² (22.4 mm/min/m²)

                          Difference = 0.15 gpm/ft² (6.1 mm/min/m²)

   b. 15 gpm/ft² divided by 5 ft (1.5 m) (difference between 20 ft (6.1 m) and 15 ft (4.6 m) = 0.03 gpm/ft² (12.2 mm/min/m²) per ft of storage

Keep in mind that the density for 18 ft (5.5 m) is going to be greater than the 20-ft (6.1-m) number of 0.55 gpm/ft² (22.4 mm/min/m²). A common error is made by assuming the density decreases as the storage height decreases.

   c. 18 ft (5.5 m) is 2 ft (0.6 m) × 0.03 gpm/ft² (12.2 mm/min/m²) greater than 0.55 gpm/
       ft² (22.4 mm/min/m²) for 20 ft (6.1 m)

20 ft (6.1 m) density 0.55 gpm/ft^2 (22.4 mm/min/m^2) + 2 ft (0.6 m) × 0.03 gpm/ft^2 (22.4 mm/min/m^2) 0.06 gpm/ft^2 (24.4 mm/min/m^2)

18 ft (5.5 m) density = 0.61 gpm/ft^2 (24.9 mm/min/m^2)

4. The density interpolated for 18 ft (5.5 m) of storage in a 24-ft (7.3-m) high building is 0.61 gpm/ft^2 (24.9 mm/min/m^2).

12.2.3.2 Large Drop Sprinklers and Specific Application Control Mode Sprinklers for Palletized or Solid Piled of Plastic and Rubber Commodities.

The large drop sprinkler, which is addressed in 12.2.3.2, is a type of specific application control mode technology as defined in Chapter 3. The names have remained separate due to the long history of the name "large drop" and its relation to the nominal K-factor of 11.2. Applications of large drop sprinklers and specific application control mode sprinklers are described in Tables 12.2.3.2.1(a) and (b). Listing of large drop sprinklers and control mode specific application sprinklers takes into consideration the ability of the sprinkler discharge pattern to penetrate a high-velocity fire plume. Only listed large drop and specific application control mode sprinklers are to be used in accordance with the design approach of 12.2.3.2.

12.2.3.2.1 Protection of palletized and solid-piled storage of unexpanded plastic and expanded plastic commodities shall be in accordance with Table 12.2.3.2.1(a) or Table 12.2.3.2.1(b).

12.2.3.2.2 Protection shall be provided as specified in Table 12.2.3.2.1(a) and Table 12.2.3.2.1(b) or appropriate NFPA standards in terms of minimum operating pressure and the number of sprinklers to be included in the design area.

12.2.3.2.2.1 For design purposes, 95 psi (6.6 bar) shall be the maximum discharge pressure at the hydraulically most remote sprinkler.

Discharge pressures in excess of 95 psi (6.6 bar) negatively impact the sprinkler's discharge pattern and droplet size, which is the reason for the requirement in 12.2.3.2.2.1.

TABLE 12.2.3.2.1(a) *Large-Drop Sprinkler Design Criteria for Palletized and Solid-Piled Storage of Plastic and Rubber Commodities*

Storage Arrangement	Commodity Class	Nominal K-Factor	Maximum Storage Height		Maximum Ceiling/ Roof Height		Type of System	Number of Design Sprinklers/ Minimum Pressure		Hose Stream Demand		Water Supply Duration (hours)
			ft	m	ft	m		/psi	/bar	gpm	L/min	
Palletized	Cartoned or exposed unexpanded plastics	11.2	20	6.1	30	9.1	Wet	25/25	25/1.7	500	1900	2
							Dry	N/A	N/A	N/A	N/A	N/A
	Cartoned or exposed expanded plastics	11.2	18	5.5	26	7.9	Wet	15/50	15/3.4	500	1900	2
							Dry	N/A	N/A	N/A	N/A	N/A
Solid pile	Cartoned or exposed unexpanded plastics	11.2	20	6.1	30	9.1	Wet	15/50	15/3.4	500	1900	2
							Dry	N/A	N/A	N/A	N/A	N/A

TABLE 12.2.3.2.1(b) *Specific Application Control Mode (16.8 K-Factor) Sprinkler Design Criteria for Palletized and Solid-Piled Storage of Plastic and Rubber Commodities*

Configuration	Commodity Class	Maximum Storage Height		Maximum Building Height		Type of System	Number of Design Sprinklers by Minimum Operating Pressure		Hose Stream Demand		Water Supply Duration (hours)
		ft	*m*	*ft*	*m*		10 psi (0.7 bar)	22 psi (1.5 bar)	gpm	L/min	
Palletized	Cartoned or exposed unexpanded plastics	25	7.6	30	9.1	Wet	—	15	500	1900	2
Solid pile	Cartoned or exposed unexpanded plastics	25	7.6	30	9.1	Wet	—	15	500	1900	1½

12.2.3.2.2.2 Open Wood Joist Construction.

(A) Where large drop K-11.2 sprinklers are installed under open wood joist construction, their minimum operating pressure shall be 50 psi (3.4 bar).

(B) Where each joist channel of open, wood joist construction is fully fire-stopped to its full depth at intervals not exceeding 20 ft (6.1 m), the lower pressures specified in Table 12.2.3.2.1(a) shall be permitted to be used.

12.2.3.2.2.3 The design area shall be a rectangular area having a dimension parallel to the branch lines at least 1.2 times the square root of the area protected by the number of sprinklers to be included in the design area. Any fractional sprinkler shall be included in the design area.

Starting with the 1996 edition, NFPA 13 provided more information about the shape of the design area where large drop sprinklers are used (see 12.2.3.2.2.3). Although earlier editions implied that the design area was to be a rectangular shape having a dimension parallel to the branch lines of at least 1.2 times the square root of the area protected by the number of sprinklers, it was not explicitly stated.

12.2.3.2.2.4 Hose stream demand and water supply duration requirements shall be in accordance with Table 12.2.3.2.1(a) and Table 12.2.3.2.1(b).

12.2.3.2.2.5 Preaction Systems.

(A) For the purpose of using 12.2.3.2.1, preaction systems shall be classified as dry pipe systems.

Paragraph 12.2.3.2.2.5(A) requires that all preaction systems be treated as dry pipe sprinkler systems when applying the requirements of Table 12.2.3.2.1(a) and Table 12.2.3.2.1(b).

(B) Where it can be demonstrated that the detection system activating the preaction system will cause water to be at the sprinklers when they operate, preaction systems shall be permitted to be treated as wet pipe systems.

If it can be demonstrated that a detection system activating the preaction system will cause water to be at the sprinklers when they operate, the wet system design criteria can be used. Preaction systems that perform to 12.2.3.2.2.5(B) are not considered dry systems.

12.2.3.2.2.6 The nominal diameter of branch line pipes (including riser nipples) shall meet the following:

(1) Pipe diameter shall not be not less than 1¼ in. (33 mm) nor greater than 2 in. (51 mm).
(2) Starter pieces shall be permitted to be 2½ in. (64 mm).
(3) Where branch lines are larger than 2 in. (51 mm), the sprinkler shall be supplied by a riser nipple to elevate the sprinkler 13 in. (330 mm) for 2½-in. (64-mm) pipe and 15 in.

◄ **FAQ**
For large drop and specific application control mode sprinklers, are all types of preaction systems treated as dry pipe systems?

◄ **FAQ**
For large drop and specific application control mode sprinklers, are preaction systems always treated as dry pipe systems?

(380 mm) for 3-in. (76-mm) pipe. These dimensions are measured from the centerline of the pipe to the deflector. In lieu of this, sprinklers shall be permitted to be offset horizontally a minimum of 12 in. (305 mm).

The purpose of limiting the maximum diameter of branch lines or riser nipples in 12.2.3.2.2.6 is to minimize the effect of pipe shadow below the sprinkler. Pipe shadow can result in significant shielded, or dry, areas with materially reduced water application and loss of sprinkler water penetration.

12.2.3.2.2.7 Building steel shall not require special protection where Table 12.2.3.2.1(a) and Table 12.2.3.2.1(b) is applied as appropriate for the storage configuration.

12.2.3.3 Early Suppression Fast-Response (ESFR) Sprinklers for Palletized, Solid Piled of Plastic and Rubber Commodities.

Applications of ESFR sprinklers are described in 12.2.3.3. The design approach for ESFR sprinklers is based on fire suppression by the first operating ring of sprinklers.

12.2.3.3.1 Protection of palletized and solid pile storage of cartoned or uncartoned unexpanded plastic and cartoned expanded plastic shall be in accordance with Table 12.2.3.3.1.

ESFR protection criteria are provided in Table 12.2.3.3.1, which addresses protection of palletized and solid-piled storage of plastic and rubber commodities. The criteria in Table 12.2.3.3.1 have been expanded to permit broader applications of ESFR sprinkler technology based on large-scale test results reviewed by the Technical Committee on Sprinkler System Discharge Criteria. Design criteria for K-11.2, K-16.8, and K-25.2 ESFR sprinkler technology have been incorporated into the tables where test data supports such inclusion.

12.2.3.3.2 ESFR sprinkler systems shall be designed such that the minimum operating pressure is not less than that indicated in Table 12.2.3.3.1 for type of storage, commodity, storage height, and building height involved.

FAQ ▶
For ESFR applications where the ceiling/roof height falls between design criteria in Table 12.2.3.3.1, is it acceptable to interpolate the design criteria?

After selecting the commodity, the ceiling height for ESFR protection is the most important factor when selecting the minimum operating pressure (see 12.2.3.3.2). ESFR performance is highly dependent on the ceiling/roof height. This is why averaging of ceiling/roof height based for pitched roofs is not acceptable; the maximum ceiling/roof height over the storage area being protected must be selected.

Where the ceiling/roof height falls above the selected criteria, the design criteria for the next higher ceiling/roof height must be chosen with a maximum ceiling/roof height limit of 45 ft as established by Table 12.2.3.3.1.

Additionally, verification that the maximum storage height does not exceed the value for the ceiling/roof height selected in Table 12.2.3.3.1 is also necessary. It is important to verify that the storage height does not exceed the maximum storage height for the maximum ceiling/roof height design selected from Table 12.2.3.3.1. Lower storage heights that result in greater commodity clearances within a given design are acceptable provided the ESFR design criteria from Table 12.2.3.3.1 are based upon the maximum ceiling/roof height.

12.2.3.3.3 The design area shall consist of the most hydraulically demanding area of 12 sprinklers, consisting of four sprinklers on each of three branch lines. The design shall include a minimum of 960 ft^2 (89 m^2).

Where additional ESFR sprinklers are added below obstructions, what is the total number of sprinklers that must be calculated?
FAQ ▶

12.2.3.3.4 Where ESFR sprinklers are installed above and below obstructions, the discharge for up to two sprinklers for one of the levels shall be included with those of the other level in the hydraulic calculations.

Additional ESFR sprinklers installed below fixed obstructions as required by the obstruction rules in Chapter 8 must be included in the hydraulic calculations. Paragraph 12.2.3.3.4 requires that up to an additional two ESFR sprinklers that are located below obstructions be

TABLE 12.2.3.3.1 *ESFR Protection of Palletized and Solid-Pile Storage of Plastic and Rubber Commodities*

Storage Arrangement	Commodity	Maximum Storage Height		Maximum Ceiling/Roof Height		Nominal K-Factor	Orientation	Minimum Operating Pressure		Hose Stream Demand		Water Supply Duration (hours)
		ft	m	ft	m			psi	bar	gpm	L/min	
Palletized and solid pile storage (no open-top containers or solid shelves)	Cartoned unexpanded plastic	20	6.1	25	7.6	11.2	Upright	50	3.4	250	946	1
						14.0	Upright or pendent	50	3.4			
						16.8	Pendent	35	2.4			
						25.2	Pendent	15	1.0			
				30	9.1	14.0	Upright or pendent	50	3.4			
						16.8	Pendent	35	2.4			
						25.2	Pendent	15	1.0			
				35	7.6	14.0	Pendent	75	5.2			
						16.8	Pendent	52	3.6			
						25.2	Pendent	20	1.4			
				40	12.2	14.0	Pendent	75	5.2			
						16.8	Pendent	52	3.6			
						25.2	Pendent	25	1.7			
				45	13.7	25.2	Pendent	40	2.8			
		25	7.6	30	9.1	14.0	Upright or pendent	50	3.4			
						16.8	Pendent	35	2.4			
						25.2	Pendent	15	1.0			
				32	9.8	14.0	Upright or pendent	60	4.1			
						16.8	Pendent	42	2.9			
				35	7.6	14.0	Upright or pendent	75	5.2			
						16.8	Pendent	52	3.6			
						25.2	Pendent	20	1.4			
				40	12.2	14.0	Upright or pendent	75	5.2			
						16.8	Pendent	52	3.6			
						25.2	Pendent	25	1.7			
				45	13.7	25.2	Pendent	40	2.8			

(Continues)

TABLE 12.2.3.3.1 *Continued*

Storage Arrangement	Commodity	Maximum Storage Height		Maximum Ceiling/Roof Height		Nominal K-Factor	Orientation	Minimum Operating Pressure		Hose Stream Demand		Water Supply Duration (hours)
		ft	m	ft	m			psi	bar	gpm	L/min	
Palletized and solid pile storage (no open-top containers or solid shelves)	Cartoned unexpanded plastic (continued)	30	9.1	35	10.7	14.0	Upright or pendent	75	5.2			
						16.8	Pendent	52	3.6			
						25.2	Pendent	20	1.4			
				40	12.2	14.0	Pendent	75	5.2			
						16.8	Pendent	52	3.6			
						25.2	Pendent	25	1.7			
				45	13.7	25.2	Pendent	40	2.8			
		35	10.7	40	12.2	14.0	Pendent	75	5.2			
						16.8	Pendent	52	3.6			
						25.2	Pendent	25	1.7			
				45	13.7	25.2	Pendent	40	2.8			
		40	12.2	45	13.7	25.2	Pendent	40	2.8			
	Exposed unexpanded plastic	20	6.1	25	7.6	14.0	Pendent	50	3.4	250	946	1
						16.8	Pendent	35	2.4			
				30	9.1	14.0	Pendent	50	3.4			
						16.8	Pendent	35	2.4			
				35	10.7	14.0	Pendent	75	5.2			
						16.8	Pendent	52	3.6			
				40	12.2	14.0	Pendent	75	5.2			
						16.8	Pendent	52	3.6			
		25	7.6	30	9.1	14.0	Pendent	50	3.4			
						16.8	Pendent	35	2.4			
				32	9.8	14.0	Pendent	60	4.1			
						16.8	Pendent	42	2.9			
				35	10.7	14.0	Pendent	75	5.2			
						16.8	Pendent	52	3.6			
				40	12.2	14.0	Pendent	75	5.2			
						16.8	Pendent	52	3.6			

TABLE 12.2.3.3.1 *Continued*

Storage Arrangement	Commodity	Maximum Storage Height		Maximum Ceiling/Roof Height		Nominal K-Factor	Orientation	Minimum Operating Pressure		Hose Stream Demand		Water Supply Duration (hours)
		ft	*m*	*ft*	*m*			*psi*	*bar*	*gpm*	*L/min*	
Palletized and solid pile storage (no open-top containers or solid shelves)	Exposed unexpanded plastic (continued)	30	9.1	35	10.7	14.0	Pendent	75	5.2	250	946	1
						16.8	Pendent	52	3.6			
				40	12.2	14.0	Pendent	75	5.2			
						16.8	Pendent	52	3.6			
		35	10.7	40	12.2	14.0	Pendent	75	5.2			
						16.8	Pendent	52	3.6			
	Cartoned expanded plastic	20	6.1	25	7.6	14.0	Upright or pendent	50	3.4			
						16.8	Pendent	35	2.4			
				30	9.1	14.0	Upright or pendent	50	3.4			
						16.8	Pendent	35	2.4			
		25	7.6	30	9.1	14.0	Upright or pendent	50	3.4			
						16.8	Pendent	35	2.4			
				32	9.8	14.0	Pendent	60	4.1			
						16.8	Pendent	42	2.9			

included with the 12 ESFR sprinkler calculations for a total of up to 14 ESFR sprinklers. This is a maximum of two additional ESFR sprinklers regardless of the number of ESFR sprinklers installed below obstructions in the remote area. Where only one additional ESFR sprinkler is needed to address an isolated obstruction, then only that one ESFR sprinkler would need to be added to the calculation. Care must be taken to identify the appropriate hydraulic remote area when such additional ESFR sprinklers are installed below fixed obstructions. The additional two ESFR sprinklers need only to be added to the 12 ESFR sprinkler demand directly above the obstruction when the combined number of sprinklers creates the hydraulically most demanding area.

12.2.3.4 Special Design for Palletized, Solid Piled, Bin Box, or Shelf Storage of Plastic and Rubber Commodities. (Reserved)

12.3 Protection of Commodities Stored on Racks

(See Section C.9.)

12.3.1 Protection Criteria—General.

12.3.1.1 This section shall apply to storage of materials representing the broad range of combustibles stored in racks.

12.3.1.2* Sprinkler Protection Criteria.

 A.12.3.1.2 The fire protection system design should consider the maximum storage height. For new sprinkler installations, maximum storage height is the usable height at which commodities can be stored above the floor while the minimum required unobstructed space below sprinklers is maintained. Where evaluating existing situations, maximum storage height is the maximum existing storage height if space between the sprinklers and storage is equal to or greater than that required.

12.3.1.2.1 Sprinkler protection criteria for the storage of materials on racks shall be in accordance with 12.3.2 or 12.3.3 for storage up to 25 ft (7.6 m), and 12.3.4 and 12.3.5 for storage over 25 ft (7.6 m).

12.3.1.2.2* Protection criteria for Group A plastics shall be permitted for the protection of the same storage height and configuration of Class I, II, III, and IV commodities.

 A.12.3.1.2.2 Information for the protection of Classes I, II, III, and IV commodities was extrapolated from full-scale fire tests that were performed at different times than the tests that were used to develop the protection for plastic commodities. It is possible that, by selecting certain points from the tables (and after applying the appropriate modifications), the protection specified by 12.3.2.4.1 exceeds the requirements of 12.3.3. In such situations, the protection specified for plastics, although less than that required by the tables, can adequately protect Classes I, II, III, and IV commodities.

This section also allows storage areas that are designed to protect plastics to store Classes I, II, III, and IV commodities without a re-evaluation of fire protection systems.

FAQ ▶

Where the sprinkler design criteria are for a higher hazard commodity (e.g., Class IV), is it acceptable to store a lower hazard commodity (e.g., Class I) within the area?

Protection that is adequate for a higher commodity classification that presents a greater fire hazard, such as Class IV commodities, is also adequate for a lower commodity classification, such as Class I (see 12.3.1.2.2).

Future changes regarding the classes of commodities to be stored at the premises should be anticipated to the extent possible, and protection for the highest anticipated commodity class likely to be stored should be provided. Designing for the most hazardous commodity anticipated when the sprinkler system is initially installed is often more cost-effective in the long run.

12.3.1.3 Hose connections shall not be required for the protection of Class I, II, III, and IV commodities stored 12 ft (3.7 m) or less in height.

FAQ ▶

Are hose connections required for all storage?

Paragraph 12.3.1.3 acknowledges the omission of hose stations for certain storage arrangements and recognizes the cost of installing hose stations in any storage facility. Hose stations would still be beneficial, but the sprinkler system in combination with fire department response is considered adequate to guard against the associated fire risk. Whenever possible, hose stations should be considered in all storage facilities regardless of storage heights because their benefits generally outweigh their expense.

12.3.1.4 The design figures indicate water demands for ordinary temperature-rated and nominal high temperature-rated sprinklers at the ceiling. The ordinary-temperature design densities correspond to ordinary temperature-rated sprinklers and shall be used for sprinklers with ordinary- and intermediate-temperature classification. The high-temperature design densities correspond to high temperature–rated sprinklers and shall be used for sprinklers having a high temperature rating.

The densities shown in the design figures discussed in 12.3.1.4 were developed from full-scale fire tests. The area of operation specified is because control-mode density/area protection with standard sprinklers for the temperature specified cannot reliably limit sprinkler operating areas below these specified minimums, even with increased discharge densities.

When intermediate-temperature sprinklers are used, the design density should follow the criteria for ordinary-temperature sprinklers. When using sprinklers with K-factors of nominal 8.0 or 5.6, the use of high-temperature sprinklers has been shown to operate fewer sprinklers in full-scale fire tests. Paragraph 12.3.1.5 allows all temperatures of sprinklers with K-factors of nominal 11.2 or greater to use the lower design densities for high-temperature sprinklers as shown in the figures. (See commentary on 12.3.1.5.)

12.3.1.5 Ordinary- and intermediate-temperature sprinklers with K-factors of 11.2 or larger, where listed for storage, shall be permitted to use the densities for high-temperature sprinklers.

◀ **FAQ**
Why are ordinary-temperature sprinklers with K-factors of 11.2 or greater permitted to utilize the densities for high-temperature sprinklers?

Full-scale fire testing has shown that ordinary-temperature sprinklers with a nominal K-factor of 11.2 or greater perform to the lower density requirements of high-temperature sprinklers in the figures. Therefore, sprinklers with these orifice sizes can utilize the lower densities of the high-temperature curves in the figures regardless of the temperature rating of the sprinkler utilized, as stated in 12.3.1.5.

12.3.1.6 Movable Racks. Rack storage in movable racks shall be protected in the same manner as multiple-row racks.

12.3.1.7 Fire Protection of Steel Columns—Columns within Storage Racks of Class I through Class IV and Plastic Commodities. *(See Section C.10.)*

Protection of steel columns, which is covered in 12.3.1.7, is necessary primarily to assure that the structural integrity of the building is maintained during sprinkler system operation.

12.3.1.7.1 Where sprinkler protection of building columns within the rack structure or vertical rack members supporting the building are required in lieu of fireproofing, sprinkler protection in accordance with one of the following shall be provided:

(1) Sidewall sprinklers at the 15-ft (4.6-m) elevation, pointed toward one side of the steel column
(2) Provision of ceiling sprinkler density for a minimum of 2000 ft^2 (186 m^2) with ordinary 165°F (74°C) or high temperature 286°F (141°C) rated sprinklers as shown in Table 12.3.1.7.1 for storage heights above 15 ft (4.6 m), up to and including 20 ft (6.1 m)
(3) Provision of large drop, specific application control mode or ESFR ceiling sprinkler protection

TABLE 12.3.1.7.1 *Ceiling Sprinkler Densities for Protection of Steel Building Columns*

	Aisle Width			
	4 ft (1.2 m)		8 ft (2.4 m)	
Commodity Classification	*gpm/ft^2*	*(L/min)/m^2*	*gpm/ft^2*	*(L/min)/m^2*
Class I	0.37	15.1	0.33	13.5
Class II	0.44	17.9	0.37	15.1
Class III	0.49	20	0.42	17.1
Class IV and Plastics	0.68	27.7	0.57	23.2

12.3.1.7.2 The flow from a column sprinkler(s) shall be permitted to be omitted from the sprinkler system hydraulic calculations.

12.3.1.8 High-Expansion Foam.

12.3.1.8.1* Where high-expansion foam systems are installed, they shall be in accordance with NFPA 11A, *Standard for Medium- and High-Expansion Foam,* and they shall be automatic in operation, unless modified by this standard.

A.12.3.1.8.1 Detection systems, concentrate pumps, generators, and other system components that are essential to the operation of the system should have an approved standby power source.

12.3.1.8.2 In-rack sprinklers shall not be required where high-expansion foam systems are used in combination with ceiling sprinklers.

12.3.1.8.3 Detectors for High-Expansion Foam Systems.

Detectors for high-expansion foam systems are covered in 12.3.1.8.3. Quick detection of a fire in a warehouse protected by high-expansion foam is essential. The foam requires a period of time to cover the burning stock. The faster the foam is discharged onto the fire, the less the amount of damage that will occur. Reducing the detector spacing at the ceiling by one-half of what is typically required helps assure faster response of the foam system.

12.3.1.8.3.1 Detectors shall be listed and shall be installed in one of the following configurations:

(1) At the ceiling only where installed at one-half the listed linear spacing [e.g., 15 ft × 15 ft (4.6 m × 4.6 m) rather than at 30 ft × 30 ft (9.1 m × 9.1 m)]; at the ceiling at the listed spacing and in racks at alternate levels
(2) Where listed for rack storage installation and installed in accordance with the listing to provide response within 1 minute after ignition using an ignition source that is equivalent to that used in a rack storage testing program

12.3.1.8.3.2 Ceiling detectors alone shall not be used where the ceiling/roof clearance from the top of the storage exceeds 10 ft (3.1 m) or the height of the storage exceeds 25 ft (7.6 m).

12.3.1.8.4 Detectors for preaction systems shall be installed in accordance with 12.3.1.8.3.

 12.3.1.9 Solid Shelving.

Solid shelving is covered in 12.3.1.9. The standard for many years has required sprinkler protection below each shelf for solid shelving in racks, but has failed to clearly define such shelving or the minimum size of solid shelf that creates the need for such protection. During the original test program that led to the development of NFPA 231C, *Standard for Rack Storage Materials*, Test 147 showed that solid shelving 3.5 ft × 7.75 ft (27 ft^2) between the flues resulted in unacceptable performance without in-rack sprinklers. The limit of 20 ft^2 is established as representing the amount of blockage typically presented by a standard pallet load, which is acceptable based on traditional testing. Above this area limit, some in-rack protection is required. Where close-spaced shelves or tiers are used, the need for sprinklers under each tier can be mitigated provided flues are spaced at reasonable intervals to prevent uninterrupted spread of fire within the tier. The 64 ft^2 area is considered a reasonable maximum area for this purpose.

Paragraph 12.3.1.9 details the requirements of sprinkler protection within a rack structure with solid shelves. A solid shelf is defined in Chapter 3 and should be reviewed prior to applying this paragraph. Solid shelf protection criteria have been divided into two sections—shelves with an area between 20 ft^2 and 64 ft^2 (1.9 m^2 and 5.9 m^2) and shelves with an area greater than 64 ft^2 (5.9 m^2). This requirement should not be interpreted to mean that racks with solid shelves that have only their required longitudinal flues or only their transverse flues obstructed have adequate flue spaces.

An inadequate number of flues result where transverse flues are only provided at the rack uprights and not between pallet loads. Lacking other protection criteria, 12.3.1.9 needs to be considered where flue spaces cannot be provided in accordance with 12.3.1.13 or 12.3.1.14.

Exhibit 12.4 shows a double-row rack storage arrangement with inadequate flue spaces. Note that the solid shelves eliminate the required flues between loads [flues every 4 ft to 5 ft (1.2 m to 1.5 m) down the rack are considered adequate] and create a very narrow flue [less than 6 in. (152 mm)] at the rack uprights.

EXHIBIT 12.4 *Double-Row Storage Racks Consisting of Solid Shelves and Inadequate Flue Spaces.*

12.3.1.9.1 Where solid shelving in single-, double-, and multiple-row racks exceeds 20 ft^2 but does not exceed 64 ft^2 in area, sprinklers shall not be required below every shelf, but shall be installed at the ceiling and below shelves at intermediate levels not more than 6 ft (2 m) apart vertically. *(See Section C.11.)*

It is reasonable to expect that when solid shelving is located close together such as 18 in. (457 mm) vertically between shelves, the fire size can be contained by in-rack sprinklers located up to 6 ft (2 m) vertically and not located at every tier, as addressed in 12.3.1.9.1. This arrangement could result in several levels of storage between levels of in-rack sprinklers due to the small vertical distance between shelves.

12.3.1.9.2 Where solid shelving in single-, double-, and multiple-row racks exceeds 64 ft^2 in area or where the levels of storage exceed 6 ft (2 m), sprinklers shall be installed at the ceiling and below each level of shelving.

Paragraph 12.3.1.9.2 applies to either shelves 64 ft^2 (5.9 m^2) and greater or all solid shelves spaced more than 6 ft (2 m) vertically. In either case, in-rack sprinklers will be located at every tier of storage.

12.3.1.10 Open-Top Combustible Containers. See Section C.12.

12.3.1.11 In-Rack Sprinklers.

12.3.1.11.1 The number of sprinklers and the pipe sizing on a line of sprinklers in racks shall be restricted only by hydraulic calculations and not by any piping schedule.

12.3.1.11.2 When in-rack sprinklers are necessary to protect a higher hazard commodity that occupies only a portion of the length of a rack, in-rack sprinklers shall be extended a minimum of 8 ft or one bay, whichever is greater, in each direction along the rack on either side of the higher hazard. The in-rack sprinklers protecting the higher hazard need not be extended across the aisle.

The requirement in 12.3.1.11.2 is similar to the 15-ft (4.6-m) extension of the higher hazard ceiling protection area specified in Section 12.1; however, it is believed that the 8-ft (2.4-m) extension of protection within the rack is adequate for in-rack protection. If the adjacent bays contain in-rack sprinklers installed to a lower hazard, then the pipe sizing should be adequate for the in-rack demand of the higher hazard for the 8-ft (2.4-m) distance.

12.3.1.11.3 Where a storage rack, due to its length, requires less than the number of in-rack sprinklers specified, only those in-rack sprinklers in a single rack need to be included in the calculation.

12.3.1.12* Horizontal Barriers and In-Rack Sprinklers. Horizontal barriers used in conjunction with in-rack sprinklers to impede vertical fire development shall be constructed of sheet metal, wood, or similar material and shall extend the full length and width of the rack. Barriers shall be fitted within 2 in. (51 mm) horizontally around rack uprights.

A **A.12.3.1.12** Where the ceiling is more than 10 ft (3.1 m) above the maximum height of storage, a horizontal barrier should be installed above storage with one line of sprinklers under the barrier for Classes I, II, and III commodities and two lines of sprinklers under the barrier for Class IV commodities. In-rack sprinkler arrays should be installed as indicated in Table 12.3.4.1.1 and Figure 12.3.4.4.1.1(a) through Figure 12.3.4.4.1.1(j).

Barriers should be of sufficient strength to avoid sagging that interferes with loading and unloading operations.

Horizontal barriers are not required to be provided above a Class I or Class II commodity with in-rack sprinkler arrays in accordance with Figure 12.3.4.4.1.1(a) and Figure 12.3.4.4.1.1(b) provided one line of in-rack sprinklers is installed above the top tier of storage.

12.3.1.13 For Storage Up to and Including 25 ft (7.6 m). In double-row and multiple-row racks without solid shelves, a longitudinal (back-to-back clearance between loads) flue space shall not be required. Nominal 6-in. (152.4-mm) transverse flue spaces between loads and at-rack uprights shall be maintained in single-row, double-row, and multiple-row racks. Random variations in the width of flue spaces or in their vertical alignment shall be permitted. *(See Section C.13.)*

FAQ ▶
What purpose do flue spaces in rack storage serve?

Flue spaces, which are discussed in 12.3.1.13, exert two primary influences on fires in racks. Flues allow a fire to spread vertically through a rack, thereby providing a means for heat to rise up through the racks and activate the sprinklers. Flues also provide the path through which water from the sprinklers reaches a fire. Where they exist, flue spaces are to extend vertically through the entire height of the rack.

Clear transverse flue spaces between pallet loads that line up vertically for the full height of the rack are required for all single-, double-, and multiple-row racks regardless of overall storage heights. However, where longitudinal flues are not provided, it is assumed that the pallet loads abut each other as indicated in Exhibit 12.5. Rack storage tests of 20-ft (6.1-m) high double-row racks indicated that where pallet loads are pushed together in the back-to-back space, thus eliminating the longitudinal flues as indicated in Exhibit 12.5, virtually no difference was observed in results from those tests that had clear longitudinal flues.

FAQ ▶
Can narrow aisles be considered flues spaces?

Where a rack storage configuration is determined to be a multiple-row rack arrangement because the aisle widths are less than 3 ft (0.9 m), the aisles are not to be considered flue spaces. Flue spaces must have a nominal width of 6 in. (152 mm). Spaces larger than the nominal 6 in. (152 mm) rising up through the rack are not to be considered flues.

Exhibit 12.6 illustrates the flue spaces required for a multiple-row rack arrangement consisting of aisles of less than 3 ft (0.9 m).

EXHIBIT 12.5 *Plan View of Double-Row Rack Without a Longitudinal Flue Space.*

Rack upright

0 in. (0 mm) longitudinal flue space

6-in. (152-mm) transverse flue space (typical)

Plan View

Plan View

Elevation View

EXHIBIT 12.6 Multiple-Row Rack Storage Arrangement Consisting of Aisles of Less Than 3 ft (0.9 m).

12.3.1.14 For Storage over 25 ft (7.6 m).

12.3.1.14.1 Nominal 6-in. (152.4-mm) transverse flue spaces between loads and at rack uprights shall be maintained in single-row, double-row, and multiple-row racks. Nominal 6-in. (152.4-mm) longitudinal flue spaces shall be provided in double-row racks. Random variations in the width of the flue spaces or in their vertical alignment shall be permitted.

Where no flue spaces exist, fire development cannot occur up through the racks (see 12.3.1.14.1). The fire can only develop and spread horizontally down the length of the rack and up along the rack face in the aisles. This type of fire development severely delays the activation of sprinklers, and when sprinklers do activate, their discharge cannot penetrate the rack and reach the fire even though a greater number of sprinklers ultimately operate. A similar phenomenon also occurs where flue spaces exist but are obstructed, limited in number or size, or do not extend vertically through the entire height of the rack. The final outcome can often result in a very significant loss or complete destruction of the storage facility.

Longitudinal flues are required for double-row racks where storage heights exceed 25 ft (7.6 m).

12.3.1.14.2 In single-row, double-row, or multiple-row racks, a minimum 6-in. (152.4-mm) vertical clear space shall be maintained between the sprinkler deflectors and the top of a tier of storage. Face sprinklers in such racks shall be located a minimum of 3 in. (76 mm) from rack uprights and no more than 18 in. (460 mm) from the aisle face of storage. Longitudinal flue in-rack sprinklers shall be located at the intersection with the transverse flue space and

◀ **FAQ**
What is the effect of having no flue spaces or obstructed flue spaces?

with the deflector located at or below the bottom of horizontal load beams or above or below other adjacent horizontal rack members. Such in-rack sprinklers shall be a minimum of 3 in. (76 mm) radially from the side of the rack uprights.

When storage exceeds 25 ft (7.6 m), the in-rack sprinklers must be located as stated in 12.3.1.14.2. This paragraph can require more clearance vertically between shelves than normal to accommodate the 6-in. (152.4-mm) clearance between the in-rack deflector and the top of the storage.

12.3.2 Protection Criteria for Rack Storage of Class I through Class IV Commodities Stored Up to and Including 25 ft (7.6 m) in Height.

12.3.2.1 Control Mode Density-Area Sprinkler Protection Criteria for Rack Storage of Class I through Class IV Commodities Stored Up to and Including 25 ft (7.6 m) in Height.

12.3.2.1.1 The area and density for the hydraulically remote area and the water supply shall be determined as specified in 12.1.10 for storage up to 12 ft (3.7 m) and 12.3.2 for storage over 12 ft (3.7 m).

Paragraph 12.3.2.1.1 clearly indicates that it is for the protection of Class I through Class IV storage above 12 ft (3.7 m). Storage 12 ft (3.7 m) and less does not apply to this paragraph and should be protected in accordance with 12.1.10.

12.3.2.1.1.1* Ceiling sprinkler water demand shall be determined in accordance with 12.3.2.1.2 for single- and double-row racks or 12.3.2.1.3 for multiple-row racks. *(See Section C.14.)*

A **A.12.3.2.1.1.1** Bulkheads are not a substitute for sprinklers in racks. Their installation does not justify reduction in sprinkler densities or design operating areas as specified in the design curves.

12.3.2.1.2* Single- or double-row racks for Class I, Class II, Class III, or Class IV commodities, encapsulated or nonencapsulated in single- or double-row racks, ceiling sprinkler water demand in terms of density (gpm/ft^2) (mm/min) and area of sprinkler operation [ft^2 (m^2) of ceiling or roof] shall be selected from the density/area curves of Figure 12.3.2.1.2(a) through Figure 12.3.2.1.2(g) that are appropriate for each commodity and configuration as shown in Table 12.3.2.1.2 and shall be modified as appropriate by 12.3.2.1.5. These requirements shall apply to portable racks arranged in the same manner as single- or double-row racks.

A **A.12.3.2.1.2** Data indicates that the sprinkler protection criteria in Figure 12.3.2.1.2(a) through Figure 12.3.2.1.2(g) is ineffective, by itself, for rack storage with solid shelves, if the required flue spaces are not maintained. Use of Figure 12.3.2.1.2(a) through Figure 12.3.2.1.2(g) along with the additional provisions that are required by this standard, can provide acceptable protection.

Tables 12.3.2.1.2, 12.3.2.1.3, and 12.3.2.1.4 provide options to ceiling densities with or without in-rack sprinklers. An example is as follows:

If a nonencapsulated Class III commodity is stored to a height of 20 ft (6.1 m) in double-row racks having 4-ft (1.2-m) aisles with high-temperature sprinklers at the ceiling, in-rack sprinklers are not required per Table 12.3.2.1.2, which references Figure 12.3.2.1.2(c) (curve G) with a density/area design of 0.43 gpm/ft^2 (17.5 mm/min) over 2000 ft^2 (186 m^2).

However, the designer has the option of using in-rack sprinklers. Where one level of in-rack sprinklers is installed, the ceiling sprinkler density is chosen from Table 12.3.2.1.2, which references Figure 12.3.2.1.2(c) (curve C). An appropriate density would be 0.29 gpm/ft^2 (11.6 mm/min) over 2000 ft^2 (186 m^2).

TABLE 12.3.2.1.2 *Single- or Double-Row Racks—Storage Height Up to and Including 25 ft (7.6 m) Without Solid Shelves*

Height	Commodity Class	Encapsulated	ft	m	Sprinklers Mandatory In-Rack	With In-Rack Sprinklers Figure	Curves	Apply Figure 12.3.2.1.5.1	Without In-Rack Sprinklers Figure	Curves	Apply Figure 12.3.2.1.5.1
Over 12 ft (3.7 m), up to and including 20 ft (6.1m)	I	No	4	1.2	No	12.3.2.1.2(a)	C and D	Yes	12.3.2.1.2(a)	G and H	Yes
			8	2.4			A and B			E and F	
		Yes	4	1.2	No	12.3.2.1.2(e)	C and D		12.3.2.1.2(e)	G and H	Yes
			8	2.4			A and B			E and F	
	II	No	4	1.2	No	12.3.2.1.2(b)	C and D		12.3.2.1.2(b)	G and H	Yes
			8	2.4			A and B			E and F	
		Yes	4	1.2	No	12.3.2.1.2(e)	C and D		12.3.2.1.2(e)	G and H	Yes
			8	2.4			A and B			E and F	
	III	No	4	1.2	No	12.3.2.1.2(c)	C and D		12.3.2.1.2(c)	G and H	Yes
			8	2.4			A and B			E and F	
		Yes	4	1.2	1 level	12.3.2.1.2(f)	C and D		—	—	—
			8	2.4			A and B				
	IV	No	4	1.2	No	12.3.2.1.2(d)	C and D		12.3.2.1.2(d)	G and H	Yes
			8	2.4			A and B			E and F	
		Yes	4	1.2	1 level	12.3.2.1.2(g)	C and D		—	—	—
			8	2.4			A and B				
Over 20 ft (6.1 m), up to and including 22 ft (6.7 m)	I	No	4	1.2	No	12.3.2.1.2(a)	C and D	No	12.3.2.1.2(a)	F and H	Yes
			8	2.4			A and B			E and G	
		Yes	4	1.2	1 level	12.3.2.1.2(e)	C and D		—	—	—
			8	2.4			A and B				
	II	No	4	1.2	No	12.3.2.1.2(b)	C and D		12.3.2.1.2(b)	G and H	Yes
			8	2.4			A and B			E and F	
		Yes	4	1.2	1 level	12.3.2.1.2(e)	C and D		—	—	—
			8	2.4			A and B				
	III	No	4	1.2	No	12.3.2.1.2(c)	C and D		12.3.2.1.2(c)	G and H	Yes
			8	2.4			A and B			E and F	
		Yes	4	1.2	1 level	12.3.2.1.2(f)	C and D		—	—	—
			8	2.4			A and B				
	IV	No	4	1.2	No	12.3.2.1.2(d)	C and D		12.3.2.1.2(d)	G and H	Yes
			8	2.4			A and B			E and F	
		Yes	4	1.2	1 level	12.3.2.1.2(g)	C and D		—	—	—
			8	2.4			A and B				

(Continues)

TABLE 12.3.2.1.2 Continued

Height	Commodity Class	Encapsulated	Aisles* ft	Aisles* m	Sprinklers Mandatory In-Rack	Ceiling Sprinkler Water Demand — With In-Rack Sprinklers — Figure	Curves	Apply Figure 12.3.2.1.5.1	Ceiling Sprinkler Water Demand — Without In-Rack Sprinklers — Figure	Curves	Apply Figure 12.3.2.1.5.1
Over 22 ft (6.7 m), up to and including 25 ft (7.6 m)	I	No	4	1.2	No	12.3.2.1.2(a)	C and D	No	12.3.2.1.2(a)	F and H	Yes
			8	2.4			A and B			E and G	
		Yes	4	1.2	1 level	12.3.2.1.2(e)	C and D		—	—	—
			8	2.4			A and B				
	II	No	4	1.2	No	12.3.2.1.2(b)	C and D		12.3.2.1.2(b)	G and H	Yes
			8	2.4			A and B			E and F	
		Yes	4	1.2	1 level	12.3.2.1.2(e)	C and D		—	—	—
			8	2.4			A and B				
	III	No	4	1.2	No	12.3.2.1.2(c)	C and D		12.3.2.1.2(c)	G and H	Yes
			8	2.4			A and B			E and F	
		Yes	4	1.2	1 level	12.3.2.1.2(f)	C and D		—	—	—
			8	2.4			A and B				
	IV	No	4	1.2	1 level	12.3.2.1.2(d)	C and D		—	—	—
			8	2.4			A and B				
		Yes	4	1.2	1 level	12.3.2.1.2(g)	C and D		—	—	—
			8	2.4			A and B				

*See 12.3.2.1.2.1 for interpolation of aisle widths.

12.3.2.1.2.1* Design densities for single- and double-row racks shall be selected to correspond to aisle width. For aisle widths between 4 ft (1.2 m) and 8 ft (2.4 m), a direct linear interpolation between densities shall be made. The density given for 8-ft (2.4-m) wide aisles shall be applied to aisles wider than 8 ft (2.4 m). The density given for 4-ft (1.2-m) wide aisles shall be applied to aisles narrower than 4 ft (1.2 m) down to 3½ ft (1.07 m). Where aisles are narrower than 3½ ft (1.07 m), racks shall be considered to be multiple-row racks. *(See Section C.15.)*

 A.12.3.2.1.2.1 The aisle width and the depth of racks are determined by material-handling methods. The widths of aisles should be considered in the design of the protection system. Storage in aisles can render protection ineffective and should be discouraged.

Sprinkler protection requirements do not continue to decrease as aisle width increases beyond 8 ft (2.4 m) (see 12.3.2.1.2.1). For aisle widths less than 8 ft (2.4 m), a higher density is needed to prevent fire from jumping the aisle. For aisles greater than 8 ft (2.4 m), aisle jump is no longer a controlling factor in protection requirements.

12.3.2.1.3 Multiple-Row Racks—Rack Depth Up to and Including 16 ft (4.9 m) with Aisles 8 ft (2.4 m) or Wider. For Class I, Class II, Class III, or Class IV commodities, encapsulated or

FIGURE 12.3.2.1.2(a) *Sprinkler System Design Curves—20-ft (6.1-m) High Rack Storage—Class I Nonencapsulated Commodities—Conventional Pallets.*

FIGURE 12.3.2.1.2(b) *Sprinkler System Design Curves—20-ft (6.1-m) High Rack Storage—Class II Nonencapsulated Commodities—Conventional Pallets.*

FIGURE 12.3.2.1.2(c) Sprinkler System Design Curves—20-ft (6.1-m) High Rack Storage—Class III Nonencapsulated Commodities—Conventional Pallets.

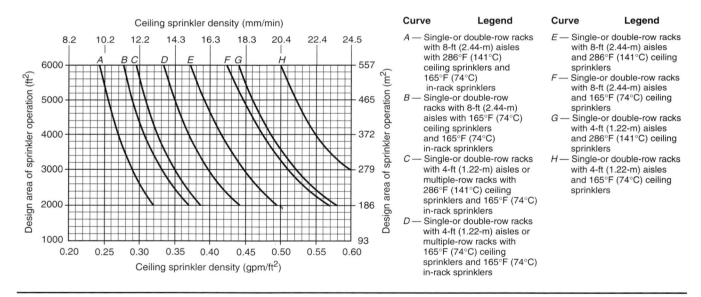

FIGURE 12.3.2.1.2(d) Sprinkler System Design Curves—20-ft (6.1-m) High Rack Storage—Class IV Nonencapsulated Commodities—Conventional Pallets.

FIGURE 12.3.2.1.2(e) *Single- or Double-Row Racks—20-ft (6.1-m) High Rack Storage—Sprinkler System Design Curves—Class I and II Encapsulated Commodities—Conventional Pallets.*

FIGURE 12.3.2.1.2(f) *Single- or Double-Row Racks—20-ft (6.1-m) High Rack Storage—Sprinkler System Design Curves—Class III Encapsulated Commodities—Conventional Pallets.*

FIGURE 12.3.2.1.2(g) *Single- or Double-Row Racks—20-ft (6.1-m) High Rack Storage—Sprinkler System Design Curves—Class IV Encapsulated Commodities—Conventional Pallets.*

nonencapsulated, ceiling sprinkler water demand in terms of density (gpm/ft^2) (mm/min) and area of sprinkler operation [ft^2 (m^2) of ceiling or roof] shall be selected from the density/area curves of Figure 12.3.2.1.2(a) through Figure 12.3.2.1.2(g) that are appropriate for each commodity and configuration as shown in Table 12.3.2.1.3 and shall be modified as appropriate by 12.3.2.1.5. The protection criteria shall apply to portable racks arranged in the same manner as single- or double-row racks.

The aisle width indicated in Table 12.3.2.1.3 refers to the aisles between rack structures and not the aisles between individual racks.

12.3.2.1.4 Multiple-Row Racks—Rack Depth Over 16 ft (4.9 m) or Aisles Narrower than 8 ft (2.4 m). For Class I, Class II, Class III, or Class IV commodities, encapsulated or nonencapsulated, ceiling sprinkler water demand in terms of density (gpm/ft^2) (mm/min) and area of sprinkler operation [ft^2 (m^2) of ceiling or roof] shall be selected from the density/area curves of Figure 12.3.2.1.2(a) through Figure 12.3.2.1.2(g) that are appropriate for each commodity and configuration as shown in Table 12.3.2.1.4 and shall be modified as appropriate by 12.3.2.1.5. The protection criteria shall apply to portable racks arranged in the same manner as single-, double-, or multiple-row racks.

The aisle width indicated in Table 12.3.2.1.4 refers to the aisles between rack structures and not the aisles between individual racks.

12.3.2.1.5 Ceiling Sprinkler Density Adjustments.

12.3.2.1.5.1 For storage height up to and including 25 ft (7.6 m) protected with ceiling sprinklers only and for storage height up to and including 20 ft (6.1 m) protected with ceiling sprinklers and minimum required in-rack sprinklers, densities obtained from design curves shall be adjusted in accordance with Figure 12.3.2.1.5.1.

12.3.2.1.5.2 For storage height over 20 ft (6.1 m) up to and including 25 ft (7.6 m) protected with ceiling sprinklers and minimum required in-rack sprinklers, densities obtained from design curves shall be used. Densities shall not be adjusted in accordance with Figure 12.3.2.1.5.1.

TABLE 12.3.2.1.3 *Multiple-Row Racks—Rack Depth Up to and Including 16 ft (4.9 m), Aisles 8 ft (2.4 m) or Wider, Storage Height Up to 25 ft (7.6 m)*

Height	Commodity Class	Encapsulated	Sprinklers Mandatory In-Racks	Ceiling Sprinkler Water Demand — With In-Rack Sprinklers: Figure	Curves	Apply Figure 12.3.2.1.5.1	1.25 × Density	Without In-Rack Sprinklers: Figure	Curves	Apply Figure 12.3.2.1.5.1	1.25 × Density
Over 12 ft (3.7 m), up to and including 15 ft (4.6 m)	I	No	No	12.3.2.1.2(a)	C and D	Yes	No	12.3.2.1.2(a)	I and J	Yes	No
	I	Yes		12.3.2.1.2(a)			Yes	12.3.2.1.2(a)	I and J		Yes
	II	No		12.3.2.1.2(b)			No	12.3.2.1.2(b)	I and J	Yes	No
	II	Yes		12.3.2.1.2(b)			Yes	12.3.2.1.2(b)	I and J		Yes
	III	No	No	12.3.2.1.2(c)			No	12.3.2.1.2(c)	I and J	Yes	No
	III	Yes	1 level	12.3.2.1.2(c)			Yes		NA	NA	NA
	IV	No	No	12.3.2.1.2(d)			No	12.3.2.1.2(d)	C and D	No	No
	IV	Yes	1 level	12.3.2.1.2(d)	A and B		1.50 × density		NA	NA	NA
Over 15 ft (4.6 m), up to and including 20 ft (6.1 m)	I	No	No	12.3.2.1.2(a)	C and D	Yes	No	12.3.2.1.2(a)	I and J	Yes	No
	I	Yes		12.3.2.1.2(a)			Yes	12.3.2.1.2(a)	I and J		Yes
	II	No		12.3.2.1.2(b)			No	12.3.2.1.2(b)	I and J	Yes	No
	II	Yes		12.3.2.1.2(b)			Yes	12.3.2.1.2(b)	I and J		Yes
	III	No	No	12.3.2.1.2(c)			No	12.3.2.1.2(c)	I and J	Yes	No
	III	Yes	1 level	12.3.2.1.2(c)			Yes	NA	NA	NA	NA
	IV	No	1 level	12.3.2.1.2(d)			No	NA	NA	NA	NA
	IV	Yes		12.3.2.1.2(d)	A nd B		1.50 × density	NA	NA	NA	NA
Over 20 ft (6.1 m), up to and including 25 ft (7.6 m)	I	No	No	12.3.2.1.2(a)	C and D	No	No	12.3.2.1.2(a)	I and J	Yes	No
	I	Yes	1 level	12.3.2.1.2(a)			Yes	NA	NA	NA	NA
	II	No		12.3.2.1.2(b)			No	NA	NA	NA	NA
	II	Yes	1 level	12.3.2.1.2(b)			Yes	NA	NA	NA	NA
	III	No		12.3.2.1.2(c)			No	NA	NA	NA	NA
	III	Yes		12.3.2.1.2(c)			Yes	NA	NA	NA	NA
	IV	No	2 levels	12.3.2.1.2(d)			No	NA	NA	NA	NA
	IV	Yes		12.3.2.1.2(d)	A and B		1.50 × density	NA	NA	NA	NA

TABLE 12.3.2.1.4 *Multiple-Row Racks—Rack Depth Over 16 ft (4.9 m) or Aisles Narrower than 8 ft (2.4 m), Storage Height Up to and Including 25 ft (7.6 m)*

Height	Commodity Class	Encapsulated	Sprinklers Mandatory In-Racks	Ceiling Sprinkler Water Demand							
				With In-Rack Sprinklers				Without In-Rack Sprinklers			
				Figure	Curves	Apply Figure 12.3.2.1.5.1	1.25× Density	Figure	Curves	Apply Figure 12.3.2.1.5.1	1.25× Density
Over 12 ft (3.7 m), up to and including 15 ft (4.6 m)	I	No	No	12.3.2.1.2(a)	C and D	Yes	No	12.3.2.1.2(a)	I and J	Yes	No
		Yes		12.3.2.1.2(a)			Yes	12.3.2.1.2(a)	I and J		Yes
	II	No		12.3.2.1.2(b)			No	12.3.2.1.2(b)	I and J	Yes	No
		Yes		12.3.2.1.2(b)			Yes	12.3.2.1.2(b)	I and J		Yes
	III	No		12.3.2.1.2(c)			No	12.3.2.1.2(c)	I and J	Yes	No
		Yes	1 level	12.3.2.1.2(c)			Yes				
	IV	No	No	12.3.2.1.2(d)			No	12.3.2.1.2(d)	C and D	No	No
		Yes	1 level	12.3.2.1.2(d)			1.50× density				
Over 15 ft (4.6 m), up to and including 20 ft (6.1 m)	I	No	1 level	12.3.2.1.2(a)	C and D	Yes	No	NA	NA	NA	NA
		Yes		12.3.2.1.2(a)			Yes				
	II	No		12.3.2.1.2(b)			No				
		Yes		12.3.2.1.2(b)			Yes				
	III	No		12.3.2.1.2(c)			No				
		Yes		12.3.2.1.2(c)			Yes				
	IV	No		12.3.2.1.2(d)			No				
		Yes		12.3.2.1.2(d)			1.50× density				
Over 20 ft (6.1 m), up to and including 25 ft (7.6 m)	I	No	1 level	12.3.2.1.2(a)	C and D	No	No	NA	NA	NA	NA
		Yes		12.3.2.1.2(a)			Yes				
	II	No		12.3.2.1.2(b)			No				
		Yes		12.3.2.1.2(b)			Yes				
	III	No		12.3.2.1.2(c)			No				
		Yes		12.3.2.1.2(c)			Yes				
	IV	No	2 levels	12.3.2.1.2(d)			No				
		Yes		12.3.2.1.2(d)			1.50× density				

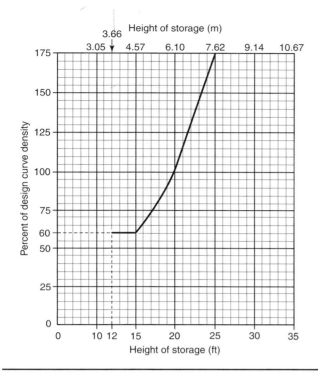

FIGURE 12.3.2.1.5.1 *Ceiling Sprinkler Density vs. Storage Height.*

12.3.2.1.5.3 For storage height up to and including 20 ft (6.1 m) protected with ceiling sprinklers and with more than one level of in-rack sprinklers, but not in every tier, densities obtained from design curves and adjusted in accordance with Figure 12.3.2.1.5.1 shall be permitted to be reduced an additional 20 percent, as indicated in Table 12.3.2.1.5.3.

TABLE 12.3.2.1.5.3 *Adjustment to Ceiling Sprinkler Density for Storage Height and In-Rack Sprinklers*

Storage Height	In-Rack Sprinklers	Apply Figure 12.3.2.1.5.1 for Storage Height Adjustment	Permitted Ceiling Sprinklers Density Adjustments Where In-Rack Sprinklers are Installed
Over 12 ft (3.7 m) through 25 ft (7.6 m)	None	Yes	None
Over 12 ft (3.7 m) through 20 ft (6.1 m)	Minimum required	Yes	None
	More than minimum, but not in every tier	Yes	Reduce density 20% from that of minimum in-rack sprinklers
	In every tier	Yes	Reduce density 40% from that of minimum in-rack sprinklers
Over 20 ft (6.1 m) through 24 ft (7.5 m)	Minimum required	No	None
	More than minimum, but not in every tier	No	Reduce density 20% from that of minimum in-rack sprinklers
	In every tier	No	Reduce density 40% from that of minimum in-rack sprinklers

Table 12.3.2.1.5.3 summarizes the adjustments to ceiling sprinkler density where a level of in-rack sprinklers is in excess of that specified by the tables and figures.

An example is as follows: With regard to the adjustment for in-rack sprinklers, if a non-encapsulated Class III commodity is stored to a height of 20 ft (6.1 m) in double-row racks having 4-ft (1.2-m) aisles with high-temperature sprinklers at the ceiling and one level of in-rack sprinklers are provided, Table 12.3.2.1.2, which references Figure 12.3.2.1.2(c) (curve C), would require a 0.29 gpm/ft² (11.6 mm/min) over 2000 ft² (186 m²). However, the designer has the option of using more than the minimum level of in-rack sprinklers required. If a second level of in-rack sprinklers were installed, the ceiling sprinkler density could be reduced by 20 percent per Table 12.3.2.1.5.3, which would result in a required density of 0.23 gpm/ft² (9.4 mm/min) over 2000 ft² (186 m²). If in-rack sprinklers are added at every level, the ceiling sprinkler density could be reduced by 40 percent per Table 12.3.2.1.5.3, which would result in a required density of 0.17 gpm/ft² (9.4 mm/min) over 2000 ft² (186 m²).

12.3.2.1.5.4 For storage height over 20 ft (6.1 m) up to and including 25 ft (7.6 m) protected with ceiling sprinklers and with more than the minimum required level of in-rack sprinklers, but not in every tier, densities obtrained from design curves shall be permitted to be reduced 20 percent as indicated in Table 12.3.2.1.5.3. Densities shall not be adjusted in accordance with Figure 12.3.2.1.5.1 for storage height.

12.3.2.1.5.5 For storage height up to and including 20 ft (6.1 m) protected with ceiling sprinklers and in-rack sprinklers at each tier, densities obtained from design curves and adjusted in accordance with Figure 12.3.2.1.5.1 shall be permitted to be reduced an additional 40 percent, as indicated in Table 12.3.2.1.5.3.

12.3.2.1.5.6 For storage height over 20 ft (6.1 m) up to and including 25 ft (7.6 m) protected with ceiling sprinklers and in-rack sprinklers at each tier, densities obtained from design curves shall be permitted to be reduced 40 percent, as indicated in Table 12.3.2.1.5.3. Densities shall not be adjusted in accordance with Figure 12.3.2.1.5.1 for storage height.

12.3.2.1.5.7 Where clearance from ceiling to top of storage is less than 4½ ft (1.37 m), the sprinkler operating area indicated in curves E, F, G, and H in Figure 12.3.2.1.2(a) through Figure 12.3.2.1.2(e) shall be permitted to be reduced as indicated in Figure 12.3.2.1.5.7 but shall not be reduced to less than 2000 ft² (185.8 m²).

12.3.2.1.5.8 Where clearance from ceiling to top of Class I or Class I encapsulated storage is 1½ ft to 3 ft (0.46 m to 0.91 m), the sprinkler operating area indicated in curve F only of Figure 12.3.2.1.2(e) shall be permitted to be reduced by 50 percent but shall not be reduced to less than 2000 ft² (186 m²).

12.3.2.1.5.9 Where solid, flat-bottom, combustible pallets are used with storage height up to and including 25 ft (7.6 m), the densities that are indicated in the design curves shown in Figure 12.3.2.1.2(a) through Figure 12.3.2.1.2(g), based on conventional pallets, shall be increased 20 percent for the given area. The percentage shall be applied to the density determined in accordance with Figure 12.3.2.1.5.1. The increase in density shall not apply where in-rack sprinklers are installed.

The most common examples of this type pallet are slave pallets as indicated in Chapter 3. See Figure A.3.10.4. The term *solid shelf* is used to indicate conditions where inadequate flues are provided. The provisions of 12.3.2.1.5.9 can be used where solid shelving materials such as slave pallets are used, provided the required number and type of flue spaces are provided. Where slave pallets or other solid materials are used in racks up to 25 ft (7.6 m) in height and only ceiling sprinklers are used, the ceiling density must be increased 20 percent.

12.3.2.1.6* The minimum water supply requirements for a hydraulically designed occupancy hazard fire control sprinkler system shall be determined by adding the hose stream demand

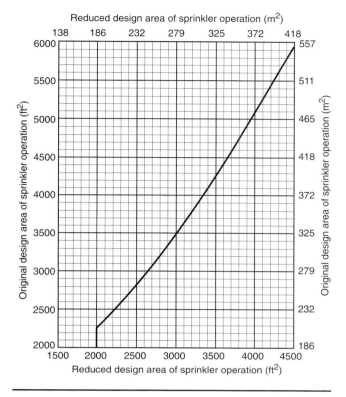

FIGURE 12.3.2.1.5.7 *Adjustment of Design Area of Sprinkler Operation for Clearance from Top of Storage to Ceiling.*

from Table 12.3.2.1.6 to the water supply for sprinklers determined in 12.3.2.1. This supply shall be available for the minimum duration specified in Table 12.3.2.1.6. *(See Section C.8.)*

A.12.3.2.1.6 Appropriate area/density, other design criteria, and water supply requirements should be based on scientifically based engineering analyses that can include submitted fire testing, calculations, or results from appropriate computational models.

Recommended water supplies anticipate successful sprinkler operation. Because of the small but still significant number of uncontrolled fires in sprinklered properties, which have various causes, there should be an adequate water supply available for fire department use.

12.3.2.1.6.1 An allowance for inside and outside hose shall not be required where tanks supply sprinklers only.

TABLE 12.3.2.1.6 *Hose Stream Demand and Water Supply Duration Requirements for Rack Storage of Class I through Class IV Commodities Stored Up to and Including 25 ft (7.6 m) in Height*

Commodity Classification	Storage Height		Inside Hose		Total Combined Inside and Outside Hose		Duration (minutes)
	ft	*m*	*gpm*	*L/min*	*gpm*	*L/min*	
Class I, II, and III	Over 12	Over 3.7	0, 50, or 100	0, 190, 380	500	1900	90
Class IV	Over 12	Over 3.7	0, 50, or 100	0, 190, 380	500	1900	120

12.3.2.1.6.2 Where pumps taking suction from a private fire service main supply sprinklers only, the pump need not be sized to accommodate inside and outside hose. Such hose allowance shall be considered in evaluating the available water supplies.

12.3.2.2 Large Drop Sprinklers and Specific Application Control Mode Sprinklers for Rack Storage of Class I through Class IV Commodities Stored Up to and Including 25 ft (7.6 m) in Height.

The large drop sprinkler, which is covered in 12.3.2.2, is a type of specific application control mode technology as defined in Chapter 3. The names have remained separate due to the long history of the name "large drop" and its relation to the nominal K-factor of 11.2. Applications of large drop sprinklers and specific application control mode sprinklers are described in Table 12.3.2.2.1(a) and Table 12.3.2.2.1(b). Listing of large drop sprinklers and control mode specific application sprinklers takes into consideration the ability of the sprinkler discharge pattern to penetrate a high-velocity fire plume. Only listed large drop and specific application control mode sprinklers are to be used in accordance with the design approach of 12.3.2.2.

12.3.2.2.1 Protection of single-, double-, and multiple-row rack storage without solid shelves for Classes I through IV commodities shall be in accordance with Table 12.3.2.2.1(a) or Table 12.3.2.2.1(b).

12.3.2.2.2 Where in-rack sprinklers are required by Table 12.3.2.2.1(a) and Table 12.3.2.2.1(b), in-rack sprinkler spacing, design pressure, and hydraulic calculation criteria shall be in accordance with the requirements of 12.3.2.4 as applicable for the commodity.

12.3.2.2.3 Protection shall be provided as specified in Table 12.3.2.2.1(a) and Table 12.3.2.2.1(b) or appropriate NFPA standards in terms of minimum operating pressure and the number of sprinklers to be included in the design area.

12.3.2.2.3.1 For design purposes, 95 psi (6.6 bar) shall be the maximum discharge pressure at the hydraulically most remote sprinkler.

Discharge pressures in excess of 95 psi (6.6 bar) negatively impact the sprinkler's discharge pattern and droplet size, which is the reason for the requirement in 12.3.2.2.3.1.

12.3.2.2.3.2 Open Wood Joist Construction.

(A) Where large drop K-11.2 sprinklers are installed under open wood joist construction, their minimum operating pressure shall be 50 psi (3.4 bar).
(B) Where each joist channel of open, wood joist construction is fully fire-stopped to its full depth at intervals not exceeding 20 ft (6.1 m), the lower pressures specified in Table 12.3.2.2.1(a) shall be permitted to be used.

12.3.2.2.3.3 The design area shall be a rectangular area having a dimension parallel to the branch lines at least 1.2 times the square root of the area protected by the number of sprinklers to be included in the design area. Any fractional sprinkler shall be included in the design area.

Starting with the 1996 edition, NFPA 13 provided more information about the shape of the design area where large drop and specific application control mode sprinklers are used (see 12.3.2.2.3.3). Although earlier editions implied that the design area was to be a rectangular shape having a dimension parallel to the branch lines of at least 1.2 times the square root of the area protected by the number of sprinklers, it was not explicitly stated.

12.3.2.2.3.4 Hose stream demand and water supply duration requirements shall be in accordance with Table 12.3.2.2.1(a) and Table 12.3.2.2.1(b).

12.3.2.2.3.5 Preaction Systems.

(A) For the purpose of using Table 12.3.2.2.1(a) and Table 12.3.2.2.1(b), preaction systems shall be classified as dry pipe systems.

TABLE 12.3.2.2.1(a) *Large Drop Sprinkler Design Criteria for Single-, Double-, and Multiple-Row Racks without Solid Shelves of Class I through Class IV Commodities Stored Up to and Including 25 ft (7.6 m) in Height*

Commodity Class	Nominal K-Factor	Maximum Storage Height		Maximum Ceiling/ Roof Height		Type of System	Number of Design Sprinklers/Minimum Pressure		Hose Stream Demand		Water Supply Duration (hours)
		ft	m	ft	m		/psi	/bar	gpm	L/min	
I, II	11.2	25	7.6	30	9.1	Wet	20/25	20/1.7	500	1900	1½
						Dry	30/25	30/1.7	500	1900	1½
I, II, III	11.2	20	6.1	30	9.1	Wet	15/25	15/1.7	500	1900	1½
						Dry	25/25	25/1.7	N/A	N/A	1½
I, II, III	11.2	25	7.6	35	10.7	Wet	15/25 + 1 level of in-rack	15/1.7 + 1 level of in-rack	500	1900	1½
						Dry	25/25 + 1 level of in-rack	25/1.7 + 1 level of in-rack	500	1900	1½
IV	11.2	20	6.1	25	7.6	Wet	15/50	15/3.4	500	1900	2
						Dry	N/A	N/A	N/A	N/A	N/A
IV	11.2	20	6.1	30	9.1	Wet	20/50	20/3.4	500	1900	2
						Dry	N/A	N/A	N/A	N/A	N/A
IV	11.2	20	6.1	30	9.1	Wet	15/75	15/5.2	500	1900	2
						Dry	N/A	N/A	N/A	N/A	N/A
IV	11.2	25	7.6	30	9.1	Wet	15/50 + 1 level of in-rack	15/3.4 + 1 level of in-rack	500	1900	2
						Dry	N/A	N/A	N/A	N/A	N/A
IV	11.2	25	7.6	35	10.7	Wet	20/50 + 1 level of in-rack	20/3.4 + 1 level of in-rack	500	1900	2
						Dry	N/A	N/A	N/A	N/A	N/A
IV	11.2	25	7.6	35	10.7	Wet	15/75 + 1 level of in-rack	15/5.2 + 1 level of in-rack	500	1900	2
						Dry	N/A	N/A	N/A	N/A	N/A

TABLE 12.3.2.2.1(b) *Specific Application Control Mode (16.8 K-factor) Sprinkler Design Criteria for Single-, Double-, and Multiple-Row Racks without Solid Shelves of Class I through Class IV Commodities Stored Up to and Including 25 ft (7.6 m) in Height*

	Maximum Storage Height		Maximum Building Height		Type of System	Number of Design Sprinklers by Minimum Operating Pressure		Hose Stream Demand		Water Supply Duration (hours)
Commodity Class	ft	m	ft	m		10 psi 0.7 bar	22 psi 1.5 bar	gpm	L/min	
I or II	25	7.6	30	9.1	Wet	15	—	500	1900	1½
III or IV	25	7.6	30	9.1	Wet	—	15	500	1900	2

FAQ ▶
For large drop and specific application control mode sprinklers, are all types of preaction systems treated as dry pipe systems?

FAQ ▶
For large drop and specific application control mode sprinklers, are preaction systems always treated as dry pipe systems?

Paragraph 12.3.2.2.3.5(A) requires that all preaction systems be treated as dry pipe sprinkler systems when applying the requirements of Table 12.3.2.2.1(a) and Table 12.3.2.2.1(b).

(B) Where it can be demonstrated that the detection system activating the preaction system will cause water to be at the sprinklers when they operate, preaction systems shall be permitted to be treated as wet pipe systems.

If it can be demonstrated that a detection system activating the preaction system will cause water to be at the sprinklers when they operate, the wet system design criteria can be used. Preaction systems that perform to paragraph 12.3.2.2.3.5(B) are not considered dry systems.

12.3.2.2.3.6 The nominal diameter of branch line pipes (including riser nipples) shall meet the following:

(1) Pipe diameter shall not be not less than 1¼ in. (33 mm) nor greater than 2 in. (51 mm).
(2) Starter pieces shall be permitted to be 2½ in. (64 mm).
(3) Where branch lines are larger than 2 in. (51 mm), the sprinkler shall be supplied by a riser nipple to elevate the sprinkler 13 in. (330 mm) for 2½ in. (64-mm) pipe and 15 in. (380 mm) for 3-in. (76-mm) pipe. These dimensions are measured from the centerline of the pipe to the deflector. In lieu of this, sprinklers shall be permitted to be offset horizontally a minimum of 12 in. (305 mm).

The purpose of limiting the maximum diameter of branch lines or riser nipples, which is discussed in 12.3.2.2.3.6, is to minimize the effect of pipe shadow below the sprinkler. Pipe shadow can result in significant shielded or dry areas with reduced water application and loss of sprinkler water penetration.

12.3.2.2.3.7 Building steel shall not require special protection where Table 12.3.2.2.1(a) and Table 12.3.2.2.1(b) is applied as appropriate for the storage configuration.

12.3.2.3* Early Suppression Fast-Response (ESFR) Sprinklers for Rack Storage of Class I through Class IV Commodities Stored Up to and Including 25 ft (7.6 m) in Height.

 A.12.3.2.3 ESFR sprinklers are designed to respond quickly to growing fires and deliver heavy discharge to suppress fires rather than to control them. ESFR sprinklers should not be relied on to provide suppression if they are used outside the design parameters.

While these sprinklers are intended primarily for use in high-pile storage situations, this section permits their use and extension into adjacent portions of an occupancy that might have a lesser classification.

Storage in single-story or multistory buildings can be permitted, provided the maximum ceiling/roof height as specified in Chapter 12 is satisfied for each storage area.

Design parameters were determined from a series of full-scale fire tests that were conducted as a joint effort between Factory Mutual Research Corporation and the National Fire Protection Research Foundation. (Copies of the test reports are available from the NFPRF.)

Applications of ESFR sprinklers are described in 12.3.2.3. The special design approach for ESFR sprinklers is based on fire suppression by the first operating ring of ESFR sprinklers.

12.3.2.3.1 Protection of single-, double-, and multiple-row rack storage of Classes I through IV shall be in accordance with Table 12.3.2.3.1.

ESFR protection criteria are provided in Table 12.3.2.3.1, which addresses protection of palletized and solid-piled storage. ESFR sprinklers are also permitted to be utilized for protection of ordinary hazard occupancies and miscellaneous storage. The criteria in Table 12.3.2.3.1 have been expanded to permit broader applications of ESFR sprinkler technology based on large-scale test results reviewed by the Technical Committee on Sprinkler System Discharge Criteria. Design criteria for K-11.2, K-16.8 and K-25.2 ESFR sprinkler technology have been incorporated into the tables where test data supports such inclusion.

12.3.2.3.1.1 ESFR protection as defined shall not apply to the following:

(1) Rack storage involving solid shelves
(2) Rack storage involving combustible, open-top cartons or containers

12.3.2.3.2 Detection systems, concentrate pumps, generators, and other system components that are essential to the operation of the system shall have an approved standby power source.

After selecting the commodity, the ceiling height for ESFR protection is the most important factor when selecting the minimum operating pressure (see 12.3.2.3.2). ESFR performance is highly dependent on the ceiling/roof height. This is why averaging of ceiling/roof height based for pitched roofs is not acceptable; the maximum ceiling/roof height over the storage area being protected must be selected.

Where the ceiling/roof height falls above the selected criteria, the design criteria for the next higher ceiling/roof height must be chosen with a maximum ceiling/roof height limit of 45 ft as established by Table 12.3.2.3.1.

◀ **FAQ**
For ESFR applications where the ceiling/roof height falls between design criteria in Table 12.3.2.3.1, is it acceptable to interpolate the design criteria?

Additionally, verification that the maximum storage height does not exceed the value for the ceiling/roof height selected in Table 12.3.2.3.1 is also necessary. It is important to verify that the storage height does not exceed the maximum storage height for the maximum ceiling/roof height design selected from Table 12.3.2.3.1. Lower storage heights that result in greater commodity clearances within a given design are acceptable provided the ESFR design criteria from Table 12.3.2.3.1 are based upon the maximum ceiling/roof height.

12.3.2.3.3 ESFR sprinkler systems shall be designed such that the minimum operating pressure is not less than that indicated in Table 12.3.2.3.1 for type of storage, commodity, storage height, and building height involved.

12.3.2.3.4 The design area shall consist of the most hydraulically demanding area of 12 sprinklers, consisting of four sprinklers on each of three branch lines. The design shall include a minimum of 960 ft² (89 m²).

12.3.2.3.5 Where ESFR sprinklers are installed above and below obstructions, the discharge for up to two sprinklers for one of the levels shall be included with those of the other level in the hydraulic calculations.

Where additional ESFR sprinklers are added below obstructions, what is the total number of sprinklers that must be calculated?
◀ **FAQ**

Additional ESFR sprinklers installed below fixed obstructions as required by the obstruction rules in Chapter 8 must be included in the hydraulic calculations. Paragraph 12.3.2.3.5 requires that up to an additional two ESFR sprinklers that are located below obstructions be included with the 12 ESFR sprinkler calculations for a total of up to 14 ESFR sprinklers. This is a maximum of two additional ESFR sprinklers regardless of the number of ESFR sprinklers

TABLE 12.3.2.3.1 *ESFR Protection of Rack Storage without Solid Shelves of Class I through Class IV Commodities Stored Up to and Including 25 ft (7.6 m) in Height*

Storage Arrangement	Commodity	Maximum Storage Height ft	m	Maximum Ceiling/Roof Height ft	m	Nominal K-Factor	Orientation	Minimum Operating Pressure psi	bar	In-Rack Sprinkler Requirements	Hose Stream Demand gpm	L/min	Water Supply Duration (hours)
Single-row, double-row, and multiple-row rack (no open-top containers)	Class I, II, III, or IV, encapsulated or unencapsulated	20	6.1	25	7.6	11.2	Upright	50	3.4	No	250	946	1
						14.0	Upright or pendent	50	3.4	No			
						16.8	Pendent	35	2.4	No			
						25.2	Pendent	15	1.0	No			
				30	9.1	14.0	Upright or pendent	50	3.4	No			
						16.8	Pendent	35	2.4	No			
						25.2	Pendent	15	1.0	No			
				35	10.7	14.0	Upright or pendent	75	5.2	No			
						16.8	Pendent	52	3.6	No			
						25.2	Pendent	20	1.4	No			
				40	12.2	14.0	Pendent	75	5.2	No			
						16.8	Pendent	52	3.6	No			
						25.2	Pendent	25	1.7	No			
				45	13.7	14.0	Pendent	90	6.2	Yes			
						16.8	Pendent	64	4.4	Yes			
						25.2	Pendent	40	2.8	No			
		25	7.6	30	9.1	14.0	Upright or pendent	50	3.4	No			
						16.8	Pendent	35	2.4	No			
						25.2	Pendent	15	1.0	No			
				32	9.8	14.0	Upright or pendent	60	4.1	No			
						16.8	Pendent	42	2.9	No			
				35	10.7	14.0	Upright or pendent	75	5.2	No			
						16.8	Pendent	52	3.6	No			
						25.2	Pendent	20	1.4	No			
				40	12.2	14.0	Pendent	75	5.2	No			
						16.8	Pendent	52	3.6	No			
						25.2	Pendent	25	1.7	No			
				45	13.7	14.0	Pendent	90	6.2	Yes			
						16.8	Pendent	64	4.4	Yes			
						25.2	Pendent	40	2.8	No			

installed below obstructions in the remote area. Where only one additional ESFR sprinkler is needed to address an isolated obstruction, then only that one ESFR sprinkler would need to be added to the calculation. Care must be taken to identify the appropriate hydraulic remote area when such additional ESFR sprinklers are installed below fixed obstructions. The additional two ESFR sprinklers need only to be added to the 12 ESFR sprinkler demand directly above the obstruction when the combined number of sprinklers creates the hydraulically most demanding area.

12.3.2.4 In-Rack Sprinklers for Rack Storage of Class I through Class IV Commodities Stored Up to and Including 25 ft (7.6 m) in Height.

Paragraph 12.3.2.4 is intended to apply only to those rack storage arrangements that contain flue spaces in accordance with 12.3.1.13. Where an inadequate number or type of flue spaces is provided or where required flue spaces are obstructed, the criteria provided by 12.3.2.4 are unlikely to provide adequate protection and the provisions of 12.3.1.9 should be considered.

12.3.2.4.1 In-Rack Sprinkler Location for Rack Storage of Class I through Class IV Commodities Stored Up to and Including 25 ft (7.6 m) in Height.

In the testing on which this standard is based, where in-rack sprinklers were used, the sprinklers were typically installed above the top of a storage tier at transverse flues (see 12.3.2.4.1). Where multiple levels of in-rack sprinklers were used, in-rack sprinklers were usually staggered among transverse flues, except when barriers were provided.

12.3.2.4.1.1 In single- or double-row racks without solid shelves, in-rack sprinklers shall be installed in accordance with Table 12.3.2.1.2.

12.3.2.4.1.2 In multiple-row racks no deeper than 16 ft (4.9 m) with aisles 8 ft (2.4 m) or wider, in-rack sprinklers shall be installed in accordance with Table 12.3.2.1.3.

12.3.2.4.1.3 In multiple-row racks deeper than 16 ft (4.9 m) or with aisles less than 8 ft (2.4 m) wide, in-rack sprinklers shall be installed in accordance with Table 12.3.2.1.4.

12.3.2.4.1.4 In-rack sprinklers at one level only for storage up to and including 25 ft (7.6 m) high shall be located at the first tier level at or above one-half of the storage height.

Exhibit 12.7 illustrates the application of the placement requirement in 12.3.2.4.1.4.

EXHIBIT 12.7 *Positioning of One Level of In-Rack Sprinklers for Storage Heights Under 25 ft (7.6 m).*

12.3.2.4.1.5 In-rack sprinklers at two levels only for storage up to and including 25 ft (7.6 m) high shall be located at the first tier level at or above one-third and two-thirds of the storage height.

Exhibit 12.8 illustrates the application of the placement requirement in 12.3.2.4.1.5.

EXHIBIT 12.8 Positioning of Two Levels of In-Rack Sprinklers for Storage Heights Under 25 ft (7.6 m).

12.3.2.4.2 In-Rack Sprinkler Spacing for Rack Storage of Class I through Class IV Commodities Stored Up to and Including 25 ft (7.6 m) in Height.

12.3.2.4.2.1* Maximum horizontal spacing of in-rack sprinklers in single- or double-row racks with nonencapsulated storage up to and including 25 ft (7.6 m) in height shall be in accordance with Table 12.3.2.4.2.1. For encapsulated storage, maximum horizontal spacing shall be 8 ft (2.44 m).

 A.12.3.2.4.2.1 Spacing of sprinklers on branch lines in racks in the various tests demonstrates that maximum spacing as specified is proper.

TABLE 12.3.2.4.2.1 In-Rack Sprinkler Spacing for Class I, II, III, and IV Commodities Stored up to 25 ft (7.6 m) in Height

| Aisle Widths | | Commodity Class | | | | | |
| | | I and II | | III | | IV | |
ft	m	ft	m	ft	m	ft	m
8	2.4	12	3.7	12	3.7	8	2.4
4	1.2	12	3.7	8	2.4	8	2.4

12.3.2.4.2.2* Maximum horizontal spacing of in-rack sprinklers on branch lines, in multiple-row racks with encapsulated or nonencapsulated storage up to and including 25 ft (7.6 m) in height, shall not exceed 12 ft (3.7 m) for Class I, II, or III commodities and 8 ft (2.4 m) for Class IV commodities, with area limitations of 100 ft² (9.3 m²) per sprinkler for Class I, II, or III commodities and 80 ft² (7.4 m²) per sprinkler for Class IV commodities. The rack plan view shall be considered in determining the area covered by each sprinkler. The aisles shall not be included in area calculations.

 A.12.3.2.4.2.2 In-rack sprinklers at one level only for storage up to and including 25 ft (7.6 m) in multiple-row racks should be located at the tier level nearest one-half to two-thirds of the storage height.

12.3.2.4.2.3* The elevation of in-rack sprinkler deflectors with respect to storage shall not be a consideration in single- or double-row rack storage up to and including 20 ft (6.1 m) high. *(See Section C.16.)*

 A.12.3.2.4.2.3 Where possible, it is recommended that in-rack sprinkler deflectors be located at least 6 in. (152.4 mm) above pallet loads.

Where in-rack sprinklers are not located above the top of a storage tier, it is important that they be located at transverse flues (see 12.3.2.4.2.3). Tests were conducted with in-rack sprinklers located one-half the way up the load and between transverse flues. Although sprinkler discharge on top of a pallet load is more advantageous, water distributed to the side of a load would limit fire development up through the flue once the sprinklers activate.

12.3.2.4.2.4* In single- or double-row racks without solid shelves with storage over 20 ft (6.1 m) high, or in multiple-row racks, or in single- or double-row racks with solid shelves and storage height up to and including 25 ft (7.6 m), a minimum of 6-in. (152.4-mm) vertical clear space shall be maintained between the in-rack sprinkler deflectors and the top of a tier of storage. Sprinkler discharge shall not be obstructed by horizontal rack members.

A.12.3.2.4.2.4 Where possible, it is recommended that in-rack sprinklers be located away from rack uprights.

12.3.2.4.2.5 For multiple-row racks, a minimum of 6 in. (152.4 mm) shall be maintained between the in-rack sprinkler deflector and the top of a tier of storage.

12.3.2.4.2.6 Sprinklers installed in racks shall be spaced without regard to rack uprights. *(See Section C.17.)*

Although NFPA 13 does not prohibit in-rack sprinklers from being positioned near rack uprights, A.12.3.2.4.2.4 recommends that in-rack sprinklers be located away from rack uprights (see 12.3.2.4.2.6).

12.3.2.4.3 In-Rack Sprinkler Water Demand for Rack Storage of Class I through Class IV Commodities Stored Up to and Including 25 ft (7.6 m) in Height. *(See Section C.18.)*

12.3.2.4.3.1 The water demand for sprinklers installed in racks shall be based on simultaneous operation of the most hydraulically remote sprinklers as follows:

(1) Six sprinklers where only one level is installed in racks with Class I, Class II, or Class III commodities
(2) Eight sprinklers where only one level is installed in racks with Class IV commodities
(3) Ten sprinklers (five on each two top levels) where more than one level is installed in racks with Class I, Class II, or Class III commodities
(4) Fourteen sprinklers (seven on each two top levels) where more than one level is installed in racks with Class IV commodities

12.3.2.4.3.2 Where a storage rack, due to its length, requires less than the number of in-rack sprinklers specified in 12.3.2.4.3.1(1) through 12.3.2.4.3.1(4), only those in-rack sprinklers in a single rack need to be included in the calculation.

12.3.2.4.4 In-Rack Sprinkler Discharge Pressure for Rack Storage of Class I through Class IV Commodities Stored Up to and Including 25 ft (7.6 m) in Height. Sprinklers in racks shall discharge at not less than 15 psi (1 bar) for all classes of commodities. *(See Section C.19.)*

12.3.2.5 Special Design for Rack Storage of Class I through Class IV Commodities Stored Up to and Including 25 ft (7.6 m) in Height.

12.3.2.5.1 Slatted Shelves.

12.3.2.5.1.1* Slatted shelves shall be considered equivalent to solid shelves where the requirements of 12.3.2.5.1 are not met. *(See Section C.20.)*

A.12.3.2.5.1.1 Slatting of decks or walkways or the use of open grating as a substitute for automatic sprinkler thereunder is not acceptable.

In addition, where shelving of any type is employed, it is for the basic purpose of providing an intermediate support between the structural members of the rack. As a result, it becomes almost impossible to define and maintain transverse flue spaces across the rack as required.

12.3.2.5.1.2 A wet pipe system that is designed to provide a minimum of 0.6 gpm/ft^2 (24.5 mm/min) density over a minimum area of 2000 ft^2 (186 m^2) or K-14.0 ESFR sprinklers operating at a minimum of 50 psi (3.5 bar), K-16.8 sprinklers operating at a minimum of 32 psi (1.7 bar), or K-25.2 ESFR sprinklers operating at a minimum of 15 psi shall be permitted to protect single-row and double-row slatted-shelf racks where all of the following conditions are met:

(1) Sprinklers shall be K-11.2, K-14.0, or K-16.8 orifice spray sprinklers with a temperature rating of ordinary, intermediate, or high and shall be listed for storage occupancies or shall be K-14.0, K-16.8, or K-25.2 ESFR.
(2) The protected commodities shall be limited to Class I-IV, Group B plastics, Group C plastics, cartoned (expanded and unexpanded) Group A plastics, and exposed (unexpanded) Group A plastics.
(3) Shelves shall be slatted using a minimum nominal 2-in. (51-mm) thick by maximum nominal 6-in. (152-mm) wide slat held in place by spacers that maintain a minimum 2-in. (51-mm) opening between each slat.
(4) Where K-11.2, K-14.0, or K-16.8 orifice sprinklers are used, there shall be no slatted shelf levels in the rack above 12 ft (3.7 m). Wire mesh (greater than 50 percent opening) shall be permitted for shelf levels above 12 ft (3.7 m).
(5) Transverse flue spaces at least 3 in. (76 mm) wide shall be provided at least every 10 ft (3.1 m) horizontally.
(6) Longitudinal flue spaces at least 6 in. (152 mm) wide shall be provided for double-row racks. Longitudinal flue spaces shall not be required where ESFR sprinklers are used.
(7) The aisle widths shall be at least 7½ ft (2.3 m).
(8) The maximum roof height shall be 27 ft (8.2 m) or 30 ft where ESFR sprinklers are used.
(9) The maximum storage height shall be 20 ft (6.1 m).
(10) Solid plywood or similar materials shall not be placed on the slatted shelves so that they block the 2-in. (51-mm) spaces between slats, nor shall they be placed on the wire mesh shelves.

Paragraph 12.3.2.5.1.2 is the result of full-scale fire tests simulating the retail display of commodity stored on racks. Rack storage configurations used in the retail industry testing included more shelving at lower levels within the reach of consumers, and larger bulk storage, usually pallet loads, was included on the upper layers in a more traditional configuration.

12.3.2.5.2 High-Expansion Foam Ceiling Sprinkler Density. Where high-expansion foam systems are used in combination with ceiling sprinklers, the minimum ceiling sprinkler design density shall be 0.2 gpm/ft^2 (8.2 mm/min) for Class I, Class II, or Class III commodities or 0.25 gpm/ft^2 (10.2 mm/min) for Class IV commodities for the most hydraulically remote 2000-ft^2 (186-m^2) operating area.

12.3.2.5.2.1 Where high-expansion foam systems are used in combination with ceiling sprinklers, the maximum submergence time shall be 7 minutes for Class I, Class II, or Class III commodities and 5 minutes for Class IV commodities.

12.3.2.5.2.2* Where high-expansion foam systems are used without sprinklers, the maximum submergence time shall be 5 minutes for Class I, Class II, or Class III commodities and 4 minutes for Class IV commodities.

A **A.12.3.2.5.2.2** Where high-expansion foam is contemplated as the protection media, consideration should be given to possible damage to the commodity from soaking and corrosion. Consideration also should be given to the problems associated with the removal of the foam after discharge.

12.3.3 Protection Criteria for Rack Storage of Plastics Commodities Stored Up to and Including 25 ft (7.6 m) in Height.

12.3.3.1 Control Mode Density-Area Sprinkler Protection Criteria for Single-, Double-, and Multiple-Row Racks for Plastics Commodities Stored Up to and Including 25 ft (7.6 m) in Height, with Clearances Up to and Including 10 ft (3.1 m).

12.3.3.1.1 Plastic commodities shall be protected in accordance with Figure 12.3.3.1.1. This decision tree also shall be used to determine protection for commodities that are not entirely Group A plastics but contain such quantities and arrangements of Group A plastics that they are deemed more hazardous than Class IV commodities. The design criteria of 12.3.3.1 for single- and double-row rack storage of plastic commodities shall be applicable where aisles are 3.5 ft or greater in width. Storage with aisles less than 3.5 ft shall be protected as multiple-row rack storage. *(See Section C.21.)*

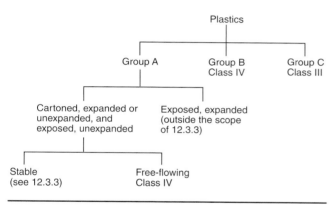

FIGURE 12.3.3.1.1 Decision Tree.

12.3.3.1.2* For the storage of Group A plastics stored 5 ft (1.5 m) or less in height, the sprinkler design criteria for miscellaneous storage specified in 12.1.10 shall be used.

A.12.3.3.1.2 All rack fire tests of plastics were run with an approximate 10-ft (3.1-m) maxi- mum clearance between the top of the storage and the ceiling sprinklers. Within 30-ft (9.1-m) high buildings, greater clearances above storage configurations should be compensated for by the addition of more in-rack sprinklers or the provision of greater areas of application, or both.

For storage of Group A plastic less than 5 ft (1.5 m), as addressed in 12.3.3.1.2, the protection criteria of 12.1.10 apply. The area of storage is not limited to the definition of miscellaneous storage for Group A plastic on racks less than 5 ft (1.5 m) in height. The remainder of 12.3.3 does not apply to storage that meets 12.3.3.1.2 and is considered miscellaneous plastics storage. See 12.1.10 for the design criteria.

12.3.3.1.3 Group B plastics and free-flowing Group A plastics shall be protected the same as Class IV commodities.

Small- and bench-scale testing of Group B plastics and large-scale testing of free-flowing Group A plastics show that Class IV commodity protection is adequate for this storage (see 12.3.3.1.3). See 12.3.2 for design criteria.

12.3.3.1.4 Group C plastics shall be protected the same as Class III commodities.

Bench-scale tests with Group C plastics and Class III commodities produced similar results as those described in the commentary to 12.3.3.1.3; they indicate that Class III protection is adequate for this storage (see 12.3.3.1.4). See 12.3.2 for design criteria.

Single-, double-, and multiple-row racks
0.30 gpm / ft² per 2000 ft²
(12.2 mm/min per 186 m²)

< 5-ft (1.5-m) ceiling clearance

Single-, double-, and multiple-row racks
0.45 gpm / ft² per 2000 ft²
(18.3 mm/min per 186 m²)

5-ft to 10-ft (1.5-m to 3.1-m) ceiling clearance

Plan View

Elevation View

Plan View

Elevation View

Note: Each square represents a storage cube measuring 4 ft to 5 ft (1.22 m to 1.53 m) on a side. Actual load heights can vary from approximately 18 in. (0.46 m) up to 10 ft (3.05 m). Therefore, there could be as few as one load or as many as six or seven loads between in-rack sprinklers that are spaced 10 ft (3.05 m) apart vertically.

FIGURE 12.3.3.1.5(a) *5-ft to 10-ft (1.5-m to 3-m) Storage.*

Single- and double-row racks
0.60 gpm / ft² per 2000 ft²
(24.5 mm/min per 186 m²)

5 ft to 10 ft (1.5 m to 3.1 m)
ceiling clearance
See 12.3.3.1.8, 12.3.3.1.10, and
Note 2

Single-, double-, and multiple-row racks
0.30 gpm / ft² per 2000 ft²
(12.2 mm/min per 186 m²)

5 ft to 10 ft (1.5 m to 3.1 m)
ceiling clearance
See Note 1

8 ft (2.44 m) maximum between sprinklers

Plan View

Elevation View

Plan View

Elevation View

Notes:

1. Single level of in-rack sprinklers [½ in. or ¹⁷⁄₃₂ in. (12.7 mm or 13.5 mm) operating at 15 psi (1.03 bar) minimum] installed as indicated in the transverse flue spaces.

2. Where sprinklers listed for storage use are installed at the ceiling only and the ceiling height in the protected area does not exceed 22 ft (6.7 m) and a minimum clearance of 7 ft (2.13 m), the ceiling sprinkler discharge criteria shall be permitted to be reduced to 0.45 gpm/ft² per 2000 ft² (18.3 mm/min per 186 m²).

3. Each square represents a storage cube measuring 4 ft to 5 ft (1.22 m to 1.53 m) on a side. Actual load heights can vary from approximately 18 in. (0.46 m) up to 10 ft (3.05 m). Therefore, there could be as few as one load or as many as six or seven loads between in-rack sprinklers that are spaced 10 ft (3.05 m) apart vertically.

FIGURE 12.3.3.1.5(b) *15-ft (4.6-m) Storage; Up to 10-ft (1.5-m to 3.1-m) Ceiling Clearance.*

Single- and double-row racks
0.60 gpm / ft² per 2000 ft²
(24.5 mm/min per 186 m²)

5 ft (1.5 m) ceiling clearance
See 12.3.3.1.8, 12.3.3.1.10

Single-, double-, and multiple-row racks
0.45 gpm / ft² per 2000 ft²
(18.3 mm/min per 186 m²)

5 ft (1.5 m) ceiling clearance
See Note 1

Single-, double-, and multiple-row racks
0.30 gpm / ft² per 2000 ft²
(12.2 mm/min per 186 m²)

5 ft (1.5 m) ceiling clearance
See Note 2

8 ft (2.44 m) maximum between sprinklers

8 ft (2.44 m) maximum between sprinklers

5 ft maximum

Plan View   **Plan View**   **Plan View**

Elevation View   **Elevation View**   **Elevation View**

Notes:

1. Single level of in-rack sprinklers [½ in. or ¹⁷⁄₃₂ in. (12.7 mm or 13.5 mm) operating at 15 psi (1.03 bar) minimum] installed as indicated in the transverse flue spaces.

2. Single level of in-rack sprinklers [¹⁷⁄₃₂ in. (13.5 mm) operating at 15 psi (1.03 bar) minimum or ½ in. (12.7 mm) operating at 30 psi (2.07 bar) minimum] installed on 4 ft to 5 ft (1.25 m to 1.56 m) spacings located, as indicated, in the longitudinal flue space at the intersection of every transverse flue space.

3. Each square represents a storage cube measuring 4 ft to 5 ft (1.22 m to 1.53 m) on a side. Actual load heights can vary from approximately 18 in. (0.46 m) up to 10 ft (3.05 m). Therefore, there could be as few as one load or as many as six or seven loads between in-rack sprinklers that are spaced 10 ft (3.05 m) apart vertically.

FIGURE 12.3.3.1.5(c) *20-ft (6.1-m) Storage; <5-ft (1.5-m) Ceiling Clearance.*

12.3.3.1.5 Ceiling Sprinkler Water Demand. For Group A plastic commodities in cartons, encapsulated or nonencapsulated in single-, double-, and multiple-row racks, ceiling sprinkler water demand in terms of density [gpm/ft² (mm/min)] and area of operation [ft² (m²)] shall be selected from Figure 12.3.3.1.5(a) through Figure 12.3.3.1.5(f). Linear interpolation of design densities and areas of application shall be permitted between storage heights with the same clearances. No interpolation between clearances shall be permitted. *(See Section C.22.)*

Ceiling sprinkler water demand is covered in 12.3.3.1.5. Unlike Class I through Class IV criteria, ceiling height and clearance from sprinklers to commodity play just as important a role as storage height. Strong fire plumes are expected in plastic protection, creating a heavier demand for greater commodity clearances resulting from higher ceilings. That is why interpolation is only allowed between storage heights with the same clearance.

For example, interpolating for an 18 ft (5.8 m) storage in a 24-ft (7.3-m) building is accomplished as follows:

1. 18 ft (5.8 m) storage in a 24-ft (7.3-m) building results in an actual 6-ft (1.8-m) clearance.
2. Figure 12.3.3.1.5(b) provides criteria for 15-ft (4.6-m) storage with 5-ft (1.5-m) to 10-ft (3.1-m) [which includes 6 ft (1.8m)] clearance. This is the first interpolation point.

0.45 gpm / ft² per 2000 ft²
(18.3 mm/min per 186 m²)

5 ft to 10 ft (1.5 m to 3.1 m) ceiling clearance
See Notes 1 and 5

8 ft (2.44 m) maximum between sprinklers

Plan View

Elevation View

0.30 gpm / ft² per 2000 ft²
(12.2 mm/min per 186 m²)

5 ft to 10 ft (1.5 m to 3.1 m) ceiling clearance
See Notes 2 and 3

8 ft (2.44 m) maximum between sprinklers

Plan View

Elevation View

0.30 gpm / ft² per 2000 ft²
(12.2 mm/min per 186 m²)

5 ft to 10 ft (1.5 m to 3.1 m) ceiling clearance
See Notes 2 and 3

8 ft (2.44 m) maximum between sprinklers

Plan View

Elevation View

0.30 gpm / ft² per 2000 ft²
(12.2 mm/min per 186 m²)

5 ft to 10 ft (1.5 m to 3.1 m) ceiling clearance
See Notes 2 and 4

8 ft (2.44 m) maximum between sprinklers

Plan View

Elevation View

Notes:

1. Single level of in-rack sprinklers [½ in. or ¹⁷⁄₃₂ in. (12.7 mm or 13.5 mm) operating at 15 psi (1.03 bar) minimum] installed as indicated in the transverse flue spaces.

2. Ceiling-only protection shall not be permitted for this storage configuration.

3. Two levels of in-rack sprinklers [½ in. or ¹⁷⁄₃₂ in. (12.7 mm or 13.5 mm) operating at 15 psi (1.03 bar) minimum] installed as indicated and staggered in the transverse flue space.

4. Single level of in-rack sprinklers [¹⁷⁄₃₂ in. (13.5 mm) operating at 15 psi (1.03 bar) minimum or ½ in. (12.7 mm) operating at 30 psi (2.07 bar) minimum] installed on 4 ft to 5 ft (1.25 m to 1.56 m) spacings located, as indicated, in the longitudinal flue space at the intersection of every transverse flue space.

5. Where K-11.2, K-14, K-16.8 spray sprinklers listed for storage use are installed at the ceiling, the in-rack sprinklers shall not be required, provided the ceiling sprinkler discharge criteria is increased to 0.6 gpm/ft² [24 (L/min)/m ²] over 2000 ft² (186 m²) and the ceiling height in the protected area does not exceed 27 ft (8.2 m).

6. Each square represents a storage cube measuring 4 ft to 5 ft (1.22 m to 1.53 m) on a side. Actual load heights can vary from approximately 18 in. (0.46 m) up to 10 ft (3.05 m). Therefore, there could be as few as one load or as many as six or seven loads between in-rack sprinklers that are spaced 10 ft (3.05 m) apart vertically.

FIGURE 12.3.3.1.5(d) *20-ft (6.1-m) Storage; 5-ft to 10-ft (1.5-m to 3.1-m) Ceiling Clearance.*

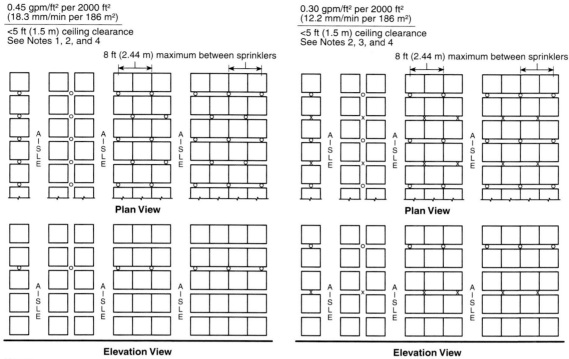

Notes:

1. Single level of in-rack sprinklers [$^{17}/_{32}$ in. (13.5 mm) operating at 15 psi (1.03 bar) minimum or ½ in. (12.7 mm) operating at 30 psi (2.07 bar) minimum] installed on 4 ft to 5 ft (1.25 m to 1.56 m) spacings located, as indicated, in the longitudinal flue space at the intersection of every transverse flue space.

2. Ceiling-only protection shall not be permitted for this storage configuration.

3. Two levels of in-rack sprinklers [½ in. or $^{17}/_{32}$ in. (12.7 mm or 13.5 mm) operating at 15 psi (1.03 bar) minimum] installed as indicated and staggered in the transverse flue space.

4. Where K-16.8 spray sprinklers listed for storage use are installed at the ceiling, the in-rack sprinklers shall not be required, provided the ceiling sprinklers criteria is increased to 0.8 gpm/ft² over 2000 ft² (32.6 mm/min over 186 m²) for wet systems and 4500 ft² (419 m²) for dry systems and the ceiling height in the protected area does not exceed 30 ft (9.1 m).

5. Each square represents a storage cube measuring 4 ft to 5 ft (1.22 m to 1.53 m) on a side. Actual load heights can vary from approximately 18 in. (0.46 m) up to 10 ft (3.05 m). Therefore, there could be as few as one load or as many as six or seven loads between in-rack sprinklers that are spaced 10 ft (3.05 m) apart vertically.

FIGURE 12.3.3.1.5(e) 25-ft (7.6-m) Storage; <5-ft (1.5-m) Ceiling Clearance. (See Note 2.)

3. Figure 12.3.3.1.5(d) provides the criteria for 20 ft (6.1 m) of storage with 5 ft (1.5 m) to 10 ft (3.1 m) (the same) clearance [a common error is to select 20 ft (6.1 m) of storage and a clearance of less than 5 ft (1.5 m) as the second point]. This is the second point used to interpolate.

4. Interpolate between the density for the 15-ft (4.6-m) and the 20-ft (6.-m) storage heights to determine the result for 18 ft (5.8 m).

12.3.3.1.6 Single-, Double-, and Multiple-Row Racks Up to 10-ft (3.1-m) Storage with Up to 10-ft (3.1-m) Clearance. The protection strategies utilizing only ceiling sprinklers, as shown in Figure 12.3.3.1.5(a), shall be acceptable for single-, double-, and multiple-row rack storage.

12.3.3.1.7 Single- and Double-Row Rack Storage Greater than 10 ft (3.1 m) Up to 15 ft (4.6 m) with Less than 5-ft (1.25-m) Clearance. The protection strategy utilizing only ceiling sprinklers, as shown in Figure 12.3.3.1.5(b), shall be acceptable only for single- and double-row rack storage.

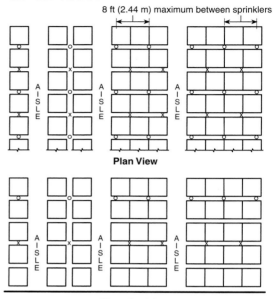

0.30 gpm/ft² per 2000 ft²
(12.2 mm/min per 186 m²)

5 ft to 10 ft (1.5 m to 3.1 m) ceiling clearance
See Notes 1, 2, and 3

8 ft (2.44 m) maximum between sprinklers

Plan View

Elevation View

Notes:

1. Two levels of in-rack sprinklers [½ in. or ¹⁷⁄₃₂ in. (12.7 mm or 13.5 mm) operating at 15 psi (1.03 bar) minimum] installed on 8 ft to 10 ft (2.5 m to 3.12 m) spacings located as indicated and staggered in the transverse flue space.

2. Ceiling-only protection shall not be permitted for this storage configuration.

3. Where K-16.8 spray sprinklers listed for storage use are installed at the ceiling, the in-rack sprinklers shall not be required, provided the ceiling sprinklers criteria is increased to 0.8 gpm/ft² over 2000 ft² (32.6 mm/min over 186 m²) for wet systems and 4500 ft² (419 m²) for dry systems and the ceiling height in the protected area does not exceed 30 ft (9.1 m).

4. Each square represents a storage cube measuring 4 ft to 5 ft (1.22 m to 1.53 m) on a side. Actual load heights can vary from approximately 18 in. (0.46 m) up to 10 ft (3.05 m). Therefore, there could be as few as one load or as many as six or seven loads between in-rack sprinklers that are spaced 10 ft (3.05 m) apart vertically.

FIGURE 12.3.3.1.5(f) *25-ft (7.6-m) Storage; 5-ft to 10-ft (1.5-m to 3.1-m) Ceiling Clearance. (See Note 2.)*

12.3.3.1.8 Single- and Double-Row Rack Storage Greater than 10 ft (3.1 m) Up to 15 ft (4.6 m) with Clearance from 5 ft to 10 ft (1.5 m to 3.1 m), and Single- and Double-Row Rack Storage Up to 20 ft (6.1 m) with Less than 5-ft (1.5-m) Clearance. The protection strategies utilizing only ceiling sprinklers, as shown in Figure 12.3.3.1.5(c) and Figure 12.3.3.1.5(d), shall be acceptable only for single- and double-row rack storage.

12.3.3.1.9 Multiple-Row Racks—15-ft (4.6-m) Storage with Less than 5-ft (1.5-m) Clearance. Where using the protection strategy utilizing only ceiling sprinklers, as shown in Figure 12.3.3.1.5(b), for multiple-row rack storage, the density to be used shall be 0.6 gpm/ft² (24.5 mm/min) over 2000 ft² (186 m²). The combination of ceiling and in-rack sprinklers specified in Figure 12.3.3.1.5(b) shall be permitted as an alternative.

12.3.3.1.10 Multiple-Row Racks—15-ft (4.6-m) Storage with 10-ft (3.1-m) Clearance, and 20-ft (6.1-m) Storage with Less than 5-ft (1.5-m) Clearance. The protection strategies utilizing only ceiling sprinklers, as shown in Figure 12.3.3.1.5(c) and Figure 12.3.3.1.5(d), shall not be permitted for multiple-row rack storage. Only the specified combinations of ceiling and in-rack sprinklers shall be used.

12.3.3.1.11* The minimum water supply requirements for a hydraulically designed occupancy hazard fire control sprinkler system shall be determined by adding the hose stream demand from Table 12.3.3.1.11 to the water supply for sprinklers determined in 12.3.3.1. This supply shall be available for the minimum duration specified in Table 12.3.3.1.11. *(See Section C.8.)*

A.12.3.3.1.11 Appropriate area/density, other design criteria, and water supply requirements should be based on scientifically based engineering analyses that can include submitted fire testing, calculations, or results from appropriate computational models.

Recommended water supplies anticipate successful sprinkler operation. Because of the small but still significant number of uncontrolled fires in sprinklered properties, which have various causes, there should be an adequate water supply available for fire department use.

12.3.3.1.11.1 An allowance for inside and outside hose shall not be required where tanks supply sprinklers only.

12.3.3.1.11.2 Where pumps taking suction from a private fire service main supply sprinklers only, the pump need not be sized to accommodate inside and outside hose. Such hose allowance shall be considered in evaluating the available water supplies.

12.3.3.2 Large Drop Sprinklers and Specific Application Control Mode Sprinklers for Rack Storage of Plastics Commodities Stored Up to and Including 25 ft (7.6 m) in Height.

The large drop sprinkler, which is covered in 12.3.3.2, is a specific application control mode technology as defined in this standard. The names have remained separate due to the long history of the name "large drop" and its relation to the nominal K-factor of 11.2. Applications of large drop sprinklers and specific application control mode sprinklers are described in 12.3.3.2. Listing of large drop sprinklers and control mode specific application sprinklers takes into consideration the ability of the sprinkler discharge pattern to penetrate a high-velocity fire plume. Only listed large drop and specific application control mode sprinklers are to be used in accordance with the special design approach of 12.3.3.2.

12.3.3.2.1 Protection of single-, double-, and multiple-row rack storage without solid shelves for unexpanded plastic commodities shall be in accordance with Table 12.3.3.2.1(a) and Table 12.3.3.2.1(b).

12.3.3.2.2 Where in-rack sprinklers are required by Table 12.3.3.2.1(a) and Table 12.3.3.2.1(b), in-rack sprinkler spacing, design pressure, and hydraulic calculation criteria shall be in accordance with the requirements of 12.3.2.4 as applicable for the commodity.

TABLE 12.3.3.1.11 Hose Stream Demand and Water Supply Duration Requirements for Rack Storage of Plastics Commodities Stored Up to and Including 25 ft (7.6 m) in Height

Commodity Classification	Storage Height		Inside Hose		Total Combined Inside and Outside Hose		Duration (minutes)
	ft	*m*	*gpm*	*L/min*	*gpm*	*L/min*	
Plastic	>5 up to 20	>1.5 up to 6.1	0, 50, or 100	0, 190, or 380	500	1900	120
	>20 up to 25	>6.1 up to 7.6	0, 50, or 100	0, 190, or 380	500	1900	150

TABLE 12.3.3.2.1(a) *Large Drop Sprinkler Design Criteria for Single-, Double-, and Multiple-Row Racks without Solid Shelves of Plastics Commodities Stored Up to and Including 25 ft (7.6 m) in Height*

Commodity Class	Nominal K-Factor	Maximum Storage Height		Maximum Ceiling/ Roof Height		Type of System	Number of Design Sprinklers/Minimum Pressure		Hose Stream Demand		Water Supply Duration (hours)
		ft	m	ft	m		/psi	/bar	gpm	L/min	
Cartoned or exposed unexpanded plastics	11.2	20	6.1	25	7.6	Wet	15/50	15/3.4	500	1900	2
						Dry	N/A	N/A	N/A	N/A	N/A
Cartoned or exposed unexpanded plastics	11.2	20	6.1	30	9.1	Wet	30/50	30/3.4	500	1900	2
						Dry	N/A	N/A	N/A	N/A	N/A
						Wet	20/75	20/5.2	500	1900	2
						Dry	N/A	N/A	N/A	N/A	N/A
Cartoned or exposed unexpanded plastics	11.2	25	7.6	30	9.1	Wet	15/50 + 1 level of in-rack	15/3.4 + 1 level of in-rack	500	1900	2
						Dry	N/A	N/A	N/A	N/A	N/A
Cartoned or exposed unexpanded plastics	11.2	25	7.6	35	10.7	Wet	30/50 + 1 level of in-rack	30/3.4 + 1 level of in-rack	500	1900	2
						Dry	N/A	N/A	N/A	N/A	N/A
						Wet	20/75 + 1 level of in-rack	20/5.2 + 1 level of in-rack	500	1900	2
						Dry	N/A	N/A	N/A	N/A	N/A

TABLE 12.3.3.2.1(b) *Specific Application Control Mode (16.8 K-factor) Sprinkler Design Criteria for Single-, Double-, and Multiple-Row Racks without Solid Shelves of Plastics Commodities Stored Up to and Including 25 ft (7.6 m) in Height*

Commodity Class	Maximum Storage Height		Maximum Building Height		Type of System	Number of Design Sprinklers by Minimum Operating Pressure		Hose Stream Demand		Water Supply Duration (hours)
	ft	m	ft	m		10 psi (0.7 bar)	22 psi (1.5 bar)	gpm	L/min	
Cartoned or exposed unexpanded plastics	25	7.6	30	9.1	Wet	—	15	500	1900	2

12.3.3.2.3 Protection shall be provided as specified in Table 12.3.3.2.1(a) and Table 12.3.3.2.1(b) or appropriate NFPA standards in terms of minimum operating pressure and the number of sprinklers to be included in the design area.

12.3.3.2.3.1 For design purposes, 95 psi (6.6 bar) shall be the maximum discharge pressure at the hydraulically most remote sprinkler.

Discharge pressures in excess of 95 psi (6.6 bar) negatively impact the sprinkler's discharge pattern and droplet size, which is the reason for the requirement in 12.3.3.2.3.1.

12.3.3.2.3.2 Open Wood Joist Construction.

(A) Where large drop K-11.2 sprinklers are installed under open wood joist construction, their minimum operating pressure shall be 50 psi (3.4 bar).

(B) Where each joist channel of open, wood joist construction is fully fire-stopped to its full depth at intervals not exceeding 20 ft (6.1 m), the lower pressures specified in Table 12.3.3.2.1(a) shall be permitted to be used.

12.3.3.2.3.3 The design area shall be a rectangular area having a dimension parallel to the branch lines at least 1.2 times the square root of the area protected by the number of sprinklers to be included in the design area. Any fractional sprinkler shall be included in the design area.

Starting with the 1996 edition, NFPA 13 provided more information about the shape of the design area where large drop sprinklers are used (see 12.3.3.2.3.3). Although earlier editions implied that the design area was to be a rectangular shape having a dimension parallel to the branch lines of at least 1.2 times the square root of the area protected by the number of sprinklers, it was not explicitly stated.

12.3.3.2.3.4 Hose stream demand and water supply duration requirements shall be in accordance with those for extra hazard occupancies in Table 12.3.3.2.1(a) and Table 12.3.3.2.1(b).

12.3.3.2.3.5 Preaction Systems.

(A) For the purpose of using Table 12.3.3.2.1(a) and Table 12.3.3.2.1(b), preaction systems shall be classified as dry pipe systems.

Paragraph 12.3.3.2.3.5(A) requires that all preaction systems be treated as dry pipe sprinkler systems when applying the requirements of Table 12.3.3.2.1(a) and Table 12.3.3.2.1(b).

◀ **FAQ**
For large drop and specific application control mode sprinklers, are all types of preaction systems treated as dry pipe systems?

(B) Where it can be demonstrated that the detection system activating the preaction system will cause water to be at the sprinklers when they operate, preaction systems shall be permitted to be treated as wet pipe systems.

◀ **FAQ**
For large drop and specific application control mode sprinklers, are preaction systems always treated as dry pipe systems?

If it can be demonstrated that a detection system activating the preaction system will cause water to be at the sprinklers when they operate, the wet system design criteria can be used. Preaction systems that perform to Paragraph 12.3.3.2.3.5(B) are not considered dry systems.

12.3.3.2.3.6 The nominal diameter of branch line pipes (including riser nipples) shall meet the following:

(1) Pipe diameter shall not be not less than 1¼ in. (33 mm) nor greater than 2 in. (51 mm).
(2) Starter pieces shall be permitted to be 2½ in. (64 mm).
(3) Where branch lines are larger than 2 in. (51 mm), the sprinkler shall be supplied by a riser nipple to elevate the sprinkler 13 in. (330 mm) for 2½-in. (64-mm) pipe and 15 in. (380 mm) for 3-in. (76-mm) pipe. These dimensions are measured from the centerline of the pipe to the deflector. In lieu of this, sprinklers shall be permitted to be offset horizontally a minimum of 12 in. (305 mm).

The purpose of limiting the maximum diameter of branch lines or riser nipples, as discussed in 12.3.3.2.3.6, is to minimize the effect of pipe shadow below the sprinkler. Pipe shadow can result in significant shielded or dry areas with reduced water application and loss of sprinkler water penetration.

12.3.3.2.3.7 Building steel shall not require special protection where Table 12.3.3.2.1(a) and Table 12.3.3.2.1(b) is applied as appropriate for the storage configuration.

12.3.3.3* Early Suppression Fast-Response (ESFR) Sprinklers for Rack Storage of Plastics Commodities Stored Up to and Including 25 ft (7.6 m) in Height.

A.12.3.3.3 ESFR sprinklers are designed to respond quickly to growing fires and deliver heavy discharge to suppress fires rather than to control them. ESFR sprinklers should not be relied on to provide suppression if they are used outside the design parameters.

While these sprinklers are intended primarily for use in high-pile storage situations, this section permits their use and extension into adjacent portions of an occupancy that might have a lesser classification.

Storage in single-story or multistory buildings can be permitted, provided the maximum ceiling/roof height as specified in Chapter 12 is satisfied for each storage area.

Design parameters were determined from a series of full-scale fire tests that were conducted as a joint effort between Factory Mutual Research Corporation and the National Fire Protection Research Foundation. (Copies of the test reports are available from the NFPRF.)

Applications of ESFR sprinklers are described in 12.3.3.3. The special design approach for ESFR sprinklers is based on fire suppression by the first operating ring of sprinklers.

12.3.3.3.1 Protection of single-, double-, and multiple-row rack storage of cartoned or uncartoned unexpanded plastic and cartoned expanded plastic shall be in accordance with Table 12.3.3.3.1.

ESFR protection criteria are provided in Table 12.3.3.3.1, which addresses protection of palletized and solid-piled storage. ESFR sprinklers are also permitted to be utilized for protection of ordinary hazard occupancies and miscellaneous storage. The criteria in Table 12.3.3.3.1 have been expanded to permit broader applications of ESFR sprinkler technology based on large-scale test results reviewed by the Technical Committee on Sprinkler System Discharge Criteria. Design criteria for K-11.2, K-16.8, and K-25.2 ESFR sprinkler technology have been incorporated into the tables where test data supports such inclusion.

12.3.3.3.1.1 ESFR protection as defined shall not apply to the following:

(1) Rack storage involving solid shelves
(2) Rack storage involving combustible, open-top cartons or containers

12.3.3.3.2 ESFR sprinkler systems shall be designed such that the minimum operating pressure is not less than that indicated in Table 12.3.3.3.1 for type of storage, commodity, storage height, and building height involved.

After selecting the commodity, the ceiling height for ESFR protection is the most important factor when selecting the minimum operating pressure (see 12.3.3.3.2). ESFR performance is highly dependent on the ceiling/roof height. This is why averaging of ceiling/roof height based for pitched roofs is not acceptable; the maximum ceiling/roof height over the storage area being protected must be selected.

FAQ ▶

For ESFR applications where the ceiling/roof height falls between design criteria in Table 12.3.3.3.1, is it acceptable to interpolate the design criteria?

Where the ceiling/roof height falls above the selected criteria, the design criteria for the next higher ceiling/roof height must be chosen with a maximum ceiling/roof height limit of 45 ft as established by Table 12.3.3.3.1.

Additionally, verification that the maximum storage height does not exceed the value for the ceiling/roof height selected in Table 12.3.3.3.1 is also necessary. It is important to verify that the storage height does not exceed the maximum storage height for the maximum ceiling/roof height design selected from Table 12.3.3.3.1. Lower storage heights that result in greater commodity clearances within a given design are acceptable provided the ESFR design criteria from Table 12.3.3.3.1 is based upon the maximum ceiling/roof height.

TABLE 12.3.3.3.1 *ESFR Protection of Rack Storage without Solid Shelves of Plastics Commodities Stored Up to and Including 25 ft (7.6 m) in Height*

Storage Arrangement	Commodity	Maximum Storage Height ft	Maximum Storage Height m	Maximum Ceiling/ Roof Height ft	Maximum Ceiling/ Roof Height m	Nominal K-Factor	Orientation	Minimum Operating Pressure psi	Minimum Operating Pressure bar	In-Rack Sprinkler Requirements	Hose Stream Demand gpm	Hose Stream Demand L/min	Water Supply Duration (hours)
Single-row, double-row and multiple-row rack (no open-top containers)	Cartoned unexpanded	20	6.1	25	7.6	11.2	Upright	50	3.4	No	250	946	1
						14.0	Upright or pendent	50	3.4	No			
						16.8	Pendent	35	2.4	No			
						25.2	Pendent	15	1.0	No			
				30	9.1	14.0	Upright or pendent	50	3.4	No			
						16.8	Pendent	35	2.4	No			
						25.2	Pendent	15	1.0	No			
				35	10.7	14.0	Upright or pendent	75	5.2	No			
						16.8	Pendent	52	3.6	No			
						25.2	Pendent	20	1.4	No			
				40	12.2	14.0	Pendent	75	5.2	No			
						16.8	Pendent	52	3.6	No			
						25.2	Pendent	25	1.7	No			
				45	13.7	14.0	Pendent	90	6.2	Yes			
						16.8	Pendent	63	4.3	Yes			
						25.2	Pendent	40	2.8	No			
		25	7.6	30	9.1	14.0	Upright or pendent	50	3.4	No			
						16.8	Pendent	35	2.4	No			
						25.2	Pendent	15	1.0	No			
				32	9.8	14.0	Upright or pendent	60	4.1	No			
						16.8	Pendent	42	2.9	No			
				35	10.7	14.0	Upright or pendent	75	5.2	No			
						16.8	Pendent	52	3.6	No			
						25.2	Pendent	20	1.4	No			
				40	12.2	14.0	Pendent	75	5.2	No			
						16.8	Pendent	52	3.6	No			
						25.2	Pendent	25	1.7	No			
				45	13.7	14.0	Pendent	90	6.2	Yes			
						16.8	Pendent	63	4.3	Yes			
						25.2	Pendent	40	2.8	No			

(Continues)

TABLE 12.3.3.3.1 *Continued*

Storage Arrangement	Commodity	Maximum Storage Height		Maximum Ceiling/ Roof Height		Nominal K-Factor	Orientation	Minimum Operating Pressure		In-Rack Sprinkler Requirements	Hose Stream Demand		Water Supply Duration (hours)
		ft	m	ft	m			psi	bar		gpm	L/min	
Single-row, double-row and multiple-row rack (no open-top containers)	Exposed unexpanded	20	6.1	25	7.6	14.0	Pendent	50	3.4	No	250	946	1
						16.8	Pendent	35	2.4	No			
				30	9.1	14.0	Pendent	50	3.4	No			
						16.8	Pendent	35	2.4	No			
				35	10.7	14.0	Pendent	75	5.2	No			
						16.8	Pendent	52	3.6	No			
				40	12.2	14.0	Pendent	75	5.2	No			
						16.8	Pendent	52	3.6	No			
				45	13.7	14.0	Pendent	90	6.2	Yes			
						16.8	Pendent	63	4.3	Yes			
		25	7.6	30	9.1	14	Pendent	50	3.4	No			
						16.8	Pendent	35	2.4	No			
				32	9.8	14.0	Pendent	60	4.1	No			
						16.8	Pendent	42	2.9	No			
				35	10.7	14.0	Pendent	75	5.2	No			
						16.8	Pendent	52	3.6	No			
				40	12.2	14.0	Pendent	75	5.2	No			
						16.8	Pendent	52	3.6	No			
				45	13.7	14.0	Pendent	90	6.2	Yes			
						16.8	Pendent	63	4.3	Yes			
	Cartoned expanded	20	6.1	25	7.6	14.0	Upright or pendent	50	3.4	No			
						16.8	Pendent	35	2.4	No			
				30	9.1	14.0	Upright or pendent	50	3.4	No			
						16.8	Pendent	35	2.4	No			
		25	7.6	30	9.1	14.0	Upright or pendent	50	3.4	No			
						16.8	Pendent	35	2.4	No			
				32	9.8	14.0	Pendent	60	4.1	No			
						16.8	Pendent	42	2.9	No			

12.3.3.3.3 The design area shall consist of the most hydraulically demanding area of 12 sprinklers, consisting of four sprinklers on each of three branch lines. The design shall include a minimum of 960 ft² (89 m²).

12.3.3.3.4 Where ESFR sprinklers are installed above and below obstructions, the discharge for up to two sprinklers for one of the levels shall be included with those of the other level in the hydraulic calculations.

Additional ESFR sprinklers installed below fixed obstructions as required by the obstruction rules in Chapter 8 must be included in the hydraulic calculations. Paragraph 12.3.3.3.4 requires that up to an additional two ESFR sprinklers that are located below obstructions be included with the 12 ESFR sprinkler calculations for a total of up to 14 ESFR sprinklers. This is a maximum of two additional ESFR sprinklers regardless of the number of ESFR sprinklers installed below obstructions in the remote area. Where only one additional ESFR sprinkler is needed to address an isolated obstruction, then only that ESFR sprinkler would need to be added to the calculation. Care must be taken to identify the appropriate hydraulic remote area when such additional ESFR sprinklers are installed below fixed obstructions. The additional two ESFR sprinklers need only to be added to the 12 ESFR sprinkler demand directly above the obstruction when the combined number of sprinklers creates the hydraulically most demanding area.

◀ **FAQ**
Where additional ESFR sprinklers are added below obstructions, what is the total number of sprinklers that must be calculated?

12.3.3.4 In-Rack Sprinklers for Rack Storage of Plastics Commodities Stored Up to and Including 25 ft (7.6 m) in Height.

12.3.3.4.1 In-Rack Sprinkler Location for Rack Storage of Plastics Commodities Stored Up to and Including 25 ft (7.6 m) in Height. In-rack sprinklers shall be installed in accordance with Figure 12.3.3.1.5(a) through Figure 12.3.3.1.5(f).

In the testing on which this standard is based (see Annex C), where in-rack sprinklers were used, the sprinklers were typically installed above the top of a storage tier at transverse flues (see 12.3.3.4.1). Where multiple levels of in-rack sprinklers were used, in-rack sprinklers were usually staggered among transverse flues, except when barriers were provided.

Paragraph 12.3.3.4.1 is intended to apply only to those rack storage arrangements that contain flue spaces in accordance with 12.3.1.13. Where an inadequate number or type of flue spaces is provided or where required flue spaces are obstructed, the criteria provided by 12.3.3.4.1 are unlikely to provide adequate protection, and the provisions of 12.3.1.9 should be considered.

12.3.3.4.2 In-Rack Sprinkler Spacing for Rack Storage of Plastics Commodities Stored Up to and Including 25 ft (7.6 m) in Height.

12.3.3.4.2.1 In-Rack Sprinkler Clearance. The minimum of 6-in. (152.4-mm) vertical clear space shall be maintained between the sprinkler deflectors and the top of a tier of storage.

12.3.3.4.2.2 The spacing of in-rack sprinklers shall be in accordance with Figure 12.3.3.1.5(a) and Figure 12.3.3.1.5(f).

12.3.3.4.3 In-Rack Sprinkler Water Demand for Rack Storage of Plastics Commodities Stored Up to and Including 25 ft (7.6 m) in Height. The water demand for sprinklers installed in racks shall be based on simultaneous operation of the most hydraulically remote sprinklers as follows:

(1) Eight sprinklers where only one level is installed in racks
(2) Fourteen sprinklers (seven on each top two levels) where more than one level is installed in racks

12.3.3.4.4 In-Rack Sprinkler Discharge Pressure for Rack Storage of Plastics Commodities Stored Up to and Including 25 ft (7.6 m) in Height. Sprinklers in racks shall discharge at not less than 15 psi (1 bar) for all classes of commodities. *(See Section C.19.)*

12.3.3.5 Special Design for Rack Storage of Plastics Commodities Stored Up to and Including 25 ft (7.6 m) in Height.

12.3.3.5.1 Slatted Shelves.

12.3.3.5.1.1* Slatted shelves shall be considered equivalent to solid shelves where the requirements of 12.3.3.5.1 are not met. *(See Section C.20.)*

A.12.3.3.5.1.1 Slatting of decks or walkways or the use of open grating as a substitute for automatic sprinkler thereunder is not acceptable.

In addition, where shelving of any type is employed, it is for the basic purpose of providing an intermediate support between the structural members of the rack. As a result, it becomes almost impossible to define and maintain transverse flue spaces across the rack as required.

12.3.3.5.1.2 A wet pipe system that is designed to provide a minimum of 0.6 gpm/ft^2 (24.5 mm/min) density over a minimum area of 2000 ft^2 (186 m^2) or K-14.0 ESFR sprinklers operating at a minimum of 50 psi (3.5 bar), K-16.8 sprinklers operating at a minimum of 32 psi (1.7 bar), or K-25.2 ESFR sprinklers operating at a minimum of 15 psi shall be permitted to protect single-row and double-row slatted-shelf racks where all of the following conditions are met:

(1)   Sprinklers shall be K-11.2, K-14.0, or K-16.8 orifice spray sprinklers with a temperature rating of ordinary, intermediate, or high and shall be listed for storage occupancies or shall be K-14.0, K-16.8, or K-25.2 ESFR.

(2)   The protected commodities shall be limited to Class I-IV, Group B plastics, Group C plastics, cartoned (expanded and unexpanded) Group A plastics, and exposed (unexpanded) Group A plastics.

(3)   Shelves shall be slatted using a minimum nominal 2-in. (51-mm) thick by maximum nominal 6-in. (152-mm) wide slat held in place by spacers that maintain a minimum 2-in. (51-mm) opening between each slat.

(4)   Where K-11.2, K-14.0, or K-16.8 orifice sprinklers are used, there shall be no slatted shelf levels in the rack above 12 ft (3.7 m). Wire mesh (greater than 50 percent opening) shall be permitted for shelf levels above 12 ft (3.7 m).

(5)   Transverse flue spaces at least 3 in. (76 mm) wide shall be provided at least every 10 ft (3.1 m) horizontally.

(6)   Longitudinal flue spaces at least 6 in. (152 mm) wide shall be provided for double-row racks. Longitudinal flue spaces shall not be required when ESFR sprinklers are used.

(7)   The aisle widths shall be at least 7½ ft (2.3 m).

(8)   The maximum roof height shall be 27 ft (8.2 m) or 30 ft where ESFR sprinklers are used.

(9)   The maximum storage height shall be 20 ft (6.1 m).

(10)   Solid plywood or similar materials shall not be placed on the slatted shelves so that they block the 2-in. (51-mm) spaces between slats, nor shall they be placed on the wire mesh shelves.

Paragraph 12.3.3.5.1.2 is the result of full-scale fire tests simulating the retail display of commodity stored on racks. Rack storage configurations used in the retail industry testing included more shelving at lower levels within the reach of consumers, and larger bulk storage, usually pallet loads, was included on the upper layers in a more traditional configuration.

12.3.4 Protection Criteria for Rack Storage of Class I through Class IV Commodities Stored Over 25 ft (7.6 m) in Height.

12.3.4.1 Control Mode Density-Area Sprinkler Protection Criteria for Rack Storage of Class I through Class IV Commodities Stored Over 25 ft (7.6 m) in Height.

Control mode density/area sprinklers used for the protection of storage that exceeds 25 ft (7.6 m), which are discussed in 12.3.4.1, are primarily used to protect the commodity between the top level of required in-rack protection and the top of storage. In addition, ceiling cooling and structural protection is provided. The in-rack protection is expected to control the growth and spread of fire within the rack structure at the lower levels, which is why there is no variation of the ceiling density for the protection of 30 ft (9.4 m) of storage as compared to 75 ft (22.9 m) of storage.

12.3.4.1.1* For single- and double-row racks, the water demand for nonencapsulated storage without solid shelves separated by aisles at least 4 ft (1.2 m) wide and with not more than 10 ft (3.1 m) between the top of storage and the sprinklers shall be based on sprinklers in a 2000-ft^2 (186-m^2) operating area, discharging a minimum of 0.25 gpm/ft^2 (10.2 mm/min) for Class I commodities, 0.3 gpm/ft^2 (12.2 mm/min) for Classes II and III commodities, and 0.35 gpm/ft^2 (14.3 mm/min) for Class IV commodities for ordinary temperature–rated sprinklers or a minimum of 0.35 gpm/ft^2 (14.3 mm/min) for Class I commodities, 0.4 gpm/ft^2 (16.3 mm/min) for Classes II and III commodities, and 0.45 gpm/ft^2 (18.3 mm/min) for Class IV commodities for high temperature–rated sprinklers. *(See Table 12.3.4.1.1 and Section C.23.)*

A.12.3.4.1.1 Water demand for storage height over 25 ft (7.6 m) on racks without solid shelves separated by aisles at least 4 ft (1.2 m) wide and with more than 10 ft (3.1 m) between the top of storage and the sprinklers should be based on sprinklers in a 2000-ft^2 (186-m^2) operating area for double-row racks and a 3000-ft^2 (278.7-m^2) operating area for multiple-row racks discharging a minimum of 0.18 gpm/ft^2 (7.33 mm/min) for Class I commodities, 0.21 gpm/ft^2 (8.56 mm/min) for Classes II and III commodities, and 0.25 gpm/ft^2 (10.2 mm/min) for Class IV commodities for ordinary temperature–rated sprinklers or a minimum of 0.25 gpm/ft^2 (10.2 mm/min) for Class I commodities, 0.28 gpm/ft^2 (11.41 mm/min) for Classes II and III commodities, and 0.32 gpm/ft^2 (13.04 mm/min) for Class IV commodities for high temperature–rated sprinklers. *(See A.12.3.1.12 and A.12.3.4.4.1.3.)*

Where such storage is encapsulated, ceiling sprinkler density should be 25 percent greater than for nonencapsulated storage.

Data indicate that the sprinkler protection criteria in 12.3.4.1.1 is ineffective, by itself, for rack storage with solid shelves, if the required flue spaces are not maintained. Use of 12.3.4.1.1, along with the additional provisions that are required by this standard, can provide acceptable protection.

12.3.4.1.2 Where storage as described in 12.3.4.1.1 is encapsulated, ceiling sprinkler density shall be 25 percent greater than for nonencapsulated storage.

12.3.4.1.3 For multiple-row racks, the water demand for nonencapsulated storage without solid shelves separated by aisles at least 4 ft (1.2 m) wide and with not more than 10 ft (3.1 m) between the top of storage and the sprinklers shall be based on sprinklers in a 2000-ft^2 (186-m^2) operating area for multiple-row racks, discharging a minimum of 0.25 gpm/ft^2 (10.2 mm/min) for Class I commodities, 0.3 gpm/ft^2 (12.2 mm/min) for Classes II and III commodities, and 0.35 gpm/ft^2 (14.3 mm/min) for Class IV commodities for ordinary temperature–rated sprinklers or a minimum of 0.35 gpm/ft^2 (14.3 mm/min) for Class I commodities, 0.4 gpm/ft^2 (16.3 mm/min) for Classes II and III commodities, and 0.45 gpm/ft^2 (18.3 mm/min) for Class IV commodities for high temperature–rated sprinklers. *(See Table 12.3.4.1.3.)*

12.3.4.1.4 Where such storage is encapsulated, ceiling sprinkler density shall be 25 percent greater than for nonencapsulated storage.

12.3.4.1.5 The minimum water supply requirements for a hydraulically designed occupancy hazard fire control sprinkler system shall be determined by adding the hose stream demand from Table 12.3.4.1.5 to the water supply for sprinklers determined in 12.3.4. This supply shall be available for the minimum duration specified in Table 12.3.4.1.5.

TABLE 12.3.4.1.1 *Double-Row Racks without Solid Shelves, of Class I through Class IV Commodities Stored Over 25 ft (7.6 m) in Height, Aisles 4 ft (1.2 m) or Wider*

Commodity Class	In-Rack Sprinklers Approximate Vertical Spacing at Tier Nearest the Vertical Distance and Maximum Horizontal Spacing[1,2,3] — Longitudinal Flue[4]	Face[5,6]	Figure	Maximum Storage Height	Stagger	Ceiling Sprinkler Operating Area — ft²	m²	Ceiling Sprinkler Density Clearance up to 10 ft (3.1 m)[7,8,9] — Ordinary Temperature — gpm/ft²	mm/min	High Temperature — gpm/ft²	mm/min
I	Vertical 20 ft (6.1 m) Horizontal 10 ft (3.1 m) under horizontal barriers	None	12.3.4.4.1.1(a)	30 ft (9.1 m)	No			0.25	10.2	0.35	14.3
	Vertical 20 ft (6.1 m) Horizontal 10 ft (3.1 m)	Vertical 20 ft (6.1 m) Horizontal 10 ft (3.1 m)	12.3.4.4.1.1(b)	Higher than 25 ft (7.6 m)	Yes	2000	186	0.25	10.2	0.35	14.3
I, II, III	Vertical 10 ft (3.1 m) or at 15 ft (4.6 m) and 25 ft (7.6 m)	None	12.3.4.4.1.1(c)	30 ft (9.1 m)	Yes			0.3	12.2	0.4	16.3
	Vertical 10 ft (3.1 m) Horizontal 10 ft (3.1 m)	Vertical 30 ft (9.1 m) Horizontal 10 ft (3.1 m)	12.3.4.4.1.1(d)		Yes			0.3	12.2	0.4	16.3
	Vertical 20 ft (6.1 m) Horizontal 10 ft (3.1 m)	Vertical 20 ft (6.1 m) Horizontal 5 ft (1.5 m)	12.3.4.4.1.1(e)		Yes			0.3	12.2	0.4	16.3
	Vertical 25 ft (7.6 m) Horizontal 5 ft (1.5 m)	Vertical 25 ft (7.6 m) Horizontal 5 ft (1.5 m)	12.3.4.4.1.1(f)	Higher than 25 ft. (7.6 m)	No	2000	186	0.3	12.2	0.4	16.3
	Horizontal barriers at 20 ft (6.1 m) Vertical intervals—two lines of sprinklers under barriers—maximum horizontal spacing 10 ft (3.1 m), staggered		12.3.4.4.1.1(g)		Yes			0.3	12.2	0.4	16.3
I, II, III, IV	Vertical 15 ft (4.6 m) Horizontal 10 ft (3.1 m)	Vertical 20 ft (6.1 m) Horizontal 10 ft (3.1 m)	12.3.4.4.1.1(h)		Yes			0.35	14.3	0.45	18.3
	Vertical 20 ft (6.1 m) Horizontal 5 ft (1.5 m)	Vertical 20 ft (6.1 m) Horizontal 5 ft (1.5 m)	12.3.4.4.1.1(i)	Higher than 25 ft (7.6 m)	No	2000	186	0.35	14.3	0.45	18.3
	Horizontal barriers at 15 ft (4.6 m) Vertical intervals—two lines of sprinklers under barriers—maximum horizontal spacing 10 ft (3.1 m), staggered		12.3.4.4.1.1(j)		Yes			0.35	14.3	0.45	18.3

[1]Minimum in-rack sprinkler discharge, 30 gpm (114 L/min).

[2]Water shields required.

[3]All in-rack sprinkler spacing dimensions start from the floor.

[4]Install sprinklers at least 3 in. (76.2 mm) from uprights.

[5]Face sprinklers shall not be required for a Class I commodity consisting of non-combustible products on wood pallets (without combustible containers), except for arrays shown in Figure 12.3.4.4.1.1(g) and Figure 12.3.4.4.1.1(j).

[6]In Figure 12.3.4.4.1.1(a) through Figure 12.3.4.4.1.1(j), each square represents a storage cube that measures 4 ft to 5 ft (1.2 m to 1.5 m) on a side. Actual load heights can vary from approximately 18 in. to 10 ft (0.46 m to 3.1 m). Therefore, there can be one load to six or seven loads between in-rack sprinklers that are spaced 10 ft (3.1 m) apart vertically.

[7]For encapsulated commodity, increase density 25 percent.

[8]Clearance is distance between top of storage and ceiling.

[9]See A.12.3.1.12 for protection recommendations where clearance is greater than 10 ft (3.1 m).

TABLE 12.3.4.1.3 Multiple-Row Racks, of Class I through Class IV Commodities Stored Over 25 ft (7.6 m) in Height

Commodity Class	Encapsulated	In-Rack Sprinklers[1,2,3] Approximate Vertical Spacing ft	m	Maximum Horizontal Spacing in A Flue ft	m	Maximum Horizontal Spacing across Flue ft	m	Height Limit (ft)	Stagger	Figure	Maximum Spacing from Top of Storage to Highest In-Rack Sprinklers ft	m	Ceiling Sprinkler Operating Area ft²	m²	Ceiling Sprinklers Density 165° Rating gpm/ft²	mm/min	286° Rating gpm/ft²	mm/min
I	No	20	6.1	12	3.7	10	3.1			12.3.4.4.1.3(a)	10	3.1			0.25	10.2	0.35	14.3
	Yes														0.31		0.44	
I, II, and III	No	15	4.6	10	3.1	10	3.1	None	Between adjacent flues	12.3.4.4.1.3(b)	10	3.1	2000	186	0.30	12.2	0.40	16.3
	Yes														0.37		0.50	20.4
I, II, III, and IV	No	10	3.1	10	3.1	10	3.1			12.3.4.4.1.3(c)	5	1.5			0.35	14.3	0.45	18.3
	Yes														0.44		0.56	

Notes: For SI units, °C = 5/9(°F–32); 1 gpm/ft² = 40.746 mm/min.

[1]All four rack faces shall be protected by sprinklers located within 18 in. (0.46 m) of the faces, as indicated in Figure 12.3.4.4.1.3(a) through Figure 12.3.4.4.1.3(c). It shall not be required for each sprinkler level to protect all faces.

[2]All in-rack sprinkler spacing dimensions start from the floor.

[3]In Figure 12.3.4.4.1.3(a) through Figure 12.3.4.4.1.3(c), each square represents a storage cube measuring 4 ft to 5 ft (1.2 m to 1.5 m) on a side. Actual load heights can vary from approximately 18 in. to 10 ft (0.46 m to 3.1 m). Therefore, there could be as few as one load or as many as six or seven loads between in-rack sprinklers that are spaced 10 ft (3.1 m) apart vertically.

TABLE 12.3.4.1.5 *Hose Stream Demand and Water Supply Duration Requirements for Rack Storage of Class I through Class IV Commodities Stored Above 25 ft (7.6 m) in Height*

Commodity Classification	Storage Height		Inside Hose		Total Combined Inside and Outside Hose		Duration (minutes)
	ft	m	gpm	L/min	gpm	L/min	
Class I, II, and III	>25	>7.6	0, 50, or 100	0, 190, 380	500	1900	90
Class IV	>25	>7.6	0, 50, or 100	0, 190, 380	500	1900	120

12.3.4.2 Large Drop Sprinklers and Specific Application Control Mode Sprinklers for Rack Storage of Class I through Class IV Commodities Stored Over 25 ft (7.6 m) in Height.

The large drop sprinkler, which is covered in 12.3.4.2, is a specific application control mode technology as defined in this standard. The names have remained separate due to the long history of the name "large drop" and its relation to the nominal K-factor of 11.2. Applications of large drop sprinklers and specific application control mode sprinklers are described in section 12.3.4.2. Listing of large drop sprinklers and control mode specific application sprinklers takes into consideration the ability of the sprinkler discharge pattern to penetrate a high-velocity fire plume. Only listed large drop and specific application control mode sprinklers are to be used in accordance with the special design approach of 12.3.4.2.

12.3.4.2.1 Protection of single-, double-, and multiple-row rack storage without solid shelves for Classes I through IV commodities shall be in accordance with Table 12.3.4.2.1.

12.3.4.2.2 Where in-rack sprinklers are required by Table 12.3.4.2.1, in-rack sprinkler spacing, design pressure, and hydraulic calculation criteria shall be in accordance with the requirements of 12.3.4.4 as applicable for the commodity.

12.3.4.2.3 Protection shall be provided as specified in Table 12.3.4.2.1 or appropriate NFPA standards in terms of minimum operating pressure and the number of sprinklers to be included in the design area.

12.3.4.2.3.1 For design purposes, 95 psi (6.6 bar) shall be the maximum discharge pressure at the hydraulically most remote sprinkler.

Discharge pressures in excess of 95 psi (6.6 bar) negatively impact the sprinkler's discharge pattern and droplet size, which is the reason for the requirement in 12.3.4.2.3.1.

TABLE 12.3.4.2.1 *Large Drop Sprinkler Design Criteria for Single-, Double-, and Multiple-Row Racks without Solid Shelves of Class I through Class IV Commodities Stored Over 25 ft (7.6 m) in Height*

Commodity Class	Nominal K-Factor	Maximum Storage Height		Maximum Ceiling/Roof Height		Type of System	Number of Design Sprinklers/Minimum Pressure		Hose Stream Demand		Water Supply Duration (hours)
		ft	m	ft	m		#/psi	#/bar	gpm	L/min	
I, II	11.2	30	9.1	35	10.7	Wet	20/25 + 1 level of in-rack	20/1.7 + 1 level of in-rack	500	1900	1½
						Dry	30/25 + 1 level of in-rack	30/1.7 + 1 level of in-rack	500	1900	1½
III, IV	Design criteria not applicable to Class III or Class IV commodities stored in excess of 25 ft (7.6 m) in height										

12.3.4.2.3.2 Open Wood Joist Construction.

(A) Where large drop K-11.2 sprinklers are installed under open wood joist construction, their minimum operating pressure shall be 50 psi (3.4 bar).

(B) Where each joist channel of open, wood joist construction is fully fire-stopped to its full depth at intervals not exceeding 20 ft (6.1 m), the lower pressures specified in Table 12.3.4.2.1 shall be permitted to be used.

12.3.4.2.3.3 The design area shall be a rectangular area having a dimension parallel to the branch lines at least 1.2 times the square root of the area protected by the number of sprinklers to be included in the design area. Any fractional sprinkler shall be included in the design area.

Starting with the 1996 edition, NFPA 13 provided more information about the shape of the design area where large drop sprinklers are used (see 12.3.4.2.3.3). Although earlier editions implied that the design area was to be a rectangular shape having a dimension parallel to the branch lines of at least 1.2 times the square root of the area protected by the number of sprinklers, it was not explicitly stated.

12.3.4.2.3.4 Hose stream demand and water supply duration requirements shall be in accordance with Table 12.3.4.2.1.

12.3.4.2.3.5 Preaction Systems.

(A) For the purpose of using Table 12.3.4.2.1, preaction systems shall be classified as dry pipe systems.

Paragraph 12.3.4.2.3.5(A) requires that all preaction systems be treated as dry pipe sprinkler systems when applying the requirements of Table 12.3.4.2.1.

(B) Where it can be demonstrated that the detection system activating the preaction system will cause water to be at the sprinklers when they operate, preaction systems shall be permitted to be treated as wet pipe systems.

If it can be demonstrated that a detection system activating the preaction system will cause water to be at the sprinklers when they operate, the wet system design criteria can be used. Preaction systems that perform to 12.3.4.2.3.5(B) are not considered dry systems.

12.3.4.2.3.6 The nominal diameter of branch line pipes (including riser nipples) shall meet the following:

(1) Pipe diameter shall not be not less than 1¼ in. (33 mm) nor greater than 2 in. (51 mm).
(2) Starter pieces shall be permitted to be 2½ in. (64 mm).
(3) Where branch lines are larger than 2 in. (51 mm), the sprinkler shall be supplied by a riser nipple to elevate the sprinkler 13 in. (330 mm) for 2½-in. (64-mm) pipe and 15 in. (380 mm) for 3-in. (76-mm) pipe. These dimensions are measured from the centerline of the pipe to the deflector. In lieu of this, sprinklers shall be permitted to be offset horizontally a minimum of 12 in. (305 mm).

The purpose of limiting the maximum diameter of branch lines or riser nipples, which is discussed in 12.3.4.2.3.6, is to minimize the effect of pipe shadow below the sprinkler. Pipe shadow can result in significant shielded or dry areas with reduced water application and loss of sprinkler water penetration.

12.3.4.2.3.7 Building steel shall not require special protection where Table 12.3.4.2.1 is applied as appropriate for the storage configuration.

12.3.4.3* Early Suppression Fast-Response (ESFR) Sprinklers for Rack Storage of Class I through Class IV Commodities Stored Over 25 ft (7.6 m) in Height.

A.12.3.4.3 ESFR sprinklers are designed to respond quickly to growing fires and deliver heavy discharge to suppress fires rather than to control them. ESFR sprinklers should not be relied on to provide suppression if they are used outside the design parameters.

◀ **FAQ**
For large drop and specific application control mode sprinklers, are all types of preaction systems treated as dry pipe systems?

◀ **FAQ**
For large drop and specific application control mode sprinklers, are preaction systems always treated as dry pipe systems?

While these sprinklers are intended primarily for use in high-pile storage situations, this section permits their use and extension into adjacent portions of an occupancy that might have a lesser classification.

Storage in single-story or multistory buildings can be permitted, provided the maximum ceiling/roof height as specified in Chapter 12 is satisfied for each storage area.

Design parameters were determined from a series of full-scale fire tests that were conducted as a joint effort between Factory Mutual Research Corporation and the National Fire Protection Research Foundation. (Copies of the test reports are available from the NFPRF.)

Applications of ESFR sprinklers are described in 12.3.4.3. The special design approach for ESFR sprinklers is based on fire suppression by the first operating ring of sprinklers.

12.3.4.3.1 Protection of single-, double-, and multiple-row rack storage of Classes I through IV shall be in accordance with Table 12.3.4.3.1.

ESFR protection criteria are provided in Table 12.3.4.3.1, which addresses protection of palletized and solid-piled storage. ESFR sprinklers are also permitted to be utilized for protection of ordinary hazard occupancies and miscellaneous storage. The criteria in Table 12.3.4.3.1 have been expanded to permit broader applications of ESFR sprinkler technology based on large-scale test results reviewed by the Technical Committee on Sprinkler System Discharge Criteria. Design criteria for K-11.2, K-16.8, and K-25.2 ESFR sprinkler technology have been incorporated into the tables where test data supports such inclusion.

12.3.4.3.1.1 ESFR protection as defined shall not apply to the following:

(1) Rack storage involving solid shelves
(2) Rack storage involving combustible, open-top cartons or containers

12.3.4.3.2 ESFR sprinkler systems shall be designed such that the minimum operating pressure is not less than that indicated in Table 12.3.4.3.1 for type of storage, commodity, storage height, and building height involved.

After selecting the commodity, the ceiling height for ESFR protection is the most important factor when selecting the minimum operating pressure (see 12.3.4.3.2). ESFR performance is highly dependent on the ceiling/roof height. This is why averaging of ceiling/roof height based for pitched roofs is not acceptable; the maximum ceiling/roof height over the storage area being protected must be selected.

FAQ ▶
For ESFR applications where the ceiling/roof height falls between design criteria in Table 12.3.4.3.1, is it acceptable to interpolate the design criteria?

Where the ceiling/roof height falls above the selected criteria, the design criteria for the next higher ceiling/roof height must be chosen, with a maximum ceiling/roof height limit of 45 ft as established by Table 12.3.4.3.1.

Additionally, verification that the maximum storage height does not exceed the value for the ceiling/roof height selected in Table 12.3.4.3.1 is also necessary. It is important to verify that the storage height does not exceed the maximum storage height for the maximum ceiling/roof height design selected from Table 12.3.4.3.1. Lower storage heights that result in greater commodity clearances within a given design are acceptable provided the ESFR design criteria from Table 12.3.4.3.1 are based upon the maximum ceiling/roof height.

12.3.4.3.3 The design area shall consist of the most hydraulically demanding area of 12 sprinklers, consisting of four sprinklers on each of three branch lines. The design shall include a minimum of 960 ft² (89 m²).

12.3.4.3.4 Where required by Table 12.3.4.3.1, one level of K-8.0 quick-response, ordinary-temperature in-rack sprinklers shall be installed at the tier level closest to but not exceeding ½ of the maximum storage height. In-rack sprinkler hydraulic design criteria shall be the most hydraulically remote eight sprinklers at 50 psi (3.4 bar). In-rack sprinklers shall be located at the intersection of the longitudinal and transverse flue space. Horizontal spacing shall not be permitted to exceed 5-ft (1.5-m) intervals.

TABLE 12.3.4.3.1 *ESFR Protection of Rack Storage without Solid Shelves of Class I through Class IV Commodities Stored Over 25 ft (7.6 m) in Height*

Storage Arrangement	Commodity	Maximum Storage Height		Maximum Ceiling/ Roof Height		Nominal K-Factor	Orientation	Minimum Operating Pressure		In-Rack Sprinkler Requirements	Hose Stream Demand		Water Supply Duration (hours)
		ft	*m*	*ft*	*m*			*psi*	*bar*		*gpm*	*L/min*	
Single-row, double-row, and multiple-row rack (no open-top containers)	Class I, II, III, or IV, encapsulated or unencapsulated	30	9.1	35	10.7	14.0	Upright or pendent	75	5.2	No	250	946	1
						16.8	Pendent	52	3.6	No			
						25.2	Pendent	20	1.4	No			
				40	12.2	14.0	Pendent	75	5.2	No			
						16.8	Pendent	52	3.6	No			
						25.2	Pendent	25	1.7	No			
				45	13.7	14.0	Pendent	90	6.2	Yes			
						16.8	Pendent	63	4.3	Yes			
						25.2	Pendent	40	2.8	No			
		35	10.7	40	12.2	14.0	Pendent	75	5.2	No			
						16.8	Pendent	52	3.6	No			
						25.2	Pendent	25	1.7	No			
				45	13.7	14.0	Pendent	90	6.2	Yes			
						16.8	Pendent	63	4.3	Yes			
						25.2	Pendent	40	2.8	No			
		40	12.2	45	13.7	14.0	Pendent	90	6.2	Yes			
						16.8	Pendent	63	4.3	Yes			
						25.2	Pendent	40	2.8	No			

12.3.4.3.5 Where ESFR sprinklers are installed above and below obstructions, the discharge for up to two sprinklers for one of the levels shall be included with those of the other level in the hydraulic calculations.

Additional ESFR sprinklers installed below fixed obstructions as required by the obstruction rules in Chapter 8 must be included in the hydraulic calculations. Paragraph 12.3.4.3.5 requires that up to an additional two ESFR sprinklers that are located below obstructions be included with the 12 ESFR sprinkler calculations for a total of up to 14 ESFR sprinklers. This is a maximum of two additional ESFR sprinklers regardless of the number of ESFR sprinklers installed below obstructions in the remote area. Where only one additional ESFR sprinkler is needed to address an isolated obstruction, then only that one ESFR sprinkler would need to be added to the calculation. Care must be taken to identify the appropriate hydraulic remote area

◄ **FAQ**
Where additional ESFR sprinklers are added below obstructions, what is the total number of sprinklers that must be calculated?

when such additional ESFR sprinklers are installed below fixed obstructions. The additional two ESFR sprinklers need only to be added to the 12 ESFR sprinkler demand directly above the obstruction when the combined number of sprinklers creates the hydraulically most demanding area.

12.3.4.4 In-Rack Sprinklers for Rack Storage of Class I through Class IV Commodities Stored Over 25 ft (7.6 m) in Height.

Paragraph 12.3.4.4 is intended to apply only to those rack storage arrangements that contain flue spaces in accordance with 12.3.1.14. Where an inadequate number or type of flue spaces is provided or where required flue spaces are obstructed, the criteria provided by 12.3.4.4 are unlikely to provide adequate protection, and the provisions of 12.3.1.9 should be considered.

12.3.4.4.1 In-Rack Sprinkler Location for Rack Storage of Class I through Class IV Commodities Stored Over 25 ft (7.6 m) in Height.

In the testing on which this standard is based, where in-rack sprinklers were used, the sprinklers were typically installed above the top of a storage tier at transverse flues (see 12.3.4.4.1). Where multiple levels of in-rack sprinklers were used, in-rack sprinklers were usually staggered among transverse flues, except when barriers were provided.

Face sprinklers must be located within racks and not over aisles. A fire spreads vertically through the flues or on the face of the pallet loads along the aisles, depending on the location of the ignition source. If the face sprinklers are located in the aisle, their activation will be significantly delayed if it occurs at all. Because face sprinklers incorrectly positioned in the aisle are likely to operate only if they are subject to direct flame impingement, it can be assumed that the fire is overwhelming the sprinkler system design and that success is not likely.

12.3.4.4.1.1* Double-Row Racks.

(A) In double-row racks without solid shelves and with a maximum of 10 ft (3.1 m) between the top of storage and the ceiling, in-rack sprinklers shall be installed in accordance with Table 12.3.4.1.1 and Figure 12.3.4.4.1.1(a) through Figure 12.3.4.4.1.1(j). The highest level of in-rack sprinklers shall be not more than 10 ft (3.1 m) below the top of storage.

Elevation   **Plan View**

Notes:
1. Symbol x indicates in-rack sprinklers.
2. Each square represents a storage cube measuring 4 ft to 5 ft (1.22 m to 1.53 m) on a side. Actual load heights can vary from approximately 18 in. (0.46 m) up to 10 ft (3.05 m). Therefore, there could be as few as one load or as many as six or seven loads between in-rack sprinklers that are spaced 10 ft (3.05 m) apart vertically.

FIGURE 12.3.4.4.1.1(a) *In-Rack Sprinkler Arrangement, Class I Commodities, Storage Height 25 ft to Maximum 30 ft (7.6 m to Maximum 9.1 m).*

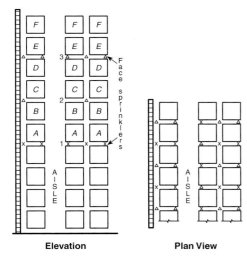

Elevation   **Plan View**

Notes:
1. Sprinklers labeled 1 (the selected array from Table 12.3.4.1.1) shall be required where loads labeled *A* or *B* represent top of storage.
2. Sprinklers labeled 1 and 2 shall be required where loads labeled *C* or *D* represent top of storage.
3. Sprinklers labeled 1 and 3 shall be required where loads labeled *E* or *F* represent top of storage.
4. For storage higher than represented by loads labeled *F,* the cycle defined by Notes 2 and 3 is repeated, with stagger as indicated.
5. Symbol Δ or x indicates sprinklers on vertical or horizontal stagger.
6. Each square represents a storage cube measuring 4 ft to 5 ft (1.22 m to 1.53 m) on a side. Actual load heights can vary from approximately 18 in. (0.46 m) up to 10 ft (3.05 m). Therefore, there could be as few as one load or as many as six or seven loads between in-rack sprinklers that are spaced 10 ft (3.05 m) apart vertically.

FIGURE 12.3.4.4.1.1(b) In-Rack Sprinkler Arrangement, Class I Commodities, Storage Height Over 25 ft (7.6 m).

Elevation   **Plan View (A or B)**

Notes:
1. Alternate location of in-rack sprinklers. Sprinklers shall be permitted to be installed above loads *A* and *C* or above loads *B* and *D.*
2. Symbol Δ or x indicates sprinklers on vertical or horizontal stagger.
3. Each square represents a storage cube measuring 4 ft to 5 ft (1.22 m to 1.53 m) on a side. Actual load heights can vary from approximately 18 in. (0.46 m) up to 10 ft (3.05 m). Therefore, there could be as few as one load or as many as six or seven loads between in-rack sprinklers that are spaced 10 ft (3.05 m) apart vertically.

FIGURE 12.3.4.4.1.1(c) In-Rack Sprinkler Arrangement, Class I, Class II, or Class III Commodities, Storage Height 25 ft to Maximum 30 ft (7.6 m to Maximum 9.1 m).

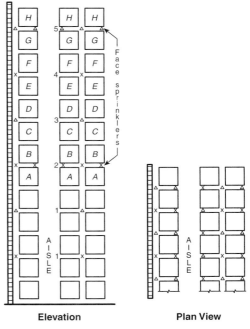

Elevation   **Plan View**

Notes:
1. Sprinklers labeled 1 shall be required where loads labeled *A* represent the top of storage.
2. Sprinklers labeled 1 and 2 shall be required where loads labeled *B* or *C* represent top of storage.
3. Sprinklers labeled 1, 2, and 3 shall be required where loads labeled *D* or *E* represent top of storage.
4. Sprinklers labeled 1, 2, 3, and 4 shall be required where loads labeled *F* or *G* represent top of storage.
5. Sprinklers labeled 1, 2, 3, 4, and 5 shall be required where loads labeled *H* represent top of storage.
6. For storage higher than represented by loads labeled *H,* the cycle defined by Notes 3, 4, and 5 is repeated with stagger as indicated.
7. The indicated face sprinklers shall be permitted to be omitted where commodity consists of unwrapped or unpackaged metal parts on wood pallets.
8. Symbol Δ or x indicates sprinklers on vertical or horizontal stagger.
9. Each square represents a storage cube measuring 4 ft to 5 ft (1.22 m to 1.53 m) on a side. Actual load heights can vary from approximately 18 in. (0.46 m) up to 10 ft (3.05 m). Therefore, there could be as few as one load or as many as six or seven loads between in-rack sprinklers that are spaced 10 ft (3.05 m) apart vertically.

FIGURE 12.3.4.4.1.1(d) In-Rack Sprinkler Arrangement, Class I, Class II, or Class III Commodities, Storage Height Over 25 ft (7.6 m)—Option 1.

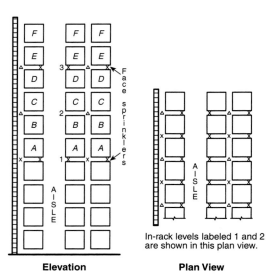

Elevation   **Plan View**

In-rack levels labeled 1 and 2
are shown in this plan view.

Notes:
1. Sprinklers labeled 1 (the selected array from Table 12.3.4.1.1) shall be required where loads labeled *A* or *B* represent top of storage.
2. Sprinklers labeled 1 and 2 shall be required where loads labeled *C* or *D* represent top of storage.
3. Sprinklers labeled 1 and 3 shall be required where loads labeled *E* or *F* represent top of storage.
4. For storage higher than represented by loads labeled *F*, the cycle defined by Notes 2 and 3 is repeated, with stagger as indicated.
5. Symbol ∆ or x indicates sprinklers on vertical or horizontal stagger.
6. Each square represents a storage cube measuring 4 ft to 5 ft (1.22 m to 1.53 m) on a side. Actual load heights can vary from approximately 18 in. (0.46 m) up to 10 ft (3.05 m). Therefore, there could be as few as one load or as many as six or seven loads between in-rack sprinklers that are spaced 10 ft (3.05 m) apart vertically.

FIGURE 12.3.4.4.1.1(e) *In-Rack Sprinkler Arrangement, Class I, Class II, or Class III Commodities, Storage Height Over 25 ft (7.6 m)—Option 2.*

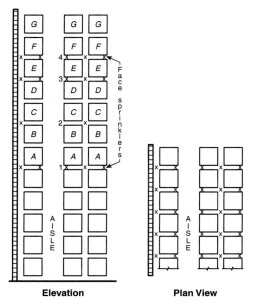

Elevation   **Plan View**

Notes:
1. Sprinklers labeled 1 (the selected array from Table 12.3.4.1.1) shall be required where loads labeled *A* or *B* represent top of storage.
2. Sprinklers labeled 1 and 2 shall be required where loads labeled *C* or *D* represent top of storage.
3. Sprinklers labeled 1 and 3 shall be required where loads labeled *E* represent top of storage.
4. Sprinklers labeled 1 and 4 shall be required where loads labeled *F* or *G* represent top of storage.
5. For storage higher than represented by loads labeled *G*, the cycle defined by Notes 2, 3, and 4 is repeated.
6. Symbol x indicates face and in-rack sprinklers.
7. Each square represents a storage cube measuring 4 ft to 5 ft (1.22 m to 1.53 m) on a side. Actual load heights can vary from approximately 18 in. (0.46 m) up to 10 ft (3.05 m). Therefore, there could be as few as one load or as many as six or seven loads between in-rack sprinklers that are spaced 10 ft (3.05 m) apart vertically.

FIGURE 12.3.4.4.1.1(f) *In-Rack Sprinkler Arrangement, Class I, Class II, or Class III Commodities, Storage Height Over 25 ft (7.6 m)—Option 3.*

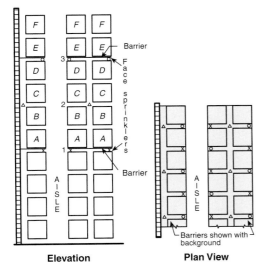

Elevation   **Plan View**

Notes:

1. Sprinklers labeled 1 (the selected array from Table 12.3.4.1.1) shall be required where loads labeled *A* or *B* represent top of storage.
2. Sprinklers labeled 1 and 2 shall be required where loads labeled *C* or *D* represent top of storage.
3. Sprinklers labeled 1 and 3 shall be required where loads labeled *E* or *F* represent top of storage.
4. For storage higher than represented by loads labeled *F*, the cycle defined by Notes 2 and 3 is repeated.
5. Symbols o, Δ, and x indicate sprinklers on vertical or horizontal stagger.
6. Each square represents a storage cube measuring 4 ft to 5 ft (1.22 m to 1.53 m) on a side. Actual load heights can vary from approximately 18 in. (0.46 m) up to 10 ft (3.05 m). Therefore, there could be as few as one load or as many as six or seven loads between in-rack sprinklers that are spaced 10 ft (3.05 m) apart vertically.

FIGURE 12.3.4.4.1.1(g) *In-Rack Sprinkler Arrangement, Class I, Class II, or Class III Commodities, Storage Height Over 25 ft (7.6 m)—Option 4.*

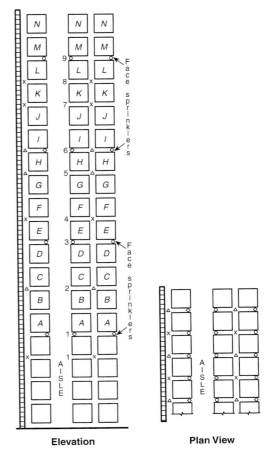

Elevation   **Plan View**

Notes:

1. Sprinklers labeled 1 (the selected array from Table 12.3.4.1.1) shall be required where loads labeled *A* or *B* represent top of storage.
2. Sprinklers labeled 1 and 2 shall be required where loads labeled *C* or *D* represent top of storage.
3. Sprinklers labeled 1, 2, and 3 shall be required where loads labeled *E* or *F* represent top of storage.
4. Sprinklers labeled 1, 2, 3, and 4 shall be required where loads labeled *G* represent top of storage.
5. Sprinklers labeled 1, 2, 3, 4, and 5 shall be required where loads labeled *H* represent top of storage.
6. Sprinklers labeled 1, 2, 3, 4, and 6 (not 5) shall be required where loads labeled *I* or *J* represent top of storage.
7. Sprinklers labeled 1, 2, 3, 4, 6, and 7 shall be required where loads labeled *K* represent top of storage.
8. Sprinklers labeled 1, 2, 3, 4, 6, and 8 shall be required where loads labeled *L* represent top of storage.
9. Sprinklers labeled 1, 2, 3, 4, 6, 8, and 9 shall be required where loads labeled *M* or *N* represent top of storage.
10. For storage higher than represented by loads labeled *N*, the cycle defined by Notes 1 through 9 is repeated, with stagger as indicated. In the cycle, loads labeled *M* are equivalent to loads labeled *A*.
11. Symbols o, x, and Δ indicate sprinklers on vertical or horizontal stagger.
12. Each square represents a storage cube measuring 4 ft to 5 ft (1.22 m to 1.53 m) on a side. Actual load heights can vary from approximately 18 in. (0.46 m) up to 10 ft (3.05 m). Therefore, there could be as few as one load or as many as six or seven loads between in-rack sprinklers that are spaced 10 ft (3.05 m) apart vertically.

FIGURE 12.3.4.4.1.1(h) *In-Rack Sprinkler Arrangement, Class I, Class II, Class III, or Class IV Commodities, Storage Height Over 25 ft (7.6 m)—Option 1.*

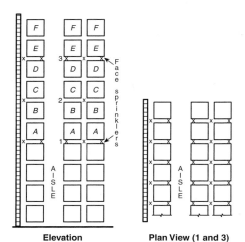

Elevation   **Plan View (1 and 3)**

Notes:

1. Sprinklers labeled 1 (the selected array from Table 12.3.4.1.1) shall be required where loads labeled *A* or *B* represent top of storage.
2. Sprinklers labeled 1 and 2 shall be required where loads labeled *C* or *D* represent top of storage.
3. Sprinklers labeled 1 and 3 shall be required where loads labeled *E* or *F* represent top of storage.
4. For storage higher than represented by loads labeled *F*, the cycle defined by Notes 2 and 3 is repeated.
5. Symbol x indicates face and in-rack sprinklers.
6. Each square represents a storage cube measuring 4 ft to 5 ft (1.22 m to 1.53 m) on a side. Actual load heights can vary from approximately 18 in. (0.46 m) up to 10 ft (3.05 m). Therefore, there could be as few as one load or as many as six or seven loads between in-rack sprinklers that are spaced 10 ft (3.05 m) apart vertically.

FIGURE 12.3.4.4.1.1(i) *In-Rack Sprinkler Arrangement, Class I, Class II, Class III, or Class IV Commodities, Storage Height Over 25 ft (7.6 m)—Option 2.*

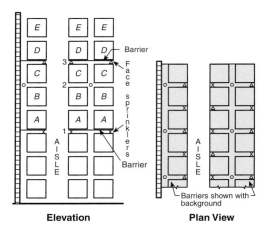

Elevation   **Plan View**

Notes:

1. Sprinklers labeled 1 (the selected array from Table 12.3.4.1.1) shall be required where loads labeled *A* or *B* represent top of storage.
2. Sprinklers labeled 1 and 2 and barrier labeled 1 shall be required where loads labeled *C* represent top of storage.
3. Sprinklers and barriers labeled 1 and 3 shall be required where loads labeled *D* or *E* represent top of storage.
4. For storage higher than represented by loads labeled *E*, the cycle defined by Notes 2 and 3 is repeated.
5. Symbol Δ or x indicates sprinklers on vertical or horizontal stagger.
6. Symbol o indicates longitudinal flue space sprinklers.
7. Each square represents a storage cube measuring 4 ft to 5 ft (1.22 m to 1.53 m) on a side. Actual load heights can vary from approximately 18 in. (0.46 m) up to 10 ft (3.05 m). Therefore, there could be as few as one load or as many as six or seven loads between in-rack sprinklers that are spaced 10 ft (3.05 m) apart vertically.

FIGURE 12.3.4.4.1.1(j) *In-Rack Sprinkler Arrangement, Class I, Class II, Class III, or Class IV Commodities, Storage Height Over 25 ft (7.6 m)—Option 3.*

Where a single-row rack is mixed with double-row racks, Table 12.3.4.1.1 and Figure 12.3.4.4.1.1(a) through Figure 12.3.4.4.1.1(j) shall be used.

(B) Figure 12.3.4.4.1.2(a) through Figure 12.3.4.4.1.2(c) shall be permitted to be used for the protection of the single-row racks.

A.12.3.4.4.1.1 Where storage tiers are not the same size on each side of the longitudinal flue, one side of the flue should be protected with sprinklers at the proper elevation above the load. The next level of sprinklers should protect the other side of the flue with the sprinklers at the proper elevation above that load as indicated in Figure A.12.3.4.4.1.1. The vertical spacing requirements for in-rack sprinklers specified in Table 12.3.4.1.1 and 12.3.3 for plastics should be followed.

12.3.4.4.1.2* Single-Row Racks. In single-row racks without solid shelves with storage height over 25 ft (7.6 m) and a maximum of 10 ft (3.1 m) between the top of storage and the ceiling, sprinklers shall be installed in accordance with Figure 12.3.4.4.1.2(a) through Figure 12.3.4.4.1.2(e). In single-row racks, where figures show in-rack sprinklers in transverse flue spaces centered between the rack faces, it shall be permitted to position these in-rack sprinklers in the transverse flue at any point between the load faces.

Elevation View

FIGURE A.12.3.4.4.1.1
Placement of In-Rack Sprinkler Where Rack Levels Have Varying Heights.

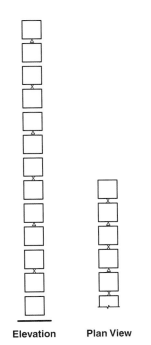

Elevation   **Plan View**

Notes:
1. For all storage heights, sprinklers shall be installed in every other tier and staggered as indicated.
2. Symbol △ or x indicates sprinklers on vertical or horizontal stagger.
3. Each square represents a storage cube measuring 4 ft to 5 ft (1.22 m to 1.53 m) on a side. Actual load heights can vary from approximately 18 in. (0.46 m) up to 10 ft (3.05 m). Therefore, there could be as few as one load or as many as six or seven loads between in-rack sprinklers that are spaced 10 ft (3.05 m) apart vertically.

FIGURE 12.3.4.4.1.2(a) *Class I, Class II, Class III, or Class IV Commodities, In-Rack Sprinkler Arrangement, Single-Row Racks, Storage Height Over 25 ft (7.6 m)— Option 1.*

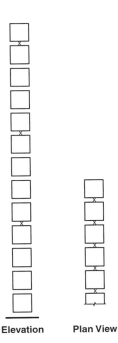

Elevation   **Plan View**

Note: Each square represents a storage cube measuring 4 ft to 5 ft (1.22 m) on a side. Actual load heights can vary from approximately 18 in. (0.46 m) up to 10 ft (3.05 m). Therefore, there could be as few as one load or as many as six or seven loads between in-rack sprinklers that are spaced 10 ft (3.05 m) apart vertically.

FIGURE 12.3.4.4.1.2(b) *Class I, Class II, or Class III Commodities, In-Rack Sprinkler Arrangement, Single-Row Racks, Storage Height Over 25 ft (7.6 m)—Option 1.*

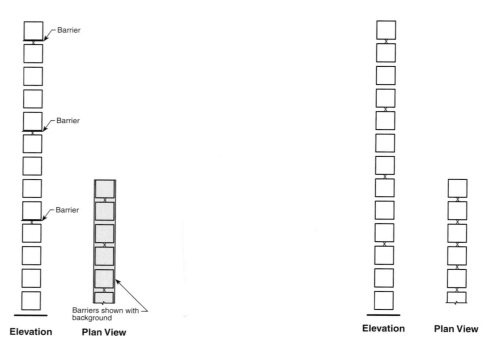

Note: Each square represents a storage cube measuring 4 ft to 5 ft (1.22 m to 1.53 m) on a side. Actual load heights can vary from approximately 18 in. (0.46 m) up to 10 ft (3.05 m). Therefore, there could be as few as one load or as many as six or seven loads between in-rack sprinklers that are spaced 10 ft (3.05 m) apart vertically.

FIGURE 12.3.4.4.1.2(c) Class I, Class II, or Class III Commodities, In-Rack Sprinkler Arrangement, Single-Row Racks, Storage Height Over 25 ft (7.6 m)—Option 2.

Note: Each square represents a storage cube measuring 4 ft to 5 ft (1.22 m to 1.53 m) on a side. Actual load heights can vary from approximately 18 in. (0.46 m) up to 10 ft (3.05 m). Therefore, there could be as few as one load or as many as six or seven loads between in-rack sprinklers that are spaced 10 ft (3.05 m) apart vertically.

FIGURE 12.3.4.4.1.2(d) Class I, Class II, Class III, or Class IV Commodities, In-Rack Sprinkler Arrangement, Single-Row Racks, Storage Height Over 25 ft (7.6 m)— Option 2.

A **A.12.3.4.4.1.2** In single-row racks with more than 10 ft (3.1 m) between the top of storage and the ceiling, a horizontal barrier should be installed above storage with one line of sprinklers under the barrier.

12.3.4.4.1.3* In-Rack Sprinkler Location—Multiple-Row Racks for Rack Storage of Class I through Class IV Commodities Stored Over 25 ft (7.6 m) in Height. In multiple-row racks with a maximum of 10 ft (3.1 m) between the top of storage and the ceiling, protection shall be in accordance with Table 12.3.4.1.3 and in-rack sprinklers shall be installed as indicated in Figure 12.3.4.4.1.3(a) through Figure 12.3.4.4.1.3(c). The highest level of in-rack sprinklers shall be not more than 10 ft (3.1 m) below maximum storage height for Class I, Class II, or Class III commodities or 5 ft (1.5 m) below the top of storage for Class IV commodities.

A **A.12.3.4.4.1.3** In multiple-row racks with more than 10 ft (3.1 m) between the maximum height of storage and ceiling, a horizontal barrier should be installed above storage with a level of sprinklers, spaced as stipulated for in-rack sprinklers, installed directly beneath the barrier. In-rack sprinklers should be installed as indicated in Figure 12.3.4.4.1.3(a) through Figure 12.3.4.4.1.3(c).

Data indicate that the sprinkler protection criteria in 12.3.4.4.1.3 is ineffective, by itself, for rack storage with solid shelves, if the required flue spaces are not maintained. Use of Table 12.3.4.1.3, along with the additional provisions that are required by this standard, can provide acceptable protection.

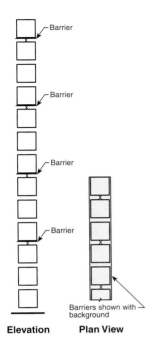

Note: Each square represents a storage cube measuring 4 ft to 5 ft (1.22 m to 1.53 m) on a side. Actual load heights can vary from approximately 18 in. (0.46 m) up to 10 ft (3.05 m). Therefore, there could be as few as one load or as many as six or seven loads between in-rack sprinklers that are spaced 10 ft (3.05 m) apart vertically.

FIGURE 12.3.4.4.1.2(e) *Class I, Class II, Class III, or Class IV Commodities, In-Rack Sprinkler Arrangement, Single-Row Racks, Storage Height Over 25 ft (7.6 m)— Option 3.*

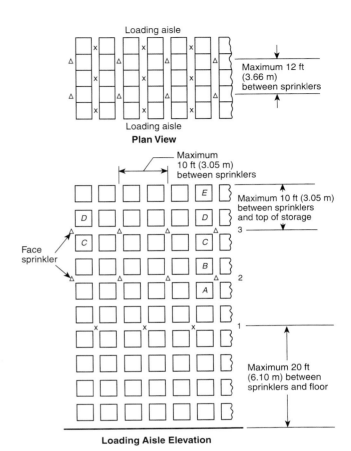

Notes:
1. Sprinklers labeled 1 shall be required if loads labeled *A* represent top of storage.
2. Sprinklers labeled 1 and 2 shall be required if loads labeled *B* or *C* represent top of storage.
3. Sprinklers labeled 1 and 3 shall be required if loads labeled *D* or *E* represent top of storage.
4. For storage higher than represented by loads labeled *E*, the cycle defined by Notes 2 and 3 is repeated, with stagger as indicated.
5. Symbol Δ or x indicates sprinklers on vertical or horizontal stagger.
6. Each square represents a storage cube measuring 4 ft to 5 ft (1.22 m to 1.53 m) on a side. Actual load heights can vary from approximately 18 in. (0.46 m) up to 10 ft (3.05 m). Therefore, there could be as few as one load or as many as six or seven loads between in-rack sprinklers that are spaced 10 ft (3.05 m) apart vertically.

FIGURE 12.3.4.4.1.3(a) *In-Rack Sprinkler Arrangement—Multiple-Row Racks, Class I Commodities, Storage Height Over 25 ft (7.6 m).*

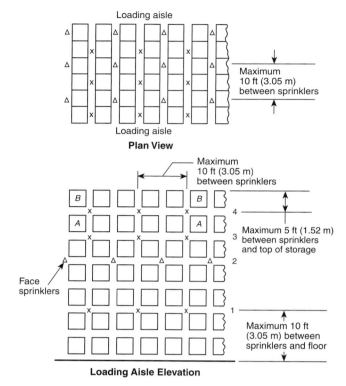

Notes:

1. Sprinklers labeled 1 and 2 shall be required if loads labeled *A* represent top of storage.
2. Sprinklers labeled 1 and 3 shall be required if loads labeled *B* or *C* represent top of storage.
3. For storage higher than represented by loads labeled *C*, the cycle defined by Notes 2 and 3 is repeated, with stagger as indicated.
4. Symbol Δ or x indicates sprinklers on vertical or horizontal stagger.
5. Each square represents a storage cube measuring 4 ft to 5 ft (1.22 m to 1.53 m) on a side. Actual load heights can vary from approximately 18 in. (0.46 m) up to 10 ft (3.05 m). Therefore, there could be as few as one load or as many as six or seven loads between in-rack sprinklers that are spaced 10 ft (3.05 m) apart vertically.

Notes:

1. Sprinklers labeled 1, 2, and 3 shall be required if loads labeled *A* represent top of storage.
2. Sprinklers labeled 1, 2, and 4 shall be required if loads labeled *B* represent top of storage.
3. For storage higher than represented by loads labeled *B*, the cycle defined by Notes 1 and 2 is repeated, with stagger as indicated.
4. Symbol Δ or x indicates sprinklers on vertical or horizontal stagger.
5. Each square represents a storage cube measuring 4 ft to 5 ft (1.22 m to 1.53 m) on a side. Actual load heights can vary from approximately 18 in. (0.46 m) up to 10 ft (3.05 m). Therefore, there could be as few as one load or as many as six or seven loads between in-rack sprinklers that are spaced 10 ft (3.05 m) apart vertically.

FIGURE 12.3.4.4.1.3(b) *In-Rack Sprinkler Arrangement —Multiple-Row Racks, Class I, Class II, or Class III Commodities, Storage Height Over 25 ft (7.6 m).*

FIGURE 12.3.4.4.1.3(c) *In-Rack Sprinkler Arrangement, Class I, Class II, Class III, or Class IV Commodities— Multiple-Row Racks, Storage Height Over 25 ft (7.6 m).*

12.3.4.4.2 In-Rack Sprinkler Spacing for Rack Storage of Class I through Class IV Commodities Stored Over 25 ft (7.6 m) in Height.

12.3.4.4.2.1 In-Rack Sprinkler Spacing. In-rack sprinklers shall be staggered horizontally and vertically where installed in accordance with Table 12.3.4.1.1, Figure 12.3.4.4.1.1(a) through Figure 12.3.4.4.1.1(j) and Figure 12.3.4.4.1.2(a) through Figure 12.3.4.4.1.2(e).

12.3.4.4.2.2 In-rack sprinklers for storage higher than 25 ft (7.6 m) in double-row racks shall be spaced horizontally and located in the horizontal space nearest the vertical intervals specified in Table 12.3.4.1.1 and Figure 12.3.4.4.1.1(a) through Figure 12.3.4.4.1.1(j).

12.3.4.4.2.3 In-Rack Sprinkler Spacing. Maximum horizontal spacing of sprinklers in multiple-row racks with storage higher than 25 ft (7.6 m) shall be in accordance with Figure 12.3.4.4.1.3(a) through Figure 12.3.4.4.1.3(c).

12.3.4.4.3 In-Rack Sprinkler Water Demand for Rack Storage of Class I through Class IV Commodities Stored Over 25 ft (7.6 m) in Height. The water demand for sprinklers installed in racks shall be based on simultaneous operation of the most hydraulically remote sprinklers as follows:

(1) Six sprinklers where only one level is installed in racks with Class I, Class II, or Class III commodities
(2) Eight sprinklers where only one level is installed in racks with Class IV commodities
(3) Ten sprinklers (five on each two top levels) where more than one level is installed in racks with Class I, Class II, or Class III commodities
(4) Fourteen sprinklers (seven on each two top levels) where more than one level is installed in racks with Class IV commodities

12.3.4.4.4 In-Rack Sprinkler Discharge for Rack Storage of Class I through Class IV Commodities Stored Over 25 ft (7.6 m) in Height. Sprinklers in racks shall discharge at a rate not less than 30 gpm (113.6 L/min) for all classes of commodities.

12.3.4.5 Special Design for Rack Storage of Class I through Class IV Commodities Stored Over 25 ft (7.6 m) in Height.

12.3.4.5.1 High-Expansion Foam Systems. Where high-expansion foam is used in combination with ceiling sprinklers, the minimum ceiling sprinkler design density shall be 0.2 gpm/ft^2 (8.2 mm/min) for Class I, Class II, or Class III commodities and 0.25 gpm/ft^2 (10.2 mm/min) for Class IV commodities for the most hydraulically remote 2000-ft^2 (186-m^2) area.

12.3.4.5.1.1 Where high-expansion foam is used in combination with ceiling sprinklers, the minimum ceiling sprinkler design density shall be 0.2 gpm/ft^2 (8.2 mm/min) for Class I, Class II, or Class III commodities and 0.25 gpm/ft^2 (10.2 mm/min) for Class IV commodities for the most hydraulically remote 2000-ft^2 (186-m^2) operating area.

12.3.4.5.1.2 Where high-expansion foam systems are used for storage over 25 ft (7.6 m) high up to and including 35 ft (10.7 m) high, they shall be used in combination with ceiling sprinklers. The maximum submergence time for the high-expansion foam shall be 5 minutes for Class I, Class II, or Class III commodities and 4 minutes for Class IV commodities.

12.3.5 Protection Criteria for Rack Storage of Plastics Commodities Stored Over 25 ft (7.6 m) in Height.

12.3.5.1 Control Mode Density-Area Sprinkler Protection Criteria for Rack Storage of Plastics Commodities Stored Over 25 ft (7.6 m) in Height for Single-, Double-, and Multiple-Row Racks.

Control mode density/area sprinklers used for the protection of storage that exceeds 25 ft (7.6 m), which are covered in 12.3.5.1, are primarily used to protect the commodity between the top level of required in-rack protection and the top of storage. In addition, ceiling cooling and structural protection is provided. The in-rack protection is expected to control the growth and spread of fire within the rack structure at the lower levels. This is why there is no variation of the ceiling density for the protection of 30 ft (9.1 m) of storage as compared to 75 ft (22.9 m) of storage. The only variation in ceiling density is based on the storage height above the top level of in-rack sprinklers.

12.3.5.1.1 Ceiling Sprinkler Water Demand. For Group A plastic commodities in cartons, encapsulated or nonencapsulated, ceiling sprinkler water demand in terms of density [gpm/ft^2 (mm/min)] and area of operation [ft^2 (m^2)] shall be selected from Table 12.3.5.1.1.

12.3.5.1.2 Where a single-row rack is mixed with double-row racks, either Figure 12.3.5.1.2(a) or Figure 12.3.5.1.2(b) shall be used in accordance with the corresponding storage height.

TABLE 12.3.5.1.1 *Control Mode Density-Area Sprinkler Discharge Criteria for Single-, Double-, and Multiple-Row Racks of Plastics Commodities with Storage Over 25 ft (7.6 m) in Height*

Storage Height above Top Level In-Rack Sprinklers	Ceiling Sprinklers Density (gpm/ft²)
5 ft or less	0.30/2000
Over 5 ft up to 10 ft	0.45/2000

Elevation View   **Plan View**

Notes:
1. Sprinklers and barriers labeled 1 shall be required where loads labeled *A* or *B* represent top of storage.
2. Sprinklers labeled 1 and 2 and barriers labeled 1 shall be required where loads labeled *C* represent top of storage.
3. Sprinklers and barriers labeled 1 and 3 shall be required where loads labeled *D* or *E* represent top of storage.
4. For storage higher than represented by loads labeled *E*, the cycle defined by Notes 2 and 3 is repeated.
5. Symbol Δ or x indicates face sprinklers on vertical or horizontal stagger.
6. Symbol o indicates longitudinal flue space sprinklers.
7. Each square represents a storage cube measuring 4 ft to 5 ft (1.22 m to 1.53 m) on a side. Actual load heights can vary from approximately 18 in. (0.46 m) up to 10 ft (3.05 m). Therefore, there could be as few as one load or as many as six or seven loads between in-rack sprinklers that are spaced 10 ft (3.05 m) apart vertically.

FIGURE 12.3.5.1.2(a) *In-Rack Sprinkler Arrangement, Group A Plastic Commodities, Storage Height Over 25 ft (7.6 m)—Option 1.*

Elevation View   **Plan View**

Notes:
1. Sprinklers labeled 1 shall be required where loads labeled *A* or *B* represent top of storage.
2. Sprinklers labeled 1 and 2 shall be required where loads labeled *C* represent top of storage.
3. Sprinklers labeled 1 and 3 shall be required where loads labeled *D* or *E* represent top of storage.
4. For storage higher than loads labeled *F*, the cycle defined by Notes 2 and 3 is repeated.
5. Symbol x indicates face and in-rack sprinklers.
6. Each square represents a storage cube measuring 4 ft to 5 ft (1.22 m to 1.53 m) on a side. Actual load heights can vary from approximately 18 in. (0.46 m) up to 10 ft (3.05 m). Therefore, there could be as few as one load or as many as six or seven loads between in-rack sprinklers that are spaced 10 ft (3.05 m) apart vertically.

FIGURE 12.3.5.1.2(b) *In-Rack Sprinkler Arrangement, Group A Plastic Commodities, Storage Height Over 25 ft (7.6 m)—Option 2.*

12.3.5.1.2.1 Figure 12.3.5.1.2.1(a) through Figure 12.3.5.1.2.1(c) shall be permitted to be used for the protection of the single-row racks.

12.3.5.1.3 The minimum water supply requirements for a hydraulically designed occupancy hazard fire control sprinkler system shall be determined by adding the hose stream demand from Table 12.3.5.1.3 to the water supply for sprinklers determined in 12.3.5. This supply shall be available for the minimum duration specified in Table 12.3.5.1.3.

TABLE 12.3.5.1.3 *Hose Stream Demand and Water Supply Duration Requirements for Rack Storage of Plastics Commodities Stored Above 25 ft (7.6 m) in Height*

Commodity Classification	Storage Height		Inside Hose		Total Combined Inside and Outside Hose		Duration (minutes)
	ft	*m*	*gpm*	*L/min*	*gpm*	*L/min*	
Plastic	>25	>7.6	0, 50, 100	0, 190, 380	500	1900	120

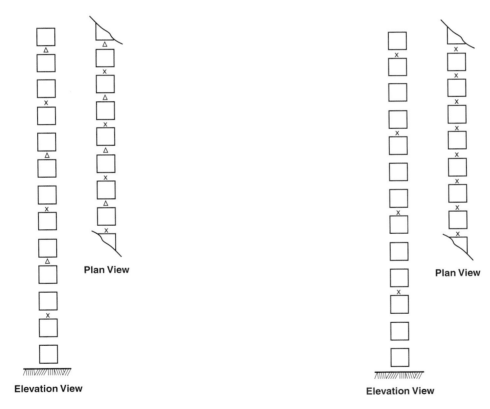

Note: Each square represents a storage cube measuring 4 ft to 5 ft (1.22 m to 1.53 m) on a side. Actual load heights can vary from approximately 18 in. (0.46 m) up to 10 ft (3.05 m). Therefore, there could be as few as one load or as many as six or seven loads between in-rack sprinklers that are spaced 10 ft (3.05 m) apart vertically.

FIGURE 12.3.5.1.2.1(a) *In-Rack Sprinkler Arrangement, Group A Plastic Commodities, Single-Row Racks, Storage Height Over 25 ft (7.6 m)—Option 1.*

Note: Each square represents a storage cube measuring 4 ft to 5 ft (1.22 m to 1.53 m) on a side. Actual load heights can vary from approximately 18 in. (0.46 m) up to 10 ft (3.05 m). Therefore, there could be as few as one load or as many as six or seven loads between in-rack sprinklers that are spaced 10 ft (3.05m) apart vertically.

FIGURE 12.3.5.1.2.1(b) *In-Rack Sprinkler Arrangement, Group A Plastic Commodities, Single-Row Racks, Storage Height Over 25 ft (7.6 m)—Option 2.*

Plan View

Elevation View

Note: Each square represents a storage cube measuring 4 ft to 5 ft (1.22 m to 1.53 m) on a side. Actual load heights can vary from approximately 18 in. (0.46 m) up to 10 ft (3.05 m). Therefore, there could be as few as one load or as many as six or seven loads between in-rack sprinklers that are spaced 10 ft (3.05 m) apart vertically.

FIGURE 12.3.5.1.2.1(c) In-Rack Sprinkler Arrangement, Group A Plastic Commodities, Single-Row Racks, Storage Height Over 25 ft (7.6 m)—Option 3.

12.3.5.2 Large Drop Sprinklers and Specific Application Control Mode Sprinklers for Rack Storage of Plastics Commodities Stored Over 25 ft (7.6 m) in Height.

Currently there are no options for the protection of plastics above 25 ft (7.6 m) in 12.3.5.2.

12.3.5.3* Early Suppression Fast-Response (ESFR) Sprinklers for Rack Storage of Plastics Commodities Stored Over 25 ft (7.6 m) in Height.

A **A.12.3.5.3** ESFR sprinklers are designed to respond quickly to growing fires and deliver heavy discharge to suppress fires rather than to control them. ESFR sprinklers should not be relied on to provide suppression if they are used outside the design parameters.

While these sprinklers are intended primarily for use in high-pile storage situations, this section permits their use and extension into adjacent portions of an occupancy that might have a lesser classification.

Storage in single-story or multistory buildings can be permitted, provided the maximum ceiling/roof height as specified in Chapter 12 is satisfied for each storage area.

Design parameters were determined from a series of full-scale fire tests that were conducted as a joint effort between Factory Mutual Research Corporation and the National Fire Protection Research Foundation. (Copies of the test reports are available from the NFPRF.)

Applications of ESFR sprinklers are described in 12.3.5.3. The special design approach for ESFR sprinklers is based on fire suppression by the first operating ring of sprinklers.

12.3.5.3.1 Protection of single-, double-, and multiple-row rack storage of cartoned or uncartoned unexpanded plastic and cartoned expanded plastic shall be in accordance with Table 12.3.5.3.1.

ESFR protection criteria are provided in Table 12.3.5.3.1, which addresses protection of palletized and solid-piled storage. ESFR sprinklers are also permitted to be utilized for protection of ordinary hazard occupancies and miscellaneous storage. The criteria in Table 12.3.5.3.1 have been expanded to permit broader applications of ESFR sprinkler technology based on large-scale test results reviewed by the Technical Committee on Sprinkler System Discharge Criteria. Design criteria for K-11.2, K-16.8, and K-25.2 ESFR sprinkler technology have been incorporated into the tables where test data supports such inclusion.

12.3.5.3.1.1 ESFR protection as defined shall not apply to the following:

(1) Rack storage involving solid shelves
(2) Rack storage involving combustible, open-top cartons or containers

12.3.5.3.2 ESFR sprinkler systems shall be designed such that the minimum operating pressure is not less than that indicated in Table 12.3.5.3.1 for type of storage, commodity, storage height, and building height involved.

After selecting the commodity, the ceiling height for ESFR protection is the most important factor when selecting the minimum operating pressure (see 12.3.5.3.2). ESFR performance is highly dependent on the ceiling/roof height. This is why averaging of ceiling/roof height based for pitched roofs is not acceptable; the maximum ceiling/roof height over the storage area being protected must be selected.

Where the ceiling/roof height falls above the selected criteria, the design criteria for the next higher ceiling/roof height must be chosen with a maximum ceiling/roof height limit of 45 ft as established by Table 12.3.5.3.1.

Additionally, verification that the maximum storage height does not exceed the value for the ceiling/roof height selected in Table 12.3.5.3.1 is also necessary. It is important to verify that the storage height does not exceed the maximum storage height for the maximum ceiling/roof height design selected from Table 12.3.5.3.1. Lower storage heights that result in greater commodity clearances within a given design are acceptable provided the ESFR design criteria from Table 12.3.5.3.1 are based upon the maximum ceiling/roof height.

◀ FAQ
For ESFR applications where the ceiling/roof height falls between design criteria in Table 12.3.5.3.1, is it acceptable to interpolate the design criteria?

12.3.5.3.3 The design area shall consist of the most hydraulically demanding area of 12 sprinklers, consisting of four sprinklers on each of three branch lines. The design shall include a minimum of 960 ft^2 (89 m^2).

12.3.5.3.4 Where required by Table 12.3.5.3.1, one level of K-8.0 quick-response, ordinary-temperature in-rack sprinklers shall be installed at the tier level closest to but not exceeding ½ of the maximum storage height. In-rack sprinkler hydraulic design criteria shall be the most hydraulically remote eight sprinklers at 50 psi (3.4 bar). In-rack sprinklers shall be located at the intersection of the longitudinal and transverse flue space. Horizontal spacing shall not be permitted to exceed 5-ft (1.5-m) intervals.

12.3.5.3.5 Where ESFR sprinklers are installed above and below obstructions, the discharge for up to two sprinklers for one of the levels shall be included with those of the other level in the hydraulic calculations.

Additional ESFR sprinklers installed below fixed obstructions as required by the obstruction rules in Chapter 8 must be included in the hydraulic calculations. Paragraph 12.3.5.3.5 requires that up to an additional two ESFR sprinklers that are located below obstructions be included with the 12 ESFR sprinkler calculations for a total of up to 14 ESFR sprinklers. This is

Where additional ESFR sprinklers are added below obstructions, what is the total number of sprinklers that must be calculated?
◀ FAQ

TABLE 12.3.5.3.1 *ESFR Protection of Rack Storage without Solid Shelves of Plastics Commodities Stored Over 25 ft (7.6 m) in Height*

Storage Arrangement	Commodity	Maximum Storage Height		Maximum Ceiling/ Roof Height		Nominal K-Factor	Orientation	Minimum Operating Pressure		In-Rack Sprinkler Requirements	Hose Stream Demand		Water Supply Duration (hours)
		ft	m	ft	m			psi	bar		gpm	L/min	
Single-row, Double-row and Multiple-row Rack (No open-top containers)	Cartoned unexpanded	30	9.1	35	10.7	14.0	Upright or pendent	75	5.2	No	250	946	1
						16.8	Pendent	52	3.6	No			
						25.2	Pendent	20	1.4	No			
				40	12.2	14.0	Pendent	75	5.2	No			
						16.8	Pendent	52	3.6	No			
						25.2	Pendent	25	1.7	No			
				45	13.7	14.0	Pendent	90	6.2	Yes			
						16.8	Pendent	63	4.3	Yes			
						25.2	Pendent	40	2.8	No			
		35	10.7	40	12.2	14.0	Pendent	75	5.2	No			
						16.8	Pendent	52	3.6	No			
						25.2	Pendent	25	1.7	No			
				45	13.7	14.0	Pendent	90	6.2	Yes			
						16.8	Pendent	63	4.3	Yes			
						25.2	Pendent	40	2.8	No			
		40	12.2	45	13.7	14.0	Pendent	90	6.2	Yes			
						16.8	Pendent	63	4.3	Yes			
						25.2	Pendent	40	2.8	No			
	Exposed unexpanded	30	9.1	35	10.7	14.0	Pendent	75	5.2	No			
						16.8	Pendent	52	3.6	No			
				40	12.2	14.0	Pendent	75	5.2	No			
						16.8	Pendent	52	3.6	No			
				45	13.7	14.0	Pendent	90	6.2	Yes			
						16.8	Pendent	63	4.3	Yes			
		35	10.7	40	12.2	14.0	Pendent	75	5.2	No			
						16.8	Pendent	52	3.6	No			
				45	13.7	14.0	Pendent	90	6.2	Yes			
						16.8	Pendent	63	4.3	Yes			
		40	12.2	45	13.7	14.0	Pendent	90	6.2	Yes			
						16.8	Pendent	63	4.3	Yes			

a maximum of two additional ESFR sprinklers regardless of the number of ESFR sprinklers installed below obstructions in the remote area. Where only one additional ESFR sprinkler is needed to address an isolated obstruction, then only that ESFR sprinkler would need to be added to the calculation. Care must be taken to identify the appropriate hydraulic remote area when such additional ESFR sprinklers are installed below fixed obstructions. The additional two ESFR sprinklers need only to be added to the 12 ESFR sprinkler demand directly above the obstruction when the combined number of sprinklers creates the hydraulically most demanding area.

12.3.5.4 In-Rack Sprinklers for Rack Storage of Plastics Commodities Stored Over 25 ft (7.6 m) in Height.

Paragraph 12.3.5.4 is intended to apply only to those rack storage arrangements that contain flue spaces in accordance with 12.3.1.14. Where an inadequate number or type of flue spaces is provided or where required flue spaces are obstructed, the criteria provided by 12.3.5.4 are unlikely to provide adequate protection, and the provisions of 12.3.1.9 should be considered.

12.3.5.4.1 In-Rack Sprinkler Location for Rack Storage of Plastics Commodities Stored Over 25 ft (7.6 m) in Height.

In the testing on which this standard is based, where in-rack sprinklers were used, the sprinklers were typically installed above the top of a storage tier at transverse flues (see 12.3.5.4.1). Where multiple levels of in-rack sprinklers were used, in-rack sprinklers were usually staggered among transverse flues, except when barriers were provided.

   Face sprinklers must be located within racks and not over aisles. A fire spreads vertically through the flues or on the face of the pallet loads along the aisles, depending on the location of the ignition source. If the face sprinklers are located in the aisle, their activation will be significantly delayed if it occurs at all. Because face sprinklers incorrectly positioned in the aisle are likely to operate only if they are subject to direct flame impingement, it can be assumed that the fire is overwhelming the sprinkler system design and that success is not likely.

12.3.5.4.1.1 In double-row racks without solid shelves and with a maximum of 10 ft (3.1 m) between the top of storage and the ceiling, in-rack sprinklers shall be installed in accordance with Figure 12.3.5.1.2(a) or Figure 12.3.5.1.2(b). The highest level of in-rack sprinklers shall be not more than 10 ft (3.1 m) below the top of storage.

12.3.5.4.1.2 In single-row racks without solid shelves with storage height over 25 ft (7.6 m) and a maximum of 10 ft (3.1 m) between the top of storage and the ceiling, sprinklers shall be installed as indicated in Figure 12.3.5.1.2.1(a), Figure 12.3.5.1.2.1(b), or Figure 12.3.5.1.2.1(c).

12.3.5.4.1.3* In multiple-row racks without solid shelves with storage height over 25 ft (7.6 m) and a maximum of 10 ft (3.1 m) between the top of storage and the roof/ceiling, in-rack sprinklers shall be installed as indicated in Figure 12.3.5.4.1.3(a) through Figure 12.3.5.4.1.3(f).

A.12.3.5.4.1.3 *Figure (a)*—The protection area per sprinkler under barriers should be no greater than 80 ft^2 (7.44 m^2).

   Figure (b)—The protection area per sprinkler under barriers should be no greater than 80 ft^2 (7.44 m^2).

   Figure (c)—The protection area per sprinkler under barriers should be no greater than 50 ft^2 (4.65 m^2).

   Figure (d)—The protection area per sprinkler under barriers should be no greater than 50 ft^2 (4.65 m^2).

   Figure (e)—The protection area per sprinkler under barriers should be no greater than 50 ft^2 (4.65 m^2).

   Figure (f)—The protection area per sprinkler under barriers should be no greater than 50 ft^2 (4.65 m^2).

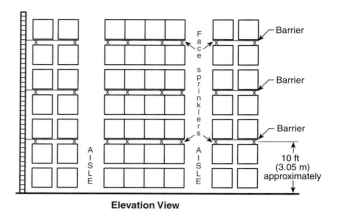

Note: Each square represents a storage cube measuring 4 ft to 5 ft (1.22 m to 1.53 m) on a side. Actual load heights can vary from approximately 18 in. (0.46 m) up to 10 ft (3.05 m). Therefore, there could be as few as one load or as many as six or seven loads between in-rack sprinklers that are spaced 10 ft (3.05 m) apart vertically.

FIGURE 12.3.5.4.1.3(a) *In-Rack Sprinkler Arrangement, Cartoned Plastic and Uncartoned Unexpanded Plastic, Multiple-Row Racks, Storage Height Over 25 ft (7.6 m)—Option 1 (10 ft Maximum Spacing).*

Note: Each square represents a storage cube measuring 4 ft to 5 ft (1.22 m to 1.53 m) on a side. Actual load heights can vary from approximately 18 in. (0.46 m) up to 10 ft (3.05 m). Therefore, there could be as few as one load or as many as six or seven loads between in-rack sprinklers that are spaced 10 ft (3.05 m) apart vertically.

FIGURE 12.3.5.4.1.3(b) *In-Rack Sprinkler Arrangement, Cartoned Plastic and Uncartoned Unexpanded Plastic, Multiple-Row Racks, Storage Height Over 25 ft (7.6 m)—Option 2 (10 ft Maximum Spacing).*

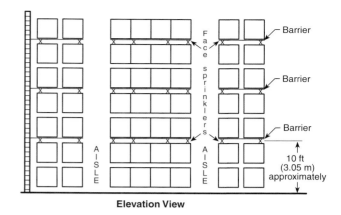

Plan View   **Elevation View**

Note: Each square represents a storage cube measuring 4 ft to 5 ft (1.22 m to 1.53 m) on a side. Actual load heights can vary from approximately 18 in. (0.46 m) up to 10 ft (3.05 m). Therefore, there could be as few as one load or as many as six or seven loads between in-rack sprinklers that are spaced 10 ft (3.05 m) apart vertically.

FIGURE 12.3.5.4.1.3(c) *In-Rack Sprinkler Arrangement, Cartoned Plastic and Uncartoned Unexpanded Plastic, Multiple-Row Racks, Storage Height Over 25 ft (7.6 m)—Option 1 (5 ft Maximum Spacing).*

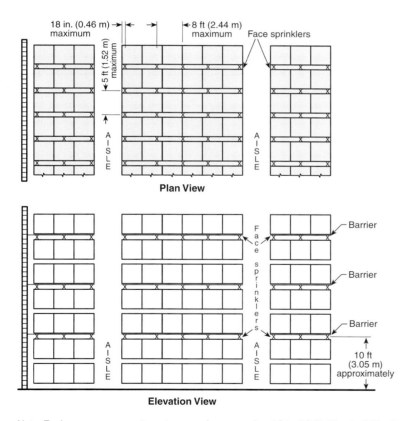

Plan View

Elevation View

Note: Each square represents a storage cube measuring 4 ft to 5 ft (1.22 m to 1.53 m) on a side. Actual load heights can vary from approximately 18 in. (0.46 m) up to 10 ft (3.05 m). Therefore, there could be as few as one load or as many as six or seven loads between in-rack sprinklers that are spaced 10 ft (3.05 m) apart vertically.

FIGURE 12.3.5.4.1.3(d) *In-Rack Sprinkler Arrangement, Cartoned Plastic and Uncartoned Unexpanded Plastic, Multiple-Row Racks, Storage Height Over 25 ft (7.6 m)—Option 2 (5 ft Maximum Spacing).*

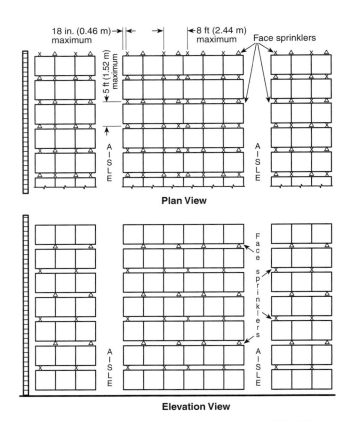

Note: Each square represents a storage cube measuring 4 ft to 5 ft (1.22 m to 1.53 m) on a side. Actual load heights can vary from approximately 18 in. (0.46 m) up to 10 ft (3.05 m). Therefore, there could be as few as one load or as many as six or seven loads between in-rack sprinklers that are spaced 10 ft (3.05 m) apart vertically.

Note: Each square represents a storage cube measuring 4 ft to 5 ft (1.22 m to 1.53 m) on a side. Actual load heights can vary from approximately 18 in. (0.46 m) up to 10 ft (3.05 m). Therefore, there could be as few as one load or as many as six or seven loads between in-rack sprinklers that are spaced 10 ft (3.05 m) apart vertically.

FIGURE 12.3.5.4.1.3(e) *In-Rack Sprinkler Arrangement, Cartoned Plastic and Uncartoned Unexpanded Plastic, Multiple-Row Racks, Storage Height Over 25 ft (7.6 m)— Option 3 (5 ft Maximum Spacing).*

FIGURE 12.3.5.4.1.3(f) *In-Rack Sprinkler Arrangement, Cartoned Plastic and Uncartoned Unexpanded Plastic, Multiple-Row Racks, Storage Height Over 25 ft (7.6 m)— Option 4 (5 ft Maximum Spacing).*

 12.3.5.4.1.4 In single-row and double-row racks without solid shelves with storage height over 25 ft (7.6 m) with aisles greater than 4 ft (1.2 m), in-rack sprinklers shall be located in accordance with Figure 12.3.5.4.1.4 and the ceiling sprinklers shall be designed for 0.45 gpm/ft^2 over a minimum design area of 2000 ft^2.

12.3.5.4.2 In-Rack Sprinkler Spacing for Rack Storage of Plastics Commodities Stored Over 25 ft (7.6 m) in Height.

12.3.5.4.2.1 In-rack sprinklers for storage higher than 25 ft (7.6 m) in double-row racks shall be spaced horizontally and shall be located in the horizontal space nearest the vertical intervals specified in Figure 12.3.5.1.2(a) or Figure 12.3.5.1.2(b).

12.3.5.4.2.2 The minimum of 6-in. (152.4-mm) vertical clear space shall be maintained between the sprinkler deflectors and the top of a tier of storage.

Plan View

Elevation View

Notes:
1. Sprinklers in alternate tiers at every transverse flue space.
2. Each square represents a storage cube measuring 4 ft to 5 ft (1.22 m to 1.53 m) on a side. Actual load heights can vary from approximately 18 in. (0.46 m) up to 10 ft (3.05 m). Therefore, there could be as few as one load or as many as six or seven loads between in-rack sprinklers that are spaced 10 ft (3.05 m) apart vertically.

FIGURE 12.3.5.4.1.4 In-Rack Sprinkler Arrangement, Cartoned Expanded and Unexpanded Plastic and Uncartoned Unexpanded Plastic Commodities, Single- and Double-Row Racks, Storage Height Over 25 ft (7.6 m).

12.3.5.4.3 In-Rack Sprinkler Water Demand for Rack Storage of Plastics Commodities Stored Over 25 ft (7.6 m) in Height. The water demand for sprinklers installed in racks shall be based on simultaneous operation of the most hydraulically remote sprinklers as follows:

(1) Eight sprinklers where only one level is installed in racks
(2) Fourteen sprinklers (seven on each top two levels) where more than one level is installed in racks

12.3.5.4.4 In-Rack Sprinkler Discharge Pressure for Rack Storage of Plastics Commodities Stored Over 25 ft (7.6 m) in Height. Sprinklers in racks shall discharge at not less than 30 gpm (113.6 L/min).

12.4 Protection of Rubber Tire Storage

The sprinkler protection of rubber tires, which is covered in Section 12.4, presents unique challenges. Because of their structure, tires possess inherent air spaces that provide a sufficient amount of air for combustion. Additionally, fires burning on the interior surface of a tire are usually shielded from sprinkler discharge.

The selection of protection criteria from Tables 12.4.2(a), 12.4.2(b), 12.4.2(c), and 12.4.2(d) requires identification of the specific tire storage configuration to be protected.

12.4.1 General. The sprinkler system criteria of Section 12.4 shall apply to buildings with ceiling slopes not exceeding 2 in 12 (16.7 percent).

12.4.1.1 Columns within Rubber Tire Storage.

12.4.1.1.1 Where fireproofing is not provided, steel columns shall be protected as follows:

(1) Storage exceeding 15 ft through 20 ft (4.6 m through 6 m) in height—one sidewall sprinkler directed to one side of the column at a 15-ft (4.6-m) level
(2) Storage exceeding 20 ft (6.1 m) in height— two sidewall sprinklers, one at the top of the column and the other at a 15-ft (4.6-m) level, both directed to the side of the column

12.4.1.1.2 The flow from a column sprinkler(s) shall be permitted to be omitted from the sprinkler system hydraulic calculations.

12.4.1.2 The protection specified in 12.3.1.7, 12.4.1.1.1(1), and 12.4.1.1.1(2) shall not be required where storage in fixed racks is protected by in-rack sprinklers.

12.4.1.3 The rate of water supply shall be sufficient to provide the required sprinkler discharge density over the required area of application plus provision for generation of high-expansion foam and in-rack sprinklers where used.

12.4.1.4 Total water supplies shall be in accordance with the following options:

(1) A minimum of not less than 750 gpm (2835 L/min) for hose streams in addition to that required for automatic sprinklers and foam systems. Water supplies shall be capable of supplying the demand for sprinkler systems and hose streams for not less than 3 hours.
(2) For on-floor storage up to and including 5 ft (1.5 m) in height, hose stream requirements shall be permitted to be 250 gpm (946 L/min) with a water supply duration of not less than 2 hours.
(3) For ESFR and large drop sprinkler systems approved for rubber tire storage, duration and hose demand shall be in accordance with Table 12.4.2(c) and Table 12.4.2(d).

12.4.1.5 Miscellaneous Tire Storage. Miscellaneous tire storage shall be protected in accordance with 12.1.10.

Miscellaneous tire storage, which is addressed in 12.4.1.5, was defined in recognition of that storage found in conjunction with another operation. The definition of *miscellaneous tire storage* can be found in Chapter 3 and also in NFPA 230, *Standard for the Fire Protection of Storage.*

12.4.2* Ceiling Systems. Sprinkler discharge and area of application shall be in accordance with Table 12.4.2(a) and Table 12.4.2(b) for standard spray sprinklers. Large drop and ESFR sprinklers shall be in accordance with Table 12.4.2(c) and Table 12.4.2(d), respectively.

A.12.4.2 The protection criteria in Table 12.4.2(a) through Table 12.4.2(d) have been developed from fire test data. Protection requirements for other storage methods are beyond the scope of this standard at the present time. From fire testing with densities of 0.45 gpm/ft^2 (18.3 mm/min) and higher, there have been indications that large-orifice sprinklers at greater than 50-ft^2 (4.6-m^2) spacing produce better results than the ½-in. (12.7-mm) orifice sprinklers at 50-ft^2 (4.6-m^2) spacing.

Table 12.4.2(a) and Table 12.4.2(c) are based on operation of standard sprinklers. Use of quick-response or other special sprinklers should be based on appropriate tests as approved by the authority having jurisdiction.

The current changes to Table 12.4.2(a) through Table 12.4.2(d) represent test results from rubber tire fire tests performed at the Factory Mutual Research Center.

Storage heights and configurations, or both, [e.g., automated material-handling systems above 30 ft (9.1 m)] beyond those indicated in the table have not had sufficient test data developed to establish recommended criteria. Detailed engineering reviews of the protection should be conducted and approved by the authority having jurisdiction.

In the 1974 tentative standard NFPA 231D, *Standard for Storage of Rubber Tires,* only the following two piling methods were listed:

1. On-floor storage (pyramid piles, on-tread, off-road tires, and arrangements with no horizontal channels)
2. Palletized rack storage (on-side and on-tread, bundled and compressed)

A third option, on-tread storage in portable metal racks, was in the appendix.

The 1974 appendix of NFPA 231D states that only on-floor and palletized rack storage had actually been tested. No other storage arrangements had been tested at that time; the appendix item for the portable metal racks was intended to be good engineering judgment.

In the 1975 edition of NFPA 231D, the sprinkler protection criteria had been expanded to include open portable racks, double- and multi-row fixed rack storage on pallets, and double- and multi-row fixed rack storage without pallets or shelves, as well as the two piling methods listed in the previous paragraph. All three of these added piling methods included tires on-side and on-tread. The height limits in NFPA 231D were 12 ft (3.7 m) for the on-floor storage, 30 ft (9.1 m) for the palletized storage, but only with high-expansion foam aiding the sprinkler protection, and 20 ft (6.1 m) for each of three added piling methods, but with high-expansion foam aiding the sprinkler protection.

By the 1986 edition, NFPA 231D increased the storage heights in piling methods for double- and multi-row fixed racks, on-tread or on-side, with or without pallets or shelves, to 30 ft (9.1 m) as long as high-expansion foam aided the sprinkler protection.

Also in 1986, the appendix reminded the user that the protection in the standard was based on standard response sprinklers. The use of quick-response sprinklers or other special sprinklers was outside the scope of the standard. If special sprinklers or quick-response sprinklers were to be used, testing needed to be conducted to establish protection criteria. This comment is still in the appendix of the 1998 edition of NFPA 231D and applies to two of the three protection tables—the third protection table is for ESFR sprinklers.

In the early 1990s, the tire industry proposed two major changes to NFPA 231D. The industry wanted to increase the storage height in several areas and to introduce laced tires as a piling or storage method. Tests were conducted at the Factory Mutual Research Center to determine if existing, accepted protection options were applicable to this higher and unique storage. This testing led to the following changes to NFPA 231D:

1. Since 1974, on-floor storage had been restricted to 12 ft (3.7 m) in height. However, testing in 1993 showed that some on-floor storage, such as pyramid piles and arrangements that had no horizontal channels, could be stored to 18 ft (5.5 m) when protected by a density of 0.60 gpm/ft^2 (24.5 mm/min).
2. Since 1974, palletized portable rack storage had been allowed to exceed 20 ft (6.1 m) up to 30 ft (9.1 m) but only when high-expansion foam aided the sprinkler protection. The 1993 testing showed that this storage could extend to 25 ft (7.6 m) and be protected with a density of 0.60 gpm/ft^2 (24.5 mm/min) when the ceiling was provided with 1-hour fireproofing. In the 1998 edition of NFPA 231D, the density was changed to 0.75 gpm/ft^2 to be more conservative.

TABLE 12.4.2(a) *Protection Criteria for Rubber Tire Storage Using Control Mode Density-Area Sprinklers*

Piling Method	Piling Height (ft)	Sprinkler Discharge Density (gpm/ft²) (see Note 1)	Areas of Application (ft²) (see Note 1) Ordinary Temperature	High Temperature (see Note 1)
(1) On-floor storage	Up to 5	0.19	2000	2000
(a) Pyramid piles, on-side	Over 5 to 12	0.30	2500	2500
(b) Other arrangements such that no horizontal channels are formed *(see Note 2)*	Over 12 to 18	0.60	Not allowed	2500
(2) On-floor storage	Up to 5	0.19	2000	2000
Tires on-tread	Over 5 to 12	0.30	2500	2500
(3) Palletized portable rack storage	Up to 5	0.19	2000	2000
On-side or on-tread	Over 5 to 20	See Table 12.4.2(b)	—	—
	Over 20 to 30	0.30 plus high-expansion foam	3000	3000
(4) Palletized portable rack storage On-side	Up to 5	0.19	2000	2000
	Over 5 to 20	See Table 12.4.2(b)	—	—
	20 to 25	0.60 and 0.90 *(see Note 3)* or 0.75 with 1-hour fire-resistive rating of roof and ceiling assembly	Not allowed Not allowed Not allowed	5000 3000 4000
(5) Open portable rack storage, on-side or on-tread	Up to 5	0.19	2000	2000
	Over 5 to 12	0.60	5000	3000
	Over 12 to 20	0.60 and 0.90 *(see Note 3)* or 0.30 plus high-expansion foam	Not allowed Not allowed 3000	5000 3000 3000
(6) Single-, double-, and multiple-row fixed rack storage on pallets, on-side or on-tread	Up to 5	0.19	2000	2000
	Over 5 to 20	See Table 12.4.2(b) or 0.40 plus one level in-rack sprinklers or 0.30 plus high-expansion foam	3000 3000	3000 3000
	Over 20 to 30	0.30 plus high-expansion foam	Not allowed	3000
(7) Single-, double-, and multiple-row fixed rack storage without pallets or shelves, on-side or on-tread	Up to 5	0.19	2000	2000
	Over 5 to 12	0.60	5000	3000
	Over 12 to 20	0.60 and 0.90 *(see Note 3)* or 0.40 plus one level in-rack sprinklers or 0.30 plus high-expansion foam	Not allowed Not allowed 3000 3000	5000 3000 3000 3000
	Over 20 to 30	0.30 plus high-expansion foam	Not allowed	3000

For SI units, 1 ft = 0.3048 m; 1 ft² = 0.0929 m²; 1 gpm/ft² = 40.746 mm/min.
Notes:

1. Sprinkler discharge densities and areas of application are based on a maximum clearance of 10 ft (3.1 m) between sprinkler deflectors and the maximum available height of storage. The maximum clearance is noted from actual testing and is not a definitive measurement.

2. Laced tires on-floor, vertical stacking on-side (typical truck tires), and off-road tires. Laced tires are not stored to a significant height by this method due to the damage inflicted on the tire (i.e., bead).

3. Water supply shall fulfill both requirements.

TABLE 12.4.2(b) *Control Mode Density-Area Sprinklers System Density for Palletized Portable Rack Storage and Fixed Rack Storage of Rubber Tires with Pallets, Over 5 ft to 20 ft in Height*

| Storage Height | Sprinkler Temperature | |
	High Temperature	Ordinary Temperature
>5 ft to 10 ft	0.32/2000	0.32/2000
>10 ft to 12 ft	0.39/2000	0.39/2600
>12 ft to 14 ft	0.45/2000	0.45/3200
>14 ft to 16 ft	0.5/2300	0.5/3700
>16 ft to 18 ft	0.55/2600	0.55/4400
>18 ft to 20 ft	0.6/3000	0.6/5000

TABLE 12.4.2(c) *Large Drop Sprinklers and Specific Application Control Mode Sprinkler Protection for Rubber Tires* (see Note 1)

Piling Method	Pile Height	Number of Sprinklers and Minimum Operating Pressures (see Note 2)	Maximum Building Height	Duration (hr)	Hose Demand
Rubber tire storage, on-side or on-tread, in palletized portable racks, or open portable racks, or fixed racks without solid shelves	Up to 25 ft (7.6 m)	15 sprinklers at 75 psi (5.2 bar) *(see Note 3)*	32 ft (9.8 m)	3	500 gpm (1893 L/min)

Notes:

1. Wet systems only.

2. Sprinkler operating pressures and number of sprinklers in the design are based on tests in which the clearance was 5 ft to 7 ft (1.5 m to 2.1 m) between the sprinkler deflector and the maximum height of storage.

3. The design area shall consist of the most hydraulically demanding area of 15 sprinklers, consisting of five sprinklers on each of three branch lines. The design shall include a minimum operating area of 1200 ft² (112 m²) and a maximum operating area of 1500 ft² (139 m²) and shall utilize a high temperature–rated sprinkler.

3. Laced tire storage was not a warehouse concern in the United States until the early 1990s. Lacing of tires was often used while shipping the tires in a tractor trailer, but no manufacturer had warehoused tires in this fashion. About this time, a manufacturer introduced this storage method to its warehouses, storing tires up to 25 ft (7.6 m) high. A test was conducted to determine if a density of 0.60 gpm/ ft² (24.5 mm/min) would provide adequate protection. In the test, 77 sprinklers operated and the steel temperatures exceeded 1500°F (816°C), forcing NFPA 231D to indicate that storage of this type did not have "sufficient test data developed to establish recommended criteria."

In 1996, another test series was conducted to introduce new technology to NFPA 231D. These tests resulted in the addition of large drop and ESFR sprinklers to the protection criteria as follows:

1. Table 12.4.2(a) applies to sprinklers ½-in., ¹⁷/₃₂-in., ⅝-in., and 0.70-in. size orifices. A version of these criteria has existed in NFPA 231D over the years.

2. Table 12.4.2(c) applies to large drop sprinklers protecting a range of piling methods except for laced tires.

3. Table 12.4.2(d) applies to ESFR sprinklers protecting a range of piling methods, including laced tires.

TABLE 12.4.2(d) *Early Suppression Fast-Response (ESFR) Sprinklers for Protection of Rubber Tires* (see Note 1)

Piling Method	Pile Height	Maximum Building Height		Nominal K-factor	Orientation	Number of Sprinklers (see Note 2)	Minimum Operating Pressure (see Note 2)		Duration (hours)	Hose Demand	
		ft	m				psi	bar		gpm	L/min
Rubber tire storage, on-side or on-tread, in palletized portable racks, open portable racks, or fixed racks without solid shelves	Up to 25 ft (7.6 m)	30	9.1	14.0	Upright or pendent	12 (*see Note 3*)	50	3.5	1	250	946
				16.8	Pendent	12 (*see Note 3*)	35	2.4	1	250	946
				25.2	Pendent	12 (*see Note 3*)	15	1.0	1	250	946
Rubber tire storage, on-side, in palletized portable racks, open portable racks, or fixed racks without solid shelves	Up to 25 ft (7.6 m)	35	10.7	14.0	Upright or pendent	12 (*see Note 3*)	75	5.2	1	250	946
				16.8	Pendent	12 (*see Note 3*)	52	3.6	1	250	946
				25.2	Pendent	12 (*see Note 3*)	25	1.7	1	250	946
Laced tires in open portable steel racks	Up to 25 ft (7.6 m)	30	9.1	14.0	Pendent	20 (*see Notes 4 and 5*)	75	5.2	3	500	1892
Rubber tire storage, on-side, in palletized portable racks	Up to 25 ft (7.6 m)	40	12.2	14.0	Pendent	12	75	5.2	1	250	946

Notes:

1. Wet systems only.

2. Sprinkler operating pressures and number of sprinklers in the design are based on tests in which the clearance was 5 ft to 7 ft (1.5 m to 2.1 m) between the sprinkler deflector and the maximum height of storage.

3. The shape of the design area shall be in accordance with 12.2.2.3.3 and 12.2.2.3.4.

4. Where used in this application, ESFR protection is expected to control rather than to suppress the fire.

5. The design area shall consist of the most hydraulically demanding area of 20 sprinklers, consisting of five sprinklers on each of four branch lines. The design shall include a minimum operating area of 1600 ft² (149 m²).

Table 12.4.2(b) is based on tests conducted at the Factory Mutual Research Center. One test was for tires stored on-tread in portable racks up to 25 ft (7.6 m). The second test was for tires stored on-side on palletized portable racks up to 25 ft (7.6 m). The sprinklers operated at 75 psi (5.2 bar). In the former test, eight sprinklers controlled the fire, and in the latter test six sprinklers controlled the fire.

Table 12.4.2(d) is based on tests conducted at the Factory Mutual Research Center. Initially only the K-14 ESFR sprinkler was permitted. Testing using plastic commodities resulted in the addition of the K-25 ESFR sprinkler when the table was transferred to NFPA 13. Rubber tires have not been used as the commodity in tests using K-25 ESFR sprinklers.

12.4.3 In-Rack Sprinkler System Requirements for Protection of Rubber Tires.

12.4.3.1 In-rack sprinklers, where provided, shall be installed in accordance with Section 12.3, except as modified by 12.4.3.2 through 12.4.3.4.

12.4.3.2 The maximum horizontal spacing of sprinklers in rack shall be 8 ft (2.4 m).

12.4.3.3 Water demand for sprinklers installed in racks shall be based on simultaneous operation of the most hydraulically remote 12 sprinklers where only one level is installed in racks.

12.4.3.4 Sprinklers in racks shall discharge at not less than 30 psi (2.1 bar).

12.4.4 Where high-expansion foam systems are installed in accordance with NFPA 11A, *Standard for Medium- and High-Expansion Foam Systems,* a reduction in sprinkler discharge density to one-half the density specified in Table 12.4.2(a) or 0.24 gpm/ft^2 (9.78 mm/min), whichever is higher, shall be permitted.

Ceiling sprinklers are necessary when protecting storage with high-expansion foam, which is discussed in 12.4.4. The sprinklers are primarily needed to maintain the integrity of the columns and ceiling structure for the time it takes to cover the storage commodity with foam. Sprinkler discharge also breaks down the foam, and the designer must take this into account when determining the amount of foam required.

    This requirement is not intended to apply when protection criteria of sprinklers plus high-expansion foam have been selected from Table 12.4.2(a) as the discharge criteria.

    In existing buildings used for tire storage, high-expansion foam can be used to augment an existing sprinkler system whose calculated density is below that required for the proposed storage height. For example, an existing system calculated to provide 0.25 gpm/ft^2 (10.2 mm/min) can be used for storage requiring up to 0.50 gpm/ft^2 (20.4 mm/min) where high-expansion foam is used. Reinforcement or redesign of the sprinkler system is an alternative.

12.5 Protection of Baled Cotton Storage

Protection of baled cotton storage is covered in Section 12.5. The 1999 edition marked the first time that NFPA 13 covered the protection of baled cotton as a requirement and not just as recommended good practice. Fire test data for fires in baled cotton is very limited. Protection criteria are largely based on empirical data gathered and observations made over the course of several years by members of the baled cotton subcommittees and task groups. With baled cotton fires, sprinkler protection should provide undelayed response over large design areas due to the possibility of rapidly spreading flameover-type fires and should provide sustained quantities of water to fight deep-seated fires. The cotton fiber itself contains enough entrained oxygen to sustain a fire deep within a compressed bale. Such a fire will slowly develop until it "breaks out" and exposes nearby bales. Flameover fires, or flashover, as it is known to baled cotton industries, can result from any number of sources, burning across the surface of bales involving areas such as exposed sample holes or fan-head bale ends where cotton ties have come loose. Current bale-wrapping practices lessen the chance of flameover, but the possibility still exists. Sustained application of water over large design areas is necessary due to both the possibility of rapid firespread and the large fuel loading (Btu content) present in baled cotton storage. Recent developments in quick-response and larger orifice sprinkler heads should aid in control of the rapidly spreading nature of some baled cotton fires and in control of more deeply seated fires.

12.5.1 General.

12.5.1.1 The total water supply available shall be sufficient to provide the recommended sprinkler discharge density over the area to be protected, plus a minimum of 500 gpm (1893 L/min) for hose streams.

12.5.1.2 Water supplies shall be capable of supplying the total demand for sprinklers and hose streams for not less than 2 hours.

12.5.2 Control Mode Density-Area Sprinkler Protection Criteria for Baled Cotton Storage.

12.5.2.1 For tiered or rack storage up to a nominal 15 ft (4.6 m) in height, sprinkler discharge densities and areas of application shall be in accordance with Table 12.5.2.1.

TABLE 12.5.2.1 Baled Cotton Storage Up to and Including 15 ft (4.6 m)

System Type	Baled Cotton Storage Up to and Including 15 ft		
	Tiered Storage	**Rack Storage**	**Untiered Storage**
Wet	0.25/3000	0.33/3000	0.15/3000
Dry	0.25/3900	0.33/3900	0.15/3900

Tiered storage of Table 12.5.2.1 is based on the criteria for protection of non-rack storage of Class IV commodities. Rack storage of Table 12.5.2.1 is an extrapolation between tiered storage and the criteria for protection of Class IV commodities in racks. Baled cotton that is not tiered is stacked one bale high on end. The additional 30 percent increase is shown for dry systems in each storage arrangement.

12.5.2.2 Where roof or ceiling heights would prohibit storage above a nominal 10 ft (3.1 m), the sprinkler discharge density shall be permitted to be reduced by 20 percent of that indicated in Table 12.5.2.1 but shall not be reduced to less than 0.15 gpm/ft^2 (6.1 mm/min).

Low roof or ceiling heights that do not permit storage above 10 ft (3 m) effectively limit storage of baled cotton to no more than two bales high on ends or five bales high on sides (see 12.5.2.2). Limited numbers of bales reduce the potential Btu content available to a fire.

12.6* Protection of Roll Paper Storage

A.12.6 This section provides a summary of the data developed from the tissue test series of full-scale roll paper tests conducted at the Factory Mutual Research Center in West Glocester, RI.

The test building is approximately 200 ft × 250 ft [50,000 ft^2 (4.65 km^2)] in area, of fire-resistive construction, and has a volume of approximately 2.25 million ft^3 (63,720 m^3), the equivalent of a 100,000-ft^2 (9.29-km^2) building 22.5 ft (6.86 m) high. The test building has two primary heights beneath a single large ceiling. The east section is 30 ft (9.1 m) high and the west section is 60 ft (18.29 m) high.

The tissue test series was conducted in the 30-ft (9.1-m) section, with clearances from the top of storage to the ceiling nominally 10 ft (3.1 m).

Figure A.12.6 illustrates a typical storage array used in the tissue series of tests.

The basic criteria used in judging test failure included one or more of the following:

(1) Firespread to the north end of the storage array
(2) Gas temperatures near the ceiling maintained at high levels for a time judged to be sufficient to endanger exposed structural steel
(3) Fire reaching the target stacks

Table A.12.6 outlines the tissue test results.

Fire tests have been conducted on 20-ft (6.1-m) and 25-ft (7.6-m) high vertical storage of tissue with 10-ft (3.1-m) and 5-ft (1.5-m) clear space to the ceiling in piles extending up to seven columns in one direction and six columns in the other direction. In these tests, target columns of tissue were located directly across an 8-ft (2.4-m) aisle from the main pile. Three tests were conducted using $^{17}/_{32}$-in. (13.5-mm) 286°F (141°C) high-temperature sprinklers on a

N

26 ft (7.9 m)

21½ ft
(6.6 m)

6 in.
(152 mm)

16 in.
(406.4 mm)

6 in.
(152 mm)

6 in.
(152 mm)

16 in.
(406.4 mm)

6 in.
(152 mm)

8 ft
(2.4 m)

← Target stack

* Ignition location
at base of array

Tissue paper —
approximately 20 ft (6 m) high

Kraft linerboard —
six rolls 20 ft (6 m) high

FIGURE A.12.6 *Plan View of Typical Tissue Storage Array.*

100-ft² (9.3-m²) spacing and at constant pressures of 14 psi, 60 psi, and 95 psi (1 bar, 4.1 bar, and 6.6 bar), respectively. One test was run using 0.64-in. (16.3-mm) 286°F (141°C) high-temperature sprinklers on a 100-ft² (9.3-m²) spacing at a constant pressure of 50 psi (3.5 bar). Two tests were conducted following a scheduled decay from an initial pressure of 138 psi (9.5 bar) to a design point of 59 psi (4.1 bar) if 40 sprinklers opened. The significant characteristic of these fire tests was the rapid initial firespread across the surface of the rolls. Ceiling temperatures were controlled during the decaying pressure tests and during the higher constant pressure tests. With the exception of the 20-ft (6.1-m) high decaying pressure test, the extent of firespread within the pile could not be clearly established. Aisle jump was experienced, except at the 95-psi (6.6-bar) constant pressure, 20-ft (6.1-m) high decaying pressure, and large drop test. Water absorption and pile instability caused pile collapse in all tests. This characteristic should be considered where manually attacking a fire in tissue storage occupancies.

Available fire experience in roll tissue storage occupancies does not correlate well with the constant pressure full-scale fire tests with respect to the number of sprinklers operating and the extent of firespread. Better correlation is noted with the decaying pressure tests. Thirteen fires reported in storage occupancies with storage piles ranging from 10 ft to 20 ft (3.1 m to 6.1 m) high and protected by wet pipe sprinkler systems ranging from ordinary hazard design densities to design densities of 0.6 gpm/ft² (24.5 mm/min) were controlled with an average of 17 sprinklers. The maximum number of wet pipe sprinklers that opened was 45 and the minimum number was five, versus 88 and 26, respectively, in the constant pressure tests. Seventeen sprinklers opened in the 20-ft (6.1-m) high decaying pressure test. One actual fire in tissue storage provided with a dry pipe system opened 143 sprinklers but was reported as controlled.

One fire test was conducted with plastic-wrapped rolls of heavyweight kraft paper. The on-end storage was in a standard configuration, 20 ft (6.1 m) high with 9½-ft (2.9-m) clearance to ceiling sprinklers. The prescribed 0.3-gpm/ft² (12.2-mm/min) density controlled the firespread, but protection to roof steel was marginal to the point where light beams and joists might be expected to distort. A lower moisture content in the paper as a result of the protective

TABLE A.12.6 *Summary of Roll Paper Tissue Tests*

Test Specifications	Test Number					
	B1[a]	B2	B3	B4	B5[b]	B6[b]
Test date	10/4/79	7/23/80	7/30/80	10/15/80	7/28/82	8/5/82
Paper type	Tissue	Tissue	Tissue	Tissue	Tissue	Tissue
Stack height [ft-in. (m)]	21–10 (6.66)	20–0 (6.1)	21–8 (6.60)	18–6 (6.64)	19–10 (6.05)	25–3 (7.69)
Paper, banded	No	No	No	No	No	No
Paper, wrapped	No	No	No	No	No	No
Fuel array	Standard	Standard	Standard	Standard	Standard	Standard
Clearance to ceiling [ft-in. (m)]	8–2 (2.49)	10–0 (3.05)	8–4 (2.54)	11–6 (3.51)	5–2 (1.58)	4–9 (1.45)
Clearance to sprinklers [ft-in. (m)]	7–7 (2.31)	9–5 (2.87)	7–9 (2.36)	10–9 (3.28)	4–7 (1.40)	4–2 (1.27)
Sprinkler orifice [in. (mm)]	$17/32$ (13.5)	$17/32$ (13.5)	$17/32$ (13.5)	0.64 (16.33)	$17/32$ (13.5)	$17/32$ (13.5)
Sprinkler temperature rating [F° (°C)]	280 (138)	280 (138)	280 (138)	280 (138)	280 (138)	280 (138)
Sprinkler spacing [ft × ft (m × m)]	10 × 10 (3.05 × 3.05)	10 × 10 (3.05 × 3.05)	10 × 10 (3.05 × 3.05)	10 × 10 (3.05 × 3.05)	10 × 10 (3.05 × 3.05)	10 × 10 (3.05 × 3.05)
Water pressure [psi (bar)]	14 (0.9)[c]	60 (4.1)	95 (6.6)	50 (3.4)	138 (9.5) initial 102 (7.0) final	138 (9.5) initial 88 (6.1) final
Moisture content of paper (%)	9.3	9.3	10.2	6.0	8.2	9.2
First sprinkler operation (min:sec)	0:43	0:32	0:38	0:31	0:28	0:22
Total sprinklers open	88	33	26	64	17	29
Final flow [gpm (L/min)]	2575 (9746)[c]	1992 (7540)	1993 (7544)	4907 (18,573)	1363 (5159)	2156 (8161)
Sprinkler demand area [ft² (m²)]	8800 (817.5)	3300 (306.6)	2600 (241.5)	6400 (595)	1700 (158)	2900 (269)
Average discharge density [gpm/ft² (mm/min)]	0.29 (11.8)[c]	0.60 (24.4)	0.77 (31.4)	—	0.92 (37.5) initial 0.80 (32.6) final	0.96 (39.1) initial 0.74 (30.2) final
Maximum 1-minute average gas temperature over ignition [°F (°C)]	1680 (916)[c]	1463 (795)	1634 (890)	1519 (826)	[d]	[e]
Duration of high temperature within acceptable limits	No	Yes	Yes	Marginal	Yes	Yes
Maximum 1-minute average fire plume gas velocity over ignition [ft/sec (m/sec)]	—	40.7 (12.4)	50.2 (15.3)	47.8 (14.6)	—	—
Target ignited	Yes	Yes	No	No	No	Briefly
Extent of fire damage within acceptable limits	No	No	Marginal	Marginal	Yes	Marginal
Test duration (min)	17.4	20	20	25.5	45	45

[a]Phase I test.

[b]Phase III tests decaying pressure.

[c]Pressure increased to 50 psi (3.5 bar) at 10 minutes.

[d]Maximum steel temperature over ignition 341°F (172°C).

[e]Maximum steel temperature over ignition 132°F (56°C).

plastic wrapping was considered to be the reason for the higher temperatures in this test as compared to a similar test where the rolls were not wrapped.

The requirements for sprinkler protection of roll paper, which are covered in Section 12.6, were developed from data obtained from full-scale fire tests of roll paper storage that were conducted at the Factory Mutual Test Center in West Glocester, RI, under flat ceilings. These sprinkler protection criteria were previously located in NFPA 231F, *Standard for the Storage of Roll Paper.*

The A.12.6 data and discussion of the full-scale roll paper tissue fire tests, which presented the highest fire challenge tested, are indicative of the overall roll paper fire test program that was conducted over a period of 3 years. Roll tissue presented the highest challenge to sprinklers in the tests because of the rapid flamespread across the surface of the rolls. A summary of the 3-year roll paper test program for tissue is shown in Table A.12.6. A summary of the test program for kraft linerboard and newsprint is shown in Commentary Table 12.1.

12.6.1 General.

12.6.1.1 The water supply system for automatic fire protection systems shall be designed for a minimum duration of 2 hours.

12.6.1.1.1 For ESFR sprinklers, the water supply duration shall be 1 hour.

12.6.1.2 At least 500 gpm (1893 L/min) shall be added to the sprinkler demand for large and small hose stream demand.

12.6.1.2.1 For ESFR sprinklers, the hose stream allowance shall be for 250 gpm (947 L/min).

12.6.1.3 The water supply design shall include the demand of the automatic sprinkler system plus the hose stream demand plus, where provided, the high-expansion foam system.

12.6.1.4 Wet pipe systems shall be used in tissue storage areas.

Tissue storage areas are addressed in 12.6.1.4. Fire tests conducted on roll paper storage demonstrate that the weight and surface characteristics of the paper determine the rate of flamespread over the surface of the paper. Lightweight and thin paper sheets burn much faster than heavyweight thick paper sheets. The surface characteristics of a paper sheet or coatings on the paper can also influence the rate of flamespread over the surface. A "fuzzy" soft sheet of paper will burn faster than paper of the same weight that has a polished surface (calendered). The rate of flamespread across the exposed surface or outer ply of a roll of paper is the most critical factor in designing a sprinkler system that will control a roll paper fire. Lightweight tissue paper exhibits a particularly rapid surface flamespread that can open an excessive number of sprinklers in a relatively short period of time and make it very difficult for a dry pipe sprinkler system to establish a controlling sprinkler density. Annex C contains a summary of the full-scale roll paper tissue tests. The classification of roll paper by basis weight can be found in Chapter 5.

12.6.1.5 Horizontal storage of heavyweight or mediumweight paper shall be protected as a closed array.

Horizontal storage of paper is addressed in 12.6.1.5. Fire tests conducted on vertical storage of roll paper in a closed array indicated a relatively slow developing fire that required a relatively small sprinkler system discharge density and area of operation to achieve fire control. A closed paper array is one in which the distance between paper columns in all directions is small—that is, not more than 2 in. (50 mm)—as shown in Exhibit 12.9. The slow fire development is due to the limited size of the flue spaces between paper rolls. Horizontal (nested) storage of paper rolls shown in Exhibit 12.10 also minimizes the size of the flue spaces in the horizontal direction, which tends to limit fire growth. See definitions of *array* in Chapter 3 for further details.

COMMENTARY TABLE 12.1 Summary of Roll Paper Fire Test Program for Kraft Linerboard and Newsprint

	Test Number										
	A1[a]	A2[a]	A3[a]	A4[a]	A5	A6	A7	C1	C2	C3	C4
Test date	9/18/79	9/25/79	10/1/79	10/9/79	7/9/80	7/16/80	8/14/80	8/16/80	8/20/80	11/19/80	12/17/80
Paper type	Kraft linerboard	Kraft linerboard	Kraft linerboard	Kraft linerboard	Kraft linerboard	Kraft linerboard	Kraft linerboard	Newsprint	Newsprint	Newsprint	Newsprint
Stack height [ft–in. (m)]	20–0 (6.1)	20–0 (6.1)	20–0 (6.1)	25–4 (7.7)	20–0 (6.1)	26–0 (7.9)	26–0 (7.9)	19–0 (5.6)	19–0 (5.6)	19–0 (5.6)	19–0 (5.6)
Paper, banded	Yes	Yes	No	Yes	No	Yes	Yes	No	No	No	No
Paper, wrapped	No	No	No	No	No	No	No	Yes	No	No	No
Fuel array	Std.	Std.	Std.	Std.	Open	Open	Open	Closed	Open	Std.	Std.
Clearance to ceiling [ft–in. (m)]	5–0 (1.5)	10–0 (3.05)	10–0 (3.05)	4–8 (1.4)	10–0 (3.05)	34–0 (10.4)	34–0 (10.4)	11–0 (3.4)	11–0 (3.4)	11–0 (3.4)	11–0 (3.4)
Clearance to sprinklers [ft–in. (m)]	4–5 (1.4)	9–5 (2.87)	9–5 (2.87)	4–1 (1.3)	9–5 (2.87)	33–5 (10.2)	33–5 (10.2)	10.5 (3.2)	10.5 (3.2)	10.5 (3.2)	10.5 (3.2)
Sprinkler orifice [in. (mm)]	$\frac{17}{32}$ (13.5)	$\frac{17}{32}$ (13.5)	$\frac{17}{32}$ (13.5)	$\frac{17}{32}$ (13.5)	$\frac{17}{32}$ (13.5)	$\frac{17}{32}$ (13.5)	0.64 (16.33)	$\frac{17}{32}$ (13.5)	$\frac{17}{32}$ (13.5)	$\frac{1}{2}$ (12.7)	$\frac{17}{32}$ (13.5)
Sprinkler temp. rating [F° (C°)]	280 (138)	280 (138)	280 (138)	280 (138)	280 (138)	280 (138)	280 (138)	280 (138)	280 (138)	280 (138)	280 (138)
Sprinkler spacing [ft × ft (m × m)]	10 × 10 (3.05 × 3.05)	10 × 10 (3.05 × 3.05)	10 × 10 (3.05 × 3.05)	10 × 10 (3.05 × 3.05)	10 × 10 (3.05 × 3.05)	10 × 10 (3.05 × 3.05)	10 × 10 (3.05 × 3.05)	10 × 10 (3.05 × 3.05)	10 × 10 (3.05 × 3.05)	10 × 10 (3.05 × 3.05)	10 × 10 (3.05 × 3.05)
Water pressure [psi (bar)]	14 (0.9)	14 (0.9)	14 (0.9)	14 (0.9)	34 (2.3)	60 (4.1)	60 (4.1)	15 (1.0)	34 (2.3)	34 (2.3)	34 (2.3)
Moisture content of paper (%)	8.4	9.9	9.2	7.8	9.2	9.4	9.6	10.6/10.9[c]	9.5	7.5	7.2
First sprinkler operation (min:sec)	1:52	1:30	1:34	1:39	1:36	2:03	2:09	2:31	0:54	0:39	0:41
Total sprinklers open	12	18	20	22	28	39	7	4	31	45	34
Final flow [gpm (L/min)]	350 (1325)	520 (1968)	575 (2176)	630 (2385)	1282 (4852)	2378 (9001)	601 (2275)	121 (458)	1414 (5352)	1538 (5821)	1550 (5867)
Sprinkler demand area [ft² (m²)]	1200 (112)	1800 (167)	2000 (186)	2200 (204)	2800 (260)	3900 (362)	700 (65)	400 (37)	3100 (288)	4500 (418)	3400 (316)
Average discharge density [gpm/ft² (mm/min)]	0.29 (11.8)	0.29 (11.8)	0.29 (11.8)	0.29 (11.8)	0.46 (18.7)	0.61 (24.9)	—	0.30 (12.2)	0.46 (18.7)	0.34 (13.9)	0.46 (18.7)
Maximum 1-minute average gas temperature over ignition [°F (°C)]	1480 (804)	1640 (893)	1550 (843)	1470 (799)	1386 (752)	1654 (901)	949 (509)	1311 (711)	1512 (822)	1851 (1011)	1646 (897)
Duration of high temperature within acceptable limits	Yes	Yes	Yes	Marginal	Yes	No	Yes	Yes	Yes	No	Marginal
Maximum 1-minute average fire plume gas velocity over ignition [ft/sec (m/sec)]	—	—	—	—	47.4 (14.4)	80.7 (24.6)	36.4 (11.1)	34.6 (10.5)	49.2 (15.0)	53.2 (16.2)	48.5 (14.8)
Target ignited	No	No	No	No	No	Yes	No	No	Yes	Yes	Yes
Extent of fire damage within acceptable limits	Yes	Yes	Yes	Yes	Yes	No	Yes	Yes	No	No	No
Test duration (min)	12.3	12.9	30.2	25.1	30	20	30	25.1	25.2	25	25.4

[a] Phase I Test.
[b] Pressure increased to 50 psi at 10 minutes.
[c] Wrapper—10.6 percent; Newsprint—10.9 percent.

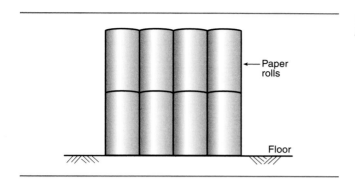

EXHIBIT 12.9 Closed Paper Roll Vertical Storage Array.

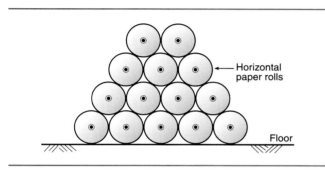

EXHIBIT 12.10 Horizontal (Nested) Storage of Paper Rolls.

Fire tests conducted on roll paper storage demonstrate that the flamespread characteristics of the exposed outer sheets of the paper rolls are the critical factor in determining the sprinkler system design required to achieve fire control. Heavyweight paper used as a protective wrapper on mediumweight newsprint and writing papers has a relatively low flamespread rating. When mediumweight papers were wrapped in heavyweight paper for testing, sprinkler systems designed to protect heavyweight paper successfully controlled the fire. See Chapter 5 for a description of paper classifications. Further, when heavyweight wrappers were used on lightweight tissue rolls, successful control of the fire was achieved by sprinkler systems designed to protect mediumweight paper.

12.6.1.6 Mediumweight paper shall be permitted to be protected as heavyweight paper where wrapped completely on the sides and both ends, or where wrapped on the sides only with steel bands. Wrapping material shall be either a single layer of heavyweight paper with a basis weight of 40 lb (18.1 kg) or two layers of heavyweight paper with a basis weight of less than 40 lb (18.1 kg).

12.6.1.7 Lightweight paper or tissue paper shall be permitted to be protected as mediumweight paper where wrapped completely on the sides and both ends, or where wrapped on the sides only with steel bands. Wrapping material shall be either a single layer of heavyweight paper with a basis weight of 40 lb (18.1 kg) or two layers of heavyweight paper with a basis weight of less than 40 lb (18.1 kg).

12.6.1.8 For purposes of sprinkler system design criteria, lightweight class paper shall be protected as tissue.

12.6.2* Protection Criteria for the Protection of Roll Paper Storage.

A.12.6.2 *Existing Systems.* Sprinkler systems protecting existing roll paper storage facilities should be evaluated in accordance with Table A.12.6.2(a) and Table A.12.6.2(b). While fire can be controlled by the protection shown in Table A.12.6.2(a) and Table A.12.6.2(b), greater

TABLE A.12.6.2(a) *Automatic Sprinkler System Design Criteria—Spray Sprinklers for Existing Storage Facilities (Discharge densities are gpm/ft² over ft².)*

| Storage Height (ft) | Clearance (ft) | Heavyweight | | | | | Mediumweight | | | |
| | | Closed Array Banded or Unbanded | Standard Array | | Open Array | | Closed Array Banded or Unbanded | Standard Array | | Open Array Banded or Unbanded |
			Banded	Unbanded	Banded	Unbanded		Banded	Unbanded	
10	≤5	0.2/2000	0.2/2000	0.2/2000	0.25/2000	0.25/2000	0.2/2000	0.25/2000	0.3/2000	0.3/2000
10	>5	0.2/2000	0.2/2000	0.2/2000	0.25/2500	0.25/2500	0.2/2000	0.25/2000	0.3/2000	0.3/2000
15	≤5	0.25/2000	0.25/2000	0.25/2500	0.3/2500	0.3/3000	0.25/2000	0.3/2000	0.45/2500	0.45/2500
15	>5	0.25/2000	0.25/2000	0.25/2500	0.3/3000	0.3/3500	0.25/2000	0.3/2500	0.45/3000	0.45/3000
20	≤5	0.3/2000	0.3/2000	0.3/2500	0.45/3000	0.45/3500	0.3/2000	0.45/2500	0.6/2500	0.6/2500
20	>5	0.3/2000	0.3/2500	0.3/3000	0.45/3500	0.45/4000	0.3/2500	0.45/3000	0.6/3000	0.6/3000
25	≤5	0.45/2500	0.45/3000	0.45/3500	0.6/2500	0.6/3000	0.45/3000	0.6/3000	0.75/2500	0.75/2500
25	>5	0.45/3000	0.45/3500	0.45/4000	0.6/3000	0.6/3500	0.45/3500	0.6/3500	0.75/3000	0.75/3000
30	≤5	0.6/2500	0.6/3000	0.6/3000	0.75/2500	0.75/3000	0.6/4000	0.75/3000	0.75/3500	0.75/3500

Note: Densities or areas, or both, can be interpolated between any 5-ft storage height increment.

TABLE A.12.6.2(b) *Automatic Sprinkler System Design Criteria—Spray Sprinklers for Existing Storage Facilities (Discharge densities are mm/min over m².)*

| Storage Height (m) | Clearance (m) | Heavyweight | | | | | Mediumweight | | | |
| | | Closed Array Banded or Unbanded | Standard Array | | Open Array | | Closed Array Banded or Unbanded | Standard Array | | Open Array Banded or Unbanded |
			Banded	Unbanded	Banded	Unbanded		Banded	Unbanded	
3.1	≤1.5	0.76/185.8	0.76/185.8	0.76/185.8	0.95/185.8	0.95/185.8	0.76/185.8	0.95/185.8	12.2/185.8	12.2/185.8
3.1	>1.5	0.76/185.8	0.76/185.8	0.76/185.8	0.95/232.3	0.95/232.3	0.76/185.8	0.95/185.8	12.2/185.8	12.2/185.8
4.6	≤1.5	0.95/185.8	0.95/185.8	0.95/232.3	12.2/232.3	12.2/278.7	0.95/185.8	12.2/185.8	18.3/232.3	18.3/232.3
4.6	>1.5	0.95/185.8	0.95/185.8	0.95/232.3	12.2/278.7	12.2/325.2	0.95/185.8	12.2/232.3	18.3/278.7	18.3/278.7
6.1	≤1.5	12.2/185.8	12.2/185.8	12.2/232.3	18.3/278.7	18.3/325.2	12.2/185.8	18.3/232.3	24.5/232.3	24.5/232.3
6.1	>1.5	12.2/185.8	12.2/232.3	12.2/278.7	18.3/325.2	18.3/371.6	12.2/232.3	18.3/278.7	24.5/278.7	24.5/278.7
7.6	≤1.5	18.3/232.3	18.3/278.7	18.3/325.2	24.5/232.3	24.5/278.7	18.3/278.7	24.5/278.7	30.6/232.3	30.6/232.3
7.6	>1.5	183/278.7	18.3/325.2	18.3/371.6	24.5/278.7	24.5/325.2	18.3/325.2	24.5/325.2	30.6/278.7	30.6/278.7
9.1	≤1.5	24.5/232.3	24.5/278.7	24.5/278.7	30.6/232.3	30.6/278.7	24.5/371.6	30.6/278.7	30.6/325.2	30.6/325.2

Note: Densities or areas, or both, can be interpolated between any 1.5-m storage height increment.

damage can occur when the densities in Table A.12.6.2(a) and Table A.12.6.2(b) are used rather than those specified in Table 12.6.2.1.3(a) and Table 12.6.2.1.3(b).

12.6.2.1 Control Mode Density-Area Sprinkler Protection Criteria for the Protection of Roll Paper Storage.

12.6.2.1.1 Storage of heavyweight or mediumweight classes of rolled paper up to 10 ft (3.1 m) in height shall be protected by sprinklers designed for ordinary hazard Group 2 densities.

Testing was used to establish the discharge densities for the control of fires in heavyweight and mediumweight paper stored up to 20 ft (6.1 m) and 25 ft (7.6 m) in height (see 12.6.2.1.1). The tests indicated that adequate protection can also be provided using an ordinary hazard (Group 2) density where the heavyweight and mediumweight paper are stored no higher than 10 ft (3.1 m).

12.6.2.1.2 Storage of tissue and lightweight classes of paper up to 10 ft (3.1 m) in height shall be protected by sprinklers in accordance with extra hazard Group 1 densities.

TABLE 12.6.2.1.3(a) *Control Mode Density-Area Sprinkler Protection Criteria for the Protection of Roll Paper Storage for Buildings or Structures with Roof or Ceilings Up to 30 ft (Discharge Densities are gpm/ft² over ft²)*

Storage Height (ft)	Clearance (ft)	Heavyweight					Mediumweight				Tissue All Storage Array
		Closed Array Banded or Unbanded	Standard Array		Open Array		Closed Array Banded or Unbanded	Standard Array		Open Array Banded or Unbanded	
			Banded	Unbanded	Banded	Unbanded		Banded	Unbanded		
10	≤5	0.3/2000	0.3/2000	0.3/2000	0.3/2000	0.3/2000	0.3/2000	0.3/2000	0.3/2000	0.3/2000	0.45/2000
10	>5	0.3/2000	0.3/2000	0.3/2000	0.3/2000	0.3/2000	0.3/2000	0.3/2000	0.3/2000	0.3/2000	0.45/2500
15	≤5	0.3/2000	0.3/2000	0.3/2000	0.3/2500	0.3/3000	0.3/2000	0.3/2000	0.45/2500	0.45/2500	0.60/2000
15	>5	0.3/2000	0.3/2000	0.3/2000	0.3/3000	0.3/3500	0.3/2000	0.3/2500	0.45/3000	0.45/3000	0.60/3000
20	≤5	0.3/2000	0.3/2000	0.3/2500	0.45/3000	0.45/3500	0.3/2000	0.45/2500	0.6/2500	0.6/2500	0.75/2500
20	>5	0.3/2000	0.3/2500	0.3/3000	0.45/3500	0.45/4000	0.3/2500	0.45/3000	0.6/3000	0.6/3000	0.75/3000
25	≤5	0.45/2500	0.45/3000	0.45/3500	0.6/2500	0.6/3000	0.45/3000	0.6/3000	0.75/2500	0.75/2500	*see Note 1*

Notes:

1. Sprinkler protection requirements for tissue stored above 20 ft have not been determined.
2. Densities or areas, or both, shall be permitted to be interpolated between any 5-ft storage height increment.

TABLE 12.6.2.1.3(b) *Control Mode Density-Area Sprinkler Protection Criteria for the Protection of Roll Paper Storage for Buildings or Structures with Roof or Ceilings Up to 9.1 m (Discharge Densities are mm/min over m²)*

Storage Height (m)	Clearance (m)	Heavyweight					Mediumweight				Tissue All Storage Arrays
		Closed Array Banded or Unbanded	Standard Array		Open Array		Closed Array Banded or Unbanded	Standard Array		Open Array Banded or Unbanded	
			Banded	Unbanded	Banded	Unbanded		Banded	Unbanded		
3.1	≤1.5	12.2/185.8	12.2/185.8	12.2/185.8	12.2/185.8	12.2/185.8	12.2/185.8	12.2/185.8	12.2/185.8	12.2/185.8	18.3/185.8
3.1	>1.5	12.2/185.8	12.2/185.8	12.2/185.8	12.2/185.8	12.2/185.8	12.2/185.8	12.2/185.8	12.2/185.8	12.2/185.8	18.3/232.3
4.6	≤1.5	12.2/185.8	12.2/185.8	12.2/185.8	12.2/232.3	12.2/278.7	12.2/185.8	12.2/185.8	18.3/232.3	18.3/232.3	24.5/185.8
4.6	>1.5	12.2/185.8	12.2/185.8	12.2/185.8	12.2/278.7	12.2/322.2	12.2/185.8	12.2/232.3	18.3/278.7	18.3/278.7	24.5/278.7
6.1	≤1.5	12.2/185.8	12.2/185.8	12.2/232.3	18.3/278.7	18.3/325.2	12.2/185.8	18.3/232.3	24.5/232.3	24.5/232.3	30.6/232.3
6.1	>1.5	12.2/185.8	12.2/232.3	12.2/278.7	18.3/325.2	18.3/371.6	12.2/232.3	18.3/278.7	24.5/278.7	24.5/278.7	30.6/278.7
7.6	≤1.5	18.3/232.3	18.3/278.7	18.3/325.2	24.5/232.3	24.5/278.7	18.3/278.7	24.5/278.7	30.6/232.3	30.6/232.3	*see Note 1*

Notes:

1. Sprinkler protection requirements for tissue stored above 6.1 m have not been determined.
2. Densities or areas, or both, shall be permitted to be interpolated between any 1.5-m storage height increment.

Because of the rapid firespread across the surface of paper rolls classified as lightweight or tissue, protection criteria must be increased to extra hazard (Group 1), as stated in 12.6.2.1.2.

12.6.2.1.3 Sprinkler design criteria for storage of roll paper 10 ft (3.1 m) high and higher in buildings or structures with roof or ceilings up to 30 ft (9.1 m) shall be in accordance with Table 12.6.2.1.3(a) and Table 12.6.2.1.3(b).

Tables 12.6.2.1.3(a) and 12.6.2.1.3(b) are based on data from a series of full-scale roll paper fire tests conducted at the Factory Mutual Research Center at West Glocester, RI. See Annex C and commentary to Table A.12.6.

12.6.2.1.4* High-temperature sprinklers shall be used for installations protecting roll paper stored 15 ft (4.6 m) or higher.

 A.12.6.2.1.4 Generally, more sprinklers open in fires involving roll paper storage protected by sprinklers rated below the high-temperature range. An increase of 67 percent in the design area should be considered.

High-temperature sprinklers, which are discussed in 12.6.2.1.4, were used in all of the fire tests conducted on roll paper that provided the data for developing the area/density design criteria. Large drop sprinklers used in the fire tests on roll paper also had high-temperature ratings. The ESFR design criteria are based on EFSR technology and tests conducted by Factory Mutual Research Corporation. ESFR sprinklers are not subject to 12.6.2.1.4.

12.6.2.1.5 The protection area per sprinkler shall not exceed 100 ft^2 (9.3 m^2) or be less than 70 ft^2 (6.5 m^2).

The protection area per sprinkler used in the roll paper fire test program described in A.12.6 was 100 ft^2 (9.3 m^2) (see 12.6.2.1.5).

12.6.2.1.6 Where high-expansion foam systems are installed in heavyweight class and mediumweight class storage areas, sprinkler discharge design densities can be reduced to not less than 0.24 gpm/ft^2 (9.8 mm/min) with a minimum operating area of 2000 ft^2 (186 m^2).

12.6.2.1.7 Where high-expansion foam systems are installed in tissue storage areas, sprinkler discharge densities and areas of application shall not be reduced below those provided in Table 12.6.2.1.3(a) and Table 12.6.2.1.3(b).

The roll paper fire test program conducted to provide data for automatic sprinkler design criteria did not include tests using high-expansion foam. However, the effect on high-expansion foam has been demonstrated on other storage commodities (see 12.6.2.1.7).

12.6.2.2 Large Drop Sprinklers and Specific Application Control Mode Sprinklers for the Protection of Roll Paper Storage. Where automatic sprinkler system protection utilizes large drop sprinklers, hydraulic design criteria shall be as specified in Table 12.6.2.2. Design discharge pressure shall be 50 psi (3.4 bar). The number of sprinklers to be calculated is indicated based on storage height, clearance, and system type.

TABLE 12.6.2.2 *Large Drop Sprinklers for the Protection of Roll Paper Storage (Number of Sprinklers to be Calculated)*

Storage Height		Clearance		System Type	Heavyweight					Mediumweight					Tissue All Storage Arrays
					Closed Array	Standard Array		Open Array		Closed Array	Standard Array		Open Array		
ft	m	ft	m		Banded or Unbanded	Banded	Unbanded	Banded	Unbanded	Banded or Unbanded	Banded	Unbanded	Banded	Unbanded	
20	6.1	<10	<3.1	W	15	15	15	15	NA	15	15	15	NA	NA	See Note 3
20	6.1	<10	<3.1	D	25	25	25	NA	NA	25	25	25	NA	NA	NA
26	7.9	<34	<10.4	W	15	15	15	15	NA	NA	NA	NA	NA	NA	NA
26	7.9	<34	<10.4	D	NA	NA	NA	NA	NA	NA	NA	NA	NA	NA	NA

Notes:
1. W = wet; D = dry; NA = not applicable.
2. For definition of storage height, see 3.9.2.
3. Twenty-five large drop sprinklers @ 75 psi (5.2 bar) for closed or standard array; other NA.

TABLE 12.6.2.3 *ESFR Sprinklers for the Protection of Roll Paper Storage (Maximum Height of Storage Permitted)*

ESFR K-Factor	Orientation	System Type	Pressure		Building Height		Heavyweight						Mediumweight						Tissue All Arrays
							Closed		Standard		Open		Closed		Standard		Open		
			psi	bar	ft	m	ft	m	ft	m	ft	m	ft	m	ft	m	ft	m	
11.2	Upright	Wet	50	3.4	25	7.6	20	6.1	20	6.1	20	6.1	20	6.1	20	6.1	20	6.1	NA
14.0	Upright or pendent	Wet	50	3.4	30	9.1	25	7.6	25	7.6	25	7.6	25	7.6	25	7.6	25	7.6	NA
14.0	Pendent	Wet	75	5.2	40	12.2	30	9.1	30	9.1	30	9.1	NA		NA		NA		NA
25.2	Pendent	Wet	15	1.0	30	9.1	25	7.6	25	7.6	25	7.6	25	7.6	25	7.6	25	7.6	NA
25.2	Pendent	Wet	25	1.7	40	12.2	30	9.1	30	9.1	30	9.1	NA		NA		NA		NA
25.2	Pendent	Wet	50	3.4	45	13.7	30	9.1	30	9.1	30	9.1	NA		NA		NA		NA

12.6.2.3 Early Suppression Fast-Response (ESFR) Sprinklers for the Protection of Roll Paper Storage. Where automatic sprinkler system protection utilizes ESFR sprinklers, hydraulic design criteria shall be as specified in Table 12.6.2.3. Design discharge pressure shall be applied to 12 operating sprinklers.

12.7 Special Designs

12.7.1* Plastic Motor Vehicle Components. Plastic automotive components and associated packaging material shall be permitted to be protected in accordance with Table 12.7.1.

A.12.7.1 Exposed, expanded plastic donnage, instrument panels, and plastic bumper facia were the automotive components with their related packaging that were utilized in the fire

TABLE 12.7.1 *K-25.2 ESFR Sprinkler Design Criteria for Portable Racks (Closed Array[1]) without Solid Shelves Containing Automotive Components*

Commodity	Maximum Storage Height		Maximum Ceiling/Roof Height		Type of System	Maximum Sprinkler Spacing[2]		Number of Design Sprinklers by Minimum Operating Pressure[3]		Maximum Deflector Distance Below Ceiling[4]		Hose Stream Demand		Water Supply Duration (hours)
	ft	m	ft	m		ft²	m²	psi	bar	in.	mm	gpm	L/min	
Automotive components and associated packaging material	25	7.6	35	10.7	Wet	100	9.3	16 at 37 psi	16 at 2.5 bar	18	457	500	1900	2

[1]Portable rack array shall be tightly nested without any flue spaces.

[2]Sprinkler spacing can exceed 100 ft² (9.3 m²) where sprinklers are listed for larger spacing.

[3]System hydraulic design shall also be capable of delivering a discharge density of 0.60 gpm/ft² over the most hydraulically remote 4000 ft² area.

[4]Maximum deflector distance below ceiling shall be permitted to exceed 18 in.2 where sprinklers are listed for greater distances.

tests. This test commodity used in the large-scale sprinklered fire test proved to be the worst challenge per the large-scale calorimeter tests of available components. See *Technical Report of Fire Testing of Automotive Parts in Portable Storage Racking,* prepared by Underwriters Laboratories, Project 99NK29106, NC4004, January 5, 2001, and *Commodity Hazard Comparison of Expanded Plastic in Portable Bins and Racking,* Project 99NK29106, NC4004, September 8, 2000.

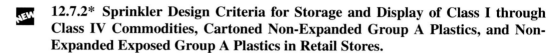

12.7.2* Sprinkler Design Criteria for Storage and Display of Class I through Class IV Commodities, Cartoned Non-Expanded Group A Plastics, and Non-Expanded Exposed Group A Plastics in Retail Stores.

A.12.7.2 These special designs are based on fire heat release calorimeter tests and 10 full-scale tests conducted by the Retail Fire Research Coalition at Underwriters Laboratories in 2000. *[See Figure A.12.7.2(a) through Figure A.12.7.2(f).]*

12.7.2.1 A wet pipe system designed to meet two separate design points—0.6 gpm/ft^2 density over 2000 ft^2 and 0.7 gpm/ft^2 density for the four hydraulically most demanding sprinklers—shall be permitted to protect single- and double-row slatted shelf racks when the following conditions are met:

(1) An extended coverage sprinkler with a nominal K-factor of 25.2 listed for storage occupancies shall be provided.

(2) Shelves shall be slatted using a 2-in. thick by maximum 6-in. wide slat held in place by spacers that maintain a minimum 2-in. opening between each slat.

(3) There shall be no slatted shelf levels in the rack above nominal 12-ft level. Wire mesh (greater than 50 percent opening) shall be permitted for shelf levels above 12 ft.

(4) Solid plywood shelving (3½ ft × 8 ft 3 in.) shall be permissible over the wood slats at the 5-ft level.

(5) Perforated metal (open area of 40 percent or more) shall be permitted over the slatted shelves up to the 60-in. level.

(6) Other than what is allowed in this section, solid plywood or similar materials shall not be placed on the slatted shelves.

(7) Solid veneered particleboard displays shall be permissible provided that all flues are maintained and only one display is installed per bay.

(8) Maximum roof height shall be 30 ft in the protected area.

(9) Maximum storage height shall be 22 ft.

(10) Aisle widths shall be a minimum of 8 ft.

(11) Minimum transverse flue spaces of 3 in. every 10 ft horizontally shall be provided.

(12) Minimum longitudinal flue spaces of 6 in. shall be provided for double-row racks.

(13) Storage in the aisle shall be permissible provided the aisle storage is no more than 4 ft high and a minimum clear aisle of 4 ft is maintained.

12.7.2.2 A wet pipe system designed to meet two separate design points—0.425 gpm/ft^2 density over 2000 ft^2 and 0.50 gpm/ft^2 density for the four hydraulically most demanding sprinklers—shall be permitted in solid steel cantilever style retail shelving racks (gondola racks) when the following conditions are met:

(1) An extended coverage sprinkler with a nominal K-factor of 25.2 listed for storage occupancies shall be provided.

(2) The storage height shall not exceed 12 ft.

(3) The ceiling height shall not exceed 22 ft in the protected area.

(4) Gondola rack structure shall not exceed 48 in. in aggregate depth or 78 in. in height.

(5) A minimum aisle of 5 ft between storage shall be maintained.

(6) Rack lengths shall be no more than 70 ft.

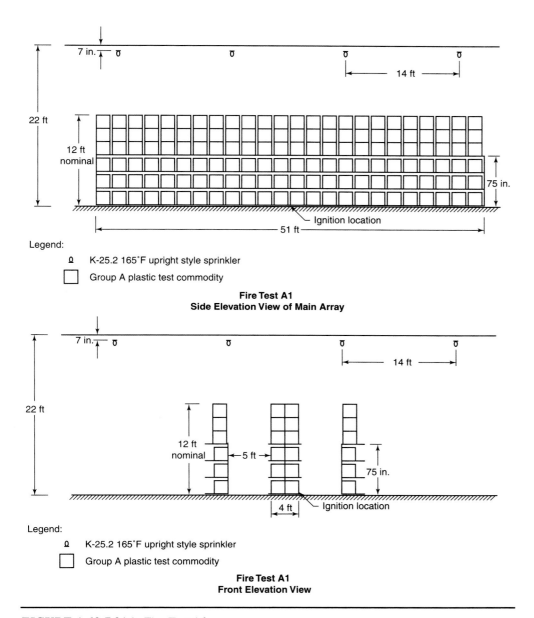

Legend:

Ω   K-25.2 165°F upright style sprinkler

▢   Group A plastic test commodity

Fire Test A1
Side Elevation View of Main Array

Legend:

Ω   K-25.2 165°F upright style sprinkler

▢   Group A plastic test commodity

Fire Test A1
Front Elevation View

FIGURE A.12.7.2(a) Fire Test A1.

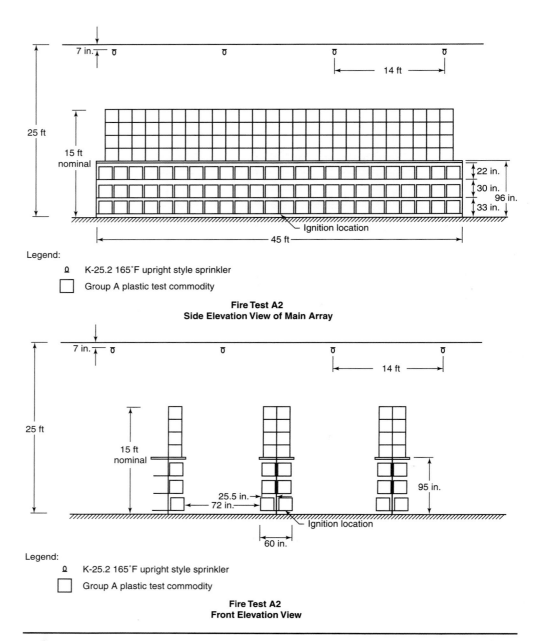

Fire Test A2
Side Elevation View of Main Array

Legend:

Ω   K-25.2 165˚F upright style sprinkler

☐   Group A plastic test commodity

Fire Test A2
Front Elevation View

Legend:

Ω   K-25.2 165˚F upright style sprinkler

☐   Group A plastic test commodity

FIGURE A.12.7.2(b) *Fire Test A2.*

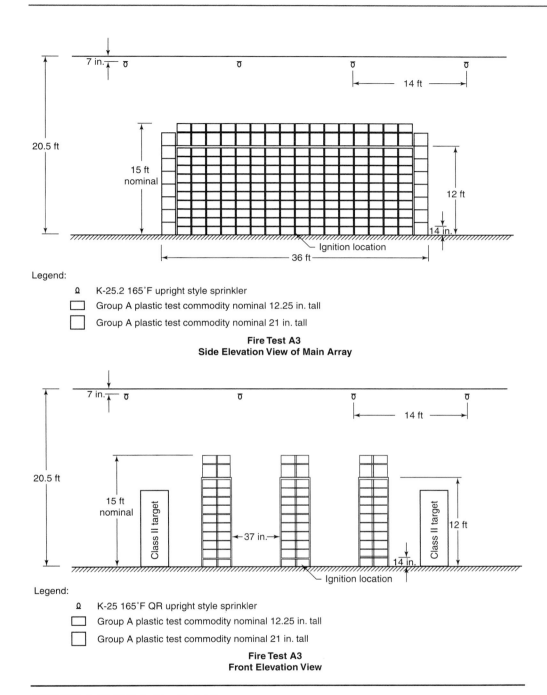

Legend:

Ω   K-25.2 165°F upright style sprinkler

☐   Group A plastic test commodity nominal 12.25 in. tall

☐   Group A plastic test commodity nominal 21 in. tall

Fire Test A3
Side Elevation View of Main Array

Legend:

Ω   K-25 165°F QR upright style sprinkler

☐   Group A plastic test commodity nominal 12.25 in. tall

☐   Group A plastic test commodity nominal 21 in. tall

Fire Test A3
Front Elevation View

FIGURE A.12.7.2(c) *Fire Test A3.*

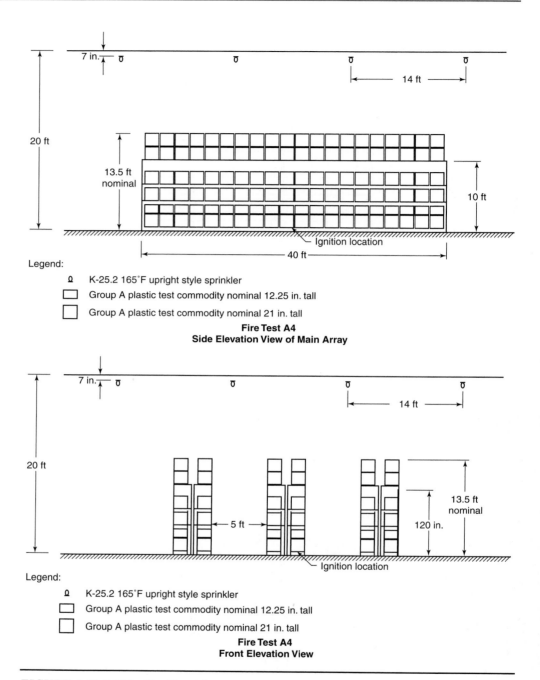

Legend:

Ω   K-25.2 165°F upright style sprinkler

☐   Group A plastic test commodity nominal 12.25 in. tall

☐   Group A plastic test commodity nominal 21 in. tall

Fire Test A4
Side Elevation View of Main Array

Legend:

Ω   K-25.2 165°F upright style sprinkler

☐   Group A plastic test commodity nominal 12.25 in. tall

☐   Group A plastic test commodity nominal 21 in. tall

Fire Test A4
Front Elevation View

FIGURE A.12.7.2(d) Fire Test A4.

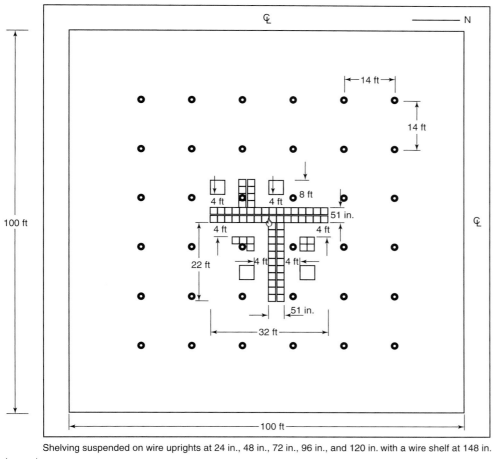

Shelving suspended on wire uprights at 24 in., 48 in., 72 in., 96 in., and 120 in. with a wire shelf at 148 in.

Legend:

● K-25 upright style sprinkler 165°F QR, 0.55 gpm/ft² water density for first four sprinkler operations, then 0.49 gpm/ft² for all additional operations

☐ Group A plastic test commodity

▢ Class II target commodity

♦ Ignition location

Fire Test A6
Plan View

FIGURE A.12.7.2(e) *Fire Test A6—Plan View.*

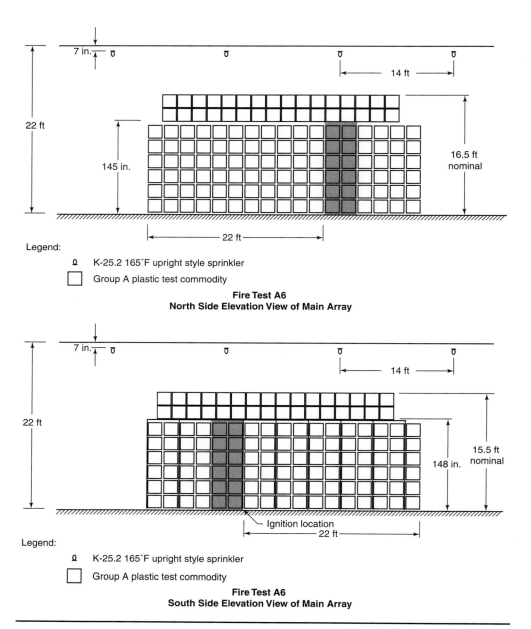

Legend:

Ω   K-25.2 165˚F upright style sprinkler

☐   Group A plastic test commodity

Fire Test A6
North Side Elevation View of Main Array

Legend:

Ω   K-25.2 165˚F upright style sprinkler

☐   Group A plastic test commodity

Fire Test A6
South Side Elevation View of Main Array

FIGURE A.12.7.2(f) *Fire Test A6—Main Array (North/South).*

12.7.2.3 A wet system designed to meet two separate design points—0.425 gpm/ft^2 density over 2000 ft^2 and 0.50 gpm/ft^2 density for the four hydraulically most demanding sprinklers— shall be permitted in solid steel cantilever-style retail shelving racks (gondola racks) when the following conditions are met:

(1) An extended coverage sprinkler with a nominal K-factor of 25.2 listed for storage occupancies shall be provided.
(2) Storage height shall not exceed 15 ft.
(3) Ceiling height shall not exceed 25 ft in the protected area.
(4) Gondola rack structure shall not exceed 60 in. in aggregate depth or 8 ft in height.
(5) A perforated metal deck at the 8-ft level shall be permissible with storage placed on top with or without flue spaces to a maximum height from floor of 15 ft.
(6) Rack lengths shall not exceed 70 ft.
(7) A minimum aisle space of 6 ft shall be provided.

12.7.2.4 A wet pipe system designed to meet two separate design points—0.45 gpm/ft^2 density over 2000 ft^2 and 0.55 gpm/ft^2 density for the four hydraulically most demanding sprinklers—shall be permitted without the use of in-rack sprinklers when the following are met:

(1) An extended coverage sprinkler with a nominal K-factor of 25.2 listed for storage occupancies shall be provided.
(2) Storage height shall not exceed 15 ft.
(3) Ceiling height shall not exceed 20 ft 6 in.
(4) Shelving structure shall not exceed 48-in. aggregate depth or 12 ft in height.
(5) Shelving shall be permitted to be made of solid particleboard.
(6) A minimum aisle space of 3 ft shall be maintained.
(7) Rack length shall be a maximum of 70 ft.

12.7.2.5 A wet pipe system designed to meet two separate design points—0.38 gpm/ft^2 density over 2000 ft^2 and 0.45 gpm/ft^2 density for the four hydraulically most demanding sprinklers—shall be permitted without the use of in-rack sprinklers in steel retail sales floor shelving racks where the following are met:

(1) An extended coverage sprinkler with a nominal K-factor of 25.2 listed for storage occupancies shall be provided.
(2) Storage height shall not exceed 14 ft.
(3) Ceiling height shall not exceed 20 ft.
(4) Solid metal shelving shall be permissible up to the 72-in. level and wire shelving shall be permissible up to the 10-ft level.
(5) The solid metal shelving shall not exceed 66 in. in aggregate depth with a 6-in. longitudinal flue between two 30-in. deep shelves.
(6) A minimum aisle space of 5 ft shall be maintained.
(7) A minimum longitudinal flue of 6 in. shall be maintained.
(8) Rack length shall be a maximum of 70 ft.

12.7.2.6 A wet pipe system designed to meet two separate design points—0.49 gpm/ft^2 density over 2000 ft^2 and 0.55 gpm/ft^2 density for the four hydraulically most demanding sprinklers— shall be permitted without the use of in-rack sprinklers in retail solid shelved steel rack structure when the following are met:

(1) An extended coverage sprinkler with a nominal K-factor of 25.2 listed for storage occupancies shall be provided.
(2) Storage height shall not exceed 16.5 ft.
(3) Ceiling height shall not exceed 22 ft.
(4) Shelving structure shall not exceed 51 in. aggregate depth or 148 in. in height.

(5) The intersection of perpendicular steel racks shall be permissible as long as no storage is placed within the void space at the junction of the racks.
(6) The top shelf shall be wire mesh.
(7) A minimum aisle width of 4 ft shall be maintained between shelf units and other displays.

SUMMARY

Chapter 12 includes all the design criteria for protection of storage occupancies. This chapter contains specific criteria for palletized, rack, rubber tire, baled cotton, and roll paper storage and for special designs.

 ## REFERENCES CITED IN COMMENTARY

National Fire Protection Association, 1 Batterymarch Park, P.O. Box 9101, Quincy, MA 02269-9101

NFPA 230, *Standard for the Fire Protection of Storage,* 1999 edition
NFPA 231C, *Standard for Rack Storage Materials* (no longer published)
NFPA 231D, *Standard for Storage of Rubber Tires* (no longer published)
NFPA 231F, *Standard for the Storage of Roll Paper* (no longer published)
NFPA 232, *Standard for the Protection of Records,* 2000 edition

National Fire Protection Research Foundation (NFPRF), 1 Batterymarch Park, Quincy, MA 02269-9101

Technical Reports of the International Fire Sprinkler/Smoke and Heat Vent/Draft Curtain Fire Test Project

Special Occupancy Requirements

The 1999 edition of NFPA 13 consolidated sprinkler criteria from other NFPA codes and standards so that sprinkler design and installation criteria would be located in one centralized location, NFPA 13. For the 1999 edition, the installation requirements were contained in Chapter 5, Installation Requirements, and the design requirements were located in Chapter 7, Design Approaches. The 2002 edition of NFPA 13 has now established Chapter 13, which centralizes all of the extracted special occupancy requirements. As with the 1999 edition, the material in Chapter 13 is extracted from other NFPA standards so that the sprinkler installation and discharge criteria are located in one place. To completely understand the criteria in these sections, the referenced standard should be consulted. In addition, the referenced NFPA document can provide options to standard sprinkler protection, such as water spray sprinklers, foam-water sprinklers, or another special extinguishing system, for the protection of those hazards.

13.1 General

13.1.1 Application.

13.1.1.1 In addition to the requirements of Chapters 8, 11, 12, and 14, the following special occupancy requirements shall apply.

13.1.1.2 Where the requirements of the reference standard differ from the requirements of this standard, the reference standard shall take precedence.

13.1.2 Definitions. For terms not defined in Chapter 3, the definitions of the reference standard shall apply.

13.2 Flammable and Combustible Liquids

Flammable and combustible liquids, which are covered in Section 13.2, are defined and classified by NFPA 30, *Flammable and Combustible Liquids Code,* as follows:

Flammable Liquid: Any liquid that has a closed-cup flash point below 37.8°C (100°F). Flammable liquids are classified by NFPA 30 as Class I and are further classified as follows:

1. *Class IA Liquid:* A liquid that has a flash point below 22.8°C (73°F) and a boiling point below 37.8°C (100°F)
2. *Class IB Liquid:* A liquid that has a flash point below 22.8°C (73°F) and a boiling point at or above 37.8°C (100°F)
3. *Class IC Liquid:* A liquid that has a flash point at or above 22.8°C (73°F), but below 37.8°C (100°F)

Combustible Liquid: Any liquid that has a closed-cup flash point at or above 37.8°C (100°F). Combustible liquids are classified by NFPA 30 as Class II or Class III as follows:

1. *Class II Liquid:* A liquid that has a flash point at or above 37.8°C (100°F) and below 60°C (140°F)
2. *Class IIIA Liquid:* A liquid that has a flash point at or above 60°C (140°F), but below 93°C (200°F)
3. *Class IIIB Liquid:* A liquid that has a flash point at or above 93°C (200°F)

It is important to note that the boiling point is only used to distinguish Class IA liquids, of which there are very few of commercial significance, from Class IB liquids.

See Section 1.7 of NFPA 30 for additional information.

 13.2.1 Design Requirements. Sprinkler system discharge criteria for the protection of flammable and combustible liquids shall comply with NFPA 30, *Flammable and Combustible Liquids Code.*

 Design requirements are covered in 13.2.1. Fire protection system design criteria for protecting containers of flammable and combustible liquids are provided in Section 4.8 of NFPA 30. The design criteria are contained in 10 tables that address different storage situations and configurations and include both sprinkler and foam-water sprinkler systems. Four "decision trees" assist the user in identifying the appropriate table to be used. One of the decision trees is reproduced here in Exhibit 13.1.

Note that Exhibit 13.1 directs the user to NFPA 13 in those cases where the design criteria therein are deemed adequate. If NFPA 13 is not considered to be appropriate, the user is directed to one of several design criteria tables in NFPA 30. Commentary Table 13.1 is an example of one of these tables. Commentary Table 13.1 is a portion of Table 4.8.2(b) from NFPA 30 and provides sprinkler design criteria for palletized storage of metal containers of flammable and combustible liquids in non-relieving-style containers. Note that this table is specific to non-miscible liquids—that is, those that do not mix with water—and water-miscible mixtures in which the flammable or combustible component constitutes more than 50 percent of the mixture. Note also that Commentary Table 13.1 represents fewer than half of the entries in the table; there are 10 more entries for relieving-style containers, which are described in Table A.4.8.1.3 of NFPA 30.

The reader's attention is directed to the last column of Commentary Table 13.1, which is titled "Fire Test Ref." Each entry in each of the 10 tables has a "fire test reference" number that is keyed to an entry in corresponding tables in Appendix D of NFPA 30. The tables in Appendix D link the criteria in the Section 4.8 tables with full-scale fire test data on which the criteria are based. The full-scale test data are summarized in the *Directory of Fire Tests Involving Storage of Flammable and Combustible Liquids In Small Containers*, by David P. Nugent of Schirmer Engineering Corporation, and are available from the Society of Fire Protection Engineers by special arrangement with Schirmer Engineering Corporation. This resource is unique to NFPA 30 and allows the user a means to investigate the source data on which the fire protection design criteria were developed.

The tests compiled in the *Directory* were conducted over a 30-year period at one of the fire test centers operated by FM Global (formerly Factory Mutual Research Corporation), Underwriters Laboratories Inc., or Southwest Research Institute. Tests were conducted using small-, intermediate-, and large-scale configurations that simulated bulk/palletized, rack, and shelf storage typical of those found in warehouse and retail facilities throughout the country. Test fuels included Class IB through Class IIIB liquids, as defined above. Container types included relieving-style and non-relieving-style steel, plastic, and glass containers. All of the tests used operating sprinkler systems discharging either water or foam-water.

EXHIBIT 13.1 *Fire Protection Criteria Decision Tree for Water-Miscible Flammable and Combustible Liquids in Plastic Containers.*

COMMENTARY TABLE 13.1 *Water Sprinkler Protection of Bulk or Palletized Storage Metal Containers (for Nonmiscible Liquids or Miscible Liquids with Flammable Liquid Concentration >50%)*

Liquid Class	Container Size and Arrangement (gal)	Maximum Storage Height (ft)	Maximum Ceiling Height (ft)	Ceiling					
				Sprinkler Type		Density (gpm/ft²)	Design Area (ft²)[b]	Notes	Fire Test Ref.[c]
				Nominal K-factor	Response[a]				
				Nonrelieving-Style Container					
IB, IC, II, or IIIA	≤5	4	18	5.6 or 8.0	SR or QR	0.21	1500	1	1
	≤5	5	18	5.6 or 8.0	SR or QR	0.30	3000	—	2
	≤5	6½	30	8.0 or 11.2	QR	0.45	3000	—	3
	>5 and ≤60	5	18	8.0 or 11.2	SR	0.40	3000	—	4
IIIB	≤5	18	30	5.6 or 8.0	SR or QR	0.25	3000	—	5
	>5 and ≤60	10	20	5.6 or 8.0	SR	0.25	3000	—	6
		18	30	5.6 or 8.0	SR	0.35	3000	—	7

For SI units, 1 gal = 3.8 L; 1 ft = 0.3 m; 1 ft² = 0.09 m²; 1 gpm/ft² = 40.7 L/min/m².
Notes:
1. Minimum hose stream demand: 250 gpm for 2 hrs.
2. Sprinklers shall also be hydraulically calculated to provide a density of 0.80 gpm/ft² over 1000 ft².
3. Use pendent-style K = 11.2 ceiling sprinklers.
4. Drums placed on open slotted pallet, not nested, to allow pressure relief from drums on lower levels.
[a]SR = standard response and QR = quick response, where both are listed.
[b]Ceiling sprinklers high temperature.
[c]See Table D.2(b) [of NFPA 30] for references to fire tests on which the protection criteria given in this table are based.
Source: Modified from NFPA 30, 2000, Table 4.8.2(b).

Several variables were identified as significant determinants of the severity of the ensuing fire and its rate of growth, as well as the ability of the fire protection system to control or suppress the fire. These variables included the following:

1. Physical properties and the fire hazard properties of the liquid
2. Style of container and its size
3. Presence or absence of packaging material (e.g., corrugated cartons)
4. Ignition scenario
5. Storage arrangement
6. Design parameters of the fire protection system

The effectiveness of the fire protection systems was typically assessed based on the following:

1. Number of sprinkler heads that operated and their time of operation
2. Temperature of fire gases at the ceiling and, where available, the temperature of ceiling structural elements
3. Extent of fire travel through the test array
4. Whether the fire was able to "jump" the aisle separating the test array from an adjacent target array
5. Assessment of the damage in both the test and target storage arrays

 More detailed discussion of these tests and the interrelationship of these factors can be found in "Fire Tests Involving Storage of Flammable and Combustible Liquids In Small Containers," authored by David P. Nugent in the *Journal of Fire Protection Engineering*.

A list of the 10 fire protection design criteria tables as they appear in NFPA 30 follows:

1. Table 4.8.2(a)—Water Sprinkler Protection of Single- or Double-Row Rack Storage of Metal Containers (for Non-Miscible Liquids or Miscible Liquids with Flammable Liquid Concentration >50%)

2. Table 4.8.2(b)—Water Sprinkler Protection of Bulk or Palletized Storage of Metal Containers (for Non-Miscible Liquids or Miscible Liquids with Flammable Liquid Concentration >50%)

3. Table 4.8.2(c)—Foam-Water Sprinkler Protection of Single- or Double-Row Rack Storage of Metal Containers (for Non-Miscible Liquids or Miscible Liquids with Flammable Liquid Concentration >50%)

4. Table 4.8.2(d)—Foam-Water Sprinkler Protection of Bulk or Palletized Storage of Metal Containers (for Non-Miscible Liquids or Miscible Liquids with Flammable Liquid Concentration >50%)

5. Table 4.8.2(e)—Water Sprinkler Protection of Single-, Double-, or Multi-Row Rack Storage of Class IIIB Liquids in Plastic Containers (for Non-Miscible Liquids or Miscible Liquids with Flammable Liquid Concentration >50%)

6. Table 4.8.2(f)—Water Sprinkler Protection of Shelf Storage of Metal Containers (for Non-Miscible Liquids or Miscible Liquids with Flammable Liquid Concentration >50%)

7. Table 4.8.2(g)—Water Sprinkler Protection of Single- or Double-Row Open-Frame Rack Storage of Water Miscible Liquids in Plastic Containers (with Flammable Liquid Concentration >50%)

8. Table 4.8.2(h)—Water Sprinkler Protection of Rack and Palletized Storage of Class IB, IC, II, IIIA, and IIIB Liquids in Relieving-Style with Minimum 7.5-ft Aisles (for Non-Miscible Liquids or Miscible Liquids with Flammable Liquid Concentration >50%)

9. Table 4.8.2(i)—Water Sprinkler Protection of Bulk or Palletized Storage of Rigid Non-Metallic Intermediate Bulk Containers (for Non-Miscible Class II and III Liquids or Miscible Class II and Class III Liquids with Flammable Liquid Concentration >50%)

10. Table 4.8.2(j)—Water Sprinkler Protection of Single- or Double-Row, Open-Frame Rack Storage of Rigid Non-Metallic Intermediate Bulk Containers (for Non-Miscible Class II and III Liquids or Miscible Class II and III Liquids with Flammable Liquid Concentration >50%)

The reader is urged to review Section 4.8 and Appendixes D and E of NFPA 30 for additional important information.

13.2.2 Installation Requirements. (Reserved)

Subsection 13.2.2 is reserved for installation requirements. Section 4.8 of NFPA 30 includes important information on installation requirements and limitations for the protection of flammable and combustible liquids storage. The reader should also refer to Table 4.2.3 of NFPA 30 for information on allowable container types.

13.3 Aerosol Products

13.3.1 Design Requirements. Sprinkler system discharge criteria for the protection of aerosol products shall comply with NFPA 30B, *Code for the Manufacture and Storage of Aerosol Products.*

The automatic fire sprinkler protection alternatives provided in Chapter 6 of NFPA 30B, *Code for the Manufacture and Storage of Aerosol Products,* are derived from a multitude of aerosol product fire tests (see 13.3.1). The testing has been conducted for over 35 years by a major insurance company, as well as through a wide range of small-, medium-, and large-scale tests sponsored by the aerosol products industry. This aerosol fire research represents a significant body of knowledge regarding aerosol fire development and control for various types of aerosol products in various storage and protection scenarios, including the most recent concerns over plastic-wrapped (uncartoned) aerosol products.

Historically, aerosol warehouse storage fires have been found to begin basically as cardboard fires. The fire grows up the flue, burning off the aerosol carton faces, and there is usually a flame above the top of the array before the first aerosol can ruptures and aerosols become involved in the fire. As aerosol containers rupture, some of the heat from the fuel added by the aerosol rises quickly to the ceiling, while some is absorbed into other aerosol containers, bringing them closer to, or exceeding, their burst pressure.

 Recently, FM Global's Technical Report No. J.I.OD2R4.PR, *Full Scale Fire Tests: Sprinkler Protection for Rack Storage of Plastic-Wrapped (Uncartoned) Aerosols,* demonstrated a significant difference in the scenario for this type of packaging. For plastic-wrapped product, the tests showed that the plastic became involved and spread over the array of cans quickly. Unlike the burning process in the cardboard carton situation, the cans did not have a sole tendency to rupture. Rupturing was present, but it was not the predominant means of fire spread. There was evidence of nozzle assembly failures that caused gradual product venting. While this gradual venting occurred, the product ignited and flames jetted from the cans. In other cases, product was expelled from the cans and created liquid pools that eventually ignited. In both of these situations, the fire burned for a longer period of time, subsequently allowing more aerosol cans to ignite due to the sustained burning.

Early application of adequate densities of sprinkler water is the most effective way to control or suppress an aerosol fire, avoiding a chain reaction that can lead to loss of control. For this reason, early suppression-fast response (ESFR) protection is especially effective for aerosol products.

Rack Storage Arrays

Understanding the dynamics of aerosol product rack storage is key to understanding and implementing the sprinkler protection for these types of products. The rack storage configuration is ideal for promoting fire development. The fuel is supported so that air has access to the fire from all sides and so that the stored commodity does not topple over, as it would in solid pile storage. A rack also has many areas that are shielded from ceiling sprinkler discharge.

Testing of rack storage configurations has demonstrated a very consistent fire development pattern. First, the fire starts at a point and widens as it moves up the storage array in a "V" pattern. When the fire reaches the second tier of storage, the flames fan out along the bottom of the pallet above and spread laterally to the face of the rack. Fireballs from rupturing aerosol cans also spread fire to the face of the rack. Once the fire is established on the face of the rack, the fire spreads rapidly upward and outward horizontally in the classic "V" pattern, thus exposing more of the commodity. The fire on the face of the rack and within the transverse flue spaces of the rack structure also causes more aerosol containers to rupture. As additional containers rupture, uninvolved containers on the interior of the pallet load are now exposed to the fire.

Additionally, fire can jump the aisle space between two rows of racks. This may happen in several different ways. Should the fire be of a severe enough nature, the radiant energy alone can be sufficient to ignite combustible cartons or commodities in the exposed rack. Fireballs from rupturing aerosol cans are large enough to engulf adjacent racks with flame. Occasionally, burning flammable liquid might be ejected from rupturing containers with enough force to reach the exposed storage.

 In-rack sprinklers, located in the longitudinal flue space, are highly effective in preventing the fire from crossing into the other half of a double-row rack. In-rack sprinklers located at the face of the rack structure have been shown to stop the spread of fire up the face of the rack. Their position within the rack structure allows them to wet down the face of the storage array along the aisle. This reduces the demand on the ceiling sprinkler system, which allows a reduction in the design density of the ceiling sprinkler system. ESFR sprinklers operate fast enough and discharge water at a high enough density that they are capable of preventing fire spread up the face of the rack. NFPA 30B, Tables 6.3.2.7(e) through 6.3.2.7(l) and their associated figures provide the requirements and sprinkler head configurations for rack storage of both cartoned and uncartoned aerosol products.

Palletized or Solid Pile Storage Arrays

On the other hand, palletized or solid pile storage configurations do not offer the same conducive conditions for fast fire growth as rack storage, but can result in persistent fires if sprinklers are not designed for proper protection.

Early aerosol fire tests showed that standard spray sprinkler protection had difficulty controlling Level 2 and Level 3 aerosol products [as defined by NFPA 30B; see below following Labeling] stacked more than 5 ft (1.5 m) high under a 30-ft (9-m) ceiling. Concerns over this prompted the aerosol industry to institute a testing program to seek more cost-effective storage and protection alternatives. The initial test series in that program investigated a wide range of packaging and formulation variables and alternatives, which produced results that demonstrated no significant benefits as compared to the existing industry practices.

Further aerosol fire testing evaluated higher water densities and larger-orifice sprinkler heads to protect higher stacking in palletized storage arrays of Level 1, 2, and 3 aerosol products under low-to-medium ceiling heights of 20 ft to 25 ft (6.1 m to 7.6 m). Numerous successful protection alternatives were found. To properly protect each class of aerosol product stored in higher stack height and higher ceiling height scenarios, it was found that higher water densities from larger-orifice (¹⁷⁄₃₂ in. to 0.64 in.) sprinklers fitted with low-temperature fusible links of 160°F (71°C) were required.

Improvement in aerosol fire protection was found by utilizing faster response ESFR sprinklers. Fitted with extremely fast-responding, low-temperature links of 160°F (71°C) and a response time index of 50, these sprinklers are capable of protecting high-stack palletized aerosol product storage under ceilings up to 30 ft (9 m) high, as well as rack storage without in-rack sprinklers. ESFR testing has demonstrated fire control, quick suppression, and, in some cases, total extinguishment. This is true for both cardboard and plastic-wrapped aerosol product arrays. NFPA 30B, Table 6.3.2.7(a) through 6.3.2.7(d) and their associated figures provide the requirements and sprinkler head configurations for palletized and solid pile storage of both cartoned and uncartoned aerosol products.

Labeling

In order to use the design information within NFPA 30B, a classification of the product being protected must be known. Precautionary labeling for aerosol products, including that for flammability hazards during use of the product, is regulated by several federal agencies, under a number of federal statutes. Labeling of aerosol pesticide products, including disinfectants and sanitizers as well as insecticides and herbicides, is strictly regulated. Also, in accordance with NFPA 30B, manufacturers of aerosol products must ensure that all cartons or packages of aerosol products are identified on at least one side with the classification of the aerosol products contained therein. Cartons or packages must be clearly marked "Level _____ Aerosols."

The level classifications are defined as follows:

1. Level 1 aerosol products are those with a total chemical heat of combustion that is less than or equal to 8600 Btu/lb (20 kJ/g).
2. Level 2 aerosol products are those with a total chemical heat of combustion that is greater than 8600 Btu/lb (20 kJ/g), but less than or equal to 13,000 Btu/lb (30 kJ/g).
3. Level 3 aerosol products are those with a total chemical heat of combustion that is greater than 13,000 Btu/lb (30 kJ/g).

13.3.2 Installation Requirements. (Reserved)

13.4 Spray Application Using Flammable and Combustible Materials

13.4.1 Design Requirements.

13.4.1.1* Automatic sprinkler systems in spray areas and mixing areas shall be designed for Extra Hazard (Group 2) occupancies. [**33:**7.2.1]

Exception: As provided for in 13.4.1.4. [33:7.2.1]

A.13.4.1.1 Spray application operations should only be located in buildings that are completely protected by an approved system of automatic sprinklers. If located in unsprinklered buildings, sprinklers should be installed to protect spray application processes where practical. Because of the rapidity and intensity of fires that involve spray operations, the available water should be ample to simultaneously supply all sprinklers likely to open in one fire without depleting the available water for use by hose streams. Noncombustible draft curtains can be used to limit the number of sprinklers that will open.

Even when areas adjacent to coating operations are considered under reasonably positive fire control by adequate automatic sprinkler protection, damage is possible if operations are conducted on floors above those containing contents that are highly susceptible to water damage. Waterproofing and drainage of spray room floors can assist in reducing water damage on floors below. The proper drainage of the large volume of water frequently necessary to extinguish spray finishing room fires often presents considerable difficulty. [**33**:A.7.2]

 It is important to understand that NFPA 33, *Standard for Spray Application Using Flammable or Combustible Materials,* requires that a spray area be protected by an automatic fire protection system, but not necessarily by a sprinkler system (see 13.4.1.1). Other types of systems, such as a dry chemical extinguishing system or a carbon dioxide system, can be used when the building itself is not protected by sprinklers. The usual situation is protection of an individual spray booth in a non-sprinklered building, such as an auto body shop. Such alternate systems might be more effective and more compatible, depending on the material being sprayed. The intent, however, is that a spray application process located in a sprinklered building should also be protected by sprinklers. By definition, the spray area includes the spray booth or room and associated exhaust systems (exhaust plenum and ductwork). These same requirements apply to any room in which the materials to be spray-applied are prepared or mixed.

NFPA 33 does not require that a building be sprinklered just because of the presence of a spray application process.

Spray application operations conducted outside of buildings are not within the scope of NFPA 33. Intermittent or occasional regular use of small portable spray application equipment or spray applications using aerosol products also are not within the scope of NFPA 33. Therefore, NFPA 33's fire protection requirements do not apply to such situations. See A.1.1.4 and A.1.1.5 of NFPA 33 for additional information.

13.4.1.2 The automatic sprinkler system shall be a wet pipe system where practical. Spray operations that require an open-head deluge system, a combination open- and closed-head automatic sprinkler system, a foam-water sprinkler system, or any other type of extinguishing system (dry chemical or gaseous agent) shall be so protected, subject to the approval of the authority having jurisdiction. [**33**:7.2.2]

Wet pipe systems are discussed in 13.4.1.2. Dry pipe systems are not recommended due to the delay in delivering water after sprinkler activation.

An example of a situation in which a wet pipe sprinkler system might not be desired would be the spray painting operations in an automobile assembly plant. Because of their sheer size, complexity, and value, such installations are typically protected with zoned deluge systems activated by fire detectors. Such systems activate much faster than a conventional sprinkler system, limiting both damage and costly downtime.

13.4.1.3 Water supply for sprinklers shall be sufficient to supply all sprinklers likely to open in any one fire incident without depleting the available water for use in hose streams. Where sprinklers are installed to protect spray areas and mixing rooms only, water shall be permitted to be furnished from the domestic supply, subject to the approval of the authority having jurisdiction and provided the domestic supply can meet the design criteria for extra hazard, Group 2 occupancies. [**33**:7.2.3]

 NFPA 33 allows the use of the building's domestic water supply to provide sprinkler protection for a spray application process, if it is capable of supplying the anticipated demand (see 13.4.1.3). This is an acceptable alternative to a special agent system, such as dry chemical or carbon dioxide, and would be a desirable means of protecting a small open-front spray booth.

13.4.1.4 Resin application areas shall be protected by an automatic sprinkler system that is designed for at least Ordinary Hazard (Group 2) occupancies. [**33**:15.3]

The requirement in 13.4.1.4 applies to the spray application of styrene/unsaturated polyester resins. The reduction of the sprinkler design density from extra hazard (Group 2) to ordinary hazard (Group 2) is based on the following:

1. Actual burn tests demonstrate that the resin does not readily ignite and does not burn rapidly when ignited, even though they are classified as a Class I flammable liquid in accordance with NFPA 30.
2. The vapor pressure of the resin is typically low enough that spray application does not generally produce vapors that exceed 25 percent of the lower flammable limit (LFL). In tests conducted in a closed area, without ventilation, maximum vapor concentration was less than 700 parts per million (ppm), far less than 25 percent of styrene's LFL, which is about 11,000 ppm.

13.4.2 Installation Requirements.

13.4.2.1* The sprinklers for each spray area and mixing room shall be controlled by a separate, accessible, listed indicating valve. Sprinkler systems in stacks or ducts shall be automatic and of a type not subject to freezing. [**33**:7.2.4]

A.13.4.2.1 Automatic sprinklers in spray areas, including the interior of spray booths and exhaust ducts, should be wet pipe, preaction, or deluge system in order that water can be placed on the fire in the shortest possible time. Automatic sprinklers in spray booths and exhaust ducts should be of the lowest practical temperature rating. Sprinklers outside the booth at ceiling level should be high temperature–rated [286°F (141°C)]. The delay in application of water with ordinary dry pipe sprinklers can permit a fire to spread so rapidly that final extinguishment is difficult without large resulting damage.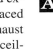

The location of the sprinklers inside spray booths should be selected with care in order to avoid sprinklers being placed in the direct path of spray and yet afford protection for the entire booth interior. When in the direct path of spray even one day's operation can result in deposits on the sprinkler head that insulate the fusible link or choke open head orifices to the extent that sprinklers cannot operate efficiently.

Automatic sprinklers should also be located so that areas subject to substantial accumulations of overspray residue are protected. Generally, sprinklers are located no more than 4 ft (1.2 m) from side walls of booths and rooms and from dry overspray collectors (where applicable). Sprinklers in booths or rooms should be on extra hazard occupancy spacing of 90 ft^2 (9.4 m^2).

Sprinklers or sprinkler systems protecting stacks or ducts should be automatic and of a type not subject to freezing. Dry pendent sprinklers are often used inside buildings near exhaust duct penetrations to the outside. Nonfreeze or dry type sprinkler systems are often used for ducts outside buildings. Sprinklers should be spaced no more than 12 ft (3.7 m) apart in the duct for adequate protection.

All sprinklers in spray areas should be controlled by an accessible control valve, preferably an OS&Y valve. [**33**:A.7.2.4]

Paragraph A.7.2.4 of NFPA 33 recommends that sprinklers in the spray booth and its exhaust duct be of the lowest practical temperature rating, but that ceiling sprinklers outside the booth be rated at 141°C (286°F) (see 13.4.2.1).

Sprinklers installed in a spray booth or spray room should be located so that they are not in the direct path of the spray. Sprinklers in exhaust ducts should be spaced no more than 3660 mm (12 ft) apart.

See A.7.2.4 of NFPA 33 for additional guidance.

13.4.2.2 Sprinklers protecting spray areas and mixing rooms shall be protected against overspray residue so that they will operate quickly in event of fire. If covered, cellophane bags having a thickness of 0.003 in. (0.076 mm) or less, or thin paper bags shall be used. Coverings shall be replaced frequently so that heavy deposits of residue do not accumulate. Sprinklers that have been painted or coated, except by the sprinkler manufacturer, shall be replaced with new listed sprinklers having the same characteristics. [**33**:7.2.5]

Overspray residue is discussed in 13.4.2.2. One day's accumulation of overspray is enough to insulate a fusible link or to choke the orifice of an open deluge head to the extent that the sprinkler will not function as intended.

13.5 Solvent Extraction Plants

Section 13.5 applies to facilities that use solvents to remove animal and vegetable oils from oil-bearing materials, a process known as "solvent extraction." Generally, what is referred to is extraction of vegetable oils from oil-bearing seeds, such as sunflower seed, rapeseed (canola), soybeans, cotton seed, and others, by the use of a flammable liquid solvent. A flow-chart for the solvent extraction process is shown in Exhibit 13.2 and a diagram of one type of extractor is shown in Exhibit 13.3.

***EXHIBIT 13.2** Flow Diagram of Extraction Process.*

 NFPA 36, *Standard for Solvent Extraction Plants,* is limited to solvent extraction using Class I flammable hydrocarbon liquids, a Class I liquid being one whose flash point is below 37.8°C (100°F). Currently, the only hydrocarbon liquid that is widely used is hexane, whose properties are particularly suited to the extraction process. Other hydrocarbons, such as pentane and heptane, have been used but have not gained acceptance. Also, there are some extraction processes that use ethyl alcohol, but these are also not widely used and are not within the scope of NFPA 36.

EXHIBIT 13.3 *Rectangular Loop Extractor.*

13.5.1* Design Requirements.

A.13.5.1 Water spray or deluge systems that are used to protect solvent extraction process equipment or structures should be designed to provide a density of not less than 0.25 gpm/ft^2 (10.2 L/min·m^2) of protected surface area. *(See NFPA 13 and NFPA 15, Standard for Water Spray Fixed Systems for Fire Protection, for additional information.)* Foam-water sprinkler or deluge systems that are used for the same purposes should be designed to provide a density of not less than 0.16 gpm/ft^2 (6.5 L/min·m^2) of protected surface area. *(See NFPA 13 and NFPA 16, Standard for the Installation of Foam-Water Sprinkler and Foam-Water Spray Systems, for additional information.)*

Preparation buildings should be protected with automatic sprinkler systems designed for Ordinary Hazard (Group 2), in accordance with NFPA 13. [**36**:A.2.9]

Design requirements are covered in 13.5.1. NFPA 36 requires a water spray system, a deluge system, or a foam water sprinkler system, or a combination of these for the extraction process equipment and the structure in which it is located. NFPA 36 also requires automatic sprinkler protection for the area where the oil-bearing seeds are prepared prior to extraction. Although no particular density is mandated, the design criteria stated above are recommended as acceptable. If the extraction process involves more than 4540 kg (10,000 lb) of flammable solvent, then the U.S. Occupational Safety and Health Administration's Process Safety Management Rule, in Title 29, Code of Federal Regulations, Part 1910.119, is applicable. (This is only about 6800 L, or about 1800 gal, of hexane.) Based on a process hazard evaluation, the sprinkler system design criteria recommended by NFPA 36 might or might not be considered adequate.

13.5.2 Installation Requirements. (Reserved)

13.6 Nitrate Film

The requirements of Section 13.6 address the storage of cellulose nitrate film. Cellulose nitrate film has not been used for approximately 50 years but there are collections of nitrate films and negatives (flat film) that are stored for archival purposes. Because of the relative scarcity of cellulose nitrate film there are few cellulose nitrate film storage facilities. However, the material that they store is often of great historical value. For example the Library of Congress has a facility that stores cellulose nitrate film documents that are of significance to the United States.

Cellulose nitrate has stringent storage requirements because it is an extremely energetic material. Cellulose nitrate was the main component of "single base" gunpowder. When ignited it will burn rapidly, and if contained it may explode. Cellulose nitrate has the potential for exothermic decomposition. Sprinklers can be effective in stopping these reactions.

13.6.1 Design Requirements.

13.6.1.1 Rooms where nitrate film is stored or handled in quantities greater than 50 lb [23 kg (10 standard rolls)] shall be protected with an automatic sprinkler system that is designed for extra hazard occupancies.

*Exception: Motion picture projection booths or rooms and rewinding rooms. [**40**:3.1.2]*

13.6.1.2 Water supplies for automatic sprinklers shall be based on 20 gpm (1.26 L/sec) per sprinkler for 20 minutes for the total number of sprinklers in one vault, plus 25 percent of the sprinklers in the communicating fire area. [**40**:3.2.2]

13.6.2 Installation Requirements.

13.6.2.1 In areas or rooms where nitrate film is handled, the area that is protected per sprinkler shall not exceed 64 ft^2 (6 m^2) with sprinklers and branch lines not being over 8 ft (2.4 m) apart. [**40**:3.1.4]

13.6.2.2 Cabinet Protection. [**40**:4.2.5]

13.6.2.2.1 Where cabinets are required to be sprinklered, they shall be provided with at least one automatic sprinkler. [**40**:4.2.5.1]

 13.6.2.2.2 Where cans are stored on more than one shelf, as shown in Figure 13.6.2.2.2 and as described in 4.2.6.1 or 4.2.6.2 of NFPA 40, *Standard for the Storage and Handling of Cellulose Nitrate Film,* one sprinkler shall be provided for each shelf. [**40**:4.2.5.2]

13.6.2.3 Vaults Other than Extended Term Storage Vaults. [**40**:4.3] *(See Figure 13.6.2.3.)*

13.6.2.3.1 Sprinkler protection utilizing regular automatic sprinklers or open sprinklers shall be calculated on the basis of one sprinkler for each 62.5 ft^3 (1.8 m^3) of the interior vault volume. [**40**:4.3.6.1]

13.6.2.3.2 The minimum number of sprinklers for a standard 750-ft^3 (21-m^3) vault shall be not less than 12. [**40**:4.3.6.2]

 13.6.2.3.3* Sprinklers or nozzles shall be arranged to provide coverage over the tops and fronts of shelves. [**40**:4.3.6.3]

  A.13.6.2.3.3 The arrangement of sprinklers or nozzles for providing distribution over the face of shelving is important and requires knowledge of sprinkler discharge patterns and locations. This arrangement should be done only by qualified personnel. [**40**:4.3.6.3]

 13.6.2.3.4 Where automatic sprinklers are used, barriers made of No. 24 U.S. gauge sheet steel or other acceptable noncombustible material shall be installed between each sprinkler. Barriers shall be fastened rigidly in place and shall extend from the ceiling down to 4 in. (10 cm) below the sprinkler deflectors. [**40**:4.3.6.4]

13.6.2.4 Extended Term Storage Vaults. See Figure 13.6.2.4.

Vent flue is equivalent to No.18 U.S. gauge riveted steel. When inside building, it is to be covered with 1 in. (2.5 cm) of insulating material.

Decomposition vent

Shelves shall fit tightly against the back and sides of cabinet.

Automatic sprinkler

Not more than 25 cans on a single shelf.

2 in. (5 cm)

Not more than 5 cans high or more than 3 piles.

2 in. (5 cm)

Shelves of, noncombustible, insulating material not less than ⅜ in. (9.5 mm) thick or hardwood not less than 1 in. (2.5 cm) thick.

1 in. (2.5 cm)

Three-point lock

Cabinet and self-closing door of insulated or hollow metal construction

Side Elevation   **Front Elevation**   **Front Elevation**

FIGURE 13.6.2.2.2 *Standard Film Cabinet for Other than Extended Term Storage Film.* [40:Figure 4.2]

Decomposition vent   Lights of fixed type at ceiling only. Lights should be guarded.

Shelves of hardwood or noncombustible, insulating material tightly fitted to walls and barriers

Shelves should be 1 in. (2.5 cm) wider than diameter of largest container.

2-hr-rated swinging-type self-closing fire door in approved frame

Elevation view

Explosion relief [1 ft² for 50 ft³ (0.1 m² for each 1.4 m³)]. Provide wing walls necessary

Vertical barriers of noncombustible, insulating material

2-hr-rated sliding-type automatic-closing fire door

Floor drain or scuppers

Switch and pilot light

Decomposition vent

Not over 3 ft (0.9 m)

Plan view

Shelves and barriers tightly fitted to walls

Spray-type fixed nozzles

Automatic sprinklers

1 in. (2.5 cm)

Barriers

Elevation view

FIGURE 13.6.2.3 *Standard Film Vault (for Other than Extended Term Storage Film).* [40:Figure 4.3]

FIGURE 13.6.2.4 *Extended Term Storage Vault. [40:Figure 4.5]*

13.6.2.4.1 Sprinklers shall be provided in a ratio of one sprinkler for each 62.5 ft³ (1.8 m³) of vault volume.

Exception: Sprinkler systems in existing extended term storage vaults that were in compliance with the provisions of NFPA 40 at the time of installation shall be permitted to be continued in use. **[40:**4.5.5.1]

13.6.2.4.2 The minimum number of sprinklers for a 1000-ft³ (28-m³) vault shall be 15 sprinklers.

Exception: Sprinkler systems in existing extended term storage vaults that were in compliance with the provisions of NFPA 40 at the time of installation shall be permitted to be continued in use. **[40:**4.5.5.2]

13.6.2.4.3 Directional sprinklers that will provide coverage into the face of the shelves shall be provided. [**40:**4.5.5.3]

13.6.2.5 Motion Picture Film Laboratories. In all cases, sprinklers shall be arranged so that not more than two machines are protected by any one sprinkler. [**40:**7.2.5.2]

Because film is more vulnerable during processing, the number of machines per sprinkler must be limited, as stated in 13.6.2.5.

13.7 Storage of Pyroxylin Plastic

 Pyroxylin plastic is covered in Section 13.7. There is no active pyroxylin plastic industry. The document that addresses storage of pyroxylin plastic, NFPA 42, *Code for the Storage of Pyroxylin Plastic,* will likely be withdrawn.

13.7.1 Design Requirements.

13.7.1.1 The water supply for automatic sprinklers shall be based on the number of sprinklers liable to be affected in any fire section between fire walls or fire-resistive partitions. It shall be assumed that any one of the following numbers of sprinklers can be affected and the condition giving maximum flow used as a basis:

(1) All sprinklers in a vault
(2) All sprinklers in a tote box storeroom
(3) Three-fourths of the sprinklers in a finished-stock storeroom
(4) All sprinklers in a section of an isolated storage building [**42**:2.4.3.1]

13.7.1.2 The water supply for an automatic sprinkler system shall be based on a flow of 20 gpm (76 Lpm) per sprinkler for 20 minutes, with a minimum rate of flow of 500 gpm (1900 Lpm). Such flow shall be with an effective pressure at the top line of sprinklers of not less than 40 psi (2.8 bar). [**42**:2.4.3.2]

13.7.2 Installation Requirements. See Figure 13.7.2(a) and Figure 13.7.2(b).

13.7.2.1 Where sprinkler systems are provided for isolated storage buildings per 3.4.3 of NFPA 42, *Code for the Storage of Pyroxylin Plastic,* sprinklers shall be spaced so that there is one sprinkler per 32 ft² (3 m²). [**42**:3.4.3]

FIGURE 13.7.2(a) *Raw Stock Storage Vault Showing General Arrangement of Sprinklers, Racks, and Baffles. [42:Figure 4.3.3.7(a)]*

FIGURE 13.7.2(b) *Details of Storage Racks in Raw Stock Storage Vault. [42:Figure 4.3.3.7(b)]*

13.7.2.2 Sprinklers in buildings used for storage of loose scrap shall be installed in the ratio of one sprinkler for each 1000 lb (454 kg) of storage.

Exception: The ratio in 13.7.2.2 shall need not apply if the scrap is in tanks or other receptacles kept filled with water. [**42**:*3.4.4*]

13.7.2.3 Where cabinets are required to be sprinklered, they shall have at least one automatic sprinkler in each compartment. [**42**:4.2.10]

13.7.2.4 Vaults Containing Pyroxylin Plastic.

13.7.2.4.1 Vaults shall be equipped with automatic sprinklers in a ratio of one sprinkler to each 834 lb (378 kg) of pyroxylin plastic or one sprinkler to each 125 ft^3 (3.5 m^3) of total vault space. [**42**:4.4.1]

13.7.2.4.2 A vault that is divided into two or more sections shall have at least one automatic sprinkler in each section. [**42**:4.4.2]

13.7.2.4.3 Sprinkler systems for vaults shall be equipped with a 1-in. (2.5-cm) drip line with a ½-in. (13-mm) outlet valve. [**42**:4.4.5]

13.7.2.5 Tote-Box Storeroom for Pyroxylin Plastic. Sprinkler protection provided for the tote box storeroom shall consist of one sprinkler in the center of the aisle immediately in front of the dividing partition between each pair of sections. Proper baffles shall be provided between heads. [**42**:4.7.9] *(See Figure 13.7.2.5(a) and Figure 13.7.2.5(b).)*

13.7.2.6 Finished Stock Storeroom for Pyroxylin Plastic. See Figure 13.7.2.6.

13.7.2.6.1 Automatic sprinklers shall be installed with proper baffles between sprinklers in the center of the aisle opposite each section. [**42**:4.8.7]

13.7.2.6.2 Special Rooms for Stock in Shipping Cases. The special room shall be protected by automatic sprinklers, with at least one sprinkler for each 64 ft^2 (6 m^2). [**42**:4.9.4]

13.8 Laboratories Using Chemicals

 13.8.1 Design Requirements. An automatic sprinkler system, where required by Table 3.1(a) of NFPA 45, *Standard on Fire Protection for Laboratories Using Chemicals,* depending on the construction of the building, the hazard class of the laboratory unit, the construction of the laboratory unit enclosure, and the area of the laboratory unit shall be in accordance with the following:

(1) Automatic sprinkler system protection for Class A and Class B laboratories shall be in accordance with ordinary hazard, Group 2 occupancies.
(2) Automatic sprinkler system protection for Class C and Class D laboratories shall be in accordance with ordinary hazard, Group 1 occupancies. [**45**:4.2.1.1]

Design requirements are discussed in 13.8.1. Both the fire hazard class of the lab as well as the requirement of sprinklers depend on the volume of chemicals in the particular lab, the construction of the building, and the size of the lab unit. For all classes of labs, sprinklering allows greater quantities of chemicals to be used in the lab; allows, in some cases, for the labs to be larger; and allows for reduced or no fire separation from nonlaboratory areas.

The fire hazard classes range from A to D, representing a potentially high fire hazard to a minimal fire hazard, respectively. As the overall potential hazard is increased, the required sprinkler application rate increases; hence, Class A and B labs are considered ordinary hazard (Group 2) occupancies, and Class C and D labs are considered ordinary hazard (Group 1) occupancies. Although the Class A and B labs are the two types of labs allowed to contain the

FIGURE 13.7.2.5(a) *Tote Box Storeroom Showing General Arrangement of Racks and Sprinklers. [42:Figure 4.7]*

FIGURE 13.7.2.5(b) *Tote Box Storeroom Showing Arrangement of Sprinklers and Baffles and Section of Tote Box Storage Rack. [42:Figure 4.7.7]*

most chemicals when compared to Class C and D labs, they are required to be sprinklered and have a greater fire separation, and they are not allowed to be over 10,000 ft². In Classes C and D labs, the presence of sprinklers allows the maximum quantities per lab unit to be approximately doubled. The comparison of the chemical quantities by lab class for sprinklered and nonsprinklered labs is shown in Commentary Tables 13.2 and 13.3 and the fire separation is shown in Commentary Tables 13.4 and 13.5.

When presented with a noncompliant lab with respect to sprinklers or lab class, the simplest, most obvious means of bringing it into compliance is to reduce the quantities of flammable and combustible liquids. Upon performing a chemical inventory, chances are that a surprising quantity of such liquids are not in frequent use or are outdated and should be

FIGURE 13.7.2.6 *Finished-Stock Storeroom Showing General Arrangement of Racks.* [42:Figure 4.8]

COMMENTARY 13.2 *Maximum Quantities of Flammable and Combustible Liquids and Liquefied Flammable Gases in Sprinklered Laboratory Units Outside of Inside Liquid Storage Areas*

Laboratory Unit Fire Hazard Class	Flammable and Combustible Liquid Class§	Excluding *Quantities in Storage Cabinets†or Safety Cans*				Including *Quantities in Storage Cabinets‡or Safety Cans*			
		Maximum Quantity# per 9.3 m² (100 ft²) of Laboratory Unit		Maximum Quantity# per Laboratory Unit		Maximum Quantity# per 9.3 m² (100 ft²) of Laboratory Unit		Maximum Quantity# per Laboratory Unit	
		L	gal	L	gal	L	gal	L	gal
A	I†	38	10	2270	600	76	20	4540	1200
	I†, II, and IIIA	76	20	3028	800	150	40	6060	1600
B	I†	20	5	1136	300	38	10	2270	600
	I†, II, and IIIA	38	10	1515	400	76	20	3028	800
C	I†	7.5	2	570	150	15	4	1136	300
	I†, II, and IIIA	15	4	757	200	30	8	1515	400
D	I†	4	1.1	284	75	7.5	2	570	150
	I†, II, and IIIA	4	1.1	284	75	7.5	2	570	150

†This category includes Class I flammable liquids and liquefied flammable gases.
‡See description of containers in Table 4.2.3 and description of storage cabinets in Section 4.3, both of NFPA 30, *Flammable and Combustible Liquids Code.*
§See 2.2.1.5 and 8.1.6.5 [of NFPA 45].
#For maximum container sizes, see Table 7.2.3.2 [of NFPA 45].
Source: NFPA 45, 2000, Table 2.2.1(a).

COMMENTARY TABLE 13.3 *Maximum Quantities of Flammable and Combustible Liquids and Liquefied Flammable Gases in Nonsprinklered Laboratory Units Outside of Inside Liquid Storage Areas*

Laboratory Unit Fire Hazard Class	Flammable and Combustible Liquid Class‡	Excluding *Quantities in Storage Cabinets†or Safety Cans*				Including *Quantities in Storage Cabinets†or Safety Cans*			
		Maximum Quantity per 9.3 m² (100 ft²) of Laboratory Unit		Maximum Quantity§ per Laboratory Unit		Maximum Quantity§ per 9.3 m² (100 ft²) of Laboratory Unit		Maximum Quantity§ per Laboratory Unit	
		L	gal	L	gal	L	gal	L	gal
A	I#	Not permitted		Not permitted		Not permitted		Not permitted	
	I#, II, and IIIA	Not permitted		Not permitted		Not permitted		Not permitted	
B	I#	Not permitted		Not permitted		Not permitted		Not permitted	
	I#, II, and IIIA	Not permitted		Not permitted		Not permitted		Not permitted	
C	I#	7.5	2	284	75	15	4	570	150
	I#, II, and IIIA	15	4	380	100	30	8	760	200
D	I#	4	1.1	140	37	7.5	2	284	75
	I#, II, and IIIA	4	1.1	140	37	7.5	2	284	75

†See description of containers in Table 4.2.3 and description of storage cabinets in Section 4.3, both of NFPA 30, *Flammable and Combustible Liquids Code.*
‡See 2.2.1.5 and 8.1.6.5 [of NFPA 45].
§For maximum container sizes, see Table 7.2.3.2 [of NFPA 45].
#This category includes Class I flammable liquids and liquefied flammable gases.
Source: NFPA 45, 2000, Table 2.2.1(b).

COMMENTARY TABLE 13.4 Fire Protection Requirements for Sprinklered Laboratory Units

Laboratory Unit	Area of Lab Unit	Fire Separation
A	< 10,000 ft^2	2 hours
	> 10,000 ft^2	Not permitted
B	< 10,000 ft^2	1 hour
	> 10,000 ft^2	Not permitted
C	Any size	Not required
D	Any size	Not required

Source: NFPA 45, 2000, Table 3.1.1(a).

COMMENTARY TABLE 13.5 Fire Protection Requirements for Nonsprinklered Laboratory Units

Laboratory Unit	Area of Lab Unit	Fire Separation
A		Not permitted
B		Not permitted
C	< 10,000 ft^2	1 hour
	> 10,000 ft^2	Not permitted
D	< 10,000 ft^2	Not required
	> 10,000 ft^2	1 hour

Source: NFPA 45, 2000, Table 3.1.1(b).

removed from the laboratory. Keep in mind that outdated chemicals can be dangerous and some, such as those that form friction-sensitive compounds upon prolonged storage, require haz-mat removal.

13.8.2 Installation Requirements. (Reserved)

13.9 Oxygen-Fuel Gas Systems for Welding, Cutting, and Allied Processes

 13.9.1 Design Requirements. Where sprinkler systems are required per 2.3.1 of NFPA 51, *Standard for the Design and Installation of Oxygen—Fuel Gas Systems for Welding, Cutting, and Allied Processes,* they shall provide a sprinkler discharge density of at least 0.25 gpm/ft^2 (10.2 mm/min) over a minimum operating area of at least 3000 ft^2 (88 m^2). [**51**:2.3.1, Exception No. 1]

13.9.2 Installation Requirements. Where sprinkler systems are provided per NFPA 51, 2.3.1, Exception No. 1, sprinklers shall be located not more than 20 ft (6 m) above the floor where the cylinders are stored. [**51**:2.3.1, Exception No. 1]

13.10 Acetylene Cylinder Charging Plants

Acetylene cylinder charging plants are covered in Section 13.10. Acetylene is an extremely energetic and unstable chemical. Under typical ambient conditions it decomposes slowly enough that it can be safely stored. However, when exposed to elevated temperatures (in the 250°C to 280°C range), the heat generated by decomposition may not be able to be safely dissipated, and the acetylene has the potential to react violently. Because of its instability, acetylene is typically dissolved in acetone or other solvents that are retained on a porous silica media in a cylinder. This configuration provides relatively stable acetylene storage.

Acetylene is produced by reacting calcium carbide with water. Sprinklers cannot be used in the acetylene production portion of a facility for this reaction.

13.10.1 Design Requirements. Where an automatic sprinkler system is required per NFPA 51A, *Standard for Acetylene Cylinder Charging Plants,* it shall be an extra hazard (Group 1) open or closed head sprinkler system. [**51A:**9.2.2]

13.10.2 Installation Requirements. (Reserved)

13.11 Storage, Use, and Handling of Compressed and Liquefied Gases in Portable Cylinders

13.11.1 Design Requirements.

13.11.1.1 Where an automatic sprinkler system is required per NFPA 55, *Standard for the Storage, Use, and Handling of Compressed and Liquefied Gases in Portable Cylinders,* the sprinkler system protecting the gas cylinder storage, and for a distance of 25 ft (7.6 m) beyond in all directions, shall be capable of providing a sprinkler density of at least 0.3 gpm/ft^2 (12.2 mm/min) over the most hydraulically remote 2500 ft^2 (232.25 m^2). [**55:**2.2.2.1]

13.11.1.2 Where sprinkler systems are provided per NFPA 55, 2.2.2.2, Exception No. 1, they shall be designed for ordinary hazard, Group 1 occupancies. [**55:**2.2.2.2]

13.11.1.3 Where sprinkler systems are provided per NFPA 55, 2.2.2.2, Exception No. 2, they shall be designed for ordinary hazard, Group 1 occupancies. [**55:**2.2.2.2]

13.11.1.4 Where sprinkler systems are required for gas cylinder storage rooms per NFPA 55, they shall be capable of providing a minimum density of 0.3 gpm/ft^2 (12.2 mm/min) over the most hydraulically remote 2500 ft^2 (232.25 m^2) or the entire room area, whichever is smaller. [**55:**2.2.3.2]

13.11.2 Installation Requirements. (Reserved)

13.12 Storage and Handling of Liquefied Petroleum Gases at Utility Gas Plants

13.12.1 Design Requirements. The design of fire water supply and distribution systems, if required by NFPA 59, *Utility LP-Gas Plant Code,* shall provide for the simultaneous supply of those fixed fire protection systems, including monitor nozzles, at their design flow and pressure, involved in the maximum single incident expected in the plant. An additional supply of 1000 gpm (3785 L/min) shall be available for hand hose streams for a period of not less than 2 hours. Manually actuated monitors shall be permitted to be used to augment hand hose streams. [**59:**10.5.2]

13.12.2 Installation Requirements. (Reserved)

13.13 Production, Storage, and Handling of Liquefied Natural Gas (LNG)

13.13.1 Design Requirements. The design of fire water supply and distribution systems, if required by NFPA 59A, *Standard for the Production, Storage, and Handling of Liquefied*

Natural Gas (LNG), shall provide for the simultaneous supply of those fixed fire protection systems, including monitor nozzles, at their design flow and pressure, involved in the maximum single incident expected in the plant plus an allowance of 1000 gpm (3785 L/min) for hand hose streams for not less than 2 hours. [**59A**:9.5.2]

13.13.2 Installation Requirements. (Reserved)

13.14 Electronic Computer Systems

13.14.1 Design Requirements. (Reserved)

 13.14.2 Installation Requirements. Where sprinkler systems are provided per NFPA 75, *Standard for the Protection of Electronic Computer/Data Processing Equipment,* they shall be valved separately from other sprinkler systems. [75:6.1.3]

13.15 Incinerators, Systems, and Equipment

13.15.1 Design Requirements. (Reserved)

13.15.2 Installation Requirements.

13.15.2.1 Chute Automatic Sprinklers. [**82**:3.2.5]

13.15.2.1.1 Gravity Chute. Gravity chutes shall be protected internally by automatic sprinklers. This requires a sprinkler at or above the top service opening of the chute, and, in addition, a sprinkler shall be installed within the chute at alternate floor levels in buildings over two stories in height with a mandatory sprinkler located at the lowest service level. [**82**:3.2.5.1] *(See Figure 13.15.2.1.1.)*

 *Exception No. 1: Lined masonry chute that complies with 3.2.2.5 of NFPA 82. [**82**:3.2.5.1]*

In order to eliminate sprinklers in a masonry waste chute, the chute must be constructed of clay or shale brickwork not less than 8 in. (203 mm) thick or be of reinforced concrete not less than 6 in. (152 mm) thick (see 13.15.2.1.1, Exception No. 1). The chute must also be lined with low-duty refractory brick that is not less than 4½ in. (114 mm) thick. The intent of this provision is to provide a separation between the chute and the building with at least a 2-hour fire resistance rating.

 *Exception No. 2: Lined metal chute that complies with 3.2.2.6 of NFPA 82. [**82**:3.2.5.1]*

Only lined metal waste chutes are permitted to have sprinklers omitted (see 13.15.2.1.1, Exception No. 2). The metal waste chute must be lined with low-duty refractory brick not less than 2½ in. (63.5 mm) thick or equivalent castable refractories. All unlined steel chutes must be protected internally by automatic sprinklers.

 *Exception No. 3: Listed medium-heat chimney that complies with 3.2.2.8 of NFPA 82, Standard on Incinerators and Waste and Linen Handling Systems and Equipment. [**82**:3.2.5.1]*

 Listed medium-heat appliance chimney sections are acceptable for use as trash chutes (see 13.15.2.1.1, Exception No. 3). These chimneys are listed to UL 103, *Factory-Built Chimneys for Residential Type and Building Heating Appliances,* and are used with appliances that produce maximum flue gas temperatures of 1800°F (982°C). They are composed of listed, factory-built components that are suitable for open, nonenclosed use at specified minimum clearances to combustibles.

FIGURE 13.15.2.1.1 *Gravity Chute. [82:Figure 3.2.5.1]*

13.15.2.1.2 Chute Sprinkler Head Protection. Automatic sprinklers installed in gravity chute service openings shall be recessed out of the chute area through which the material travels. [**82**:3.2.5.2]

13.15.2.2 Automatic Sprinklers, Full Pneumatic Systems. Full pneumatic-type risers shall be protected internally by automatic sprinklers. A sprinkler shall be required at or above the top loading station and at alternate floor levels in buildings over two stories in height, with a mandatory sprinkler located at the lowest loading station. Sprinklers shall be recessed out of the station area through which the material travels. [**82**:3.3.4] *(See Figure 13.15.2.2.)*

Full pneumatic waste transport systems, which are discussed in 13.15.2.2, consist of full vacuum stations equipped with inner doors and a locked outer door, an air source at the top of the riser, an air inlet control damper, flanged riser piping, transport piping, collectors (receivers), and a fan and fan damper. It is important to note that sprinklers are only required in the riser portions of full pneumatic systems. Figure 13.15.2.2 illustrates a full pneumatic system with an offset. Note the sprinklers positioned in each of the risers.

13.15.2.3 Commercial-Industrial Compactors. All chute-fed compactors shall have an automatic special fine water spray sprinkler with a minimum ½-in. (13-mm) orifice installed in the hopper of the compactor. This sprinkler shall be an ordinary temperature-rated sprinkler. The sprinklers shall be supplied by a minimum 1-in. (25.4-mm) ferrous piping or ¾-in. (19-mm) copper tubing line from the domestic cold water supply. The sprinkler shall provide a suitable spray into the hopper. A cycling (on-off), self-actuating, snap-action, heat-actuated sprinkler shall be permitted to be used, or the sprinkler shall be permitted to be controlled by a temperature sensor operating a solenoid valve. Sprinkler water piping shall be protected from freezing in outdoor installations. [**82**:5.2.5.2.1]

FIGURE 13.15.2.2 *Full Pneumatic System.* [82: *Figure 3.3.4]*

13.16   Industrial Furnaces Using a Special Process Atmosphere

13.16.1   Design Requirements. (Reserved)

 13.16.2   Installation Requirements. Where sprinkler systems are provided per NFPA 86C, *Standard for Industrial Furnaces Using a Special Processing Atmosphere,* 18.1.2(b), sprinklers shall be of extra high-temperature rating [325°F to 650°F (163°C to 343°C] to avoid premature operation from localized flashing. [**86C:**18.1.2(b)]

13.17   Ventilation Control and Fire Protection of Commercial Cooking Operations

 13.17.1   Design Requirements. (Reserved)

13.17.2   Installation Requirements. (Reserved)

13.18   Class A Hyperbaric Chambers

13.18.1   Design Requirements.

13.18.1.1 In chambers that consist of more than one chamber compartment (lock), the design of the deluge system shall ensure adequate operation when the chamber compartments are at different depths (pressures). The design shall also ensure the independent or simultaneous operation of deluge systems.

Exception: Chamber compartments that are used strictly as personnel transfer compartments (locks), and for no other purposes, are not required to have a fixed deluge system. [99:19.2.5.2]

13.18.1.2* Manual activation and deactivation deluge controls shall be located at the operator's console and in each chamber compartment (lock) containing a deluge system. Controls shall be designed to prevent unintended activation. [**99**:19.2.5.2.1]

A.13.18.1.2 More than one control station could be required in a compartment (lock) depending on its size. [**99**:A.19.2.5.2.1]

13.18.1.3 Water shall be delivered from the sprinkler heads as specified in 13.18.1.4 within 3 seconds of activation of any affiliated deluge control. [**99**:19.2.5.2.2]

13.18.1.4* Average spray density at floor level shall be not less than 2 gpm/ft^2 (81.5 L/min/m^2) with no floor area larger than 1 m^2 receiving less than 1 gpm/ft^2 (40.75 L/min/m^2). [**99**:19.2.5.2.3]

A.13.18.1.4 Experience has shown that when water is discharged through conventional sprinklers into a hyperbaric atmosphere, the spray angle is reduced because of increased resistance to water droplet movement in the denser atmosphere. This is so even though the water pressure differential is maintained above chamber pressure. Therefore, it is necessary to compensate by increasing the number of sprinklers. It is recommended that spray coverage tests be conducted at maximum chamber pressure.

Some chamber configurations, such as small-diameter horizontal cylinders, might have a very tiny "floor," or even no floor at all. For horizontal cylinder chambers and spherical chambers, "floor level" shall be taken to mean the level at ¼ diameter below the chamber centerline or actual "floor level," whichever gives the larger floor area. [**99**:A.19.2.5.2.3]

13.18.1.5* The number and positioning of sprinklers shall be sufficient to provide reasonably uniform spray coverage with vertical and horizontal (or near horizontal) jets. [**99**:19.2.5.2.3]

A.13.18.1.5 Experience has shown that when water is discharged through conventional sprinklers into a hyperbaric atmosphere, the spray angle is reduced because of increased resistance to water droplet movement in the denser atmosphere. This is so even though the water pressure differential is maintained above chamber pressure. Therefore, it is necessary to compensate by increasing the number of sprinklers. It is recommended that spray coverage tests be conducted at maximum chamber pressure.

Some chamber configurations, such as small-diameter horizontal cylinders, could have a very tiny "floor," or even no floor at all. For horizontal cylinder chambers and spherical chambers, "floor level" should be taken to mean the level at ¼ diameter below the chamber centerline or actual "floor level," whichever gives the larger floor area. [**99**:A.19.2.5.2.3]

13.18.1.6 There shall be sufficient water available in the deluge system to maintain the flow specified in 13.18.1.4 simultaneously in each chamber compartment (lock) containing the deluge system for 1 minute. The limit on maximum extinguishment duration shall be governed by the chamber capacity (bilge capacity also, if so equipped) and/or its drainage system. [**99**:19.2.5.2.4]

13.18.1.7 The deluge system shall have stored pressure to operate for at least 15 seconds without electrical branch power. [**99**:19.2.5.2.5]

13.18.2 Installation Requirements. (Reserved)

13.19 Fixed Guideway Transit Systems

Fixed guideway transit systems are discussed in Section 13.19. NFPA 130, *Standard for Fixed Guideway Transit and Passenger Rail Systems,* contains requirements for sprinklers in two areas—stations, such as train or subway, and vehicle storage areas. In the requirements for stations, NFPA 130 makes a direct reference to NFPA 13 with further specific guidance provided. For vehicle storage areas, NFPA 130 requires a minimum ordinary hazard classification.

13.19.1 Design Requirements. In all areas of enclosed structures used for storage and maintenance of vehicles the sprinkler system shall be of a closed-head type for Ordinary Hazard classification. [**130:**6.4.1]

13.19.2 Installation Requirements. (Reserved)

13.20 Race Track Stables

13.20.1 Design Requirements. Automatic sprinkler systems shall be designed in accordance with Ordinary Hazard Group 2 classification. [**150:**4.1.2]

13.20.2 Installation Requirements. (Reserved)

13.21 Water Cooling Towers

13.21.1 Design Requirements.

13.21.1.1 Types of Systems.

13.21.1.1.1* Because the counterflow tower design lends itself to either closed- or open-head systems, wet-pipe, dry-pipe, preaction, or deluge systems shall be permitted to be used. [**214:**3.2.2.1]

 A.13.21.1.1.1 A deluge system provides a higher degree of protection where water supplies are adequate. In climates that are subject to freezing temperatures, a deluge system minimizes the possibility of failure due to pipes freezing. [**214:**A.3.2.2.1]

13.21.1.1.2* The open-head deluge system shall be used in crossflow towers to maximize the water distribution and heat detection activation. [**214:**3.2.2.2]

A.13.21.1.1.2 The crossflow design is such that it is difficult to locate sprinklers in the most desirable spots for both water distribution and heat detection. This situation can be solved by separating these two functions and using separate water discharge and detection systems. [**214:**A.3.2.2.2]

13.21.1.2 Minimum Rate of Application.

13.21.1.2.1 Under the fan decks of counterflow towers, the rate of application of water shall be 0.5 gpm/ft^2 (20.4 L/min·m^2) (including fan opening). [**214:**3.2.3.1]

13.21.1.2.2 Under the fan decks of crossflow towers, the rate of application of water shall be 0.33 gpm/ft^2 (13.45 L/min·m^2) (including fan opening). [**214:**3.2.3.2]

13.21.1.2.3 Over the fill areas of crossflow towers, the rate of application of water shall be 0.5 gpm/ft^2 (20.4 L/min·m^2). [**214:**3.2.3.3]

13.21.1.3 Extended Fan Decks. On towers having extended fan decks that completely enclose the distribution basin, the discharge outlets protecting the fill area shall be located over the basin, under the extension of the fan deck. These discharge outlets shall be open directional spray nozzles or other approved spray devices arranged to discharge 0.35 gpm/ft^2 (14.26 L/min·m^2) directly on the distribution basin and 0.15 gpm/ft^2 (6.11 L/min·m^2) on the underside of the fan deck extension. On towers having extended fan decks that do not completely enclose the hot water basin, outlets protecting the fill shall be located under the distribution basin as set out in 3.2.4.2. of NFPA 214, *Standard on Water-Cooling Towers.* [**214:**3.2.4.3]

13.21.1.4 Combustible Fan Decks. For deluge systems using directional spray nozzles in the pendent position, provisions shall be made to protect the underside of a combustible fan deck at a minimum of 0.15 gpm/ft^2 (6.11 L/min·m^2), which shall be included as part of the application rate specified in 13.21.1.3. [**214:**3.2.4.4]

13.21.1.5 Water Basin Covers. On film-filled towers that have solid, hot-water basin covers over the complete basin, the discharge outlets protecting the fill area shall be permitted to be located under the basin covers. These discharge outlets shall be open directional spray nozzles or other approved devices arranged to discharge 0.35 gpm/ft^2 (14.26 L/min·m^2) directly on the distribution basin, and 0.15 gpm/ft^2 (6.11 L/min·m^2) on the underside of the water basin covers. [**214:**3.2.4.5]

13.21.1.6 Exterior Protection. Systems for exterior protection shall be designed with the same attention and care as interior systems. Pipe sizing shall be based on hydraulic calculations. Water supply and discharge rate shall be based on a minimum 0.15 gpm/ft^2 (6.11 L/min·m^2) for all surfaces being protected. [**214:**3.2.10.2]

13.21.1.7 Sprinkler System Water Supply.

13.21.1.7.1 Deluge Systems.

13.21.1.7.1.1* Where all cells of a cooling tower are protected by a single deluge system, the water supply shall be adequate to supply all discharge outlets on that system. [**214:**3.6.1.1]

A.13.21.1.7.1.1 Where a single deluge system protects an entire water-cooling tower, regardless of the number of cells, the water supply needs to be based on the entire deluge system coverage. Refer to Figure A.13.21.1.7.1.1. [**214:**A.3.6.1.1]

FIGURE A.13.21.1.7.1.1 *Single Deluge System.* *[214:Figure A.3.6.1.1]*

13.21.1.7.1.2 Where two or more deluge systems are used to protect a cooling tower and fire-resistant partitions are not provided between the deluge systems, the water supply shall be adequate to supply all discharge outlets in the two most hydraulically demanding adjacent systems. [**214:**3.6.1.2]

13.21.1.7.1.3* Where two or more deluge systems are separated by fire-resistant partitions, the water supply shall be adequate to supply all discharge outlets in the single most hydraulically demanding system. [**214:**3.6.1.3]

A.13.21.1.7.1.3 Deluge systems separated by fire-resistant partitions can be treated independently as worst-case water supply situations. Refer to Figure A.13.21.1.7.1.3. [**214:**A.3.6.1.3]

FIGURE A.13.21.1.7.1.3 *Multiple Deluge Systems.*
[214:Figure A.3.6.1.3]

13.21.1.7.2 Wet, Dry, and Preaction Systems.

13.21.1.7.2.1* Where each cell of the cooling tower is separated by a fire-resistant partition, the water supply shall be adequate to supply all discharge outlets in the hydraulically most demanding single cell. [**214:**3.6.2.1]

A.13.21.1.7.2.1 Water-cooling towers with each cell separated by a fire-resistant partition and protected by wet, dry, or preaction system(s) should have the water supply based on the most demanding individual cell. Refer to Figure A.13.21.1.7.2.1. [**214:**A.3.6.2.1]

FIGURE A.13.21.1.7.2.1 *Multiple Wet, Dry, or Preaction Systems with Fire-Resistant Partitions. [214: Figure A.3.6.2.1]*

13.21.1.7.2.2* Where fire-resistant partitions are not provided between each cell of a cooling tower, the water supply shall be adequate to supply all discharge outlets in the two most hydraulically demanding adjoining cells. [**214:**3.6.2.2]

A.13.21.1.7.2.2 Without fire-resistant partitions between cells, the worst-case situation involves the most demanding adjoining cells. Refer to Figure A.13.21.1.7.2.2. [**214:**A.3.6.2.2]

13.21.1.7.3 Hose Streams. Water supplies shall be sufficient to include a minimum of 500 gpm (1892.5 L/min) for hose streams in addition to the sprinkler requirements. [**214:**3.6.3]

13.21.1.7.4 Duration. An adequate water supply of at least 2-hour duration shall be provided for the combination of the water supply specified in 13.21.1.7.1 or 13.21.1.7.2, plus the hose stream demand specified in 13.21.1.7.3. [**214:**3.6.4]

13.21.2 Installation Requirements.

13.21.2.1* Counterflow Towers. [**214:**3.2.4.1]

A.13.21.2.1 See Figure A.13.21.2.1(a) through Figure A.13.21.2.1(d).

FIGURE A.13.21.1.7.2.2 *Multiple Wet, Dry, or Preaction Systems with No Fire-Resistant Partitions.* [214: Figure A.3.6.2.2]

FIGURE A.13.21.2.1(a) *Typical Deluge Fire Protection Arrangement for Counterflow Towers, Illustration 1.* [214: Figure A.3.2.4.1(a)]

13.21.2.1.1 The discharge outlets shall be located under the fan deck and fan opening. [**214**:3.2.4.1.1]

13.21.2.1.2 Except under the fan opening, all discharge outlets shall have deflector distances installed in accordance with Section 8.5. [**214**:3.2.4.1.2]

13.21.2.1.3 Closed-head discharge outlets for dry-pipe and preaction systems shall be installed in the upright position only. [**214**:3.2.4.1.3]

13.21.2.2* Crossflow Towers. [**214**:3.2.4.2]

A.13.21.2.2 See Figure A.13.21.2.2(a) through Figure A.13.21.2.2(d).

13.21.2.2.1 The discharge outlets protecting the plenum area shall be located under the fan deck and in the fan opening. [**214**:3.2.4.2.1]

Section A-A

FIGURE A.13.21.2.1(b) *Typical Deluge Fire Protection Arrangement for Counterflow Towers, Illustration 2. [214: Figure A.3.2.4.1(b)]*

FIGURE A.13.21.2.1(c) *Typical Deluge or Dry Pipe Fire Protection Arrangement for Counterflow Towers, Illustration 1. [214: Figure A.3.2.4.1(c)]*

FIGURE A.13.21.2.1(d) *Typical Deluge or Dry Pipe Fire Protection Arrangement for Counterflow Towers, Illustration 2. [214: Figure A.3.2.4.1(d)]*

FIGURE A.13.21.2.2(a) *Typical Deluge Fire Protection Arrangement for Crossflow Towers, Illustration 1. [214: Figure A.3.2.4.2(a)]*

FIGURE A.13.21.2.2(b) *Typical Deluge Fire Protection Arrangement for Crossflow Towers, Illustration 2. [214: Figure A.3.2.4.2(b)]*

Note: Where air seal boards prevent installation of cooling tower nozzles on drift eliminator side of fill, this nozzle location should be used.

FIGURE A.13.21.2.2(c) *Typical Deluge Fire Protection Arrangement for Crossflow Towers, Illustration 3. [214: Figure A.3.2.4.2(c)]*

Section A-A

Note: Where air seal boards prevent installation of cooling tower nozzles on drift eliminator side of fill, this nozzle location should be used.

FIGURE A.13.21.2.2(d) *Typical Deluge Fire Protection Arrangement for Crossflow Towers, Illustration 4. [214: Figure A.3.2.3.2(d)]*

13.21.2.2.2 Discharge outlets protecting the fill shall be located under the distribution basin on either the louver or drift eliminator side, discharging horizontally through the joist channels. [**214**:3.2.4.2.2]

13.21.2.2.3 Towers with a fill area longer than the maximum allowable for the discharge device being used shall have discharge devices placed on both sides of the fill area in each joist channel. The pressure at each discharge device shall be adequate to provide protection for half of the length of the fill area. [**214**:3.2.4.2.3]

13.21.2.2.4 Where joist channels are wider than 2 ft (0.6 m), more than one discharge device shall be required per joist channel.

*Exception: If the discharge device being used is listed for the width of the joist channel being protected. [**214**:3.2.4.2.4]*

13.21.2.3* Extended Fan Decks. On towers having extended fan decks that completely enclose the distribution basin, the discharge outlets protecting the fill area shall be located over the basin, under the extension of the fan deck. [**214**:3.2.4.3]

A.13.21.2.3 Location of the nozzle relative to surfaces to be protected should be determined by the particular nozzle's discharge characteristics. Care should also be taken in the selection of nozzles to obtain waterways not easily obstructed by debris, sediment, sand, and so forth, in the water. *[See Figure A.13.21.2.3(a) and Figure A.13.21.2.3(b).]*

13.21.2.4 Combustible Fan Decks. For deluge systems using directional spray nozzles in the pendent position, provisions shall be made to protect the underside of a combustible fan deck. [**214**:3.2.4.4]

13.21.2.5* Water Basin Covers. On towers having basin covers that do not completely enclose the hot water basin, outlets protecting the fill shall be located under the distribution basin as set out in 13.21.2.2. [**214**:3.2.4.5]

FIGURE A.13.21.2.3(a) Typical Deluge Fire Protection Arrangement for Crossflow Towers with Completely Enclosed Distribution Basins, Illustration 1. [214: Figure A.3.2.4.3(a)]

FIGURE A.13.21.2.3(b) Typical Deluge Fire Protection Arrangement for Crossflow Towers with Completely Enclosed Distribution Basins, Illustration 2. [214: Figure A.3.2.4.3(b)]

A.13.21.2.5 See Figure A.13.21.2.5.

13.21.2.6 Valves. [214:3.2.6]

13.21.2.6.1 General. Shutoff valves and automatically operated water control valves, if provided, shall be located:

(1) Outside the fire-exposed area
(2) As close to the cooling tower as possible to minimize the amount of pipe to the discharge device
(3) Where they will be accessible during a fire emergency [**214:**3.2.6.1]

13.21.2.6.2 Manual Release Valve. Remote manual release valves, where required, shall be conspicuously located and readily accessible during a fire emergency. If remote, manual release valves are not required, an inspector's test valve shall be provided for each pilot-head-operated system. [**214:**3.2.6.2]

13.21.2.7 Strainers. Strainers shall be required for systems utilizing discharge devices with waterways of less than 0.375-in. (9.5-mm) diameter. *(See NFPA 15, Standard for Water Spray Fixed Systems for Fire Protection, for further details.)* [**214:**3.2.7]

13.21.2.8 Heat Detectors. [214:3.2.8]

13.21.2.8.1 Where deluge or preaction systems are used, heat detectors shall be installed in ac- cordance with the applicable sections of *NFPA 72, National Fire Alarm Code.* [**214:***3.2.8.1]*

13.21.2.8.2 In mechanical induced-draft towers, heat detectors shall be located under the fan deck at the circumference of the fan opening and under the fan opening where necessary to comply with the following spacing requirements. *(For extended fan decks, see 3.2.8.3 in NFPA 214.)* [**214:**3.2.8.2]

FIGURE A.13.21.2.5 *Typical Deluge Fire Protection Arrangement for Crossflow Towers with Covers Completely Enclosing Distribution Basins. [214: Figure A.3.2.4.5]*

13.21.2.8.2.1 Fixed-temperature detectors shall be spaced not more than 8 ft (2.4 m) apart in any direction including the fan opening. Temperature ratings shall be selected in accordance with operating conditions, but shall be no less than intermediate. [**214:**3.2.8.2.1]

13.21.2.8.2.2 Rate-of-rise detectors shall be spaced not more than 15 ft (4.6 m) apart in any direction. In pneumatic-type systems, for detectors inside the tower, there shall be no more than one detector for each mercury check in towers operating in cold climates, and two detectors for each mercury check in towers used during the warm months only or year-round in warm climates. There shall be no more than four detectors for each mercury check where the detectors are located outside the tower. [**214:**3.2.8.2.2]

 13.21.2.8.3 On towers having extended fan decks that completely enclose the distribution basin, detectors shall be located under the fan deck extension in accordance with standard, indoor-spacing rules for the type detectors used. *(See NFPA 72, National Fire Alarm Code.)*

*Exception: Where the fan deck extension is 16 ft (4.9 m) or less and this dimension is the length of the joist channel, then only one row of detectors centered on and at right angles to the joist channels shall be required. Spacing between detectors shall be in accordance with NFPA 72, National Fire Alarm Code. On towers having extended fan decks that do not completely enclose the hot water basin, detectors shall not be required under the fan deck extension. [**214:**3.2.8.3]*

13.21.2.8.4 Where the total number of deluge systems exceeds the number for which the water supply was designed, heat barriers shall be installed under the extended fan deck to separate the systems. Heat barriers shall extend from the fan deck structure to the distribution basin dividers. [**214:**3.2.8.4]

13.21.2.8.5 Where heat detectors are inaccessible during tower operation, an accessible test detector shall be provided for each detection zone. [**214:**3.2.8.5]

13.21.2.8.6 Heat detector components exposed to corrosive vapors or liquids shall be protected by materials of suitable construction or by suitable, protective coatings applied by the equipment manufacturer. [**214:**3.2.8.6]

13.21.2.9 Protection for Fan Drive Motor. [**214:**3.2.9]

13.21.2.9.1 A heat detector and water discharge outlet shall be provided over each fan drive motor when the motor is located so that it is not within the protected area of the tower. [**214:**3.2.9.1]

13.21.2.9.2 Provision shall be made to interlock the fan motors with the fire protection system so that the cooling tower fan motors will be stopped in the cell(s) for which the system is actuated. Where the continued operation of the fans is vital to the process, a manual override switch may be provided to reactivate the fan when it is determined that there is no fire. [**214:**3.2.9.2]

13.21.2.10 Corrosion Protection. [**214:**3.3]

 13.21.2.10.1 Piping, fittings, hangers, braces, and attachment hardware including fasteners shall be hot-dip galvanized steel per ASTM A 153, *Standard Specification for Zinc Coating (Hot Dip) on Iron and Steel Hardware,* or other materials having a superior corrosion resistance. Exposed pipe threads and bolts on fittings shall be protected against corrosion. All other components shall be corrosion resistant or protected against corrosion by a suitable coating. [**214:**3.3.1]

13.21.2.10.2* Wax-type coatings shall not be used on devices without fusible elements. [**214:**3.3.2]

 A.13.21.2.10.2 Approved sprinklers are made of nonferrous material and are corrosion resistant to normal atmospheres. Some atmospheres require special coatings on the discharge devices.

13.21.2.10.3* Special care shall be taken in the handling and installation of wax-coated or similar sprinklers to avoid damaging the coating. Corrosion-resistant coatings shall not be applied to the sprinklers by anyone other than the manufacturer of the sprinklers, except that in all cases any damage to the protective coating occurring at the time of installation shall be repaired at once using only the coating of the manufacturer of the sprinkler in an approved manner so that no part of the sprinkler will be exposed after the installation has been completed. [**214**:3.3.3]

A.13.21.2.10.3 Otherwise, corrosion will attack the exposed metal and will, in time, creep under the wax coating.

13.22 Piers, Terminals, and Wharves

13.22.1 Design Requirements.

13.22.1.1* Piers and Wharves.

A.13.22.1.1 The use of firestops for draft control to bank heat, facilitate the opening of sprinklers, and prevent the overtaxing of the sprinkler system is particularly important in the design of sprinkler protection for combustible substructures. The fire walls and firestops of 3.3.3.6 of NFPA 307, *Standard for the Construction and Fire Protection of Marine Terminals, Piers, and Wharves,* should be incorporated into the sprinkler system design for this purpose to the maximum extent practical; however, due to limitations in the size of the design area for the sprinkler system, additional firestops will normally be needed. These additional or supplemental firestops need only have limited fire resistance but should be as deep as possible and be of substantial construction, such as double 3-in. (76.2-mm) planking where exposed to the elements. Where not exposed to physical damage, ¾-in. (19.05-mm) treated plywood extending 48 in. (1219.2 mm) below stringers with solid blocking between stringers should provide adequate durability and reasonable effectiveness. [**307**:A.3.3.3.3(a)(5)]

13.22.1.1.1 Sprinklers shall be 12.7-mm (½-in.) orifice and shall discharge at a minimum pressure of 85 kPa (12.5 psi). [**307**:3.3.3.1.3(a)5]

13.22.1.1.2 Design area shall be based upon the largest area between firestops plus an additional area embracing at least two branch lines on opposite sides of the fire-stop. [**307**:3.3.3.1.3(a)5b]

13.22.1.1.3 Minimum design area shall be not less than 465 m² (5000 ft²). [**307**:3.3.3.1.3(a)5c]

13.22.1.1.4 The maximum area to be protected by any one system shall be limited to 2325 m² (25,000 ft²). [**307**:3.3.3.1.3(a)7]

13.22.1.2 Terminal Buildings.

13.22.1.2.1 Due to the widely varying nature of commodities that might pass through transit sheds, container freight stations, transload facilities, and similar buildings used for handling and temporary storage of general cargo, minimum sprinkler design shall be based upon Extra Hazard (Group 1) classification. [**307**:4.4.2]

13.22.1.2.2 If the maximum storage height that the building will permit exceeds 3.7 m (12 ft), the requirements shall be followed for the protection of Class I, II, III, IV, or plastic commodities piled to the maximum height permitted by building construction, and the clearance requirements of 8.5.6 of NFPA 307, *Standard for the Construction and Fire Protection of Marine Terminals, Piers, and Wharves.* [**307**:4.4.3]

13.22.1.2.3 If racks or shelving are present or likely to be present, the requirements shall be followed for the protection of Class I, II, III, IV, or plastic commodities. Protection in warehouses for the long-term storage of specific commodities shall be designed for the specific use unless the buildings exceed 465 m² (5000 ft²) total floor area. [**307**:4.4.4]

13.22.2 Installation Requirements.

13.22.2.1 Where there is danger of damage to sprinkler equipment by floating objects, physical barriers shall be provided to exclude such objects. [**307**:3.3.3.1.2]

13.22.2.2 The following installation criteria shall also apply.

(1) Where narrow horizontal channels or spaces are caused by caps, stringers, ties, and other structural members, the standard upright sprinkler might not project sufficient water upward to extinguish or control fires on the underside of the pier or wharf deck. In these cases, a sprinkler that projects water upward to wet the overhead, such as a pendent sprinkler installed in an upright position, or the old-style sprinkler shall be used. Location, spacing, and deflector position shall be governed by the discharge pattern of the sprinkler and the structure being protected. The following design and installation guides shall apply where pendent sprinklers in the upright position or old-style sprinklers are to be utilized:

   (a) The maximum coverage per sprinkler head shall be limited to 7.5 m^2 (80 ft^2).

   (b) Where spacing or arrangement of stringers constitutes typical open-joist construction directly supporting the deck, sprinkler branch lines shall be installed between the bents at right angles to the stringers. Spacing between branch lines shall not exceed 3 m (10 ft). Sprinklers on branch lines shall be staggered and spaced not to exceed 2.5 m (8 ft) on centers.

   (c) Where crisscross construction (typically ties on stringers—see diagram in Appendix B of NFPA 307) is involved, closer spacing of sprinklers shall be permitted as necessary to provide wetting of the entire structure.

   (d) The deflectors of sprinklers on lines under stringers shall be located not less than 100 mm (4 in.) nor more than 250 mm (10 in.) below the bottom plane of the stringer, and not more than 450 mm (18 in.) below the underside of the pier or wharf deck.

   (e) The temperature rating of the sprinkler shall not exceed 74°C (165°F).

   (f) The maximum area to be protected by any one system shall be limited to 2325 m^2 (25,000 ft^2).

(2) Sprinklers designed and approved specifically for protection of combustible substructures shall be installed in conformity with their listing.

(3) The pipe hangers shall be placed in a location where they will be in the wetting pattern of the sprinkler to prevent the lag screws from burning or charring out, dropping sprinkler piping, and bleeding the system. The distance from the sprinkler to the hanger shall not exceed 460 mm (18 in.).

(4) Horizontal and vertical bracing shall be provided at not more than 6-m (20-ft) intervals on all sprinkler piping 76 mm (3 in.) or larger that is parallel to and within 15 m (50 ft) of the face of the pier or wharf and where it might be subjected to heavy fireboat nozzle streams.

(5) Sprinkler systems, including hanger assemblies and bracing, in underdeck areas shall be properly protected throughout against corrosion. Sprinklers shall be of corrosion-resistant type. When the fire protection design for substructures involves the use of detectors or other electrical equipment for smoke or heat detection, pre-action or deluge-type sprinkler protection, all detectors and wiring systems shall be moisture- and corrosion-proof to protect against unfavorable atmospheric conditions that exist beneath these structures. Frequent inspection and testing of these systems shall be conducted in accordance with applicable NFPA standards.

(6) Water supply systems, hydrants, fire hose valves, and sprinkler systems shall be installed with adequate protection against freezing and physical damage. [**307**:3.3.3.1.3]

13.23   Cleanrooms

13.23.1 Design Requirements.

13.23.1.1* Automatic sprinklers for cleanrooms or clean zones shall be hydraulically designed for a density of 0.20 gpm/ft^2 (8.15 L/min·m^2) over a design area of 3000 ft^2 (278.8 m^2). [**318**:2.1.2.1]

A.13.23.1.1 Typical configurations of cleanrooms and their chases and plenums create numerous areas that might be sheltered from sprinkler protection. These areas can include air-mixing boxes, catwalks, hoods, protruding lighting, open waffle slabs, equipment, piping, ducting, and cable trays. Care should be taken to relocate or supplement sprinkler protection to ensure that sprinkler discharge covers all parts of the occupancy. Care should also be taken to ensure that sprinklers are located where heat will be satisfactorily collected for reliable operation of the sprinkler.

Gaseous fire suppression systems are not substitutes for automatic sprinkler protection. The large number of air changes in cleanrooms can cause dilution or stratification of the gaseous agent.

It is recommended that sprinkler systems be inspected at least semiannually by a qualified inspection service *(see NFPA 25, Standard for the Inspection, Testing, and Maintenance of Water-Based Fire Protection Systems)*. The length of time between such inspections can be decreased due to ambient atmosphere, water supply, or local requirements of the authority having jurisdiction.

Prior to taking a sprinkler system out of service, one should be certain to receive permission from all authorities having jurisdiction and notify all personnel who might be affected during system shutdown. A fire watch during maintenance periods is a recommended precaution. Any sprinkler system taken out of service for any reason should be returned to service as promptly as possible.

A sprinkler system that has been activated should be thoroughly inspected for damage and components replaced or repaired promptly. Sprinklers that did not operate but were subjected to corrosive elements of combustion or elevated temperatures should be inspected, and replaced if necessary, in accordance with the minimum replacement requirements of the authority having jurisdiction. Such sprinklers should be destroyed to prevent their reuse. [**318:**A.2.1.2.1]

13.23.1.2 Automatic sprinkler protection shall be designed and installed in the plenum and interstitial space above cleanrooms for a density of 0.20 gpm/ft^2 (8.15 L/min·m^2) over a design area of 3000 ft^2 (278.8 m^2).

Exception: Automatic sprinklers can be omitted if the construction and occupancy of these spaces are noncombustible. [318:2.1.2.6]

13.23.1.3* Sprinklers installed in duct systems shall be hydraulically designed to provide 0.5 gpm (1.9 L/min) over an area derived by multiplying the distance between the sprinklers in a horizontal duct by the width of the duct. Minimum discharge shall be 20 gpm (76 L/min) per sprinkler from the five hydraulically most remote sprinklers. [**318:**2.1.2.6.1]

A.13.23.1.3 Small-orifice sprinklers, ⅜ in. (9.5 mm) or larger, can be used. [**318:**A.2.1.2.1.6.1]

13.23.2 Installation Requirements.

13.23.2.1 Wet pipe automatic sprinkler protection shall be provided throughout facilities containing cleanrooms and clean zones. [**318:**2.1.1]

13.23.2.2* Quick response sprinklers shall be utilized for sprinkler installations within down-flow airstreams in cleanrooms and clean zones. [**318:**2.1.2.2]

A.13.23.2.2 The use of quick-response sprinklers, while still delayed in opening by the downward airflow, would respond to a smaller size fire quicker than conventional sprinklers. (Glass bulb-type quick response sprinklers might be preferable to other types of quick-response sprinklers.) [**318:**A.2.1.2.2]

13.23.2.3* Sprinklers installed in ductwork shall be spaced a maximum of 20 ft (6.1 m) apart horizontally and 12 ft (3.7 m) apart vertically. [**318:**2.1.2.6.1]

A.13.23.2.3 Small orifice sprinklers, ⅜ in. (9.5 mm) or larger, can be used. [**318:**A.2.1.2.6.1]

13.23.2.4 A separate indicating control valve shall be provided for sprinklers installed in ductwork. [**318**:2.1.2.6.2]

13.23.2.5 The sprinklers shall be accessible for periodic inspection and maintenance. [**318**:2.1.2.6.5]

13.24 Aircraft Hangars

13.24.1 Design Requirements. Sprinkler systems installed in aircraft hangars shall comply with NFPA 409, *Standard on Aircraft Hangars.*

13.24.2 Installation Requirements. Sprinkler systems installed in aircraft hangars shall comply with NFPA 409, *Standard on Aircraft Hangars.*

13.25 Airport Terminal Buildings, Fueling Ramp Drainage, and Loading Walkways.

13.25.1 Design Requirements.

13.25.1.1 Passenger handling areas [in airport terminal buildings] shall be classified as ordinary hazard, Group 1 occupancy for the purpose of sprinkler system design. [**415**:2.5.1.1]

13.25.1.2* Other areas of the airport terminal building shall be classified in accordance with Chapter 5 of NFPA 13, based on the occupancy of the area. [**415**:2.5.1.2]

A.13.25.1.2 The exposure to the airport terminal building from the airport ramp is significant. The number of building sprinklers operating from the exposure fire can be greater than from an internal ignition source. [**415**:A.2.5.1.2]

13.25.1.3 Sprinkler System Water Supply. Water supply from public or private sources shall be adequate to supply maximum calculated sprinkler demand plus a minimum of 500 gpm (1893 L/min) for hose streams. The supply shall be available at the rate specified for a period of at least 1 hour. [**415**:2.5.5]

13.25.2 Installation Requirements. (Reserved)

13.26 Aircraft Engine Test Facilities

13.26.1 Design Requirements.

13.26.1.1* In engine test cells, the minimum design discharge density shall be 0.5 gpm/ft^2 (20.4 mm/min) of protected area. [**423**:5.6.3]

A.13.26.1.1 Because of the nature of the test cell fire potential, deluge systems are considered more appropriate than automatic sprinklers due to their speed of operation and simultaneous discharge of all nozzles; however, automatic sprinklers can be used under the following conditions.

(1) In small cells [600 ft^2 (56 m^2) or less] where it is likely that all sprinklers would fuse at the same time
(2) As a backup to a manual water spray or other manual system [**423**:A.5.6.3]

13.26.1.2 In engine test cells, water supplies shall be capable of meeting the largest demand at the design rate plus hose stream demand for a period of 30 minutes. Hose stream demand shall be a minimum of 250 gpm (946 L/min). The hydraulic calculation and the water supply shall be based on the assumption that all sprinklers in the test cell are operating simultaneously. [**423**:5.6.4]

13.26.2 Installation Requirements. (Reserved)

13.27 Liquid and Solid Oxidizers

Liquid and solid oxidizers are covered in Section 13.27. Oxidizers are materials that react to provide oxygen, which has the potential to increase oxidization reaction rates. Oxidizers do not contain fuel; however, more powerful oxidizers may react rapidly enough that they produce significant overpressure. Because oxidizers increase oxidization reaction rates, they have the potential to turn ordinary combustible material into highly potent fuel sources.

Oxidizers are classified qualitatively in potency from Class 1 to Class 4 (Class 4 is the most powerful). They are frequently used for water purification. Examples of oxidizers commonly used for water purification are calcium hypochlorite (a Class 3 oxidizer) and trichloro-s-triazinetrione (trichloroisocyanuric) (a Class I oxidizer usually referred to as trichlor).

Although water is an effective extinguishing agent, chlorine gas can be produced when water is present during the decomposition of calcium hypochlorite by the reaction of calcium hypochlorite and calcium chloride.

13.27.1 Design Requirements.

13.27.1.1 Dry-pipe and double-interlock pre-action sprinkler systems shall not be permitted for protection of buildings or areas containing oxidizers.

Exception: Dry-pipe and double-interlock pre-action systems shall be permitted for protection of Class I oxidizers in noncombustible structures. [430:2.11.3]

13.27.1.2 Sprinkler System Water Supplies.

13.27.1.2.1 Water supplies shall be adequate for the protection of the oxidizer storage by hose streams and automatic sprinklers. The water system shall be capable of providing not less than 750 gpm (2840 L/min) where protection is by means of hose streams, or 500 gpm (1890 L/min) for hose streams in excess of the automatic sprinkler water demand. [**430**:2.11.4.1]

13.27.1.2.2 Duration of the water supply shall be a minimum of 2 hours. [**430**:2.11.4.2]

13.27.1.3 Class 1 Oxidizers. Class 1 oxidizers in noncombustible or combustible containers (paper bags or noncombustible containers with removable combustible liners) shall be designated as a Class 1 commodity; as a Class 2 commodity where contained in fiber packs or noncombustible containers in combustible packaging; and as a Class 3 commodity where contained in plastic containers. [**430**:3.3.2]

13.27.1.4 Class 2 Oxidizers.

13.27.1.4.1* Sprinkler protection for Class 2 oxidizers shall be designed in accordance with Table 13.27.1.4.1. [**430**:4.4.1]

A.13.27.1.4.1 For the purposes of Table 13.27.1.4.1, the fire hazard potential of Class 2 oxidizers has been considered as approximately equal to Group A plastic (non-expanded), stable cartoned. [**430**:A.4.4.1]

13.27.1.4.2 Storage Protection with In-Rack Sprinklers. In-rack sprinklers shall be designed to provide 30 psi (2.1 bar) on the hydraulically most remote six sprinklers on each level. [**430**:4.4.4, 4.4.4.1]

TABLE 13.27.1.4.1 *Sprinkler Protection for Class 2 Oxidizers*

| | Ceiling Sprinklers | | | | | | |
| | Storage Height | | Density | | Area of Application | | |
Type of Storage	ft	m	gpm/ft²	L/min/m²	ft²	m²	In-Rack Sprinklers
Palletized or bulk	8	2.4	0.20	8	3750	348	—
Palletized or bulk	12	3.7	0.35	14	3750	348	—
Rack	12	3.7	0.20	8	3750	348	One line above each level of storage except the top level
Rack	16	4.9	0.30	12	2000	186	One line above each level of storage except the top level

13.27.1.5 Class 3 Oxidizers.

13.27.1.5.1* Sprinkler protection for Class 3 oxidizers shall be designed in accordance with Table 13.27.1.5.1. [**430:**5.4.1]

TABLE 13.27.1.5.1 *Sprinkler Protection for Class 3 Oxidizers [430:Table 5.4.1]*

| | Storage Height | | Density | | Area of Application | | |
Type of Storage	ft	m	gpm/ft²	L/min/m²	ft²	m²	In-Rack Sprinklers
Palletized or bulk	5	1.5	0.35	14	5000	465	
Palletized rack or bulk	10	3	0.65	26	5000	465	
Rack	10	3	0.35	14	5000	465	1 level at midpoint of rack

A.13.27.1.5.1 For the purposes of Table 13.27.1.5.1, the sprinkler density has been derived from fire loss history. [**430:**A.5.4.1]

13.27.1.5.2 Where more than 200 lb but less than 2300 lb of Class 3 oxidizers are stored in racks, height of such storage shall be limited to 6 ft, and a level of in-rack sprinklers spaced at maximum 8 ft intervals shall be provided over each level of storage.

13.27.1.5.3 Storage Protection with In-Rack Sprinklers. In-rack sprinklers shall be designed to provide 30 psi (2.1 bar) on the hydraulically most remote six sprinklers on each level. [**430:**5.4.4, 5.4.4.1]

13.27.1.6 Class 4 Oxidizers. Sprinkler protection for Class 4 oxidizers shall be installed on a deluge sprinkler system to provide water density of 0.35 gpm (14.3 mm/min) over the entire storage area. [**430:**6.4.1]

13.27.2* Installation Requirements. See NFPA 430, *Code for the Storage of Liquid and Solid Oxidizers.*

A.13.27.2 At the time of the publication of this standard, the Technical Committee on Sprinkler System Installation Criteria is aware of ongoing research concerning the sprinkler protection of solid oxidizers. This research is being conducted by the National Fire Protection Research Foundation.

13.28 Storage of Organic Peroxide Formulations

An organic peroxide, which is covered in Section 13.28, is any organic compound having a double oxygen or peroxy (-O-O-) group in its chemical structure. This oxygen-oxygen bond is relatively weak and can be broken at low temperatures, resulting in reactive free radical compounds that can initiate chain reactions. Organic peroxides vary in potency from materials that burn with less intensity than ordinary combustibles to materials that can deflagrate. The NFPA classification scheme goes from Class I (most potent) to Class V (least potent). NFPA also gives recommended classifications for many organic peroxides. These classifications are based on a specific container size, unlike most other recommended material classifications.

Class I formulations present a deflagration hazard through easily initiated, rapid explosive decomposition. Class I includes some formulations that are relatively safe only under closely controlled temperatures. Either excessively high or low temperatures can increase the potential for severe explosive decomposition.

Class V formulations do not present severe fire hazards. Those that do burn, do so with less intensity than ordinary combustibles.

13.28.1 Design Requirements.

13.28.1.1 Where [automatic sprinkler systems are required per NFPA 432, *Code for the Storage of Organic Peroxide Formulations,* they] shall provide the following discharge densities:

Class I [organic peroxides]—0.5 gpm/ft^2 (20. 4 mm/min)

Class II [organic peroxides]—0.4 gpm/ft^2 (16.3 mm/min)

Class III [organic peroxides]—0.3 gpm/ft^2 (12.2 mm/min)

Class IV [organic peroxides]—0.25 gpm/ft^2 (10.2 mm/min) [**432:**2.8.2]

There is not a sprinkler density given for Class V organic peroxides in 13.28.1.1 because the primary fire safety concern is the combustibility of containers in which the material is stored.

13.28.1.2 The system shall be designed to provide the required density over a 3000-ft^2 (279-m^2) area for areas protected by a wet pipe sprinkler system or 3900 ft^2 (363 m^2) for areas protected by a dry pipe sprinkler system. The entire area of any building of less than 3000 ft^2 (279 m^2) shall be used as the area of application. [**432:**2.8.2.1]

13.28.1.3 Sprinkler System Water Supply. Water supplies for automatic sprinkler systems, fire hydrants, and so forth, shall be capable of supplying the anticipated demand for at least 90 minutes. [**432:**2.8.3]

13.28.1.4 Detached Storage of Class I Organic Peroxide Formulations. Sprinkler protection for Class I organic peroxide formulations in quantities exceeding 2000 lb (908 kg) in detached storage shall be of the deluge type. [**432:**5.5.2]

13.28.2 Installation Requirements. Where automatic sprinkler protection is provided for Class I organic peroxide formulations in quantities exceeding 2000 lb (907 kg), it shall be a deluge system. [**432:**5.5.2]

13.29 Advanced Light Water Reactor Electric Generating Plants

13.29.1 Design Requirements.

13.29.1.1* Sprinkler System Water Supply. The fire water supply shall be calculated on the basis of the largest expected flow rate for a period of 2 hours, but shall not be less than 300,000 gal (1,135,500 L). This flow rate shall be based on 500 gpm (1892.5 L/min) for manual hose streams plus the largest design demand of any sprinkler system. The fire water supply shall be capable of delivering this design demand with the hydraulically least demanding portion of fire main loop out of service. [**804**:7.2.1]

 A.13.29.1.1 The water supply for the permanent fire protection water system should be based on providing a 2-hour water supply for both items (1) and (2) as follows:

(1) Either of the following items, a or b, whichever is larger:

    (a) The largest fixed fire suppression system demand

    (b) Any fixed fire suppression system demand that could be reasonably expected to operate simultaneously during a single event (e.g., turbine underfloor protection in conjunction with other fire protection systems in the turbine area)

(2) The hose stream demand of not less than 500 gpm (1892.5 L/min). [**804**:A.7.2.1]

 It is important that fire protection water supplies for nuclear power plants, which are discussed in 13.29.1.1, be highly reliable and of adequate quantity and duration. Although NFPA 805, *Performance-Based Standard for Fire Protection for Light Water Reactor Electric Generating Plants,* allows for performance-based options, it also details minimum requirements in Chapter 3. Fundamental requirements for water supplies are contained in Section 3.5 of NFPA 805.

A minimum fire protection water supply of not less than two separate 300,000-gallon water supplies is specified. This supply can be met by two separate water storage tanks with a minimum of 300,000 gallons reserved for fire protection use. To increase reliability, the tanks must be interconnected such that fire pumps can take suction from either or both tanks. The tanks and piping must be arranged such that a failure in one tank or its piping will not allow both tanks to drain.

In some cases, fire pumps may take suction from a large body of water, such as a lake or river. In those cases, two fire protection water supplies are not required. However, in those cases, each fire pump must have a separate suction and each suction and fire pump must be adequately separated.

The minimum duration of fire protection water supplies for nuclear power plants is not less than two hours. The minimum hose stream demand is specified to be not less than 500 gpm. The flow rate must also include the largest demand of any sprinkler or water spray system. For many installations, the largest demand is for generator step-up transformer deluge water spray systems. Unique to nuclear power plants is the requirement to base the flow and pressure demand on the least demanding section of the fire protection water supply distribution piping system out of service. This provides for a higher reliability of the fire protection water supply with a single impairment to the distribution system.

13.29.1.2 Yard Mains. The underground yard fire main loop shall be installed to furnish anticipated water requirements. The type of pipe and water treatment shall be design considerations, with tuberculation as one of the parameters. Means for inspecting and flushing the systems shall be provided. [**804**:7.4.1]

13.29.1.3 Cable Tunnels. [**804**:8.4.2]

 NFPA 804, *Standard for Fire Protection for Advanced Light Water Reactor Electric Generating Plants,* requires that cable tunnels, which are covered in 13.29.1.3, be provided with automatic fixed suppression systems (see 8.4.2.2.1 in NFPA 804). Where automatic sprinkler systems are used to meet this requirement, the sprinkler system must be designed to provide a density of 0.30 gpm/ft^2 (12.2 L/min·m^2) for the most remote 100 linear ft (30.5 m) of the cable tunnel up to the most remote 2500 ft^2 (232.2 m^2). This assures that an adequate water supply and sprinkler system discharge can be provided at the far end of any cable tunnel. Additionally, NFPA 804 requires that the location of sprinklers or water spray nozzles be arranged to provide adequate coverage for cable trays and any potential exposures (such as transient combustibles) to the cable trays (see 8.4.2.2.2 in NFPA 804). This requires careful engineering design for the actual installation and arrangement in the cable tunnel.

13.29.1.3.1 Automatic sprinkler systems shall be designed for a density of 0.3 gpm/ft^2 (12.2 mm/min) for the most remote 100 linear feet (30.5 linear meters) of cable tunnel up to the most remote 2500 ft^2 (232.2 m^2). [**804:**8.4.2.2.1]

13.29.1.3.2 Deluge sprinkler systems or deluge spray systems shall be zoned to limit the area of protection to that which the drainage system can handle with any two adjacent systems actuated. The systems shall be hydraulically designed with each zone calculated with the largest adjacent zone flowing. [**804:**8.4.2.2.3]

Deluge systems in cable tunnels must be zoned, as stated in 13.29.1.3.2. The flow demand is based on the demand of the most remote 2500 ft^2 (232.2 m^2) area operating as well as the largest adjacent zone. Drainage should contemplate two adjacent systems being actuated simultaneously.

13.29.1.4 Cable Spreading Room. The cable spreading room shall have an automatic water-based suppression system. The location of sprinklers or spray nozzles shall consider cable tray arrangements to ensure adequate water coverage for areas that could present exposure fire hazards to the cable raceways. Automatic sprinkler systems shall be designed for a density of 0.30 gpm/ft^2 (12.2 L/min·m^2) over the most remote 2500 ft^2 (232.2 m^2). [**804:**8.4.1.1]

The cable spreading room is covered in 13.29.1.4. Paragraph 8.4.1.1 in NFPA 804 requires that cable tunnels be provided with automatic water-based suppression systems. The location of sprinklers or water spray nozzles should be arranged to provide adequate coverage for cable trays and any potential exposures (such as transient combustibles) to the cable trays. This requires careful engineering design for the actual installation and arrangement in the cable tunnel. Automatic sprinkler systems must be designed to provide a density of 0.30 gpm/ft^2 (12.2 L/min·m^2) for the most remote 2500 ft^2 (232.2 m^2).

Additionally, 8.4.1.2 in NFPA 804 requires that suppression systems in cable spreading rooms be zoned. The flow demand is based on the demand of the most remote 2500 ft^2 (232.2 m^2) area operating as well as the largest adjacent zone. Drainage should contemplate two adjacent systems being actuated simultaneously.

13.29.1.5* Beneath Turbine Generator Operating Floor. All areas beneath the turbine generator operating floor shall be protected by an automatic sprinkler or foam-water sprinkler system. The sprinkler system beneath the turbine generator shall take into consideration obstructions from structural members and piping and shall be designed to a minimum density of 0.3 gpm/ft^2 (12.2 mm/min) over a minimum application of 5000 ft^2 (464.5 m^2). [**804:**8.8.2.1]

A.13.29.1.5 To avoid water application to hot parts or other water-sensitive areas and to provide adequate coverage, designs that incorporate items such as fusible element operated spray nozzles might be necessary. [**804:**A.8.8.2.1]

Areas beneath the turbine generator operating floor are covered in 13.29.1.5. Sprinkler protection is not required at the roof of a high-bay turbine generator building. However, due to the oil hazards that can introduce combustible oils anywhere in the turbine building, wherever oil might flow, as well as other combustible materials that may be present in the turbine building, automatic sprinkler protection should be provided throughout all areas of the turbine building below the turbine operating deck level. This is currently specified as a single point density of 0.30 gpm/ft^2 (12.2 L/min·m^2) over the most remote 2500 ft^2 (232.2 m^2).

13.29.1.6* Turbine Generator Bearings.

A.13.29.1.6 Additional information concerning turbine generator fire protection can be found in EPRI Research Report 1843-2, "Turbine Generator Fire Protection by Sprinkler System," July 1985. [**804**:A.8.8.3]

Turbine generator bearings are addressed in 13.29.1.6. Pressurized lube oil piping presents the potential for three-dimensional, pressurized oil fires that are extremely difficult to control and extinguish. During emergencies, the duration of oil flow and fire can be extensive as lube oil continues to be provided as the turbine slows to a stop. Automatic water spray systems should be provided to protect the lube oil lines, including the piping that is located beneath the turbine skirt or lagging.

13.29.1.6.1 Lubricating oil lines above the turbine operating floor shall be protected with an automatic sprinkler system covering those areas subject to oil accumulation, including the area within the turbine lagging (skirt). The automatic sprinkler system shall be designed to a minimum density of 0.30 gpm/ft^2 (12.2 mm/min). [**804**:8.8.4]

13.29.1.6.2 If shaft-driven ventilation systems are used, an automatic preaction sprinkler system providing a density of 0.3 gpm/ft^2 (12.2 mm/min) over the entire area shall be provided. [**804**:8.8.6]

13.29.1.7 Standby Emergency Diesel Generators and Combustion Turbines. Sprinkler and water spray protection systems shall be designed for a 0.25-gpm/ft^2 (10.2-mm/min) density over the entire area. [**804**:8.9.2]

Diesel generators or combustion turbines, which are addressed in 13.29.1.7, combine fuel oil and lube oil hazards with continuous ignition sources when operating. Automatic sprinkler, water spray, or foam-water sprinkler systems should be provided.

13.29.1.8 Fire Pump Room/House. If sprinkler and water spray systems are provided for fire pump houses, they shall be designed for a minimum density of 0.25 gpm/ft^2 (10.2 mm/min) over the entire fire area. [**804**:8.22]

If fire pump rooms, which are covered in 13.29.1.8, contain diesel engine drivers, automatic sprinkler, water spray, or foam-water sprinkler systems should be provided.

13.29.1.9 Oil-Fired Boilers. Sprinkler and water spray systems shall be designed for a minimum density of 0.25 gpm/ft^2 (10.2 mm/min) over the entire area. [**804**:8.24.2]

Oil-fired boilers or boilers using oil ignition, which are covered in 13.29.1.9, should be provided with automatic sprinkler, water spray, or foam-water sprinkler systems designed for a minimum density of 0.25 gpm/ft^2 (10.19 L/min·m^2) over the entire areas.

13.29.2 Installation Requirements.

 13.29.2.1 Yard Mains, Hydrants, and Building Standpipes. [**804**:7.4]

 13.29.2.1.1 Approved visually indicating sectional control valves such as post-indicator valves shall be provided to isolate portions of the main for maintenance or repair without simultaneously shutting off the supply to both primary and backup fire suppression systems. [**804**:7.4.2]

 13.29.2.1.2* Sectional control valves shall permit maintaining independence of the individual loop around each unit. For such installations, common water supplies shall also be permitted to be utilized. For multiple-reactor sites with widely separated plants [approaching 1 mi. (1.6 km) or more], separate yard fire main loops shall be used. [**804**:7.4.4]

  A.13.29.2.1.2 A common yard fire main loop can serve multi-unit nuclear power plant sites if it is cross-connected between units.

13.29.2.1.3 Sprinkler systems and manual hose station standpipes shall have connections to the plant underground water main so that a single active failure or a crack in a moderate-energy line can be isolated so as not to impair both the primary and backup fire suppression systems. Alternatively, headers fed from each end are permitted inside buildings to supply both sprinkler and standpipe systems, provided steel piping and fittings meeting the requirements of ANSI/ASME B31.1, *Code for Power Piping,* are used for the headers (up to and including the first valve) supplying the sprinkler systems where such headers are part of the seismically analyzed hose standpipe system. Where provided, such headers are considered an extension of the yard main system. Each sprinkler and standpipe system shall be equipped with an outside screw and yoke (OS&Y) gate valve or other approved shutoff valve. [**804:**7.4.7]

The requirement in 13.29.2.1.3 is unique to nuclear power plants. The intent is that a single failure will not impair both the primary (automatic sprinkler) protection and the backup (manual hose stations) fire suppression systems. In most cases, this means separate connections for sprinkler systems and standpipes to the underground fire protection water distribution system. Alternatively, internal piping headers fed from two directions can feed both sprinkler and standpipe systems provided that steel piping and fittings meet the requirements of ANSI/ASME B31.1, *Code for Power Piping,* and the piping is part of a seismically analyzed hose standpipe system.

13.29.2.2 Cable Concentrations. The location of sprinklers or spray nozzles shall consider cable array arrangements and possible transient combustibles to ensure adequate water coverage for areas that could present exposure fire hazards to the cable raceways. [**804:**8.4.2.2.2]

13.29.2.3 Turbine Building. Deluge sprinkler systems or deluge spray systems shall be zoned to limit the area of protection to that which the drainage system can handle with any two adjacent systems actuated. The systems shall be hydraulically designed with each zone calculated with the largest adjacent zone flowing. [**804:**8.4.2.2.3]

Deluge systems in cable tunnels must be zoned, as stated in 13.29.2.3. The flow demand is based on the demand of the most remote 2500 ft^2 (232.2 m^2) area operating as well as the largest adjacent zone. Drainage should contemplate two adjacent systems being actuated simultaneously.

13.30 Light Water Nuclear Power Plants

13.30.1* Design Requirements. A fire protection water supply of adequate reliability, quantity, and duration shall be provided by one of the two following methods:

(1) Provide a fire protection water supply of not less than two separate 300,000-gal (1,135,500-L) supplies.
(2) Calculate the fire flow rate for 2 hours. This fire flow rate shall be based on 500 gpm (1892.5 L/min) for manual hose streams plus the largest design demand of any sprinkler or fixed water spray system(s) in the power block as determined in accordance with NFPA 13 or NFPA 15, *Standard for Water Spray Fixed Systems for Fire Protection.* The fire water supply shall be capable of delivering this design demand with the hydraulically least demanding portion of fire main loop out of service. [**805:**3.5.1]

A.13.30.1 Cement-lined pipe 12 in. (304.8 mm) in diameter is recommended. Main sizes should be designed to encompass any anticipated expansion.

The underground main should be arranged such that any one break will not put both a fixed water extinguishing system and hose lines protecting the same area out of service. [**805:**A.3.5.1]

Design requirements for light water nuclear power plants are given in 13.30.1. See commentary following A.13.29.1.1.

13.30.2 Installation Requirements. (Reserved)

13.31   Electric Generating Plants and High Voltage Direct Current Converter Stations. [NFPA 850]

13.31.1*   Design Requirements.

A.13.31.1 Sprinkler System Discharge Criteria for Electric Generating Plants and High-Voltage Direct Current Converter Stations. See NFPA 850, *Recommended Practice for Fire Protection for Electric Generating Plants and High Voltage Direct Current Converter Stations,* for applicable terms not defined in Chapter 3.

(1)   *Sprinkler System Water Supply.* The water supply for the permanent fire protection installation should be based on providing a 2-hour supply for both items (a) and (b) as follows:

    (a)   Either of items i or ii below, whichever is larger:
       i.   The largest fixed fire suppression system demand
       ii.   Any fixed fire suppression system demands that could reasonably be expected to operate simultaneously during a single event [e.g., turbine underfloor protection in conjunction with other fire protection system(s) in the turbine area; coal conveyor protection in conjunction with protection for related coal handling structures during a conveyor fire; adjacent transformers not adequately separated according to 3.1.3 of NFPA 850].

    (b)   The hose stream demand of not less than 500 gpm (31.5 L/sec).
       [**850**:4.2.1]
       Where an adequate and reliable water supply, such as a lake, cooling pond, river, or municipal water system, is unavailable, at least two separate water supplies should be provided for fire protection purposes with each supply capable of meeting the fire waterflow requirements determined by 4.2.1 of NFPA 850. [**850**:4.2.2]

(2)   *Yard Mains.* The supply mains should be looped around the main power block and should be of sufficient size to supply the flow requirements determined by 4.2.1 of NFPA 850 to any point in the yard loop considering the most direct path to be out of service. Pipe sizes should be designed to encompass any anticipated expansion and future water demands. [**850**:4.4.1.3]

(3)   *Coal Handling Structures.* Sprinkler systems should be designed for a minimum of 0.25 gpm/ft^2 (10.2 mm/min) density over a 2500 ft^2 (232 m^2) area. [**850**:5.4.6.1]

(4)   *Coal Conveyors.* Sprinklers should be designed for a minimum of 0.25 gpm/ft^2 (10.2 mm/min) density over 2000 ft^2 (186 m^2) of enclosed area or the most remote 100 linear ft (30 m) of conveyor structure up to 2000 ft^2 (186 m^2). [**850**:5.4.6.2]

(5)   [In areas over conveyor belts and striker plates within the stacker reclaimer,] the water supply [should] be from a 3000-gal to 5000-gal (11,355-L to 18,925-L) capacity pressure tank located on-board. [**850**:5.4.6.4]

(6)   Sprinklers for bag-type dust collectors should be designed for ordinary hazard systems. Sprinkler systems should be designed for a density of 0.2 gpm (8.2 mm/min) over the projected plan area of the dust collector. [**850**:5.4.6.5.1]

(7)   *Steam Generator.* Boiler front fire protection systems should be designed to cover the fuel oil burners and ignitors, adjacent fuel oil piping and cable, a 20 ft (6.1 m) distance from the burner and ignitor including structural members and walkways at these levels. Additional coverage should include areas where oil may collect. Sprinkler and water spray systems should be designed for a density of 0.25 gpm/ft^2 (10.2 mm/min) over the protected area. [**850**:5.5.1.2]

(8)   *Flue Gas Bag-Type Dust Collectors.* The design density should be 0.2 gpm/ft^2 (8.2 mm/min) over the plan area of the dust collector. [**850**:5.6.3.3]

(9)   *Electrostatic Precipitators.* If mineral oil insulating fluids are used, hydrants or standpipes should be located so that each transformer-rectifier set can be reached by at least

one hose stream. In addition the following should be provided:

Automatic sprinkler protection. Automatic sprinkler systems should be designed for a density of 0.25 gpm/ft^2 (10.2 mm/min) over 3500 ft^2 (325 m^2). The drain system should be capable of handling oil spillage plus the largest design waterflow from the fire protection system. [**850:**5.6.4.3]

(10) *Scrubber Buildings.* Where scrubbers have plastic or rubber linings, one of the following methods of protection for the building should be provided:

Automatic sprinkler protection at ceiling level sized to provide a density 0.2 gpm/ft^2 (8.2 mm/min). The area of operation should be the area of the building or 10,000 ft^2 (930 m^2). Where draft curtains are provided the area of operation can be reduced to the largest area subdivided by draft curtains. [**850:**5.6.5.2.2]

(11) *Turbine-Generator Area.* The sprinkler system beneath the turbine-generator should take into consideration obstructions from structural members and piping and should be designed to a density of 0.3 gpm/ft^2 (12.2 mm/min) over a minimum application of 5000 ft^2 (464 m^2).

NOTE: To avoid water application to hot parts or other water sensitive areas and to provide adequate coverage, designs that incorporate items such as fusible element operated directional spray nozzles may be necessary. [**850:**5.7.4.1, 5.7.4.1.1]

The automatic sprinkler system [protecting the lubricating oil lines above the turbine operating floor] should be designed to a density of 0.3 gpm/ft^2 (12.2 mm/min). [**850:**5.7.4.1.2]

(12) *Turbine-Generator Bearings.* Fire protection systems for turbine-generator bearings should be designed for a density of 0.25 gpm/ft^2 (10.2 mm/min) over the protected area. [**850:**5.7.4.2.1]

(13) *Cable Spreading Room and Cable Tunnels.* Automatic sprinkler systems should be designed for a density of 0.3 gpm/ft^2 (12.2 mm/min) over 2500 ft^2 (232 m^2) or the most remote 100 linear ft (30 m) of cable tunnels up to 2500 ft^2 (232 m^2). [**850:**5.8.2.1]

(14) *Emergency Generators.* Sprinkler systems should be designed for a 0.25 gpm/ft^2 (10.2 mm/min) density over the fire area. [**850:**5.9.1.2.1]

(15) *Fire Pumps.* If sprinkler systems are provided for fire pump houses, they should be designed for a density of 0.25 gpm/ft^2 (10.2 mm/min) over the fire area. [**850:**5.9.4]

(16) *Oil- or Coal-Fueled Auxiliary Boilers.* If a sprinkler system is provided it should be designed for a density of 0.25 gpm/ft^2 (10.2 mm/min) over the entire room.

(17) *Alternative Fuels.*

(a) *Hydraulic Equipment, Reservoirs, Coolers, and Associated Oil-Filled Equipment.* Sprinklers should be over oil-containing equipment and for 20 ft (6.1 m) beyond in all directions. A density of 0.25 gpm/ft^2 (10.2 mm/min) should be provided. [**850:**7.3.4.3]

(b) *Tipping/Receiving Building.* Systems should be designed for a minimum of 0.25 gpm/ft^2 (10.2 mm/min) over the most remote 3000 ft^2 (279 m^2) (increase by 30 percent for dry pipe systems) of floor area with the protection area per sprinkler not to exceed 130 ft^2 (12 m^2). High temperature sprinklers [250°F to 300°F (121°C to 149°C)] should be used.

NOTE: The above requirements are based on storage heights not exceeding 20 ft (6.1 m). [**850:**7.3.4.4]

(c) *The MSW Storage Pit, Charging Floor, and Grapple Laydown Areas.* Systems should be designed for a minimum of 0.2 gpm/ft^2 (8.2 mm/min) over the most remote 3000 ft^2 (279 m^2) (increase by 30 percent for dry pipe systems) of pit/floor area with the protection area per sprinkler not to exceed 100 ft^2 (9.3 m^2). High temperature sprinklers [250°F to 300°F (121°C to 149°C)] should be used. [**850:**7.3.4.5.1]

(18) *Refuse Derived Fuels.*

(a) *Hydraulic Equipment, Reservoirs, Coolers, and Associated Oil-Filled Equipment.* Sprinklers should be over oil-containing equipment and for 20 ft (6.1 m) beyond in all directions. A density of 0.25 gpm/ft^2 (10.2 mm/min) should be provided. [**850:**7.4.4.6]

(b) *Tipping/Receiving Building.* Systems should be designed for a minimum of 0.25 gpm/ft^2 (10.2 mm/min) over the most remote 3000 ft^2 (279 m^2) (increase by 30 percent for dry pipe systems) of floor area with the protection area per sprinkler not to exceed 130 ft^2 (12.0 m^2). High temperature sprinklers [250°F to 300°F (121°C to 149°C)] should be used.
NOTE: The above requirements are based on storage heights not exceeding 20 ft (6.1 m). [**850**:7.4.4.7]

(c) *Processing Building.* Systems should be designed for a minimum of 0.25 gpm/ft^2 (10.2 mm/min) over the most remote 3000 ft^2 (279 m^2) (increase by 30 percent for dry pipe systems) of floor area with the protection area per sprinkler not to exceed 130 ft^2 (12.0 m^2). [**850**:7.4.4.8)]

(d) *RDF Storage Building.* Systems should be designed for a minimum of 0.35 gpm/ft^2 (14.3 mm/min) over the most remote 3000 ft^2 (279 m^2) (increase by 30 percent for dry pipe systems) of floor area with the protection area per sprinkler not to exceed 100 ft^2 (9.3 m^2). High temperature sprinklers [250°F to 300°F (121°C to 149°C)] should be used. Storage heights in excess of 20 ft (6.1 m) will require higher design densities. [**850**:7.4.4.9]

(e) *RDF Boiler Feed System Area, Including Bins, Hoppers, Chutes, Conveyors, and So Forth.* Where provided, the systems should be designed for a minimum of 0.2 gpm/ft^2 (8.2 mm/min) over the most remote 2000 ft^2 (186 m^2) (increase by 30 percent for dry pipe systems) of floor area with the protection area per sprinkler not to exceed 130 ft^2 (12.0 m^2). Internal, as well as external, protection also should be considered depending upon specific equipment design, ceiling heights, and accessibility for manual fire fighting. [**850**:7.4.4.10]

(f) *Shredder Enclosures.* Systems should be designed for a minimum of 0.25 gpm/ft^2 (10.2 mm/min) over the most remote 3000 ft^2 (279 m^2) (increase by 30 percent for dry pipe systems) of floor area with the protection area per sprinkler not to exceed 100 ft^2 (9.3 m^2). [**850**:7.4.4.11]

(19) *Biomass Fuels.*

(a) *Biomass Storage Buildings.* Systems should be designed for a minimum of 0.25 gpm/ft^2 (10.2 mm/min) over the most remote 3000 ft^2 (279 m^2) (increase by 30 percent for dry pipe systems) of floor area with the protection area per sprinkler not to exceed 130 ft^2 (12.0 m^2).
NOTE: Biomass fuels exhibit a wide range of burning characteristics and upon evaluation can require increased levels of protection.
[**850**:7.5.4.4]

(b) *Hydraulic Equipment, Reservoirs, Coolers, and Associated Oil-Filled Equipment.* Sprinklers or spray nozzles should be over oil-containing equipment and for 20 ft (6.1 m) beyond in all directions. A density of 0.25 gpm/ft^2 (10.2 mm/min) should be provided. [**850**:7.5.4.6]

(20) *Rubber Tire Fuel—Hydraulic Equipment, Reservoirs, Coolers, and Associated Oil-Filled Equipment.* Sprinklers should be over oil-containing equipment and for 20 ft (6.1 m) beyond in all directions. A density of 0.25 gpm/ft^2 (10.2 mm/min) should be provided. [**850**:7.6, 7.6.4.10]

13.31.2* Installation Requirements.

A **A.13.31.2** Where an adequate and reliable water supply, such as a lake, cooling pond, river, or municipal water system, is unavailable, at least two separate water supplies should be provided for fire protection purposes with each supply capable of meeting the fire waterflow requirements determined by 4.2.1 of NFPA 850. [**850**:4.2.2]

Each water supply should be connected to the yard main by separate connections arranged and valve controlled to minimize the possibility of multiple supplies being impaired simultaneously. [**850**:4.2.3]

Indicator control valves should be installed to provide adequate sectional control of the fire main loop to minimize plant protection impairments. [**850**:4.4.1.4)]

Each hydrant should be equipped with a separate shutoff valve located on the branch connection to the supply main. [**850**:4.4.1.5]

Interior fire protection loops are considered an extension of the yard main and should be provided with at least two valved connections to the yard main with appropriate sectional control valves on the interior loop. [**850**:4.4.1.6]

If a sprinkler system is used to protect the coal conveyor, particular care should be exercised in locating closed sprinkler so that they will be in the path of the heat produced by the fire and still be in a position to provide good coverage of all belt surfaces along the conveyor. [**850**:5.4.6.2.1]

Protection inside dust collectors should include the clean air plenum and the bag section. If the hopper is shielded from water discharge, sprinklers also should be provided in the hopper section.

All areas beneath the turbine-generator operating floor that are subject to oil flow, oil spray, or oil accumulation should be protected by an automatic sprinkler of foam-water sprinkler system. This coverage normally includes all areas beneath the operating floor in the turbine building. [**850**:5.7.4.1.1]

Lubricating oil lines above the turbine operating floor should be protected with an automatic sprinkler system covering those areas subject to oil accumulation including the area within the turbine lagging (skirt). [**850**:5.7.4.1.2]

Turbine-generator bearings should be protected with a manually or automatically operated closed-head sprinkler system utilizing directional nozzles. [**850**:5.7.4.2.1]

Due to the large quantity of platforms, equipment, and walkways, care should be taken to include coverage under all obstructions greater than 4 ft (1.2 m) wide. (**850**:7.4.4.8)

13.32 Hydroelectric Generating Plants [NFPA 851]

13.32.1* Design Requirements.

A.13.32.1 Sprinkler System Discharge Criteria for Hydroelectric Generating Plants. See NFPA 851, *Recommended Practice for Fire Protection for Hydroelectric Generating Plants,* for applicable terms not defined in Chapter 3.

(1) *Sprinkler Systems Water Supply.* The water supply for the permanent fire protection installation should be based on the largest fixed fire suppression system demand plus the maximum hose stream demand of not less than 500 gpm (31.5 L/sec) for a 2-hour duration. [**851**:4.2.2]

(2) If a single water supply is utilized, two independent connections should be provided. If a situation can arise in which the primary water supply can become unavailable (e.g., dewatering of penstocks), an auxiliary supply should be provided. Each supply should be capable of meeting the requirements in 4.2.2 of NFPA 851. [**851**:4.2.3]

(3) Fixed fire protection for this equipment, where provided, should be automatic wet pipe sprinkler systems utilizing a design density of 0.25 gpm/ft^2 (10.2 mm/min) for the entire hazard area *(see 3.5.3 of NFPA 803).* [**851**:5.2.4]

(4) Sprinkler or water spray systems should be designed for a density of 0.3 gpm/ft^2 (12.2 mm/min) over 2500 ft^2 (232 m^2). This coverage is for area protection. Individual cable tray tier coverage could be required based on the Fire Risk Evaluation. [**851**:5.5.3]

(5) *Cable Tunnels.* Automatic sprinkler systems should be designed for a density of 0.3 gpm/ft^2 (12.2 mm/min) over 2500 ft^2 (232 m^2) or the most remote 100 linear ft (30 m) of cable tunnel up to 2500 ft^2 (232 m^2). [**851**:5.6.1]

(6) *Emergency Generators.* Sprinkler and water spray protection systems should be designed for a 0.25 gpm/ft^2 (10.2 mm/min) density over the fire area. [**851**:5.11.2]

(7) *Air Compressors.* Automatic sprinkler protection, with a density of 0.25 gpm/ft^2 (10.2 mm/min) over the postulated oil spill, should be considered for air compressors containing a large quantity of oil. *(See 4.8.2 of NFPA 851.)* [**851**:5.12]

(8) *Hydraulic Systems for Gate and Valve Operators.* Automatic sprinkler protection designed for a density of 0.25 gpm/ft^2 (10.2 mm/min) over the fire area should be considered for hydraulic systems not using a listed fire-resistant fluid. *(See 4.8.2 of NFPA 851.)* [**851**:5.13]

(9) *Fire Pumps.* If sprinkler systems are provided they should be designed for a density of 0.25 gpm/ft^2 (10.2 mm/min) over the fire area. For automatic foam-water sprinkler systems, a density of 0.16 gpm/ft^2 (6.5 mm/min) should be provided. [**851**:5.14]

13.32.2* Installation Requirements.

A.13.32.2 Upstream water is frequently the fire protection water supply. Water for fire suppression should not be taken downstream from any closure device in a penstock, flume, or forebay. [**851**:4.2.6]

Fire extinguishing systems, where installed for lube oil systems employing combustible-type oil, should include protection for the reservoirs, pumps, and all oil lines, especially where unions exist on piping and beneath any shielded area where flowing oil can collect. Facilities not provided with curbs or drains should extend coverage for a distance of 20 ft (6.1 m) from the oil lines, when measured from the outermost oil line. [**851**:5.2.7]

13.33 Fire Protection in Places of Worship. [NFPA 909]

13.33.1* Design Requirements.

A.13.33.1 Sprinkler systems for specific areas associated with religious facilities should be designed as follows:

(1) All assembly areas, except state—Light Hazard
(2) Stages—Ordinary Hazard (Group 2)
(3) Kitchens—Ordinary Hazard (Group 1)
(4) Storage rooms—Ordinary Hazard (Group 2)
(5) Unused attics/lofts/steeples/concealed spaces— Light Hazard
(6) Schools/day-care centers—Light Hazard
(7) Gift shops—Ordinary Hazard (Group 1)
(8) Special exhibit area—Ordinary Hazard (Group 2)
(9) Libraries—Ordinary Hazard (Group 2)
(10) Offices—Light Hazard
[**909**:A.10.4.2]

13.33.2 Installation Requirements. (Reserved)

SUMMARY

Chapter 13 consolidates and centralizes sprinkler design and installation criteria for special occupancies extracted into NFPA 13. When applying the requirements of Chapter 13, the referenced standard should be consulted in all applications. As previously stated, the referenced NFPA document can provide options to standard sprinkler protection, such as water spray sprinklers, foam-water sprinklers, or another special extinguishing system, for the protection of those hazards.

REFERENCES CITED IN COMMENTARY

National Fire Protection Association, 1 Batterymarch Park, P.O. Box 9101, Quincy, MA 02269-9101

NFPA 30, *Flammable and Combustible Liquids Code,* 2000 edition

NFPA 30B, *Code for the Manufacture and Storage of Aerosol Products,* 2002 edition

NFPA 33, *Standard for Spray Application Using Flammable or Combustible Materials,* 2000 edition

NFPA 36, *Standard for Solvent Extraction Plants,* 2001 edition

NFPA 42, *Code for the Storage of Pyroxylin Plastic,* 2002 edition

NFPA 45, *Standard on Fire Protection for Laboratories Using Chemicals,* 2000 edition

NFPA 130, *Standard for Fixed Guideway Transit and Passenger Rail Systems,* 2000 edition

NFPA 804, *Standard for Fire Protection for Advanced Light Water Reactor Electric Generating Plants,* 2001 edition

NFPA 805, *Performance-Based Standard for Fire Protection for Light Water Reactor Electric Generating Plants,* 2001 edition

American Society of Mechanical Engineers, Three Park Avenue, New York, NY 10016-5990

ANSI/ASME B31.1, *Code for Power Piping,* 2001 edition

FM Global, 1151 Boston-Providence Turnpike, Norwood, MA 02061

Technical Report No. J.I.OD2R4.PR, *Full Scale Fire Tests: Sprinkler Protection for Rack Storage of Plastic-Wrapped (Uncartoned) Aerosols*

Underwriters Laboratories Inc., 333 Pfingsten Road, Northbrook, IL 60062

UL 103, *Factory-Built Chimneys for Residential Type and Building Heating Appliances*

U.S. Government Printing Office, Washington, DC 20402

U.S. Occupational Safety and Health Administration's Process Safety Management Rule, in Title 29, Code of Federal Regulations, Part 1910.119

Nugent, D. P., *Directory of Fire Tests Involving Storage of Flammable and Combustible Liquids in Containers,* Second Edition, Schirmer Engineering Corp., Deerfield, IL, October 2000

Nugent, D. P., "Fire Tests Involving Storage of Flammable and Combustible Liquids In Small Containers," *Journal of Fire Protection Engineering,* 6(1): 1994

CHAPTER 14

Plans and Calculations

Chapter 14 describes the procedures and information necessary to calculate the hydraulic demand of a sprinkler system and to verify that the system's overall layout is compliant with NFPA 13. Emphasis is placed on the methodology used to calculate and verify the system's hydraulic demand and available water supply. Chapter 14 was Chapter 8 in the 1999 edition of NFPA 13.

14.1* Working Plans

A.14.1 Preliminary plans should be submitted for review to the authority having jurisdiction prior to the development of working plans *[see Figure A.14.1(a)]*. The preliminary plans can be part of the construction documents submitted in order to obtain a building permit. However, working drawings in accordance with Section 14.1 should be submitted and approved prior to the installation of system equipment. Preliminary plans should include as much information as is required to provide a clear representation of the hazard to be protected, the system design concept, the proposed water supply configuration, and building construction information pertinent to system layout and detailing.

The Owner's Information Certificate shown as Figure A.14.1(b) should be used to obtain a declaration of the intended use of the occupancy to be protected.

Drawings that accompany the certificate should include the following:

(1) Name of owner and occupant.
(2) Location, including street address.
(3) Point of compass.
(4) Construction and occupancy of each building.
(5) Building height in feet.
(6) Waterflow test information. If a waterflow test of the city main is available, the drawings should indicate the date and time of the test, the name of the party that conducted the test, the location of the hydrants where the flow was taken and where static and residual pressure readings were recorded *(see A.15.2.1)*, the size and configuration of mains supplying the hydrants, the size and number of open hydrant butts flood, and results of the test.
(7) Building features such as combustible concealed spaces, floor openings, areas subject to freezing, and areas from which it is intended to omit sprinkler protection.
(8) Proposed location and approximate size, if a water supply employing pumps or tanks is contemplated.
(9) Name and address of party submitting the preliminary plans.
(10) Tentative location of underground major piping, including mains, risers, overhead mains, and fire department connections.

The preliminary plans discussed in A.14.1 are different from the working plans contained in the body of Chapter 14. Typically, the preliminary plans are prepared by an engineer or other

FIGURE A.14.1(a) *Typical Preliminary Plan.*

design professional as a part of the conceptual phase of building construction and are submitted along with other construction documents in the application for a building permit. The purpose of these preliminary plans is to make sure that basic information about the building and the structure is incorporated into the design of the sprinkler system.

FAQ ▶
Why was the Owner's
Information Certificate
added to NFPA 13?

In preparing the preliminary plans, the engineer should take the concerns of the owner into account so that the sprinkler system will meet the present and future needs of the owner's intended use of the space. To facilitate this discussion, the Owner's Information Certificate [Figure A.14.1(b)] was added to the standard. It is hoped that in filling out this certificate the owner or the owner's agent (who may be the design professional) will describe the intended use of the building so that the preliminary plans and the working plans will reflect the owner's needs. Preliminary plans are also useful in assessing the adequacy of an available water supply system and in assessing if the basis of the overall design is flawed. For example, in A.14.1(6), an out-of-date water test would indicate that more current information is needed for an accurate evaluation.

Another example involves A.14.1(4). An inexperienced architect or engineer might specify a design approach based on an ordinary hazard (Group 2) occupancy classification for a

Owner's Information Certificate

Name/Address of property to be protected with sprinkler protection:

_____

_____

Name of Owner: _____

Existing or planned construction is:

❏ Fire resistive or noncombustible

❏ Wood frame or ordinary (masonry walls with wood beams)

❏ Unknown

Is the system installation intended for one of the following special occupancies:

Aircraft hangar	❏ Yes	❏ No
Fixed guideway transit system	❏ Yes	❏ No
Race track stable	❏ Yes	❏ No
Marine terminal, pier, or wharf	❏ Yes	❏ No
Airport terminal	❏ Yes	❏ No
Aircraft engine test facility	❏ Yes	❏ No
Power plant	❏ Yes	❏ No
Water-cooling tower	❏ Yes	❏ No

If the answer to any of the above is "yes," the appropriate NFPA standard should be referenced for sprinkler density/area criteria.

Indicate whether any of the following special materials are intended to be present:

Flammable or combustible liquids	❏ Yes	❏ No
Aerosol products	❏ Yes	❏ No
Nitrate film	❏ Yes	❏ No
Pyroxylin plastic	❏ Yes	❏ No
Compressed or liquefied gas cylinders	❏ Yes	❏ No
Liquid or solid oxidizers	❏ Yes	❏ No
Organic peroxide formulations	❏ Yes	❏ No
Idle pallets	❏ Yes	❏ No

If the answer to any of the above is "yes," describe type, location, arrangement, and intended maximum quantities.

_____

_____

(NFPA 13, 1 of 2)

FIGURE A.14.1(b) *Owner's Information Certificate.*

rack storage operation in a proposed single-story, 35-ft (10.7-m) high building. A more accurate approach would consider a 30-ft to 34-ft (9.1-m to 10.4-m) storage height and the appropriate design criteria for the type of commodity in question. Although preliminary plans are not always submitted or required, they are very helpful during the design process and can eliminate costly problems and delays later in the design process.

Working plans are different from the preliminary plans discussed above. These documents are typically prepared by technicians in conformance with the concepts of the preliminary plans and are typically submitted for approval prior to system installation but after the issuance of a building permit. Working plans are prepared primarily for the qualified workers who conduct the actual system installation and for those responsible for verifying that the sprinkler system complies with NFPA 13. They also generally reflect coordination with other

Indicate whether the protection is intended for one of the following specialized occupancies or areas:

Spray area or mixing room	❏ Yes	❏ No
Solvent extraction	❏ Yes	❏ No
Laboratory using chemicals	❏ Yes	❏ No
Oxygen-fuel gas system for welding or cutting	❏ Yes	❏ No
Acetylene cylinder charging	❏ Yes	❏ No
Production or use of compressed or liquefied gases	❏ Yes	❏ No
Commercial cooking operation	❏ Yes	❏ No
Class A hyperbaric chamber	❏ Yes	❏ No
Cleanroom	❏ Yes	❏ No
Incinerator or waste handling system	❏ Yes	❏ No
Linen handling system	❏ Yes	❏ No
Industrial furnace	❏ Yes	❏ No
Water-cooling tower	❏ Yes	❏ No

If the answer to any of the above is "yes," describe type, location, arrangement, and intended maximum quantities.

_____

_____

Will there be any storage of products over 12 ft (3.6 m) in height?

❏ Yes   ❏ No

If the answer is "yes," describe product, intended storage arrangement, and height. _____

_____

_____

_____

Will there be any storage of plastic, rubber, or similar products over 5 ft (1.5 m) high except as described above?

❏ Yes   ❏ No

If the answer is "yes," describe product, intended storage arrangement, and height. _____

_____

_____

_____

I certify that I have knowledge of the intended use of the property and that the above information is correct.

Signature of owner's representative or agent: _____

Date: _____

Name of owner's representative or agent completing certificate (print): _____

Relationship and firm of agent (print): _____

(NFPA 13, 2 of 2)

FIGURE A.14.1(b) Continued

trades. The plans also serve to protect the interest of the owner, who usually is not knowledgeable about sprinkler systems and who usually relies on others to verify that the proposed sprinkler system is acceptable.

Several parties usually conduct a review of the proposed working plans. These parties typically include the owner's representatives, such as the engineer or architect of record via the services of a registered fire protection engineer, and society's representatives, such as the fire department or building department. Representatives from the associated insurance companies will also most likely take part in the review process. Regardless of the type of building in which the system is installed, the success of the overall fire and life safety system depends on proper sprinkler system design and installation. Verification of compliance with NFPA 13 is critical.

With a speculative-type building in which the nature of the future tenants or their operations is uncertain during the building's design and construction stage, the difficulties associated with the verification process increase. Many of the installation criteria of NFPA 13 hinge on the determination of the building's occupancy hazard classification. This determination usually cannot be made without knowing the type of tenant and the tenant's intended operations. To address these concerns, some jurisdictions have implemented additional regulations for speculative-type buildings. One example is to require any speculative building to be designed based on the criteria for an ordinary hazard (Group 2) occupancy. This approach provides a sprinkler system capable of protecting a wide range of hazards, and it allows the building owner more latitude in attracting prospective tenants. However, the limitations of this approach must also be acknowledged. Tenants with operations that present a greater hazard than those addressed by an ordinary hazard (Group 2) classification will be inadequately protected by the sprinkler system. The owner needs to be aware of the limits of the sprinkler system.

NFPA 25, *Standard for the Inspection, Testing, and Maintenance of Water-Based Fire* *Protection Systems,* requires the owner to retain the initial working plans and specifications because this facilitates the necessary inspection, testing, and maintenance activities. Any future modifications or additions of the sprinkler system also become more workable.

Some of the symbols commonly used in plan drawings can be found in NFPA 170, *Stan-* *dard for Fire Safety Symbols.* Any symbol used in the plan drawings that is not a standard symbol needs to be explained in the legend or some other obvious location on the working plans.

14.1.1* Working plans shall be submitted for approval to the authority having jurisdiction before any equipment is installed or remodeled.

A.14.1.1 See Figure A.14.1.1. Underground mains should be designed so that the system can be extended with a minimum of expense. Possible future plant expansion should also be considered and the piping designed so that it will not be covered by buildings.

14.1.2 Deviation from approved plans shall require permission of the authority having jurisdiction.

14.1.3 Working plans shall be drawn to an indicated scale, on sheets of uniform size, with a plan of each floor, and shall show those items from the following list that pertain to the design of the system:

(1) Name of owner and occupant
(2) Location, including street address
(3) Point of compass
(4) Full height cross section, or schematic diagram, including structural member information if required for clarity and including ceiling construction and method of protection for nonmetallic piping
(5) Location of partitions
(6) Location of fire walls
(7) Occupancy class of each area or room
(8) Location and size of concealed spaces, closets, attics, and bathrooms
(9) Any small enclosures in which no sprinklers are to be installed
(10) Size of city main in street and whether dead end or circulating; if dead end, direction and distance to nearest circulating main; and city main test results and system elevation relative to test hydrant *(see A.15.1.8).*
(11) Other sources of water supply, with pressure or elevation
(12) Make, type, model, and nominal K-factor of sprinklers including sprinkler identification number
(13) Temperature rating and location of high-temperature sprinklers

FIGURE A.14.1.1 *Typical Working Plans.*

(14) Total area protected by each system on each floor

(15) Number of sprinklers on each riser per floor

(16) Total number of sprinklers on each dry pipe system, preaction system, combined dry pipe-preaction system, or deluge system

(17) Approximate capacity in gallons of each dry pipe system

(18) Pipe type and schedule of wall thickness

(19) Nominal pipe size and cutting lengths of pipe (or center-to-center dimensions). Where typical branch lines prevail, it shall be necessary to size only one typical line

(20) Location and size of riser nipples

(21) Type of fittings and joints and location of all welds and bends. The contractor shall specify on drawing any sections to be shop welded and the type of fittings or formations to be used

(22) Type and locations of hangers, sleeves, braces, and methods of securing sprinklers when applicable

(23) All control valves, check valves, drain pipes, and test connections

(24) Make, type, model, and size of alarm or dry pipe valve

(25) Make, type, model, and size of preaction or deluge valve

(26) Kind and location of alarm bells

(27) Size and location of standpipe risers, hose outlets, hand hose, monitor nozzles, and related equipment

(28) Private fire service main sizes, lengths, locations, weights, materials, point of connection to city main; the sizes, types and locations of valves, valve indicators, regulators, meters, and valve pits; and the depth that the top of the pipe is laid below grade

(29) Piping provisions for flushing

(30) Where the equipment is to be installed as an addition to an existing system, enough of the existing system indicated on the plans to make all conditions clear

(31) For hydraulically designed systems, the information on the hydraulic data nameplate

(32) A graphic representation of the scale used on all plans

(33) Name and address of contractor

(34) Hydraulic reference points shown on the plan that correspond with comparable reference points on the hydraulic calculation sheets

(35) The minimum rate of water application (density), the design area of water application, in-rack sprinkler demand, and the water required for hose streams both inside and outside

(36) The total quantity of water and the pressure required noted at a common reference point for each system

(37) Relative elevations of sprinklers, junction points, and supply or reference points

(38) If room design method is used, all unprotected wall openings throughout the floor protected

(39) Calculation of loads for sizing and details of sway bracing

(40) The setting for pressure-reducing valves

(41) Information about backflow preventers (manufacturer, size, type)

(42) Information about antifreeze solution used (type and amount)

(43) Size and location of hydrants, showing size and number of outlets and if outlets are to be equipped with independent gate valves. Whether hose houses and equipment are to be provided, and by whom, shall be indicated. Static and residual hydrants that were used in flow tests shall be shown

(44) Size, location, and piping arrangement of fire department connections

Even though 14.1.3(22) requires hanger locations to be indicated on the working plans, there is no intent to require that the locations be specifically dimensioned. Instead, sufficient information needs to be included on the working plans to determine that the rules of Chapter 9 have been met.

 FAQ
Is it the intent of 14.1.3(22) that hanger locations be dimensioned?

With regard to 14.1.3(34), hydraulic reference points are important to both the designer and the plan reviewer because the points help ensure that all essential components of the system are included in the calculations. Hydraulic reference points serve to provide coordination between the plans and the hydraulic calculations. The reference points are especially important for more hydraulically complex systems such as those that are gridded.

Effective coordination between calculations and plans is also essential for system verification and where modifications or additions are proposed. The plan reviewer's job becomes more straightforward in this regard.

The information given in 14.1.3(35) establishes the basis for the majority of the design options. If an incorrect discharge density was selected or if the area of system operation is not large enough for the occupancy hazard, the proposed system design is subject to rejection. It should be noted that a growing number of sprinklers are not designed to operate at any specific density. Instead, these sprinklers are listed for their ability to control or suppress fires at some specific flow or pressure. For these sprinklers, the minimum flow of the sprinkler should be an acceptable substitute for the density. If the minimum flow is known from the listing, it can be stated here. If the pressure is known from the listing, the flow can be calculated by using the following formula:

$$Q = K\sqrt{P}$$

where:

Q = the flow

K = the constant associated with the orifice size of the sprinkler

P = the pressure from the listing

If it is necessary to report the density for these sprinklers, the flow can be divided by the largest area of coverage to determine the density for these sprinklers.

The following information, which is associated with the water supply requirements, must be shown on the plans:

1. Density (or flow required from sprinklers not listed for a specific density)
2. Area of water application
3. In-rack sprinkler demand, if applicable
4. Inside hose demand, if applicable
5. Outside hose demand

The sum of the inside and outside hose demands must always be equal to or greater than the values given in Table 11.2.3.1.1.

With regard to 14.1.3(36), the actual calculated demand is normally referenced at the base of the riser in buildings containing several systems. In single-system buildings, the reference point can be at the riser's base or the connection point to the water supply (city main).

With regard to 14.1.3(41), the friction loss through the backflow preventer must be accounted for in the calculations. Because each model device has different friction loss characteristics, the model on the plans, the model on the calculations, and the model installed all have to be the same. A change during the construction phase could cause an inadequate sprinkler system discharge.

14.1.4 The working plan submittal shall include the manufacturer's installation instructions for any specially listed equipment, including descriptions, applications, and limitations for any sprinklers, devices, piping, or fittings.

NFPA 13 does not address specially listed equipment and system components in detail (see 14.1.4). Therefore, when specially listed equipment is used in the system, a proper evaluation cannot be conducted using NFPA 13 alone.

FAQ ▶
Why are manufacturer's instructions required to be submitted?

Specific instructions and information about the component must be obtained from the manufacturer or listing agency and included on the plans and hydraulic calculations. Examples of specially listed equipment include the use of special fittings whose equivalent lengths—that is, hydraulic characteristics—are not addressed in NFPA 13, and special sprinklers with minimum flows and pressures not addressed within NFPA 13.

14.1.5* Working Plans for Automatic Sprinkler Systems with Non–Fire Protection Connections. Special symbols shall be used and explained for auxiliary piping, pumps, heat exchangers, valves, strainers, and the like, clearly distinguishing these devices and piping runs from those of the sprinkler system. Model number, type, and manufacturer's name shall be identified for each piece of auxiliary equipment.

 A.14.1.5 See Figure A.14.1.5(a) and Figure A.14.1.5(b).

14.2 Water Supply Information

14.2.1 Water Supply Capacity Information. The following information shall be included:

(1) Location and elevation of static and residual test gauge with relation to the riser reference point
(2) Flow location

FIGURE A.14.1.5(a) *Working Plans for Circulating Closed-Loop Systems (Example 1).*

Notes:
1. Wet pipe automatic sprinkler system with auxiliary connections for heating and air conditioning equipment. Ordinary hazard occupancy, 130 ft² maximum spacing.
2. A dotted line (............) denotes auxiliary heating and air-conditioning piping.

Globe valve in auxiliary piping system

Check valve in auxiliary piping system

Heat pump in auxiliary piping system

Heat pump detail:
Typical section of connections between sprinkler branch lines and heat pump
1. Branch line
2. "World-wide" model "E" globe valve
3. "Wunway" model "S" check valve
4. Dielectric union
5. "Farenheit" model #72 heat pump

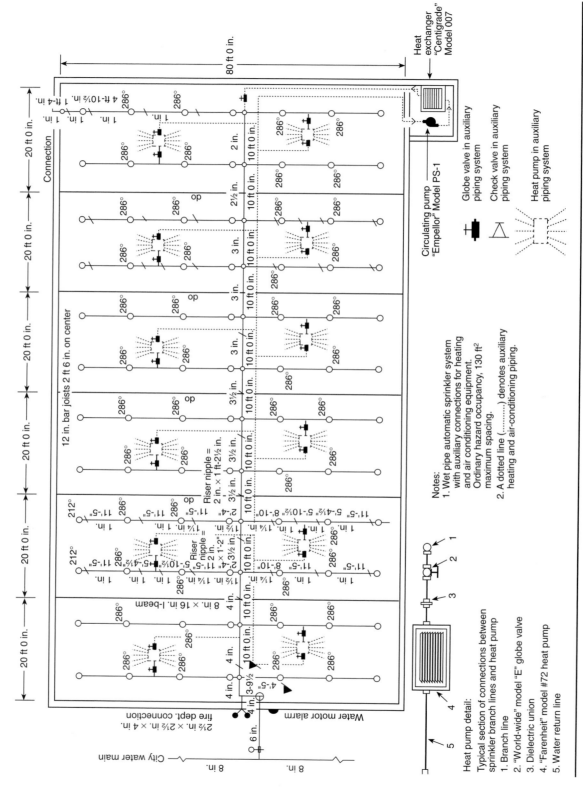

FIGURE A.14.15(b) *Working Plans for Circulating Closed-Loop Systems (Example 2).*

Notes:
1. Wet pipe automatic sprinkler system with auxiliary connections for heating and air conditioning equipment. Ordinary hazard occupancy, 130 ft² maximum spacing.
2. A dotted line (..........) denotes auxiliary heating and air-conditioning piping.

Heat pump detail:
Typical section of connections between sprinkler branch lines and heat pump
1. Branch line
2. "World-wide" model "E" globe valve
3. Dielectric union
4. "Farenheit" model #72 heat pump
5. Water return line

Globe valve in auxiliary piping system

Check valve in auxiliary piping system

Heat pump in auxiliary piping system

(3) Static pressure, psi (bar)
(4) Residual pressure, psi (bar)
(5) Flow, gpm (L/min)
(6) Date
(7) Time
(8) Test conducted by or information supplied by
(9) Other sources of water supply, with pressure or elevation

Water supply capacity information is discussed in 14.2.1. Waterflow test data must be current, analyzed during periods of peak usage, and handled in such a manner that it represents the supply's true orientation, or direction, to the system being designed.

Determining when peak demands occur can be difficult, but water departments will usually have information readily available concerning the time of year and time of day when the highest distribution system demand occurs.

Waterflow tests are rarely actually conducted on the day and at the time of the peak demand of the water system. Instead, some reduction in the results is usually applied to account for peak demand conditions. If such a deduction is made in the reporting of the results, it should be indicated so that additional safety factors are not applied that would make the system unnecessarily expensive.

A growing number of water utilities are no longer performing waterflow tests to determine available flows and pressures. Instead, an analysis is being performed using knowledge of the flows and pressures in the system taking into account future expected growth and demand of the community. From this analysis, a design flow and pressure can be computed for any location on the distribution network.

14.2.2 Water Supply Treatment Information. The following information shall be included where required by 12.1.5:

(1) Type of condition that requires treatment
(2) Type of treatment needed to address the problem
(3) Details of treatment plan

As part of the overall water supply information it is important to document any required water supply treatments including the condition requiring treatment, the type of treatment, and details of the treatment plan, as stated in 14.2.2. Microbiologically induced corrosion (MIC) is a relatively rare but growing problem. Microbes in the water attach themselves to the pipe and then eat their way through, creating pinhole leaks in the pipe. Microbe byproducts can also build up and restrict the effective diameter of the pipe. Neither situation is beneficial for a sprinkler system. See Supplement 2 for more information on MIC.

Subsection 15.1.5 requires that MIC be dealt with once it is known to be a problem and specifies some methods of dealing with MIC. If MIC has built up within a system or eaten through the pipes, the affected pipes must be cleaned or replaced, and then the water entering the system needs to be treated with a biocide so that the microbes are destroyed.

Proper treatment depends on the type of microbes causing the corrosion or buildup. Different microbes respond differently to each kind of biocide. Each site where MIC is known to be a problem needs its own plan for how to deal with the particular microbes in question.

NFPA 25 provides more information on identification and treatment of systems with MIC. The NFSA report "Detection, Treatment and Prevention of Microbiologically Influenced Corrosion in Water-Based Fire Protection Systems" also provides information on the subject.

◄ FAQ
What considerations should be made when evaluating the water capacity information?

◄ FAQ
What other methods are available to determine the available flow and pressure from a water supply?

14.3 Hydraulic Calculation Forms

14.3.1 General. Hydraulic calculations shall be prepared on form sheets that include a summary sheet, detailed worksheets, and a graph sheet. *[See copies of typical forms in Figure A.14.3.2(a), Figure A.14.3.3, and Figure A.14.3.4.]*

The calculation forms in Section 14.3 are tools that help monitor the waterflow through the system, summarize system design information, and allow for a quick evaluation of the system. As illustrated in Figure A.14.3.2(c), waterflow through the system is tracked in a direction opposite to that of the actual waterflow—that is, the first evaluation point begins at the hydraulically most demanding sprinkler, which many times is the furthest sprinkler from the system riser, and ends at the point of connection to the system water supply. These forms permit the designer or other persons reviewing the plans to account for individual pipe lengths and fittings and to keep track of changes in pressure and flow that result from friction loss and elevation changes.

14.3.2* Summary Sheet. The summary sheet shall contain the following information, where applicable:

(1) Date
(2) Location
(3) Name of owner and occupant
(4) Building number or other identification
(5) Description of hazard
(6) Name and address of contractor or designer
(7) Name of approving agency
(8) System design requirements, as follows:

    (a) Design area of water application, ft^2 (m^2)
    (b) Minimum rate of water application (density), gpm/ft^2 (mm/min)
    (c) Area per sprinkler, ft^2 (m^2)

(9) Total water requirements as calculated, including allowance for inside hose, outside hydrants, and water curtain and exposure sprinklers
(10) Allowance for in-rack sprinklers, gpm (L/min)
(11) Limitations (dimension, flow, and pressure) on extended coverage or other listed special sprinklers

A **A.14.3.2** See Figure A.14.3.2(a) through Figure A.14.3.2(d).

The summary sheet shown in Figure A.14.3.2(a) is normally used as the cover sheet for the calculations and contains the information required by 14.3.2 concerning the system design parameters. This information is useful in estimating the total amount of water needed for sprinkler system demand. For example, multiplying the value given in 14.3.2(8)(a) by the value given in 14.3.2(8)(b) will give an estimation of the minimum flow rate needed to supply the sprinklers, assuming no friction loss in the system. More specifically, for a light hazard occupancy with a density of 0.1 gpm/ft^2 operating over 1500 ft^2 (see Figure 11.2.3.1.5), the water from demand for the sprinklers cannot be less than 150 gpm (0.1 × 1500).

This estimation technique assumes that there will be no friction loss in the system. In reality, the actual minimum flow rate will be greater than the value obtained by the above estimation technique because there will be friction loss in the system. Experienced designers and plan reviewers can apply a correction factor for the pipe sizes and arrangement and make rough estimates regarding sprinkler demand.

The area of sprinkler operation is selected from the area/density curve shown in Figure 11.2.3.1.5 or the appropriate criteria in Chapter 12 and is subject to modification due to the rules of Chapter 11 and Chapter 12.

FAQ ▶
How is the area of operation affected by the size of the building?

The area of sprinkler operation is independent of the total area of the building. For example, when a design area of 1500 ft^2 (139 m^2) is selected for an office building, the fire is anticipated to be controlled to an area no larger than 1500 ft^2 (139 m^2), regardless of the size of the building.

Controlling a fire with fewer sprinklers than the number required within the operating area is rather common. Safety factors are incorporated in the design approach and the calculation technique to account for uncertainties such as the potential for a fire to be shielded from

Hydraulic Calculations

for

ABC Company, employee garage
_____

7499 Franklin Road
_____

Charleston, SC
_____

Contract No. _____4001_____

Date_____1 – 7 – 99_____

Design data:

Occupancy classification ___ORD. GR. 1___

Density___0.15___ gpm/ft²

Area of application __1500__ ft

Coverage per sprinkler ___130___ ft

Special sprinklers _____

No. of sprinklers calculated _____12_____

In-rack demand _____

Hose streams _____250 gpm_____

Total water required ____510.4____ gpm
including hose streams

Name of contractor _____

Name of designer _____

Address _____

Authority having jurisdiction _____

FIGURE A.14.3.2(a) *Summary Sheet.*

sprinkler discharge or a plugged sprinkler. Additionally, the design approach anticipates relatively worst-case fire situations for each respective occupancy hazard.

Selecting the hydraulically most demanding area of operation for calculation ensures that an area located hydraulically closer to the water supply will also control the fire. In buildings containing two or more occupancy hazards, multiple sets of hydraulic calculations are usually necessary to verify that each hazard is adequately protected.

Figure A.14.3.2(b) shows the floor plan and elevation of a hydraulically calculated sprinkler system in a small building that is 130 ft × 200 ft (39 m × 60 m) in area. The density of 0.15 gpm/ft² (6.1 mm/min) over an area of operation of 1500 ft² (139 m²) is obtained from Figure 11.2.3.1.5 and is sufficient for an ordinary hazard (Group 1) occupancy. This design approach requires that only a single point from the curve be satisfied. For example, a density of 0.12 gpm/ft² (4.5 mm/min) operating over an area of 3000 ft² (279 m²) is also acceptable for protecting an ordinary hazard (Group 1) occupancy. The person performing the hydraulic calculations has the option to choose any point along the curve. However, many people find that the most efficient selection is one with a higher density operating over a smaller area of operation, which can be found at the lower ends of the density/area curves.

A quick way to identify the approximate size of the remote area and to determine the number of operating sprinklers for the system is to divide the area of operation by the area of coverage per sprinkler. The area of coverage per sprinkler is determined by the methodology discussed in 8.5.2.1.

FIGURE A.14.3.2(b) *Hydraulic Calculation Example (Plan View and Elevation View).*

FAQ ▶

How are fractional numbers of sprinklers handled when determining the number of operating sprinklers?

Using the information provided in Figure A.14.3.2(b), 1500 ft² is divided by 130 ft² (139 m² is divided by 12 m²), giving a value of 11.54 sprinklers. Because a fraction of a sprinkler is not possible, this value is always rounded up to the next whole number. Therefore, the number of sprinklers in the operating area is 12.

When the spacing of sprinklers along a branch line is fairly uniform, the number of sprinklers required to operate on a branch line in the area of operation is determined by dividing

Contract Name _____ GROUP I 1500 ft² Sheet _2_ Of _3_

Step No.	Nozzle Ident. and Location	Flow in gpm	Pipe Size	Pipe Fittings and Devices	Equiv. Pipe Length	Friction Loss psi Foot	Pressure Summary	Normal Pressure	D = 0.15 GPM/ ft² Notes K = 5.6	Ref. Step
1	1 BL-1	q	1		L 13.0	C=120	P_t 12.1	P_t	$Q = 130 \times 0.15 = 19.5$	
					F		P_e	P_v	$P = (19.5/5.6)^2 = 12.1$ psi	
		Q 19.5			T 13.0	0.124	P_f 1.6	P_n		
2	2	q 20.7	1¼		L 13.0		P_t 13.7	P_t	$q = 5.65 \sqrt{13.7}$	
					F		P_e	P_v		
		Q 40.2			T 13.0	0.125	P_f 1.6	P_n		
3	3	q 21.9	1½		L 13.0		P_t 15.3	P_t	$q = 5.65 \sqrt{15.3}$	4
					F		P_e	P_v		
		Q 62.1			T 13.0	0.131	P_f 1.7	P_n		
4	4 DN RN	q 23.1	1½	2T-16	L 20.5		P_t 17.0	P_t	$q = 5.65 \sqrt{17}$	5
					F 16.0		P_e 0.4	P_v	$P_e = 1 \times 0.433$	
		Q 85.2			T 36.5	0.236	P_f 8.6	P_n		
5	CM TO BL-2	q	2		L 10.0		P_t 26.0	P_t	$K = \dfrac{85.2}{\sqrt{26}}$	
					F		P_e	P_v	$K = 16.71$	
		Q 85.2			T 10.0	0.07	P_f 0.7	P_n		
6	BL-2 CM TO BL-3	q 86.3	2½		L 10.0		P_t 26.7	P_t	$q = 16.71 \sqrt{26.1}$	6
					F		P_e	P_v		
		Q 171.5			T 10.0	0.107	P_f 1.1	P_n		
7	BL-3 CM	q 88.1	2½		L 70.0		P_t 27.8	P_t	$q = 16.7 \sqrt{27.8}$	
					F		P_e	P_v		
		Q 259.6			T 70.0	0.231	P_f 16.2	P_n		
8	CM TO FIS	q	3	E5 AV15 GV1	L 119.0		P_t 44.0	P_t	$P_e = 15 \times 0.433$	8
					F 21		P_e 6.5	P_v		
		Q 259.6			T 140.0	0.081	P_f 11.2	P_n		
9	THROUGH UNDER-GROUND TO CITY MAIN	q	3	E5 GV1 T15	L 50.0	C=150	P_t 61.7	P_t	$F = F_{40} \times 1.51 \times F_c$	9
					F 27.6	TYPE'M'	P_e	P_v	$F_c = [2.981/3.068]^{4.87} = 0.869$	
		Q 259.6			T 77.6	0.061	P_f 4.7	P_n	$F = 21 \times 1.51 \times 0.869$ $F = 27.6$	
		q			L		P_t 66.4	P_t		
					F		P_e	P_v		
		Q			T		P_f	P_n		
		q			L		P_t	P_t		
					F		P_e	P_v		
		Q			T		P_f	P_n		
							P_t			

FIGURE A.14.3.2(c) *Hydraulic Calculations.*

1.2 times $\sqrt{A}$ (where *A* is the total operating area) by the distance between sprinklers on the branch line. This calculation ensures that the area of operation takes the shape of a rectangle, with the longer dimension parallel to the direction of the branch lines. (See A.14.4.4 for more discussion on this procedure.) In this case, the number of sprinklers along the branch line is 4— that is, $1.2 \times (1500)^{0.5} \div 13 = 3.58$ sprinklers. The length of the rectangle's longer side in the design area is measured in terms of a number of sprinklers rather than an actual length dimension.

FIGURE A.14.3.2(d) *Hydraulic Graph.*

FAQ ▶
How are fractional numbers of sprinklers handled when determining the number of operating sprinklers on each branch line?

Because 0.58 or any other fractional part of a sprinkler cannot operate, the resulting number must always be rounded up to the next whole number. Therefore, 4 sprinklers must be used. Any fractional number in this calculation technique is always rounded up to the next whole number, even if the calculation result has a fractional value less than 0.5—for example, 4.1 sprinklers would be rounded up to 5 sprinklers.

Once these values are determined, the actual operating area can be laid out based on a relative minimum length of 4 sprinklers per branch line. Because the first calculation in this example indicated that at least 12 sprinklers must be considered, the shorter length of the design area—that is, the length parallel to the cross main—is determined by counting the number of branch lines along the cross main, which produces 12 sprinklers with 4 sprinklers on each branch line. In this case, 3 branch lines need to be included in the operation area. It is important to note that the designer must also verify that the operating area at least covers or exceeds the operating area determined from Chapter 11, 12 or 13, as applicable. Where the actual floor area protected is less than the design parameters, additional sprinklers must be added to ensure that the minimum area is evaluated.

The operating area is the hydraulically most demanding rectangle encompassing 4 sprinklers on each of 3 branch lines, which provides the required total of 12 sprinklers. This area is indicated by cross-hatching, and, because this system is symmetrical about the cross main, this area can be located as shown in Figure A.14.3.2(b), or, since the branch lines are laid out perfectly symmetrical around the cross main, the sprinklers in the lower left corner of the building shown in Figure A.14.3.2(b) would also be correct.

If the sprinkler spacing along the branch line were not uniform, the operating area would be a little more difficult to identify. The rectangle would need to have a length parallel to the branch line equal to 1.2 times the square root of the operating area. Any sprinkler on the first branch line that covered any portion of space in that length would need to be in the operating area. Additional branch lines would need to be added, counting the sprinklers adjacent to the length identified on the first branch line, until the total operating area was reached. Sprinklers on the last branch line can be dropped from the operating area if they are not the most demanding and if the total operating area is being protected without considering these sprinklers.

In Step 1 of Figure A.14.3.2(c), sprinkler 1 and branch line 1 (BL-1) are identified in the Nozzle Identification and Location column. The flow for the first sprinkler is determined using the formula $Q = D \times A$ where the selected density of 0.15 gpm/ft² (D) is multiplied by the area of coverage per sprinkler, 130 ft² (A). This results in a flow of 19.5 gpm from sprinkler 1. The final pipe size is determined through a combination of trial and error and experience. An initial pipe sizing can be based on the pipe schedule tables and then modified through hydraulic analysis to determine the most ideal pipe size. In this case, a 1-in. pipe has been selected. Note that the pipe size is given as a nominal dimension.

The fitting directly connected to a sprinkler is not usually included in the calculations because it is accounted for in the sprinkler's K-factor. [See 14.4.4.5(9) for more information.] As a result, no values are shown under the Pipe Fittings and Devices column in Figure A.14.3.2(c). The equivalent pipe length is the total center-to-center distance between sprinklers, which in this case is the actual pipe length of 13 ft (3.9 m) because no fittings were used. The friction loss (psi/ft) is determined by using the Hazen-Williams formula shown in 14.4.2.1.1. When using 1-in. Schedule 40 pipe with a C factor of 120, the formula becomes the following:

$$p = 5.10 \times 10^{-4} \times Q^{1.85}$$

(Note that the actual inside diameter of 1-in. Schedule 40 pipe is 1.049 in.)

When the flow (Q) is 19.5 gpm, then the following is the result:

$$p = 0.124 \text{ psi/ft}$$

By multiplying 0.124 psi/ft by 13 ft, a friction loss of 1.6 psi (0.11 bar) from sprinkler 1 to sprinkler 2 exists.

The total pressure (P_t) at sprinkler 1 is determined by using the following formula:

$$P_t = \left(\frac{Q}{K}\right)^2$$

where:

P_t = pressure (psi)

Q = flow from sprinkler (gpm)

K = K-factor of sprinkler

The total pressure in the case of the example is as follows:

$$\left(\frac{19.5 \text{ gpm}}{5.6}\right)^2 = 12.1 \text{ psi}$$

The pressure at sprinkler 2 is determined by adding the pressure at sprinkler 1 plus the pressure drop caused by friction loss. In this case, the pressure at sprinkler 2 is 13.7 psi (0.93 bar) [12.1 psi (0.82 bar) at sprinkler 1 plus 1.6 psi (0.11 bar) for friction loss]. The flow (Q) from sprinkler 2 is determined using the following formula:

$$Q = K\sqrt{P}$$

where:

K = the K-factor of sprinkler 2 (5.6)

P = the pressure at sprinkler 2 (13.7 psi)

The flow at sprinkler 2 is therefore 20.7 gpm (78 L/min). This flow is added to sprinkler 1, and the same procedures for determining friction loss and flow for the pipe between sprinklers 1 and 2 are followed for determining the information for the pipe between sprinklers 2 and 3.

In Step 4 of Figure A.14.3.2(c), the four sprinklers have been calculated, and the pressure loss between sprinkler 4 and the cross main needs to be determined. The pipe length (*L*) includes the 13.0 ft (4.0 m) between sprinklers plus 6.5 ft (2.0 m) for a starter piece plus 1.0 ft (0.3 m) for a riser nipple for a total of 20.5 ft (6.3 m). The tees at the top and bottom of the riser nipple are included in the analysis of the friction loss and are equal to 8 ft (2.4 m) of pipe each. (See Table 14.4.3.1.1.) The change in elevation [1 ft × 0.433 psi/ft (0.31 m × 0.0979 bar/m)] also needs to be taken into account at this point.

A K-factor is established for branch line 1 (BL-1) by dividing the flow (*Q*) by $\sqrt{P}$, which in this case is 85.2 divided by $\sqrt{26}$, or 16.71. This K-factor is used in predicting the flow in subsequent branch lines that are identical to BL-1. This K-factor is based on the same hydraulic principle as the K-factor assigned to a sprinkler—namely, that the K-factor for BL-1 describes the physical characteristics of the pipe opening in the cross main for the branch line and identifies the constant relationship between the flow and the pressure at this point. When a pressure is associated with the branch line K-factor, a corresponding flow can then be established for the branch line. If the system design area is of such a nature that it is not symmetrical and if sprinklers for the design area occur on both sides of the branch line, then two K-factors must be determined and the flow must be balanced to properly reflect the effect of the higher pressure.

In Step 8 of Figure A.14.3.2(c), the pressure due to elevation (P_e) of 6.5 psi (15 ft × 0.433) is added. The elevation pressure is considered here because the change in elevation occurs within the step with no additional water flowing from the system between the two points considered by this step. Any change in elevation needs to be taken into account where it occurs.

In Step 9 of Figure A.14.3.2(c), as indicated by the note, copper pipe is used, so the *C* factor is 150 (see Table 14.4.4.5). The fitting and device equivalent lengths are totaled and multiplied by 1.51 (see 14.4.3.2) due to the different *C* factor. The total of the equivalent lengths also needs to be multiplied by 0.869 due to the different internal pipe diameter. The factor 0.869 is derived by taking the ratio of the internal diameter of copper tube to the internal diameter of Schedule 40 steel and raising this ratio to the 4.87 power (see 14.4.3.1.3).

In Figure A.14.3.2(d), the water supply curve is based on a 90-psi (6.2-bar) static pressure and a 60-psi (4.1-bar) residual pressure with 1000 gpm (3785 L/min) flowing.

The system demand curve is started at the 6.5-psi (0.5-bar) point on the ordinate to consider the pressure due to elevation (P_e) and is continued to the demand point of 260 gpm (984 L/min) at 66.4 psi (4.5 bar). The system demand curve represents the friction loss in the system. The horizontal dashed line drawn from the above demand point to the city water supply curve represents the amount of water available for hose streams. In this case, about 610 gpm (2309 L/min) are available, but only 250 gpm (946 L/min) are required. The design demand in this example falls well below the water supply curve and, therefore, is acceptable.

Some authorities having jurisdiction will lower the water supply curve to take into account daily and seasonal fluctuations in available pressures and to prepare for future growth of areas to be developed.

Because the demand curve falls well below the water supply curve, some pipe sizes may be reduced to utilize the excess pressure and reduce the cost of the sprinkler system. If the system demand point reached beyond the city water supply curve, some of the piping could be enlarged to decrease friction loss. Some adjustments can also be made to reduce the system demand to a point at or below the water supply curve. These adjustments include the use of sprinklers with larger K-factors (orifice sizes), selection of a lower discharge density with a larger area of operation, or a reduction in sprinkler spacing. If these actions do not correct the situation, then a more detailed analysis of the water supply is needed. If the system demand point cannot be reduced, then the water supply pressure needs to be increased through the installation of a fire pump, and/or the flow can be increased through the installation of a water storage tank.

14.3.3* Detailed Worksheets. Detailed worksheets or computer printout sheets shall contain the following information:

(1) Sheet number
(2) Sprinkler description and discharge constant *(K)*
(3) Hydraulic reference points
(4) Flow in gpm (L/min)
(5) Pipe size
(6) Pipe lengths, center-to-center of fittings
(7) Equivalent pipe lengths for fittings and devices
(8) Friction loss in psi/ft (bar/m) of pipe
(9) Total friction loss between reference points
(10) In-rack sprinkler demand balanced to ceiling demand
(11) Elevation head in psi (bar) between reference points
(12) Required pressure in psi (bar) at each reference point
(13) Velocity pressure and normal pressure if included in calculations
(14) Notes to indicate starting points or reference to other sheets or to clarify data shown
(15)*Diagram to accompany gridded system calculations to indicate flow quantities and directions for lines with sprinklers operating in the remote area
(16) Combined K-factor calculations for sprinklers on drops, armovers, or sprigs where calculations do not begin at the sprinkler

A.14.3.3 See Figure A.14.3.3.   **A**

Figure A.14.3.3 illustrates just one of several worksheets used in the sprinkler industry today. Many of the computer printouts are similar. The form is used to track the waterflow and hydraulic characteristics of the system. The form allows the calculation procedure to be followed from the last sprinkler in the hydraulically most remote area to the point in the system where the water supply is connected. Pipe diameters, fittings, and friction loss values are tabulated based on the information retrieved from the sheet.

A.14.3.3(15) See Figure A.14.3.3(15).   **A**

Figure A.14.3.3(15) depicts a gridded system that has been calculated. The dotted lines outline the calculated area, and the numbers in circles are reference points. The arrows on the pipe indicate the flow directions, and the numbers alongside indicate quantity in gpm. The flow directions are of particular importance in a gridded system due to the various flow paths that the water can take from the source to the operating sprinklers.

To facilitate the review of a proposed system, a diagram similar to Figure A.14.3.3(15) must accompany hydraulic calculations for a gridded system. Most of the commonly used software programs available today produce similar flow diagrams.

14.3.4* Graph Sheet. A graphic representation of the complete hydraulic calculation shall be plotted on semiexponential graph paper ($Q^{1.85}$) and shall include the following:

(1) Water supply curve
(2) Sprinkler system demand
(3) Hose demand (where applicable)
(4) In-rack sprinkler demand (where applicable)

A.14.3.4 See Figure A.14.3.4.

The graph sheet in Figure A.14.3.4 is used to plot the water supply curve and the sprinkler system demand. The graph sheet is referred to as hydraulic graph paper. The scale along the abscissa (x-axis) must be to the 1.85 power because, in the Hazen-Williams formula, pressure (*p*) is proportional to the flow (*Q*) to the 1.85 power. Without this exponential adjustment, the

Contract no. _____   Sheet no. _____ of _____

Name and location _____

Reference	Nozzle type and location	Flow in gpm (L/min)	Pipe size (in.)	Fitting and devices	Pipe equivalent length		Friction loss psi/ft (bar/m)	Required psi (bar)		Normal Pressure	Notes
	q				length			P_t	P_t		
					fitting			P_f	P_v		
	Q				total			P_e	P_n		
	q				length			P_t	P_t		
					fitting			P_f	P_v		
	Q				total			P_e	P_n		
	q				length			P_t	P_t		
					fitting			P_f	P_v		
	Q				total			P_e	P_n		
	q				length			P_t	P_t		
					fitting			P_f	P_v		
	Q				total			P_e	P_n		
	q				length			P_t	P_t		
					fitting			P_f	P_v		
	Q				total			P_e	P_n		
	q				length			P_t	P_t		
					fitting			P_f	P_v		
	Q				total			P_e	P_n		
	q				length			P_t	P_t		
					fitting			P_f	P_v		
	Q				total			P_e	P_n		
	q				length			P_t	P_t		
					fitting			P_f	P_v		
	Q				total			P_e	P_n		
	q				length			P_t	P_t		
					fitting			P_f	P_v		
	Q				total			P_e	P_n		
	q				length			P_t	P_t		
					fitting			P_f	P_v		
	Q				total			P_e	P_n		
	q				length			P_t	P_t		
					fitting			P_f	P_v		
	Q				total			P_e	P_n		
	q				length			P_t	P_t		
					fitting			P_f	P_v		
	Q				total			P_e	P_n		
	q				length			P_t	P_t		
					fitting			P_f	P_v		
	Q				total			P_e	P_n		
	q				length			P_t	P_t		
					fitting			P_f	P_v		
	Q				total			P_e	P_n		
	q				length			P_t	P_t		
					fitting			P_f	P_v		
	Q				total			P_e	P_n		
	q				length			P_t	P_t		
					fitting			P_f	P_v		
	Q				total			P_e	P_n		
	q				length			P_t	P_t		
					fitting			P_f	P_v		
	Q				total			P_e	P_n		
	q				length			P_t	P_t		
					fitting			P_f	P_v		
	Q				total			P_e	P_n		

P_t = total pressure; P_f = friction loss pressure; P_v = velocity pressure; P_e = elevation pressure

FIGURE A.14.3.3 *Sample Worksheet.*

FIGURE A.14.3.3(15) *Example of Hydraulically Remote Area—Grid System.*

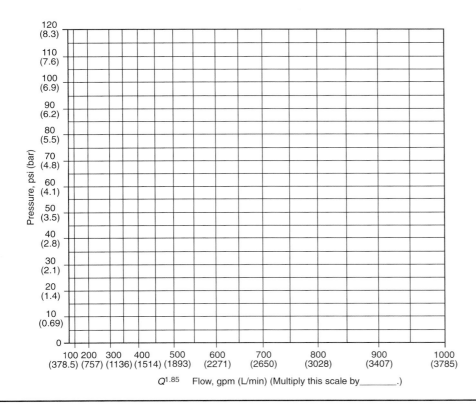

FIGURE A.14.3.4 *Sample Graph Sheet.*

water supply graph would be in the shape of a curve (similar to a fire pump curve) rather than a straight-line function. The straight line allows the water supply information to be more easily plotted using two data points.

The flow ($Q^{1.85}$) axis can be multiplied by any number to extend the range of the flow value. For example, if no adjustment is desired, the flow numbers are merely multiplied by 1. If a flow of 2500 gpm (9463 L/min) needs to be evaluated, the scale could be multiplied by 3, resulting in an extension of the scale to 3000 gpm (11,355 L/min).

14.4 Hydraulic Calculation Procedures

The procedure for hydraulically calculating a sprinkler system, which is covered in Section 14.4, is different than that for other types of systems that use waterflow. A combination of factors must be integrated into the design, including the hazard, the spacing of sprinklers, the type of pipe, and the type of sprinkler system.

14.4.1* General.

A.14.4.1 When additional sprinkler piping is added to an existing system, the existing piping does not have to be increased in size to compensate for the additional sprinklers, provided the new work is calculated and the calculations include that portion of the existing system that can be required to carry water to the new work. It is not necessary to restrict the water velocity when determining friction losses using the Hazen-Williams formula.

FAQ ▶
Can a pipe schedule system be connected to the hydraulically designed system?

Can pipe or tube with a diameter of less than 1 in. be utilized?
FAQ ▶

Is there a limit to the number of sprinklers that can be supplied by a given pipe size when utilizing the hydraulic calculation procedure?
FAQ ▶

FAQ ▶
Does NFPA 13 limit water velocity in any of the pipes?

Under no circumstances should a new pipe schedule system be connected to or supplied from an existing hydraulically designed system (see 14.4.1). Extending an existing pipe schedule system with a new hydraulically designed system can be acceptable in some cases where a careful analysis of the resultant hybrid system has been done. This analysis might need to include shifting the remote area design to include a part of the existing pipe schedule design.

The restriction on ¾-in. (19-mm) steel pipe was included in NFPA 13 in 1940, about 30 years before the advent of hydraulically calculated systems. This change was made to improve the discharge characteristics of the sprinkler and to reduce the likelihood of the smaller diameter line becoming clogged.

It should be noted that ¾-in. (19-mm) nonmetallic piping and copper tube are currently listed and are acceptable. Additionally, NFPA 13D, *Standard for the Installation of Sprinkler Systems in One- and Two-Family Dwellings and Manufactured Homes,* allows the use of ½-in. (12.7-mm) nonmetallic pipe when specific criteria are followed.

A number of sprinkler systems are still in service that use ¾-in. (19-mm) steel pipe. No requirements are in NFPA 13 to replace all such pipe. During a routine internal pipe investigation required by NFPA 25, if the smaller diameter pipe appears blocked, the obstruction needs to be cleared or the pipe needs to be replaced.

The use of the hydraulic calculation procedure, which is favored over the pipe schedule procedure, does not impose any limit on the number of sprinklers supplied by certain diameters of pipe. The determining factor for any such limit rests with the capacity of the water supply.

The last sentence of A.14.4.1 was added to state definitively that NFPA 13 has no limits on water velocity in any of the pipes. The impact of high water velocities tends to be self-correcting. When the velocity of water in a pipe is high, the pressure loss in that pipe is also high. If the pressure loss is too high, the pipe size will be increased to reduce the pressure loss, and the velocity will correspondingly go down.

Additional information on the impact of water velocity can be found in the AFSA report "Water Velocity: Its impact on the Accuracy of Hydraulic Calculations."

14.4.1.1 A calculated system for a building, or a calculated addition to a system in an existing sprinklered building, shall supersede the rules in this standard governing pipe schedules, except that all systems shall continue to be limited by area.

14.4.1.2 Pipe sizes shall be no less than 1 in. (25.4 mm) nominal for ferrous piping and ¾ in. (19 mm) nominal for copper tubing or nonmetallic piping listed for fire sprinkler service.

14.4.1.3 The size of pipe, number of sprinklers per branch line, and number of branch lines per cross main shall otherwise be limited only by the available water supply.

14.4.1.4 However, sprinkler spacing and all other rules covered in this and other applicable standards shall be observed.

14.4.2 Formulas.

14.4.2.1 Friction Loss Formula.

The Hazen-Williams formula is the most common of the empirical formulas used to determine relationships between flow, friction loss, and available pressure when designing a sprinkler system (see 14.4.2.1). Allen Hazen (a civil engineer) and Gardner Stewart Williams (Professor of Civil Engineering at the University of Michigan) developed the formula at the beginning of the 20th century. A different method of calculating friction loss, known as the Darcy-Weisbach equation, can provide a more precise method for establishing these relationships, but it is not commonly used for fire protection calculations due to its complexity and the fact that standardized values for aged pipe have not been agreed upon by the fire protection community.

The Hazen-Williams formula depends on the relationship between the pipe type (the C factor), the pipe diameter, and the flow through the pipe. The C factor describes the relative roughness of the pipe interior and is similar to the epsilon factor used in the Darcy-Weisbach calculation technique. C factors for various pipe types are shown in Table 14.4.4.5.

Although NFPA 13 does not stipulate a maximum limit on velocities, some insurance companies modify this standard and incorporate such limits. Other mechanical piping standards impose limits on velocity because of concerns over noise and pipe erosion. These concerns are not relevant in fire protection pipe systems because water is not normally flowing through them. Automatic sprinkler systems only operate during a fire or during testing.

NFPA 13 does not require individual detailed calculations using the Hazen-Williams formula for individual pipe segments. As an alternative, friction loss tables or internal hydraulic calculations that are part of a software program are usually used to establish the friction loss. These tables and programs provide a set of accurate friction loss values for a combination of pipe types and flows, all of which are based on the Hazen-Williams formula.

14.4.2.1.1 Pipe friction losses shall be determined on the basis of the Hazen-Williams formula, as follows:

$$p = \frac{4.52Q^{1.85}}{C^{1.85}d^{4.87}}$$

where:

p = frictional resistance in psi per foot of pipe

Q = flow in gpm

C = friction loss coefficient

d = actual internal diameter of pipe in inches

14.4.2.1.2 For SI units, the following equation shall be used:

$$p_m = 6.05\left(\frac{Q_m^{1.85}}{C^{1.85}d_m^{4.87}}\right)10^5$$

where:

p_m = frictional resistance in bar per meter of pipe

Q_m = flow in L/min

C = friction loss coefficient

d_m = actual internal diameter in mm

 14.4.2.2 Velocity Pressure Formula. Velocity pressure shall be determined on the basis of the following formula:

$$P_v = \frac{0.001123Q^2}{D^4}$$

where:

P_v = velocity pressure in psi (SI: 1 psi = 0.0689 bar)

Q = flow in gpm (SI: 1 gal = 3.785 L)

D = inside diameter in inches (SI: 1 in. = 25.4 mm)

 The velocity pressure, which is addressed in 14.4.2.2, is a measure of the energy required to keep the water in a pipe in motion and is necessary for certain hydraulic calculations (see 14.4.4.7.2). The velocity pressure always acts in the direction of waterflow. The basic formula for velocity pressure is as follows:

$$P_v = \left(\frac{V^2}{2g}\right)0.433 \text{ psi/ft}$$

where:

P_v = velocity pressure in psi

V = velocity in ft/sec

g = 32.2 ft/sec^2 (Earth's gravitational constant)

By substituting Q/A for V in the previous formula and using proper units, the more usable formula that appears in the text is found. In this approach, Q is the volumetric flow rate ft^3/sec, and A is the cross-sectional area (ft^2) of the pipe.

 14.4.2.3 Normal Pressure Formula. Normal pressure (P_n) shall be determined on the basis of the following formula:

$$P_n = P_t - P_v$$

where:

P_n = normal pressure

P_t = total pressure in psi (bar)

P_v = velocity pressure in psi (bar)

The normal pressure, which is addressed in 14.4.2.3, is the pressure acting against, or perpendicular to, the pipe wall. Therefore, the normal pressure usually acts perpendicular to the velocity pressure, because the general direction of waterflow is parallel to the pipe wall. When no flow occurs, the velocity pressure is zero, and the normal pressure is equal to the total pressure. See Exhibits 14.1 and 14.2, which illustrate velocity and normal pressures when water flows through a pipe.

EXHIBIT 14.1 *Velocity and Normal Pressures.*

EXHIBIT 14.2 Normal Pressure Is Responsible for Flow from Sprinklers Where Additional Flow Is Downstream of the Operating Sprinkler.

NFPA 13 allows the user to choose between two methods of hydraulic calculations—the total pressure method and the velocity pressure method. Hydraulic calculations of sprinkler systems using the total pressure method (P_t) are the most common. Use of the total pressure method simplifies the calculations and, in most cases, builds a safety factor into the calculations because the assumption is made that the total pressure is responsible for pushing the water out of the pipe through the sprinkler. This assumption is somewhat conservative because it is the normal pressure that is really responsible for pushing the water out of the pipe. The normal pressure is always less than the total pressure. By using a higher pressure to calculate the flow, the demand is overestimated, creating a safety factor.

The two places where the normal pressure does not apply are at the last sprinkler on the branch line and the last branch line on a cross main. In these places, the total pressure should be used to calculate the discharge because the velocity pressure and the normal pressure will be acting in the same direction, adding up to the total pressure. When using the normal pressure method of calculations, the user must be careful that all of the sprinklers have sufficient flow. Due to the additional safety factors built into the total pressure method of calculations, no additional considerations are necessary when using this calculation method for fire sprinkler systems.

NFPA 15, *Standard for Water Spray Fixed Systems for Fire Protection,* requires the use of the normal pressure method of hydraulic calculations because of the possibility of long runs of small diameter pipe to the end nozzle. These long runs cause a greater than acceptable disparity between the flow predicted by the total pressure method and the flow predicted by the normal pressure method. Because sprinkler systems do not generally have long runs of small diameter pipe to the end sprinkler, the same concerns are not shared by the Technical Committee on Sprinkler System Installation Criteria.

See the commentary after 14.4.4.4.6 for more information on the effect of velocity pressure and normal pressure on the discharge from an open sprinkler.

14.4.2.4 Hydraulic Junction Points.

14.4.2.4.1 Pressures at hydraulic junction points shall balance within 0.5 psi (0.03 bar).

14.4.2.4.2 The highest pressure at the junction point, and the total flows as adjusted, shall be carried into the calculations.

Calculations for loops and grids need to be done using an iterative technique in which an assumption is made and a series of calculations are made to test the assumption (see 14.4.2.4.1 and 14.4.2.4.2). If the calculated value is the same as the assumed value, the assumption is correct. Due to the number of significant figures used in the calculations and the method of rounding, getting exactly the same number between the assumed value and the calculation is not always possible. Therefore, a value needs to be selected to let the user know how close is close enough to continue with the calculations.

The value of 0.5 psi (0.03 bar) was selected because it provides a reasonable degree of accuracy for balancing at hydraulic junction points. Most computer programs can easily obtain this value without an excessive number of iterations. By requiring a balance at the hydraulic junction points, the designer will be assured that an excess system demand is not concealed in the calculations. Several software programs have the capability to carry the balance to four significant digits. The use of four significant digits does not necessarily mean that the design is better but, rather, that the computer can do a faster calculation with more significant digits to the right of the decimal point.

 14.4.2.4.3 Pressure balancing shall be permitted through the use of a K-factor developed for branch lines or portions of systems using $K_p=Q/(p)^{0.5}$.

Pressure balancing, which is addressed in 14.4.2.4.3, is the act of adjusting demand flows when calculations for different portions of the system require different pressures at the same point. Since there can only be one pressure at any point, the highest of all the demands needs to be provided. Once the higher pressure is provided, greater flows than necessary will go to the other portions of the system. The balancing procedure calculates and accounts for these higher flows.

The formula shown in 14.4.2.4.3 is a simplification of the true physics involved. A more accurate K-factor for the portion of the system can be determined without respect to the elevation changes in the system. However, such a calculation technique would be difficult to perform by hand, so the simplified formula is allowed. Many of the computer programs on the market perform this balancing feature using the more precise method and discounting the elevation changes in establishing a K-factor. These computer programs produce more accurate results than hand calculations due to this feature.

14.4.3 Equivalent Pipe Lengths of Valves and Fittings.

14.4.3.1 Pipe and Fittings.

14.4.3.1.1 Table 14.4.3.1.1 shall be used to determine the equivalent length of pipe for fittings and devices unless manufacturer's test data indicate that other factors are appropriate.

The fitting and valve losses shown in Table 14.4.3.1.1 are experimentally derived values that have been rounded to a whole number for convenience. The exception is the swing check valve, in which several makes of valves were averaged to produce the numbers in the table. Where possible, the designer should use the friction loss value for the specific check valve that is to be installed. This information can usually be obtained from the manufacturer.

TABLE 14.4.3.1.1 *Equivalent Schedule 40 Steel Pipe Length Chart*

Fittings and Valves	Fittings and Valves Expressed in Equivalent Feet of Pipe														
	½ in.	¾ in.	1 in.	1¼ in.	1½ in.	2 in.	2½ in.	3 in.	3½ in.	4 in.	5 in.	6 in.	8 in.	10 in.	12 in.
45° elbow	—	1	1	1	2	2	3	3	3	4	5	7	9	11	13
90° standard elbow	1	2	2	3	4	5	6	7	8	10	12	14	18	22	27
90° long-turn elbow	0.5	1	2	2	2	3	4	5	5	6	8	9	13	16	18
Tee or cross (flow turned 90°)	3	4	5	6	8	10	12	15	17	20	25	30	35	50	60
Butterfly valve	—	—	—	—	—	6	7	10	—	12	9	10	12	19	21
Gate valve	—	—	—	—	—	1	1	1	1	2	2	3	4	5	6
Swing check*	—	—	5	7	9	11	14	16	19	22	27	32	45	55	65

For SI units, 1 in. = 25.4 mm; 1 ft = 0.3048 m.

Note: Information on ½-in. pipe is included in this table only because it is allowed under 8.14.19.3 and 8.14.19.4.

*Due to the variation in design of swing check valves, the pipe equivalents indicated in this table are considered average.

Where valves or fittings that are not in Table 14.4.3.1.1 are used in the system, the user must account for the friction loss by obtaining the equivalent length from the manufacturer or by obtaining the actual friction loss at the specific flow. This figure needs to be included in the calculations.

Some specially listed 1-in. (25.4-mm) saddle-type fittings have a friction loss equivalent to 21 ft (6.4 m) of pipe as opposed to the 5 ft (1.5 m) shown in Table 14.4.3.1.1. This difference in friction loss is another case in which the listing information for a given product is of utmost importance. Ignoring this increased loss would introduce an appreciable error into the calculations.

To make the equivalent pipe length table even more accurate, the modification formula shown in 14.4.3.1.3.1 is intended to account for the difference in the internal diameter between Schedule 40 pipe and other pipe types.

Values for ½-in. (12.7-mm) and ¾-in. (19-mm) pipe appear in Table 14.4.3.1.1 because when hydraulic and pipe schedule systems are redesigned or modified, 8.14.19.3 and 8.14.19.4 allow the use of pipe nipples up to 4 in. (102 mm) in length with a pipe diameter smaller than 1 in. (25.4 mm) under certain conditions.

14.4.3.1.2 For saddle-type fittings having friction loss greater than that shown in Table 14.4.3.1.1, the increased friction loss shall be included in hydraulic calculations.

14.4.3.1.3 Equivalent Feet Modifier.

14.4.3.1.3.1 For internal pipe diameters different from Schedule 40 steel pipe, the equivalent feet shown in Table 14.4.3.1.1 shall be multiplied by a factor derived from the following formula:

$$\left(\frac{\text{Actual inside diameter}}{\text{Schedule 40 steel pipe diameter}}\right)^{4.87} = \text{Factor}$$

14.4.3.1.3.2 The factor thus obtained shall be further modified as required by Table 14.4.3.1.1. This table shall apply to other types of pipe listed in Table 14.4.3.1.1 only where modified by factors from 14.4.3.1.1 and 14.4.3.2.

14.4.3.2 C-Factors. Table 14.4.3.1.1 shall be used with a Hazen-Williams *C* factor of 120 only. For other values of *C*, the values in Table 14.4.3.1.1 shall be multiplied by the factors indicated in Table 14.4.3.2.

TABLE 14.4.3.2 C *Value Multiplier*

Value of *C*	100	130	140	150
Multiplying factor	0.713	1.16	1.33	1.51

Note: These factors are based upon the friction loss through the fitting being independent of the *C* factor available to the piping.

C-factors are discussed in 14.4.3.2. The method of hydraulic calculations used for sprinkler systems mathematically represents the friction loss for a valve or fitting as an extra length of pipe. This assumed extra length of pipe is referred to as the fitting's or valve's *equivalent length*. In an effort to make the calculations easier, the equivalent length of pipe is added to the actual length of pipe attached to the fitting. To correctly add the equivalent pipe length to the actual pipe length, the two pipes need to be of the same material, with the same internal diameter, and the same *C* factor.

Table 14.4.3.1.1 contains equivalent lengths for various types of fittings and valves for Schedule 40 pipe with a *C* factor of 120. Where other types of pipe are used, the length of pipe to create the same amount of friction will be different. The formula in 14.4.3.1.3.1 is used to adjust for different pipe diameter (other schedules of pipe), and 14.4.3.2, including the table, is used to adjust for differing *C* factors.

The following example illustrates the effect of differing C factors. The base formula for friction loss through a given length of pipe using the Hazen-Williams approach is as follows:

$$p_f = L \times \frac{4.52Q^{1.85}}{(C^{1.85})(d^{4.87})}$$

where:

P_f = friction loss in psi

L = length in ft

(The other factors are as described in the commentary on 14.4.2.1.)

The example illustrates why an adjustment is needed and considers a 2-in., Schedule 40, 10-ft length of steel pipe with a C factor of 100 when 135 gpm is flowing through the pipe. The actual internal diameter of the pipe must be used. Tables A.6.3.2 and A.6.3.5 provide information in this regard.

When the C factor is 100, the friction loss is as follows:

$$p_{f(100)} = 10\left[\frac{4.52(135^{1.85})}{(100^{1.85})(2.067^{4.87})}\right] = 2.7 \text{ psi}$$

From Table 14.4.3.2, the multiplier for pipe having a C value of 100 is 0.713. The correction to the friction loss value is as follows:

$$p_{f(100)} = 2.7 \text{ psi} \times 0.713 = 1.9 \text{ psi}$$

When the C factor is 120, the friction loss is as follows:

$$p_{f(100)} = 10\left[\frac{4.52(135^{1.85})}{(120^{1.85})(2.067^{4.87})}\right] = 1.9 \text{ psi}$$

Therefore, the values from Table 14.4.3.1.1 need to be adjusted accordingly when C factors of other than 120 are used.

Another example specifically considers the adjustment needed for a fitting. Determine the equivalent length of a 1¼-in. (31.8-mm) 90-degree elbow used in a system employing Schedule 10 steel pipe on a dry pipe system.

In Step 1, determine the internal diameter of Schedule 10 and Schedule 40 steel pipe. From Table A.6.3.2, Schedule 10 is 1.442 in. (36.6 mm) and Schedule 40 is 1.380 in. (35.1 mm).

In Step 2, derive the factor using the following equation (see also 8.4.3.1.3):

$$factor = \left(\frac{1.442 \text{ in.}}{1.380 \text{ in.}}\right)^{4.87} = 1.2387$$

In Step 3, establish the equivalent length of a 1¼-in., Schedule 10, 90-degree elbow with a C value of 120. Multiply the equivalent length obtained from Table 14.4.3.1.1 for a 1¼-in., Schedule 40, 90-degree elbow by the factor determined in Step 2, as follows: 3 ft × 1.2387 = 3.716 ft (1.13 m)

In Step 4, make a final adjustment for the different C factor for a dry pipe system. From Table 14.4.4.5, the C value for a dry system using black steel is 100. From Table 14.4.3.2, the multiplier for pipe with a C value of 100 is 0.713. Therefore, the equivalent length of a 1¼-in. 90-degree elbow used in a system employing Schedule 10 steel pipe on a dry pipe system is as follows: 0.713 × 3.716 = 2.6495 ft.

14.4.3.3 Valves. Specific friction loss values or equivalent pipe lengths for alarm valves, dry pipe valves, deluge valves, strainers, and other devices shall be made available to the authority having jurisdiction.

14.4.3.4 Differing Values. Specific friction loss values or equivalent pipe lengths for listed fittings not in Table 6.4.1 shall be used in hydraulic calculations where these losses or equivalent pipe lengths are different from those shown in Table 14.4.3.1.1.

Differing values are addressed in 14.4.3.4. A number of special fittings that are listed for various pipe types are available on the market. These fittings often have friction loss characteristics that are different than the values given in Table 14.4.3.1.1. Although these fittings tend to facilitate the installation of a system, they do come with a pressure penalty that must be accounted for in the hydraulic calculations. As indicated in 14.1.3, the working plans are required to include manufacturer's instructions and information on these specially listed fittings.

14.4.4* Calculation Procedure.

A.14.4.4 See Figure A.14.4.4.

Details on how to properly calculate the water demand of a sprinkler system are provided in 14.4.4. The various concepts and equations described throughout Chapters 11, 12, and 14 to hydraulically design a system are tied together in 14.4.4.

The concepts in Chapters 11, 12, and 13 are used to determine the amount of water each sprinkler will need to discharge, the pressure necessary to achieve this flow, the number of sprinklers to calculate, the duration of the water supply, and the existence and demand of hose connections. Hydraulic calculations are then typically done by starting with the flow and pressure demand at the most hydraulically demanding single point in the system, which is usually

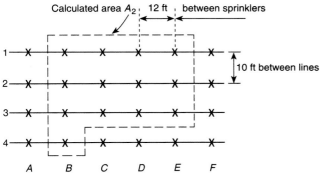

Notes:
1. For gridded systems, the extra sprinkler (or sprinklers) on branch line 4 can be placed in any adjacent location from *B* to *E* at the designer's option.
2. For tree and looped systems, the extra sprinkler on line 4 should be placed closest to the cross main.

Assume a remote area of 1500 ft^2 with sprinkler coverage of 120 ft^2

Total sprinklers to calculate $= \dfrac{\text{Design area}}{\text{Area per sprinkler}}$

$= \dfrac{1500}{120} = 12.5$, calculate 13

Number of sprinklers on branch line $= \dfrac{1.2\sqrt{A}}{S}$

Where:
A = design area
S = distance between sprinklers on branch line

Number of sprinklers on branch line $= \dfrac{1.2\sqrt{1500}}{12} = 3.87$

For SI units, 1 ft = 0.3048 m; 1 ft^2 = 0.0929 m^2.

FIGURE A.14.4.4 *Example of Determining the Number of Sprinklers to Be Calculated.*

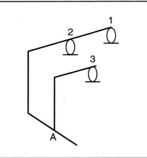

EXHIBIT 14.3 *Branch Line Schematic.*

the most distant sprinkler from the water supply. Working back towards the water supply, pressure losses and additional flows are added to determine the total water demand.

At some points within a system, the waterflow will split and travel in two or more directions. This flow split happens on cross mains with multiple branch lines, at connections to lines supplying in-rack sprinklers, and at connections to hose stations. When this type of flow split occurs, the demand for each leg of the split needs to be calculated independently. Because only one pressure reading can exist at a single point in the system, the more demanding pressure reading is used at the point of separation. Therefore, the flow through the line that requires less pressure needs to be adjusted to the higher pressure. This adjustment results in a greater waterflow because the greater the amount of pressure, the greater the amount of flow when all other variables remain unchanged. The adjustment is accomplished using a combined K-factor as shown in the following example and as permitted by 14.4.2.4.3 (see commentary for 14.4.2.4.3).

For example, consider the portion of a sprinkler system shown in Exhibit 14.3. The flow through sprinklers 1 and 2 is calculated on the first branch line and the flow through sprinkler 3 is calculated on the second branch line. Hydraulic calculations for the first branch at point A indicate a demand of 37 gpm at 15 psi. This includes discharge through sprinklers 1 and 2 and the associated pressure and elevation losses. Hydraulic calculations for the second branch line when sprinkler 3 is operating indicate a demand of 18 gpm (68.1 L/min) at 12 psi (0.8 bar) at point B. Because only one pressure can exist at point A, the higher pressure of 15 psi (1.0 bar) will need to be provided so that the proper discharge from sprinklers 1 and 2 is obtained. Supplying a pressure of 12 psi (0.8 bar) will result in less than 37 gpm (140.1 L/min) through the first branch line. At point A, 15 psi (1.0 bar) will create a waterflow in excess of 18 gpm (68.1 L/min) through the second branch line to sprinkler 3. The increased flow can be calculated by determining a K-factor at point A using the demand information of 18 gpm at 12 psi and rearranging the formula $Q = K\sqrt{P}$ to solve for K. This equation yields a K-factor of 5.2, as follows:

$$(18 \text{ gpm}) \div \sqrt{12} \text{ psi}$$

The K-factor is used to determine the flow at sprinkler 3 if the pressure is increased to 15 psi with the formula $Q = K\sqrt{P}$. In this case, $Q = 5.2\sqrt{15} = 20$ gpm. The total demand at point A becomes 57 gpm (37 + 20) at 15 psi.

Calculations at the point of connection of the line that supplies in-rack sprinklers are done as indicated in the preceding example. At the point of connection to the ceiling sprinkler system, the two demands are evaluated with the higher pressure demand selected and the flow at the lower demand adjusted to the higher pressure. For some specific storage commodities stored in racks, the protection criteria do not require the in-rack sprinkler water demand to be added to the ceiling system demand. One example includes combustible liquids in plastic containers protected in accordance with NFPA 30, *Flammable and Combustible Liquids Code*. The protection criteria for this commodity employ ceiling sprinklers, in-rack sprinklers, and solid barriers throughout the rack. In this circumstance, only the most demanding flow from among the ceiling system and in-rack lines needs to be met.

Hose connections to sprinkler systems that are a part of a standpipe system required to meet NFPA 14, *Standard for the Installation of Standpipe, Private Hydrant, and Hose Systems,* also may need to be adjusted as described in the previous example. The requirements of NFPA 14 for combined systems provide more information on this piping arrangement.

Hose connections to sprinkler systems that are not a part of a standpipe system, such as those installed for first aid in warehouses, are not required to follow the adjustments described in the previous example. Instead, the flow demand is added to the sprinkler demand at the point of connection using the pressure available in the system at that point. In effect, no minimum pressure requirement exists for hose connections that are not part of a standpipe system.

Figure A.14.4.4 illustrates how to determine the number of sprinklers in the gridded system's area of operation and how to determine the number of sprinklers on each branch line in the area of operation. To apply to a tree or loop system to this figure, the branch line would terminate at the last sprinkler on the right in the calculated area, and the cross main would be to the left. Also, Note 1 only applies to gridded systems. The extra sprinkler on branch line 4 would have to be *B* for tree and loop systems, because it is closest to the supply and would be the hydraulically most demanding on that branch line.

14.4.4.1* For all systems the design area shall be the hydraulically most demanding based on the criteria of Chapter 11, Chapter 12, or the special design approaches in accordance with the requirements of Chapter 13.

The last portion of the text of 14.4.4.1 recognizes that the use of specially listed sprinklers or alternative design approaches can result in some design areas that are not rectangular. In a design involving listed residential sprinklers, the design area of operation can be a perfect square.

A.14.4.4.1 See Figure A.14.4.4.1(a) and Figure A.14.4.4.1(b).

A

1 This sprinkler is not in the selected area of operation.

FIGURE A.14.4.4.1(a) *Example of Hydraulically Most Demanding Area.*

System *A* in Figure A.14.4.4.1(a) shows the design area for 12 sprinklers with three branch lines and four sprinklers per branch line. Systems *B* and *C* indicate the location of the extra sprinkler on the fourth branch line.

System *D* illustrates the situation described in 14.4.4.1.1.3.

System *E* illustrates that sprinklers on both sides of the cross main can be required to fulfill the required design area and the $1.2\sqrt{A}$ restriction on the branch line sprinklers.

Figure A.14.4.4.1(b) illustrates the design area for looped systems with various riser locations and branch line configurations.

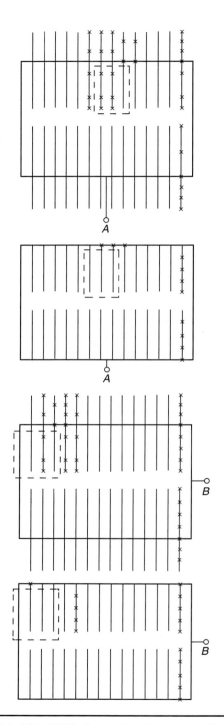

FIGURE A.14.4.4.1(b) *Example of Hydraulically Most Demanding Area.*

14.4.4.1.1 Density-Area Method.

14.4.4.1.1.1 Where the design is based on the density-area method, the design area shall be a rectangular area having a dimension parallel to the branch lines at least 1.2 times the square root of the area of sprinkler operation *(A)* used, which shall permit the inclusion of sprinklers on both sides of the cross main.

14.4.4.1.1.2 Any fractional sprinkler shall be carried to the next higher whole sprinkler.

14.4.4.1.1.3 In systems having branch lines with an insufficient number of sprinklers to fulfill the 1.2 requirement, the design area shall be extended to include sprinklers on adjacent branch lines supplied by the same cross main.

The 1966 edition of NFPA 13 was the first to include a chapter that dealt with hydraulic calculations. The following sentence is from that edition: "The design area shall be the hydraulically most remote area and shall include all sprinklers on both sides of the cross main." This sentence meant that if the system shown in Figure A.14.3.2(b) were to be calculated, the 10 sprinklers on the end of the system (five on each side of the cross main) plus two on the next line would be calculated.

However, under certain conditions, such as where sprinklers were spaced 13 ft (3.96 m) apart on a branch line and the branch lines were spaced 10 ft (3.05 m) apart and where the design area included 12 sprinklers, some designers were calculating three sprinklers on the line (3 × 13 ft = 39 ft) over four branch lines (4 × 10 ft = 40 ft). This approach resulted in a design area that was almost a perfect square. The square shape for the design area would be inadequate if four sprinklers operated on the branch line. Therefore, the requirement that the area of operation take the shape of a rectangle with the length of the longer side having a dimension of $1.2 \sqrt{A}$ was eventually added.

Gridded systems, along with the mention of a square-shaped design area, first appeared in the 1975 edition of NFPA 13 as follows: "For gridded systems, the design area shall be the hydraulically most remote area which approaches a square." This approach was adopted because it did not seem logical to calculate all of the sprinklers on one line of a grid, which had been done on tree systems since 1966.

In later editions of NFPA 13, the characteristic square design area was changed to represent a rectangular area. The rectangle must have its longer side at least 1.2 times greater in length than its shorter side. The rectangle must be longer in the dimension parallel to the branch lines because this arrangement accounts for the possibility that a fire could spread in this direction and open multiple sprinklers on a single branch line before opening sprinklers on other branch lines. To require a smaller number of individual branch lines to flow more water through them is hydraulically more demanding than to require the same demand to be supplied by more branch lines with fewer sprinklers operating on them. Obviously, a worst-case scenario would be to make the designer calculate all of the sprinklers on the remote branch line. However, at a certain point in time the fire is much more likely to spread to areas under adjacent branch lines than to spread entirely under one branch line. Part of the rationale behind design areas is an attempt to predict where heat from a fire will travel. To provide an even greater factor of safety, some insurance companies require the longer side of the design area to have a dimension of $1.4 \sqrt{A}$. This more conservative approach, however, is not considered necessary by NFPA 13.

The number of sprinklers to be calculated in the design area can be calculated using the area of coverage for the sprinklers in the design area. For example, with a design area of 1500 ft^2 and an area of coverage of 130 ft^2 per sprinkler, the total number of sprinklers to be considered in the design area is 1500 ft^2 divided by 130 ft^2, which gives a total of 12 sprinklers (the actual number of 11.5 needs to rounded up to the next whole number).

The number of sprinklers along a branch line can be determined by dividing the length of the design area's longer side by the spacing of the sprinklers along the branch line. For example, with a design area of 1500 ft^2 and a sprinkler spacing of 13 ft along the branch lines and

10 ft between branch lines, the number of sprinklers along the branch line is four—that is, $(1.2\sqrt{1500})/13$. With a total of 12 sprinklers to be considered and four sprinklers required per branch line, a total of three branch lines must be considered in the design area—that is, 12 divided by 4 equals 3. This technique applies only where all sprinklers are uniformly spaced.

When determining the total number of sprinklers in the design area and along a branch line, the proper geometric area for system design, which is selected from the curves in Chapters 11 and 12 or the design criteria in Chapter 13, must be verified. Additionally, the number of sprinklers to be calculated must also be verified against the geometry of the design area. This requirement is frequently misinterpreted and misapplied. This situation usually arises when sprinklers are not symmetrically spaced and when they are not spaced exactly at one-half the allowable distance from the wall. In actuality, a large percentage of sprinkler systems falls into this situation.

Exhibit 14.4 illustrates one example of how the design area can incorrectly be calculated to an area less than that selected from Chapter 11. The area of coverage for the sprinklers in Exhibit 14.4 appears to be 104 ft² ($A_s = S \times L$ = 13 ft × 8 ft). Sprinklers labeled E, F, H, and I are covering this actual area. However, sprinklers labeled A, B, C, D, and G are covering a physical area of something less than 104 ft² because of their position adjacent to the walls. The actual areas of coverage for sprinklers A, B, C, D, and G are 80.5 ft² (11.5 ft × 7 ft), 91 ft² (7 ft × 13 ft), 91 ft² (7 ft × 13 ft), 92 ft² (11.5 ft × 8 ft), and 92 ft² (11.5 ft × 8 ft), respectively. If the determination of the total number of sprinklers is based on 104 ft², the actual design area will be less than 1500 ft², which is only permitted under certain conditions as specified in Chapter 11. To provide the required design area of 1500 ft², additional sprinklers must be included, which will increase the overall system demand in terms of flow and pressure.

The requirements of 14.4.4.1.1.3 were added in 1980 for clarification and are illustrated by System D in Figure A.14.4.4.1(a). Note that the design area's longer dimension is along the cross main.

In all cases shown in Figure A.14.4.4.1(a), the area of sprinkler operation becomes a unit of measurement defined by the number of sprinklers rather than by a unit of length such as feet or meters. Because fractional parts of a sprinkler cannot operate, the conventional rules for rounding off numbers do not apply and the numbers are always rounded up. Thus, if the

EXHIBIT 14.4 Sprinkler Spacing.

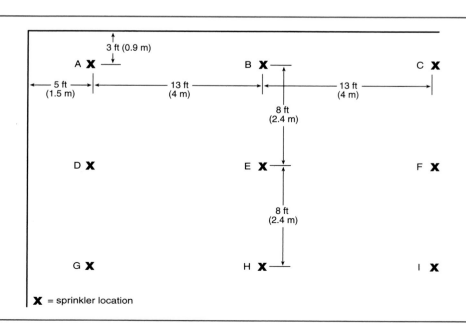

application of the rectangular area rule results in the need to calculate 5.07 sprinklers on a branch line, six sprinklers must be included.

14.4.4.1.2 Room Design Method. Where the design is based on the room design method, the calculation shall be based on the room and communicating space, if any, that is hydraulically the most demanding. *(See 11.2.3.3.)*

The use of the room design method, which is addressed in 14.4.4.1.2, is popular in highly compartmented occupancies. In effect, this method predicts that the number of sprinklers that will open during a fire is all of the sprinklers in the room or compartment. If the openings from the room to other spaces are not protected as required by 11.2.3.3, then additional sprinklers are accounted for in these adjoining spaces.

   Users must remember when utilizing the room design method that a corridor is a room. In many compartmented occupancies (like guest room areas of hotels) the corridor will be the most demanding room. In this case, Chapter 11 does not require that all of the sprinklers in the corridor be considered as opening during a fire. The probability that so many sprinklers would open in a long narrow line with water spraying in the corridor is so remote that the decision has been made to limit the number of sprinklers in this design to five (if doors to the corridor are protected) or seven (if doors are not protected). See 11.2.3.3.6, 11.2.3.3.7, and 11.2.3.3.8. These numbers holds true for both wet pipe and dry pipe systems.

14.4.4.2* Gridded Systems.

A.14.4.4.2 See Figure A.14.4.4.2.

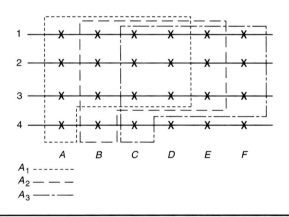

FIGURE A.14.4.4.2 *Example of Determining the Most Remote Area for a Gridded System.*

Gridded systems are covered in 14.4.4.2. In the 1975 edition of NFPA 13, the shape of the design area for a gridded system was shown as a square area located along the far cross main (not the supply cross main). However, this configuration did not necessarily represent the hydraulically most demanding area. Because of the complexity of the flow in a gridded system and the bidirectional flows that often occur within the same branch line, the hydraulically most demanding area is not readily obvious.

   To determine the appropriate design area, 14.4.4.2 requires that an initial design area be selected and that two additional areas be considered on either side of the initially selected area. This approach results in three separate design areas that overlap each other as illustrated in Figure A.14.4.4.2. A_2 represents the initially chosen design area. Hydraulic calculations for each of the three design areas are required in order to determine which is the most demanding area. If the initially chosen area (A_2) is determined not to be the most demanding, then an additional area (A_4) adjacent to the area with the highest demand of the three (either A_1 or A_3) needs to be calculated to verify that A_4 is not more demanding. This technique is typically referred to as peaking the system.

Hydraulic calculations for a gridded system verify the hydraulically most demanding area and determine the system demand. These calculations are very tedious and time consuming. Conducting the calculations with a hydraulics computer program is most economical.

14.4.4.2.1 For gridded systems, the designer shall verify that the hydraulically most demanding area is being used.

14.4.4.2.2 A minimum of two additional sets of calculations shall be submitted to demonstrate peaking of demand area friction loss when compared to areas immediately adjacent on either side along the same branch lines, unless the requirements of 14.4.4.2.3 are met.

14.4.4.2.3 Computer programs that show the peaking of the demand area friction loss shall be acceptable based on a single set of calculations.

14.4.4.3 Design Densities.

14.4.4.3.1 System piping shall be hydraulically designed using design densities and areas of operation in accordance with 11.2.3.2 or Chapter 12 as required for the occupancies or hazards involved.

14.4.4.3.2* The density shall be calculated on the basis of floor area of sprinkler operation.

A.14.4.4.3.2 See Figure A.14.4.4.3.2.

FIGURE A.14.4.4.3.2 Sprinkler Design Area.

14.4.4.3.3 The area covered by any sprinkler used in hydraulic design and calculations shall be the horizontal distances measured between the sprinklers on the branch line and between the branch lines in accordance with 8.5.2.

Paragraphs 14.4.4.3.2 and 14.4.4.3.3 have been in NFPA 13 for several years and were originally two sentences in a single paragraph. In writing the 2002 edition, these two sentences were broken out into separate paragraphs. Although there are two separate sentences here, they really need to be enforced together since they both apply to cases in which the sprinklers are installed under a sloping roof or ceiling. Under sloped ceilings, where the design area on the floor is 1500 ft[2] (139 m[2]), the area projected along the ceiling will be larger than this depending on the slope of the ceiling, and the additional sprinklers in this area need to be accounted for in the sprinkler system calculations.

When evaluating remote area requirements for sprinkler systems installed under sloping roofs or ceilings, the actual horizontal floor area calculated must be equal to or greater than the required remote area.

The area of coverage per sprinkler for spacing and density purposes is based on the area of coverage of the sprinkler as determined by 8.5.2.1—that is, along branch lines and between branch lines. Even though the branch line adjacent to the wall in Figure A.14.4.4.3.2 is only 2 ft (0.62 m) from the wall, the L dimension is considered to be 12 ft (3.72 m). Similarly, the last sprinkler on this branch line is also 2 ft (0.62 m) from the wall. However, the S dimension is considered to be 10 ft (3.1 m). Therefore, the area of coverage of sprinklers in this figure is 120 ft^2 (11.1 m^2) [10 ft × 12 ft (3.1 m × 3.72 m)].

Where small rooms as defined in 3.3.20 are considered, the area of sprinkler coverage is defined as the area of the room divided by the number of sprinklers in that room. See 8.6.2.1.2 and 8.6.3.2.4 for additional information regarding small rooms.

The piping layout of many systems are not as uniform as the one illustrated in Figure A.14.4.4.3.2. Due to building features, sprinkler placement and piping layouts can take on a more varied arrangement. This varied arrangement can result in differing areas of coverage for sprinklers in the design area and requires evaluation of several portions of a system to determine the hydraulically most demanding area so that the system demand is properly determined. Once the area of coverage per sprinkler and the appropriate dimensions for S and L are determined, other sprinklers are not required to be uniformly spaced in this arrangement. However, any other sprinkler layout that results in a greater hydraulic demand will need to be calculated separately to verify that it will work.

14.4.4.3.4* Where sprinklers are installed above and below a ceiling or in a case where more than two areas are supplied from a common set of branch lines, the branch lines and supplies shall be calculated to supply the largest water demand.

A.14.4.4.3.4 This subsection assumes a ceiling constructed so as to reasonably ensure that a fire on one side of the ceiling will operate sprinklers on one side only. Where a ceiling is sufficiently open, or of such construction that operation of sprinklers above and below the ceiling can be anticipated, the operation of such additional sprinklers should be considered in the calculations.

14.4.4.4* Design Area Sprinklers.

A.14.4.4.4 When it is not obvious by comparison that the design selected is the hydraulically most remote, additional calculations should be submitted. The most distant area is not necessarily the hydraulically most remote.

Paragraph A.14.4.4.4 warns that the most remote area is not necessarily the hydraulically most demanding and that a hydraulic evaluation would be necessary to verify the location of the area. Figures A.14.4.4.1(a) and A.14.4.4.1(b) provide examples of the location and the shape of the hydraulically most demanding areas for tree and looped systems. These examples illustrate uniform piping and sprinkler layouts in a space assumed to have the same occupancy classification throughout. However, in many situations, the system layout is not so uniform, more than one occupancy hazard exists, and the hydraulically most demanding area is not so obvious.

Occupancy hazard classification, piping configuration, and sprinkler spacing are factors that must be considered when determining the location of the design area. Exhibit 14.5 illustrates a building that has three different operations and hazards in it. Even though the office space, which is a light hazard occupancy, is the furthest from the riser, it may not represent the hydraulically most demanding area. The space used for the storage of finished product up to 14 ft (4.27 m) in height needs to be protected for the appropriate commodity classification in accordance with Chapter 12. The flow-coating operation is considered an extra-hazard (Group 2) occupancy. An evaluation of areas in each of the three spaces is needed to verify the most demanding area.

◀ FAQ
When determining the remote area for a sprinkler system installed under sloping roofs or ceilings, is the remote area measured along the slope or on the floor?

EXHIBIT 14.5 Building Containing Various Operations and Fire Hazards.

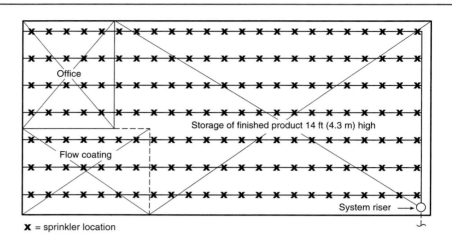

X = sprinkler location

The difficulties associated with determining the hydraulically most demanding area for gridded systems are addressed in 14.4.4.2.

14.4.4.4.1 Each sprinkler in the design area and the remainder of the hydraulically designed system shall discharge at a flow rate at least equal to the stipulated minimum water application rate (density) multiplied by the area of sprinkler operation.

14.4.4.4.2 The requirements of 14.4.4.4.1 to include every sprinkler in the design area to be included in the system discharge shall not apply and where the area of application is equal to or greater than the minimum allowable area of Figure 11.2.3.1.5 for the appropriate hazard classification (including a 30 percent increase for dry pipe systems), sprinkler discharge in closets, washrooms, and similar small compartments requiring only one sprinkler shall be permitted to be omitted from hydraulic calculations within the area of application. Sprinklers in these small compartments shall, however, be capable of discharging minimum densities in accordance with Figure 11.2.3.1.5.

The intent of 14.4.4.4.2 is to allow sprinklers in small spaces (compartments) to be considered as not open (closed) during a fire in the area around that compartment. In order to use this rule, the area of operation for calculations must be at least 1500 ft^2 (139 m^2) for wet pipe systems in light and ordinary hazard occupancies and at least 2500 ft^2 (232 m^2) for wet pipe systems in extra hazard occupancies. For dry pipe systems, the area of operation for calculations must be at least 1950 ft^2 (181 m^2) for light and ordinary hazard and at least 3250 ft^2 (302 m^2) for extra hazard occupancies.

If quick response sprinklers are used in a wet pipe system in a light or ordinary hazard system and the design area is decreased below 1500 ft^2 (139 m^2), the sprinklers in the small compartments are not allowed to be considered closed. In other words, this rule is not allowed to be applied because the design area falls below the minimum stated in the density/area Figure 11.2.3.1.5.

In most cases when the room design method is utilized, the area of operation is usually below 1500 ft^2 (139 m^2). Since the area is less than the minimum, this rule cannot be applied when using the room design option.

In order to use this rule, these spaces (compartments) are to be of a size that only one sprinkler is required to protect them. The sprinkler within the small compartment must be verified as capable of producing the appropriate discharge density as identified in Figure 11.2.3.1.5. The intent of this provision is to prevent designers from falsely minimizing system demands by omitting sprinkler discharge from the compartments addressed by this rule.

It is compelling to note the types of areas described in this rule. Small compartments are intended not only to be physically small but also to contain a relatively small fuel load. For example, the size of a small office, because of its size, can require only one sprinkler. However, this rule is not intended to apply to small offices because the anticipated fuel load is greater than that expected in closets and washrooms.

In compartmented areas, such as the small spaces just described, the simultaneous operation of all of the sprinklers in the design area is unlikely. On the other hand, the sprinklers in the foyer, closet, and bathroom of a hotel room could all operate in response to a fire in the bedroom.

The intent of this rule is not to eliminate the rooms that constitute the primary occupancy of a building or space from the calculations. If sprinklers in these spaces are not included in the calculations, the proper water demand will not be determined and can cause unfavorable sprinkler system performance. The sprinkler discharge in small compartments can be omitted from the calculations, but the design area needs to include the square footage of the small compartments.

Small compartments, such as bathrooms, closets, or foyers in hotels, can be protected with small-orifice sprinklers—that is, those with nominal K-factors less than 5.6 (K_M less than 80)—even though the sprinklers in the bedrooms and hallways have a nominal K-factor of 5.6 (K_M of 80) or more. See 14.4.4.6.2.

◀ FAQ
Is it the intent of 14.4.4.4.2 to omit sprinklers in all areas protected by one sprinkler only?

14.4.4.4.3 The requirements of 14.4.4.4.1 to include every sprinkler in the design area to be included in the system discharge shall not apply and where spray sprinklers and large drop sprinklers are provided above and below obstructions such as wide ducts or tables, the water supply for one of the levels of sprinklers shall be permitted to be omitted from the hydraulic ceiling design calculations within the area of application.

The basic idea of hydraulic calculations is to account for all of the sprinklers that might open in case of a fire (including reasonable safety factors). When spray sprinklers or large drop sprinklers (specific application sprinklers), which are covered in 14.4.4.4.3, are being used and sprinklers are installed both above and below obstructions, it is unlikely that the sprinklers above and below the obstructions are all going to open. Rather than force the user to calculate both sets of sprinklers simultaneously, the user is directed to prove the most demanding situation with calculations. In most cases, this will be the ceiling sprinklers unless significant quantities of sprinklers are installed under obstructions with long runs of relatively small diameter pipe.

The presence of a permanent or temporary obstruction, such as an overhead garage door, is treated in a similar manner to a ceiling configuration that requires sprinklers above and below it where spray sprinklers and large drop sprinklers are installed.

◀ FAQ
When calculating a sprinkler system utilizing spray sprinklers or large drop (specific application sprinklers), are additional sprinklers required to be added to the system demand where additional sprinklers are installed to address obstructions?

14.4.4.4.4 The requirements of 14.4.4.4.1 to include every sprinkler in the design area to be included in the system discharge shall not apply, and where ESFR sprinklers are installed above and below obstructions, the discharge for up to two sprinklers from one of the levels shall be included with those of the other level in the hydraulic calculation.

The basic idea of hydraulic calculations is to account for all of the sprinklers that might open in case of a fire (including reasonable safety factors). Unlike spray sprinklers or large drop sprinklers (covered by 14.4.4.4.3 above), ESFR sprinklers, which are covered in 14.4.4.4.4, at the ceiling might also activate even when the sprinklers below obstructions activate. This tendency is due to the extremely sensitive nature of the ESFR sprinkler's link or bulb.

To account for the additional sprinklers that might open, an additional two sprinklers need to be included in the calculation where additional sprinklers are positioned around obstructions. Additionally, due to the orifice size of ESFR sprinklers, this is a significant flow of water that must be accounted for in the total system demand.

When calculating an ESFR sprinkler system, are additional sprinklers required to be added to the system demand where additional sprinklers are installed to address obstructions?
◀ FAQ

14.4.4.4.5 Calculations shall begin at the hydraulically most remote sprinkler.

14.4.4.4.6 The calculated pressure at each sprinkler shall be used to determine the discharge flow rate for that particular sprinkler.

When applying velocity pressure, sometimes the discharge from the second sprinkler from the end of the branch line is less than the discharge from the end sprinkler. To correct this deficiency, either the pipe sizing should be changed or the end sprinkler discharge should be slightly increased.

Paragraph 14.4.4.4.6 requires that the discharge from each sprinkler in the design area be calculated based on the pressure acting at that sprinkler. The intent of this statement is to prevent the calculation of the discharge from each sprinkler in the design area based on the discharge from the most remote sprinkler by manipulating the density/area requirements. For instance, if the hydraulically most demanding sprinkler produces a flow of 20.8 gpm (847 L/min) based on its area of coverage and design density, it is not correct to assume that the remaining sprinklers in the design area will also flow at 20.8 gpm (847 L/min). When water flows through a piping network, pressure changes result throughout the system due to friction, turbulence, and elevation changes. Therefore, the pressures acting at each sprinkler in the design area can vary, resulting in different amounts of flow at each sprinkler. These pressure changes must be accounted for, thereby increasing the complexity of the hydraulic calculations.

Paragraph 14.4.4.4.2 allows the sprinkler discharge in certain small compartments to be omitted from the hydraulic calculations if specific conditions are met. These conditions include a requirement for the design area to be equal to or greater than the minimum allowable area identified in Figure 11.2.3.1.5 for the appropriate hazard. This limitation includes the area increase for dry pipe systems.

14.4.4.5 Friction Loss. Pipe friction loss shall be calculated in accordance with the Hazen-Williams formula with *C* values from Table 14.4.4.5, as follows:

(1) Include pipe, fittings, and devices such as valves, meters, flow switches in pipes 2 in. or less in size, and strainers, and calculate elevation changes that affect the sprinkler discharge.
(2) Tie-in drain piping shall not be included in the hydraulic calculations.
(3) Calculate the loss for a tee or a cross where flow direction change occurs based on the equivalent pipe length of the piping segment in which the fitting is included.
(4) The tee at the top of a riser nipple shall be included in the branch line, the tee at the base of a riser nipple shall be included in the riser nipple, and the tee or cross at a cross main-feed main junction shall be included in the cross main.
(5) Do not include fitting loss for straight-through flow in a tee or cross.
(6) Calculate the loss of reducing elbows based on the equivalent feet value of the smallest outlet.
(7) Use the equivalent feet value for the standard elbow on any abrupt 90-degree turn, such as the screw-type pattern.

TABLE 14.4.4.5 *Hazen-Williams* C *Values*

Pipe or Tube	C Value*
Unlined cast or ductile iron	100
Black steel (dry systems including preaction)	100
Black steel (wet systems including deluge)	120
Galvanized (all)	120
Plastic (listed) all	150
Cement-lined cast or ductile iron	140
Copper tube or stainless steel	150
Asbestos cement	140
Concrete	140

*The authority having jurisdiction is permitted to consider other *C* values.

(8) Use the equivalent feet value for the long-turn elbow on any sweeping 90-degree turn, such as a flanged, welded, or mechanical joint-elbow type. *(See Table 14.4.3.1.1.)*

(9) Friction loss shall be excluded for the fitting directly connected to a sprinkler.

(10) Losses through a pressure-reducing valve shall be included based on the normal inlet pressure condition. Pressure loss data from the manufacturer's literature shall be used.

With regard to 14.4.4.5(1), water flowing through a pipe, a fitting, or any other attachment, such as a valve or strainer, results in a pressure loss due to friction and turbulent flow. In the 2002 edition, the friction loss for paddle type flow switches in small pipe was added to this list since most designers were forgetting about this source of friction loss and not accounting for it. In larger pipes (greater than 2 in.) the paddle has less of an effect on the friction loss and can be ignored.

Additionally, changes in elevation also cause pressure changes because the force of gravity either acts against or aids waterflow. Therefore, the type of pipe, any devices attached to the pipe, and changes in elevation must be accounted for in the hydraulic calculations. However, NFPA 13 does allow certain devices to be excluded because their effects are incorporated into other parts of the system—for example, the fitting addressed in 14.4.4.5(9).

With regard to 14.4.4.5(4), the evaluation of the waterflow from the supply to the last branch line in the system is illustrated in Exhibit 14.6. Tee A is included with the 1½-in. (38.1-mm) starting piece. Tee B is included with the 2-in. (50.8-mm) riser nipple. Tees C, D, and E are not included because the flow is straight through them. Tee F is included with the 3-in. (76.2-mm) piece of cross main.

With regard to 14.4.4.5(9), on branch lines with upright or pendent sprinklers screwed into the line tee, the fitting losses associated with the line tee are excluded from the calculations because it is assumed that one fitting is included in the approval tests of a sprinkler. The presence of this fitting is accounted for by the sprinkler's K-factor.

In cases where sprinklers are installed on sprigs or drops, the reducing coupling at the sprinkler is ignored, but the tee on the branch line must be included. In this situation, a new K-factor for the entire assembly, which includes the tee fitting, the sprig or drop, and the sprinkler, could be determined. This K-factor allows individual calculations to be simplified for each junction between the branch line and the sprig.

◀ **FAQ**
**Is it required to account
for friction loss caused by
paddle type flow switches?**

*EXHIBIT 14.6 Typical
Sprinkler System Used in
Making Sample Calculations.*

With regard to 14.4.4.5(10), pressure-reducing devices would be installed where system pressures are in excess of the system component's pressure rating. Many components are limited to a maximum working pressure of 175 psi (12.1 bar). These devices act to intentionally reduce the available pressure so that system components will not be damaged by high pressures. The manufacturer's instructions must be closely followed to establish the correct outlet pressure and flow parameters.

NFPA 13 requires the use of the Hazen-Williams formula when determining friction losses—that is, pressure changes between pipe segments. (Refer to 14.4.2.1.1 for the formula.) One variable in this formula is represented by the letter C. This variable, often referred to as the C value, is a coefficient that reflects the roughness of the internal surface of the piping material. The lower the C value, the rougher the inner surface of the pipe material.

C values for steel and iron pipe materials tend to decrease with time due to the buildup of scale and the effects of corrosion. The values shown in Table 14.4.4.5 include C values for aged pipe. If pipe could remain in its original condition after installation, the C factors would be somewhat higher than those shown in Commentary Table 14.1. A comparison between new pipe C factors and the design C factors required by NFPA 13 is shown in Commentary Table 14.1. For ferrous and cement-lined products, an adjustment is applied to compensate for the aging process of the pipe.

COMMENTARY TABLE 14.1 Comparison of C Values for New Pipe

Pipe Type	C New	C Design	Upscale Factor (%)
Steel (welded or seamless)	140	120*	16
Unlined and ductile iron	130	100*	23
Plastic	150	150*	0
Copper	150	150*	0
Cement-lined cast iron	150	140*	7

*Wet pipe system.

Factors that can affect the C value for a particular piece of pipe include the pipe's manufacturing process, the rate of pipe corrosion, and the buildup of scale and other materials that decrease the inside diameter of the pipe. The synergistic effect of these contributing factors is accounted for by reducing the pipe's C value.

Pipe manufacturing techniques do not usually produce a perfectly round piece of pipe, and some inherent imperfections exist. However, these imperfections are usually very subtle and cannot be detected without taking precise measurements.

Corrosion of ferrous materials is very difficult, if not impossible, to prevent in sprinkler systems. Degradation of pipe in this manner can actually cause a slight increase in the internal diameter of the pipe. However, the effects of corrosion should not be considered as having a positive effect on system performance. Corrosion causes the internal surface of the pipe to become much rougher, thus increasing the associated pressure loss due to friction.

Tuberculation of pipe is a function of the naturally occurring elements and chemicals added to the water supply by the water purveyor. These waterborne chemicals can fall out over time and cause buildups on the internal portions of the pipe network. The result is a rougher internal pipe surface and a smaller internal diameter. Exhibit 14.7 illustrates a pipe that has experienced tuberculation.

If the Darcy-Weisbach method of calculations is going to be used as an alternative to Hazen-Williams or in conformance with NFPA 11, *Standard for Low-, Medium-, and High-Expansion Foam,* and NFPA 16, *Standard for the Installation of Foam-Water Sprinkler and Foam-Water Spray Systems,* standardized values for degradation of the pipe's interior condition will need to be determined and appropriate safety factors applied.

EXHIBIT 14.7 *Tuberculated Pipe.*

Table 14.4.4.5 includes the types of materials that are commonly used in the design and installation of sprinkler systems. If the water quality is poor and the pipe deteriorates faster than would be expected in most water supplies, further adjustments to the *C* value should then be made. Commentary Table 14.1 identifies the adjustments (safety factors) used for a particular type of pipe material. Because plastic and copper piping materials do not experience the same effects as ferrous pipe, their *C* values are not adjusted.

14.4.4.6* Orifice Plates.

A.14.4.4.6 The use of sprinklers with differing orifice sizes in situations where different protection areas are needed is not considered balancing. An example would be a room that could be protected with sprinklers having different orifice size in closet, foyer, and room areas. However, this procedure introduces difficulties when restoring a system to service after operation since it is not always clear which sprinklers go where.

14.4.4.6.1 Unless the requirements of 14.4.4.6.2 or 14.4.4.6.3 are met, orifice plates or sprinklers of different orifice sizes shall not be used for balancing the system.

14.4.4.6.2 Sprinklers with different orifice sizes shall be acceptable for special use such as exposure protection, small rooms or enclosures, or directional discharge. *(See 3.3.20 for definition of small rooms.)*

14.4.4.6.3 Extended-coverage sprinklers with a different orifice size shall be acceptable for part of the protection area where installed in accordance with their listing.

Orifice plates are prohibited because they can be removed while modifying a system and not be reinstalled. This removal would invalidate the hydraulic calculations supporting the initial system design. Also, if installed in a horizontal run of pipe, orifice plates are subject to the accumulation of debris on the surface facing the direction of waterflow. This accumulation would further impact the hydraulics as well as affect proper system drainage.

In general, the use of sprinklers with differing orifice sizes is prohibited. The concern is that if sprinklers with various orifice sizes are used and if some of those sprinklers have to be replaced at a future date, a sprinkler with a differing orifice size might be installed.

Paragraphs 14.4.4.6.2 and 14.4.4.6.3 recognize the following:

1. Certain arrangements can require a reduced sprinkler discharge; thus, a sprinkler with a smaller orifice is permitted.
2. The use of extended coverage sprinklers with a different orifice size than the other sprinklers in the room can be needed to provide proper coverage of a space.

An example of where 14.4.4.6.3 applies is illustrated in Exhibit 14.8. The center portions of the room can be protected with extended coverage sprinklers that have a nominal K-factor of 8. However, the space under the 3-ft (0.91-m) wide soffit also needs to be protected. Because the areas under the soffits are so small, 14.4.4.6.3 permits the use of a smaller orifice sprinkler.

◀ **FAQ**
Why are orifice plates prohibited by 14.4.4.6.1?

◀ **FAQ**
Why are sprinklers of differing office sizes prohibited for balancing by 14.4.4.6.1?

◀ **FAQ**
Where can sprinklers of differing orifice sizes be utilized?

14.4.4.7* Pressures.

A.14.4.4.7 Where the normal pressure (P_n) is used to calculate the flow from an orifice, the following assumptions should be used:

(1) At any flowing outlet along a pipe, except the end outlet, only the normal pressure (P_n) can act on the outlet. At the end outlet the total pressure (P_t) can act. The following should be considered end outlets:
   (a) The last flowing sprinkler on a dead-end branch line
   (b) The last flowing branch line on a dead-end cross main
   (c) Any sprinkler where a flow split occurs on a gridded branch line
   (d) Any branch line where a flow split occurs on a looped system

EXHIBIT 14.8 Sprinkler Layout Using Multiple-Orifice Approach.

Standard spray sprinkler ○ Extended coverage sprinkler EC

(2) At any flowing outlet along a pipe, except the end outlet, the pressure acting to cause flow from the outlet is equal to the total pressure (P_t) minus the velocity pressure (P_v) on the upstream (supply) side.

(3) To find the normal pressure (P_n) at any flowing outlet, except the end outlet, assume a flow from the outlet in question and determine the velocity pressure (P_v) for the total flow on the upstream side. Because normal pressure (P_n) equals total pressure (P_t) minus velocity pressure (P_v), the value of the normal pressure (P_n) so found should result in an outlet flow approximately equal to the assumed flow; if not, a new value should be assumed, and the calculations should be repeated.

14.4.4.7.1 When calculating flow from an orifice, the total pressure (P_t) shall be used, unless the calculation method of 14.4.4.7.2 is utilized.

14.4.4.7.2 Use of the normal pressure (P_n) calculated by subtracting the velocity pressure from the total pressure shall be permitted. Where the normal pressure is used, it shall be used on all branch lines and cross mains where applicable.

The total pressure, which is addressed in 14.4.4.7.1 and 14.4.4.7.2, acts on the remote outlet at the point where the flow enters the outlet from opposing directions. Velocity pressure is usually small compared to the total pressure and normally does not have a major impact on the outcome of the hydraulic calculation.

14.4.4.7.3 Flow from a sprinkler shall be calculated using the nominal K-factor.

14.4.4.8 Minimum Operating Pressure.

14.4.4.8.1 Minimum operating pressure of any sprinkler shall be 7 psi (0.5 bar).

14.4.4.8.2 Where a higher minimum operating pressure for the desired application is specified in the listing of the sprinkler, this higher pressure shall be required.

When sprinklers are submitted to testing laboratories for examination and listing, they are subjected to water distribution and fire tests (see 14.4.4.8.1 and 14.4.4.8.2). These tests are conducted at a minimum flow of 15 gpm (57 L/min) per sprinkler. The pressure required to produce this flow through sprinklers with a nominal K-factor of 5.6 is approximately 7 psi

(0.5 bar), as illustrated in the equation that follows. The requirement recognizes that specially listed sprinklers might have minimum operating pressures greater than 7 psi (0.5 bar). In some cases, the minimum operating pressure can be as high as 75 psi (1.93 bar).

$$p = \frac{Q^2}{K^2} = \frac{15^2}{5.6^2} = 7.17 \text{ psi}$$

In recent years, some sprinklers were listed with operating pressures less than 7 psi (0.5 bar). NFPA 13 no longer permits such pressures. The concern was that, at these lower pressures, sprinklers that had been installed for an extended period of time would not operate properly. These lower pressures' ability to blow off the orifice cap on activation of the operating element was uncertain. Additional concerns were that sprinklers operating at pressures less than 7 psi (0.5 bar) could produce unsuitable discharge patterns.

14.4.4.9 Maximum Operating Pressure. For extra hazard occupancies, palletized, solid-pile, in bin box, on shelf storage, the maximum operating pressure of any sprinkler shall be 175 psi.

The requirements for a maximum operating pressure, which are given in 14.4.4.9, were added in the 2002 edition of NFPA 13. In extra hazard occupancies or higher challenge fire risks, excessive discharge pressures may adversely impact the effectiveness of sprinkler discharge in these high-challenge fire conditions.

◀ **FAQ**
Why does NFPA 13 limit the maximum pressure to 175 psi?

14.5 Pipe Schedules

Pipe schedules shall not be used, except in existing systems and in new systems or extensions to existing systems described in Chapter 11. Water supplies shall conform to 11.2.2.

Pipe schedules are covered in Section 14.5. As noted in 11.2.2, the use of pipe schedule design approaches is restricted to rather small systems, unless relatively high residual pressures are available. Although the pipe schedule approach has previously served as an acceptable design option for a wider range of operations and fire hazards, its misuse has resulted in its restricted application.

14.5.1* General.

A.14.5.1 The demonstrated effectiveness of pipe schedule systems is limited to their use with ½-in. (13-mm) orifice sprinklers. The use of other size orifices can require hydraulic calculations to prove their ability to deliver the required amount of water within the available water supply.

14.5.1.1 The pipe schedule sizing provisions shall not apply to hydraulically calculated systems.

14.5.1.2 Sprinkler systems having sprinklers with K-factors other than 5.6 nominal, listed piping material other than that covered in Table 6.3.1.1, extra hazard Groups 1 and 2 systems, and exposure protection systems shall be hydraulically calculated.

The numbers of sprinklers shown in the pipe schedule tables are maximum numbers for the minimum size pipes shown (see 14.5.1.2). The graduated type of system—that is, larger pipe serving increasingly smaller pipe—is not mandatory as long as the minimum pipe sizes established in the pipe schedule tables are met.

14.5.1.3 The number of automatic sprinklers on a given pipe size on one floor shall not exceed the number given in 14.5.2, 14.5.3, or 14.5.4 for a given occupancy.

The number of sprinklers per branch line is limited (see 14.5.2.1, 14.5.3.1, and A.14.5.4) on pipe schedule systems, and, prior to 1966, the number of branch lines on a cross main was limited to 14 (see 14.5.1.3). These rules do not apply to hydraulically designed systems.

14.5.1.4* Size of Risers. Each system riser shall be sized to supply all sprinklers on the riser on any one floor as determined by the standard schedules of pipe sizes in 14.5.2, 14.5.3, or 14.5.4.

A.14.5.1.4 Where the construction or conditions introduce unusually long runs of pipe or many angles in risers or feed or cross mains, an increase in pipe size over that called for in the schedules can be required to compensate for increased friction losses.

14.5.1.5 Slatted Floors, Large Floor Openings, Mezzanines, and Large Platforms. Buildings having slatted floors or large unprotected floor openings without approved stops shall be treated as one area with reference to pipe sizes, and the feed mains or risers shall be of the size required for the total number of sprinklers.

Fire spreads readily through grated or slatted floors, which are discussed in 14.5.1.5. Therefore, an area with such divisions must be treated as a single fire area when sizing pipe.

14.5.1.6 Stair Towers. Stairs, towers, or other construction with incomplete floors, if piped on independent risers, shall be treated as one area with reference to pipe sizes.

Stair towers are covered in 14.5.1.6. A fire in a stair or tower can open a large number of sprinklers in that area. An independent riser supplying such an area must be sized to supply all the sprinklers in the area.

14.5.2 Schedule for Light Hazard Occupancies.

14.5.2.1 Branch Lines.

14.5.2.1.1 Unless permitted by 14.5.2.1.2 or 14.5.2.1.3, branch lines shall not exceed eight sprinklers on either side of a cross main.

14.5.2.1.2 Where more than eight sprinklers on a branch line are necessary, lines shall be permitted to be increased to nine sprinklers by making the two end lengths 1 in. (25.4 mm) and 1¼ in. (33 mm), respectively, and the sizes thereafter standard.

14.5.2.1.3 Ten sprinklers shall be permitted to be placed on a branch line, making the two end lengths 1 in. (25.4 mm) and 1¼ in. (33 mm), respectively, and feeding the tenth sprinkler by a 2½-in. (64-mm) pipe.

The amount of pressure lost to friction in long runs of small-diameter pipe is significant. To ensure that pressure is not excessively reduced, the number of sprinklers on a branch line is limited to eight sprinklers in light hazard occupancies. Paragraph 14.5.2.1.3 allows up to 10 sprinklers on branch lines in light hazard occupancies, provided that pipe sizing is increased to reduce the pressure drop along the run of pipe.

14.5.2.2 Pipe Sizes.

14.5.2.2.1 Pipe sizes shall be in accordance with Table 14.5.2.2.1.

A system riser in a light hazard occupancy is limited to the protection area of 52,000 ft^2 (4831 m^2). Piping is sized in accordance with Table 14.5.2.2.1, unless more than 100 sprinklers are in an area without subdividing partitions. Piping supplying such sprinklers must be sized in accordance with 14.5.2.4 to minimize the friction loss.

14.5.2.2.2 Each area requiring more sprinklers than the number specified for 3½-in. (89-mm) pipe in Table 14.5.2.2.1 and without subdividing partitions (not necessarily fire walls) shall be supplied by mains or risers sized for ordinary hazard occupancies.

14.5.2.3 Where sprinklers are installed above and below ceilings in accordance with Figure 14.5.2.3(a) through Figure 14.5.2.3(c), and such sprinklers are supplied from a common set of branch lines or separate branch lines from a common cross main, such branch lines shall not

TABLE 14.5.2.2.1 *Light Hazard Pipe Schedules*

Steel		Copper	
1 in.	2 sprinklers	1 in.	2 sprinklers
1¼ in.	3 sprinklers	1¼ in.	3 sprinklers
1½ in.	5 sprinklers	1½ in.	5 sprinklers
2 in.	10 sprinklers	2 in.	12 sprinklers
2½ in.	30 sprinklers	2½ in.	40 sprinklers
3 in.	60 sprinklers	3 in.	65 sprinklers
3½ in.	100 sprinklers	3½ in.	115 sprinklers
4 in.	See Section 8.2	4 in.	See Section 8.2

For SI units, 1 in. = 25.4 mm.

exceed eight sprinklers above and eight sprinklers below any ceiling on either side of the cross main.

The intent of the committee is that a ceiling separate the two areas. The requirements of 14.5.2.3 do not require a rated assembly.

14.5.2.4 Unless the requirements of 14.5.2.5 are met, pipe sizing up to and including 2½ in. (64 mm) shall be as shown in Table 14.5.2.4 utilizing the greatest number of sprinklers to be found on any two adjacent levels.

◄ **FAQ**
Is the ceiling, as referenced in 14.5.2.3, required to be a rated assembly (i.e., 1-hour, 2-hour, etc.)?

2 in. 2 in.   2 in. 1½ in.   1½ in. 1½ in.   1¼ in. 1¼ in.   1 in. 1 in.

For SI units, 1 in. = 25.4 mm.

FIGURE 14.5.2.3(a) *Arrangement of Branch Lines Supplying Sprinklers Above and Below a Ceiling.*

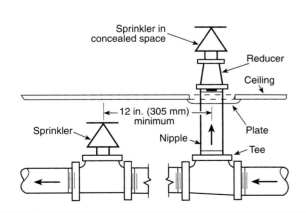

FIGURE 14.5.2.3(b) *Sprinkler on Riser Nipple from Branch Line in Lower Fire Area.*

FIGURE 14.5.2.3(c) *Arrangement of Branch Lines Supplying Sprinklers Above, in Between, and Below Ceilings.*

TABLE 14.5.2.4 *Number of Sprinklers Above and Below a Ceiling*

Steel		Copper	
1 in.	2 sprinklers	1 in.	2 sprinklers
1¼ in.	4 sprinklers	1¼ in.	4 sprinklers
1½ in.	7 sprinklers	1½ in.	7 sprinklers
2 in.	15 sprinklers	2 in.	18 sprinklers
2½ in.	50 sprinklers	2½ in.	65 sprinklers

For SI units, 1 in. = 25.4 mm.

14.5.2.5 Branch lines and cross mains supplying sprinklers installed entirely above or entirely below ceilings shall be sized in accordance with Table 14.5.2.2.1.

A fire either above or below a ceiling in a light hazard occupancy will normally be contained in that area by operating sprinklers (see 14.5.2.5). In light hazard pipe schedule systems, NFPA 13 permits more sprinklers on a branch line in the above or below configuration than are permitted on a branch line protecting a single area. NFPA 13 also permits more total sprinklers to be supplied by a given pipe size. When determining if sprinkler protection is needed above the ceiling, 8.14.1.2 should be consulted.

The requirement recognizes that piping dedicated to a given area—that is, above a ceiling or below a ceiling—can be sized to accommodate the sprinklers for that area only.

14.5.2.6* Where the total number of sprinklers above and below a ceiling exceeds the number specified in Table 14.5.2.2.1 for 2½-in. (64-mm) pipe, the pipe supplying such sprinklers shall be increased to 3 in. (76 mm) and sized thereafter according to the schedule shown in Table 14.5.2.2.1 for the number of sprinklers above or below a ceiling, whichever is larger.

A.14.5.2.6 For example, a 2½-in. (64-mm) steel pipe, which is permitted to supply 30 sprinklers, can supply a total of 50 sprinklers where not more than 30 sprinklers are above or below a ceiling.

The probability of a fire involving the areas both above and below a ceiling in a light hazard occupancy and opening in excess of 50 sprinklers is extremely remote. When sizing piping for systems with more than 50 sprinklers, the pipe diameter is increased to 3 in. (76 mm) in 14.5.2.6 to reduce friction loss.

14.5.3 Schedule for Ordinary Hazard Occupancies.

14.5.3.1 Unless permitted by 14.5.3.2 or 14.5.3.3, branch lines shall not exceed eight sprinklers on either side of a cross main.

14.5.3.2 Where more than eight sprinklers on a branch line are necessary, lines shall be permitted to be increased to nine sprinklers by making the two end lengths 1 in. (25.4 mm) and 1¼ in. (33 mm), respectively, and the sizes thereafter standard.

14.5.3.3 Ten sprinklers shall be permitted to be placed on a branch line, making the two end lengths 1 in. (25.4 mm) and 1¼ in. (33 mm), respectively, and feeding the tenth sprinkler by a 2½-in. (64-mm) pipe.

14.5.3.4 Pipe sizes shall be in accordance with Table 14.5.3.4.

14.5.3.5 Where the distance between sprinklers on the branch line exceeds 12 ft (3.7 m) or the distance between the branch lines exceeds 12 ft (3.7 m), the number of sprinklers for a given pipe size shall be in accordance with Table 14.5.3.5.

The requirement in 14.5.3.5 recognizes the increased friction loss when either the distance between sprinklers on branch lines or the distance between branch lines exceeds 12 ft (3.7 m). The requirement also recognizes that the sprinkler's area of coverage needs to reach or over-

TABLE 14.5.3.4 *Ordinary Hazard Pipe Schedule*

Steel		Copper	
1 in.	2 sprinklers	1 in.	2 sprinklers
1¼ in.	3 sprinklers	1¼ in.	3 sprinklers
1½ in.	5 sprinklers	1½ in.	5 sprinklers
2 in.	10 sprinklers	2 in.	12 sprinklers
2½ in.	20 sprinklers	2½ in.	25 sprinklers
3 in.	40 sprinklers	3 in.	45 sprinklers
3½ in.	65 sprinklers	3½ in.	75 sprinklers
4 in.	100 sprinklers	4 in.	115 sprinklers
5 in.	160 sprinklers	5 in.	180 sprinklers
6 in.	275 sprinklers	6 in.	300 sprinklers
8 in.	See Section 8.2	8 in.	See Section 8.2

For SI units, 1 in. = 25.4 mm.

TABLE 14.5.3.5 *Number of Sprinklers—Greater than 12-ft (3.7-m) Separations*

Steel		Copper	
2½ in.	15 sprinklers	2½ in	20 sprinklers
3 in.	30 sprinklers	3 in.	35 sprinklers
3½ in.	60 sprinklers	3½ in.	65 sprinklers

For SI units, 1 in. = 25.4 mm.
Note: For other pipe and tube sizes, see Table 14.5.3.4.

lap any adjacent sprinkler's area of coverage so that a uniform water discharge and density are achieved. Increasing the pipe sizing as required reduces pressure losses due to friction and results in a greater amount of pressure at the sprinkler. The higher pressure increases sprinkler discharge and improves water distribution.

The pipe sizes specified in Table 14.5.3.4 take into consideration normal water supplies and friction loss. The pipe sizes tend to be somewhat smaller for branch lines and somewhat larger for cross mains, feed mains, and system risers when compared to hydraulically designed systems.

14.5.3.6 Where sprinklers are installed above and below ceilings and such sprinklers are supplied from a common set of branch lines or separate branch lines supplied by a common cross main, such branch lines shall not exceed eight sprinklers above and eight sprinklers below any ceiling on either side of the cross main.

14.5.3.7 Pipe sizing up to and including 3 in. (76 mm) shall be as shown in Table 14.5.3.7 in accordance with Figure 14.5.2.3(a), Figure 14.5.2.3(b), and Figure 14.5.2.3(c) utilizing the greatest number of sprinklers to be found on any two adjacent levels.

14.5.3.8 Branch lines and cross mains supplying sprinklers installed entirely above or entirely below ceilings shall be sized in accordance with Table 14.5.3.4 or Table 14.5.3.5.

A fire either above or below a ceiling in an ordinary hazard occupancy will normally be contained in that area by operating sprinklers (see 14.5.3.8). In ordinary hazard pipe schedule systems, NFPA 13 permits more sprinklers on a branch line in the above or below configuration than are permitted on a branch line protecting a single area. NFPA 13 also permits more total sprinklers to be supplied by a given pipe size. When determining if sprinkler protection is needed above the ceiling, 8.14.1.2 should be consulted.

TABLE 14.5.3.7 Number of Sprinklers Above and Below a Ceiling

Steel		Copper	
1 in.	2 sprinklers	1 in.	2 sprinklers
1¼ in.	4 sprinklers	1¼ in.	4 sprinklers
1½ in.	7 sprinklers	1½ in.	7 sprinklers
2 in.	15 sprinklers	2 in.	18 sprinklers
2½ in.	30 sprinklers	2½ in.	40 sprinklers
3 in.	60 sprinklers	3 in.	65 sprinklers

For SI units, 1 in. = 25.4 mm.

14.5.3.9* Where the total number of sprinklers above and below a ceiling exceeds the number specified in Table 14.5.3.7 for 3-in. (76-mm) pipe, the pipe supplying such sprinklers shall be increased to 3½ in. (89 mm) and sized thereafter according to the schedule shown in Table 14.5.2.2.1 or Table 14.5.3.4 for the number of sprinklers above or below a ceiling, whichever is larger.

A.14.5.3.9 For example, a 3-in. (76-mm) steel pipe, which is permitted to supply 40 sprinklers in an ordinary hazard area, can supply a total of 60 sprinklers where not more than 40 sprinklers protect the occupied space below the ceiling.

14.5.3.10 Where the distance between the sprinklers protecting the occupied area exceeds 12 ft (3.7 m) or the distance between the branch lines exceeds 12 ft (3.7 m), the branch lines shall be sized in accordance with either Table 14.5.3.5, taking into consideration the sprinklers protecting the occupied area only, or 14.5.3.7, whichever requires the greater size of pipe.

The probability of a fire involving the areas both above and below a ceiling in an ordinary hazard occupancy and opening in excess of 60 sprinklers is extremely remote (see 14.5.3.10). When sizing piping or tubing for systems with more than 60 sprinklers with steel pipe and more than 65 sprinklers with copper tubing, the pipe or tubing diameter is increased to reduce friction loss.

14.5.4* Extra Hazard Occupancies. Extra hazard occupancies shall be hydraulically calculated.

A.14.5.4 The piping schedule shown in Table A.14.5.4 is reprinted only as a guide for existing systems. New systems for extra hazard occupancies should be hydraulically calculated as required in 14.5.4.

TABLE A.14.5.4 Extra Hazard Pipe Schedule

Steel		Copper	
1 in.	1 sprinklers	1 in.	1 sprinklers
1¼ in.	2 sprinklers	1¼ in.	2 sprinklers
1½ in.	5 sprinklers	1½ in.	5 sprinklers
2 in.	8 sprinklers	2 in.	8 sprinklers
2½ in.	15 sprinklers	2½ in.	20 sprinklers
3 in.	27 sprinklers	3 in.	30 sprinklers
3½ in.	40 sprinklers	3½ in.	45 sprinklers
4 in.	55 sprinklers	4 in.	65 sprinklers
5 in.	90 sprinklers	5 in.	100 sprinklers
6 in.	150 sprinklers	6 in.	170 sprinklers

For SI units, 1 in. = 25.4 mm.

Extra hazard occupancies are covered in 14.5.4. A set of pipe schedule design tables and flow values for extra hazard occupancies were provided in NFPA 13 until 1991. Since then, concern about pipe schedule systems intended to protect facilities with fire hazards that are likely to operate a large number of sprinklers has placed a restriction on the pipe schedule method for extra hazard occupancies. Because many existing pipe schedule systems are currently in place, the selection table for extra hazard occupancies has been retained in Annex A and appears as Table A.14.5.4.

14.6 Deluge Systems

Open sprinkler and deluge systems shall be hydraulically calculated according to applicable standards.

Pipe schedule systems are designed with a safety margin that presumes that only some of the sprinklers will operate in a fire. In open and deluge systems, which are covered in Section 14.6, water discharges from all sprinklers, including those outside the fire area. Therefore, the system must be specifically designed to provide the density of coverage required to suppress or control the fire over the entire protected area.

14.7* Exposure Systems

Exposure sprinklers shall be hydraulically calculated using Table 14.7 and a relative classification of exposures guide number.

Table 14.7 *Exposure Protection*

		Section A—Window Sprinklers				
		Window Sprinkler Orifice Size		*Discharge Coefficient*	*Flow Rate*	*Application Rate Over 25 ft of Window*
Guide Number	*Level of Window Sprinkler*	*in.*	*mm*	*(K-factor)*	*(Q) (gpm)*	*Area (gpm/ft²)*
1.50 or less	Top 2 levels	⅜	9.5	2.8	7.4	0.30
	Next lower 2 levels	5/16	7.9	1.9	5.0	0.20
	Next lower 2 levels	¼	6.4	1.4	3.7	0.15
1.51–2.20	Top 2 levels	½	12.7	5.6	14.8	0.59
	Next lower 2 levels	7/16	11.1	4.2	11.1	0.44
	Next lower 2 levels	⅜	9.5	2.8	7.4	0.30
2.21–13.15	Top 2 levels	⅝	15.9	11.2	29.6	1.18
	Next lower 2 levels	17/32	13.5	8.0	21.2	0.85
	Next lower 2 levels	½	12.7	5.6	14.8	0.59

	Section B—Cornice Sprinklers		
	Cornice Sprinkler Orifice Size		*Application Rate per*
Guide Number	*in.*	*mm*	*Lineal Foot (gpm)*
1.50 or less	⅜	9.5	0.75
1.51–2.20	½	12.7	1.50
2.21–13.15	⅝	15.9	3.00

For SI units, 1 in. = 25.4 mm; 1 gpm = 3.785 L/min; 1 gpm/ft² = 40.76 mm/min.

A.14.7 In the design of an exposure protection system, the flow rate from window and cornice sprinklers is shown in Table 14.7. The flow rates are based on the guide numbers selected from Table 4.3.7.3 of NFPA 80A, *Recommended Practice for Protection of Buildings from Exterior Fire Exposures.*

Section A of the table is for window sprinklers. The orifice size is selected according to the level on which the sprinkler is located. Section B of the table is for cornice sprinklers.

Recognizing that sprinkler systems for exposure protection require a unique design approach, included in Table 14.7 are the techniques to be followed. An analysis of the level of exposure protection needed for an adjacent structure must be completed. This study includes an evaluation of the building construction materials used and the area and height of the exposing structure. The resultant guide number is based on the values derived from NFPA 80A, *Recommended Practice for Protection of Buildings from Exterior Fire Exposures.*

14.8 In-Rack Sprinklers

14.8.1 Pipes to in-rack sprinklers shall be sized by hydraulic calculations.

14.8.2 Water demand of sprinklers installed in racks shall be added to ceiling sprinkler water demand over the same protected area at the point of connection.

The flow and pressure demand associated with in-rack sprinklers must be hydraulically balanced to the higher pressure in the same manner that is required for branch lines on opposite sides of a cross main (see 14.8.2). There are multiple acceptable locations for the point of connection, from the cross main directly over the racks to the system riser manifold. The separate water demands are still balanced even at a remote point of connection. See commentary to A.14.4.4.

14.8.3 The demand shall be balanced to the higher pressure.

SUMMARY

Chapter 14 provides the necessary information to calculate the hydraulic demand of a sprinkler system and to verify that the system's overall hydraulic layout complies with NFPA 13.

REFERENCES CITED IN COMMENTARY

National Fire Protection Association, 1 Batterymarch Park, P.O. Box 9101, Quincy, MA 02269-9101

NFPA 11, *Standard for Low-, Medium-, and High-Expansion Foam,* 2002 edition

NFPA 13D, *Standard for the Installation of Sprinkler Systems in One- and Two-Family Dwellings and Manufactured Homes,* 2002 edition

NFPA 14, *Standard for the Installation of Standpipe, Private Hydrant, and Hose Systems,* 2000 edition

NFPA 15, *Standard for Water Spray Fixed Systems for Fire Protection,* 2001 edition

NFPA 16, *Standard for the Installation of Foam-Water Sprinkler and Foam-Water Spray Systems,* 1999 edition

NFPA 25, *Standard for the Inspection, Testing, and Maintenance of Water-Based Fire Protection Systems,* 2002 edition

NFPA 30, *Flammable and Combustible Liquids Code,* 2000 edition

NFPA 80A, *Recommended Practice for Protection of Buildings from Exterior Fire Exposures,* 2001 edition

NFPA 170, *Standard for Fire Safety Symbols,* 2002 edition

National Fire Sprinkler Association, 40 Jon Barrett Road, P.O. Box 1000, Patterson, NY 12563

"Detection, Treatment and Prevention of Microbiologically Influenced Corrosion in Water-Based Fire Protection Systems," June 1998

American Fire Sprinkler Association, 9696 Sillman Street, Suite 300, Dallas, TX 75243

"Water Velocity: Its Impact on the Accuracy of Hydraulic Calculations" (available at www.sprinklenet.org)

CHAPTER 15

Water Supplies

The effectiveness of even the most conservative sprinkler system design depends on its water supply. Unless the sprinkler system discharge criteria can be satisfied by the water supply in terms of pressure, flow, and duration, the system will not perform as intended. Sprinkler system design considerations such as sprinkler spacing, hazard classification, design density, and pipe sizes will have little or no bearing without sufficient water.

In many cases, efforts are made to design a sprinkler system so that an existing water supply can adequately supply the system's demand—that is, larger pipes or sprinklers with larger orifices are selected so that the system demand will not exceed the water supply curve of the city water main. If the water supply, which includes a pressure, flow, and capacity (duration times flow) component, is deficient, supplemental measures in increasing the water supply will be needed for proper system operation. In some situations, a fire pump can be needed to compensate for a lack of pressure and flow even if a sufficient volume of water is available. For other cases, such as a large industrial complex, the installation of a gravity tank could be needed to provide the necessary water supply capacity. Chapter 15 identifies water supply sources that are acceptable for sprinkler systems.

15.1 General

15.1.1 Number of Supplies.
Every automatic sprinkler system shall have at least one automatic water supply.

The requirement in 15.1.1 for each sprinkler system to have at least one automatic water supply does not mean that each sprinkler system (system riser) in a building must have its own dedicated water supply.

It is not necessary for a single water supply source to be sized to account for the simultaneous operation of all systems. The water supply must be capable of meeting the most hydraulically demanding area of the systems.

If a building's size requires it to have three separate sprinkler systems, each system is not required to be connected to its own water supply. Instead, the water supply must be capable of meeting the demands of the hydraulically most demanding areas of the three systems. NFPA 13 assumes that only one fire will occur in a building at any given time.

The term *automatic water supply* means that the activation of the water supply does not depend on human intervention. When a sprinkler activates due to heat from a fire, the waterflow out of the sprinkler causes a pressure drop in the sprinkler system. This drop in pressure initiates waterflow through the system to the open sprinkler. An automatic sprinkler system cannot be arranged in such a manner that the operation of a sprinkler sounds an alarm that notifies someone to either turn on a fire pump or open a control valve to the water supply.

15.1.2 Capacity.
Water supplies shall be capable of providing the required flow and pressure for the required duration as specified in Chapter 11, Chapter 12, and Chapter 13.

Where a building requires multiple sprinkler systems, how many water supplies are required?
◀ FAQ

◀ FAQ
Where a building requires multiple sprinkler systems, is it required that the water supply meet the combined demand of all systems?

◀ FAQ
What does the term *automatic water supply* mean?

Capacity is discussed in 15.1.2. As with all components critical to the effective operation of the sprinkler system, water supply sources must be reliable. The sources must be capable of meeting the system demand at all times. It is important to note that no matter how well the sprinkler system was designed and installed, if the water supply fails, the sprinkler system will fail. If the water supply is taken from a municipal water works system, potential future degradation of water supply conditions, as well as seasonal and daily fluctuations, must be considered. Additionally, waterflow tests should be conducted on a routine basis to monitor the condition of the water supply. Over time, water supply systems are likely to be degraded by pipe corrosion, scale buildup, and inadvertently closed valves. The impact of future users of the water supply must also be evaluated. Additionally, if water supplies employ fire pumps or water tanks, certain requirements are placed on this equipment to maintain their reliability. See NFPA 20, *Standard for the Installation of Stationary Pumps for Fire Protection,* and NFPA 22, *Standard for Water Tanks for Private Fire Protection,* for additional information. NFPA 25, *Standard for the Inspection, Testing, and Maintenance of Water-Based Fire Protection Systems,* further requires that specific inspection, testing, and maintenance activities be conducted to ensure the integrity of the water supply.

Where a waterworks system serves as the sprinkler system's supply, 11.2.3.1.8(9) requires that the supply be of sufficient capacity so that it meets the sprinkler system's discharge criteria, any inside hose demand, and a waterflow allowance for outside hose. The outside hose allowance is to be added at either the connection to the water main or a yard hydrant, whichever is closer.

Regardless of its arrangement, the underground supply must have sufficient capacity to satisfy the calculated system demand based on the selected design approach from Chapters 11, 12, or 13. In all cases, this supply must require no human intervention to operate and must be capable of supplying the system for the necessary duration.

15.1.3 Size of Fire Mains.

15.1.3.1 No pipe smaller than 6 in. (152.4 mm) in diameter shall be installed as a private service main.

15.1.3.2 For mains that do not supply hydrants, sizes smaller than 6 in. (152.4 mm) shall be permitted to be used subject to the following restrictions:

(1) The main supplies only automatic sprinkler systems, open sprinkler systems, water spray fixed systems, foam systems, or Class II standpipe systems.

 (2) Hydraulic calculations show that the main will supply the total demand at the appropriate pressure. Systems that are not hydraulically calculated shall have a main at least as large as the system riser.

Size of fire mains is addressed in 15.1.3.1 and 15.1.3.2. Private fire service mains must be at least 6 in. in diameter where they supply hydrants. In some cases, the use of a minimum 8-in. (203-mm) pipe for dead-end mains is advised. Where the fire service mains do not supply hydrants, they are permitted to be sized based on hydraulic calculations or to be as large the riser under certain conditions. Fire mains need sufficient supply to meet the demands of the sprinkler systems, inside hose, outside hose, and other anticipated water demands.

 15.1.4 Underground Supply Pipe. For pipe schedule systems, the underground supply pipe shall be at least as large as the system riser.

The minimum diameter of the underground pipe connecting the water supply with a pipe schedule sprinkler system, regardless of the type of water supply used, is specified in 15.1.4.

 15.1.5* Water Supply Treatment. Water supplies and environmental conditions shall be evaluated for the existence of microbes and conditions that contribute to microbiologically influenced corrosion (MIC). Where conditions are found that contribute to MIC, the owner(s) shall notify the sprinkler system developed to treat the system using one of the following methods:

(1) Install a water pipe that will not be affected by the MIC microbes.
(2) Treat all water that enters the system using an approved biocide.
(3) Implement an approved plan for monitoring the interior conditions of the pipe at established time intervals and locations.

A.15.1.5 Evaluation of the water supply and environmental conditions does not necessarily require a water sample analysis by a laboratory. Instead, general knowledge of the long-term condition of sprinkler systems with similar piping materials in similar environments on the same water supply can be a sufficient evaluation.

There are several options to address the effects of MIC on sprinkler systems. Some types of sprinkler pipe such as CPVC have not shown to be affected by MIC. Other types of pipe are being manufactured with a biofilm that resists the effects of MIC.

Where water supplies are treated with biocides, evaluation of the effects of the biocide on sprinkler system components (pipe, fittings, sprinklers, gaskets, valves, and seals) is just as important as evaluating the effect the biocide has on the organisms. Where water treatment is selected as the method to deal with MIC, all water entering the system during testing or flushing needs to be treated so that the organisms don't get a chance to establish themselves.

Since all of the conditions that can effect the growth of MIC are unknown, a plan to sample randomly selected interior positions in the system can be effective. The frequency and location of the interior inspections will depend on the extent of the known MIC problem with the same water supply and similar environmental conditions.

Microbiologically influenced corrosion (MIC), which is discussed in 15.1.5, is caused in part by microorganisms in the water supply that react with system piping. The overall effect can result in the formation of deposits and pitting of system piping in a relatively short period of time.

Over the past several years, additional data on the effects of MIC have become available. MIC can cause severe problems with metallic pipe in areas with specific water supply and system factors. These provisions in 15.1.5 were introduced to guard against the effects of MIC on sprinkler system performance when the sprinkler system is installed. Because the effects of MIC are often not a one-time event, follow-up evaluation and treatment of the water supply is likely to be necessary once the system is in service. Additional information on MIC can be found in the NFSA report "Detection, Treatment and Prevention of Microbiologically Influenced Corrosion in Water-Based Fire Protection Systems" and in Supplement 2.

15.1.6 Arrangement.

15.1.6.1 Connection Between Underground and Aboveground Piping.

15.1.6.1.1 The connection between the system piping and underground piping shall be made with a suitable transition piece and shall be properly strapped or fastened by approved devices.

15.1.6.1.2 The transition piece shall be protected against possible damage from corrosive agents, solvent attack, or mechanical damage.

The provisions of 15.1.6.1 imply that piping serving as the transition piece between the underground supply piping and the aboveground system piping at the base of the riser be of a metallic material. Many of the types of pipe acceptable for use as underground fire service mains are limited to conditions involving below-grade applications only. The use of certain pipe materials, such as plastic and concrete, for aboveground fire service mains is restricted by their listings. As indicated by 15.1.6.1.2, these transition pieces must be able to withstand damage from likely corrosive agents, solvent attack, and mechanical damage. As a result, the need to use steel, iron, or copper pipe materials at these transition areas is evident.

15.1.6.2* Connection Passing Through or Under Foundation Walls. When system piping pierces a foundation wall below grade or is located under the foundation wall, clearance shall be provided to prevent breakage of the piping due to building settlement.

 A.15.1.6.2 Where the system riser is close to an outside wall, underground fittings of proper length should be used in order to avoid pipe joints located in or under the wall. Where the connection passes through the foundation wall below grade, a 1-in. to 3-in. (25-mm to 76-mm) clearance should be provided around the pipe and the clear space filled with asphalt mastic or similar flexible waterproofing material.

Without clearance around the wall, which is required by 15.1.6.2, normal building movement and settlement can cause the failure of pipe that is rigidly held in place by foundation walls.

15.1.7* Meters. Where meters are required by other authorities, they shall be listed.

 A.15.1.7 Where water meters are in the supply lines to a sprinkler system, they should be rated to deliver the proper system demand. The amount of water supplied through a water meter varies with its size and type and might not provide the required demand, regardless of the water supply available.

Meters, which are covered in 15.1.7, are not necessary for the proper performance of a sprinkler system. However, meters could be required by the local water authority. Because of the pressure loss they introduce, the use of meters on automatic sprinkler systems should be discouraged. Meters also introduce an additional expense and maintenance concern.

Figure B.1 of NFPA 13 provides guidance on possible arrangements for metering water that is used for purposes other than fire protection, such as domestic and industrial uses. Where a concern about possible leakage or loss from the fire protection piping exists, a detector check valve can be substituted for the check valve indicated.

15.1.8* Connection from Waterworks System.

 A.15.1.8 Where connections are made from public waterworks systems, such systems should be guarded against possible contamination as follows *(see AWWA M14, Recommended Practice for Backflow Prevention and Cross Connection Control):*

(1) For private fire service mains with direct connections from public waterworks mains only or with booster pumps installed in the connections from the street mains, no tanks or reservoirs, no physical connection from other water supplies, no antifreeze or other additives of any kind, and with all drains discharging to atmosphere, dry well, or other safe outlets, no backflow protection is recommended at the service connection.

(2) For private fire service mains with direct connection from the public water supply main plus one or more of the following: elevated storage tanks or fire pumps taking suction from aboveground covered reservoirs or tanks (all storage facilities are filled or connected to public water only and the water in the tanks is to be maintained in a potable condition), an approved double check valve assembly is recommended.

(3) For private fire service mains directly supplied from public mains with an auxiliary water supply such as a pond or river on or available to the premises and dedicated to fire department use; or for systems supplied from public mains and interconnected with auxiliary supplies, such as pumps taking suction from reservoirs exposed to contamination or rivers and ponds; driven wells, mills, or other industrial water systems; or for systems or portions of systems where antifreeze or other solutions are used, an approved reduced pressure zone-type backflow preventer is recommended.

15.1.8.1 Where connections are made from public waterworks systems, it might be necessary to guard against possible contamination of the public supply.

15.1.8.2 The requirements of the public health authority having jurisdiction shall be determined and followed.

15.1.8.3 Where equipment is installed to guard against possible contamination of the public water system, such equipment and devices shall be listed for fire protection service.

Connections from waterworks systems are covered in 15.1.8.1 through 15.1.8.3. The most common type of equipment utilized to guard against possible contamination of the public water supply is a listed backflow prevention device. These devices typically impact the system's hydraulic characteristics and are a potential point of system impairment if performance is not properly monitored.

Backflow prevention devices are not a requirement of NFPA 13 and serve no benefit to the sprinkler system. Backflow prevention devices are typically required by public health authorities for non–fire protection purposes.

Where installed, the pressure loss through a backflow prevention device must be accounted for, and the valves on the device must be supervised as any other system control valve. If a backflow prevention device is installed retroactively, the pressure loss through the additional pipe and fittings used in conjunction with the preventor must also be taken into account.

See 8.16.4.6 for more details. Additionally, the backflow prevention device must be properly inspected, tested, and maintained to ensure proper operation.

Are backflow prevention devices required by NFPA 13?
◀ FAQ

◀ FAQ
When backflow prevention devices are installed, what pressure losses must be accounted for?

15.2 Types

Section 15.2 describes those sources of water that are acceptable for use as the permanent, automatic supply for the sprinkler system.

Although not specifically mentioned, suction tanks (see Exhibit 15.1), embankment tanks (see Exhibit 15.2), wells, and ponds (see Exhibit 15.3) could also be considered as water supply sources for automatic sprinkler systems. Along with the other water supply sources identified, the sources must be reliable and have enough capacity to meet the sprinkler system demand at all times.

When water supplies other than circulating public waterworks systems are used, the proper installation of system components such as piping, pumps, or tanks should be verified. Even though private systems are designed to provide adequate water capacity, flow, and pressure, the reliability of these systems needs to be monitored through the implementation of a periodic inspection, testing, and maintenance program and through the proper supervision of certain system components. Public systems are tested and supervised continually by the daily demands placed on them. Private systems can remain idle for longer periods of time.

◀ FAQ
What are some additional types of water supplies?

15.2.1* Connections to Water Works Systems.

A.15.2.1 Care should be taken in making water tests to be used in designing or evaluating the capability of sprinkler systems. The water supply tested should be representative of the supply that might be available at the time of a fire. For example, testing of public water supplies should be done at times of normal demand on the system. Public water supplies are likely to fluctuate widely from season to season and even within a 24-hour period. Allowance should be made for seasonal or daily fluctuations, for drought conditions, for possibility of interruption by flood, or for ice conditions in winter. Testing of water supplies also normally used for industrial use should be done while water is being drawn for industrial use. The range of industrial-use demand should be taken into account. In special situations where the domestic water demand could significantly reduce the sprinkler water supply, an increase in the size of the pipe supplying both the domestic and sprinkler water can be justified.

Future changes in water supplies should be considered. For example, a large, established, urban supply is not likely to change greatly within a few years. However, the supply in a

EXHIBIT 15.1 *Suction Tank.*

EXHIBIT 15.2 *Embankment Supported Tank.*

EXHIBIT 15.3 *Pond. (Courtesy of Kenneth Isman)*

growing suburban industrial park might deteriorate quite rapidly as greater numbers of plants draw more water.

Dead-end mains should be avoided, if possible, by arranging for mains supplied from both directions. When private fire service mains are connected to dead-end public mains, each situation should be examined to determine if it is practical to request the water utility to loop the mains in order to obtain a more reliable supply.

Testing of Water Supply. To determine the value of public water as a supply for automatic sprinkler systems, it is generally necessary to make a flow test to determine how much water can be discharged at a residual pressure at a rate sufficient to give the required residual pressure under the roof (with the volume flow hydraulically translated to the base of the riser)—that is, a pressure head represented by the height of the building plus the required residual pressure.

The proper method of conducting this test is to use two hydrants in the vicinity of the property. The static pressure should be measured on the hydrant in front of or nearest to the property and the water allowed to flow from the hydrant next nearest the property, preferably the one farthest from the source of supply if the main is fed only one way. The residual pressure will be that indicated at the hydrant where water is not flowing.

Referring to Figure A.15.2.1, the method of conducting the flow tests is as follows:

(1) Attach the gauge to the hydrant *(A)* and obtain static pressure.
(2) Either attach a second gauge to the hydrant *(B)* or use the pitot tube at the outlet. Have hydrant *(B)* opened wide and read pressure at both hydrants.
(3) Use the pressure at *(B)* to compute the gallons flowing and read the gauge on *(A)* to determine the residual pressure or that which will be available on the top line of sprinklers in the property.

Gauge attached to hydrant to show static and residual pressures

Gauge attached to hydrant or pitot tube to register flowing pressure

Pitot tube →

Public main

FIGURE A.15.2.1 *Method of Conducting Flow Tests.*

Water pressure in pounds per square inch for a given height in feet equals height multiplied by 0.434.

In making flow tests, whether from hydrants or from nozzles attached to hose, always measure the size of the orifice. While hydrant outlets are usually 2½ in. (64 mm), they are sometimes smaller and occasionally larger. The Underwriters Laboratories play pipe is 1⅛ in. (29 mm) and 1¾ in. (44 mm) with the tip removed, but occasionally nozzles will be 1 in. (25.4 mm) or 1¼ in. (33 mm), and with the tip removed the opening can be only 1½ in. (38 mm).

The pitot tube should be held approximately one-half the diameter of the hydrant or nozzle opening away from the opening. It should be held in the center of the stream, except that in using hydrant outlets the stream should be explored to ascertain the average pressure.

For further information on water supply testing, see NFPA 291, *Recommended Practice for Fire Flow Testing and Marking of Hydrants.*

Connection to a public or private water works system, which is covered in 15.2.1, is often the first choice when considering water supply options. Such systems are typically very reliable, accessible, and capable of accommodating the demand for a wide range of sprinkler systems.

If a waterworks system is contemplated for the supply source, the associated water supply test data must be current. Peak loads on the system, as well as any seasonal fluctuations and likely interruptions of waterflow, must be contemplated. When considering a waterworks system, the least amount of water in terms of pressure and flow available should be used as the water supply, because the sprinkler system demand must be met 24 hours a day, 7 days a week, 365 days a year.

15.2.1.1 A connection to a reliable water works system shall be an acceptable water supply source.

15.2.1.2 The volume and pressure of a public water supply shall be determined from waterflow test data. An adjustment to the waterflow test data to account for daily and seasonal fluctuations, possible interruption by flood or ice conditions, large simultaneous industrial use, future demand on the water supply system, or any other condition that could affect the water supply shall be made as appropriate.

15.2.2* Pumps. A single automatically controlled fire pump installed in accordance with NFPA 20, *Standard for the Installation of Stationary Pumps for Fire Protection,* shall be an acceptable water supply source.

A.15.2.2 An automatically controlled vertical turbine pump taking suction from a reservoir, pond, lake, river, or well complies with 15.2.2.

See sections dealing with sprinkler equipment supervisory and waterflow alarm services in *NFPA 72, National Fire Alarm Code.*

FAQ ▶
Can a fire pump be utilized to increase the capacity of a water supply?

Pumps are discussed in 15.2.2. Fire pumps cannot create water, which is important to understand. Fire pumps serve to increase the pressure and resultant flow from an existing supply of water such as a waterworks system. If a sufficient capacity of water does exist, means in addition to the fire pump, such as a tank, are necessary.

Listed fire pumps installed in accordance with NFPA 20 and connected to a sufficient supply of water are an acceptable water supply source. A vertical turbine pump, such as the one shown in Exhibit 15.4, is a type of centrifugal fire pump that operates in a vertical position. In that position, the first impeller, or bowl, of the pump is always submerged. Therefore, the first pump impeller has a positive suction pressure on it. This type of pump, with its first impeller submerged, does not actually take suction but, rather, pumps from a water source located below the pump. NFPA's *Fire Pump Handbook* and *Pumps for Fire Protection Systems* provide additional information on fire pumps and their proper application.

One of the most common types of fire pumps installed is the horizontal split case fire pump shown in Exhibit 15.5.

To provide sufficient reliability of a single fire pump that can serve as the sole supply for a sprinkler system, supervisory service of pump conditions to a constantly attended location is required. Conditions to be supervised should include pump-running indication, pump power supply availability, and other conditions that could render the pump inoperative. These requirements, as well as additional details, are contained in NFPA 20.

15.2.3 Pressure Tanks.

Unlike gravity tanks or suction tanks, pressure tanks, which are covered in 15.2.3, contain both water and air under pressure. A sufficient capacity of air must be available to discharge the water from the tank at the necessary rate. See 15.2.3 for details on water level and air pressure requirements for pressure tanks.

15.2.3.1 Acceptability.

15.2.3.1.1 A pressure tank installed in accordance with NFPA 22, *Standard for Water Tanks for Private Fire Protection,* shall be an acceptable water supply source.

EXHIBIT 15.4 *Vertical Turbine Pump. (Courtesy of ITT A-C Pump)*

Electric driver

Pump head

Discharge flange

Pump column

Impellers covered by bowls and submerged in water source

EXHIBIT 15.5 *Horizontal Split Case Fire Pump. (Courtesy of ITT A-C Pump)*

15.2.3.1.2 Pressure tanks shall be provided with an approved means for automatically maintaining the required air pressure.

15.2.3.1.3 Where a pressure tank is the sole water supply, there shall also be provided an approved trouble alarm to indicate low air pressure and low water level with the alarm supplied from an electrical branch circuit independent of the air compressor.

As with fire pumps, certain features and conditions about the pressure tank should be supervised to increase the reliability of this sole source of water supply (see 15.2.3.1.3). Trouble alarms that indicate low air pressure and low water levels should be received at a constantly attended location. *NFPA 72®, National Fire Alarm Code®*, provides additional details on acceptable supervisory methods.

15.2.3.1.4 Pressure tanks shall not be used to supply other than sprinklers and hand hose attached to sprinkler piping.

15.2.3.2 Capacity.

15.2.3.2.1 In addition to the requirements of 15.1.2, the water capacity of a pressure tank shall include the extra capacity needed to fill dry pipe or preaction systems where installed.

15.2.3.2.2 The total volume shall be based on the water capacity plus the air capacity required by 15.2.3.3.

Unlike wet pipe systems, dry pipe and preaction systems are filled with air immediately before a fire. (See Chapter 7 for requirements on dry pipe and preaction systems.) Therefore, if a pressure tank serves as the water supply, it must be sized so that it has sufficient capacity to fill the system piping in addition to the capacity needed to meet the system's discharge requirements (see 15.2.3.2.2).

15.2.3.3* Water Level and Air Pressure.

 A.15.2.3.3 For pipe schedule systems, the air pressure to be carried and the proper proportion of air in the tank can be determined from the following formulas where:

P = air pressure carried in pressure tank

A = proportion of air in tank

H = height of highest sprinkler above tank bottom

 When the tank is placed above the highest sprinkler, use the following formula:

$$P = \frac{30}{A} - 15$$

If $A = \frac{1}{3}$, then $P = 90 - 15 = 75$ lb psi

If $A = \frac{1}{2}$, then $P = 60 - 15 = 45$ lb psi

If $A = \frac{2}{3}$, then $P = 45 - 15 = 30$ lb psi

 When the tank is below the level of the highest sprinkler, use the following formula:

$$P = \frac{30}{A} - 15 + \frac{0.434H}{A}$$

If $A = \frac{1}{3}$, then $P = 75 + 1.30H$

If $A = \frac{1}{2}$, then $P = 45 + 0.87H$

If $A = \frac{2}{3}$, then $P = 30 + 0.65H$

The respective air pressures above are calculated to ensure that the last water will leave the tank at a pressure of 15 psi (1 bar) when the base of the tank is on a level with the highest sprinkler or at such additional pressure as is equivalent to a head corresponding to the distance between the base of the tank and the highest sprinkler when the latter is above the tank.

 For hydraulically calculated systems, the following formula should be used to determine the tank pressure and ratio of air to water:

$$P_i = \frac{P_f + 15}{A} - 15$$

where:

P_i = tank pressure

P_f = pressure required from hydraulic calculations

A = proportion of air

Example: Hydraulic calculations indicate 75 psi (5.2 bar) is required to supply the system. What tank pressure will be required?

$$P_i = \frac{75 + 15}{0.5} - 15$$

$$P_i = 180 - 15 = 165 \text{ psi}$$

For SI units, 1 ft = 0.3048 m; 1 psi = 0.0689 bar.

In this case, the tank would be filled with 50 percent air and 50 percent water, and the tank pressure would be 165 psi (11.4 bar). If the pressure is too high, the amount of air carried in the tank will have to be increased.

Pressure tanks should be located above the top level of sprinklers but can be located in the basement or elsewhere.

15.2.3.3.1 Pressure tanks shall be kept with a sufficient supply of water to meet the demand of the fire protection system as calculated in Chapter 14 for the duration required by Chapter 11, Chapter 12, or Chapter 13.

15.2.3.3.2 The pressure shall be sufficient to push all of the water out of the tank while maintaining the necessary residual pressure (required by Chapter 14) at the top of the system.

Table 11.2.2.1 requires that certain residual pressures be provided at the elevation of the highest sprinkler for pipe schedule systems (see 15.2.3.3.2). Table 11.2.2.1 also requires a minimum flow at the base of the riser. Residual pressure and minimum flow need to be considered when contemplating a pressure tank for pipe schedule systems.

15.2.4 Gravity Tanks. An elevated tank installed in accordance with NFPA 22, *Standard for Water Tanks for Private Fire Protection,* shall be an acceptable water supply source.

Gravity tanks are addressed in 15.2.4. Gravity tanks, such as the one shown in Exhibit 15.6, are not as common as they were years ago. The availability of a wider range of fire pump capacities in terms of flow–pressure combinations has made pumps a more desirable option in many cases.

EXHIBIT 15.6 Gravity Tank.

If gravity tanks are used, they must be of a capacity that satisfies the system discharge requirements of Chapters 11, 12, and 13. If gravity tanks are also used to supply domestic or industrial needs, the arrangement must be such that the entire volume of water needed for fire protection is available during and after other demands have been placed on the tank.

15.2.5 Penstocks or Flumes, Rivers, or Lakes. Water supply connections from penstocks, flumes, rivers, lakes, or reservoirs shall be arranged to avoid mud and sediment and shall be provided with approved double removable screens or approved strainers installed in an approved manner.

When contemplating the use of naturally occurring water supply sources, such as lakes, rivers, wells, and ponds, their reliability and ability to meet the system demand at all times must be verified (see 15.2.5). For example, seasonal fluctuations must be considered. Because of the degree of uncertainty associated with some naturally occurring water supplies, local regulations and insurance company guidelines may limit the use of these water supply sources.

SUMMARY

The effectiveness of any sprinkler system design depends on its water supply. In the event that the water supply fails to provide the required system demand when called upon will, in most cases, result in the failure of the system and, in many case, result in significant damage or loss of the facility. Unless the sprinkler system discharge criteria can be satisfied by the water supply in terms of pressure, flow, and duration, the system will not perform as intended. Sprinkler system design considerations such as sprinkler spacing, hazard classification, design density, and pipe sizes will have little or no bearing without sufficient water.

 ## REFERENCES CITED IN COMMENTARY

National Fire Protection Association, 1 Batterymarch Park, P.O. Box 9101, Quincy, MA 02269-9101

NFPA 20, *Standard for the Installation of Stationary Pumps for Fire Protection,* 1999 edition
NFPA 22, *Standard for Water Tanks for Private Fire Protection,* 1998 edition
NFPA 25, *Standard for the Inspection, Testing, and Maintenance of Water-Based Fire Protection Systems,* 2002 edition
NFPA 72®, National Fire Alarm Code®, 2002 edition
Isman, K. E., and Puchosvsky, M. T., *Pumps for Fire Protection Systems,* NFPA, Quincy, MA, 2002
Puchosvsky, M. T., and Isman, K. E., *Fire Pump Handbook,* NFPA, Quincy, MA, 1998

National Fire Sprinkler Association, P.O. Box 1000, Patterson, NY 12463

"Detection, Treatment and Prevention of Microbiologically Influenced Corrosion in Water-Based Fire Protection Systems"

Systems Acceptance

Chapter 16 contains information concerning systems acceptance for the aboveground portions of sprinkler systems. See the requirements of Section 10.10 for the testing and acceptance of underground piping.

The approval process for system acceptance is important in verifying the design and installation of the system and should receive top priority. These final steps in the design and installation of a sprinkler system are to confirm that the basic requirements of NFPA 13 are satisfied, that the work was completed in an acceptable manner, and that the customer receives a system that performs as intended. Failure to comply with system acceptance requirements will likely delay the issuance of the building's certificate of occupancy. The remedy of any deficiency in the sprinkler system design or installation discovered after the building is occupied is likely to be extremely costly.

16.1 Approval of Sprinkler Systems and Private Fire Service Mains

The installing contractor shall do the following:

(1) Notify the authority having jurisdiction and owner's representative of the time and date testing will be performed
(2) Perform all required acceptance tests *(see Section 16.2)*
(3) Complete and sign the appropriate contractor's material and test certificate(s) *(see Figure 16.1)*

Occasionally the authority having jurisdiction wants to be present during acceptance tests, which is the reason for the requirement in Section 16.1. The authority having jurisdiction is responsible for informing the building owner either directly or through the installing contractor or design engineer that he or she wants to be present. The building owner is obligated to comply with such a request and to give the authority having jurisdiction advance notice. Failure to do so can result in the need to repeat the tests.

The material and test certificate for aboveground installations referenced in 16.1.3(3) is shown in Figure 16.1. This certificate helps in verifying that the materials used and the tests performed are in accordance with the requirements of NFPA 13. The certificate also provides a record of the test results that can be used for comparison with any tests conducted in the future. It is important to complete all applicable portions of this certificate for each installed system.

16.2 Acceptance Requirements

16.2.1 Hydrostatic Tests.

16.2.1.1 Unless permitted by 16.2.1.2 through 16.2.1.6, all piping and attached appurtenances subjected to system working pressure shall be hydrostatically tested at 200 psi (13.8 bar) and shall maintain that pressure without loss for 2 hours.

Contractor's Material and Test Certificate for Aboveground Piping

PROCEDURE

Upon completion of work, inspection and tests shall be made by the contractor's representative and witnessed by an owner's representative. All defects shall be corrected and system left in service before contractor's personnel finally leave the job.

A certificate shall be filled out and signed by both representatives. Copies shall be prepared for approving authorities, owners, and contractor. It is understood the owner's representative's signature in no way prejudices any claim against contractor for faulty material, poor workmanship, or failure to comply with approving authority's requirements or local ordinances.

Property		Date
Property address		

	Accepted by approving authorities (names)		
Plans	Address		
	Installation conforms to accepted plans	☐ Yes	☐ No
	Equipment used is approved	☐ Yes	☐ No
	If no, explain deviations		

	Has person in charge of fire equipment been instructed as to location of control valves and care and maintenance of this new equipment? If no, explain	☐ Yes	☐ No
Instructions	Have copies of the following been left on the premises?		
	1. System components instructions	☐ Yes	☐ No
	2. Care and maintenance instructions	☐ Yes	☐ No
	3. NFPA 25	☐ Yes	☐ No

Location of system	Supplies buildings

	Make	Model	Year of manufacture	Orifice size	Quantity	Temperature rating
Sprinklers						

Pipe and fittings	Type of pipe _____ Type of fittings _____

Alarm valve or flow indicator	Alarm device			Maximum time to operate through test connection	
	Type	Make	Model	Minutes	Seconds

	Dry valve			Q. O. D.		
	Make	Model	Serial no.	Make	Model	Serial no.
Dry pipe operating test						

		Time to trip through test connection[1,2]		Water pressure	Air pressure	Trip point air pressure	Time water reached test outlet[1,2]		Alarm operated properly	
		Minutes	Seconds	psi	psi	psi	Minutes	Seconds	Yes	No
	Without Q.O.D.									
	With Q.O.D.									
	If no, explain									

[1] Measured from time inspector's test connection is opened
[2] NFPA 13 only requires the 60-second limitation in specific sections

FIGURE 16.1 *Contractor's Material and Test Certificate for Aboveground Piping.*

	Operation								
	☐ Pneumatic ☐ Electric ☐ Hydraulics								

	Piping supervised	☐ Yes	☐ No	Detecting media supervised			☐ Yes	☐ No

	Does valve operate from the manual trip, remote, or both control stations?	☐ Yes	☐ No

Deluge and preaction valves

Is there an accessible facility in each circuit for testing? ☐ Yes ☐ No	If no, explain

Make	Model	Does each circuit operate supervision loss alarm?		Does each circuit operate valve release?		Maximum time to operate release	
		Yes	No	Yes	No	Minutes	Seconds

Pressure reducing valve test

Location and floor	Make and model	Setting	Static pressure		Residual pressure (flowing)		Flow rate
			Inlet (psi)	Outlet (psi)	Inlet (psi)	Outlet (psi)	Flow (gpm)

Test description

Hydrostatic: Hydrostatic tests shall be made at not less than 200 psi (13.6 bar) for 2 hours or 50 psi (3.4 bar) above static pressure in excess of 150 psi (10.2 bar) for 2 hours. Differential dry-pipe valve clappers shall be left open during the test to prevent damage. All aboveground piping leakage shall be stopped.

Pneumatic: Establish 40 psi (2.7 bar) air pressure and measure drop, which shall not exceed 1½ psi (0.1 bar) in 24 hours. Test pressure tanks at normal water level and air pressure and measure air pressure drop, which shall not exceed 1½ psi (0.1 bar) in 24 hours.

Tests

All piping hydrostatically tested at _____ psi (____ bar) for ____ hours Dry piping pneumatically tested ☐ Yes ☐ No Equipment operates properly ☐ Yes ☐ No	If no, state reason

Do you certify as the sprinkler contractor that additives and corrosive chemicals, sodium silicate or derivatives of sodium silicate, brine, or other corrosive chemicals were not used for testing systems or stopping leaks?
☐ Yes   ☐ No

Drain test	Reading of gauge located near water supply test connection: _____ psi (____ bar)	Residual pressure with valve in test connection open wide: _____ psi (____ bar)

Underground mains and lead-in connections to system risers flushed before connection made to sprinkler piping Verified by copy of the Contractor's Material and Test Certificate for Underground Piping. ☐ Yes ☐ No Flushed by installer of underground sprinkler piping ☐ Yes ☐ No	Other Explain

If powder-driven fasteners are used in concrete, has representative sample testing been satisfactorily completed? ☐ Yes ☐ No	If no, explain

Blank testing gaskets

Number used	Locations	Number removed

Welding

Welding piping   ☐ Yes ☐ No
If yes. . .

Do you certify as the sprinkler contractor that welding procedures comply with the requirements of at least AWS B2.1?	☐ Yes ☐ No

Do you certify that the welding was performed by welders qualified in compliance with the requirements of at least AWS B2.1?	☐ Yes ☐ No

Do you certify that the welding was carried out in compliance with a documented quality control procedure to ensure that all discs are retrieved, that openings in piping are smooth, that slag and other welding residue are removed, and that the internal diameters of piping are not penetrated?	☐ Yes ☐ No

Cutouts (discs)

Do you certify that you have a control feature to ensure that all cutouts (discs) are retrieved?	☐ Yes ☐ No

FIGURE 16.1 Continued

Hydraulic data nameplate	Nameplate provided ☐ Yes ☐ No	If no, explain

Remarks	Date left in service with all control valves open

Signatures	Name of sprinkler contractor		
	Tests witnessed by		
	For property owner (signed)	Title	Date
	For sprinkler contractor (signed)	Title	Date

Additional explanations and notes

FIGURE 16.1 *Continued*

16.2.1.2 Portions of systems normally subjected to system working pressures in excess of 150 psi (10.4 bar) shall be tested as described in 16.2.2.1 at a pressure of 50 psi (3.5 bar) in excess of system working pressure.

Hydrostatic tests are described in 16.2.1.1 and 16.2.1.2. When conducting a hydrostatic test, it is important to note that temperature changes affect the pressure readings of the tested systems. The expansion or contraction of the air in the system changing due to the temperature affects the pressure shown on the gauge. These fluctuations due to temperature apply to both hydrostatic and pneumatic tests because trapped air is in the system even in a hydrostatic test. This pressure reading is not an indication of a change in the amount of internal air or water or a leak but, rather, is an indication that the expansion or contraction of the air molecules has caused the pressure to fluctuate. For example, if the system were to be put under pressure when the temperature was 65°F and the temperature dropped to 40°F by the end of the test, the gauge would indicate less pressure, even if no leaks occurred. Conversely, if the temperature were to rise to 90°F, the pressure would increase, even though no additional air or water had been pumped into the system.

Where system pressures are in excess of 150 psi (10.4 bar), the hydrostatic test must be conducted at a pressure 50 psi (3.5 bar) in excess of the working pressure as indicated in 16.2.1.2. This requirement is intended to ensure system integrity for these high-pressure systems.

16.2.1.3 Where cold weather will not permit testing with water, an interim air test shall be permitted to be conducted as described in 16.2.3.

The air test for dry pipe and double interlock systems in 16.2.2.1 is permitted by 16.2.1.3 as an interim substitution for the hydrostatic test where a danger of water freezing in the system exists. The standard hydrostatic test must be made, however, when it is possible to do so without danger of freezing.

16.2.1.4 Modifications affecting 20 or fewer sprinklers shall not require testing in excess of system working pressure.

16.2.1.5 Where addition or modification is made to an existing system affecting more than 20 sprinklers, the new portion shall be isolated and tested at not less than 200 psi (13.8 bar) for 2 hours.

16.2.1.6 Modifications that cannot be isolated, such as relocated drops, shall not require testing in excess of system working pressure.

All new systems must be tested hydrostatically at a pressure of at least 200 psi (13.8 bar) (see 16.2.1.6). This value is set to ensure that pipe joints are made to withstand that pressure without coming apart or leaking. Although the hydrostatic test is primarily a workmanship test and not a materials performance test, damaged materials—for example, cracked fittings or leaky valves—are routinely discovered during the hydrostatic test. All materials used must be rated for a minimum working pressure of 175 psi (12.1 bar), which is the maximum pressure at which the system is normally maintained.

Paragraphs 16.2.1.4, 16.2.1.5, and 16.2.1.6 address additions and modifications and specify when new piping installations are to be isolated and tested. In many cases, segregating new work from existing work is difficult. The Technical Committee on Sprinkler System Installation Criteria believes that to require the entire system to undergo another hydrostatic test when only relatively minor changes are made is unreasonable. When new portions of a system cannot be isolated, such as relocated drops, NFPA 13 provides some flexibility and permits hydrostatic tests to be conducted at the system's normal static pressure. In general, existing portions of the system do not need to be subjected to a new hydrostatic test.

16.2.1.7 Loss shall be determined by a drop in gauge pressure or visual leakage.

The measures of success for inside sprinkler piping under hydrostatic test are no visible leakage and no loss of pressure in the 2-hour test period, as stated in 16.2.1.7. Often a very small bead of water forms on a fitting during the test. Unless the bead continues to grow and drip, it is not considered visible leakage.

16.2.1.8 The test pressure shall be read from a gauge located at the low elevation point of the system or portion being tested.

The hydrostatic test pressure is measured at the lowest elevation within the system or portion of the system being tested as stated in 16.2.1.8. Testing at the high point of the system, which, due to static head, would increase the test pressure significantly, is not considered necessary. The procedure is carried out in this way due to the fact that application of pressure typically occurs at the lower elevation, and these high pressures would not be anticipated at the higher elevations within the system.

◀ **FAQ**
Where is the hydrostatic test pressure measured during the test?

16.2.1.9 Additives, corrosive chemicals such as sodium silicate, or derivatives of sodium silicate, brine, or other chemicals shall not be used while hydrostatically testing systems or for stopping leaks.

Additives are addressed in 16.2.1.9. Water additives, such as sodium silicate, that are intended to plug small system leaks during hydrostatic testing can clog small orifices, bind sprinkler parts, and prevent or delay operation. These chemicals tend to harden when exposed to air and can create significant obstructions later when they detach themselves from the internal portions of the pipe. Water additives for stopping leaks should never be used on sprinkler systems.

16.2.1.10 Piping between the exterior fire department connection and the check valve in the fire department inlet pipe shall be hydrostatically tested in the same manner as the balance of the system.

A reminder that the fire department connection must be tested is contained in 16.2.1.10. The fact that the piping from the check valve to the hose connection is not normally subjected to water pressure can lead the contractor to believe testing of that portion is not required. Other portions of pipe, such as the inspector's test connection drain and auxiliary drains, are not typically

Is it required that the fire department connection piping be hydrostatically tested?
◀ **FAQ**

subject to high pressures and do not have to be tested in accordance with this requirement to ensure integrity of the entire system. Any buried piping connecting the fire department connection to the system can be tested in accordance with the requirements of 10.10.2.2.4.

The trench must be backfilled prior to hydrostatic testing to prevent movement of underground piping. The backfilling can take place between joints if it is desired to observe the joints for leakage and if the backfill depth is sufficient to prevent movement. As an alternative, the joints can also be covered, but the contractor remains responsible for locating and correcting excessive leakage. The latter is usually preferred where a delay is expected in scheduling the hydrostatic test, since it is not desirable to leave trenches open for any length of time from a safety standpoint.

A 2-hour hydrostatic test is required at not less than 200 psi (13.8 bar), but at least 50 psi (3.4 bar) above the maximum expected static pressure. The piping between an exterior fire department connection and the check valve in the connection's inlet pipe must also be hydrostatically tested. All thrust blocks should be hardened before testing.

It is recommended that the underground piping be filled with water for a 24-hour period prior to the hydrostatic test to stabilize the system. It is also recommended that the test pressure be held for one hour, the pressure then be decreased to zero to look for signs of leakage, and then re-pressurized for the second hour.

16.2.1.11 When deluge systems are being hydrostatically tested, plugs shall be installed in fittings and replaced with open sprinklers after the test is completed, or the operating elements of automatic sprinklers shall be removed after the test is completed.

16.2.1.12* The trench shall be backfilled between joints before testing to prevent movement of pipe.

 A.16.2.1.12 Hydrostatic tests should be made before the joints are covered so that any leaks can be readily detected. Thrust blocks should be sufficiently hardened before hydrostatic testing is begun. If the joints are covered with backfill prior to testing, the contractor remains responsible for locating and correcting any leakage in excess of that permitted.

The pipeline should be prepared 24 hours prior to testing by filling it with water in such a manner as to remove all air. The test pressure should be applied to stabilize the system, which should minimize losses due to entrapped air, changes in water temperature, distention of components under pressure, movement of gaskets, and absorption of air by the water and water by the pipe wall.

16.2.1.13 Where required for safety measures presented by the hazards of open trenches, the pipe and joints shall be permitted to be backfilled provided the installing contractor takes the responsibility for locating and correcting leakage in excess of that permitted in 16.2.1.8.

16.2.1.14 Provision shall be made for the proper disposal of water used for flushing or testing.

16.2.1.15* Test Blanks.

 A.16.2.1.15 Valves isolating the section to be tested might not be "drop-tight." When such leakage is suspected, test blanks of the type required in 16.2.1.15 should be used in a manner that includes the valve in the section being tested.

16.2.1.15.1 Test blanks shall have painted lugs protruding in such a way as to clearly indicate their presence.

16.2.1.15.2 The test blanks shall be numbered, and the installing contractor shall have a recordkeeping method ensuring their removal after work is completed.

All test blanks must be removed after the work is completed, as stated in 16.2.1.15.2. This procedure is extremely important. A test blank without a protruding lug is virtually impossible to detect by visual inspection. Test blanks are commonly referred to as frying pans because of their characteristic shape.

16.2.1.16 When subject to hydrostatic test pressures, the clapper of a differential-type valve shall be held off its seat to prevent damaging the valve.

The design of differential dry pipe valves incorporates flexible gaskets, which prevent water from entering the system (see 16.2.1.16). Pressures in excess of 50 psi (3.4 bar) can damage the mechanism of the valve.

16.2.2 Dry Pipe and Double Interlock System(s) Air Test.

16.2.2.1 In addition to the standard hydrostatic test, an air pressure leakage test at 40 psi (2.8 bar) shall be conducted for 24 hours. Any leakage that results in a loss of pressure in excess of 1½ psi (0.1 bar) for the 24 hours shall be corrected.

The air pressure leakage test described in 16.2.2.1 verifies the integrity of the system, since both types of systems use pressurized air or nitrogen for system monitoring. Under non-fire conditions, dry pipe and double interlock preaction systems are subject to lower pressures than when the system is operating and is charged with water.

Because these systems are subjected to pressures from both air and water, they must be pressure tested using both air and water. Differences in physical properties between air and water make it impossible to judge system integrity based on only one of these tests. See the commentary following 16.2.1.6 regarding the impact on temperature changes during the test.

16.2.2.2 Where systems are installed in spaces that are capable of being operated at temperatures below 32°F (0°C), air pressure leakage tests required in 16.2.2 shall be conducted at the lowest nominal temperature of the space.

16.2.3 System Operational Tests.

16.2.3.1 Waterflow Devices. Waterflow detecting devices including the associated alarm circuits shall be flow tested through the inspector's test connection and shall result in an audible alarm on the premises within 5 minutes after such flow begins and until such flow stops.

An audible alarm is required on the premises when the inspector's test is operated, as stated in 16.2.3.1. The alarm is to sound within 5 minutes after flow begins and must continue to sound until the flow stops. The 5-minute requirement in NFPA 13 was prompted by conditions created when a sprinkler system incorporates both a strong water supply and a backflow device or check valve.

Pressure differentials in water supplies can cause surges through the system. In strong water supplies, these surges can force water into the sprinkler system. Air pockets, which can be trapped in the system, become compressed and provide space for the added water. The presence of a backflow device or check valve does not allow the water to flow back out of the system.

Over a period of such occurrences, the system's static pressure continues to increase. As a result, when the inspector's test valve is opened, there can be enough pressure in the system to allow flow out of the test connection for a period of time, without requiring water from the water supply. If the built-up pressure in the system is large enough, the alarm device cannot operate until the system pressure is reduced sufficiently to initiate flow from the source of supply.

16.2.3.2* Dry Pipe.

A.16.2.3.2 When the acceptance test is being performed during freezing conditions, a partial flow trip test should be conducted at that time and the full flow trip test specified should be conducted as soon as conditions permit.

16.2.3.2.1 A working test of the dry pipe valve alone and with a quick-opening device, if installed, shall be made by opening the inspector's test connection.

16.2.3.2.2 The test shall measure the time to trip the valve and the time for water to be discharged from the inspector's test connection. All times shall be measured from the time the inspector's test connection is completely opened.

16.2.3.2.3 The results shall be recorded using the contractor's material and test certificate for aboveground piping.

Full operational tests of dry pipe valves are required, in accordance with 16.2.3.2.1 through 16.2.3.2.3. The Contractor's Material and Test Certificate (see Figure 16.1) includes provisions for recording the following information:

1. Time it takes for the valve to trip after opening the system test valve
2. Air and water pressures before the test
3. Air pressure at trip point
4. Delivery time for water to reach the test outlet
5. Indication of whether or not alarms operated properly

The valve should operate in accordance with the tolerance specified by the manufacturer for the trip point. When this test is conducted, no maximum time limit is imposed by NFPA 13 as long as the system capacity is less than 750 gal (2850 L). For example, a 3-minute interval from the time the inspector's test valve is opened until the water is delivered to that inspector's test valve is an acceptable time lapse. The 60-second time limit imposed by 7.2.3.2 only applies to systems that exceed a capacity of 750 gal (2850 L) and are not calculated for water delivery as permitted by 7.2.3.3.

16.2.3.3 Deluge System.

16.2.3.3.1 The automatic operation of a deluge or preaction valve shall be tested in accordance with the manufacturer's instructions.

16.2.3.3.2 The manual and remote control operation, where present, shall also be tested.

16.2.3.4 Main Drain.

16.2.3.4.1 The main drain valve shall be opened and remain open until the system pressure stabilizes.

16.2.3.4.2 The static and residual pressures shall be recorded on the contractor's test certificate.

FAQ ▶
What is the purpose of the main drain test?

The main drain test, which is discussed in 16.2.3.4.1 and 16.2.3.4.2, is crucial in that it establishes a baseline against which future tests can be compared. By recording available static and residual pressures during each test, a database can be established and used for tracking the relative condition of the water supply during the life of the system. Decreases in the static pressure, residual pressure, or both could indicate a deteriorating water supply, an obstructed supply pipe, or a partially closed valve.

 Chapters 5 and 12 of NFPA 25, *Standard for the Inspection, Testing, and Maintenance of Water-Based Fire Protection Systems,* requires periodic tests of the main drain valve.

16.2.3.5 Operating Test.

16.2.3.5.1 Each hydrant shall be fully opened and closed under system water pressure, and dry barrel hydrants shall be checked for proper drainage.

16.2.3.5.2 Where fire pumps are available, this check shall be done with the pumps running.

16.2.3.5.3 All control valves shall be fully closed and opened under system water pressure to ensure proper operation.

16.2.4 Pressure Reducing Valves.

16.2.4.1 Each pressure-reducing valve shall be tested upon completion of installation to ensure proper operation under flow and no-flow conditions.

16.2.4.2 Testing shall verify that the device properly regulates outlet pressure at both maximum and normal inlet pressure conditions.

16.2.4.3 The results of the flow test of each pressure-reducing valve shall be recorded on the contractor's test certificate.

16.2.4.4 The results shall include the static and residual inlet pressures, static and residual outlet pressures, and the flow rate.

If pressure-reducing valves (see Exhibit 16.1) are installed to control excessive pressures—for example, greater than 175 psi (12.1 bar) for most systems—they must be flow tested to ensure that they are correctly set (see 16.2.4.1 through 16.2.4.4). Pressure-reducing valves can also be required for combined sprinkler/standpipe systems. The flow-testing requirements of these devices originated not from a potential functional failure of the device but to ensure that the installer properly followed the installation instructions. Following the manufacturer's instructions is very important when determining the appropriate pressure and flow values for these types of devices. An improperly set pressure-reducing device can have catastrophic results.

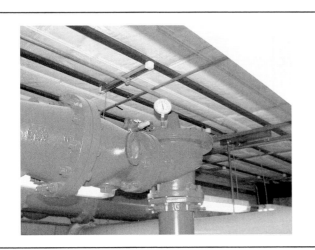

EXHIBIT 16.1 Pressure-Reducing Valve. (Courtesy of John Jensen)

16.2.5 Backflow Prevention Assemblies.

16.2.5.1 The backflow prevention assembly shall be forward flow tested to ensure proper operation.

16.2.5.2 The minimum flow rate shall be the system demand, including hose stream demand where applicable.

Backflow prevention assemblies are covered in 16.2.5.1 and 16.2.5.2. Additional information on the testing of backflow devices is provided in 8.16.4.6. Due to their effect on sprinkler systems, backflow prevention devices must be accounted for through hydraulic analysis and flow testing.

16.2.6 Exposure Systems.
Operating tests shall be made of exposure protection systems upon completion of the installation, where such tests do not risk water damage to the building on which they are installed or to adjacent buildings.

Exposure systems are covered in 16.2.6. Acceptance tests should reveal that all surfaces to be protected from radiant and connective heat are uniformly wetted and that the most remote sprinkler has an adequate discharge pressure. The designer needs to consider the potential effects of wind and other drafts so that they do not substantially impact the sprinkler's intended discharge and spray pattern and do not prevent the proper wetting of the surfaces to be protected.

16.3 Circulating Closed Loop Systems

16.3.1 For sprinkler systems with non–fire protection connections, additional information shall be appended to the Contractor's Material and Test Certificate for Aboveground Piping shown in Figure 16.1 as follows:

(1) Certification that all auxiliary devices, such as heat pumps, circulating pumps, heat exchangers, radiators, and luminaries, if a part of the system, have a pressure rating of at least 175 psi or 300 psi (12.1 bar or 20.7 bar) if exposed to pressures greater than 175 psi (12.1 bar).

(2) All components of sprinkler system and auxiliary system have been pressure tested as a composite system in accordance with 16.2.2.

(3) Waterflow tests have been conducted and waterflow alarms have operated while auxiliary equipment is in each of the possible modes of operation.

(4) With auxiliary equipment tested in each possible mode of operation and with no flow from sprinklers or test connection, waterflow alarm signals did not operate.

(5) Excess temperature controls for shutting down the auxiliary system have been properly field tested.

16.3.2 Discharge tests of sprinkler systems with non–fire protection connections shall be conducted using system test connections described in 6.8.2.

16.3.3 Pressure gauges shall be installed at critical points and readings shall be taken under various modes of auxiliary equipment operation.

16.3.4 Waterflow alarm signals shall be responsive to discharge of water through system test pipes while auxiliary equipment is in each of the possible modes of operation.

16.4 Instructions

The installing contractor shall provide the owner with the following:

(1) All literature and instructions provided by the manufacturer describing proper operation and maintenance of any equipment and devices installed

(2) NFPA 25, *Standard for the Inspection, Testing, and Maintenance of Water-Based Fire Protection Systems*

Following the requirements of Section 16.4 is important so that the system is operable during its entire life expectancy. Many systems installed more than 50 years ago are still in service, are being properly maintained, and continue to protect lives and property. Therefore it is imperative that the owner be provided with all literature and instructions from the manufacturer describing proper operation and maintenance and NFPA 25 to ensure that the system(s) are properly inspected, tested and maintained.

16.5* Hydraulic Design Information Sign

A.16.5 See Figure A.16.5.

This system as shown on . . . . company

print no . . . . dated . . . .

for . . . .

at . . . . contract no . . . .

is designed to discharge at a rate of . . . . gpm/ft^2

(L/min/m^2) of floor area over a maximum area of . . . .

ft^2 (m^2) when supplied with water at a rate of . . . .

gpm (L/min) at . . . . psi (bar) at the base of the riser.

Hose stream allowance of . . . . gpm (L/min)

is included in the above.

Occupancy classification . . . .

Commodity classification . . . .

Maximum storage height . . . .

FIGURE A.16.5 *Sample Nameplate.*

16.5.1 The installing contractor shall identify a hydraulically designed sprinkler system with a permanently marked weatherproof metal or rigid plastic sign secured with corrosion-resistant wire, chain, or other approved means. Such signs shall be placed at the alarm valve, dry pipe valve, preaction valve, or deluge valve supplying the corresponding hydraulically designed area.

In more cases than not, as-built drawings become lost or misplaced over time. By keeping a permanent record of the design parameters attached to the system riser, as required in 16.5.1, any future modifications or work on the system are much easier and less costly to perform. The information contained on the nameplate is also of vital importance in assessing the ability of the system to control fires as the building's occupancy changes or the water supply's strength deteriorates. Exhibit 16.2 illustrates a hydraulic nameplate.

EXHIBIT 16.2 *Hydraulic Nameplate.*

16.5.2 The sign shall include the following information:

(1) Location of the design area or areas
(2) Discharge densities over the design area or areas
(3) Required flow and residual pressure demand at the base of the riser
(4) Occupancy classification or commodity classification and maximum permitted storage height and configuration
(5) Hose stream demand included in addition to the sprinkler demand

SUMMARY

System acceptance is the important final step in verifying the design and installation of the system. These final steps in the design and installation of a sprinkler system are to confirm that the basic requirements of NFPA 13 are satisfied, that the work was completed in an acceptable manner, and that the customer receives a system that performs as intended. Additionally, the acceptance tests assure that the final installed sprinkler system is designed to protect the actual hazard present. The remedy of any deficiencies found during the acceptance tests, in the sprinkler system design or installation is more easily corrected than if discovered after the building is occupied when correction can be extremely costly.

 ## REFERENCE CITED IN COMMENTARY

National Fire Protection Association, 1 Batterymarch Park, P.O. Box 9101, Quincy, MA 02269-9101

NFPA 25, *Standard for the Inspection, Testing, and Maintenance of Water-Based Fire Protection Systems,* 2002 edition

Marine Systems

Chapter 17 covers the specifics for marine (shipboard) applications of automatic sprinkler systems. The requirements of Chapter 17 include general requirements; system components, hardware and use; system-specific requirements; installation requirements; design approaches; plans and calculations; water supplies; system acceptance; and system instruction and maintenance. The additional requirements of Chapter 17 are intended to be applied to marine applications only. Where a sprinkler system on a floating structure takes its water supply from the water on which the structure floats, as opposed to from a permanent water main, the sprinkler system should comply with Chapter 17.

17.1 General

17.1.1 Chapter 17 outlines the deletions, modifications, and additions that shall be required for marine application.

17.1.2 All other requirements of this standard shall apply to merchant vessel systems except as modified by this chapter.

The chapter on marine systems first appeared in the 1996 edition of NFPA 13. Prior to the 1990s, relatively few automatic sprinkler systems were installed on commercial ships in the United States. Because sprinkler installations on ships were relatively rare, the sprinkler system design and installation requirements contained in the Code of Federal Regulations applicable to ships had not kept pace with modern technology.

However, changes in the demographics of the passenger vessel fleet in the United States—from ships with overnight accommodations that resembled hotel-type occupancies to vessels with no overnight accommodations that served as assembly occupancies—prompted changes in vessel construction and fire protection requirements. These changes favored sprinkler system installations.

Internationally, a number of fire casualties led the International Maritime Organization to require installation of sprinkler systems on all new passenger vessels and the retrofitting of sprinkler systems on existing ships. Similarly, NFPA 301, *Code for Safety to Life from Fire on Merchant Vessels,* which was first published in 1998, requires installation of sprinkler systems on most passenger vessels.

In Exhibit 17.1, the fire on the cruise ship Ecstasy is shown being extinguished. More than 2500 people were aboard the cruise ship in 1998 when a fire began in the laundry room. Fire boats and on-board fire fighters were needed to extinguish the fire.

Instead of revising its regulations applicable to sprinkler systems, the U.S. Coast Guard, which is the authority having jurisdiction for commercial ships in the United States, looked to NFPA 13 for shipboard sprinkler system design and installation requirements. Although the fire hazards and the purpose of a sprinkler system on marine vessels closely resemble those of

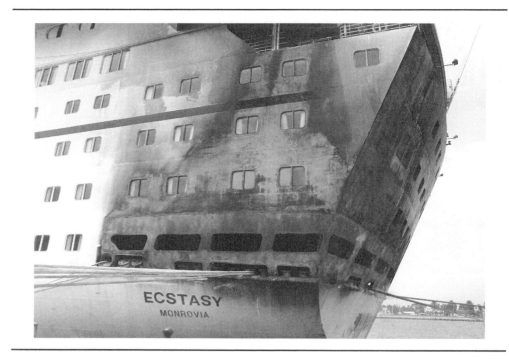

shore-side structures, certain modifications to the requirements in NFPA 13 are necessary for marine applications (see 17.1.1 and 17.1.2).

    As an initial step, the U.S. Coast Guard informally adopted the 1991 edition of NFPA 13 and published a set of changes to the standard that were necessary to make NFPA 13 applicable to shipboard installations. These changes were published in Navigation and Vessel Inspection Circular (NVIC) 10-93. The Technical Committee on Automatic Sprinklers subsequently reviewed NVIC 10-93 and included the necessary changes in the 1996 edition of NFPA 13. The U.S. Coast Guard subsequently replaced its sprinkler regulations and NVIC 10-93 by referencing the 1996 edition of NFPA 13 in the Code of Federal Regulations.

The differences in Chapter 17 primarily reflect unique shipboard factors such as operating environment, the unavailability of outside fire-fighting assistance, and egress philosophy. Because passengers and crew of a passenger ship cannot simply egress to safety, the overall shipboard fire protection system also demands a slightly higher level of protection from the sprinkler system. Although the entire standard applies to shipboard sprinkler systems, the requirements in Chapter 17 take precedence over those found in other chapters of NFPA 13.

The marine chapter was revised in 1999 and in 2002 to reflect experience gained through its application over the preceding years.

17.1.3 The following definitions shall be applicable to this chapter *(see Section 3.14):*

The definitions that are included in 17.1.3, while they appear in Chapter 3 of NFPA 13, are also duplicated here to assist the user with definitions that are applicable to the requirements of Chapter 17 only. These definitions should be utilized where these terms appear in Chapter 17.

(1) *A-Class Boundary*—A boundary designed to resist the passage of smoke and flame for 1 hour when tested in accordance with ASTM E 119, *Standard Test Methods for Fire Tests of Building Construction and Materials.*
(2) *B-Class Boundary*—A boundary designed to resist the passage of flame for ½ hour when tested in accordance with ASTM E 119, *Standard Test Methods for Fire Tests of Building Construction and Materials.*

(3) *Central Safety Station*—A continuously manned control station from which all of the fire control equipment is monitored. If this station is not the bridge, direct communication with the bridge shall be provided by means other than the ship's service telephone.

The central safety station, as defined in 17.1.3(3), is typically the bridge.

(4)* *Heat-Sensitive Material*—A material whose melting point is below 1700°F (926.7°C).

A.17.1.3(4) The backbone of the fire protection philosophy for U.S. flagged vessels and passenger vessels that trade internationally is limiting a fire to the compartment of origin by passive means. Materials that do not withstand a 1-hour fire exposure when tested in accordance with ASTM E 119, *Standard Test Methods for Fire Tests of Building Construction and Materials,* are considered "heat sensitive." *[See Figure A.17.1.3(4).]*

International Shore Connection

Threads to mate hydrants and hose at shore facilities

Threads to mate hydrants and hose on ship

9/16 in. (14 mm) minimum

2.75 in. (70 mm)
3.5 in. (89 mm)
1.25 in. (32 mm)
0.75 in. (19 mm)

2.75 in. (70 mm)
3.5 in. (89 mm)
1.25 in. (32 mm)
0.75 in. (19 mm)

Shore

Material: Any suitable for 150 psi (10.3 bar) service (shore)
Flange surface: Flat face
Gasket material: Any suitable for 150 psi (10.3 bar) service
Bolts: Four 5/8-in. (16-mm) minimum diameter, 2-in. (51-mm) long, threaded to within 1 in. (25.4 mm) of bolt head
Nuts: Four, to fit bolts
Washers: Four, to fit bolts

Ship

Material: Brass or bronze suitable for 150 psi (10.3 bar) service (ship)

FIGURE A.17.1.3(4) *International Shore Fire Connection.*

Heat-sensitive material is defined in 17.1.3(4). Ships are highly compartmentalized by passive fire barrier systems, such as bulkheads (walls) and decks (floors). Overall, shipboard fire protection places a greater emphasis on passive fire safety systems than on active fire suppression systems, such as automatic sprinklers. An assembly that is not expected to withstand fire exposure for 1 hour in accordance with the time–temperature profile of ASTM E 119, *Standard Test Methods for Fire Tests of Building Construction and Materials,* is considered heat sensitive. The fire endurance of materials, such as piping, that penetrate fire barriers on ships must be tested dry so that a failure of the sprinkler system would not cause a failure of the passive system.

(5) *Heel*—The inclination of a ship to one side.

(6) *Heel Angle*—The angle defined by the intersection of a vertical line through the center of a vessel and a line perpendicular to the surface of the water.

Exhibit 17.2 illustrates measurement of the heel angle, which is defined in 17.1.3(6).

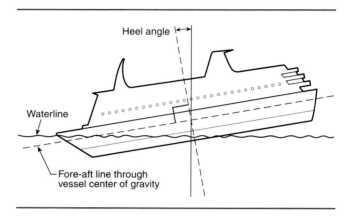

EXHIBIT 17.2 *Measurement of the Heel Angle. (Courtesy of Morgan Hurley)*

(7) *International Shore Connection*—A universal connection complying with ASTM F 1121, *Standard Specification for International Shore Connections for Marine Fire Applications,* to which shoreside fire-fighting hose are to be connected.

(8)* *Marine System*—A sprinkler system installed on a ship, boat, or other floating structure that takes its supply from the water on which the vessel floats.

A.17.1.3(8) Some types of sprinkler systems can closely resemble marine systems, such as a system installed on a floating structure that has a permanent water supply connection to a public main. For these types of systems, judgment should be used in determining if certain aspects of Chapter 17 are applicable.

FAQ ▶
Do the requirements of Chapter 17 apply to float structures such as restaurants and casinos that are either mobile or permanently moored?

Marine system is defined in 17.1.3(8). Although originally intended only for application to ships, other types of waterborne structures were recognized to more closely resemble ships than buildings. Examples include restaurants and casinos that are built on permanently moored barges. Where a sprinkler system on a floating structure takes its water supply from the water on which the structure floats, as opposed to from a permanent water main, the sprinkler system must comply with Chapter 17.

(9)* *Marine Thermal Barrier*—An assembly that is constructed of noncombustible materials and made intact with the main structure of the vessel, such as shell, structural bulkheads, and decks. A marine thermal barrier shall meet the requirements of a B-Class boundary. In addition, a marine thermal barrier shall be insulated such that, if tested in accordance with ASTM E 119, *Standard Test Methods for Fire Tests of Building Construction and Materials,* for 15 minutes, the average temperature of the unexposed side does not rise more than 250°F (193°C) above the original temperature, nor does the temperature at any one point, including any joint, rise more than 405°F (225°C) above the original temperature.

A.17.1.3(9) A marine thermal barrier is typically referred to as a B-15 boundary.

(10) *Supervision*—A visual and audible alarm signal given at the central safety station to indicate when the system is in operation or when a condition that would impair the satisfactory operation of the system exists. Supervisory alarms shall give a distinct indication for each individual system component that is monitored.

(11) *Survival Angle*—The maximum angle to which a vessel is permitted to heel after the assumed damage required by stability regulations is imposed.

The survival angle, which is defined in 17.1.3(11), for a ship is typically calculated when the ship is designed. A sprinkler designer would likely need to consult with a vessel's representative, such as the captain or naval architect, to determine the survival angle. The sprinkler system equipment is selected to remain functional at this angle of inclination.

(12) *Type 1 Stair*—A fully enclosed stair that serves all levels of a vessel in which persons can be employed.

(13) *Marine Water Supply*—The supply portion of the sprinkler system from the water pressure tank or the sea suction of the designated sprinkler system pump up to and including the valve that isolates the sprinkler system from these two water sources.

17.1.4* Occupancy Classifications. Marine environment classifications shall be in accordance with Section 5.1.

A.17.1.4 In addition to the examples provided in A.5.1, Table A.17.1.4 provides additional examples of occupancy definitions of typical shipboard spaces.

The classifications in Table A.17.1.4 are not meant to be applied without giving consideration to the definition of each occupancy hazard given in the standard. Table A.17.1.4 is general guidance for classification of typical spaces. Where a space is outfitted such that the occupancy definitions indicate that another classification would be more appropriate, the most representative and most demanding occupancy classification should be used. For example, it would certainly be possible to outfit a stateroom to require upgrading the occupancy to ordinary hazard, Group 1.

When a vessel undergoes modifications, alterations, or service changes that significantly affect the fire risk of the occupancy of one or more compartments, the occupancy classification should be reevaluated to determine if it has changed.

TABLE A.17.1.4 Examples of Shipboard Space Occupancy Classification

| Occupancy Type | Space Types Included | | Examples |
	CFR[1]	SOLAS[2]	
Light hazard	1[3], 2, 3, 4, 5, 6, 7, 8[4], 13	1[3], 2, 3, 4, 5, 6, 7, 8, 9	Accommodation spaces Small pantries
Ordinary hazard (Group 1)	8[4], 9[4]	12, 13[4]	Galleys Storage areas Sales shops Laundries Pantries with significant storage
Ordinary hazard (Group 2)	9[4], 11[4]	12[4], 13[4]	Sales shops Storage areas Stages (with sets) Machine shops
Extra hazard (Group 1)	1, 9[4], 10, 11[4]	1, 12[4], 13[4]	Auxiliary machinery—limited combustible liquids[5] Steering rooms—combustible hydraulic fluid in use[5]
Extra hazard (Group 2)	1, 9[4], 10, 11[4]	1, 12[4], 13[4]	Auxiliary machinery—with combustible liquids[5] Machinery spaces[5]

[1]Space type designations are given in 46 CFR 72.05-5.

[2]Space type designations are given in the *International Convention for the Safety of Life at Sea*, 1974 (SOLAS 74), as amended, regulations II-2/3 and II-2/26.

[3]Primarily for accommodation-type control stations, such as the wheel house, which would not include generator rooms or similar-type spaces.

[4]Depends on storage type, quantity, and height and distance below sprinkler.

[5]Automatic sprinklers typically will not be the primary means of protection in these areas; total flooding systems are usually used.

17.1.5* Partial Installations.

A.17.1.5 Experience has shown that structures that are partially sprinklered can be overrun by well-developed fires originating in unsprinklered areas. Therefore, the entire vessel should be sprinklered whenever sprinkler systems are considered.

Partial installations are discussed in 17.1.5. Although limited area systems are discussed by the standard, partial sprinkler systems are not acceptable for shipboard fire protection. Paragraph 17.1.5.2 recognizes that some areas of a ship, such as the engine room, are typically not protected by an automatic sprinkler system but would be protected by another type of fire protection system such as a carbon dioxide system. However, these spaces need to be separated by a 1-hour-rated assembly. Paragraph 17.1.5.3 recognizes that sprinkler coverage in certain areas of a ship might not be necessary and maintains the exception for their omission under certain conditions.

17.1.5.1 Partial installation of automatic sprinklers shall not be permitted, unless the requirements of 17.1.5.2 or 17.1.5.3 are met.

17.1.5.2 Spaces shall be permitted to be protected with an alternative, approved fire suppression system where such areas are separated from the sprinklered areas with a 1 hour–rated assembly.

17.1.5.3 The requirements of 17.1.5.1 shall not apply where specific sections of this standard permit the omission of sprinklers.

17.2 System Components, Hardware, and Use

17.2.1* Sprinklers shall have a nominal discharge coefficient greater than 1.9.

A.17.2.1 Sprinklers with a nominal K-factor of 2.8 or less coupled with a system strainer minimize the potential for clogging.

Experience has shown that sprinklers with nominal K-factors smaller than 2.8 have a greater likelihood of becoming clogged by scale (see 17.2.1). Additionally, piping that is exposed to salt water has a tendency to develop more scale than piping that is exposed to fresh water.

FAQ ▶
What happened to the requirements for a minimum sprinkler operating pressure of 10 psi?

The 1996 edition required a minimum operating pressure of 10 psi (0.69 bar) to account for changes in elevation between sprinklers and their water supply as the vessel lists (leans to a side) or heels (points upwards or downwards). However, this 10-psi (0.69-bar) minimum was replaced with the more performance-oriented requirements contained in 17.6.4

17.2.2* Sprinkler piping penetrations shall be designed to preserve the fire integrity of the ceiling or bulkhead penetrated.

A.17.2.2 Where a marine thermal barrier is penetrated, limiting the opening around the sprinkler pipe to 1/16 in. (1.6 mm) is considered as meeting this requirement.

Because of the importance of passive fire protection systems, piping that penetrates walls, floors, and ceilings must not compromise the integrity of the passive fire protection system, as stated in 17.2.2. For an A-Class (1-hour) barrier, the penetration is usually protected with an approved fire stop or the piping is welded or flanged to the vessel structure at the penetration. For vessels that are subject to the International Convention for the Safety of Life at Sea (SOLAS), all penetrations of A-Class divisions must be fire tested in accordance with the IMO Fire Test Procedures Code. On domestic vessels, a small 1/16-in. (1.6-mm) gap is considered acceptable for penetrations of any B-Class (30-minute) division, such as a marine thermal barrier. On vessels in international service, penetrations in B-Class divisions are subject to regulation II-2/9.3.2 of SOLAS.

17.2.3 Spare Sprinklers.

17.2.3.1 The required stock of spare sprinklers shall be carried for each type of sprinkler installed onboard the vessel.

17.2.3.2 Where fewer than six sprinklers of a particular type are installed, 100 percent spares shall be kept in stock.

In the event of sprinkler system activation at sea, obtaining replacement sprinklers can be impossible for a long period of time, which is the reason for the requirement in 17.2.3.2. Additionally, because of the variety of spaces that are found on a large ship, it would not be unusual to find a wide variety of sprinkler types installed. The requirement for spare sprinklers is increased in 17.2.3 to ensure that if, for example, a sprinkler actuation occurs in a small compartment that is protected by sprinklers that do not match the majority found on the ship, it would be possible to replace the sprinklers at sea.

17.2.3.3 Where applicable, at least one elastometric gasket shall be kept in the cabinet for each fire department connection that is installed onboard the vessel.

The marine environment can also accelerate aging of the gaskets in fire department connections. Readily available spares are important (see 17.2.3.3).

17.2.3.4 The cabinet containing spare sprinklers, special wrenches, and elastometric gaskets shall be located in the same central safety station that contains the alarm annunciator panel(s) and supervisory indicators.

17.2.4 System Pipe and Fittings.

System pipe and fittings are covered in 17.2.4. The 1996 edition prohibited the use of brazing filler metal because of concerns regarding saltwater corrosion. However, further evaluation has indicated that brazing filler metal has acceptable corrosion resistance qualities when exposed to salt water, and the prohibition was removed in the 1999 edition.

17.2.4.1* When ferrous materials are used for piping between the sea chest and zone control valves, these materials shall be protected against corrosion by hot dip galvanizing or by the use of Schedule 80 piping.

A.17.2.4.1 When nonferrous materials are used, consideration should be given to protecting against galvanic corrosion where the nonferrous materials connect to steel pipe. Consideration should also be given to protection against galvanic corrosion from pipe hangers in areas of high humidity.

The piping between the sea chest and the sprinkler zone valves are likely to see the frequent flow of salt water when testing. Sprinkler zone piping will rarely, if ever, be exposed to salt water. In such an event, NFPA 25, *Standard for the Inspection, Testing, and Maintenance of Water-Based Fire Protection Systems,* requires flushing of the piping. Even if the piping is not flushed, the salt water will not be replenished and will lose oxygen content in fairly short order.

Even if galvanized, the failure from corrosion from the interior of the pipe is likely to be at all threaded connections, welded assembly connections, and where brass sprinklers thread into ferrous pipe. Only hot dipped galvanized after fabrication of assembly (as opposed to simply hot dipped galvanized pipe and fittings) will protect against some of those failures. Hot dipped galvanized after fabrication of assembly is practical from the sea chest to the sprinkler manifold where spaces are open and pipe is relatively large and uses flanged takedown joints instead of threaded unions. Hot dipped galvanized after fabrication of assembly is not practical in the sprinkler zone pipe where it is mainly field fit.

The additional requirements in 17.2.4.1 aimed at protecting ferrous materials reflect the concerns regarding the potential of corrosion damage caused by salt water. The 1996 edition required all sprinkler piping used in marine systems to be protected against corrosion by either hot dip galvanization or the use of extra heavy schedule material. However, this requirement was removed in the 1999 edition for all but the piping between the sea chest and sprinkler zone valves, because 17.7.4.3 requires charging of all other piping with fresh water, and NFPA 25, *Standard for the Inspection, Testing, and Maintenance of Water-Based Fire Protection Systems,* requires that piping be flushed following exposure to salt water.

Galvanic corrosion could occur where piping transitions from copper to steel or where a metal different from the piping is used for hangers.

17.2.4.2 Maximum design pressure for copper and brass pipe shall not exceed 250 psi (17.2 bar).

Vessel construction regulations typically do not permit copper or brass piping to be subjected to pressures in excess of 250 psi (17.2 bar) (see 17.2.4.2).

17.2.5 Pipe Support.

The additional requirements for pipe support in 17.2.5 are intended to protect sprinkler piping from the motions typically found on ships. When in doubt as to the magnitude of these motions, consultation with a naval architect may be necessary.

17.2.5.1* Pipe supports shall comply with the following:

(1) Pipe supports shall be designed to provide adequate lateral, longitudinal, and vertical sway bracing.
(2) The design shall account for the degree of bracing, which varies with the route and operation of the vessel.
(3) Bracing shall be designed to ensure the following:
  (a) Slamming, heaving, and rolling will not shift sprinkler piping, potentially moving sprinklers above ceilings, bulkheads, or other obstructions.
  (b) Piping and sprinklers will remain in place at a steady heel angle at least equal to the maximum required damaged survival angle.
(4) Pipe supports shall be welded to the structure.
(5) Hangers that can loosen during ship motion or vibration, such as screw-down-type hangers, shall not be permitted.
(6) Hangers that are listed for seismic use shall be permitted to be used in accordance with their listing.

 A.17.2.5.1 When designing supports, the selection and spacing of pipe supports should take into account the pipe dimensions, mechanical and physical properties of piping materials and supports, operating temperature, thermal expansion effects, external loads, thrust forces, vibration, maximum accelerations, differential motions to which the system might be subjected, and the type of support.

The route of the vessel is intended to be descriptive of its usual operating area. For example, expected motion of the system on an ocean vessel is expected to be considerably greater than the motion of a vessel that operates on a river. A vessel that operates within the confines of any of the Great Lakes is expected to subject the system pipe to greater motion than would a vessel that operates on a lake such as Lake Tahoe.

It is recommended that the designer review the requirements for automatic sprinkler systems that are subject to earthquakes. While it is obvious that shipboard motions and accelerations differ from those that occur during an earthquake, the general principle of protecting the piping system against damage applies. Individual hanger design, however, will be very similar.

Earthquake protection does not apply to ships; however, motions are similar to those that a ship will experience in a seaway. The design principles discussed in this section should be used as a guide for shipboard system design.

17.2.5.2 Sprinkler piping shall be supported by the primary structural members of the vessel such as beams, girders, and stiffeners.

17.2.5.3* The components of hanger assemblies that are welded directly to the ship structure shall not be required to be listed.

A.17.2.5.3 Use of heat-sensitive materials for pipe hangers and supports might be desirable in some cases. Where heat-sensitive materials are used, the hangers and supports should be adequately protected by either the direct application of insulation or installation behind a marine thermal barrier. Insulation materials applied directly to hangers should be insulated in accordance with the method provided in Society of Naval Architects and Marine Engineers Technical Research Bulletin 2-21, "Aluminum Fire Protection Guidelines."

17.2.5.4* U-hook sizes shall be no less than that specified in Table 9.1.2.3.

A.17.2.5.4 Consideration should be given to increasing the size of rods and U-hooks as necessary, to account for service and operational loading, including ship motion and vibrations.

17.2.6 Valves.

17.2.6.1* All indicating, supply, and zone control valves shall be supervised open from a central safety station.

A.17.2.6.1 Shipboard installations will normally require more than one valve per water supply. Locking valves in the open position is not an acceptable substitute for the requirement of 17.2.6.1 but can be done in addition to the supervision requirement.

By supervising all indicating, supply, and zone control valves from the central safety station, as required in 17.2.6.1, any system impairment is intended to be quickly detected and corrected.

17.2.6.2 Drain and test valves shall meet the applicable requirements of 46 CFR 56.20 and 56.60.

A requirement of 46 CFR 56.20, which is cited in 17.2.6.2, is that the valve have limited leakage after removal of all resilient material. The removal of the resilient material simulates extended aging or exposure of the valve to a fire. The intention is to ensure that failure of a drain line does not allow large quantities of water to flow uncontrolled into the structure of a vessel.

A requirement of 46 CFR 56.60 is that valve castings meet ASTM A 47, *Standard Specification for Ferritic Malleable Iron Castings,* or ASTM A 197, *Standard Specification for Cupola Malleable Iron,* for malleable iron, ASTM A 126, *Standard Specification for Gray Iron Castings for Valves, Flanges and Pipe Fittings,* for gray iron, or ASTM A 395, *Standard Specification for Ferritic Ductile Iron Pressure-Retaining Castings for Use at Elevated Temperatures,* for ductile iron. Additionally, the valve itself is required by 46 CFR 56.60 to meet ANSI B16.34, *Valves—Flanged, Threaded, and Welding End.*

17.2.6.3 Valve markings shall include the information required by 46 CFR 56.20-5(a).

A requirement of 46 CFR 56.20-5(a), which is cited in 17.2.6.3, is that the valve be marked with the manufacturer's name and the service conditions for which it is intended.

17.2.7 Fire Department Connections and International Shore Connections.

17.2.7.1* A fire department connection and an International Shore Connection shall be installed.

A.17.2.7.1 International Shore Connections are portable universal couplings that permit connections of shipboard sprinkler or firemain systems between one ship and another or between a shore facility and a ship. Both the ship and the shore facility are expected to have an International Shore Connection fitting such that in an emergency they can be attached to their respective fire hoses and bolted together to permit charging the ship's system. It must be portable to accommodate hose-to-hose connection and allow assistance from any position.

Installation of an additional fire boat connection might be required on-board vessels whose route is such that regular access to fire boats is possible. An additional fire boat connection might not be necessary where fire boats are equipped to connect to the regular fire department connection. *(See A.17.2.7.7.)*

17.2.7.2 The requirements for a fire department connection in 17.2.7.1 shall not apply to vessels that operate primarily on international voyages.

17.2.7.3 Connections shall be located near the gangway or other shore access point so that they are readily accessible to the land-based fire department.

17.2.7.4 Fire department and International Shore Connections shall be colored and marked so that the connections are easily located from the shore access point (i.e., gangway location) and will not be confused with a firemain connection.

 17.2.7.5 An 18 in. × 18 in. (0.46 m × 0.46 m) sign displaying the symbol for fire department connection as shown in Table 5.2.1 of NFPA 170, *Standard for Fire Safety Symbols,* shall be placed at the connection so that it is in plain sight from the shore access point.

17.2.7.6 Connections on both sides of the vessel shall be provided where shore access arrangements make it necessary.

17.2.7.7* Fire department connection thread type shall be compatible with fire department equipment.

A **A.17.2.7.7** Selection of the pipe thread for the fire department connection should be done very carefully. It is recommended that a 2½-in. (63.5-mm) siamese connection with National Standard Hose Thread be used since a majority of fire department hose lines will be compatible with this thread. However, it must be noted that some fire jurisdictions might not be compatible with a connection of this type. Serious consideration should be given to the vessel's typical operating area. Precautions and planning should avert the possibility of the vessel being forced ashore by fire at a location where the fire department equipment is not compatible with this connection. Carriage of extra fittings and pre-voyage arrangements with all applicable jurisdictions should be considered. The International Shore Connection is required to ensure that all vessels fitted with sprinkler systems have at least one type of common connection.

17.3 System Requirements

17.3.1* Relief Valves. Relief valves shall be provided on all wet pipe systems.

A **A.17.3.1** Special consideration should be given to the installation of relief valves in all wet pipe systems. Ambient ship temperatures can vary greatly depending on operating environment, duration of voyage, and failure of climate control systems.

FAQ ▶
Why are relief valves required on all wet pipe sprinkler systems?

Large ambient temperature variations occur on ships because of changes in climate or solar heating. Relief valves are required by 17.3.1 on all wet pipe systems to protect against piping failure caused by pressure buildup. This provision extends beyond that required for gridded systems in shore-side structures, as indicated in 7.1.2.

17.3.2 Spare Detection Devices. The number of spare detection devices or fusible elements used for protection systems that shall be carried per temperature rating is as follows:

(1) Vessels shall have two spare detection devices or fusible elements when operating voyages are normally less than 24 hours.
(2) Vessels shall have four spare detection devices or fusible elements when operating voyages are normally more than 24 hours.

FAQ ▶
Why are spare detection devices required?

The provisions of 7.3.1.4 are amplified in 17.3.2 by requiring additional detection devices for preaction and deluge systems for vessels with routes that routinely exceed 24 hours.

As previously discussed for spare sprinklers (see commentary on 17.2.3), in the event of a shipboard fire while at sea, replacement detection devices are critical to returning the system to service. These requirements work to ensure that the system will be able to remain in service until additional detection devices can be obtained.

17.3.3 System Piping Supervision. All preaction sprinkler systems shall be supervised regardless of the number of sprinklers supplied.

Because of the large number of small spaces on a ship and the level of reliability required of all shipboard fire protection systems, all preaction systems—not just those with more than 20 sprinklers—need to be supervised, as stated in 17.3.3.

17.3.4 Circulating Closed Loop Systems. Circulating closed loop systems shall not be permitted.

17.4 Installation Requirements

17.4.1 Temperature Zones. Intermediate temperature–rated sprinklers shall be installed under a noninsulated steel deck that is exposed to sunlight.

To reduce the possibility of sprinkler operation caused by solar heating, intermediate temperature–rated sprinklers are required by 17.4.1 under uninsulated steel decks, such as ceilings, that are exposed to sunlight.

17.4.2* Residential Sprinklers. Residential sprinklers shall be permitted for use only in sleeping accommodation areas.

A.17.4.2 Areas fitted primarily with multiple staterooms and corridors should be considered sleeping accommodation areas.

On ships, sleeping accommodation areas, which are discussed in 17.4.2, are the only spaces that should be considered and treated as dwelling units.

◀ **FAQ**
What portions of the ship can be considered dwelling units?

17.4.3 Window Protection. Where required, windows shall be protected by sprinklers installed at a distance not exceeding 1 ft (0.3 m) from the glazing at a spacing not exceeding 6 ft (1.8 m) such that the entire glazing surface is wetted at a linear density not less than 6 gpm/ft (75 mm/min), unless listed window sprinkler protection systems are installed in accordance with their installation and testing criteria.

Vessel construction codes require protection of windows that face areas where passengers can be expected to gather in the event of a fire. The requirements for sprinkler spacing and design densities, which are discussed in 17.4.3, are based on research conducted by Richardson and Oleszkiewicz [1987]. The requirement recognizes that sprinklers specifically listed for window protection are available. It is noteworthy that the required density is based on protection of ordinary, non–fire-rated glazing.

17.4.4* Concealed Spaces.

A.17.4.4 If combustibles are present such that they constitute a threat, the space should be sprinklered. One example would be the presence of large bundles of unsheathed computer or electrical cable. Typical amounts of lighting or control cabling should not be considered to constitute a fire threat.

17.4.4.1 Concealed spaces that are constructed of combustible materials, or materials with combustible finishes or that contain combustible materials, shall be sprinklered.

17.4.4.2 The requirements of 17.4.4.1 shall not apply to concealed spaces that contain only nonmetallic piping that is continuously filled with water.

Paragraph 17.4.4.2 exceeds the requirements of 8.14.1. Ships, particularly passenger ships, typically have large concealed spaces, such as interstitial spaces above ceilings, that can contain large quantities of combustible piping, cabling, and so forth. The intent of this requirement is to protect against possible avenues where a fire could spread undetected.

17.4.5 Vertical Shafts.

17.4.5.1 Sprinklers are not required in vertical shafts used as duct, electrical, or pipe shafts that are nonaccessible, noncombustible, and enclosed in an A-Class-rated assembly.

Paragraph 17.4.5.1 states that sprinklers are not required in vertical shafts, which echoes the requirements in 8.14.2.1 and allows for the omission of sprinklers in vertical shafts enclosed by A-Class (1-hour) assemblies. Many of the concealed spaces alluded to in 17.4.4 are enclosed by B-Class (30-minute) assemblies or non-rated assemblies.

17.4.5.2 Stairway enclosures shall be fully sprinklered.

The stairways on passenger ships typically contain more combustible materials, such as carpeting and small amounts of furniture, than their shore-side counterparts. Therefore, the requirement in 8.14.3 is expanded to require sprinklers in all levels of stairways (see 17.4.5.2).

17.4.6 Bath Modules.
Sprinklers shall be installed in bath modules (full room modules) constructed with combustible materials, regardless of room fire load.

Bath modules are addressed in 17.4.6. Modern marine construction often utilizes bathrooms that are prefabricated from combustible composite materials. Because of concern over the potential combustible load that these materials would contribute to a fire, the provision in 8.14.8.1 that allows for the omission of sprinklers in certain bathrooms does not apply to combustible bathroom modules on ships. The amount of combustible materials should be considered in this regard.

17.4.7 Ceiling Types.
Drop-out ceilings shall not be used in conjunction with sprinklers.

Because drop-out ceilings can affect sprinkler operation, they are not permitted on ships in accordance with 17.4.7.

17.4.8 Return Bends.

17.4.8.1 To prevent sediment buildup, return bends shall be installed in all shipboard sprinkler systems where pendent-type or dry pendent-type sprinklers are used in wet systems *(see Figure 8.14.18.2)*.

17.4.8.2 Consideration shall be given concerning the intrusion of saltwater into the system.

17.4.8.3 Specifically, sprinklers shall not be rendered ineffective by corrosion related to saltwater entrapment within the return bend.

FAQ ▶
Why are return bends required on all shipboard wet pipe sprinkler systems where pendent type sprinklers are utilized?

All ships use a raw water source; therefore, return bends are required (see 17.4.8.1 through 17.4.8.3). Research has indicated that sprinklers constructed using silicon brass alloy (UNS C87800) are susceptible to corrosion caused by salt water; this provides an additional reason for the use of return bends on shipboard applications.

17.4.9 Hose Connections.
Sprinkler system piping shall not be used to supply hose connections or hose connections for fire department use.

Hose connections are addressed in 17.4.9. Ships are generally required to have an independent fire main or standpipe system dedicated to manual fire-fighting operations. Although 8.16.5 permits hose connections to be supplied by sprinkler system piping in shore-side structures, hose connections for manual fire fighting are not permitted to be supplied by the ship's sprinkler system piping. Due to the limited stored water supply requirements contained in Section 17.7, there is concern that operation of a hose connection supplied by the sprinkler system piping will very quickly deplete the stored water supply dedicated solely for the sprinkler system.

17.4.10 Heat-Sensitive Piping Materials.

The requirements in 17.4.10 are intended to ensure that where heat-sensitive piping materials, such as plastic pipe, are used, they will not be susceptible to failure caused by exposure to fire, even if the sprinkler system is impaired, such as by a closed valve.

17.4.10.1 Portions of the piping system constructed with a heat-sensitive material shall be subject to the following restrictions:

(1) Piping shall be of non–heat-sensitive type from the sea suction up through the penetration of the last A-Class barrier enclosing the space(s) in which the heat-sensitive piping is installed.

(2) B-Class draft stops shall be fitted not more than 45 ft (13.7 m) apart between the marine thermal barrier *(see definitions in Chapter 3 and 17.1.3)* and the deck or shell.

(3) Portions of a system that are constructed from heat-sensitive materials shall be installed behind a marine thermal barrier, unless the provisions of item (4) are met.

(4)* Piping materials with brazed joints shall not be required to be installed behind a marine thermal barrier, provided the following conditions are met:

   (a) The system is of the wet pipe type.

   (b) The piping is not located in spaces containing boilers, internal combustion engines, or piping containing flammable or combustible liquids or gases under pressure, cargo holds, or vehicle decks.

   (c) A relief valve in compliance with 7.1.2 is installed in each section of piping that is capable of being isolated by a valve(s).

   (d) A valve(s) isolating the section of piping from the remainder of the system is installed in accordance with 17.4.10.2 and 17.4.10.3.

A.17.4.10.1(4) Because of its melting point, brazing would be considered heat sensitive. The criterion of this paragraph is intended to permit brazed joints without requiring that they be installed behind a marine thermal barrier, while maintaining the fire endurance performance as stated in 17.4.10.1 under reasonably foreseeable failure modes.

The 1996 edition only permitted brazed copper piping when it was installed behind a marine thermal barrier. The brazing material would have been considered heat sensitive because it melts at a temperature less than 1700°F (926.7°C). This exception was added to the 1999 edition to permit brazing of copper tube, while maintaining the fire endurance performance as stated in 17-4.10.1.

The 1700°F (926.7°C) definition of heat-sensitive materials was derived from the end-point temperature of a 1-hour ASTM E 119 exposure. Brazing filler metals have a solidous melting temperature between 1125°F and 1310°F (607°C and 710°C) [*Copper Tube Handbook,* 1995]. However, while dry piping could be expected to reach temperatures approaching 1700°F (926.7°C) after a 1-hour exposure, stagnant water–filled piping would likely not reach temperatures hot enough to melt brazing metals as indicated in 17.4.10.1(a). Soldered joints, which are permitted for non-marine systems under 6.5.4.3 and 6.5.4.4, are not permitted for marine systems, because solders have melting temperatures ranging from 361°F to 464°F (183°C to 240°C) [*Copper Tube Handbook,* 1995]. Under foreseeable circumstances, such as exposure to a fire when a valve is shut, the solder could melt.

Section 17.4.10.1(b) recognizes that hydrocarbon fires or fires in cargo spaces or vehicle decks could easily reach temperatures that could jeopardize the integrity of brazed joints. For example, a fuel spray fire on the USS Conyngham caused failure of a brazed joint in a fire main that was filled with stagnant water.

Section 17.4.10.1(c) is intended to allow for the expansion of boiling water in piping when there is no waterflow.

Section 17.4.10.1(d) is intended to ensure that valves that could prevent waterflow to a protected space are accessible in the event of a fire.

17.4.10.2 Each zone in which heat-sensitive piping is installed shall be fitted with a valve capable of segregating that zone from the remainder of the system.

17.4.10.3 The valve shall be supervised and located outside of the zone controlled and within a readily accessible compartment having A-Class boundaries or within a Type 1 stair.

17.4.11 Discharge of Drain Lines.

17.4.11.1 Drain lines shall not be connected to housekeeping, sewage, or deck drains. Drains shall be permitted to be discharged to bilges.

17.4.11.2 Overboard discharges shall meet the requirements of 46 CFR 56.50-95 and shall be corrosion resistant in accordance with 46 CFR 56.60.

17.4.11.3 Systems that contain water additives that are not permitted to be discharged into the environment shall be specially designed to prevent such discharge.

Ships typically have two wastewater systems—gray and black (see 17.4.11.3). Black water includes piping from toilets, while gray water typically consists of drainage from sinks, deck drains, showers, and so forth. Gray water can often be discharged directly into the sea, but black water must be held or processed on the ship. Introduction of any pressurized water source into gray or black water piping could result in overflowing the system. Bilges are similar in function to sumps, and drainage from bilge pumps is always overboard.

17.4.11.4 Discharges shall be provided with a down-turned elbow.

The down-turned elbow specified in 17.4.11.4 serves to direct the water discharge in a downward direction and minimizes the likelihood of water spray hitting people or other objects on the deck and adjacent boats.

17.4.12 Alarm Signals and Devices.

17.4.12.1* A visual and audible alarm signal shall be given at the central safety station to indicate when the system is in operation or when a condition that would impair the satisfactory operation of the system exists.

 A.17.4.12.1 While not required, a dual annunciator alarm panel system is recommended. One panel should show the piping system layout and indicate status of zone valves, tank pressures, water supply valves, pump operation, and so forth. The second panel should show the vessel's general arrangement and indicate status of waterflow (i.e., fire location) alarms.

17.4.12.2 Alarm signals shall be provided for, but not limited to, each of the following: monitoring position of control valves, fire pump power supplies and operating condition, water tank levels and temperatures, zone waterflow alarms, pressure of tanks, and air pressure on dry pipe valves.

17.4.12.3 Alarms shall give a distinct indication for each individual system component that is monitored.

17.4.12.4 An audible alarm shall be given at the central safety station within 30 seconds of waterflow.

17.4.12.5 Waterflow alarms shall be installed for every zone of the sprinkler system.

17.4.12.6 Sprinkler zones shall not encompass more than two adjacent decks or encompass more than one main vertical zone.

Many passenger vessels are subdivided into areas referred to as main vertical zones, which are specified in 17.4.12.6. These spaces have a function similar to that of horizontal exits in buildings, allowing people to egress away from the hazard. Main vertical zones are usually about 131 ft (40 m) in length. Sprinkler zones are limited to not more than two decks in any main vertical zone.

17.4.12.7 Electrically operated aarm attachments shall comply with, meet, and be installed in accordance with the requirements of 46 CFR, Subchapter J, "Electrical Engineering."

NFPA 70, *National Electrical Code*®, does not fully apply to shipboard electrical systems. The requirements for electric systems on ships are contained in 46 CFR110-113, Subchapter J, as stated in 17.4.12.7.

17.4.12.8 All wiring shall be chosen and installed in accordance with IEEE 45, *Recommended Practice for Electrical Installations on Shipboard.*

17.4.13 Test Connections. Where test connections are below the bulkhead deck, they shall comply with the overboard discharge arrangements of 46 CFR 56.50-95.

The bulkhead deck is the highest deck that can be expected to be submerged when the vessel's hull is breached (see 17.4.13). Any penetration of the hull below the bulkhead deck must be protected so that it does not serve as a path for water ingress.

17.4.14 Protection of Copper Tubing. Copper tubing materials shall be protected against physical damage in areas where vehicles and stores handling equipment operate.

Copper tubing has a lower yield strength and thinner walls than steel pipe. Therefore, copper is more prone to damage such as pinching, which is the reason for the requirement in 17.4.14.

17.5 Design Approaches

17.5.1 Design Options.

17.5.1.1 Marine sprinkler systems shall be designed using the hydraulic calculation procedure of Chapter 10.

17.5.1.2 The pipe schedule method shall not be used to determine the water demand requirements.

Marine sprinkler systems must be fully operational when the vessel is upright or inclined as a result of damage in accordance with 17.5.1.1 and 17.5.1.2 (see 17.6.4).

17.5.2* Window Protection. Minimum water demand requirements shall include sprinklers that are installed for the protection of windows as described in 17.4.3.

A.17.5.2 For example, a design area of 1500 ft^2 (139.3 m^2) is used to design a sprinkler system for an unobstructed light hazard occupancy. In this case, the system must supply at least seven sprinklers that are installed within that area. If eight sprinklers are installed to protect windows within this design area, the water demand of these sprinklers is added to the total water demand. Thus, 15 sprinklers must be supplied by this system.

17.5.3* Hose Stream Allowance. No allowance for hose stream use shall be required.

A.17.5.3 Hose stream flow need not be added to the water demand. The water supply for fire streams is supplied by separate fire pump(s) that supply the vessel's fire main.

FAQ ▶
Why is there no inside or outside hose stream allowance required for shipboard sprinkler systems?

As stated in 17.4.9, sprinkler system piping is not permitted to be used to supply hose connections (see 17.5.3).

17.6 Plans and Calculations

17.6.1 Additional Information. The pressure tank size, high-pressure relief setting, high and low water alarm settings, low-pressure alarm setting, and pump start pressure shall be provided.

17.6.2 Sprinklers specifically installed for the protection of windows under 17.4.3 shall be permitted to be of a different size from those protecting the remainder of the occupancy classification.

17.6.3 All of the window sprinklers, however, shall be of the same size.

17.6.4* Marine sprinkler systems shall be designed and installed to be fully operational without a reduction in system performance when the vessel is upright and inclined at the angles of inclination specified in 46 CFR 58.01-40.

A.17.6.4 In vessels, the elevation of sprinklers with respect to the water supply varies as the vessel heels to either side or trims by the bow or stern. The water demand requirements can be increased or decreased under these conditions. This requirement aligns the operational parameters of this safety system with that required for other machinery vital to the safety of the vessel.

A list of 22.5 degrees and a trim of 7.5 degrees is specified in 46 CFR 58.01-40, which is cited in 17.6.4. Also, 46 CFR 58.01-40 contains flexibility where lesser angles can be accepted. For example, lesser angles are accepted on vessels that operate only in calm waters or do not get under way.

  Verification of the requirement of performance with the specified list and trim requires hydraulic calculation of the hydraulically most remote area with the vessel in the following three conditions:

FAQ ▶
Why are multiple sets of hydraulic calculations required for each system?

1. Upright
2. Listing to port
3. Listing to starboard

17.7 Water Supplies

Water supplies are covered in Section 17.7. The water supply for a sprinkler system on a ship typically comes from two sources. The initial supply comes from a small limited water source stored on the vessel. This stored supply is sized to provide for 1 minute of system demand plus the volume of the piping if a dry pipe, preaction, or deluge system is used. During the discharge of the stored water source, a pump that takes suction from the sea activates. Because of concerns regarding drawing large quantities of mud into the fire pump suction when the vessel is close to shore or on an inland waterway, a single water supply that takes suction from the sea is not considered sufficiently reliable.

17.7.1 General. The water supply requirements for marine applications shall be in accordance with Section 17.7.

17.7.2 Pressure Tank.

A pressure tank, which is covered in 17.7.2, is the preferred source of initial water supply because, during a loss of power, it will still operate. As indicated in 17.7.2.1(1), the tank must be sized to provide the system demand for at least 1 minute plus the volume of any dry piping used.

17.7.2.1 Unless the requirements of 17.7.2.2 are met, a pressure tank shall be provided. The pressure tank shall be sized and constructed so that the following occurs:

(1) The tank shall contain a standing charge of fresh water equal to that specified by Table 17.7.2.1.
(2) The pressure tank shall be sized in accordance with 12.2.3.2.
(3) A glass gauge shall be provided to indicate the correct level of water within the pressure tank.
(4) Arrangements shall be provided for maintaining an air pressure in the tank such that, while the standing charge of water is being expended, the pressure will not be less than that necessary to provide the design pressure and flow of the hydraulically most remote design area.
(5) Suitable means of replenishing the air under pressure and the fresh water standing charge in the tank shall be provided.
(6) Tank construction shall be in accordance with the applicable requirements of 46 CFR, Subchapter F, "Marine Engineering."

TABLE 17.7.2.1 *Required Water Supply*

System Type	Additional Water Volume
Wet pipe system	Flow requirement of the hydraulically most remote system demand for 1 minute
Preaction system Deluge system Dry pipe system	Flow requirement of the hydraulically most remote system demand for 1 minute of system demand plus the volume needed to fill all dry piping

17.7.2.2 Pressure Tank Alternative. In lieu of a pressure tank, a dedicated pump connected to a fresh water tank shall be permitted to be used, provided the following conditions are met:

(1) The pump is listed for marine use and is sized to meet the required system demand.
(2) The suction for the fire pump is located below the suction for the fresh water system so that there shall be a minimum water supply of at least 1 minute for the required system demand.
(3) Pressure switches are provided in the system and the controller for the pump that automatically start the pump within 10 seconds after detection of a pressure drop of more than 5 percent.
(4) There shall be a reduced pressure zone backflow preventer to prevent contamination of the potable water system by salt water.
(5) There are at least two sources of power for this pump. Where the sources of power are electrical, these shall be a main generator and an emergency source of power. One supply shall be taken from the main switchboard, by separate feeder reserved solely for that purpose. This feeder shall be run to an automatic changeover switch situated near the sprinkler unit and the switch shall normally be kept closed to the feeder from the emergency switchboard. The changeover switch shall be clearly labeled, and no other switch shall be permitted in these feeders.

The requirement in 17.7.2.2 permits a dedicated pump that takes suction from a freshwater tank. Because of concerns regarding contamination of the vessel's potable water tank with seawater, a single pump that takes suction from both the sea and the potable water tank is not permitted. The suction from the pump must be located at a lower elevation from any other pumps, ensuring that the minimum required volume of water is always available. When the option permitted by 17.7.2.2(5) is used, both the pump dedicated to the potable water tank and the pump that takes suction from seawater must be powered by the emergency switchboard.

17.7.2.3 Relief Valves.

17.7.2.3.1 Relief valves shall be installed on the tank to avoid overpressurization and false actuation of any dry pipe valve.

 17.7.2.3.2 Relief valves shall comply with 46 CFR 54.15-10.

17.7.2.4 Power Source.

17.7.2.4.1 There shall be not less than two sources of power for the compressors that supply air to the pressure tank.

17.7.2.4.2 Where the sources of power are electrical, these shall be a main generator and an emergency source of power.

17.7.2.4.3 One supply shall be taken from the main switchboard, by separate feeders reserved solely for that purpose.

17.7.2.4.4 Such feeders shall be run to a changeover switch situated near the air compressor, and the switch normally shall be kept closed to the feeder from the emergency switchboard.

17.7.2.4.5 The changeover switch shall be clearly labeled, and no other switch shall be permitted in these feeders.

17.7.2.5 Multiple Tanks.

17.7.2.5.1 More than one pressure tank can be installed provided that each is treated as a single water source when determining valve arrangements.

Where sufficient space on the vessel is not available to install a single pressure tank meeting the requirements of Table 17.7.2.1, several smaller tanks can be considered, as stated in 17.7.2.5.1. Each tank must be fitted with valves to keep seawater out of the tank and keep water out of the air supply.

17.7.2.5.2 Check valves shall be installed to prohibit flow from tank to tank or from pump to tank, unless the tank is designed to hold only pressurized air.

The requirement in 17.7.2.5.2 permits the omission of check valves in piping between a supplemental pressurized air tank and a pressure tank containing water.

17.7.2.6 In systems subject to use with saltwater, valves shall be so arranged as to prohibit contamination of the pressure tank with saltwater.

17.7.2.7* Where applicable, a means shall be provided to restrict the amount of air that can enter the pressure tank from the air supply system. A means shall also be provided to prevent water from backflowing into the air supply system.

 A.17.7.2.7 The purpose of this is to ensure that the pressure tank air supply will not keep the tank "fully" pressurized while water is expelled, thus preventing pump actuation.

17.7.3 Fire Pump.

17.7.3.1 A dedicated, automatically controlled pump that is listed for marine service, which takes suction from the sea, shall be provided to supply the sprinkler system.

17.7.3.2 Where two pumps are required to ensure the reliability of the water supply, the pump that supplies the fire main shall be allowed to serve as the second fire pump.

The requirement given in 17.7.3.2 for the installation of multiple fire pumps to increase system reliability would typically come from a vessel construction standard, such as NFPA 301.

17.7.3.3* The pump shall be sized to meet the water demand of the hydraulically most demanding area.

A.17.7.3.3 NFPA 20, *Standard for the Installation of Stationary Pumps for Fire Protection*, requires that fire pumps furnish not less than 150 percent of their rated capacity at not less than 65 percent of their rated heat. The intention of the requirement of 17.7.3.3 is to limit designers to 120 percent of the rated capacity of the pump to provide an additional factor of safety for marine systems.

As a means of increasing the overall level of system reliability, pumps may not be sized in excess of 120 percent of their rated capacity (see 17.7.3.3).

17.7.3.4 Pumps shall be designed to not exceed 120 percent of the rated capacity of the pump.

17.7.3.5 The system shall be designed so that, before the supply falls below the design criteria, the fire pump shall be automatically started and shall supply water to the system until manually shut off.

17.7.3.6 Where pump and fresh water tank arrangement is used in lieu of the pressure tank, there must be a pressure switch that senses a system pressure drop of 25 percent, and the controller must automatically start the fire pump(s) if pressure is not restored within 20 seconds.

17.7.3.7 There shall be not less than two sources of power supply for the fire pumps. Where the sources of power are electrical, these shall be a main generator and an emergency source of power.

17.7.3.8 One supply shall be taken from the main switchboard by separate feeders reserved solely for that purpose.

17.7.3.9 Such feeders shall be run to a changeover switch situated near to the sprinkler unit, and the switch normally shall be kept closed to the feeder from the emergency switchboard.

17.7.3.10 The changeover switch shall be clearly labeled, and no other switch shall be permitted in these feeders.

17.7.3.11 Test Valves.

17.7.3.11.1 A test valve(s) shall be installed on the discharge side of the pump with a short open-ended discharge pipe.

17.7.3.11.2 The area of the pipe shall be adequate to permit the release of the required water output to supply the demand of the hydraulically most remote area.

17.7.3.12 Multiple Pumps.

17.7.3.12.1 Where two fire pumps are required to ensure the reliability of the water supply, each fire pump shall meet the requirements of 17.7.3.1 through 17.7.3.4.

17.7.3.12.2 In addition, a system that is required to have more than one pump shall be designed to accommodate the following features:

(1)* Pump controls and system sensors shall be arranged such that the secondary pump will automatically operate if the primary pump fails to operate or deliver the required water pressure and flow. *[Figure A.17.7.3.12.2(1) is an example of an acceptable dual pump arrangement.]*

(2) Both pumps shall be served from normal and emergency power sources. However, where approved by the authority having jurisdiction, the secondary pump shall be permitted to be nonelectrically driven.

(3) Pump failure or operation shall be indicated at the central safety station.

 A.17.7.3.12.2(1) Pumps should not be located within the same compartment. However, where this is not reasonable or practical, special attention should be given to protecting pumps such that a single failure will not render the sprinkler system inoperative. *[See Figure A.17.7.3.12.2(1).]*

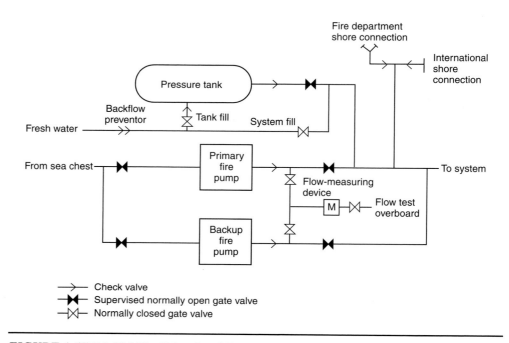

FIGURE A.17.7.3.12.2(1) *Abbreviated Example of a Dual Fire Pump Water Supply.*

17.7.3.13* If not specifically prohibited, the fire pump that supplies the fire main shall be permitted to be used as the second pump, provided the following conditions are met:

(1) The pump is adequately sized to meet the required fire hose and sprinkler system pressure and flow demands simultaneously.

(2) The fire main system is segregated from the sprinkler system by a normally closed valve that is designed to automatically open upon failure of the designated fire pump.

(3) The fire pump that supplies the fire main is automatically started in the event of dedicated fire pump failure or loss of pressure in the sprinkler main. *(See Figure A.17.7.3.13.)*

 A.17.7.3.13 See Figure A.17.7.3.13.

17.7.4 Water Supply Configurations.

17.7.4.1 The pressure tank and fire pump shall be located in a position reasonably remote from any machinery space of Category A.

Why are the pressure tank and the fire pump required to be remote from any Category A machinery space?
FAQ ▶

Many shipboard fires start in machinery spaces. The intent of 17.7.4.1 is to locate the fire pumps and pressure tanks so that a fire in the machinery space does not cause an impairment of the sprinkler system.

FIGURE A.17.7.3.13 *Abbreviated Example of a Water Supply with Fire Pump Backup.*

17.7.4.2 All valves within the water supply piping system shall be supervised.

17.7.4.3 Only fresh water shall be used as the initial charge within the piping network.

Limiting the initial charge of water in the piping network to fresh water, as stated in 17.7.4.3, is intended to minimize the potential for corrosion. See NFPA 25 for information on flushing of piping following introduction of seawater.

17.7.4.4 The sprinkler system shall be cross-connected with the ship's fire main system and fitted with a lockable screw-down nonreturn valve such that backflow from the sprinkler system to the fire main is prevented.

The fire main (standpipe) used for manual fire-fighting operations also has one or more pumps that take suction from the sea (see 17.7.4.4). The cross-connection between these two systems minimizes the effects caused by a pump failure in either the sprinkler system piping or the fire main and increases the reliability of the overall fire protection system.

17.7.4.5 The piping, tanks, and pumps that make up the water supply shall be installed in accordance with the applicable requirements of 46 CFR, Subchapter F, "Marine Engineering."

17.7.4.6* When a shore water supply is to be used during extended dockside periods, the water supply shall be qualified in the manner described in 15.2.1.

A.17.7.4.6 This procedure should be used to qualify each water supply to which the vessel is to be attached. For example, this might require testing of multiple hydrants or connections in the same mooring area. The pressure loss effect of the hose or piping leading from the water supply to the ship should also be considered when qualifying each hydrant.

Some vessels, such as casino vessels, can operate at the dock for extended periods of time, which is discussed in 17.7.4.6. These vessels can use a water supply independent of the vessel, such as a connection to a shore-side water main.

17.7.4.7 Tests shall be conducted in accordance with the requirements of the local shore-based authority having jurisdiction.

17.7.4.8 The water supply information listed in Section 11.3 shall then be provided to the authority having jurisdiction.

17.8 System Acceptance

17.8.1 Hydrostatic Tests. In addition to the interior piping, the test required by 16.2.1.10 shall also be conducted on all external water supply connections including international shore and fireboat connections.

17.8.2 Alarm Test. A waterflow test shall result in an alarm at the central safety station within 30 seconds after flow through the test connection begins.

17.8.3 Operational Tests.

17.8.3.1 Pressure tank and pump operation, valve actuation, and waterflow shall also be tested.

17.8.3.2 Pump operation and performance shall be tested in accordance with Chapter 14 of NFPA 20, *Standard for the Installation of Stationary Pumps for Fire Protection.*

17.9 System Instructions and Maintenance

17.9.1 Instructions for operation, inspection, maintenance, and testing shall be kept on the vessel.

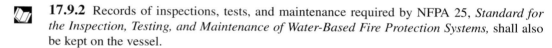 **17.9.2** Records of inspections, tests, and maintenance required by NFPA 25, *Standard for the Inspection, Testing, and Maintenance of Water-Based Fire Protection Systems,* shall also be kept on the vessel.

The requirements in NFPA 25 for the inspection, testing, and maintenance of sprinkler systems are applicable for marine purposes (see 17.9.2). NFPA 25 is referenced in Chapter 16. Chapter 15 expands on the requirements of NFPA 25 as indicated in Section 17.9.

Although NFPA 25 requires keeping records of inspections, tests, and maintenance, these records could be kept in a location other than on the vessel and still meet the requirements of NFPA 25.

FAQ ▶
Where are the records required by NFPA 25 required to be kept?

Subsection 17.9.2 specifically requires that instructions and records be kept on the vessel.

NFPA 25 requires flushing of piping following a system activation to limit corrosion caused by seawater ingress into the sprinkler system.

SUMMARY

Chapter 17 covers the specifics for marine (shipboard) applications of automatic sprinkler systems. These requirements are in addition to the requirements of the remainder of NFPA 13. The additional requirements of Chapter 17 are intended to be applied to marine applications only.

REFERENCES CITED IN COMMENTARY

National Fire Protection Association, 1 Batterymarch Park, P.O. Box 9101, Quincy, MA 02269-9101

NFPA 25, *Standard for the Inspection, Testing, and Maintenance of Water-Based Fire Protection Systems,* 2002 edition
NFPA 70, *National Electrical Code®,* 2002 edition
NFPA 301, *Code for Safety to Life from Fire on Merchant Vessels,* 2001 edition

American National Standards Institute, Inc., 11 West 42nd Street, 13th floor, New York, NY 10036

ANSI B16.34, *Valves—Flanged, Threaded, and Welding End,* 1988

American Society for Testing and Materials, 100 Barr Harbor Drive, West Conshohocken, PA 19428-2959

ASTM A 47, *Standard Specification for Ferritic Malleable Iron Castings,* 1995 edition
ASTM A 126, *Standard Specification for Gray Iron Castings for Valves, Flanges, and Pipe Fittings,* 1995 edition
ASTM A 197, *Standard Specification for Cupola Malleable Iron,* 1992 edition
ASTM A 395, *Standard Specification for Ferritic Ductile Iron Pressure-Retaining Castings for Use at Elevated Temperatures,* 1998 edition
ASTM E 119, *Standard Test Methods for Fire Tests of Building Construction and Materials,* 2000 edition

International Maritime Organization, 4 Albert Embankment, London, SEI 7SR, United Kingdom

IMO Fire Test Procedures Code

U.S. Government Printing Office, Washington, DC 20402

Navigation and Vessel Inspection Circular 10-93, "Guide to the Acceptance of National Fire Protection Association Code No. 13 for Automatic Sprinkler System Design, Installation and Maintenance," U.S. Coast Guard, 1993
Title 46, Code of Federal Regulations, Parts 56.20, 56.20-5(a), 56.60, and 58.01-40
Title 46, Code of Federal Regulations, Parts 110–113, Subchapter J, "Electrical Engineering"

Richardson and Oleszkiewicz, *Fire Technology,* Vol. 23, No. 2, May 1987, pp. 115–132.
Copper Tube Handbook, Copper Development Association, 1995

CHAPTER 18

System Inspection, Testing, and Maintenance

Chapter 18 specifically requires that sprinkler systems be inspected, tested, and maintained in accordance with NFPA 25, *Standard for the Inspection, Testing, and Maintenance of Water-Based Fire Protection Systems.* Inspection and testing activities are critical in ensuring proper system operation. Additionally, many insurance companies insist that an ongoing program be in place. NFPA 25 identifies the activities that need to be conducted and the frequency at which they need to be conducted.

18.1* General

A sprinkler system installed in accordance with this standard shall be properly inspected, tested, and maintained in accordance with NFPA 25, *Standard for the Inspection, Testing, and Maintenance of Water-Based Fire Protection Systems*, to provide at least the same level of performance and protection as designed.

A.18.1 *Impairments.* Before shutting off a section of the fire service system to make sprinkler system connections, notify the authority having jurisdiction, plan the work carefully, and assemble all materials to enable completion in the shortest possible time. Work started on connections should be completed without interruption, and protection should be restored as promptly as possible. During the impairment, provide emergency hose lines and extinguishers and maintain extra watch service in the areas affected.

When changes involve shutting off water from any considerable number of sprinklers for more than a few hours, temporary water supply connections should be made to sprinkler systems so that reasonable protection can be maintained. In adding to old systems or revamping them, protection should be restored each night so far as possible. The members of the private fire brigade as well as public fire departments should be notified as to conditions.

Maintenance Schedule. The items shown in Table A.18.1 should be checked on a routine basis.

Inspection, testing, and maintenance issues are beyond the scope of NFPA 13, but they are critical for effective sprinkler system performance. Inspection, testing, and maintenance are especially important because of the inactive nature of a sprinkler system. Unlike other types of building systems that are used on a routine basis, the sprinkler system is only used during emergency situations. The system's proper operating condition is not verifiable through day-to-day operations, as are the heating, air-conditioning, and plumbing systems. Therefore, the building owner or representative must employ and follow an inspection, testing, and maintenance program as specified by NFPA 25, as stated in Section 18.1.

A system that does not comply with the requirements of NFPA 25 is not in compliance with NFPA 13. An improperly maintained system is likely to be impaired in some way and cannot be expected to meet its fire protection objectives. An impaired system is likely to have the same effect as no sprinkler protection at all.

737

TABLE A.18.1 Maintenance Schedule

Parts	Activity	Frequency
Flushing piping	Test	5 years
Fire department connections	Inspection	Monthly
Control valves	Inspection	Weekly—sealed
	Inspection	Monthly—locked
	Inspection	Monthly—tamper switch
	Maintenance	Yearly
Main drain	Flow test	Quarterly—annual
Open sprinklers	Test	Annually
Pressure gauge	Calibration test	
Sprinklers	Test	50 years
Sprinklers—high temperature	Test	5 years
Sprinklers—residential	Test	20 years
Waterflow alarms	Test	Quarterly
Preaction/deluge detection system	Test	Semiannually
Preaction/deluge systems	Test	Annually
Antifreeze solution	Test	Annually
Cold weather valves	Open and close valves	Fall, close; spring, open
Dry/preaction/deluge systems		
Air pressure and water pressure	Inspection	Weekly
Enclosure	Inspection	Daily—cold weather
Priming water level	Inspection	Quarterly
Low-point drains	Test	Fall
Dry pipe valves	Trip test	Annually—spring
Dry pipe valves	Full flow trip	3 years—spring
Quick-opening devices	Test	Semiannually

 It is critical that steps be taken to compensate for the lack of protection in a building when the sprinkler system is impaired. NFPA 25 provides information on dealing with system impairments. One step that can be taken regarding life safety is evacuation of the building. Provisions for emergency hose lines, extinguishers, and/or an approved fire watch are alternatives to an evacuation. See Chapter 14 of NFPA 25 for a more complete discussion of impairments and recommendations on how to handle the occupation of a building with an impaired system.

Table A.18.1 was added to NFPA 13 to provide guidance on the kinds of activities that need to be performed and some general sense as to how frequently such activities should be carried out. The table was extracted from the 1995 edition of NFPA 25 and was not updated. As a result, some of the frequencies for activities no longer match the 2002 edition of NFPA 25. Because this table is in the annex, and because the reference to NFPA 25 is a mandatory requirement of NFPA 13, the rules of NFPA 25 apply if a conflict arises.

For example, the table shows that a main drain test needs to be conducted on the sprinkler system at quarterly intervals, which was consistent with the 1995 edition of NFPA 25. However, the 2002 edition of NFPA 25 revised this requirement to annual intervals and after each time a valve is closed. Because the 2002 edition is the one that is referenced as the mandatory requirement of NFPA 13, the annual test and the test after each valve closure is the enforceable requirement.

SUMMARY

Inspection, testing, and maintenance are beyond the scope of NFPA 13, but they are critical for effective sprinkler system performance. In all cases NFPA 25 should be followed for inspection, testing, and maintenance of automatic sprinkler systems. As previously stated, this is especially important because sprinkler systems are called upon during an emergency situation, and their failure could be catastrophic. For additional information on inspection, testing and maintenance the following two resources should be used:

1. *Inspection, Testing, and Maintenance of Water-Based Fire Protection Systems: The 25 Handbook*
2. *Fire Protections Systems: Inspection, Test and Maintenance Manual*

REFERENCES CITED IN COMMENTARY

National Fire Protection Association, 1 Batterymarch Park, P.O. Box 9101, Quincy, MA 02269-9101

NFPA 25, *Standard for the Inspection, Testing, and Maintenance of Water-Based Fire Protection Systems,* 2002 edition

Hague, D. R., ed., *Inspection, Testing, and Maintenance of Water-Based Fire Protection Systems: The 25 Handbook,* NFPA, Quincy, MA, 2002

Carson, W. G., and Klinker, R. L., *Fire Protections Systems: Inspection, Test and Maintenance Manual,* 3rd edition, NFPA, Quincy, MA, 2000

Explanatory Material

Annex A is not a part of the requirements of this NFPA document but is included for informational purposes only. This annex contains explanatory material, numbered to correspond with the applicable text paragraphs.

The material contained in Annex A of NFPA 13 is included within the text of this handbook, and, therefore, is not repeated here.

Miscellaneous Topics

This annex is not a part of the requirements of this NFPA document but is included for informational purposes only.

B.1 Figure B.1 shows acceptable methods for interconnection of the fire protection and domestic water supply.

FIGURE B.1 *Permitted Arrangements Between the Fire Protection Water Supply and the Domestic Water Supply.*

B.2 Sprinkler System Performance Criteria

B.2.1 Sprinkler system performance criteria have been based on test data. The factors of safety are generally small, are not definitive, and can depend on expected (but not guaranteed) inherent characteristics of the sprinkler systems involved. These inherent factors of safety consist of the following:

(1) The flow-declining pressure characteristic of sprinkler systems whereby the initial operating sprinklers discharge at a higher flow than with all sprinklers operating within the designated area.

(2) The flow-declining pressure characteristic of water supplies, which is particularly steep where fire pumps are the water source. This characteristic similarly produces higher than design discharge at the initially operating sprinklers.

The user of these standards can elect an additional factor of safety if the inherent factors are not considered adequate.

B.2.1.1 Performance-specified sprinkler systems, as opposed to scheduled systems, can be designed to take advantage of multiple loops or gridded configurations. Such configurations result in minimum line losses at expanded sprinkler spacing, in contrast to the older tree-type configurations, where advantage cannot be taken of multiple path flows.

Where the water supply characteristics are relatively flat with pressures being only slightly above the required sprinkler pressure at the spacing selected, gridded systems with piping designed for minimal economic line losses can all but eliminate the inherent flow-declining pressure characteristic generally assumed to exist in sprinkler systems. In contrast, the economic design of a tree-type system would likely favor a system design with closer sprinkler spacing and greater line losses, demonstrating the inherent flow-declining pressure characteristic of the piping system.

Elements that enter into the design of sprinkler systems include the following:

(1) Selection of density and area of application
(2) Geometry of the area of application (remote area)
(3) Permitted pressure range at sprinklers
(4) Determination of the water supply available
(5) Ability to predict expected performance from calculated performance
(6) Future upgrading of system performance
(7) Size of sprinkler systems

In developing sprinkler specifications, each of these elements needs to be considered individually. The most conservative design should be based on the application of the most stringent conditions for each of the elements.

B.2.1.2 Selection of Density and Area of Application. Specifications for density and area of application are developed from NFPA standards and other standards. It is desirable to specify densities rounded upward to the nearest 0.005 gpm/ft^2 (0.2 mm/min).

Prudent design should consider reasonable-to-expect variations in occupancy. This design would include not only variations in type of occupancy, but also, in the case of warehousing, the anticipated future range of materials to be stored, clearances, types of arrays, packaging, pile height, and pile stability, as well as other factors.

Design should also consider some degree of adversity at the time of a fire. To take this into account, the density and/or area of application can be increased. Another way is to use a dual-performance specification where, in addition to the normal primary specifications, a secondary density and area of application are specified. The objective of such a selection is to control the declining pressure-flow characteristic of the sprinkler system beyond the primary design flow.

A case can be made for designing feed and cross mains to lower velocities than branch lines to achieve the same result as specifying a second density and area of application.

B.2.1.3 Geometry of the Area of Application (Remote Area). It is expected that, over any portion of the sprinkler system equivalent in size to the area of application, the system will achieve the minimum specified density for each sprinkler within that area.

Where a system is computer-designed, ideally the program should verify the entire system by shifting the area of application the equivalent of one sprinkler at a time so as to cover all portions of the system. Such a complete computer verification of performance of the system is most desirable, but unfortunately not all available computer verification programs currently do this.

This selection of the proper Hazen-Williams coefficient is important. New unlined steel pipe has a Hazen-Williams coefficient close to 140. However, it quickly deteriorates to 130 and, after a few years of use, to 120. Hence, the basis for normal design is a Hazen-Williams coefficient of 120 for steel-piped wet systems. A Hazen-Williams coefficient of 100 is generally used for dry pipe systems because of the increased tendency for deposits and corrosion in these systems. However, it should be realized that a new system will have fewer line losses than calculated, and the distribution pattern will be affected accordingly.

Conservatism can also be built into systems by intentionally designing to a lower Hazen-Williams coefficient than that indicated.

B.2.1.4 Ability to Predict Expected Performance from Calculated Performance. Ability to accurately predict the performance of a complex array of sprinklers on piping is basically a function of the pipe line velocity. The greater the velocity, the greater is the impact on difficult-to-assess pressure losses. These pressure losses are presently determined by empirical means that lose validity as velocities increase. This is especially true for fittings with unequal and more than two flowing ports.

The inclusion of velocity pressures in hydraulic calculations improves the predictability of the actual sprinkler system performance. Calculations should come as close as practicable to predicting actual performance. Conservatism in design should be arrived at intentionally by known and deliberate means. It should not be left to chance.

B.2.1.5 Future Upgrading of System Performance. It is desirable in some cases to build into the system the capability to achieve a higher level of sprinkler performance than needed at present. If this is to be a consideration in conservatism, consideration needs to be given to maintaining sprinkler operating pressures on the lower side of the optimum operating range and/or designing for low pipe line velocities, particularly on feed and cross mains, to facilitate future reinforcement.

Explanation of Test Data and Procedures for Rack Storage

This annex is not a part of the requirements of this NFPA document but is included for informational purposes only.

C.1 Annex C provides an explanation of the test data and procedures that led to the development of sprinkler system discharge criteria for rack storage applications. Numbers in brackets refer to paragraphs in the text.

C.2 [5.6] A review of full-scale fire tests run on the standard commodity (double tri-wall carton with metal liner), of Hallmark products and 3M products (e.g., abrasives, pressure-sensitive tapes of plastic fiber, and paper), and of the considerable number of commodity tests conducted provides a guide for commodity classifications. Such guidance is not related to any other method of classification of materials; therefore, sound engineering judgment and analysis of the commodity and the packaging should be used when selecting a commodity classification.

C.3 [8.13.3.1] Tests 71, 73, 81, 83, 91, 92, 95, and 100 in the 20-ft (6.1-m) high array involving a single level of in-rack sprinklers were conducted without heat or water shields. Results were satisfactory.

Test 115 was conducted with two levels of sprinklers in racks with shields. Test 116, identical to Test 115 but without water shields, produced a lack of control. Visual observation of lower level in-rack sprinklers that did not operate although they were in the fire area indicated a need for water shields.

Tests 115 and 116 were conducted to investigate the necessity for water shields where multiple levels of in-rack sprinklers are installed. Where water shields were not installed in Test 116, the fire jumped the aisle, and approximately 76 boxes were damaged. In Test 115 with water shields, the fire did not jump the aisle, and only 32 boxes were damaged. Water shields are, therefore, suggested wherever multiple levels of in-rack sprinklers are installed, except for installations with horizontal barriers or shelves that serve as water shields.

C.4 [8.16.1.8] The time of operation of the first sprinkler varied from 52 seconds to 3 minutes and 55 seconds, with most tests under 3 minutes, except in Test 64 (Class III), where the first sprinkler operated in 7 minutes and 44 seconds. Fire detection more sensitive than waterflow is, therefore, considered necessary only in exceptional cases.

C.5 [8.16.5.1] In most tests conducted, it was necessary to use small hose for mop-up operations. Small hose were not used in the high-expansion foam test.

Test 97 was conducted to evaluate the effect of dry pipe sprinkler operation. Test results were approximately the same as the base test with a wet pipe system. A study of NFPA records, however, indicates an increase in area of operation of 30 percent to be in order for dry pipe systems as compared with wet pipe systems.

C.6 [12.1.1] Tests were conducted as a part of this program with eave line windows or louvers open to simulate smoke and heat venting. These tests opened 87.5 percent and 91 percent more sprinklers than did comparative tests without windows or louvers open. Venting tests that have been conducted in other programs were without the benefit of sprinkler protection and, as such, are not considered in this report, which covers only buildings protected by sprinklers. The design curves are based upon the absence of roof vents or draft curtains in the building. During mop-up operations, ventilating systems, where installed, should be capable of manual exhaust operations.

C.7 [12.1.9.1.3] No tests were conducted with idle pallets in racks using standard spray sprinklers. However, tests were conducted using ESFR and large drop sprinklers. Such storage conceivably would introduce fire severity in excess of that contemplated by protection criteria for an individual commodity classification.

C.8 [12.2.1.2, 12.3.2.1.7, 12.3.3.1.11] In all valid tests with double-row racks, sprinkler water supplies were shut off at approximately 60 minutes. In only one test did the last sprinkler operate in excess of 30 minutes after ignition; the last sprinkler operated in excess of 25 minutes in three tests, with the majority of tests involving the last sprinkler operating within 20 minutes.

C.9 [12.3] The discharge criteria of Section 12.3 use as a basis the large-scale fire test series conducted at the Factory Mutual Research Center, West Glocester, Rhode Island.

The test building is approximately 200 ft × 250 ft (61 m × 76 m) [50,000 ft^2 (4.65 km^2) in area], of fire-resistive construction, and contains a volume of approximately 2.25 million ft^3 (63,720 m^3), the equivalent of a 100,000-ft^2 (9.29-km^2) building that is 22.5 ft (6.86 m) high. The test building has two primary heights beneath a single large ceiling. The east section is 30 ft (9.1 m) high, and the west section is 60 ft (18.29 m) high.

The test series for storage height of 20 ft (6.1 m) was conducted in the 30-ft (9.1-m) section with clearances from the top of storage to the ceiling nominally 10 ft (3.1 m).

Doors at the lower and intermediate levels and ventilation louvers at the tops of walls were kept closed during the majority of the fire tests, which minimized the effect of exterior conditions.

The entire test series was fully instrumented with thermocouples attached to rack members, simulated building columns, bar joists, and the ceiling.

Racks were constructed of steel vertical and horizontal members designed for 4000-lb (1814-kg) loads. Vertical members were 8 ft (2.4 m) on center for conventional racks and 4 ft (1.2 m) on center for simulated automated racks. Racks were 3½ ft (1.07 m) wide with 6-in. (152.4-mm) longitudinal flue space for an overall width of 7½ ft (2.29 m). Simulated automated racks and slave pallets were used in the main central rack in the 4-ft (1.2-m) aisle tests. Conventional racks and conventional pallets were used in the main central rack in the 8-ft (2.4-mm) aisle tests. The majority of the tests were conducted with 100-ft^2 (9.29-m^2) sprinkler spacing.

The test configuration for storage heights of 15 ft (4.6 m), 20 ft (6.1 m), and 25 ft (7.6 m) covered an 1800-ft^2 (167.2-m^2) floor area, including aisles between racks. Tests that were used in producing this standard limited fire damage to this area. The maximum water damage area anticipated in the standard is 6000 ft^2 (557.4 m^2), the upper limit of the design curves.

The test data shows that, as density is increased, both the extent of fire damage and sprinkler operation are reduced. The data also indicates that, with sprinklers installed in the racks, a reduction is gained in the area of fire damage and sprinkler operations (e.g., water damage).

Table C.9 illustrates these points. The information shown in the table is taken from the test series for storage height of 20 ft (6.1 m) using the standard commodity.

The fact that there is a reduction in both fire damage and area of water application as sprinkler densities are increased or where sprinklers are installed in racks should be considered carefully by those responsible for applying this standard to the rack storage situation.

In the test for storage height of 25 ft (7.6 m), a density of 0.55 gpm/ft^2 (22.4 mm/min) produced 42 percent, or 756 ft^2 (70.26 m^2), fire damage in the test array and a sprinkler-wetted area of 1400 ft^2 (130.1 m^2). Lesser densities would not be expected to achieve the same limited degree of control. Therefore, if the goal of smaller areas of fire damage is to be achieved, sprinklers in racks should be considered.

The test series for storage height over 25 ft (7.6 m) was conducted in the 60-ft (18.3-m) section of the test building with nominal clearances from the top of storage to the ceiling of either 30 ft (9.1 m) or 10 ft (3.1 m).

Doors at the lower and intermediate levels and ventilation louvers at the top of walls were kept closed during the fire tests, which minimized the effect of exterior wind conditions.

The purpose of the tests for storage height over 25 ft (7.6 m) was to accomplish the following:

(1) Determine the arrangement of in-rack sprinklers that can be repeated as pile height increases and that provide control of the fire
(2) Determine other protective arrangements, such as high-expansion foam, that provide control of the fire

Control was considered to have been accomplished if the fire was unlikely to spread from the rack of origin to adjacent racks or spread beyond the length of the 25-ft (7.6-m) test rack. To aid in this judgment, control was considered to have been achieved if the fire failed to exhibit the following characteristics:

(1) Jump the 4-ft (1.2-m) aisles to adjoining racks
(2) Reach the end face of the end stacks (north or south ends) of the main rack

TABLE C.9 *Summary of Relationship Between Sprinkler Discharge Density and the Extent of Fire Damage and Sprinkler Operation*

Density (gpm/ft²)	Fire Damage in Test Array		Sprinkler Operation (165°F) Area (ft²)
	%	ft²	
0.30 (ceiling only)	22	395	4500–4800
0.375 (ceiling only)	17	306	1800
0.45 (ceiling only)	9	162	700
0.20 (ceiling only)	28–36	504–648	13,100–14,000
0.20 (sprinklers at ceiling and in racks)	8	144	4100
0.30 (sprinklers at ceiling and in racks)	7	126	700

For SI units: 1 ft = 0.3048 m; °C = ⁵⁄₉(°F – 32); 1 gpm/ft^2 = 40.746 mm/min.

Control is defined as holding the fire in check through the extinguishing system until the commodities initially involved are consumed or until the fire is extinguished by the extinguishing system or manual aid.

The standard commodity as selected in the 20-ft (6.1-m) test series was used in the majority of tests for storage over 25 ft (7.6 m). Hallmark products and 3M products described in the 20-ft (6.1-m) test series report also were used as representative of Class III or Class IV commodities, or both, in several tests. The results of privately sponsored tests on Hallmark products and plastic encapsulated standard commodities also were made available to the committee.

A 25-ft (7.6-m) long test array was used for the majority of the tests for storage over 25 ft (7.6 m). The decision to use such an array was made because it was believed that a fire in racks over 25 ft (7.6 m) high that extended the full length of a 50-ft (15.24-m) long rack could not be considered controlled, particularly as storage heights increased.

One of the purposes of the tests was to determine arrangements of in-rack sprinklers that can be repeated as pile height increases and that provide control of the fire. The tests for storage height of 30 ft (9.1 m) explored the effect of such arrays. Many of these tests, however, produced appreciable fire spread in storage in tiers above the top level of protection within the racks. (In some cases, a total burnout of the top tiers of both the main rack and the target rack occurred.) In the case of the 30-ft (9.1-m) Hallmark Test 134 on the 60-ft (18.3-m) site, the material in the top tiers of storage burned vigorously, and the fire jumped the aisle above the fourth tier. The fire then burned downward into the south end of the fourth tier. In the test on the floor, a nominal 30-ft (9.1-m) clearance occurred between the top of storage and the ceiling sprinklers, whereas on the platform this clearance was reduced to nominal 10 ft (3.1 m). In most cases, the in-rack sprinklers were effective in controlling fire below the top level of protection within the racks. It has been assumed by the Test Planning Committee that, in an actual case with a clearance of 10 ft (3.1 m) or less above storage, ceiling sprinklers would be expected to control damage above the top level of protection within the racks. Tests have been planned to investigate lesser clearances.

Tests 114 and 128 explore the effect of changing the ignition point from the in-rack standard ignition point to a face ignition location. It should be noted, however, that both of these tests were conducted with 30-ft (9.1-m) clearance from the ceiling sprinklers to the top of storage and, as such, ceiling sprinklers had little effect on the fire in the top two tiers of storage. Firespread in the three lower tiers is essentially the same. A similar change in the firespread where the ignition point is changed was noted in Tests 126 and 127. Once again, 30-ft (9.1-m) clearance occurred between the top of storage and the ceiling sprinklers, and, as such, the ceiling sprinklers had little effect on the face fire. Comparisons of Tests 129, 130, and 131 in the test series for storage height of 50 ft (15.24 m) indicate little effect of point of ignition in the particular configuration tested.

Test 125, when compared with Test 133, indicates no significant difference in result between approved low-profile sprinklers and standard sprinklers in the racks.

C.10 [12.3.1.7] Temperatures in the test column were maintained below 1000°F (538°C) with densities, of roof ceiling sprinklers only, of 0.375 gpm/ft^2 (15.3 mm/min) with 8-ft (2.4-m) aisles and 0.45 gpm/ft^2 (18.3 mm/min) with 4-ft (1.2-m) aisles using the standard commodity.

C.11 [12.3.1.9.1] Test 98 with solid shelves 24 ft (7.3 m) long and 7½ ft (2.3 m) deep at each level produced total destruction of the commodity in the main rack and jumped the aisle. Density was 0.3 gpm/ft^2 (12.2 mm/min) from the ceiling sprinklers only. Test 108 with shelves 24 ft (7.3 m) long and 3½ ft (1.07 m) deep and with a 6-in. (152.4-mm) longitudinal flue space and one level of sprinklers in the rack resulted in damage to most of the commodity in the main rack but did not jump the aisle. Density from ceiling sprinklers was 0.375 gpm/ft^2 (15.3 mm/min), and rack sprinklers discharged at 15 psi (1 bar).

These tests did not yield sufficient information to develop a comprehensive protection standard for solid shelf racks. Items such as increased ceiling density, use of bulkheads, other configurations of sprinklers in racks, and limitation of shelf length and width should be considered.

Where such rack installations exist or are contemplated, the damage potential should be considered, and sound engineering judgment should be used in designing the protection system.

Test 98, with solid shelving obstructing both the longitudinal and transverse flue space, produced unsatisfactory results and indicates a need for sprinklers at each level in such a rack structure.

Test 147 was conducted with ceiling sprinklers only. Density was 0.45 gpm/ft^2 (18.3 mm/min) with a sprinkler spacing of 100 ft^2 (9.29 m^2). A total of 47 sprinklers opened, and 83 percent of the commodity was consumed. The fire jumped both aisles and spread to both ends of the main and target racks. The test was considered unsuccessful.

Test 148 was conducted with ceiling sprinklers and in-rack sprinklers. In-rack sprinklers were provided at each level (top of first, second, and third tiers) and were located in the longitudinal flue. They were directly above each other and 24 ft (7.3 m) on center or 22 ft (6.7 m) on each side of the ignition flue. Ceiling sprinkler discharge density was 0.375 gpm/ft^2 (15.3 mm/min). In-rack sprinkler discharge pressure was 30 psi (2.1 bar). A total of 46 ceiling sprinklers and three in-rack sprinklers opened, and 34 percent of the commodity was consumed. The fire consumed most of the material between the in-rack sprinklers and jumped both aisles.

C.12 [12.3.1.10] Fire tests with open-top containers in the upper tier of storage and a portion of the third tier of storage produced an increase in sprinkler operation from 36 to 41 sprinklers and a more pronounced aisle jump and increase in firespread in the main array. The smooth underside of the containers closely approximates fire behavior of slave pallets.

Installation of in-rack sprinklers or an increase in ceiling sprinkler density should be considered.

C.13 [12.3.1.13] Test 80 was conducted to determine the effect of closing back-to-back longitudinal 6-in. (152.4-mm) flue spaces in conventional pallet racks. Test results indicated fewer sprinklers operating than with the flue space open, and, as such, no minimum back-to-back clearance is necessary if the transverse flue space is kept open.

Tests 145 and 146 were conducted to investigate the influence of longitudinal and transverse flue dimensions in double-row racks without solid shelves. Results were compared with Tests 65 and 66. Flue dimensions in Tests 65, 66, 145, and 146 were 6 in. (152.4 mm), 6 in. (152.4 mm), 3 in. (76.2 mm), and 12 in. (0.3 m), respectively. All other conditions were the same.

In Tests 65 and 66, 45 and 48 sprinklers operated compared with 59 and 58 for Tests 145 and 146, respectively. Fire damage in Tests 145 and 146 was somewhat less than in Tests 65 and 66; 2100 ft^3 (59.51 m^3) and 1800 ft^3 (51 m^3) in Tests 145 and 146, respectively, versus 2300 ft^3 (65.13 m^3) and 2300 ft^3 (65.13 m^3) in Tests 65 and 66, respectively, of combustible material were consumed.

Test results indicate narrow flue spaces of about 3 in. (76.2 mm) allow reasonable passage of sprinkler water down through the racks.

Tests 96 and 107, on multiple-row racks, used 6-in. (152.4-mm) transverse flue spaces. The water demand recommended in the standard is limited to those cases with nominal 6-in. (152.4-mm) transverse flues in vertical alignment.

C.14 [12.3.2.1.1.1] Tests 65 and 66, compared with Test 69, and Test 93, compared with Test 94, indicated a reduction in areas of application of 44.5 percent and 45.5 percent, respectively, with high temperature–rated sprinklers as compared with ordinary temperature–rated sprinklers. Other extensive Factory Mutual tests produced an average reduction of 40 percent. Design curves are based on this area reduction. In constructing the design curves, the high-temperature curves above 3600 ft^2 (334.6 m^2) of application, therefore, represent 40 percent reductions in area of application of the ordinary temperature curves in the 6000-ft^2 to 10,000-ft^2 (557.6-m^2 to 929.41-m^2) range.

Test 84 indicated the number of intermediate temperature–rated sprinklers operating is essentially the same as ordinary temperature–rated sprinklers.

C.15 [12.3.2.1.2.1] Tests were not conducted with aisles wider than 8 ft (2.4 m) or narrower than 4 ft (1.2 m). It is, therefore, not possible to determine whether lower ceiling densities should be used for aisle widths greater than 8 ft (2.4 m) or if higher densities should be used for aisle widths less than 4 ft (1.2 m).

C.16 [12.3.2.4.2.3] In one 20-ft (6.1-m) high test, sprinklers were buried in the flue space 1 ft (0.3 m) above the bottom of the pallet load, and results were satisfactory. Coverage of aisles by in-rack sprinklers is, therefore, not necessary, and distribution across the tops of pallet loads at any level is not necessary for the occupancy classes tested.

C.17 [12.3.2.4.2.6] In all tests with in-rack sprinklers, obstructions measuring 3 in. × 3 ft (76.2 mm × 0.3 m) were introduced on each side of the sprinkler approximately 3 in. (76.2 mm) from the sprinkler to simulate rack structure member obstruction. This obstruction had no effect on sprinkler performance in the 20-ft (6.1-m) high tests.

Tests 103, 104, 105, and 109 in the 30-ft (9.1-m) high test with in-rack sprinklers obstructed by rack uprights produced unsatisfactory results. Tests 113, 114, 115, 117, 118, and 120 in the 30-ft (9.1-m) high test series with in-rack sprinklers located a minimum of 2 ft (0.61 m) from rack uprights produced improved results.

C.18 [12.3.2.4.3] In all except one case, using the standard commodity with one line of sprinklers installed in racks, only two sprinklers opened. In the one exception, two sprinklers opened in the main rack, and two sprinklers opened in the target rack.

C.19 [12.3.2.4.4 and 12.3.3.4.4] Operating pressures were 15 psi (1 bar) on all tests of sprinklers in racks with storage 20 ft (6.1 m) high and 30 psi (2.1 bar) for storage 30 ft (9.1 m) and 50 ft (15.24 m) high.

Tests 112 and 124 were conducted to compare the effect of increasing sprinkler discharge pressure at in-rack sprinklers from 30 psi to 75 psi (2.1 bar to 5.2 bar). With the higher discharge pressure, the fire did not jump the aisle, and damage below the top level of protection within the racks was somewhat better controlled by the higher discharge pressure of the in-rack sprinklers. A pressure of 15 psi (1 bar) was maintained on in-rack sprinklers in the first 30-ft (9.1-m) high tests (Tests 103 and 104). Pressure on in-rack sprinklers in subsequent tests was 30 psi (2.1 bar), except in Test 124, where it was 75 psi (5.2 bar).

C.20 [12.3.2.5.1.1 and 12.3.3.5.1.1] A full-scale test program was conducted with various double-row rack storage arrangements of a cartoned Group A unexpanded plastic commodity at the Factory Mutual Research Corporation (FMRC) test facility. The series of nine tests included several variations, one of which involved the use of the following four distinct shelving arrangements: slatted wood, solid wood, wire mesh, and no shelving. The results of the testing program, specifically Tests 1, 2, 3, and 5, clearly demonstrate the acceptable performance of sprinkler systems protecting storage configurations that involve the use of slated shelving as described in 12.3.2.5.1.1 and 12.3.3.5.1.1. As a result of the test program, Factory Mutual has amended FM Loss Prevention Data Sheet 8–9 to allow slatted shelving to be protected in the same manner as an open rack arrangement.

Complete details of the test program are documented in the FMRC technical report FMRC J. I. 0X1R0.RR, "Large-Scale Fire Tests of Rack Storage Group A Plastics in Retail Operation Scenarios Protected by Extra Large Orifice (ELO) Sprinklers."

C.21 [12.3.3.1.1] In the RSP rack storage test series as well as the stored plastics program palletized test series, compartmented 16-oz (0.47-L) polystyrene jars were found to produce significantly higher protection requirements than the same commodity in a nested configuration. Polystyrene glasses and expanded polystyrene plates were comparable to the nested jars.

Different storage configurations within cartons or different products of the same basic plastic might, therefore, require reduced protection requirements.

In Test RSP-7, with nominal 15-ft (4.6-m) high storage with compartmented jars, a 0.6 gpm/ft^2 (24.5 mm/min) density, 8-ft (2.4-m) aisles, and a 10-ft (3.1-m) ceiling clearance, 29 sprinklers opened. In Tests RSP-4 with polystyrene glasses, RSP-5 with expanded polystyrene plates, and RSP-16 with nested polystyrene jars all stored at nominal 15-ft (4.6-m) height, 10-ft (3.1-m) ceiling clearance, 8-ft (2.4-m) aisles, and 0.6 gpm/ft^2 (24.5 mm/min) density, only four sprinklers opened.

However, Test RSP-11, with expanded polystyrene plates and 6-ft (1.8-m) aisles, demonstrated an increase in the number of operating sprinklers to 29. Test RSP-10 with expanded polystyrene plates, nominally 15 ft (4.6 m) high with a 10-ft (3.1-m) clearance and 8-ft (2.4-m) aisles, but protected only by 0.45 gpm/ft^2 (18.3 mm/min) density, opened 46 sprinklers and burned 100 percent of the plastic commodity.

At a nominal 20-ft (6.1-m) storage height with 8-ft (2.4-m) aisles, a 3-ft (0.9-m) ceiling clearance, and a 0.6 gpm/ft^2 (24.5 mm/min) density opened four sprinklers with polystyrene glasses in Test RSP-2 and 11 sprinklers with expanded polystyrene plates in Test RSP-6. In Test RSP-8, however, with the ceiling clearance increased to 10 ft (3.1 m) and other variables held constant, 51 sprinklers opened, and 100 percent of the plastic commodity burned.

Test RSP-3 with polystyrene glasses at a nominal height of 25 ft (7.6 m) with a 3-ft (0.9-m) ceiling clearance, 8-ft (2.4-m) aisles, and 0.6 gpm/ft^2 (24.5 mm/min) ceiling sprinkler density in combination with one level of in-rack sprinklers, resulted in four ceiling sprinklers and two in-rack sprinklers operating. Test RSP-9, with the same configuration but with polystyrene plates, opened 12 ceiling sprinklers and three in-rack sprinklers.

No tests were conducted with compartmented polystyrene jars at storage heights in excess of a nominal 15 ft (4.6 m) as a part of this program.

C.22 [12.3.3.1.5] The protection of Group A plastics by extra large orifice (ELO) sprinklers designed to provide 0.6 gpm/ft^2/2000 ft^2 (24.5 mm/min/186 m^2) or 0.45 gpm/ft^2/2000 ft^2 (18.3 mm/min/186 m^2) without the installation of in-rack sprinklers was developed from full-scale testing conducted with various double-row rack storage arrangements of a cartoned

Group A unexpanded plastic commodity at the Factory Mutual Research Corporation (FMRC) test facility. The results of this test program are documented in the FMRC technical report, FMRC J.I. 0X1R0.RR, "Large-Scale Fire Tests of Rack Stored Group A Plastics in Retail Operation Scenarios Protected by Extra Large Orifice (ELO) Sprinklers." The test program was initiated to address the fire protection issues presented by warehouse-type retail stores with regard to the display and storage of Group A plastic commodities including, but not limited to, acrylonitrile-butadiene-styrene copolymer (ABS) piping, polyvinyl chloride (PVC) hose and hose racks, tool boxes, polypropylene trash and storage containers, and patio furniture. Tests 1 and 2 of this series included protection of the Group A plastic commodity stored to 20 ft (6.1 m) under a 27-ft (8.2-m) ceiling by a design density of 0.6 gpm/ft^2 (24.5 mm/min) utilizing ELO sprinklers. The results of the testing program clearly demonstrate the acceptable performance of sprinkler systems that protect storage configurations involving Group A plastics up to 20 ft (6.1 m) in height under a 27-ft (8.2-m) ceiling where using ELO sprinklers to deliver a design density of 0.6 gpm/ft^2 (24.5 mm/min) and Group A plastics up to 14 ft (4.3 m) in height under a 22-ft (6.7-m) ceiling where using ELO sprinklers to deliver a design density of 0.45 gpm/ft^2 (18.3 mm/min). The tabulation of the pertinent tests shown in Table C.22 demonstrates acceptable performance.

C.23 [12.3.4.1.1] The recommended use of ordinary temperature–rated sprinklers at ceiling for storage higher than 25 ft (7.6 m) was determined by the results of fire test data. A test with high temperature–rated sprinklers and 0.45 gpm/ft^2 (18.3 mm/min) density resulted in fire damage in the two top tiers just within acceptable limits, with three ceiling sprinklers operating. A test with 0.45 gpm/ft^2 (18.3 mm/min) density and ordinary temperature–rated sprinklers produced a dramatic reduction in fire damage with four ceiling sprinklers operating.

The four ordinary temperature-rated ceiling sprinklers operated before the first of the three high temperature–rated ceiling sprinklers. In both tests, two in-rack sprinklers at two levels operated at approximately the same time. The high temperature–rated sprinklers were at all times fighting a larger fire with less water than the ordinary temperature–rated ceiling sprinklers.

Tests 115 and 119 compare ceiling sprinkler density of 0.3 gpm/ft^2 (12.2 mm/min) with 0.45 gpm/ft^2 (12.2 mm/min) with 0.45 gpm/ft^2 (18.3 mm/min). Damage patterns coupled with the number of boxes damaged in the main rack suggest that the increase in density produces improved control, particularly in the area above the top tier of in-rack sprinklers.

Tests 119 and 122 compare ceiling sprinkler temperature ratings of 286°F (141°C) and 165°F (74°C). A review of the number of boxes damaged and the firespread patterns indicates that the use of ordinary temperature–rated ceiling sprinklers on a rack configuration that incorporates in-rack sprinklers dramatically reduces the amount of firespread. Considering that in-rack sprinklers in the tests for storage over 25 ft (7.6 m) operated prior to ceiling sprinklers, it would seem that the installation of in-rack sprinklers converts an otherwise rapidly developing fire, from the standpoint of ceiling sprinklers, to a slower developing fire with a lower rate of heat release.

In the 20-ft (6.1-m) high test series, ceiling sprinklers operated before in-rack sprinklers. In the 30-ft (9.1-m) high series, ceiling sprinklers operated after in-rack sprinklers. The 50-ft (15.24-m) high test did not operate ceiling sprinklers. Ceiling sprinklers would, however, be needed if fire occurred in upper levels.

The results of these tests indicate the effect of in-rack sprinklers on storage higher than 25 ft (7.6 m). From the ceiling sprinkler operation standpoint, a fire with an expected high heat release rate was converted to a fire with a much lower heat release rate.

Since the fires developed slowly and opened sprinklers at two levels in the racks, only a few ceiling sprinklers were needed to establish control. Thus, the sprinkler operating area does not vary with height for storage over 25 ft (7.6 m) or for changes in sprinkler temperature rating and density.

All tests with sprinklers in racks were conducted using nominal ½-in. (12.7-mm) orifice size sprinklers of ordinary temperature.

TABLE C.22 *Summary of Test Results for Plastic Commodities Using ⅝-in. (15.9-mm) Orifice Sprinklers*

Test Parameters	Date of Test						
	8/20/93	8/25/93	9/2/93	10/7/93	2/17/94	2/25/94	4/27/94
Type of shelving	Slatted wood	Slatted wood	Slatted wood	Slatted wood	Slatted wood	Slatted wood	Wire mesh
Other conditions/inclusions	—	—	—	—	Draft curtains	Draft curtains	—
Storage height (ft-in.)	19-11	19-11	15-4	15-4	19-11	19-11	13-11
Number of tiers	6[a]	6[a]	5[b]	5[b]	6[a]	6[b]	3
Clearance to ceiling/sprinklers (ft-in.)	6-10/6-3	6-10/6-3	11-5/10-10	11-5/10-10	6-10/6-3	6-10/6-3	8-4/7-9
Longitudinal/transverse flues (in.)	6/6 to 7½	6/6 to 7½	6/6 to 7	6/6 to 7½	6/6 to 7½	6/6 to 7½	6/3[c]
Aisle width (ft)	7½	7½	7½	7½	7½	7½	7½
Ignition centered below (number of sprinklers)	2	2	1	1	2	2	1
Sprinkler orifice size (in.)	0.64	0.64	0.64	0.64	0.64	0.64	0.64
Sprinkler temperature rating (°F)	165	286	286	165	165	286	286
Sprinkler RTI (ft-sec)^½	300	300	300	300	300	300	300
Sprinkler spacing (ft × ft)	8 × 10	8 × 10	8 × 10	8 × 10	8 × 10	8 × 10	10 × 10
Sprinkler identification	ELO-231	ELO-231	ELO-231	ELO-231	ELO-231	ELO-231	ELO-231
Constant water pressure (psi)	19	19	19	19	19	19	15.5
Minimum density (gpm/ft²)	0.6	0.6	0.6	0.6	0.6	0.6	0.45
First sprinkler operation (min:sec)	2:03	2:25	1:12	0:44	1:25	0:52	0:49
Last sprinkler operation (min:sec)	2:12	15:19	6:34	7:34	15:54	14:08	10:58
Total sprinklers opened	4	9	7	13	35	18	12
Total sprinkler discharge (gpm)	205	450	363	613	1651	945	600
Average discharge per sprinkler (gpm)	51	50	52	47	47	52	50
Peak/maximum 1-min average gas temperature (°F)	1107/566	1412/868	965/308	662/184	1575/883	1162/767	1464/895
Peak/maximum 1-min average steel temperature (°F)	185/172	197/196	233/232	146/145	226/225	255/254	502/500
Peak/maximum 1-min average plume velocity (ft/sec)	27/15	25/18	18/15[d]	14/10[d]	26/23	20/18[d]	33/20
Peak/maximum 1-min heat flux (Btu/ft²/sec)	0.6/0.5	2.0/1.9	2.8/2.5	1.1/0.8	1.0/0.9	4.8/3.0	1.6/1.4
Aisle jump, east/west target ignition (min:sec)	None	8:24/None	5:35/10:10	None	None	[e]/8:18	[e]/None
Equivalent number of pallet loads consumed	3	9	6	5	12	13	12
Test duration (min)	30	30	30	30	30	30	30
Results acceptable	Yes	Yes	Yes	Yes	No[f]	No[g]	Yes

For SI units, 1 ft = 0.305 m; 1 in. = 25.4 mm; °F = (1.8 × °C) + 32; °C = (°F – 32)/1.8; 1 psi = 0.069 bar; 1 gpm = 3.8 L/min; 1 ft/sec = 0.31 m/sec; 1 gpm/ft² = 40.746 mm/min.

[a]Main (ignition) racks divided into five or six tiers; bottom tiers each approximately 2 ft (0.6 m) high and upper tiers each about 5 ft (1.5 m) high; wood shelving below commodity at second through fifth tiers.

[b]Main (ignition) racks divided into five or six tiers; bottom tiers each approximately 2 ft (0.6 m) high and upper tiers each about 5 ft (1.5 m) high; wood shelving below commodity at second through fifth tiers; wire mesh shelving below commodity at sixth tier or below fifth (top) tier commodity.

[c]Transverse flues spaced 8 ft (2.4 m) apart [versus 3½ ft (1.1 m) apart in all other tests].

[d]Instrumentation located 5 ft (1.5 m) north of ignition.

[e]Minor surface damage to cartons.

[f]High water demand.

[g]Excessive firespread; marginally high water demand.

Sprinkler System Information from the 1997 Edition of the *Life Safety Code*

This annex is not a part of the requirements of this NFPA document but is included for informational purposes only.

D.1 Introduction

This annex is provided as an aid to the user of NFPA 13 by identifying those portions of the 1997 edition of *101, Life Safety Code,* that pertain to sprinkler system design and installation. It is not intended that this annex provide complete information regarding all aspects of fire protection addressed by NFPA *101*. It is important to note that this information was not copied from NFPA *101* using NFPA's extract policy and is not intended to be a part of the requirements of NFPA 13. While the 1997 edition of the *Life Safety Code* was the most current at the time of the publication of the 1999 edition of NFPA 13, a 2000 edition of the *Life Safety Code* is in preparation.

D.2 Definitions

See NFPA *101, Life Safety Code,* for terms not defined in Chapter 3.

D.3 Atriums

Glass walls and inoperable windows shall be permitted in lieu of the fire barriers where automatic sprinklers are spaced 6 ft (1.8 m) apart or less along both sides of the glass wall and inoperable windows, not more than 1 ft (0.3 m) from the glass, and with the automatic sprinklers located so that the entire surface of the glass is wet upon operation of the sprinklers. The glass shall be tempered, wired, or laminated glass held in place by a gasket system that permits the glass framing system to deflect without breaking (loading) the glass before the sprinklers operate. Automatic sprinklers shall not be required on the atrium side of the glass wall and inoperable windows where there is no walkway or other floor area on the atrium side above the main floor level. Doors in such walls shall be glass or other material that will resist the passage of smoke. Doors shall be self-closing or automatic-closing upon detection of smoke. [*101:*6.2.4.6, Exception No. 2 to (a)]

D.4 Connection to Domestic Water Supply

Sprinkler piping serving not more than six sprinklers for any isolated hazardous area shall be permitted to be connected directly to a domestic water supply system having a capacity sufficient to provide 0.15 gpm/sq ft (6.1 L/min/sq m) of floor area throughout the entire enclosed area. An indicating shut-off valve shall be installed in an accessible location between the sprinklers and the connection to the domestic water supply. [*101:*7.7.1.2]

D.5 Supervision [*101:* 7.7.2]

 D.5.1 Supervisory Signals. Where supervised, automatic sprinkler systems are required by another section of NFPA *101*, supervisory attachments shall be installed and monitored for integrity in accordance with *NFPA 72, National Fire Alarm Code,* and a distinctive supervisory signal shall be provided to indicate a condition that would impair the satisfactory operation of the sprinkler system. This shall include, but not be limited to, monitoring of control valves, fire pump power supplies and running conditions, water tank levels and temperatures, pressure of tanks, and air pressure on dry-pipe valves. Supervisory signals shall sound and shall be displayed either at a location within the protected building that is constantly attended by qualified personnel or at an approved, remotely located receiving facility. [*101:*7.7.2.1]

D.5.2 Alarm Signal Transmission. Where supervision of automatic sprinkler systems is provided in accordance with another provision of NFPA *101*, waterflow alarms shall be transmitted to an approved, proprietary alarm receiving facility, a remote station, a central station, or the fire department. Such connection shall be installed in accordance with 7.6.1.4 of NFPA *101*. [*101:*7.7.2.2]

D.6 Stages

D.6.1 Sprinklers shall not be required for stages 1000 sq ft (93 sq m) or less in area and 50 ft (15 m) or less in height where curtains, scenery, or other combustible hangings are not retractable vertically. Combustible hangings shall be limited to a single main curtain, borders, legs, and a single backdrop. [*101:*8.4.5.10, Exception No. 1]

D.6.2 Sprinklers shall not be required under stage areas less than 4 ft (1.2 m) in clear height used exclusively for chair or table storage and lined on the inside with ⅝-in. (1.6-cm) Type X gypsum wallboard or the approved equivalent. [*101:*8.4.5.10, Exception No. 2]

D.7 Exhibition Booths

The following shall be protected by automatic extinguishing systems:

(1) Single-level exhibit booths greater than 300 sq ft (27.9 sq m) and covered with a ceiling.
(2) Throughout each level of multilevel exhibit booths, including the uppermost level if the uppermost level is covered with a ceiling.
(3) A single exhibit or group of exhibits with ceilings that do not require sprinklers shall be separated by a minimum of 10 ft (3 m) where the aggregate ceiling exceeds 300 sq ft (27.9 sq m).

The water supply and piping for the sprinkler system shall be permitted to be of approved temporary means taken from an existing domestic water supply, an existing standpipe system, or an existing sprinkler system.

Exception No. 1: Ceilings that are constructed of open grate design or listed dropout ceilings in accordance with NFPA 13, Standard for the Installation of Sprinkler Systems, shall not be considered ceilings within the context of this section.

Exception No. 2: Vehicles, boats, and similar exhibited products having over 100 sq ft (9.3 sq m) of roofed area shall be provided with smoke detectors acceptable to the authority having jurisdiction.

Exception No. 3: Where fire protection of multilevel exhibit booths is consistent with the criteria developed through a life safety evaluation of the exhibition hall in accordance with 8.4.1 of NFPA 101, subject to approval of the authority having jurisdiction. (See A.8.2.3.2 of NFPA 101.)

*[**101**:8.7.5.3.7]*

D.8 Proscenium Curtain

The proscenium opening of every legitimate stage shall be provided with a curtain constructed and mounted so as to intercept hot gases, flames, and smoke and to prevent flame from a fire on the stage from becoming visible from the auditorium side for a 5-min period where the curtain is of asbestos. Other materials shall be permitted if they have passed a 30-min fire test in a small scale 3 ft × 3 ft (0.9 m × 0.9 m) furnace with the sample mounted in the horizontal plane at the top of the furnace and subjected to the standard time-temperature curve.

The curtain shall be automatic-closing without the use of applied power.

All proscenium curtains shall be in the closed position except during performances, rehearsals, or similar activities.

Exception No. 1: In lieu of the protection required herein, all the following shall be provided:

(1) *A noncombustible opaque fabric curtain shall be arranged so that it will close automatically; and*

(2) *An automatic, fixed waterspray deluge system shall be located on the auditorium side of the proscenium opening and shall be arranged so that the entire face of the curtain will be wetted. The system shall be activated by combination of rate-of-rise and fixed-temperature detectors located on the ceiling of the stage. Detectors shall be spaced in accordance with their listing. The water supply shall be controlled by a deluge valve and shall be sufficient to keep the curtain completely wet for 30 min or until the valve is closed by fire department personnel; and*

(3) *The curtain shall be automatically operated in case of fire by a combination of rate-of-rise and fixed-temperature detectors that also activates the deluge spray system. Stage sprinklers and vents shall be automatically operated by fusible elements in case of fire; and*

(4) *Operation of the stage sprinkler system or spray deluge valve shall automatically activate the emergency ventilating system and close the curtain; and*

(5) *The curtain, vents, and spray deluge system valve shall also be capable of manual operation.*

*Exception No. 2: Proscenium fire curtains or water curtains complying with 8.4.5.7 of NFPA 101. [**101**:9.4.5.7]*

D.9 Listed quick response or listed residential sprinklers shall be used throughout smoke compartments containing patient sleeping rooms. [**101**:12.3.5.2]

The requirements for use of quick response sprinklers intends that quick response sprinklers be the predominant type of sprinkler installed in the smoke compartment. It is recognized, however, that quick response sprinklers may not be approved for installation in all areas such as those where NFPA 13, *Standard for the Installation of Sprinkler Systems*, requires sprinklers of the intermediate- or high-temperature classification. It is not the intent of the 12-3.5.2 of NFPA *101* requirements to prohibit the use of standard sprinklers in limited areas of a smoke compartment where intermediate- or high-temperature sprinklers are required.

Where the installation of quick response sprinklers is impracticable in patient sleeping room areas, appropriate equivalent protection features acceptable to the authority having jurisdiction should be provided. It is recognized that the use of quick response sprinklers may be limited in facilities housing certain types of patients, or due to the installation limitations of quick response sprinklers. [*101:*A.12.3.5.2]

D.10 Where an automatic sprinkler system is installed, either for total or partial building coverage, the system shall be installed in accordance with Section 7.7 of NFPA *101*. In buildings up to and including four stories in height, systems installed in accordance with NFPA 13R, *Standard for the Installation of Sprinkler Systems in Residential Occupancies up to and Including Four Stories in Height,* shall be permitted.

Exception No. 1: In individual dwelling units, sprinkler installation shall not be required in closets not over 12 sq ft (1.1 sq m). Closets that contain equipment such as washers, dryers, furnaces, or water heaters shall be sprinklered regardless of size.

Exception No. 2: The draft stop and closely spaced sprinkler requirements of NFPA 13, Standard for the Installation of Sprinkler Systems, shall not be required for convenience openings complying with 6.2.4.8 of NFPA 101a where the convenience opening is within the dwelling unit.

[101:18.3.5.1]

Informational References

E.1 Referenced Publications

The following documents or portions thereof are referenced within this standard for informational purposes only and are thus not part of the requirements of this document unless also listed in Chapter 2.

E.1.1 NFPA Publications. National Fire Protection Association, 1 Batterymarch Park, P.O. Box 9101, Quincy, MA 02269-9101.

NFPA 13E, *Recommended Practice for Fire Department Operations in Properties Protected by Sprinkler and Standpipe Systems,* 2000 edition.

NFPA 13R, *Standard for the Installation of Sprinkler Systems in Residential Occupancies up to and Including Four Stories in Height,* 2002 edition.

NFPA 14, *Standard for the Installation of Standpipe, Private Hydrant, and Hose Systems,* 2000 edition.

NFPA 15, *Standard for Water Spray Fixed Systems for Fire Protection,* 2001 edition.

NFPA 16, *Standard for the Installation of Foam-Water Sprinkler and Foam-Water Spray Systems,* 1999 edition.

NFPA 20, *Standard for the Installation of Stationary Pumps for Fire Protection,* 1999 edition.

NFPA 22, *Standard for Water Tanks for Private Fire Protection,* 1998 edition.

NFPA 25, *Standard for the Inspection, Testing, and Maintenance of Water-Based Fire Protection Systems,* 2002 edition.

NFPA 36, *Standard for Solvent Extraction Plants,* 1997 edition.

NFPA 72®, *National Fire Alarm Code®,* 2002 edition.

NFPA 80A, *Recommended Practice for Protection of Buildings from Exterior Fire Exposures,* 2001 edition.

NFPA *101®, Life Safety Code®,* 2000 edition.

NFPA 220, *Standard on Types of Building Construction,* 1999 edition.

NFPA 291, *Recommended Practice for Fire Flow Testing and Marking of Hydrants,* 2002 edition.

NFPA 307, *Standard for the Construction and Fire Protection of Marine Terminals, Piers, and Wharves,* 2000 edition.

NFPA 409, *Standard on Aircraft Hangars,* 2001 edition.

NFPA 850, *Recommended Practice for Fire Protection for Electric Generating Plants and High Voltage Direct Current Converter Stations,* 2000 edition.

NFPA 851, *Recommended Practice for Fire Protection for Hydroelectric Generating Plants,* 2000 edition.

E.1.2 Other Publications.

E.1.2.1 ACPA Publication. American Concrete Pipe Association, 222 W. Las Collinas Boulevard, Suite 641, Irving, TX 75039.

Concrete Pipe Handbook.

E.1.2.2 ASCE Publication. American Society of Civil Engineers, 1801 Alexander Bell Drive, Reston, VA 20191-4400.

ASCE 19, *Standard Guidelines for the Structural Applications of Steel Cables for Buildings,* 1996.

E.1.2.3 ASME Publications. American Society of Mechanical Engineers, 345 East 47th Street, New York, NY 10017.

ASME B16.1, *Cast-Iron Pipe Flanges and Flanged Fittings,* 1989.

ASME A17.1, *Safety Code for Elevators and Escalators,* 1996.

ASME B1.20.1, *Pipe Threads, General Purpose (Inch),* 1983.

E.1.2.4 ASTM Publications. American Society for Testing and Materials, 100 Barr Harbor Drive, West Conshohocken, PA 19428-2959.

ASTM A 126, *Standard Specification for Gray Iron Casting for Valves, Flanges, and Pipe Fittings,* 1995.

ASTM A 135, *Standard Specification for Electric-Resistance-Welded Steel Pipe,* 1997.

ASTM A 197, *Standard Specification for Cupola Malleable Iron,* 1987.

ASTM A 307, *Standard Specification for Carbon Steel Bolts and Studs,* 1997.

ASTM A 603, *Standard Specification for Zinc-Coated Steel Structural Wire Rope,* 1998.

ASTM C 296, *Standard Specification for Asbestos-Cement Pressure Pipe,* 1988.

ASTM D 3309, *Standard Specification for Polybutylene (PB) Plastic and Hot- and Cold-Water Distribution Systems,* 1996.

ASTM E 8, *Structural Test Method for Tension Testing of Metallic Materials,* 2001.

ASTM E 119, *Standard Test Methods for Fire Tests of Building Construction and Materials,* 1998.

ASTM F 437, *Standard Specification for Threaded Chlorinated Poly (Vinyl Chloride) (CPVC) Plastic Pipe Fittings, Schedule 80,* 1996.

ASTM F 438, *Standard Specification for Socket-Type Chlorinated Poly (Vinyl Chloride) (CPVC) Plastic Pipe Fittings, Schedule 40,* 1997.

ASTM F 439, *Standard Specification for Socket-Type Chlorinated Poly (Vinyl Chloride) (CPVC) Plastic Pipe Fittings, Schedule 80,* 1997.

ASTM F 442, *Standard Specification for Chlorinated Poly (Vinyl Chloride) (CPVC) Plastic Pipe (SDR-PR),* 1997.

E.1.2.5 AWWA Publications. American Water Works Association, 6666 West Quincy Avenue, Denver, CO 80235.

AWWA C104, *Cement Mortar Lining for Ductile Iron Pipe and Fittings for Water,* 1995.

AWWA C105, *Polyethylene Encasement for Ductile Iron Pipe Systems,* 1993.

AWWA C110, *Ductile Iron and Gray Iron Fittings, 3-in. Through 48-in., for Water and Other Liquids,* 1993.

AWWA C111, *Rubber-Gasket Joints for Ductile Iron Pressure Pipe and Fittings,* 1990.

AWWA C115, *Flanged Ductile Iron Pipe with Ductile Iron or Gray Iron Threaded Flanges,* 1994.

AWWA C150, *Thickness Design of Ductile Iron Pipe,* 1996.

AWWA C151, *Ductile Iron Pipe, Centrifugally Cast for Water,* 1996.

AWWA C153, *Ductile Iron Compact Fittings, 3 in. through 24 in. and 54 in. through 64 in. for Water Service,* 1994.

AWWA C203, *Coal-Tar Protective Coatings and Linings for Steel Water Pipelines Enamel and Tape—Hot Applied,* 1997.

AWWA C205, *Cement-Mortar Protective Lining and Coating for Steel Water Pipe 4 in. and Larger—Shop Applied,* 1995.

AWWA C206, *Field Welding of Steel Water Pipe,* 1997.

AWWA C208, *Dimensions for Fabricated Steel Water Pipe Fittings,* 1996.

AWWA C300, *Reinforced Concrete Pressure Pipe, Steel-Cylinder Type, for Water and Other Liquids,* 1997.

AWWA C301, *Prestressed Concrete Pressure Pipe, Steel-Cylinder Type, for Water and Other Liquids,* 1992.

AWWA C302, *Reinforced Concrete Pressure Pipe, Non-Cylinder Type, for Water and Other Liquids,* 1995.

AWWA C303, *Reinforced Concrete Pressure Pipe, Steel-Cylinder Type, Pretensioned, for Water and Other Liquids,* 1995.

AWWA C400, *Standard for Asbestos-Cement Distribution Pipe, 4 in. Through 16 in., for Water and Other Liquids,* 1993.

AWWA C401, *Standard Practice for the Selection of Asbestos-Cement Water Pipe,* 1993.

AWWA C600, *Standard for the Installation of Ductile-Iron Water Mains and Their Appurtenances,* 1993.

AWWA C602, *Cement-Mortar Lining of Water Pipe Lines 4 in. and Larger—in Place,* 1995.

AWWA C603, *Standard for the Installation of Asbestos-Cement Water Pipe,* 1996.

AWWA C606, *Grooved and Shouldered Joints,* 1997.

AWWA C900, *Polyvinyl Chloride (PVC) Pressure Pipe, 4 in. Through 12 in., for Water and Other Liquids,* 1997.

AWWA M11, *A Guide for Steel Pipe Design and Installation,* 3rd edition, 1989.

AWWA M14, *Recommended Practice for Backflow Prevention and Cross Connection Control,* 2nd edition, 1990.

AWWA M41, *Ductile Iron and Pipe Fittings.*

E.1.2.6 DIRPA Publication. Ductile Iron Pipe Research Association, 245 Riverchase Parkway, East, Suite 0, Birmingham, AL 35244.

Installation Guide for Ductile Iron Pipe.

Thrust Restraint Design for Ductile Iron Pipe.

E.1.2.7 EPRI Publication. EPRI, 3412 Hillview Avenue, Palo Alto, CA 94304.

1843-2, "Turbine Generator Fire Protection by Sprinkler System," July 1985.

E.1.2.8 FMRC Publication. Factory Mutual Research Corporation, 1151 Boston-Providence Turnpike, Norwood, MA 02061.

FMRC J. I. 0X1R0.RR, "Large-Scale Fire Tests of Rack Storage Group A Plastics in Retail Operation Scenarios Protected by Extra Large Orifice (ELO) Sprinklers."

E.1.2.9 IMO Publication. International Maritime Organization, 4 Albert Embankment, London, SEI 7SR, United Kingdom.

International Convention for the Safety of Life at Sea, 1974 (SOLAS 74), as amended, regulations II-2/3 and II-2/26.

E.1.2.10 SNAME Publication. Society of Naval Architects and Marine Engineers, 601 Pavonia Ave., Suite 400, Jersey City, NJ 07306.

Technical Research Bulletin 2-21, "Aluminum Fire Protection Guidelines."

E.1.2.11 UL Publication. Underwriters Laboratories Inc., 333 Pfingsten Road, Northbrook, IL 60062.

"Commodity Hazard Comparison of Expanded Plastic in Portable Bins and Racking," Project 99NK29106, NC4004, September 8, 2000.

"Technical Report of Fire Testing of Automotive Parts in Portable Storage Racking," Project 99NK29106, NC4004, January 5, 2001.

E.1.2.12 Uni-Bell Plastic Pipe Publication. Uni-Bell Plastic Pipe Association, 2655 Villa Creek Drive, Suite 155, Dallas, TX 75234.

Handbook of PVC Pipe.

E.1.2.13 U.S. Government Publications. U.S. Government Printing Office, Washington, DC 20402.

Title 46, *Code of Federal Regulations,* Part 72.05-5.

U.S. Federal Standard No. 66C, *Standard for Steel Chemical Composition and Harden Ability,* April 18, 1967, change notice No. 2, April 16, 1970.

E.2 Informational References (Reserved)

E.3 References for Extracts

The following documents are listed here to provide reference information, including title and edition, for extracts given throughout this standard as indicated by a reference in brackets [] following a section or paragraph. These documents are not a part of the requirements of this document unless also listed in Chapter 2 for other reasons.

NFPA 33, *Standard for Spray Application Using Flammable or Combustible Materials,* 2000 edition.

NFPA 36, *Standard for Solvent Extraction Plants,* 2001 edition.

NFPA 40, *Standard for the Storage and Handling of Cellulose Nitrate Film,* 2001 edition.

NFPA 42, *Code for the Storage of Pyroxylin Plastic,* 2002 edition.

NFPA 45, *Standard on Fire Protection for Laboratories Using Chemicals,* 2000 edition.

NFPA 51, *Standard for the Design and Installation of Oxygen–Fuel Gas Systems for Welding, Cutting, and Other Hot Work,* 1999 edition.

NFPA 51A, *Standard for Acetylene Cylinder Charging Plants,* 2001 edition.

NFPA 55, *Standard for the Storage, Use, and Handling of Compressed and Liquefied Gases in Portable Cylinders,* 1998 edition.

NFPA 59, *Utility LP-Gas Plant Code,* 2001 edition.

NFPA 59A, *Standard for the Production, Storage, and Handling of Liquefied Natural Gas (LNG),* 2001 edition.

NFPA 75, *Standard for the Protection of Electronic and Computer/Data Processing Equipment,* 1999 edition.

NFPA 82, *Standard on Incinerators and Waste and Linen Handling Systems and Equipment,* 1999 edition.

NFPA 86C, *Standard for Industrial Furnaces Using a Special Processing Atmosphere,* 1999 edition.

NFPA 99, *Standard for Health Care Facilities,* 2002 edition.

NFPA 130, *Standard for Fixed Guideway Transit and Passenger Rail Systems,* 2000 edition.

NFPA 150, *Standard on Fire Safety in Racetrack Stables,* 2000 edition.

NFPA 214, *Standard on Water-Cooling Towers,* 2000 edition.

NFPA 307, *Standard for the Construction of Marine Terminals, Piers, and Wharves,* 2000 edition.

NFPA 318, *Standard for the Protection of Semiconductor Fabrication Facilities,* 2002 edition.

NFPA 415, *Standard on Airport Terminal Buildings, Fueling Ramp Drainage, and Loading Walkways,* 2002 edition.

NFPA 423, *Standard for Construction and Protection of Aircraft Engine Test Facilities,* 1999 edition.

NFPA 430, *Code for the Storage of Liquid and Solid Oxidizers,* 2000 edition.

NFPA 432, *Code for the Storage of Organic Peroxide Formulations,* 2002 edition.

NFPA 804, *Standard for Fire Protection for Advanced Light Water Reactor Electric Generating Plants,* 2001 edition.

NFPA 805, *Performance-Based Standard for Fire Protection for Light Water Reactor Electric Generating Plants,* 2001 edition.

NFPA 850, *Recommended Practice for Fire Protection for Electric Generating Plants and High Voltage Direct Current Converter Stations,* 2000 edition.

NFPA 851, *Recommended Practice for Fire Protection for Hydroelectric Generating Plants,* 2000 edition.

NFPA 909, *Code for the Protection of Cultural Resources,* 2001 edition.

PART TWO

NFPA 13D,

Standard for the Installation of Sprinkler Systems in One- and Two-Family Dwellings and Manufactured Homes, 2002 Edition, with Commentary

P art Two of this handbook includes the complete text and illustrations of the 2002 edition of NFPA 13D, *Standard for the Installation of Sprinkler Systems in One- and Two-Family Dwellings and Manufactured Homes.* The text and illustrations from the standard are printed in black and are the official requirements of NFPA 13D. Line drawings and photographs from the standard are labeled "Figures."

Paragraphs that begin with the letter "A" are extracted from Annex A of the standard. Although printed in black ink, this nonmandatory material is purely explanatory in nature. For ease of use, this handbook places Annex A material immediately after the standard paragraph to which it refers.

In addition to the standard text and annexes, Part Two includes commentary that provides the history and other background information for specific paragraphs in the standard. This insightful commentary takes the reader behind the scenes, into the reasons underlying the requirements.

To make commentary material readily identifiable, commentary text, captions, and tables are printed in blue. Line drawings and photographs in the commentary are labeled "Exhibits."

CHAPTER 1

Administration

The 1973 publication of the report "America Burning" by the National Commission on Fire Prevention and Control focused national attention on the residential fire problem. This report, with its cover shown in Exhibit 1.1, indicated that the majority of fire deaths occurred in residential occupancies. As the magnitude of the U.S. residential fire problem became clear, the Technical Committee on Residential Sprinkler Systems expanded its focus to help address the residential fire problem.

EXHIBIT 1.1 "America Burning," the Report of the National Commission on Fire Prevention and Control.

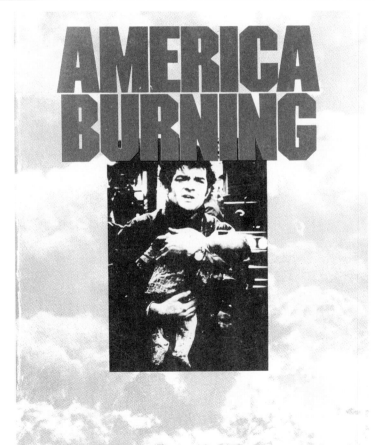

In the summer of 1973, the Technical Committee on Residential Sprinkler Systems established the Subcommittee on Residential and Light Hazard Occupancies. This subcommittee was charged with developing a standard that would produce a reliable but inexpensive sprinkler system for these occupancies. In its first meeting, the subcommittee established the philosophies and principles of NFPA 13D. These philosophies and principles still apply to the current edition and include the following:

1. Cost is a major factor. A system that was slightly less reliable and had fewer operational features than those described in NFPA 13, *Standard for the Installation of Sprinkler Systems,* but that could be effective and installed at a substantially lower cost, was necessary to achieve acceptance of a residential system. This goal was a statement of "America Burning."
2. Life safety is the primary goal of NFPA 13D, with property protection a secondary goal.
3. System design should be such that a fire could be controlled for a sufficient time to enable people to escape—that is, a 10-minute stored water supply with an adequate local audible alarm.
4. Piping arrangements, components, and hangers must be compatible with residential construction techniques. Combined sprinkler/plumbing systems are acceptable from a fire protection standpoint.
5. The fire record in residential properties can reasonably serve as a baseline to permit omission of sprinklers in areas of low incidence of fire deaths, thus lowering costs. NFPA 13D gives permission to omit sprinklers in spaces where fires result in a small percentage of fatalities compared to other spaces in the dwelling.

The first draft document produced by the subcommittee addressed residential systems for one- and two-family dwellings, mobile homes, and multifamily housing up to four stories in height. However, when finally adopted in 1975, the multifamily housing portion had been removed because the Technical Committee on Residential Sprinkler Systems believed that such occupancies needed to include a system with more safety factors due to the greater number of people living there and the buildings' larger, more complex layout. As a result, multifamily buildings were required to be protected with sprinkler systems complying with NFPA 13. It would be another 13 years before sufficient understanding about fires and people's response to them in such occupancies allowed for the development of NFPA 13R, *Standard for the Installation of Sprinkler Systems in Residential Occupancies up to and Including Four Stories in Height.*

The first edition of NFPA 13D was developed with a relatively limited scientific understanding of residential fires and how sprinklers should protect against them. As a result, the first edition was based on technology that was largely applicable to property protection of commercial and industrial facilities such as factories and warehouses. In 1975, these types of buildings had a more prevalent use of sprinkler systems. Although the technical committee had good intentions, the first edition of NFPA 13D did not provide the type of cost-effective fire protection system recommended by the report "America Burning." However, the efforts of the technical committee clearly indicated that more scientific research would be necessary if the overall goals were to be realized.

In 1976, the National Fire Prevention and Control Administration (NFPCA), later renamed the U.S. Fire Administration (USFA), began to fund a number of research programs to scientifically evaluate the residential fire problem with the intent of developing a viable solution. The overall goals and objectives documented in the report "America Burning," which were embraced by the technical committee, centered on the system's ability to permit adequate time for occupants to escape from the dwelling. The NFPCA/USFA programs included studies that assessed the impact of using sprinklers on reducing the incidence of deaths and injuries in residential fires [Halpin 1978]. Other studies evaluated the practicality, design, installation, and user acceptance of residential systems while focusing on the reliability of these systems [Yurkonis 1978]; the evaluation of sprinkler discharge rates, spray patterns, response sensitivity, and overall design criteria [Henderson 1978, Kung 1978]; and the evaluation of prototype systems using full-scale tests [Cote 1980, Kung 1980, Kung 1982, Moore 1980].

Research and development programs also included evaluation of factors that contributed to the death of humans in a fire event—for example, the determination of threshold values of carbon monoxide, temperature, and oxygen depletion. These factors served as test criteria for evaluating whether a sprinkler could maintain occupant tenability in the room of fire origin. These research efforts collectively provided a greater understanding of the associated phenomenon of residential fires and created a new class of sprinkler—the residential sprinkler. This development resulted in a complete revision of NFPA 13D, published in 1980, at which time residential sprinkler technology was developed to a level where it could begin to be standardized and used commercially.

This part, Part Two, of the *Automatic Sprinkler Systems Handbook* addresses the 2002 edition of NFPA 13D. The commentary provides background information to the reader on the standard's requirements. Beginning with the 1999 edition, the Technical Committee on Residential Sprinkler Systems was established to specifically address NFPA 13D and NFPA 13R and to continue the efforts of increasing the effectiveness and appeal of residential sprinkler systems in terms of both their cost and their ability to save lives. Since 1980, a number of special situations such as the protection of piping in areas subject to freezing, placement of sprinklers beneath other than smooth, flat ceilings, the use of specially listed piping materials, alternative design options for limited area dwellings, and multipurpose piping systems have been addressed. For example, the 1996 edition was the first to allow the use of ½-in. nonmetallic pipe when certain conditions are met, and the 1999 edition provided for reduced system working pressures for multipurpose piping systems.

While many improvements have been incorporated into the standard over the years, associated efforts in terms of scientific research and overall acceptance of residential sprinklers are needed. One such effort includes the development of the Home Fire Sprinkler Coalition (HFSC) that was established in 1997 to make the general public more aware of the potential for fire in their homes and to promote the option of residential fire sprinklers. The HFSC acts independently from the technical committee and is a nonprofit organization made up of various interests. For more information on HFSC, call 1-888-635-7222 or contact them at www.homefiresprinkler.org.

Users of NFPA 13D are encouraged to review the publications presented in Chapter 2 to obtain additional information on residential sprinkler systems. Also, users should be aware that research efforts are ongoing in the rapidly changing field of residential fire protection and that more current information could become available.

A sprinkler system installed in accordance with NFPA 13D greatly enhances the chance for occupant escape. However, the residential sprinkler system is not considered a substitute for smoke detectors, which is indicated in the preface to NFPA 13D. The installation of smoke detectors is considered an important element in a balanced approach to residential fire safety.

1.1* Scope

This standard shall cover the design and installation of automatic sprinkler systems for protection against the fire hazards in one- and two-family dwellings and manufactured homes.

A.1.1 NFPA 13D is appropriate for protection against fire hazards only in one- and two-family dwellings and manufactured homes. Residential portions of any other type of building or occupancy should be protected with residential sprinklers in accordance with NFPA 13, or in accordance with NFPA 13R. Other portions of such buildings should be protected in accordance with NFPA 13 or NFPA 13R as appropriate for areas outside the dwelling unit.

The criteria in this standard are based on full-scale fire tests of rooms containing typical furnishings found in residential living rooms, kitchens, and bedrooms. The furnishings were arranged as typically found in dwelling units in a manner similar to that shown in Figure A.1.1(a),

FIGURE A.1.1(a) *Bedroom.*

FIGURE A.1.1(b) *Manufactured Home Bedroom.*

FIGURE A.1.1(c) *Living Room.*

Figure A.1.1(b), and Figure A.1.1(c). Sixty full-scale fire tests were conducted in a two-story dwelling in Los Angeles, California, and 16 tests were conducted in a 14 ft (4.3 m) wide mobile home in Charlotte, North Carolina.

Sprinkler systems designed and installed according to this standard are expected to prevent flashover within the compartment of origin where sprinklers are installed in the compartment. A sprinkler system designed and installed according to this standard cannot, however, be expected to completely control a fire involving fuel loads that are significantly higher than average for dwelling units [10 lb/ft^2 (49 kg/m^2)] and where the interior finish has an unusually high flame spread rating (greater than 225).

(For protection of multifamily dwellings, see NFPA 13, Standard for the Installation of Sprinkler Systems, or NFPA 13R, Standard for the Installation of Sprinkler Systems in Residential Occupancies up to and Including Four Stories in Height.)

The scope of NFPA 13D is covered in Section 1.1. NFPA 13D applies only to one- and two-family dwellings and manufactured homes, formerly referred to as mobile homes, as defined in 3.3.5, regardless of size.

Because of a number of factors such as a two-sprinkler design discharge, the allowance for the omission of sprinklers in certain spaces, and a 10-minute water supply (7 minutes under specific conditions), a sprinkler system installed in accordance with NFPA 13D is inappropriate for multifamily occupancies. (A multifamily occupancy contains three or more dwelling units.) Sprinkler systems using residential sprinklers that are intended for multifamily facilities should be designed and installed in accordance with either NFPA 13R or NFPA 13. It should also be noted that the development of NFPA 13D did not consider the application of NFPA 13D for residential board and care facilities.

The requirements of NFPA 13D are based on full-scale fire tests conducted in dwellings in Los Angeles and Charlotte, NC [Cote 1980, Cote, 1982, Kung 1982, Moore 1980], and

◀ **FAQ**
What are the limits of the application of NFPA 13D, and are the size of the dwelling units limited?

earlier laboratory tests conducted by Factory Mutual Research Corporation and Battelle Columbus Laboratories [Henderson 1978, Kung 1978]. Some of these tests indicated that the associated life safety objectives could possibly be achieved with water application rates as low as 0.025 gpm/ft^2 [1.02 L/min · m^2]. However, these tests usually involved smoldering fires in typical residential room configurations and flaming fires generated by a gas burner rather than by a fuel package consisting of household combustibles such as furniture and draperies. Subsequent tests at FM Global [Kung 1980] and at the test sites in Los Angeles and Charlotte, NC [Cote 1980, Cote 1982, Kung 1982, Moore 1980] established that sprinkler discharge had to be in accordance with the design parameters as indicated in Section 8.1. Using these parameters, the basic design density acceptable is 0.09/gpm ft^2 [3.7 L/min · m^2]. The likelihood of successfully achieving life safety and reducing injuries and property damage is reduced when smaller discharge densities are used.

FAQ ▶
Why was the minimum water spray density of 0.05 gpm/ft^2 (2.0 L/m^2) added to the 2002 edition of NFPA 13D?

With the 2002 edition, a minimum water spray density of 0.05 gpm/ft^2 (2.0 L/m^2) for sprinklers is required for systems designed according to this standard. The Technical Committee on Residential Sprinkler Systems proposed this change after considering (1) laboratory test data by Underwriters Laboratories and FM Global, (2) the variability of fire challenges, (3) the excellent residential sprinkler system performance record in field installations, and (4) the need for cost-effective sprinkler protection to encourage the use of sprinklers in residential occupancies.

FAQ ▶
Why was the chapter on limited area dwellings eliminated from the 2002 edition of NFPA 13D?

Another major change in this edition is the removal of the limited area dwelling system, which had been added to the standard in 1994. The system was based on a specialized sprinkler that required a minimum flowing pressure of 25 psi (1.72 bar). Since no such sprinkler has been manufactured to date, the system could not be used. Hence the system has been removed from the standard. Removal of the limited area dwelling system does not in any way change the scope or applicability of NFPA 13D.

1.2* Purpose

The purpose of this standard shall be to provide a sprinkler system that aids in the detection and control of residential fires and thus provides improved protection against injury, life loss, and property damage. A sprinkler system designed and installed in accordance with this standard shall be expected to prevent flashover (total involvement) in the room of fire origin, where sprinklered, and to improve the chance for occupants to escape or be evacuated. The layout, calculation, and installation of systems installed in accordance with this standard shall only be performed by people knowledgeable and trained in such systems.

 A.1.2 Various levels of fire safety are available to dwelling occupants to provide life safety and property protection.

This standard recommends, but does not require, sprinklering of all areas in a dwelling; it permits sprinklers to be omitted in certain areas. These areas have been proved by NFPA statistics *[see Table A.1.2(a) and Table A.1.2(b)]* to be those where the incidence of life loss from fires in dwellings is low. Such an approach provides a reasonable degree of fire safety. Greater protection to both life and property is achieved by sprinklering all areas.

Guidance for the installation of smoke detectors and fire detection systems is found in *NFPA 72®, National Fire Alarm Code®*.

The purpose of NFPA 13D is covered in Section 1.2. Both Underwriters Laboratories Inc. and FM Global have developed test standards for the evaluation of residential sprinklers. These test standards include significantly different test parameters than those used to evaluate non-residential sprinklers such as the standard spray sprinkler. The criteria used in UL 1626 for residential sprinklers during a fire test are as follows:

TABLE A.1.2(a) *Causal Factors in One- and Two-Family Dwelling Fires that Caused One or More Deaths*

Area of Origin	Percent Occurrence[1]
Living room	41%
Bedroom	27%
Kitchen	15%
Storage area	4%
Heating equipment room	3%
Structural area	2%
Other areas	8%

Form of Materials Ignited	Percent Occurrence[2]
Furniture	27%
Bedding	18%
Combustible liquid or gas	13%
Interior finish	9%
Structural member	9%
Waste, rubbish	4%
Clothing (on a person)	3%
Cooking materials	3%
Electrical insulation	2%
Curtains, draperies	2%
Other	10%

Form of Heat of Ignition	Percent Occurrence[3]
Smoking materials	36%
Heat from fuel-fire or powered object	25%
Heat from miscellaneous open flame (including match)	15%
Heat from electrical equipment arcing or overload	14%
Hot objects, including properly operating electrical equipment	7%
Other	3%

Note: Total number of incidents reported: 10,194.

[1]Based on 6066 incidents where area of origin was reported.

[2]Based on 5080 incidents where form of material ignited was reported.

[3]Based on 5016 incidents where form of heat of ignition was reported.

(Source: FIDO Database 1973 to 1982, NFPA Fire Analysis Department.)

1. The maximum gas or air temperature adjacent to the sprinkler—3 in. (76.2 mm) below the ceiling and 8 in. (203 mm) horizontally away from the sprinkler—must not exceed 600°F (316°C).
2. The maximum temperature—5 ft, 3 in. (1.6 m) above the floor and half the room length away from each wall—must be less than 200°F (93°C) during the entire test. This temperature must not exceed 130°F (54°C) for more than a 2-minute period.
3. The maximum temperature ¼ in. (6.3 mm) behind the finished surface of the ceiling material directly above the test fire must not exceed 500°F (260°C).
4. No more than two residential sprinklers in the test enclosure can operate.

The UL 1626 fuel package and test procedure was recently revised to (1) enhance the reproducibility of the tests and (2) increase the similarity between the fire performance of the fuel

TABLE A.1.2(b) *Fires and Associated Deaths and Injuries in Dwellings, Duplexes, and Manufactured Homes by Area of Origin: Annual Average of 1986–1990 Structure Fires Reported to U.S. Fire Departments*

Area of Origin	Civilian Deaths	Civilian Percent	Fires	Percent	Injuries	Percent
Living room, family room, or den	1,330	37.1	42,600	10.5	2,546	18.6
Bedroom	919	25.6	50,200	12.4	3,250	23.7
Kitchen	541	15.1	92,670	22.9	3,987	29.1
Dining room	83	2.3	3,780	0.9	189	1.4
Heating equipment room or area	62	1.7	15,130	3.7	374	2.7
Hallway or corridor	48	1.3	3,690	0.9	155	1.1
Laundry room or area	47	1.3	15,370	3.8	363	2.7
Garage or carport*	45	1.2	14,580	3.6	524	3.8
Bathroom	44	1.2	8,040	2.0	271	2.0
Unclassified structural area	43	1.2	4,530	1.1	104	0.8
Crawl space or substructure space	41	1.2	11,200	2.8	317	2.3
Multiple areas	41	1.1	3,350	0.8	96	0.7
Ceiling/floor assembly or concealed space	32	0.9	3,470	0.9	64	0.5
Wall assembly or concealed space	27	0.8	7,090	1.8	93	0.7
Closet	23	0.6	5,020	1.2	186	1.4
Exterior balcony or open porch	22	0.6	5,570	1.4	121	0.9
Exterior wall surface	22	0.6	14,620	3.6	118	0.9
Unclassified area	21	0.6	2,590	0.6	87	0.6
Attic or ceiling/roof assembly or concealed space	21	0.6	10,740	2.7	98	0.7
Tool room or other supply storage room or area	20	0.5	4,160	1.0	133	1.0
Lobby or entrance way	17	0.5	1,410	0.3	44	0.3
Interior stairway	17	0.5	1,100	0.3	41	0.3
Chimney	17	0.5	60,530	14.9	75	0.5
Unclassified function area	17	0.5	1,090	0.3	43	0.3
Unclassified storage area	14	0.4	2,460	0.6	80	0.6
Area not applicable	11	0.3	1,180	0.3	22	0.2
Exterior stairway	8	0.2	1,090	0.3	25	0.2
Lawn or field	7	0.2	1,670	0.4	24	0.2
Trash room or area	5	0.1	1,140	0.3	14	0.1
Product storage area	5	0.1	780	0.2	23	0.2
Unclassified means of egress	5	0.1	610	0.2	15	0.1
Unclassified service or equipment area	4	0.1	380	0.1	12	0.1
Library	3	0.1	180	0.0	11	0.0
Other known area	26	0.7	12,880	3.2	195	1.4
Total	3,589	100.0	404,900	100.0	13,691	100.0

Note: Fires are estimated to the nearest 10; civilian deaths and injuries are estimated to the nearest 1.

*Does not include dwelling garages coded as a separate property, which averaged 19 deaths, 259 injuries, and 21,170 fires per year.

(Source: 1986–1990 NFIRS and NFPA survey.)

package used in the standard tests and that of the fuel packages used as part of the principle residential sprinkler research effort.

The details of the UL 1626 simulated furniture are shown in Exhibit 1.2. The fuel package is composed of several different components: a wood crib, two simulated sofa ends covered with foam, two sheets of ¼ in. (6.3 mm) Douglas fir plywood, a pan with heptane, and two heptane-soaked cotton wicks. The arrangement of the fuel package within the test room is shown at the upper left of the exhibit.

EXHIBIT 1.2 *Simulated Fuel Package for UL 1626. (Courtesy of Underwriters Laboratories Inc.)*

The three fire test configurations are shown in Exhibits 1.3 through 1.5. Exhibit 1.3 shows the configuration used to test pendent, upright, flush, recessed pendent and concealed sprinklers. Exhibits 1.4 and 1.5 present the configurations used to test sidewall sprinklers. In the first case the sprinklers are located opposite the fuel package, and in the second case the sprinklers are located on the same wall as the fuel package.

Compliance with the preceding criteria serves to provide an indication that flashover will not occur, the environment through which occupants must evacuate is tenable, and that both of these criteria can be accomplished with the water supply specified by NFPA 13D.

The basic laboratory test configuration is a 12 ft × 24 ft (3.7 m × 7.3 m) room with a combustible array simulating residential furnishings. The test facility is adjustable so that it can be configured to evaluate other sprinkler spacing parameters as permitted by 8.1.3.2.

The technical committee adopted the concept of "levels of protection" in order to achieve a reasonable degree of safety while controlling the cost of the system. Because sprinklers may be omitted from certain spaces in the dwelling as indicated by Section 8.6, the level of protection is

EXHIBIT 1.3 *Fire Test Arrangement for UL 1626 for Pendent, Upright, Flush Recessed Pendent and Concealed Sprinklers.*

L = Coverage length
W = Coverage width

less than if those spaces were sprinklered. The areas where omission of sprinklers is permitted are those where NFPA fire statistics indicate a relatively low incidence of fire deaths. See Table A.1.2(a).

FAQ ▶
Why are dry pipe systems prohibited from NFPA 13D?

Dry pipe systems in dwellings are not desirable for life safety because of the delay in application of water from activated sprinklers. This delay was noted in early FM Global tests and substantiated in the Los Angeles and Charlotte, NC, fire tests [Cote 1980, Cote 1982, Kung 1982, Moore 1980]. The key to achieving control of a residential fire is the rapid appli-

EXHIBIT 1.4 *Fire Test Arrangement from UL 1626 for Sidewall Sprinklers, Test Arrangement 1.*

Thermocouple
¼ in. (6.3 mm)
above ceiling
10 in. diagonally
from corner

L

4 ft (1.2 m) plywood

42 in. (1.06 m)

35 in. (0.89 m)

19 in. (0.48 m)

Wood crib

Simulated furniture

W/2

4 ft (1.2 m) plywood

42 in. (1.06 m)

Thermocouple
3 in. (76.2 mm)
below ceiling and
5¼ in. (1.6 m)
above floor

½L + 8 in. (203 mm)

1½ W +
9 ft (2.7 m)

W

Thermocouple
3 in. (76.2 mm)
below ceiling
(room center)

Sidewall sprinkler
(typical)

8 ft
(2.4 m)
minimum

1 ft (0.3 m)

L = Coverage length
W = Coverage width

41 in.
(1.04 m)

cation of water upon activation of the sprinkler. Additionally, residential systems must be simple and easy to maintain. Because dry pipe systems are more complex than wet pipe systems, their maintenance requires greater effort.

In the 2002 edition, wording has been added to Section 1.2 to remind users of the standard that a residential sprinkler system is a life safety system and as such should be designed and installed only by persons trained and skilled in the design and installation of residential sprinkler systems.

EXHIBIT 1.5 *Fire Test Arrangement from UL 1626 for Sidewall Sprinklers, Test Arrangement 2.*

1.3 Retroactivity

The provisions of this standard reflect a consensus of what is necessary to provide an acceptable degree of protection from the hazards addressed in this standard at the time the standard was issued. Unless otherwise specified, the provisions of this standard shall not apply to facilities, equipment, structures, or installations that existed or were approved for construction or installation prior to the effective date of the standard. Where specified, the provisions of this standard shall be retroactive. In those cases where the authority having jurisdiction determines that the existing situation presents an unacceptable degree of risk, the authority having jurisdiction shall be permitted to apply retroactively any portions of this standard deemed appropriate. The retroactive requirements of this standard shall be permitted to be modified if their application clearly would be impractical in the judgment of the authority having jurisdiction, and only where it is clearly evident that a reasonable degree of safety is provided.

1.4 Equivalency

Nothing in this standard is intended to restrict new technologies or alternative arrangements, provided that the level of safety prescribed by the standard is not reduced.

1.5 Units

1.5.1* Metric units of measurement in this standard shall be in accordance with the modernized metric system known as the International System of Units (SI).

A.1.5.1 For additional conversions and information, see ASTM SI 10, *Standard for Use of the International System of Units (SI): the Modernized Metric System.*

1.5.2 The liter and bar units shall be permitted to be used in this standard.

1.5.3 The conversion factors for liter, pascal, and bar shall be in accordance with Table 1.5.3.

TABLE 1.5.3 *Metric Conversions*

Name of Unit	Unit Symbol	Conversion Factor
liter	L	1 gal = 3.785 L
pascal	Pa	1 psi = 6894.757 Pa
bar	bar	1 psi = 0.0689 bar
bar	bar	1 bar = 10^5 Pa

1.5.4* Where a value for measurement as specified in this standard is followed by an equivalent value in other units, the first stated value shall be regarded as the requirement.

A.1.5.4 A given equivalent value is considered to be approximate.

1.5.5 The equivalent value for a measurement in SI shall be converted by multiplying the value by the conversion factor and then rounding the result to the appropriate number of significant digits.

REFERENCES CITED IN COMMENTARY

National Fire Protection Association, 1 Batterymarch Park, P.O. Box 9101, Quincy, MA 02269-9101

NFPA 13, *Standard for the Installation of Sprinkler Systems,* 2002 edition

NFPA 13R, *Standard for the Installation of Sprinkler Systems in Residential Occupancies up to and Including Four Stories in Height,* 2002 edition

Cote, A. E., "Final Report on Field Test and Evaluation of Residential Sprinkler Systems," National Fire Protection Association, Quincy, MA, July 1982

Cote, A., and Moore, D., "Field Test and Evaluation of Residential Sprinkler Systems, Los Angeles Test Series," National Fire Protection Association, Boston, MA, April 1980 (This report was done for the NFPA 13D subcommittee and included a series of fire tests in actual dwellings with sprinkler systems installed in accordance with the data resulting from all prior test work and the criteria included in the proposed 1980 revisions to NFPA 13D so as to evaluate the effectiveness of the system under conditions approaching actual use.)

Factory Mutual Research Corporation/Underwriters Laboratories Inc., *Standard for Residential Automatic Sprinklers for Fire Protection Service,* Northbrook, IL, April 1980 (This study developed a performance standard for testing residential sprinklers under room fire conditions that conform with the requirements of NFPA 13D.)

Halpin, B. M., Dinan, J. J., and Deters, O. J., "Assessment of the Potential Impact of Fire Protection Systems on Actual Fire Incidents," Johns Hopkins University—Applied Physics Laboratory (JHU/APL), Laurel, MD, October 1978 (This study describes an in-depth analysis of fires involving fatalities and includes an assessment of how use of detectors, sprinklers, or remote alarms would have changed the results.)

Henderson, N. C., Riegel, P. S., Patton, R. M., and Larcomb, D. B., "Investigation of Low-Cost Residential Sprinkler Systems," Battelle Columbus Laboratories (BCL), Columbus, OH, June 1978 (This study addresses fire tests of commercial nozzles and evaluates piping methods to achieve low-cost systems based on propane burner, wood crib, and furniture fire tests.)

Kung, H., Haines, D., and Green, R., Jr., "Development of Low-Cost Residential Sprinkler Protection," Factory Mutual Research Corporation, Norwood, MA, February 1978 (This study addresses development of low-cost residential sprinkler systems having minimal water discharge rates providing adequate life and property from smoldering fires.)

Kung, H. C., Spaulding, R. D., and Hill, E. E., Jr., "Sprinkler Performance in Residential Fire Tests," Factory Mutual Research Corporation, Norwood, MA, December 1980 (This study includes fire tests on representative living room and bedroom residential configurations with combinations of furnishings, with open and closed windows, and with variations in sprinkler application rates and response sensitivity of sprinklers. This work has been closely evaluated by the NFPA 13D subcommittee during its conduct, and the subcommittee was responsible for directing many of the test conditions that were evaluated.)

Kung, H. C., Spaulding, R. D., Hill, E. E., Jr., and Symonds, A. P., "Technical Report Field Evaluation of Residential Prototype Sprinkler, Los Angeles Fire Test Program," Factory Mutual Research Corporation, Norwood, MA, February 1982

Moore, D., "Data Summary of the North Carolina Test Series of USFA Grant 79027 Field Test and Evaluation of Residential Sprinkler Systems," National Fire Protection Association, Boston, MA, September 1980 (This report was done for the NFPA 13D subcommittee and included a series of fire tests in actual mobile homes with sprinkler systems installed in accordance with the data resulting from prior test work and following criteria described in the 1980 edition of NFPA 13D in order to evaluate the effectiveness of the system under conditions approaching actual use.)

National Commission on Fire Prevention and Control, "America Burning," U.S. Government Printing Office, Washington, DC, 1973

Underwriters Laboratories Inc., "Proposed Standard for Residential Automatic Sprinklers for Fire Protection Service," UL 1626, Northbrook, IL, October 1980 (This standard describes the requirements for the testing of residential sprinklers by a testing laboratory. Factory Mutual Research Corporation has a similar standard.)

Yurkonis, Peter, "Study to Establish the Existing Automatic Fire Suppression Technology for Use in Residential Occupancies," Rolf Jensen & Associates, Inc., Deerfield, IL, December 1978 (This study identifies suppression systems and evaluates design and cost factors affecting practical usage and user acceptance.)

CHAPTER 2

Referenced Publications

2.1 General

The documents or portions thereof listed in this chapter are referenced within this standard and shall be considered part of the requirements of this document.

2.2 NFPA Publications

National Fire Protection Association, 1 Batterymarch Park, P.O. Box 9101, Quincy, MA 02269-9101.

NFPA 13, *Standard for the Installation of Sprinkler Systems,* 2002 edition.

NFPA 72®, National Fire Alarm Code®, 2002 edition.

NFPA 220, *Standard on Types of Building Construction,* 1999 edition.

2.3 Other Publications

2.3.1 ANSI Publication. American National Standards Institute, Inc., 11 West 42nd Street, 13th floor, New York, NY 10036.

ANSI B36.10M, *Welded and Seamless Wrought Steel Pipe,* 1996.

2.3.2 ASME Publications. American Society of Mechanical Engineers, Three Park Avenue, New York, NY 10016-5990.

ASME B16.1, *Cast Iron Pipe Flanges and Flanged Fittings,* 1989.

ASME B16.3, *Malleable Iron Threaded Fittings,* 1992.

ASME B16.4, *Gray Iron Threaded Fittings,* 1992.

ASME B16.5, *Pipe Flanges and Flanged Fittings,* 1996.

ASME B16.9, *Factory-Made Wrought Steel Buttwelding Fittings,* 1993.

ASME B16.11, *Forged Fittings, Socket-Welding and Threaded,* 1996.

ASME B16.18, *Cast Copper Alloy Solder Joint Pressure Fittings,* 1984.

ASME B16.22, *Wrought Copper and Copper Alloy Solder Joint Pressure Fittings,* 1995.

ASME B16.25, *Buttwelding Ends,* 1997.

2.3.3 ASTM Publications. American Society for Testing and Materials, 100 Barr Harbor Drive, West Conshohocken, PA 19428-2959.

ASTM A 53, *Standard Specification for Pipe, Steel, Black and Hot-Dipped, Zinc-Coated, Welded and Seamless,* 1998.

ASTM A 135, *Standard Specification for Electric-Resistance-Welded Steel Pipe*, 1997.

ASTM A 234, *Standard Specification for Piping Fittings of Wrought Carbon Steel and Alloy Steel for Moderate and Elevated Temperatures*, 1997.

ASTM A 795, *Standard Specification for Black and Hot-Dipped Zinc-Coated (Galvanized) Welded and Seamless Steel Pipe for Fire Protection Use*, 1997.

ASTM B 32, *Standard Specification for Solder Metal*, 1996.

ASTM B 75, *Standard Specification for Seamless Copper Tube*, 1999.

ASTM B 88, *Standard Specification for Seamless Copper Water Tube*, 1999.

ASTM B 251, *Standard Specification for General Requirements for Wrought Seamless Copper and Copper-Alloy Tube*, 1997.

ASTM B 813, *Standard Specification for Liquid and Paste Fluxes for Soldering Applications of Copper and Copper-Alloy Tube*, 2000.

ASTM B 828, *Standard Practice for Making Capillary Joints by Soldering of Copper and Copper Alloy Tube and Fittings*, 2000.

ASTM D 3309, *Standard Specification for Polybutylene (PB) Plastic Hot- and Cold-Water Distribution Systems*, 1996.

ASTM F 437, *Standard Specification for Threaded Chlorinated Poly (Vinyl Chloride) (CPVC) Plastic Pipe Fittings, Schedule 80*, 1996.

ASTM F 438, *Standard Specification for Socket-Type Chlorinated Poly (Vinyl Chloride) (CPVC) Plastic Pipe Fittings, Schedule 40*, 1997.

ASTM F 439, *Standard Specification for Socket-Type Chlorinated Poly (Vinyl Chloride) (CPVC) Plastic Pipe Fittings, Schedule 80*, 1997.

ASTM F 442, *Standard Specification for Chlorinated Poly (Vinyl Chloride) (CPVC) Plastic Pipe (SDR-PR)*, 1997.

2.3.4 AWS Publication. American Welding Society, 550 N.W. LeJeune Road, Miami, FL 33126.

AWS A5.8, *Specification for Filler Metals for Brazing and Braze Welding*, 1992.

CHAPTER 3

Definitions

With the *Manual of Style* rewrite of NFPA 13D, definitions are no longer in alphabetical order; the definitions are listed by category. For example, *antifreeze systems* is categorized under 3.3.9 *Systems*.

In the 2002 edition, many of the definitions were changed to adopt the preferred definitions from the NFPA glossary of terms. Terms modified include *dry pipe sprinkler system, multipurpose piping system, manufactured home, residential sprinkler, sprinkler system,* and *wet pipe sprinkler system.*

The definitions of the terms *preaction sprinkler system* and *network system* were added. It should be noted that dry systems and preaction systems are not approved for use in NFPA 13D systems.

3.1 Definitions

The definitions contained in this chapter shall apply to the terms used in this standard. Where terms are not included, common usage of the terms shall apply.

3.2 NFPA Official Definitions

3.2.1* Approved. Acceptable to the authority having jurisdiction.

A.3.2.1 Approved. The National Fire Protection Association does not approve, inspect, or certify any installations, procedures, equipment, or materials; nor does it approve or evaluate testing laboratories. In determining the acceptability of installations, procedures, equipment, or materials, the authority having jurisdiction may base acceptance on compliance with NFPA or other appropriate standards. In the absence of such standards, said authority may require evidence of proper installation, procedure, or use. The authority having jurisdiction may also refer to the listings or labeling practices of an organization that is concerned with product evaluations and is thus in a position to determine compliance with appropriate standards for the current production of listed items.

The term *approved,* which is defined in 3.2.1 and which means acceptable to the authority having jurisdiction, differs from the term *listed,* which is defined in 3.2.4. An item that is approved is not necessarily listed. In accordance with 5.1.3, tanks, pumps, hangers, waterflow devices, and waterflow valves are not required to be listed. Residential sprinklers, however, must be listed per 5.1.2, and certain types of pipe and fittings are also required to be listed in accordance with 5.2.2 and 5.2.9.

◀ **FAQ**
What is the difference between Listed and Approved?

3.2.2* Authority Having Jurisdiction (AHJ). The organization, office, or individual responsible for approving equipment, materials, an installation, or a procedure.

A.3.2.2 Authority Having Jurisdiction (AHJ). The phrase "authority having jurisdiction," or its acronym AHJ, is used in NFPA documents in a broad manner, since jurisdictions and approval agencies vary, as do their responsibilities. Where public safety is primary, the authority having jurisdiction may be a federal, state, local, or other regional department or individual such as a fire chief; fire marshal; chief of a fire prevention bureau, labor department, or health department; building official; electrical inspector; or others having statutory authority. For insurance purposes, an insurance inspection department, rating bureau, or other insurance company representative may be the authority having jurisdiction. In many circumstances, the property owner or his or her designated agent assumes the role of the authority having jurisdiction; at government installations, the commanding officer or departmental official may be the authority having jurisdiction.

3.2.3 Labeled. Equipment or materials to which has been attached a label, symbol, or other identifying mark of an organization that is acceptable to the authority having jurisdiction and concerned with product evaluation, that maintains periodic inspection of production of labeled equipment or materials, and by whose labeling the manufacturer indicates compliance with appropriate standards or performance in a specified manner.

3.2.4* Listed. Equipment, materials, or services included in a list published by an organization that is acceptable to the authority having jurisdiction and concerned with evaluation of products or services, that maintains periodic inspection of production of listed equipment or materials or periodic evaluation of services, and whose listing states that either the equipment, material, or service meets appropriate designated standards or has been tested and found suitable for a specified purpose.

 A.3.2.4 Listed. The means for identifying listed equipment may vary for each organization concerned with product evaluation; some organizations do not recognize equipment as listed unless it is also labeled. The authority having jurisdiction should utilize the system employed by the listing organization to identify a listed product.

3.2.5 Shall. Indicates a mandatory requirement.

3.2.6 Should. Indicates a recommendation or that which is advised but not required.

3.2.7 Standard. A document, the main text of which contains only mandatory provisions using the word "shall" to indicate requirements and which is in a form generally suitable for mandatory reference by another standard or code or for adoption into law. Nonmandatory provisions shall be located in an appendix or annex, footnote, or fine-print note and are not to be considered a part of the requirements of a standard.

3.3 General Definitions

3.3.1 Compartment. See Section 4.1.

3.3.2 Design Discharge. The rate of water discharged by an automatic sprinkler expressed in gpm (mm/min).

3.3.3 Dwelling. Any building that contains not more than one or two dwelling units intended to be used, rented, leased, let, or hired out to be occupied or that are occupied for habitation purposes.

3.3.4 Dwelling Unit. One or more rooms, arranged for the use of one or more individuals living together, as in a single housekeeping unit, that normally have cooking, living, sanitary, and sleeping facilities.

3.3.5* Manufactured Home. A structure, transportable in one or more sections, that is 8 body-ft (2.4 m) or more in width or 40 body-ft (12.2 m) or more in length in the traveling mode or, when erected on-site, is 320 ft² (29.7 m²) or more; which is built on a chassis and designed to be used as a dwelling, with or without a permanent foundation, when connected to the required utilities, including the plumbing, heating, air conditioning, and electrical systems contained therein. Calculations used to determine the number of square feet in a structure are based on the structure's exterior dimensions, measured at the largest horizontal projections when erected on-site. These dimensions include all expandable rooms, cabinets, and other projections containing interior space, but do not include bay windows.

A.3.3.5 Manufactured Home. Manufactured homes were formerly referred to as "mobile homes" or "trailer coaches."

In the United States, the Department of Housing and Urban Development (HUD) regulates manufactured homes, which are defined in 3.3.5. The regulation of manufactured homes is unique when compared to modular housing units or stick-built homes. Both of these types of housing tend to be governed more by local codes. The previous reputation of manufactured homes as rural, low- to middle-income housing units no longer applies. Developments that are exclusively reserved for these units are widely used and accepted. In some southern and southwestern states, more manufactured homes are estimated to be brought in than stick-built and modular homes are to be constructed. The units' cost, functionality, and appearance make them attractive, viable, and economically feasible for many people.

3.3.6 Pressure.

3.3.6.1 Supply Pressure. The pressure within the supply (e.g., city or private supply water source).

Supply pressure, which is defined in 3.3.6.1, is the pressure that can be expected from the municipal or stored water supply, which is discussed in A.8.4.4.

3.3.6.2 System Pressure. The pressure within the system (e.g., above the control valve).

System pressure, which is defined in 3.3.6.2, is determined by subtracting friction losses between the street connection and the residence's water supply valve from the water pressure in the street after making any necessary adjustments for changes in friction loss in the pipe, fittings, appurtenances, and elevation. (See A.8.4.4.)

3.3.6.3 System Working Pressure. The maximum anticipated static (nonflowing) or flowing pressure applied to sprinkler system components exclusive of surge pressures.

The definition of *system working pressure,* which is contained in 3.3.6.3, was added to the 1999 edition to clearly indicate that this pressure pertains to the installed system. The maximum static pressure could be the result of surge pressures held in a system by a check valve or backflow preventer and are not to be considered the system's working pressure.

3.3.7 Pump. A mechanical device that transfers or raises, or transfers and raises, the pressure of a fluid (water).

3.3.8 Sprinkler.

3.3.8.1 Automatic Sprinkler. A fire suppression or control device that operates automatically when its heat-actuated element is heated to its thermal rating or above, allowing water to discharge over a specific area.

Depending on the type used, automatic sprinklers, which are defined in 3.3.8.1, are intended to achieve fire control or fire suppression. Additionally, automatic sprinklers can be used for property protection or life safety, or both. Residential sprinklers that are specifically listed automatic devices are intended to achieve life safety as their primary objective. Property protection is considered a secondary benefit. NFPA 13 provides more information with regard to the types and styles of automatic sprinklers.

 3.3.8.2 Residential Sprinkler. A type of fast-response sprinkler that meets the criteria of NFPA 13, *Standard for the Installation of Sprinkler Systems,* that has been specifically investigated for its ability to enhance survivability in the room of fire origin and is listed for use in the protection of dwelling units.

 Residential sprinklers, which are defined in 3.3.8.2, are specifically listed by Underwriters Laboratories Inc. and FM Global for residential service and have been tested for compliance with NFPA 13D. The primary purpose of residential sprinklers is to achieve life safety in residential occupancies. The sprinklers contain fast-response operating elements and can be of the upright, pendent, or sidewall configuration, although no upright devices are available at this time. The discussion on sprinkler sensitivity in the commentary to 3.6.1 of NFPA 13 provides additional information with regard to sprinklers with fast-response operating elements.

3.3.9 Systems.

3.3.9.1 Antifreeze System. An antifreeze system is an automatic sprinkler system containing an antifreeze solution and connected to a water supply. The antifreeze solution, followed by water, discharges immediately from sprinklers opened by a fire.

 3.3.9.2 Dry Pipe Sprinkler System. A sprinkler system employing automatic sprinklers that are attached to a piping system containing air or nitrogen under pressure, the release of which (as from the opening of a sprinkler) permits the water pressure to open a valve known as a dry pipe valve, and the water then flows into the piping system and out the opened sprinkler.

Dry pipe sprinkler system is defined in 3.3.9.2. Because of the concern for delayed water delivery and the fact that there are no residential sprinklers listed for use on dry pipe systems, residential dry pipe systems are not allowed. Furthermore, data from residential fire tests do not support the four-sprinkler design that was included in the 1980 edition of NFPA 13D. Rather than deleting all references to dry pipe systems in NFPA 13D, the technical committee left selective wording in place to allow for the development and listing of a residential sprinkler that can be used in a dry pipe system.

> **Since dry pipe systems are prohibited, how can areas subject to freezing be addressed?**
> **FAQ ▶**

Areas subject to freezing can be protected by antifreeze systems or by the use of standard dry pendent or dry sidewall sprinklers (see 8.3.2). Additionally, piping passing through areas subject to freezing can be protected with insulation as indicated in A.8.3.1.

 3.3.9.3 Multipurpose Piping System. A piping system within a residential occupancy intended to serve both domestic and fire protection needs.

 3.3.9.4 Network System. A type of multipurpose system utilizing a common piping system supplying domestic fixtures and fire sprinklers where each sprinkler is supplied by a minimum of three separate paths.

> **FAQ ▶**
> **What is a network system as defined in 3.3.9.4?**

A *network system,* which is defined in 3.3.9.4, is a type of multipurpose system that is unique to NFPA 13D systems. Typically the system utilizes nominal ½ in. (12.7 mm) nonmetallic pipe. The requirements for using ½ in. (12.7 mm) nonmetallic pipe are given in 8.4.3.3 and the requirements for a multipurpose piping system are given in Section 6.3. Exhibit 3.1 shows a network fitting.

 3.3.9.5 Preaction Sprinkler System. A sprinkler system employing automatic sprinklers that are attached to a piping system that contains air that might or might not be under pressure, with a supplemental detection system installed in the same areas as the sprinklers.

EXHIBIT 3.1 *Network Fitting, Simple Single Story System Design. (Courtesy of Uponor Wirsbo)*

3.3.9.6 Preengineered System. A packaged sprinkler system including all components connected to the water supply and designed to be installed according to pretested limitations.

3.3.9.7 Sprinkler System. For fire protection purposes, an integrated system of underground and overhead piping designed in accordance with fire protection engineering standards. The installation includes one or more automatic water supplies. The portion of the sprinkler system aboveground is a network of specially sized or hydraulically designed piping installed in a building, structure, or area, generally overhead, and to which sprinklers are attached in a systematic pattern. The system is usually activated by heat from a fire and discharges water over the fire area.

The definition of *sprinkler system,* which is contained in 3.3.9.7, includes water supplies and underground piping. These components are critical to proper sprinkler system performance and must be treated as part of the system.

3.3.9.8 Wet Pipe Sprinkler System. A sprinkler system employing automatic sprinklers attached to a piping system containing water and connected to a water supply so that water discharges immediately from sprinklers opened by heat from a fire.

3.3.10 Valve.

3.3.10.1 Check Valve. A valve that allows flow in one direction only.

3.3.10.2* Control Valve. A valve employed to control (shut) a supply of water to a sprinkler system.

A.3.3.10.2 Control Valve. System control valves should be of the indicating type, such as plug valves, ball valves, butterfly valves, or OS&Y gate valves.

Control valve is defined in 3.3.10.2. The type of control valve used should be an indicating type. An indicating valve has some external means to indicate to the occupant that the valve is either in the open or closed position.

3.3.11 Waterflow Alarm. A sounding device activated by a waterflow detector or alarm check valve.

3.3.12 Waterflow Detector. An electric signaling indicator or alarm check valve actuated by waterflow in one direction only.

 REFERENCES CITED IN COMMENTARY

Factory Mutual Research Corporation/Underwriters Laboratories Inc., *Standard for Residential Automatic Sprinklers for Fire Protection Service,* Northbrook, IL, April 1980

Underwriters Laboratories Inc., "Proposed Standard for Residential Automatic Sprinklers for Fire Protection Service," UL 1626, Northbrook, IL, October 1980

CHAPTER 4

General Requirements

4.1 Compartments

4.1.1 A compartment, for the purposes of this standard, shall be a space that is completely enclosed by walls and a ceiling.

4.1.2 A compartment enclosure shall be permitted to have openings in walls, provided the openings have a minimum lintel depth of 8 in. (203 mm) from the ceiling.

A room compartment, which is addressed in 4.1.2, is determined by the enclosing walls and soffits or lintels along the ceiling over a compartment opening that have a minimum depth of 8 in. (203 mm). [See Figures A.8.1.2(a) and A.8.1.2(b).] The 8-in. (203-mm) lintel depth allows for the collection of heat in the compartment of fire origin and was confirmed by the Los Angeles test series.

 Large, beamed ceilings are not intended to be given credit as a compartment enclosure even if they have an 8-in. (203-mm) depth. The openings from the compartment are generally based on a 36-in. (914-mm) wide door opening. Larger openings or beamed ceilings allow for large furnishings to be located beneath the openings or the beams. A fire originating on the furniture could activate more than two sprinklers on both sides of the opening and overtax the water supply. As indicated in 8.1.2, the designer should select no more than two sprinklers to determine the area of sprinkler application. When a compartment is of a size that only one sprinkler is needed to provide proper coverage, the compartment boundaries define the area of sprinkler operation.

◀ **FAQ**
How is a room compartment determined?

4.2 Maintenance

4.2.1* The installer shall provide to the owner/occupant instructions on inspecting, testing, and maintaining the system.

A.4.2.1 The responsibility for properly maintaining a sprinkler system is that of the owner or manager, who should understand the sprinkler system operation. A minimum monthly maintenance program should include the following:

(1) Visual inspection of all sprinklers to ensure against obstruction of spray.
(2) Inspection of all valves to ensure that they are open.
(3) Testing of all waterflow devices.
(4) Testing of the alarm system, where installed. Note that where it appears likely that the test will result in a fire department response, notification to the fire department should be made prior to the test.

(5) Operation of pumps, where employed. *(See NFPA 20, Standard for the Installation of Stationary Pumps for Fire Protection.)*

(6) Checking of the pressure of air used with dry systems.

(7) Checking of water level in tanks.

(8) Special attention to ensure that sprinklers are not painted either at the time of installation or during subsequent redecoration. When sprinkler piping or areas next to sprinklers are being painted, the sprinklers should be protected by covering them with a bag, which should be removed immediately after painting is finished.

(For further information, see NFPA 25, Standard for the Inspection, Testing, and Maintenance of Water-Based Fire Protection Systems.)

An excellent resource for the maintenance of sprinkler systems, which is cited in 4.2.1, is in NFPA 25, *Standard for the Inspection, Testing, and Maintenance of Water-Based Fire Protection Systems.* Further guidance on maintenance of the sprinkler system can be obtained from a local sprinkler contractor. Because of their simplicity, residential sprinkler systems generally need no more maintenance than residential plumbing systems. However, the owner may need to be educated on issues unique to sprinkler systems, such as obstructing discharge patterns, painting of sprinklers, hanging items from sprinklers, and maintaining control valves in the open position at all times.

FAQ ▶
Are NFPA 13D systems required to be maintained in accordance with NFPA 25?

Sprinkler systems installed in accordance with NFPA 13D are generally exempt from the requirements contained within NFPA 25, which applies to sprinkler systems in commercial, industrial, and multifamily residential facilities.

4.2.2 Operated or damaged sprinklers shall be replaced with sprinklers having the same performance characteristics as the original equipment.

FAQ ▶
How should damaged or painted sprinklers be addressed?

Operated and damaged sprinklers are covered in 4.2.2. Underwriters Laboratories Inc. has conducted a program in which field samples of automatic sprinklers were tested to determine their operating characteristics. According to the test program, a sprinkler that is damaged or painted after leaving the factory is unlikely to operate properly and should be replaced. Installing replacement sprinklers with performance characteristics differing from those of the original sprinklers will likely negatively impact overall system performance.

4.2.3 Any sprinklers that have been painted outside of the factory shall be replaced with a new listed sprinkler.

It is extremely important that only manufacturers that have had their procedures listed apply paint or ornamental finishes to residential sprinklers, as indicated in 4.2.3. The installing contractor or homeowner does not have the facilities available to properly duplicate the manufacturer's procedures. Do-it-yourself applications will seriously impair the sprinkler's operation, render it inoperable, or impact the discharge pattern's characteristics.

4.2.4* Antifreeze Systems. Before freezing weather each year, the following procedure shall be performed:

(1) Solution in the entire antifreeze system emptied into convenient containers

(2) Solution brought to the proper specific gravity by adding concentrated liquid as needed, or a new solution be prepared, in accordance with 8.3.3

(3) System refilled with the new or remixed solution

A.4.2.4 Tests should be made by drawing a sample of the solution from valve B, as shown in Figure 8.3.3.3.1.1, two or three times during the freezing season, especially if it has been necessary to drain the building sprinkler system for reasons such as repairs or changes. A small hydrometer should be used so that a small sample is sufficient. Where water appears at valve

B or where the test sample indicates that the solution has become weakened, the entire system should be emptied and then recharged as previously described.

4.3* Hydrostatic Tests

A.4.3 Testing of a system can be accomplished by filling the system with water and checking visually for leakage at each joint or coupling.

Fire department connections are not required for systems covered by this standard but can be installed at the discretion of the owner. In these cases, hydrostatic tests in accordance with NFPA 13, *Standard for the Installation of Sprinkler Systems,* are necessary.

Dry systems also should be tested by placing the system under air pressure. Any leak that results in a drop in system pressure greater than 2 psi (0.14 bar) in 24 hours should be corrected. Leaks should be identified using soapy water brushed on each joint or coupling. The presence of bubbles indicates a leak. This test should be made prior to concealing the piping.

Although A.4.3 describes the test procedures for a dry system, at this time, dry systems are not permitted. (See Section 7.5 and commentary to 8.1.2 and 8.3.2(3) Exception.)

Unlike the requirements of NFPA 13, *Standard for the Installation of Sprinkler Systems,* and in some cases NFPA 13R, *Standard for the Installation of Sprinkler Systems in Residential Occupancies up to and Including Four Stories in Height,* residential systems do not require a hydrostatic test unless the system is equipped with a fire department connection. If a hydrostatic test was required, it would complicate the installation and add significantly to the system's cost. Plumbing systems have been successfully installed in homes without special hydrostatic testing for years. Because the residential sprinkler system is intended to be similar to or integrated with the plumbing system, the technical committee concluded that a special hydrostatic test was not generally required.

Although a fire department connection to a residential system is not required, one can be installed. When a fire department connection is added, the system pressure can be increased using a fire department pumper. In such instances, the installer and owner should verify that the system has the integrity to withstand such pressures, and a hydrostatic test should be done in accordance with NFPA 13. Normally, the test would be a pressure of 200 psi (13.8 bar).

4.3.1 Where a fire department pumper connection is not provided, the system shall be hydrostatically tested for leakage at normal system operating pressure.

4.3.2 Where a fire department pumper connection is provided, the system shall pass a hydro- static pressure test performed in accordance with NFPA 13, *Standard for the Installation of Sprinkler Systems.*

4.4 Sprinkler Temperature Ratings

4.4.1 Sprinklers having a temperature rating of 135°F to 170°F (57°C to 77°C) shall be classified as ordinary temperature–rated sprinklers.

4.4.2 Sprinklers having a temperature rating of 175°F to 225°F (79°C to 107°C) shall be classified as intermediate temperature–rated sprinklers.

4.5 Tube

Wherever the word *pipe* is used in this standard, it shall also mean *tube.*

For the purposes of NFPA 13D, the term *pipe* also means *tube,* as stated in Section 4.5.

REFERENCES CITED IN COMMENTARY

National Fire Protection Association, 1 Batterymarch Park, P.O. Box 9101, Quincy, MA 02269-9101

NFPA 13, *Standard for the Installation of Sprinkler Systems,* 2002 edition

NFPA 13R, *Standard for the Installation of Sprinkler Systems in Residential Occupancies up to and Including Four Stories in Height,* 2002 edition

NFPA 25, *Standard for the Inspection, Testing, and Maintenance of Water-Based Fire Protection Systems,* 2002 edition

CHAPTER 5

System Components

5.1 General

5.1.1* Only new sprinklers shall be installed in sprinkler systems.

A.5.1.1 Where fused sprinklers are replaced by the owner, fire department, or others, care should be taken to ensure that the replacement sprinkler has the same operating characteristics.

In agreement with NFPA 13, *Standard for the Installation of Sprinkler Systems,* and NFPA 13R, *Standard for the Installation of Sprinkler Systems in Residential Occupancies up to and Including Four Stories in Height,* only new sprinklers are permitted to be used in NFPA 13D systems, which is discussed in 5.1.1. The performance and reliability of used sprinklers are not easily verified. The installation of new, listed residential sprinklers provides a much higher degree of reliability.

Sprinklers used in residential systems are a special type that have been tested for residential use (UL 1626, *Proposed Standard for Residential Automatic Sprinklers for Fire Protection Service*). Residential sprinklers are one-time operating devices that must be treated carefully during installation. When the system is originally installed, only new sprinklers should be used to ensure proper operating condition and type.

On those occasions when it is necessary to replace a sprinkler that has operated (fused) or has been damaged, the orifice size, the temperature rating, and the deflector configuration should be carefully checked so that the replacement sprinkler is the same as the original. Many sprinklers—for example, upright, pendent, or sidewall—have unique operating characteristics, and some have differing areas of coverage.

5.1.2 Devices and materials used in sprinkler systems shall be listed unless permitted not to be by 5.1.3.

5.1.3 Tanks, pumps, hangers, waterflow detection devices, and waterflow valves shall not be required to be listed.

When the original edition of NFPA 13D was prepared, testing laboratories had not listed or evaluated tanks, pumps, hangers, waterflow devices, and water control valves in the sizes needed for residential use (see 5.1.3).

Although some of these components are now listed, they are not required to be listed. One exception exists, however, involving the use of specially listed pipe materials. Subsection 7.4.1 requires the use of listed hangers for these materials.

The technical committee anticipated that the type of equipment used would be similar to that commonly found in residential plumbing systems. The economic impact of requiring listed tanks, pumps, and valves could increase the system cost by as much as 500 percent in some cases, which works against the low-cost objective established by USFA and adopted by the technical committee when they initiated their residential sprinkler program. Such a large

When utilizing listed pipe, is it required that listed hangers be utilized?

◄ **FAQ**

◄ **FAQ**
Why are so many of the components not required to be listed?

cost increase would discourage installation of residential sprinkler systems. Although the use of listed components would increase the overall reliability of the system, the technical committee is of the opinion that the use of some nonlisted components still provides a sufficient level of reliability and performance.

5.2 Pipe

Pipe is covered in Section 5.2. Piping components manufactured to the material standards of Table 5.2.1 and Table 5.2.5 are not required to be listed even though testing laboratories have evaluated and listed many of these materials. The most commonly used piping materials in residential sprinkler systems are listed and are of nonmetallic materials, such as chlorinated polyvinyl chloride (CPVC) pipe and polybutylene (PB) pipe. Although Table 5.2.2.2 only identifies plastic pipe, it does not preclude the listing of metallic piping materials that are not identified in Table 5.2.1.

Although listed PB pipe is acceptable for use in sprinkler systems, PB pipe is no longer manufactured due to problems associated with its use in domestic plumbing systems. PB pipe's overall use in fire protection systems has been favorable. The development of other flexible pipe is being pursued as an alternative to PB pipe.

Paragraph 5.2.1.3 provides reduced system working pressure criteria and temperature criteria for piping used in multipurpose piping systems. The original intent in the development of NFPA 13D was to provide standards for residential sprinkler systems that would be economically feasible to encourage installation and save lives. The installation of a multipurpose piping system could provide significant cost savings and potentially increase system reliability.

The pressure criterion was developed from the maximum pressure requirement of 80 psi (5.5 bar) for plumbing fixtures as provided by Section 604.8 of the *International Plumbing Code* and Section 608.2 of the *Uniform Plumbing Code.* The Technical Committee on Residential Sprinkler Systems believed that a safety factor should be included over and beyond 80 psi (5.5 bar) because of the associated life safety objectives. The technical committee chose a pressure rating of 130 psi (9.0 bar) at 120°F (49°C) for piping used in multipurpose systems where specific conditions exist. (See commentary to 5.2.1 and 5.2.5.) The temperature criterion of 120°F (49°C) was selected because it is included in Section 8.1 of UL 1821, *Standard for Safety-Thermoplastic Sprinkler Pipe and Fittings for Fire Protection Service,* based on attic temperature conditions from a 1977 UL study. A similar study conducted by the National Bureau of Standards, which is now the National Institute of Standards and Technology, in 1977 measured the attic temperatures of a house in Houston, TX. The maximum temperature at the top of the peak was 115°F (46°C) and 84°F (29°C) at the attic floor on the insulation's underside. This temperature criterion also prompted new requirements concerning the installation of plastic pipe in attics. (See Section 7.7.)

5.2.1* Pipe or tube used in sprinkler systems shall be of the materials specified in Table 5.2.1 or shall be in accordance with 5.2.2.

A.5.2.1 This standard anticipates the water supply for the system to be in compliance with the governing plumbing code for the jurisdiction. It is intended that any pipe material or diameter permitted by a plumbing code for one- or two-family dwellings and satisfying the hydraulic criteria of NFPA 13D is considered to be in compliance.

Because a number of systems conforming to NFPA 13D are installed retroactively, existing underground pipe and materials are to be used (see 5.2.1). A careful analysis of the existing pipe's size, condition, and type must be completed to ensure that it will provide the necessary flow and pressure to the system. When new systems are installed, the underground pipe network only needs to comply with the requirements of the local plumbing code. The calculation procedures discussed in Chapter 8 and the associated commentary must be completed to ensure that the piping materials will allow for the proper system performance.

TABLE 5.2.1 *Pipe or Tube Materials and Dimensions*

Materials and Dimensions	Standard
Specification for Black and Hot-Dipped Zinc-Coated (Galvanized) Welded and Seamless Steel Pipe for Fire Protection Use	ASTM A 795
Specification for Welded and Seamless Pipe	ASTM A 53
Wrought Steel Pipe	ANSI B 36.10M
Specification for Electric-Resistance-Welded Steel Pipe	ASTM A 135
Standard Specification for Seamless Copper Tube [Copper Tube (Drawn, Seamless)]	ASTM B 75
Standard Specification for Seamless Copper Water Tube	ASTM B 88
Standard Specification for General Requirements for Wrought Steamless Copper and Copper-Alloy Tube	ASTM B 251
Standard Specification for Liquid and Paste Fluxes for Soldering Applications of Copper and Copper-Alloy Tube	ASTM B 813
Specification for Filler Metals for Brazing and Braze Welding (BCuP, copper-phosphorus, or copper-phosphorus-silver brazing filler metal)	AWS A5.8
Standard Specification for Solder Metal [alloy grades containing less than 0.2 percent lead as identified in ASTM B 32, Table 5, Section 1, and having a solidus temperature that exceeds 400°F (204°C)]	ASTM B 32

5.2.1.1 The chemical properties, physical properties, and dimensions of pipe materials shall be at least equivalent to the standards cited in Table 5.2.1.

5.2.1.2 Pipe used in sprinkler systems other than those addressed in 5.2.1.3 shall be designed to withstand a working pressure of not less than 175 psi (12.1 bar).

5.2.1.3 Nonmetallic pipe used in multipurpose piping systems not equipped with a fire department connection shall be designed to withstand a working pressure of not less than 130 psi (8.9 bar) at 120°F (49°C).

5.2.2 Types of pipe other than those specified in Table 5.2.1 shall be permitted to be used where listed for sprinkler system use.

5.2.2.1 Pipe differing from those specified in Table 5.2.1 shall be installed in accordance with their listings and the manufacturers' installation instructions.

5.2.2.2* Chlorinated polyvinyl chloride (CPVC) and polybutylene (PB) pipe shall comply with the portions of the American Society for Testing and Materials (ASTM) standards specified in Table 5.2.2.2 that apply to fire protection service.

TABLE 5.2.2.2 *Specially Listed Pipe or Tube Materials and Dimensions*

Materials and Dimensions	Standard
Nonmetallic Piping:	
Specification for Chlorinated Polyvinyl Chloride (CPVC) Pipe	ASTM F 442
Specification for Polybutylene (PB) Pipe	ASTM D 3309

A.5.2.2.2 Not all pipe or tube made to ASTM D 3309, *Standard Specification for Polybutylene (PB) Plastic Hot- and Cold-Water Distribution Systems,* and ASTM F 442, *Standard*

Specification for Chlorinated Poly (Vinyl Chloride) (CPVC) Plastic Pipe (SDR-PR), as described in 5.2.2.2 is listed for fire sprinkler service. Listed pipe is identified by the logo of the listing agency.

Paragraph 5.2.2.2 and Table 5.2.2.2 specifically address the use of specially listed pipe. These pipe materials are now widely accepted and deserve specific recognition.

No material is prohibited from use as long as it is listed for use in sprinkler systems and is installed in accordance with its listing. This paragraph is intended to encourage development of either more efficient or more cost-effective materials.

Not all pipe made to a particular standard is listed. Listed piping is identified by the logo of the listing agency. Similar piping that is required to be listed and that is manufactured with less exacting quality control must not be used in sprinkler systems. This provision precludes the use of nonmetallic pipe materials available at a building supply store, because these materials are not suitable for use in sprinkler systems.

FAQ ▶
Is plastic pipe permitted for use in NFPA 13D installations?

At this time, two synthetic piping materials are listed for sprinkler system application—CPVC and PB pipe. The listings of these materials often include restrictions such as the pipe cannot be left exposed. (CPVC pipe can be installed exposed under special conditions.) The listings are specific and indicate for which standard (e.g., NFPA 13D or NFPA 13R) or hazard classification (e.g., light hazard in accordance with NFPA 13) the pipe is listed. The user must refer to the extensive listing information to correctly install the system components. See the additional discussion on these materials in Chapter 5 of NFPA 13.

FAQ ▶
Is PB pipe still manufactured?

Although permitted by NFPA 13D, PB pipe is no longer manufactured due to problems associated with its use in domestic plumbing systems. PB pipe used in fire protection systems is subject to certain restrictions and installation practices that do not necessarily apply to its use in domestic plumbing systems. Overall, the use of PB pipe in fire protection systems has been favorable. The development of other flexible pipe is being pursued as an alternative to PB pipe.

5.2.3 Schedule 10 steel pipe shall be permitted to be joined with mechanical groove couplings approved for service.

5.2.4 Where mechanical groove couplings are used to join pipe, grooves shall be rolled on the pipe by an approved groove-rolling machine.

5.2.5 Fittings used in sprinkler systems shall be of the materials listed in Table 5.2.5 or shall be in accordance with 5.2.9.

Fittings of the types and materials indicated in Table 5.2.5 are not required to be listed provided they are manufactured to the indicated standards or to a standard meeting or exceeding those indicated.

5.2.5.1 The chemical properties, physical properties, and dimensions of fitting materials shall be at least equivalent to the standards cited in Table 5.2.5.

5.2.5.2 Fittings used in sprinkler systems other than those addressed in 5.2.5.3 shall be designed to withstand a working pressure of not less than 175 psi (12.1 bar).

5.2.5.3 Nonmetallic fittings used in multipurpose piping systems not equipped with a fire department connection shall be designed to withstand a working pressure of not less than 130 psi (8.9 bar) at 120°F (49°C).

5.2.6 Joints for the connection of copper tube shall be brazed on dry pipe and preaction systems.

5.2.7 Joints for the connection of copper tube for wet pipe systems and antifreeze systems shall be solder joints or be brazed.

TABLE 5.2.5 *Fitting Materials and Dimensions*

Materials and Dimensions	Standard
Cast Iron:	
Gray Iron Threaded Fittings	ASME B16.4
Cast Iron Pipe Flanges and Flanged Fittings	ASME B16.1
Malleable Iron:	
Malleable Iron Threaded Fittings	ASME B16.3
Steel:	
Factory-Made Wrought Steel Buttweld Fittings	ASME B16.9
Buttwelding Ends	ASME B16.25
Specification for Piping Fittings of Wrought Carbon Steel and Alloy Steel for Moderate and Elevated Temperatures	ASTM A 234
Pipe Flanges and Flanged Fittings	ASME B16.5
Forged Fittings, Socket-Welding and Threaded	ASME B16.11
Copper:	
Wrought Copper and Copper Alloy Solder Joint Pressure Fittings	ASME B16.22
Cast Copper Alloy Solder Joint Pressure Fittings	ASME B16.18

5.2.8 Solder joints, where permitted, shall be fabricated in accordance with the methods and procedures listed in ASTM B 828, *Standard Practice for Making Capillary Joints by Soldering of Copper and Copper Alloy Tube and Fittings.*

Solder joints are addressed in 5.2.8. Previous editions allowed 50-50 solder because it was the type normally used in domestic plumbing systems. The 1986 amendments to the *Federal Safe Drinking Water Act* prohibited the use of 50-50 solder in plumbing systems. Although this act does not specifically apply to residential sprinkler systems, the technical committee considered it poor practice to use this leaded solder in close proximity to potable water systems. The solder alloys that conform to Table 5, Section 1 of ASTM B 32, *Standard Specification for Solder Metal,* have a higher melting point, contain no lead, and are permitted under the *Federal Safe Drinking Water Act.*

5.2.9 Types of fittings other than those specified in Table 5.2.5 shall be permitted to be used where listed for sprinkler system use.

5.2.9.1 Fittings differing from those specified in Table 5.2.5 shall be installed in accordance with their listings and the manufacturers' installation instructions.

5.2.9.2* Chlorinated polyvinyl chloride (CPVC) and polybutylene (PB) fittings shall comply with the portions of the American Society for Testing and Materials (ASTM) standards specified in Table 5.2.9.2 that apply to fire protection service.

TABLE 5.2.9.2 *Specially Listed Fittings and Dimensions*

Materials and Dimensions	Standard
Specification for Schedule 80 CPVC Threaded Fittings	ASTM F 437
Specification for Schedule 40 CPVC Socket-Type Fittings	ASTM F 438
Specification for Schedule 80 CPVC Socket-Type Fittings	ASTM F 439

A.5.2.9.2 Not all fittings made to ASTM F 437, *Standard Specification for Threaded Chlorinated Poly (Vinyl Chloride) (CPVC) Plastic Pipe Fittings, Schedule 80,* ASTM F 438, *Standard Specification for Socket-Type Chlorinated Poly (Vinyl Chloride) (CPVC) Plastic Pipe*

Fittings, Schedule 40, and ASTM F 439, *Standard Specification for Socket-Type Chlorinated Poly (Vinyl Chloride) (CPVC) Plastic Pipe Fittings, Schedule 80,* as described in 5.2.9.2 are listed for fire sprinkler service. Listed fittings are identified by the logo of the listing agency.

 The types of fittings acceptable as required in 5.2.9.2 are those that have been found satisfactory and listed by a testing and inspection agency laboratory. Although Table 5.2.9.2 identifies only plastic materials, specially listed metallic fittings are also available. These fittings are compatible with the pipe materials listed in Table 5.2.2.2. (See Sections 6.3 and 6.4 of NFPA 13 for additional information on pipe and fittings.)

5.3 Preengineered Systems

Where listed preengineered systems are installed, they shall be installed within the limitations that have been established by the testing laboratories.

Preengineered systems are covered in Section 5.3. Approval laboratories have sometimes tested and listed complete systems that include all of the components necessary for an application. In this case, the system could include sprinklers, water supply tanks, valves, pumps, and special piping limitations. A manufacturer is permitted to develop such a system for application as a residential sprinkler system but does not require the use of such a packaged system.

 REFERENCES CITED IN COMMENTARY

National Fire Protection Association, 1 Batterymarch Park, P.O. Box 9101, Quincy, MA 02269-9101

NFPA 13, *Standard for the Installation of Sprinkler Systems,* 2002 edition
NFPA 13R, *Standard for the Installation of Sprinkler Systems in Residential Occupancies up to and Including Four Stories in Height,* 2002 edition

American Society for Testing and Materials, 100 Barr Harbor Drive, West Conshohocken, PA 19428-2959

ASTM B 32, *Standard Specification for Solder Metal,* 2000 edition

Building Officials and Code Administrators International, 4051 W. Flossmoor Road, Country Club Hills, IL 60478-5795

International Plumbing Code, Section 604.8, 1997

International Association of Plumbing and Mechanical Officials, 20001 E. Walnut Drive South, Walnut, CA 91789-2825

Uniform Plumbing Code, Section 608.2, 1997

Underwriters Laboratories Inc., 333 Pfingsten Road, Northbrook, IL 60062

UL 1626, *Proposed Standard for Residential Automatic Sprinklers for Fire Protection Service,* October 1980
UL 1821, *Standard for Safety-Thermoplastic Sprinkler Pipe and Fittings for Fire Protection Service,* 1st edition, 1994

U.S. Government, U.S. Government Printing Office, Washington, DC 20402

Federal Safe Drinking Water Act, 1974

CHAPTER 6

Water Supply

6.1 General Provisions

6.1.1 Every automatic sprinkler system shall have at least one automatic water supply.

6.1.2 Where stored water is used as the sole source of supply, the minimum quantity shall equal the water demand rate times 10 minutes unless permitted otherwise by 6.1.3.

6.1.3 Where stored water is used as the sole source of supply, the minimum quantity shall be permitted to equal the two-sprinkler water demand rate times 7 minutes where dwelling units meet the following criteria:

(1) One story in height
(2) Less than 2000 ft^2 (186 m^2) in area

A sprinkler system's effectiveness greatly depends on its water supply, which must be automatic and reliable. The adequacy of a public water supply is determined in the manner described in 8.4.4 and A.8.4.4 of NFPA 13D. When a stored water supply is used, as discussed in 6.1.3, it must provide the required amount of water and pressure for a minimum of 10 minutes. For dwellings that satisfy the limitations of 6.1.3, a 7-minute water supply can be used.

When considering a system design using the prototype residential sprinkler discussed in Chapter 8, the tank capacity must be at least 260 gal (984 L), which is based on two sprinklers operating at a total of 26 gpm (98 L/min). The tank would have sufficient water to control a fire while giving occupants enough time to evacuate the residence. The 10-minute supply includes an implied safety factor to account for a delay in the response of an occupant while the fire condition is recognized.

Given the limitations on the design (one story in height) and the size (less than 2000 ft^2 (186 m^2)) of the residence, 7 minutes was determined to provide a reasonable time for egress from the structure. This time also includes an implied safety factor to account for a delay in the response of the occupant, just as in the 10-minute supply.

◄ **FAQ**
Why is a 7-minute water supply permitted for some dwellings?

6.2* Water Supply Sources

The following water supply sources shall be considered to be acceptable by this standard:

(1) A connection to a reliable waterworks system with or without an automatically operated pump
(2) An elevated tank
(3) A pressure tank designed to American Society of Mechanical Engineers (ASME) standards for a pressure vessel with a reliable pressure source
(4) A stored water source with an automatically operated pump

A **A.6.2** The connection to city mains for fire protection is often subject to local regulation of metering and backflow prevention requirements. Preferred and acceptable water supply arrangements are shown in Figure A.6.2(a), Figure A.6.2(b), and Figure A.6.2(c). Where it is necessary to use a meter between the city water main and the sprinkler system supply, an acceptable arrangement as shown in Figure A.6.2(c) can be used. Under these circumstances, the flow characteristics of the meter are to be included in the hydraulic calculation of the system [*see Table 8.4.4(g)*]. Where a tank is used for both domestic and fire protection purposes, a low water alarm that actuates when the water level falls below 110 percent of the minimum quantity specified in 6.1.2 should be provided.

FIGURE A.6.2(a) *Preferable Arrangement.*

FIGURE A.6.2(b) *Acceptable Arrangement with Valve Supervision—Option 1.*

FIGURE A.6.2(c) *Acceptable Arrangement with Valve Supervision—Option 2.*

The effect of pressure-reducing valves on the system should be considered in the hydraulic calculation procedures.

Pumps can be used on municipal supplies as well as on stored supplies, as indicated in Section 6.2(1). If the municipal supply is not sufficient, the technical committee does not intend that a stored supply be used. A pump can be used to boost the pressure of a municipal supply provided a sufficient quantity of water is available.

◀ FAQ
Can pumps be utilized to boost the municipal supply?

With regard to Section 6.2(2), a system can occasionally be supplied from an elevated tank. Where an elevated tank is used, it must have an elevation sufficient to provide adequate pressure to supply the system. Adequate pressure is determined by the methods described in 8.4.4 and 8.4.6.

Where a pressure tank is used for the water supply in accordance with Section 6.2(3), the amount of water and air in the tank is determined according to the information in 8.4.6. NFPA 13, *Standard for the Installation of Sprinkler Systems,* contains criteria for pressure tanks that are acceptable as a water source for NFPA 13 systems. Pressure tanks used as a water supply do not have to meet the requirements of NFPA 22, *Standard for Water Tanks for Private Fire Protection.* Tanks constructed in accordance with the ASME *Boiler and Pressure Vessel Code* can be acceptable, provided the authority having jurisdiction considers the air or nitrogen supply reliable.

With regard to Section 6.2(4), a water supply source, whether stored or from a municipal supply used in conjunction with an automatically operated pump, must be as follows:

1. Have a pump with adequate capacity to supply the water demand as described in 8.1.1.
2. Have adequate pressure to overcome friction and elevation pressure losses
3. Meet the operating pressure established by the testing laboratory for the sprinkler being used

NFPA 13D does not require that a fire pump conforming to NFPA 20, *Standard for the Installation of Stationary Pumps for Fire Protection,* be installed. The type of pump and the arrangement of power supplies to that pump only need to satisfy the system demand and to be electrically wired to conform to NFPA 70, *National Electrical Code®.*

◀ FAQ
Where a pump is utilized, must it meet the requirements of NFPA 20?

Figures A.6.2(a), A.6.2(b), and A.6.2(c) show preferred and acceptable arrangements of connections to city mains and include appropriately located control valves, meters, domestic takeoffs, waterflow detectors, pressure gauges, and check valves. Where the local water authority requires backflow preventers, the devices are normally located in the position where the rubber-faced check valve is shown on the figures. The piping arrangement, including valves and fittings, must be taken into account when performing the calculations for system adequacy described in 8.4.4.

From a fire protection standpoint, meters and backflow preventers are undesirable because of the high friction loss characteristic of the devices, which must be included in the system's hydraulic calculation in accordance with 8.4.4. Unfortunately, many water authorities require metering of all water connections to a residence. In addition, clean water environmental concerns are leading more jurisdictions to require backflow preventers instead of traditional, less costly check valves. Check valves have performed satisfactorily, and no case histories involving backflow contamination from fire protection systems using check valves are available. Nonetheless, local jurisdictions often require the use of backflow devices.

6.3* Multipurpose Piping System

A piping system serving both sprinkler and domestic needs shall be considered to be acceptable by this standard where the following conditions are met:

(1)* In common water supply connections serving more than one dwelling unit, 5 gpm (19 L/min) shall be added to the sprinkler system demand to determine the size of common piping and the size of the total water supply requirements where no provision is made to prevent flow into the domestic water system upon operation of a sprinkler.

 (2) Smoke detectors are provided in accordance with *NFPA 72®, National Fire Alarm Code®*.

(3) All piping in the system supplying sprinklers is listed and conforms to the piping specifications of this standard.

(4) Piping connected to the system that supplies only plumbing fixtures complies with local plumbing and health authority requirements but is not required to be listed.

(5) Permitted by the local plumbing or health authority.

(6) A sign is affixed adjacent to the main shutoff valve that states in minimum ¼-inch letters, "Warning, the water system for this home supplies a fire sprinkler system that depends on certain flows and pressures being available to fight a fire. Devices that restrict the flow or decrease the pressure such as water softeners shall not be added to this system without a review of the fire sprinkler system by a fire protection specialist. Do not remove this sign."

 (7) Devices that restrict the flow or decrease the pressure, such as water treatment and filtration equipment, shall not be added to the system. Where water treatment and filtration equipment are installed, a listed automatic flow sensing bypass shall be installed in the supply piping that directs all water directly to the system.

A.6.3 Figure A.6.3(a), Figure A.6.3(b), and Figure A.6.3(c) illustrate acceptable water supply arrangements. When contemplating the use of a multipurpose piping system, consideration should be given to possible future modifications for domestic purposes, such as the installation of a water softener or a water filtration system, which affect the performance of the sprinkler system.

A.6.3(1) In dwellings where long-term use of lawn sprinklers is common, provision should be made for such usage.

FIGURE A.6.3(a) *Multipurpose Piping System with Separate Supply.*

FIGURE A.6.3(b) *Multipurpose Piping System Calculation Procedure.*

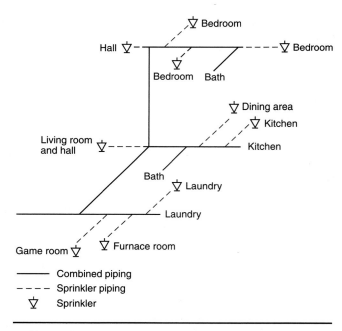

FIGURE A.6.3(c) *Multipurpose Piping System Arrangement.*

Multipurpose piping systems are discussed in Section 6.3. Any impairments to the sprinkler system will be more quickly recognized and corrected when a combined piping system is used—that is, a system concurrently serving both domestic and sprinkler needs. In a residence, a lack of water for normal usage, such as because of a shower, is likely to be corrected promptly.

Figures A.6.3(a) and A.6.3(b) show two arrangements for a multipurpose piping system. Figure A.6.3(a) shows a common point where domestic water and fire protection water are divided. A common piping line that is tapped to supply laundry fixtures is shown in Figure A.6.3(b). Figure A.6.3(c) shows an isometric view of a multilevel dwelling and one possible arrangement of the multipurpose piping. System design can be adjusted for simultaneous sprinkler flow and one or more domestic fixture outlets by adding 5 gpm (19 L/min) to the sprinkler system demand where the supply serves a townhouse, for example.

A multipurpose piping system can sometimes be used to obtain a waiver for special backflow devices. The health concerns associated with long-term water quality deterioration are reduced significantly because water circulates through most portions of the system.

Section 6.3 also clarifies under what circumstances the domestic use must be added to the sprinkler system demand.

With regard to Section 6.3(1), the technical committee recognized that periods of typical domestic water usage do not occur over great lengths of time except for an automatic long-term demand, such as a lawn sprinkler system. Although NFPA 13D only requires an adjustment to the waterflow requirements for domestic usage where the water source supplies two dwelling units, proper system performance can be better ensured where a peak domestic water demand is anticipated and added to the sprinkler demand when designing the system.

Section 6.3(1) allows an alternative to considering the added demand by making an arrangement that shuts down the waterflow to the domestic demand upon operation of a sprinkler. One way to accomplish this shutdown is through the use of an automatically controlled solenoid valve. On actuation of the sprinkler system waterflow switch, an electrical signal can be sent to the solenoid valve, which closes and shuts down the supply to the domestic demand or the individual appliance. The result is that no water is diverted from the sprinkler system.

◀ **FAQ**
Can the domestic demand be omitted from the design?

Section 6.3(4) was revised for the 1999 edition to further promote the use of multipurpose residential sprinkler systems in one- and two-family dwellings. Section 6.3(4) permits the limited use of non-listed pipe in a sprinkler system other than that specified in Table 5.2.1.

Section 6.3(6) was added to the 1999 edition to make the homeowner aware of the impact of retroactively installing devices such as water softeners on the system. Unless properly accounted hydraulically, water softeners and other such devices can have an adverse effect on system performance by decreasing the available pressure and resultant waterflow to the sprinklers. This lower pressure ultimately affects the amount of water discharged from the sprinklers and the sprinklers' discharge pattern.

6.4 Manufactured Home Water Supply

For sprinklered buildings manufactured off-site, the minimum pressure needed to satisfy the system design criteria on the system side of the meter shall be specified on a data plate by the manufacturer.

Manufactured home water supply is covered in Section 6.4. The piping for a sprinkler system installed in a manufactured home is typically installed by the home's manufacturer. NFPA 13D anticipates that the manufacturer will specify the water capacity and pressure needed to supply the system. The water supply that ultimately serves the manufactured home sprinkler system must meet the demand specified for the 7-minute or 10-minute duration, as appropriate.

◀ **FAQ**
Where a system is installed in a manufactured home, how should the water supply be addressed?

REFERENCES CITED IN COMMENTARY

National Fire Protection Association, 1 Batterymarch Park, P.O. Box 9101, Quincy, MA 02269-9101

NFPA 13, *Standard for the Installation of Sprinkler Systems,* 2002 edition
NFPA 20, *Standard for the Installation of Stationary Pumps for Fire Protection,* 1999 edition
NFPA 22, *Standard for Water Tanks for Private Fire Protection,* 1998 edition
NFPA 70, *National Electrical Code®,* 2002 edition

American Society of Mechanical Engineers, Three Park Avenue, New York, NY 10016-5990

ASME *Boiler and Pressure Vessel Code,* 1998 edition

CHAPTER 7

Installation

7.1 Valves

7.1.1 A single control valve arranged to shut off both the domestic system and the sprinkler system shall be installed unless a separate shutoff valve for the sprinkler system is installed in accordance with 7.1.2.

A control valve, which is specified in 7.1.1, permits anyone to shut off the water supply to the sprinkler system. That the control valve remains in the open position at all times is critical. The only exception should be for system maintenance or modification.

    With only one control valve serving both the domestic and sprinkler water supplies, the possibility of inadvertently shutting off the sprinkler system is significantly reduced. The need for domestic water such as for a toilet would necessitate that the water supply situation be promptly corrected. A separate control valve for the sprinkler system is acceptable only when the valve is supervised as described in 7.1.2.

◀ **FAQ**
What is the benefit of utilizing one control valve to serve both domestic and sprinkler supplies?

7.1.2 The sprinkler system piping shall not have a separate control valve installed unless supervised by one of the following methods:

(1) Central station, proprietary, or remote station alarm service
(2) Local alarm service that causes the sounding of an audible signal at a constantly attended location
(3) Valves that are locked open

7.1.3 A separate shutoff valve shall be installed for the domestic water supply in installations other than those complying with Section 6.3.

With regard to 7.1.3, the status of the water supply on a multipurpose piping system is essentially self-supervising. If the water supply is not available for the sprinkler system, it will also not be available for the toilets, sinks, and other domestic fixtures. This condition is likely to result in prompt corrective action regarding the water supply.

◀ **FAQ**
Why is a separate control valve not required for multipurpose systems in accordance with the requirements of 7.1.3?

7.2 Drains and Test Connections

7.2.1 Each sprinkler system shall have a drain on the system side of the control valve.

The drain arrangement described in 7.2.1 allows for the verification of waterflow and permits the system piping to be drained for maintenance or repairs. See 7.2.4 for requirements pertaining to waterflow alarms.

7.2.2 A valve shall be installed in the drain piping.

7.2.3 A drain shall be installed for each trapped portion of a dry system that is subject to freezing temperatures.

Exhibit 7.1 illustrates a trapped section of piping and how a drain is arranged to comply with 7.2.3. Such portions of the system are important to be carefully drained before freezing weather each year. If water from the system's operation or condensation collects in a trapped section of piping, it can freeze and break the piping, possibly causing extensive water damage.

7.2.4* Where waterflow alarms are provided, inspector's test connections shall be installed at locations that allow flow testing of water supplies, connections, and alarm mechanisms.

A.7.2.4 These connections should be installed so that the valve can be opened fully and for a sufficient time period to ensure a proper test without causing water damage. The test connection should be designed and sized to verify the sufficiency of the water supply and alarm mechanisms.

This inspector's test connection installation, which is addressed in 7.2.4, provides a means of verifying the waterflow alarm's operation if installed and of verifying the flow through the system. Although a full-flow test is not required, a flowmeter, such as that used on lawn sprinkler systems, can be attached to this connection to determine the available flow rate. The orifice of the inspector's test must be the same size as that of the sprinkler with the smallest orifice. This ensures that the inspector's test simulates minimum fire flow conditions and that the waterflow alarm sounds at this flow.

7.2.5 Where sprinklers used in the system have a nominal K-factor smaller than 5.6, inspector's test connections shall contain an orifice of the same size as the smallest sprinkler installed in the system.

EXHIBIT 7.1 Drain Connection for a Trapped Section of Piping.

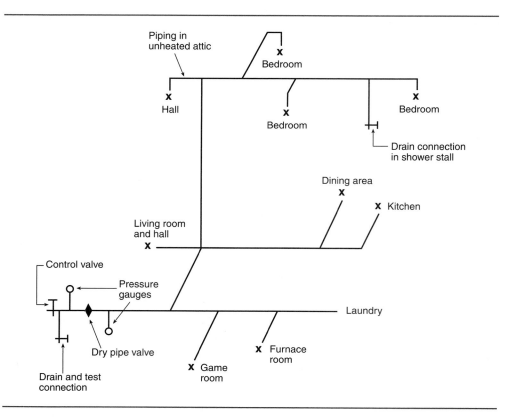

7.3 Pressure Gauges

7.3.1 Where a dry system is installed, a pressure gauge shall be installed to indicate system air pressure.

Residential sprinklers for use on a dry pipe system do not exist at the current time. Therefore, the requirement in 7.3.1 to monitor air pressure does not apply until dry pipe systems are used. The pressure tank's gauge indicates whether adequate operating pressure is available to the system.

7.3.2 Where a pressure tank is used for the water supply, a pressure gauge shall be installed to indicate tank pressure.

7.4 Piping Support

7.4.1 Listed pipe shall be supported in accordance with any listing limitations.

7.4.2 Pipe that is not listed, and listed pipe with listing limitations that do not include piping support requirements, shall be supported from structural members using support methods comparable to those required by local plumbing codes.

Unlike the hanging requirements for sprinkler systems installed according to NFPA 13, *Standard for the Installation of Sprinkler Systems,* NFPA 13D simply requires adequate support by methods recognized in local plumbing codes for the piping materials (see 7.4.2).

Generally, residential systems deal with pipe sizes of ½ in. to 1¼ in. (12.7 mm to 33 mm), and pipe sizes are not expected to exceed 2 in. (51 mm). The dynamic loads and forces that can be generated by waterflow in a residential sprinkler system are considerably lower than those experienced in a sprinkler system in compliance with NFPA 13 or NFPA 13R, *Standard for the Installation of Sprinkler Systems in Residential Occupancies up to and Including Four Stories in Height.* Most plumbing code hangers provide adequate support for these piping materials. Subsection 7.4.1 recognizes that listed piping can have specific hanging requirements as a condition of its listing.

◄ **FAQ**
Do the hanging requirements of NFPA 13 apply to NFPA 13D installations?

7.4.3 Piping laid on open joists or rafters shall be supported in a manner that prevents lateral movement.

7.4.4* Sprinkler piping shall be supported in a manner that prevents the movement of piping upon sprinkler operation.

A.7.4.4 The reaction forces caused by the flow of water through the sprinkler could result in displacement of the sprinkler, thereby adversely affecting sprinkler discharge.

Many residential sprinkler designs use flush- or recessed-mounted configurations. The reaction force created by the discharge of water can cause the piping to lift, thereby resulting in a severe obstruction to the sprinkler spray pattern, which is the reason for the requirement in 7.4.4. This phenomenon is not considered in a plumbing code and requires special treatment.

7.5 Sprinklers

7.5.1 Listed residential sprinklers shall be used unless another type is permitted by 7.5.3 or 7.5.4.

Listed residential sprinklers are required by 7.5.1. Since the listing of the first residential sprinkler, manufacturers have listed other types, including both pendent and sidewall types.

The newer residential sprinklers are more aesthetically pleasing in design, which should alleviate the homeowner's concern over the device's appearance.

   Both Underwriters Laboratories Inc. and FM Global publish standards for testing and evaluating residential sprinklers. The protocol of these standards includes a room fire test, verification of the sprinkler's thermal sensitivity, and an evaluation of the water distribution characteristics. Standard spray sprinklers of the type used in NFPA 13 sprinkler systems are evaluated under a different set of criteria. The residential sprinkler test requirements were verified in testing at FM Global [Kung 1980] and in the Los Angeles and Charlotte, NC, residential sprinkler fire tests [Cote 1980, Kung 1982, Moore 1980].

7.5.2 Residential sprinklers shall not be used on systems other than wet pipe systems unless specifically listed for use on that particular type of system.

7.5.3 Listed standard dry-pendent or dry-sidewall sprinklers shall be permitted to be extended into unheated areas not intended for living purposes.

   No residential sprinklers are available that are listed for use in a dry pipe sprinkler system (see 7.5.3). Residential sprinklers utilized in NFPA 13, NFPA 13D, and NFPA 13R are bound by this limitation.

   7.5.4 Quick-response sprinklers shall be permitted to be used in mechanical closets.

7.5.5 Temperature Ratings.

Temperature ratings are covered in 7.5.5. The requirements of 7.5.5.1 through 7.5.5.3 apply to the environmentally controlled portions of the occupancy. The intent of the requirements is to use ordinary-temperature sprinklers in areas not subject to unusually high ambient temperatures.

7.5.5.1 Sprinklers installed where maximum ambient ceiling temperatures do not exceed 100°F (38°C) shall be ordinary temperature–rated sprinklers unless modified by the requirements of 7.5.5.3.

7.5.5.2 Sprinklers installed where maximum ambient ceiling temperatures are between 101°F and 150°F (39°C and 66°C) shall be intermediate temperature–rated sprinklers unless modified by 7.5.5.3.

7.5.5.3 The following practices shall be observed when installing residential sprinklers unless higher expected ambient temperatures require a higher temperature rating:

(1) Sprinklers under glass or plastic skylights exposed to direct rays of the sun shall be of intermediate temperature classification.
(2) Sprinklers in an unventilated concealed space under uninsulated roof or in an unventilated attic shall be of intermediate temperature classification.
(3) Sprinklers installed near specific heat sources that are identified in shall be of the temperature rating indicated in Table 7.5.5.3 unless sprinklers are listed for positioning closer to the heat source.

Conditions in a residence that can result in high ambient ceiling temperatures, which are discussed in 7.5.5.3, are attributable to track lighting units, fireplaces, wood-burning stoves, cooking equipment, and attics with insufficient ventilation.

Sprinkler spacing and positioning in the immediate vicinity of these areas must be considered. Steps must be taken to ensure that sprinklers are correctly selected for such areas. Recommendations and advice from the suppliers of heat-producing equipment and sprinklers should be solicited to allow for the placement of sprinklers in such areas. The necessary rules for applications of this concept are given in 7.5.5.3. These rules assist but do not completely

TABLE 7.5.5.3 *Minimum Distances for Ordinary and Intermediate Temperature Residential Sprinklers*

Heat Source	Minimum Distance from Edge of Source to Ordinary Temperature Sprinkler		Minimum Distance from Edge of Source to Intermediate Temperature Sprinkler	
	in.	*mm*	*in.*	*mm*
Side of open or recessed fireplace	36	914	12	305
Front of recessed fireplace	60	1524	36	914
Coal- or wood-burning stove	42	1067	12	305
Kitchen range	18	457	9	229
Wall oven	18	457	9	229
Hot air flues	18	457	9	229
Uninsulated heat ducts	18	457	9	229
Uninsulated hot water pipes	12	305	6	152
Side of ceiling- or wall-mounted hot air diffusers	24	607	12	305
Front of wall-mounted hot air diffusers	36	914	18	457
Hot water heater or furnace	6	152	3	76
Light fixture:				
0 W – 250 W	6	152	3	76
250 W – 499 W	12	305	6	152

cover all situations involving residential sprinkler placement. Certain limitations with regard to all types of fast-response sprinklers and their respective temperature ratings exist. Specifically, increases in the temperature ratings result in a decrease in sensitivity, and the ability to maintain the fast-response characteristic is diminished.

Air temperature surrounding a sprinkler can exceed 100°F (38°C) when a skylight permits direct sun exposure to that area. Unventilated attics tend to develop rather high temperatures in the summer months. Thus, a similar precaution to prevent false activation should also be undertaken. Selecting the appropriate temperature rating for a given environment is always important. Proper selection helps to ensure that sprinklers will not operate prematurely and that an excessive number of sprinklers will not operate during a fire.

With regard to 7.5.5.3(3), positioning sprinklers closer than that allowed by Table 7.5.5.3 is likely to result in their false activation. Similar to other NFPA 13D provisions, if a sprinkler is listed so that it can be positioned closer to a heat source than that indicated by NFPA 13D, this smaller dimension can be used.

7.5.6* Painting and Ornamental Finishes. Sprinklers shall not be painted or enameled unless applied by the manufacturer and the sprinkler has been listed with such finishes.

A.7.5.6 Decorative painting of a residential sprinkler is not to be confused with the temperature identification colors as specified in 6.2.5 of NFPA 13, *Standard for the Installation of Sprinkler Systems*.

7.5.7 Escutcheon Plates. Where escutcheons plates or recessed escutcheons are used, they shall be part of a listed sprinkler assembly.

Escutcheon plates, which are addressed in 7.5.7, must be tested and listed by the listing laboratory as part of the residential sprinkler assembly. The tests are intended to determine that the escutcheon will not interfere with the operation and discharge characteristics of the sprinkler.

7.5.8 Solvent Cement. Where solvent cement is used as the pipe and fittings bonding agent, sprinklers shall not be installed in the fittings prior to the fittings being cemented in place.

FAQ ▶
**Why does 7.5.8 require that
the sprinklers be installed
after fittings have been
cemented in place?**

In the 1999 edition, the installation requirement in 7.5.8, which is often part of the installation instructions issued by the pipe manufacturer, was added to ensure that solvent cement will not drip into the piping drop and obstruct or clog the sprinkler.

7.6* Alarms

Local waterflow alarms shall be provided on all sprinkler systems in homes not equipped with smoke detectors in accordance with *NFPA 72®, National Fire Alarm Code®*.

A.7.6 Alarms should be of sufficient intensity to be clearly audible in all bedrooms over background noise levels while all intervening doors are closed. The tests of audibility level should be conducted with all household equipment that operates at night in full operation. Examples of such equipment are window air conditioners and room humidifiers. Where off-premises alarms are provided, the waterflow and the control valve position, as a minimum, should be monitored.

An exterior alarm can be of benefit in areas where a neighbor could alert the fire department or to enhance the ability for an assisted rescue by a passerby.

A waterflow test is normally conducted using the system drain. Figure A.6.2(a), Figure A.6.2(b), and Figure A.6.2(c) show examples of this arrangement.

NFPA 13D expects that smoke detectors be installed throughout the dwelling unit. When the detectors are present, the waterflow alarm, which is addressed in Section 7.6, is not required. However, the use of a waterflow alarm allows for the prompt notification of sprinkler activation or other waterflow through the system if no occupants are present to witness such flow. If arranged properly, notification allows for immediate response to the waterflow situation and minimizes any water damage.

NFPA 13D's basic philosophy is to provide a system that controls a fire for either 7 minutes or 10 minutes, depending on the design employed, so occupants can safely evacuate. As a result, an alarm is needed to warn occupants and initiate evacuation. NFPA 13D suggests two methods by which notification can be done. If smoke detectors are installed in accordance with *NFPA 72®, National Fire Alarm Code®*, NFPA 13D anticipates that they will give an adequate warning for evacuation. However, if smoke detectors are not installed, then the sprinkler system must be equipped with a waterflow device that sounds an audible alarm throughout the residence to initiate evacuation.

When determining whether the alarm device is of sufficient intensity, the following procedure can be used. To conduct audibility tests, the household occupants should position themselves on each level of the house inside a room, such as a bedroom, with the door closed. The alarm should be operated and the occupants should report whether or not it can be heard. The alarm must be loud enough to wake a person who is asleep.

7.7 Attics

When nonmetallic piping is installed in attics, adequate insulation shall be provided on the attic side of the piping to avoid exposure of the piping to temperatures in excess of the pipe's rated temperature.

Attics are covered in Section 7.7. At the request of the technical committee, Hughes Associates, Inc. performed a heat transfer analysis based on 145°F (63°C) attic temperatures and 100°F (38°C) temperatures in the room below. A 6-in. (152 mm) thickness of R-30 insulation above the pipe resulted in a pipe temperature of 104°F (40°C). A 2-in. (51 mm) thickness of the same insulation yielded a pipe temperature of 109°F (43°C). A lack of insulation resulted in a pipe temperature of 129°F (54°C). This analysis demonstrated the importance of adequate insulation for pipe protection in climates where the insulation might not be required because of cold weather. This lack of insulation is especially important in nonmetallic pipe in compliance with the conditions of 5.2.1.3 and 5.2.5.3.

REFERENCES CITED IN COMMENTARY

National Fire Protection Association, 1 Batterymarch Park, P.O. Box 9101, Quincy, MA 02269-9101

NFPA 13, *Standard for the Installation of Sprinkler Systems,* 2002 edition
NFPA 13R, *Standard for the Installation of Sprinkler Systems in Residential Occupancies up to and Including Four Stories in Height,* 2002 edition
NFPA 72®, National Fire Alarm Code®, 2002 edition

Cote, A., and Moore, D., "Field Test and Evaluation of Residential Sprinkler Systems, Los Angeles Test Series," National Fire Protection Association, Boston, MA, April 1980 (This report was done for the NFPA 13D subcommittee and included a series of fire tests in actual dwellings with sprinkler systems installed in accordance with the data resulting from all prior test work and the criteria included in the proposed 1980 revisions to NFPA 13D so as to evaluate the effectiveness of the system under conditions approaching actual use.)
Factory Mutual Research Corporation/Underwriters Laboratories Inc., *Standard for Residential Automatic Sprinklers for Fire Protection Service,* Northbrook, IL, April 1980 (This study developed a performance standard for testing residential sprinklers under room fire conditions that conform with the requirements of NFPA 13D.)
Kung, H. C., Spaulding, R. D., and Hill, E. E., Jr., "Sprinkler Performance in Residential Fire Tests," Factory Mutual Research Corporation, Norwood, MA, December 1980 (This study includes fire tests on representative living room and bedroom residential configurations with combinations of furnishings, with open and closed windows, and with variations in sprinkler application rates and response sensitivity of sprinklers. This work has been closely evaluated by the NFPA 13D subcommittee during its conduct, and the subcommittee was responsible for directing many of the test conditions that were evaluated.)
Kung, H. C., Spaulding, R. D., Hill, E. E., Jr., and Symonds, A. P., "Technical Report Field Evaluation of Residential Prototype Sprinkler, Los Angeles Fire Test Program," Factory Mutual Research Corporation, Norwood, MA, February 1982
Moore, D., "Data Summary of the North Carolina Test Series of USFA Grant 79027 Field Test and Evaluation of Residential Sprinkler Systems," National Fire Protection Association, Boston, MA, September 1980 (This report was done for the NFPA 13D subcommittee and included a series of fire tests in actual mobile homes with sprinkler systems installed in accordance with the data resulting from prior test work and following criteria described in the 1980 edition of NFPA 13D in order to evaluate the effectiveness of the system under conditions approaching actual use.)
Underwriters Laboratories Inc., "Proposed Standard for Residential Automatic Sprinklers for Fire Protection Service," UL 1626, Northbrook, IL, October 1980 (This standard describes the requirements for the testing of residential sprinklers by a testing laboratory. Factory Mutual Research Corporation has a similar standard.)

CHAPTER 8

System Design

8.1 Design Criteria

The design criteria for residential sprinkler systems, which are covered in Section 8.1, are a radical departure from the conventional area/density methods of NFPA 13, *Standard for the Installation of Sprinkler Systems*. The goal for an NFPA 13D design is to obtain fire control with no more than two sprinklers. Chapter 8 illustrates how to accomplish this goal. The design criteria covered in Section 8.1 were developed through laboratory and full-scale fire tests conducted at FM Global and at test sites in Los Angeles and Charlotte, NC. The design criteria identified in Chapter 8 of NFPA 13D can be considered as baseline criteria. Although these criteria are the basis for several listed residential sprinklers, additional research and development efforts over the years have resulted in the creation of sprinklers that use differing design criteria.

8.1.1 Design Discharge.

8.1.1.1 Sprinklers That Are Not Listed with Specific Discharge Criteria.

8.1.1.1.1 The system shall provide a discharge of not less than 13 gpm (49 L/min) per sprinkler simultaneously to all of the design sprinklers.

8.1.1.1.2 The system shall provide a discharge of not less than 18 gpm (68 L/min) to any sprinkler in the system.

Paragraph 8.1.1.1.2 requires a discharge of 18 gpm (68 L/min) for a single operating sprinkler and 13 gpm (49 L/min) per sprinkler for two sprinklers operating in a compartment. These flow rates can be extrapolated to a density of 0.125 gpm/ft^2 (5.1 L/min · m^2) for one sprinkler and 0.09 gpm/ft^2 (3.7 L/min · m^2) for two sprinklers at a maximum spacing of 144 ft^2 (13.4 m^2) per sprinkler. Test data indicate that the primary criterion for a residential system should be a flow rate rather than discharge density over an operating area [Cote 1980, Cote 1982, Kung 1982, Moore 1980].

The flow rates are based primarily on the Los Angeles and Charlotte, NC, fire tests [Cote 1980, Cote 1982, Kung 1982, Moore 1980]. A high percentage (95 percent) of the full-scale tests that were conducted were successful. Actual fire experience has also demonstrated the ability of one sprinkler and under certain conditions two sprinklers to control the fire. Operation Life Safety tracked the number of residential sprinkler operations for over 10 years. Their records indicate that a high percentage of fires involving residential sprinklers usually only result in the operation of a single device.

Residential sprinklers that are listed in accordance with 8.1.1.2 can discharge more or less water than that required in 8.1.1.1. Where sprinklers listed and installed in accordance with 8.1.1.2 are used, the waterflow rates established by the listing evaluation should be used to determine pipe sizes and adequacy of the water supply.

◄ **FAQ**
Are residential sprinklers that are listed for more or less water than required by 8.1.1.1 permitted by NFPA 13D to be utilized?

8.1.1.2* Sprinklers That Are Listed with Specific Discharge Criteria.

A.8.1.1.2 The minimum pressure and flow requirements need to be satisfied while also meeting the requirements of the formula $q = K(p)^{0.5}$. If a sprinkler with a K-factor of 4.3 is listed to

815

EXHIBIT 8.1 *UL 1626 Fire Test Arrangement for Pendent or Upright Sprinklers.*

cover an area of 18 ft × 18 ft at 16.2 gpm, the minimum pressure is required to be 14.2 psi so that the flow is achieved. Likewise, if a sprinkler with a K-factor of 5.6 is covering an area 12 ft × 12 ft, the minimum flow is required to be 14.8 gpm (the flow at 7 psi) even though a flow of 7.2 gpm will satisfy the density criteria.

 Sprinklers that are listed with specific discharge criteria are covered in 8.1.1.2. The design criteria for spacing and sprinkler discharge in Section 8.1 were determined from the Los Angeles and Charlotte, NC, fire tests [Cote 1980, Cote 1982, Kung 1982, Moore 1980]. Because these tests were conducted with prototype residential sprinklers, the Technical Committee on Residential Sprinkler Systems has recognized that future models of residential sprinklers might be able to achieve the intended life safety objectives with waterflow rates, design areas, areas of coverage, and minimum design pressures other than those determined in the Los Angeles and Charlotte, NC, test series. Such sprinklers are permitted to be used provided their performance has been verified through an evaluation process and listed for such use. (See definition of *listed* in 3.2.4.)

Some residential sprinklers have been listed to cover areas up to 400 ft² (36 m²), which is approximately 277 percent more than the prototype sprinkler. Although this larger area of coverage is advantageous because fewer sprinklers would be required for a large compartment, the use of such sprinklers requires a discharge of 30 gpm (114 L/min) for one sprinkler and 21 gpm (79 L/min) for two sprinklers. Greater operating pressures would also be required—for example, 30 psi (2.06 bar) for one sprinkler and 15 psi (1.03 bar) for two sprinklers. Also available are sprinklers that can discharge less than 18 gpm (68 L/min) for a single sprinkler and less than 13 gpm (49 L/min) for each of two operating sprinklers.

In each case, these devices would have been evaluated in the test enclosure built to suit the proposed listed spacing criteria. Exhibit 8.1 illustrates the arrangement of the test enclosure in accordance with UL 1626, *Residential Sprinklers for Fire-Protection Service.*

8.1.1.2.1 The system shall provide at least the flow required for the multiple and single sprinkler operating criteria specified by the sprinkler listing.

8.1.1.2.2* The system shall provide at least the flow required to produce a minimum discharge density of 0.05 gpm/ft^2 (2.04 mm/min) to the design sprinklers.

A.8.1.1.2.2 Sprinklers need to be used in accordance with their listed areas and density. *(See* *Figure A.8.1.1.2.2).*

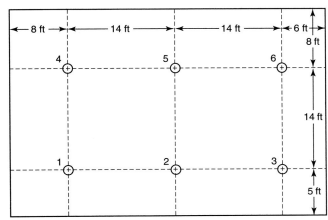

Sprinkler 1, 4, 5, 6 — 16 ft × 16 ft coverage used to determine flow
Sprinkler 2, 3 — 14 ft × 14 ft coverage used to determine flow

FIGURE A.8.1.1.2.2 *Determining Required Flow.*

8.1.2* Number of Design Sprinklers. The number of design sprinklers under flat, smooth, horizontal ceilings shall include all sprinklers within a compartment, up to a maximum of two sprinklers, that requires the greatest hydraulic demand.

A.8.1.2 Residential sprinklers are currently listed for use under flat, smooth, horizontal ceilings only. Sloped, beamed, and pitched ceilings could require special design features such as larger flow, a design for three or more sprinklers to operate in the compartment, or both. Figure A.8.1.2(a) and Figure A.8.1.2(b) show examples of a design configuration.

Since 1980 when the first residential sprinkler was listed, the installation criteria have limited its use to flat, smooth, horizontal ceilings, which are specified in 8.1.2. While this type of ceiling is not representative of all ceilings in which residential sprinklers are used, it is a limitation of the device. Some manufacturers will provide guidance on installations where the ceilings are not horizontal, smooth, and flat. Some guidance for sloped and beamed ceilings is also given in A.8.2.4.

Even if more than two sprinklers are required to cover the floor area in a compartment, the maximum number of sprinklers that need to be included in the design calculations for

Where a compartment has more than two sprinklers within it, how many sprinklers are required to be calculated?
◀ **FAQ**

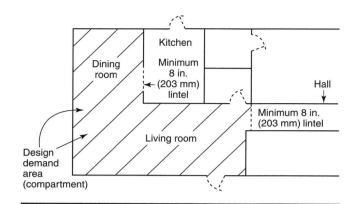

FIGURE A.8.1.2(a) *Sprinkler Design Areas for Typical Residential Occupancy—without Lintel.*

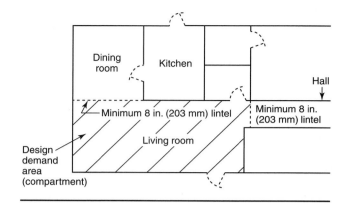

FIGURE A.8.1.2(b) *Sprinkler Design Areas for Typical Residential Occupancy—with Lintel.*

water supply is two. This requirement is frequently misinterpreted to mean that the room size must be limited to make sure that only two sprinklers cover the floor area.

The calculation procedure also requires that both the single- and two-sprinkler discharge criteria be satisfied. For example, if the largest compartment contains three sprinklers, one calculation must be submitted to verify that the single-sprinkler criteria can be satisfied. A separate calculation must also be submitted to show that the two-sprinkler criteria can be satisfied.

Available data from fire tests of residential sprinklers do not support the four-sprinkler design criteria for dry systems that were included in the 1980 edition of NFPA 13D. Currently, residential sprinklers are not listed for use in dry pipe systems, and NFPA 13D provides no design criteria for dry pipe systems.

 In the Los Angeles and Charlotte, NC, fire tests [Cote 1980, Cote 1982, Kung 1982, Moore 1980], all of the test fires used typical residential room configurations. These fires were controlled or extinguished with one or two sprinklers under specific sprinkler waterflow rates, spacing, and discharge (spray pattern) characteristics established by the test. When one of these factors, such as spacing, was not met, the test failed because an acceptance criterion, such as temperature (see commentary to Section 1.2), was exceeded or because the water supply was overtaxed when more than two sprinklers operated. Accordingly, residential system design should be based on two sprinklers operating unless each compartment is protected with only one sprinkler. With the two-sprinkler design, each sprinkler must produce a minimum flow of 13 gpm (49 L/min) when calculations are done in accordance with 8.4.4. With only one sprinkler in any room, the design is based on an 18-gpm (68-L/min) flow rate.

8.1.3 Sprinkler Coverage.

8.1.3.1 Residential Sprinklers That Have Not Been Listed with Specific Coverage Criteria.

8.1.3.1.1 Sprinklers shall be spaced so that the maximum area protected by a single sprinkler does not exceed 144 ft^2 (13.4 m^2).

Paragraph 8.1.3.1.1 indicates that the design area for a single sprinkler should not exceed 144 ft^2 (13.4 m^2). The actual area covered by the sprinklers will normally be as included in the design and specified under 8.1.2.

FAQ ▶
Are residential sprinklers permitted to protect larger areas than 144 ft^2 (13.4 m^2) where listed?

However, 8.1.3.2 allows for a greater spacing to be used if the sprinkler is listed for such coverage. This larger spacing usually requires a greater waterflow rate to achieve proper sprinkler performance.

8.1.3.1.2 The maximum distance between sprinklers shall not exceed 12 ft (3.7 m) on or between pipelines.

8.1.3.1.3 The maximum distance from a wall or partition to a sprinkler shall not exceed 6 ft (1.8 m).

The 6-ft (1.8-m) spacing limit from walls stated in 8.1.3.1.3 ensures that the sprinklers' spray will strike the wall at a distance of not more than 18 in. (457 mm) below the ceiling for the single-sprinkler operating criteria and not more than 24 in. (610 mm) below the ceiling for the multiple-sprinkler operating criteria. The high wall-wetting criteria of a residential sprinkler are critical to its ability to maintain tenable conditions in the room of fire origin. Specially listed sprinklers in accordance with 8.1.3.2 could have spacing requirements in excess of those specified in 8.1.3.1.

8.1.3.1.4 The minimum distance between sprinklers within a compartment shall be 8 ft (2.4 m).

8.1.3.2 Residential Sprinklers That Have Been Listed with Specific Coverage Criteria. Sprinklers shall be installed in accordance with the coverage criteria specified by the listing.

8.1.3.3 Non-Residential Sprinklers. Sprinklers other than residential sprinklers shall be installed in accordance with the coverage criteria specified by NFPA 13, *Standard for the Installation of Sprinkler Systems.*

8.1.4 Operating Pressure. The minimum operating pressure of any sprinkler shall be the higher of the minimum operating pressure specified by the listing or 7 psi (0.5 bar).

The 1996 edition of NFPA 13D was modified to require that residential sprinklers have a minimum operating pressure of 7 psi (0.5 bar), as stated in 8.1.4. This provision is the same provision found in NFPA 13. This minimum was established because of the likelihood that sprinklers operating at pressures below 7 psi (0.5 bar) will not perform satisfactorily.

8.2 Position of Sprinklers

8.2.1 Residential Pendent and Upright Sprinklers.

8.2.1.1 Pendent and upright sprinklers that have not been listed with specific positioning criteria shall be positioned so that the deflectors are within 1 in. to 4 in. (25.4 mm to 102 mm) from the ceiling unless otherwise permitted by 8.2.1.3.

The positioning limitation in 8.2.1.1 is based on the results of the Los Angeles and Charlotte, NC, fire tests [Cote 1980, Cote 1982, Kung 1982, Moore 1980]. When a residential sprinkler is tested and specifically listed for installation with a greater distance from the ceiling, the requirements of 8.2.1.2 and 8.1.2.3 allow the larger distance to be used.

8.2.1.2 Pendent and upright sprinklers that have been listed with specific positioning criteria shall be positioned in accordance with their listing unless permitted otherwise by 8.2.1.3.

8.2.1.3 Pendent and upright sprinklers in closets shall be permitted to be installed within 12 in. (30.5 cm) of the ceiling in order to avoid obstructions near the ceiling.

8.2.2 Residential Sidewall Sprinklers.

8.2.2.1 Sidewall sprinklers that have not been listed with specific positioning criteria shall be positioned so that the deflectors are within 4 in. to 6 in. (102 mm to 152 mm) from the ceiling.

Dead-air spaces in corners can affect a sprinkler's operation time. The 4-in. to 6-in. (102-mm to 152-mm) limitation in 8.2.2.1 ensures that the sprinkler will operate properly.

8.2.2.2 Sidewall sprinklers that have been listed with specific positioning criteria shall be installed in accordance with their listing.

8.2.3 Non-Residential Sprinklers. Sprinklers other than residential sprinklers shall be positioned in accordance with the positioning criteria specified by NFPA 13, *Standard for the Installation of Sprinkler Systems.*

8.2.4* Sprinklers shall be positioned so that the response time and discharge are not unduly affected by obstructions such as ceiling slope, beams, or light fixtures.

A.8.2.4 Fire testing has indicated the need to wet walls in the area protected by residential sprinklers at a level closer to the ceiling than that accomplished by standard sprinkler distribution. Where beams, light fixtures, sloped ceilings, and other obstructions occur, additional residential sprinklers are necessary to achieve proper response and distribution. In addition, for sloped ceilings, higher flow rates could be needed. Guidance should be obtained from the manufacturer.

A series of 33 full-scale tests were conducted in a test room with a floor area of 12 ft × 24 ft (3.6 m × 7.2 m) to determine the effect of cathedral (sloped) and beamed ceiling construction, and combinations of both, on fast-response residential sprinkler performance. The testing was performed using one pendent-type residential sprinkler model, two ceiling slopes (0 degrees and 14 degrees), and two beam configurations on a single enclosure size. In order to judge the effectiveness of sprinklers in controlling fires, two baseline tests, in which the ceiling was smooth and horizontal, were conducted with the pendent sprinklers installed and with a total water supply of 26 gpm (98 L/min) as required by this standard. The results of the baseline tests were compared with tests in which the ceiling was beamed or sloped, or both, and two pendent sprinklers were installed with the same water supply. Under the limited conditions used for testing, the comparison indicates that sloped or beamed ceilings, or a combination of both, represent a serious challenge to the fire protection afforded by fast-response residential sprinklers. However, further tests with beamed ceilings indicated that fire control equivalent to that obtained in the baseline tests can be obtained where one sprinkler is centered in each bay formed by the beams and a total water supply of 36 gpm (136 L/min) is available. Fire control equivalent to that obtained in the baseline tests was obtained for the smooth, sloped ceiling tests where three sprinklers were installed with a total water supply of 54 gpm (200 L/min). In a single smoldering-started fire test, the fire was suppressed.

Small areas created by architectural features such as planter box windows, bay windows, and similar features can be evaluated as follows:

(1) Where no additional floor area is created by the architectural feature, no additional sprinkler protection is required.

(2) Where additional floor area is created by an architectural feature, no additional sprinkler protection is required, provided all of the following conditions are met:

(a) The floor area does not exceed 18 ft² (1.7 m²).

(b) The floor area is not greater than 2 ft (0.65 m) in depth at the deepest point of the architectural feature to the plane of the primary wall where measured along the finished floor.

(c) The floor area is not greater than 9 ft (2.9 m) in length where measured along the plane of the primary wall.

Measurement from the deepest point of the architectural feature to the sprinkler should not exceed the maximum listed spacing of the sprinkler. The hydraulic design is not required to consider the area created by the architectural feature.

Location of sprinklers too near obstructions such as ceiling slope, beams, and light fixtures is likely to result in obstructed sprinkler discharge and could prevent the sprinkler from controlling the fire, which is the reason for the requirement in 8.2.4. Fire control characteristics of residential sprinklers depend on a sprinkler discharge pattern that has a higher wall-wetting characteristic than does the discharge of standard spray sprinklers. The obstruction spacing rules are necessary to allow the spray pattern to reach areas behind furnishings that can be located at the perimeter of a room. Chairs, couches, desks, and shelves are typically placed along a wall and can serve as the initial fuel package during a fire. This reason is one of the reasons why a higher horizontal discharge pattern is required for residential sprinklers.

Paragraph A.8.2.4 also offers additional information with regard to the sprinkler positioning in relation to planter box windows, bay windows, and similar architectural features. Overall, these features are usually smaller in area than a closet and in some cases do not add floor space. If this is the case, these small architectural features are not anticipated to significantly increase the residence's fire hazard, nor will they adversely impact sprinkler performance.

Furthermore, adherence to the spacing rules NFPA 13D often cannot be achieved without placing a sprinkler within the bay window or planter box window. An alternative evaluation procedure was added because sprinkler location within these spaces raises concerns about system performance.

Small bay windows protected with sprinklers usually require piping run along an outside wall to feed the sprinkler in the bay window. Because the bay window is added onto the side of the house, the space is subject to greater temperature fluctuations and cannot always be protected by insulation. This fluctuation increases the potential of freezing during cold temperatures. Additionally, in areas where warmer climates prevail, solar heating of the window glass creates the potential for false actuation of the sprinkler.

◀ **FAQ**
Why are small bay windows addressed differently when determining sprinkler requirements?

An increased number of sprinklers operating within the compartment is also a concern. Activating more sprinklers than anticipated by the design in a compartment can overtax the water supply and reduce the effectiveness of the sprinkler system.

8.2.5 In basements where ceilings are not required for the protection of piping or where metallic pipe is installed, residential sprinklers shall be permitted to be positioned in a manner that anticipates future installation of a finished ceiling.

The provision in 8.2.5 provides guidance when installing sprinklers in unfinished basements. NFPA 13D requires sprinklers in areas where the basement is not finished. If other than nonmetallic pipe is used, the deflectors can be installed as if the ceiling were installed.

8.2.6 In closets and storage areas with both a volume not larger than 300 ft^3 (8.93 m^3) and with a ceiling height less than 5 ft (1.5 m) at the lowest ceiling, a single sprinkler located at the highest ceiling shall be permitted to protect that space.

Closets less than 5 ft (1.5 m) in height at the lowest ceiling and less than 300 ft^3 (8.93 m^3) in volume only need a single sprinkler located at the highest ceiling to achieve fire control, as stated in 8.2.6. These closet types are typically found under stairs and roofs. In some cases, multiple sprinklers are installed within a single closet or storage compartment in order to ensure proper floor coverage. Experience suggests that fire development within a small confined space, such as a closet, is not comparable with that of a larger space. Fire control in these smaller compartments results primarily from the buildup of steam and the associated cooling of the space. Also, the presence of a sprinkler on lower ceiling surfaces within the closet can create the potential for unsatisfactory sprinkler activation and operation.

8.3 System Types

8.3.1* Wet Pipe Systems. A wet pipe system shall be used where all piping is installed in areas maintained above 40°F (4°C).

A.8.3.1 In areas subject to freezing, care should be taken to cover sprinkler piping completely in unheated attic spaces with insulation. Installation should follow the guidelines of the insulation manufacturer. Figure A.8.3.1(a) through Figure A.8.3.1(e) show several methods that can be considered.

Caution: It is important that the insulation be installed tight against the joists. In unheated areas, any spaces or voids between the insulation and the joists causes the water in the fire sprinkler piping to freeze.

FIGURE A.8.3.1(a) *Insulation Recommendations—Arrangement 1.*

Caution: For areas having temperatures of 0°F (−18°C) or lower, an additional batt of insulation covering the joist and the fire sprinkler piping should be used. If this is not done, freeze-ups can occur in the sprinkler piping.

FIGURE A.8.3.1(b) *Insulation Recommendations—Arrangement 2.*

Caution: Boring holes in the joist is one method of locating the fire sprinkler piping in the ceiling. As an alternative, when temperatures are expected to be 0°F (−18°C) or lower, loose pieces of insulation should be stuffed in the bored holes around the piping.

FIGURE A.8.3.1(c) *Insulation Recommendations—Arrangement 3.*

Caution: Care should be taken to avoid compressing the insulation. This reduces its *R* value. To prevent potential freeze-ups of the sprinkler piping, the insulation should be installed tight against the joists.

FIGURE A.8.3.1(d) *Insulation Recommendations—Arrangement 4.*

Caution: Care should be taken to avoid compressing the insulation. This reduces its *R* value. To prevent potential freeze-ups of the sprinkler piping, the insulation should be installed tight against the joists.

FIGURE A.8.3.1(e) *Insulation Recommendations—Arrangement 5.*

Wet pipe systems are covered in 8.3.1. The installation of sprinkler systems in one- and two-family dwellings typically requires that the system piping be installed in the attic space. During cold temperatures, system piping needs to be adequately insulated to protect it from freezing. The type of insulation used, the construction of the attic space, and anticipated low temperatures affect the means of protection. The associated concerns and recommendations on how the insulation could be installed are provided in A.8.3.1. Overall, the insulation should be installed according to the manufacturer's instructions.

8.3.2 Where system piping is located in areas not maintained above 40°F (4°C), the pipe shall be protected against freezing by use of one of the following methods:

(1) Dry pipe system
(2) Antifreeze system in accordance with 8.3.3
(3) Listed standard dry-pendent or dry-sidewall sprinklers extended from pipe in heated areas into unheated areas not intended for living purposes

As of the publishing of the 2002 handbook, no residential sprinkler is listed for dry pipe use, and, therefore, dry pipe systems cannot be installed in accordance with NFPA 13D (see 8.3.2).

◀ **FAQ**
Are any sprinklers listed for dry pipe use?

8.3.3 Antifreeze Systems.

Antifreeze systems are covered in 8.3.3. Although long recognized in NFPA 13, antifreeze systems were not specifically discussed nor specifically prohibited in NFPA 13D prior to 1989. This type of system has additional costs associated with it and requires more maintenance than a wet pipe system. Antifreeze systems also usually require the installation of backflow prevention equipment that further increases the system's costs and depletes the system's available pressure. The pressure losses caused by the backflow device need to be addressed by the system design.

Concerns regarding the use of antifreeze systems are that homeowners might not check antifreeze levels on a routine basis. Homeowners might not be able to acquire and use the types of antifreeze specified by 8.3.3.

If the precautions associated with an antifreeze system are understood and an active maintenance program is employed, then an antifreeze system can be safely and effectively used in accordance with NFPA 13D. See commentary on Section 7.5 of NFPA 13 for more information about antifreeze systems.

8.3.3.1* Conformity with Health Regulations. The use of antifreeze solutions shall be in conformity with any state or local health regulations.

A.8.3.3.1 Antifreeze solutions can be used for maintaining automatic sprinkler protection in small, unheated areas. Antifreeze solutions are recommended only for systems not exceeding 40 gal (151 L).

Because of the cost of refilling the system or replenishing small leaks, small, dry valves should be used where more than 40 gal (151 L) are to be supplied.

Propylene glycol or other suitable material can be used as a substitute for priming water to prevent evaporation of the priming fluid and thus reduce ice formation within the system.

8.3.3.2* Antifreeze Solutions.

A.8.3.3.2 Listed CPVC sprinkler pipe and fittings should be protected from freezing with glycerine only. The use of diethylene glycol, ethylene glycol, or propylene glycol are specifically prohibited. Laboratory testing shows that glycol-based antifreeze solutions present a chemical environment detrimental to CPVC. Listed PB sprinkler pipe and fittings can be protected with glycerine, diethylene glycol, ethylene glycol, or propylene glycol.

FAQ ▶

Is it acceptable to utilize glycol-based antifreeze solutions with chlorinated polyvinyl chloride (CPVC) sprinkler piping?

Chlorinated polyvinyl chloride (CPVC) sprinkler piping is not compatible with some of the recognized antifreeze solutions, which are listed in 8.3.3.2. The glycol-based solutions react with CPVC. Only glycerin solutions are acceptable for CPVC pipe systems.

8.3.3.2.1 For the purposes of this standard, pure glycerine shall mean chemically pure or United States Pharmacopeia 96.5 percent grade.

8.3.3.2.2 Where sprinkler systems are supplied by public water connections, the use of antifreeze solutions other than water solutions of pure glycerine or propylene glycol shall not be permitted.

8.3.3.2.3 Percent solution by volume of glycerine-water and propylene glycol–water mixtures shall be in accordance with Table 8.3.3.2.3.

TABLE 8.3.3.2.3 *Antifreeze Solutions to Be Used Where Public Water Is Connected to Sprinklers*

Material	Solution (by Volume)	Specific Gravity at 60°F (15.6°C)*	Freezing Point °F	°C
Glycerine	50% water	1.133	–15	–26.1
	40% water	1.151	–22	–30.0
	30% water	1.165	–40	–40.0
Propylene glycol	70% water	1.027	+9	–12.8
	60% water	1.034	–6	–21.1
	50% water	1.041	–26	–32.2
	40% water	1.045	–60	–51.1

*Measured with hydrometer having scale of 1.000 to 1.200

8.3.3.2.4 Where public water is not connected to sprinklers, water solutions of glycerine, diethylene glycol, ethylene glycol, and propylene glycol shall be permitted to be used in antifreeze solutions.

8.3.3.2.5 Percent solution by volume of diethylene glycol-water and ethylene glycol–water shall be in accordance with Table 8.3.3.2.5.

8.3.3.2.6* An antifreeze solution with a freezing point below the expected minimum temperature for the locality shall be installed.

FIGURE A.8.3.3.2.6 *Freezing Points of Water Solutions of Ethylene Glycol and Diethylene Glycol.*

TABLE 8.3.3.2.5 *Antifreeze Solutions to Be Used Where Public Water Is Not Connected to Sprinklers*

Material	Solution (by Volume)	Specific Gravity at 60°F (15.6°C)*	Freezing Point	
			°F	°C
Glycerine	50% water	1.133	−15	−26.1
	40% water	1.151	−22	−30.0
	30% water	1.165	−40	−40.0
Diethylene glycol	50% water	1.078	−13	−25.0
	45% water	1.081	−27	−32.8
	40% water	1.086	−42	−41.1
Ethylene glycol	61% water	1.056	−10	−23.3
	56% water	1.063	−20	−28.9
	51% water	1.069	−30	−34.4
	47% water	1.073	−40	−40.0
Propylene glycol	70% water	1.027	+9	−12.8
	60% water	1.034	−6	−21.1
	50% water	1.041	−26	−32.2
	40% water	1.045	−60	−51.1

*Measured with hydrometer having scale of 1.0000 to 1.120

A.8.3.3.2.6 Beyond certain limits, an increased proportion of antifreeze does not lower the freezing point of the solution (*see Figure A.8.3.3.2.6*). Glycerine, diethylene glycol, ethylene glycol, and propylene glycol never should be used without mixing with water in the proper proportions, because these materials tend to thicken near 32°F (0°C).

8.3.3.2.7 The specific gravity of the antifreeze solution shall be checked by a hydrometer with a scale having 0.002 subdivisions.

8.3.3.3* Arrangement of Supply Piping and Valves.

A.8.3.3.3 All permitted antifreeze solutions are heavier than water. At the point of contact (interface), provisions are required by 8.3.3.3 to prevent the diffusion of water into unheated areas.

To avoid leakage, the quality of materials and workmanship should be superior, the threads should be clean and sharp, and the joints should be tight. Only metal-faced valves should be used.

Arrangement of supply piping and valves is covered in 8.3.3.3. An expansion chamber is needed to prevent damage to the antifreeze system components when a backflow prevention device is installed in the supply to the antifreeze system.

8.3.3.3.1 Connections Between Antifreeze System and Wet Pipe System with No Backflow Prevention Device.

8.3.3.3.1.1 A 5 ft (1.5 m) drop pipe, or U-loop, shall be installed in the connection between the antifreeze system and the wet pipe system as illustrated in Figure 8.3.3.3.1.1.

8.3.3.3.1.2 If sprinklers are above the level of the water supply to the antifreeze system, a check valve with a ¹⁄₃₂ in. (0.8 mm) hole in the clapper shall be provided in the U-loop.

8.3.3.3.1.3 Valves shall be provided as illustrated in Figure 8.3.3.3.1.1.

Notes:
1. Check valve shall be permitted to be omitted where sprinklers are below the level of valve A.
2. The ¹⁄₃₂-in. (0.8-mm) hole in the check valve clapper is needed to allow for expansion of the solution during a temperature rise, thus preventing damage to sprinklers.

FIGURE 8.3.3.3.1.1 *Arrangement of Supply Piping and Valves.*

8.3.3.3.2 Connections Between Antifreeze System and Wet Pipe System with Backflow Prevention Device Installed.

8.3.3.3.2.1 Valves shall be provided as illustrated in Figure 8.3.3.3.2.1.

FIGURE 8.3.3.3.2.1 *Arrangement of Supply Piping with Backflow Device.*

8.3.3.3.2.2 An expansion chamber shall be provided as illustrated in Figure 8.3.3.3.2.1.

8.3.3.3.2.3 The expansion chamber shall be sized based on the minimum and maximum volume of the antifreeze solution over the life of the system.

8.4 Pipe Sizing

8.4.1 The pipe sizes shall be verified for each of the single sprinkler and multiple sprinkler design discharge.

8.4.2 For specially listed piping products, friction loss for pipe and fittings shall be permitted to be calculated based on the manufacturer's data.

Pipe sizing is addressed in 8.4.1 and 8.4.2. As indicated in 8.1.2, the single- and multiple-sprinkler design criteria must be verified. The flow–pressure combinations for each of these design points establish the size of branch lines and feed mains, respectively.

The dual discharge requirements of 8.1.1 and 8.1.2 result in two separate sets of calculations that need to be performed where two or more sprinklers are contained within a compartment.

Hydraulic calculations are required for grid-type or looped systems as indicated by 8.4.7 and 8.4.8. These types of systems are required to be hydraulically calculated in accordance with NFPA 13.

Commentary Tables 8.1 and 8.2 (see commentary following A.8.4.4) provide friction loss information for nonmetallic piping materials with regard to 8.4.4.

◀ **FAQ**
Are hydraulic calculations in accordance with NFPA 13 required for any NFPA 13D installations?

8.4.3 Minimum Pipe Size.

8.4.3.1 The minimum size of steel pipe shall be 1 in. (25.4 mm).

The requirements for the minimum pipe size of metallic pipe are the same as those in NFPA 13—that is, 1 in. (25.4 mm) for steel, as stated in 8.4.3.1. The minimum size requirement decreases the possibility of pipe becoming obstructed due to scale and rust.

8.4.3.2 The minimum size of pipe other than steel pipe shall be ¾ in. (19 mm) unless smaller sizes are permitted by 8.4.3.3.

The minimum size for types of pipe or tube other than for copper or steel, including nonmetallic piping materials, would be included as part of the product's listing information (see 8.4.3.2). Because of the concerns with obstructing waterflow through small diameter pipe, sizes less than ¾ in. (19 mm) are unlikely to be listed for ferrous pipe.

8.4.3.3* ½-in. (12.7-mm) nonmetallic pipe and ½-in. (12.7-mm) copper pipe along with listed special fittings shall be permitted to be used only in network systems under the following conditions:

(1)* Each sprinkler shall be supplied through a minimum of three separate paths from the supply shutoff valve assembly within the dwelling unit.
(2) Calculations shall clearly indicate the pipes that create the paths to each sprinkler.
(3) Sprinkler supply lines shall not terminate in a dead end.
(4) Hydraulic calculations shall be prepared for each sprinkler flowing individually within the system and for each pair of sprinklers within the same compartment.
(5) The location of the most demanding single sprinkler and pair of sprinklers, including their pressure and flow requirements, shall be indicated on the plan review documents.
(6) The system shall be hydraulically calculated in accordance with the provisions of NFPA 13, *Standard for the Installation of Sprinkler Systems,* except that the friction loss straight through a fitting shall be included.
(7) The system shall be supplied from a potable water source, or it shall be equipped with a strainer at the connection to the supply line.
(8) The method of joining the pipe to fittings or to other pipe shall be covered by the listing.
(9) When insert tees are installed, each sprinkler shall have four separate paths from the water supply. A maximum of one insert fitting shall be permitted in each pipe section between sprinklers to serve only domestic fixtures.

With the 2002 edition, insert tees may be installed on piping between sprinklers to supply a domestic fixture, as indicated in 8.4.3.3(9). Insert tees may only be used when the sprinkler is supplied from four separate paths and only one insert fitting is allowed between each sprinkler.

(10) The piping to the plumbing fixtures shall be of copper or listed pipe.

Paragraph 8.4.3.3 allows the use of ½-in. (12.7-mm) nonmetallic pipe and copper tube. The previous limitation was ¾ in. (19 mm). A growing effort exists to make residential sprinkler systems a more affordable and attractive fire safety feature for the home. Allowing for smaller diameter pipe provides more options in this regard.

FAQ ▶
What are some of the conditions required when utilizing ½-in (12.7-mm) sprinkler piping?

However, in order to utilize the ½-in. (12.7-mm) pipe, a number of conditions must be met. The system must be hydraulically calculated in accordance with the provisions of NFPA 13 and friction loss through fittings must be accounted for in the design. These conditions ensure that a thorough hydraulic analysis of the system will be conducted. Additionally, due to small pipe sizes, pressure losses through fittings will have a greater overall impact and also must be accounted for in the design. Hydraulic calculations must be prepared for each sprinkler flowing individually within the system and for each pair of sprinklers flowing within the same compartment. This requirement applies to all NFPA 13D systems. The location of the most demanding single sprinkler and pair of sprinklers along with their pressure and flow requirements need to be indicated on the plan review documents. This information allows for easier plan review and system verification.

In addition to verifying the system's hydraulic performance, supply piping in a system utilizing ½-in. (12.7-mm) pipe must be arranged so that each sprinkler is supplied by at least three separate flow paths with no supply lines terminating in a dead end. This results in a more hydraulically advantageous arrangement. Methods for joining pipe must be addressed by product listings, and insert fittings are only to be utilized in accordance with 8.4.3.3(9). Following listing requirements for joining of pipe serves to increase the system's overall reliability. Piping to any plumbing fixtures must be copper or listed. Finally, water sources must be potable or equipped with a strainer at the connection to the supply line. The small diameter piping is subject to a greater incidence of obstruction that must be guarded against. Overall, this type of system (one that uses ½ in. pipe) does not allow for a large margin of error in either its design or installation. However, when designed and installed correctly, the system will achieve the desired fire protection objectives.

A.8.4.3.3 Any special listing of products covered in 8.4.3.3 should include certification by the manufacturer of personnel involved in the layout, calculation, and installation of their product.

A.8.4.3.3(1) Where a four-port fitting is used, and one of the ports is not being used to satisfy this requirement or to feed a domestic fixture, the extra port should be connected to another open port at a sprinkler, or should be connected to the water supply pipe (manifold).

8.4.4* Pipe shall be sized by hydraulic calculations in accordance with the methods described in NFPA 13, *Standard for the Installation of Sprinkler Systems,* in accordance with 8.4.5, or in accordance with the following general method for straight-run systems connected to a city water main of at least 4 in. (102 mm) in diameter [See Table 8.4.4(a) through Table 8.4.4(g)]:

(1) The system flow rate shall be established in accordance with Section 8.1, and it shall be determined that the flow allowed by the water meter is adequate to supply the system demand and that the total demand flow does not exceed the maximum flow allowed by the piping system components.

(2) The water pressure in the street shall be determined.

(3) Pipe sizes shall be selected.

(4) Meter pressure losses, if any, shall be deducted. [*See Table 8.4.4(g).*] Higher pressure losses specified by the manufacturer shall be used in place of those specified in Table

TABLE 8.4.4(a) *Pressure Losses in psi/ft for Schedule 40 Steel Pipe (C = 120)*

Pipe Size (in.)	Flow Rate (gpm)											
	10	**12**	**14**	**16**	**18**	**20**	**25**	**30**	**35**	**40**	**45**	**50**
1	0.04	0.05	0.07	0.09	0.11	0.13	0.20	0.28	0.37	0.47	0.58	0.71
1¼	0.01	0.01	0.02	0.02	0.03	0.03	0.05	0.07	0.10	0.12	0.15	0.19
1½	0.01	0.01	0.01	0.01	0.01	0.02	0.02	0.03	0.05	0.06	0.07	0.09
2	—	—	—	—	—	0.01	0.01	0.01	0.01	0.02	0.02	0.03

NOTE: For SI units, 1 gal = 3.785 L; 1 psi = 0.0689 bar; 1 in. = 25.4 mm; 1 ft = 0.3048 m.

TABLE 8.4.4(b) *Pressure Losses in psi/ft for Copper Tubing—Types K, L, and M (C = 150)*

Tubing Size (in.)	Type	Flow Rate (gpm)											
		10	**12**	**14**	**16**	**18**	**20**	**25**	**30**	**35**	**40**	**45**	**50**
¾	M	0.08	0.12	0.16	0.20	0.25	0.30	0.46	0.64	0.85	—	—	—
	L	0.10	0.14	0.18	0.23	0.29	0.35	0.53	0.75	1.00	—	—	—
	K	0.13	0.18	0.24	0.30	0.38	0.46	0.69	0.97	1.28	—	—	—
1	M	0.02	0.03	0.04	0.06	0.07	0.08	0.13	0.18	0.24	0.30	0.38	0.46
	L	0.03	0.04	0.05	0.06	0.08	0.10	0.15	0.20	0.27	0.35	0.43	0.53
	K	0.03	0.04	0.06	0.07	0.09	0.11	0.17	0.24	0.31	0.40	0.50	0.61
1¼	M	0.01	0.01	0.02	0.02	0.03	0.03	0.05	0.07	0.09	0.11	0.15	0.17
	L	0.01	0.01	0.02	0.02	0.03	0.03	0.05	0.07	0.10	0.12	0.16	0.19
	K	0.01	0.01	0.02	0.02	0.03	0.04	0.06	0.08	0.11	0.13	0.17	0.20
1½	M	—	0.01	0.01	0.01	0.01	0.01	0.02	0.03	0.04	0.05	0.06	0.08
	L	—	0.01	0.01	0.01	0.01	0.01	0.02	0.03	0.04	0.05	0.07	0.08
	K	—	0.01	0.01	0.01	0.01	0.02	0.02	0.03	0.05	0.06	0.07	0.09
2	M	—	—	—	—	—	—	0.01	0.01	0.01	0.01	0.02	0.02
	L	—	—	—	—	—	—	0.01	0.01	0.01	0.01	0.02	0.02
	K	—	—	—	—	—	—	0.01	0.01	0.01	0.01	0.02	0.02

NOTE: For SI units, 1 gal = 3.785 L; 1 psi = 0.0689 bar; 1 in. = 25.4 mm; 1 ft = 0.3048 m.

TABLE 8.4.4(c) *Equivalent Length of Fittings and Valves for Schedule 40 Steel Pipe in Feet*

Diameter (in.)	45-Degree Elbows	90-Degree Elbows	Long-Radius Elbows	Tee or Cross (flow turned 90 degrees)	Tee Run	Gate Valve	Angle Valve	Globe Valve	Globe "Y" Pattern Valve	Cock Valve	Check Valve
1	1	2	2	5	2	0	12	28	15	4	5
1¼	1	3	2	6	2	0	15	35	18	5	7
1½	2	4	2	8	3	0	18	43	22	6	9
2	2	5	3	10	3	1	24	57	28	7	11

TABLE 8.4.4(d) *Equivalent Length of Fittings and Valves for Type K Copper Tube in Feet*

Diameter (in.)	45-Degree Elbows	90-Degree Elbows	Long-Radius Elbows	Tee or Cross (flow turned 90 degrees)	Tee Run	Gate Valve	Angle Valve	Globe Valve	Globe "Y" Pattern Valve	Cock Valve	Check Valve
¾	0	1	0	3	1	0	7	14	7	2	0
1	1	2	2	6	2	0	14	33	18	5	6
1¼	1	3	2	5	2	0	14	32	16	5	6
1½	2	4	2	8	3	0	18	43	22	6	9
2	2	6	3	12	4	1	28	66	33	8	13

TABLE 8.4.4(e) *Equivalent Length of Fittings and Valves for Type L Copper Tube in Feet*

Diameter (in.)	45-Degree Elbows	90-Degree Elbows	Long-Radius Elbows	Tee or Cross (flow turned 90 degrees)	Tee Run	Gate Valve	Angle Valve	Globe Valve	Globe "Y" Pattern Valve	Cock Valve	Check Valve
¾	0	2	0	4	1	0	8	18	10	3	0
1	1	3	3	7	2	0	16	38	20	5	7
1¼	1	3	2	6	2	0	15	35	18	5	7
1½	2	4	2	9	3	0	20	47	24	7	10
2	2	6	4	12	4	1	30	71	35	9	14

TABLE 8.4.4(f) *Equivalent Length of Fittings and Valves for Type M Copper Tube in Feet*

Diameter (in.)	45-Degree Elbows	90-Degree Elbows	Long-Radius Elbows	Tee or Cross (flow turned 90 degrees)	Tee Run	Gate Valve	Angle Valve	Globe Valve	Globe "Y" Pattern Valve	Cock Valve	Check Valve
¾	0	2	0	4	1	0	10	21	11	3	0
1	2	3	3	8	3	0	19	43	23	6	8
1¼	1	3	2	7	2	0	16	38	20	5	8
1½	2	5	2	9	3	0	21	50	26	7	11
2	3	7	4	13	5	1	32	75	37	9	14

TABLE 8.4.4(g) *Pressure Losses in psi in Water Meters*

Meter Size (in.)	Flow (gpm)					
	18	23	26	31	39	52
⅝	9	14	18	26	†	†
¾	4	8	9	13	†	†
1	2	3	3	4	6	10
1½	††	1	2	2	4	7
2	††	††	††	1	2	3

NOTE: For SI units, 1 gpm = 3.785 L/min; 1 in. = 25.4 mm; 1 psi = 0.0689 bar.

†Above maximum rated flow of commonly available meters.

††Less than 1 psi (0.689 bar).

8.4.4(g). Lower pressure losses shall be permitted to be used where supporting data is provided by the meter manufacturer.

(5) Pressure loss for elevation shall be deducted as follows:

(a) Building height above street (in ft) × 0.434 = pressure loss (in psi)
(b) Building height above street (in m) × 0.098 = pressure loss (in bar)

(6) Pressure losses from the city main to the inside control valve shall be deducted by multiplying the factor from Table 8.4.4(a) or Table 8.4.4(b) by the total length(s) of pipe in feet (meters). [The total length includes equivalent length of fittings as determined by applying Table 8.4.4(c), Table 8.4.4(d), Table 8.4.4(e), or Table 8.4.4(f).]

(7) Pressure losses for piping within the building shall be deducted by multiplying the factor from Table 8.4.4(a) or Table 8.4.4(b) by the total length in feet (meters) of each size of pipe between the control valve and the farthest sprinkler.

(8) Valve and fitting pressure losses shall be deducted. The valves and fittings from the control valve to the farthest sprinkler shall be counted. The equivalent length for each valve and fitting as shown in Table 8.4.4(c), Table 8.4.4(d), Table 8.4.4(e), or Table 8.4.4(f) shall be determined and the values added to obtain the total equivalent length for each pipe size. The equivalent length for each size shall be multiplied by the factor from Table 8.4.4(a) or Table 8.4.4(b) and the values totaled.

(9) In multilevel buildings, the steps in 8.4.4(1) through 8.4.4(8) shall be repeated to size piping for each floor.

(10) If the remaining pressure is less than the operating pressure established by the testing laboratory for the sprinkler being used, the sprinkler system shall be redesigned. If the remaining pressure is higher than required, smaller piping shall be permitted to be used where justified by calculations.

(11) The remaining piping shall be sized the same as the piping up to and including the farthest sprinkler unless smaller pipe sizes are justified by calculations.

A.8.4.4 The determination of public water supply pressure should take into account the probable minimum pressure conditions prevailing during such periods as during the night or during the summer months when heavy usage can occur; the possibility of interruption by floods or ice conditions in winter also should be considered. [*See Figure A.8.4.4(a) and Figure A.8.4.4(b).*]

Section 8.4 describes a simplified method of sizing pipe in a residence to ensure that the flow rate from the sprinklers in the design area will meet the design discharge criteria of 8.1.1 (see 8.4.4). This approximation method is only permitted for tree-type systems connected to an automatic water supply. When the supply source is a city main, the main size must be at least 4 in. (102 mm) in diameter in order to utilize this procedure.

In performing the calculation for a specific system that has at least two sprinklers in any compartment, the calculation procedure must be repeated twice. When using a residential sprinkler that uses the generic waterflow requirements discussed in 8.1.1, the first calculation is made for a single sprinkler flowing at 18 gpm (68 L/min), and the second calculation is made for two sprinklers flowing at 26 gpm (98 L/min) [13 gpm (49 L/min) each]. The pressure required to produce this flow at the sprinkler will depend on the coefficient of discharge (K-factor), which must be obtained from the sprinkler manufacturer. In multilevel dwellings, calculations will need to be done for all levels of the building to ensure that pipe is sized for the variations in flow that can occur due to elevation differences between floors and differences in piping geometry between floors.

Additionally, the first step of the calculation takes into account any maximum flow limits of system components. Some components such as meters, valves, backflow devices, and relief valves have associated flow limits. Exceeding these values could result in improper system operation. Therefore, the designer must investigate whether the use of any system components is restricted by its flow limitation.

	Individual Loss	Net Total
(1) Water pressure in street _____	_____	_____
(2) Arbitrarily select pipe size _____		
(3) Deduct meter loss (size) _____	_____	_____
(4) Deduct head loss for elevation		
(_____ ft × 0.434) _____		
(5) Deduct pressure loss from city main to sprinkler system		
control valve* _____		
____ Pipe _____ ft	_____	_____
____ Valves _____ ft	_____	_____
____ Elbows _____ ft	_____	_____
____ Tee _____ ft	_____	_____
____ Total _____ ft × _____	_____	_____
(6) Deduct pressure loss for piping-control valve to farthest sprinkler*		

Size	Quantity	Description	Total Equivalent (ft)
_____	_____	90-degree elbow	_____
_____	_____	45-degree elbow	_____
_____	_____	Tee	_____
_____	_____	Check valve	_____
_____	_____	Valve (_____)	_____
_____	_____	Total	___ ft × ___ = ___

Size	Quantity	Description	Total Equivalent (ft)
_____	_____	90-degree elbow	_____
_____	_____	45-degree elbow	_____
_____	_____	Tee	_____
_____	_____	Check valve	_____
_____	_____	Valve (_____)	_____
_____	_____	Total	___ ft × ___ = ___

Remaining pressure for sprinkler operation _____

For SI units, 1 ft = 0.3048 m; 1 psi = 0.0689 bar.

* Factors from Table 8.4.4(a) through Table 8.4.4(e).

FIGURE A.8.4.4(a) *Calculation Sheet.*

	Individual Loss	Net Total
Water pressure at supply outlet		
(1) Deduct head loss for elevation	_____	_____
(_____ ft × 0.434)	_____	_____
(2) Deduct pressure loss from piping within building*	_____	_____
Remaining pressure for sprinkler operation _____	_____	

For SI units, 1 ft = 0.3048 m; 1 psi = 0.0689 bar.

* Factors from Table 8.4.4(a) through 8.4.4(g).

FIGURE A.8.4.4(b) *Calculation Sheet—Elevated Tank, Booster Pump, Pump Tank Supply.*

The second step is to determine the water pressure in the street in front of the property. This is done by obtaining information on the public water supply pressure from the local water company or by placing a pressure gauge on the water supply inlet connection in the dwelling.

After flow demands are determined, pipe sizes are arbitrarily selected and valves and fittings laid out to meet the piping arrangements described in Figures A.6.2(a), A.6.2(b), and A.6.2(c) and A.6.3(a), A.6.3(b), and A.6.3(c). Losses in piping, fittings, meters, and valves and

COMMENTARY TABLE 8.1 *Pressure Losses in psi/ft for PB Pipe*

Tubing Size (in.)	Flow Rate (gpm)											
	10	12	14	16	18	20	25	30	35	40	45	50
¾	0.1655	0.2319	0.3084	0.3948	0.4909	0.5966	0.9014	1.2630	1.6799	2.1506		
1	0.0475	0.0666	0.0886	0.1134	0.1410	0.1714	0.2590	0.3629	0.4826	0.6179	0.7683	0.9336
1	0.0180	0.0253	0.0336	0.0430	0.0535	0.0650	0.0982	0.1375	0.1829	0.2342	0.2912	0.3539
1½	0.0080	0.0112	0.0149	0.0191	0.0237	0.0288	0.0436	0.0611	0.0812	0.1040	0.1293	0.1571
2	0.0022	0.0030	0.0040	0.0051	0.0064	0.0078	0.0118	0.0165	0.0219	0.0281	0.0349	0.0424

For SI units, 1 gal = 3.785 L; 1 psi = 0.0689 bar; 1 in. = 25.4 mm; 1 ft = 0.305 m.

COMMENTARY TABLE 8.2 *Pressure Losses in psi/ft for Listed CPVC Pipe (C = 150)*

Tubing Size (in.)	Flow Rate (gpm)											
	10	12	14	16	18	20	25	30	35	40	45	50
1	0.0182	0.0255	0.0340	0.0435	0.0541	0.0657	0.0993	0.1391	0.1850	0.2368	0.2944	0.3578
1¼	0.0059	0.0082	0.0109	0.0140	0.0174	0.0211	0.0319	0.0447	0.0595	0.0761	0.0947	0.1150
1½	0.0030	0.0043	0.0057	0.0072	0.0090	0.0110	0.0166	0.0232	0.0308	0.0395	0.0491	0.0597
2	0.0010	0.0014	0.0019	0.0024	0.0030	0.0037	0.0056	0.0078	0.0104	0.0133	0.0165	0.0201
2½	0.0004	0.0006	0.0008	0.0010	0.0012	0.0015	0.0022	0.0031	0.0041	0.0053	0.0065	0.0080

For SI units, 1 gal = 3.785 L; 1 psi = 0.0689 bar; 1 in. = 25.4 mm; 1 ft = 0.305 m.

for elevation are then determined in accordance with 8.4.4(4) through 8.4.4(8). These losses are deducted from the city pressure to determine the pressure at the sprinkler design area on each floor of the residence. If this pressure is less than the operating pressure determined in the calculation to meet flow demands (see commentary for 8.1.1), a redesign is necessary and pipe must be increased or the water supply must be improved. If the remaining pressure is higher than required to supply the demand rate at the sprinkler, the designer can either stop and submit the calculation for approval or reduce the pipe sizes to achieve a more cost-effective system. (See Commentary Tables 8.1 and 8.2 for PB and CPVC pipe pressure losses.)

A sample calculation for a typical residence is as follows. This example is based on the dwelling illustrated by Exhibit 8.2, which is also a plot plan showing an existing city main. Exhibits 8.3 and 8.4 show the sprinkler and piping layouts for the basement and first floor of the dwelling, respectively.

The following is assumed for the calculation:

1. The sprinkler used is listed for application rate, design area, and area of coverage as indicated in 8.1.1, 8.1.2, and 8.1.3.
2. The flow from one sprinkler is 18 gpm (68 L/min) and from two sprinklers is 13 gpm (49 L/min) each [26 gpm (98 L/min) total] per 8.1.1.
3. The sprinkler used has a coefficient (K-factor) of 3.9. Thus, the pressure needed for the system at the flowing sprinkler is calculated as follows:

$$Q = K\sqrt{p} \text{ or } p = \left(\frac{Q}{K}\right)^2$$

For 18 gpm: $p = \left(\frac{18}{3.9}\right)^2 = 4.61^2 = 21.3$ psi

For 13 gpm: $p = \left(\frac{13}{3.9}\right)^2 = 3.33^2 = 11.1$ psi

EXHIBIT 8.2 *Typical Residence for Sample Sprinkler System Hydraulic Calculation.*

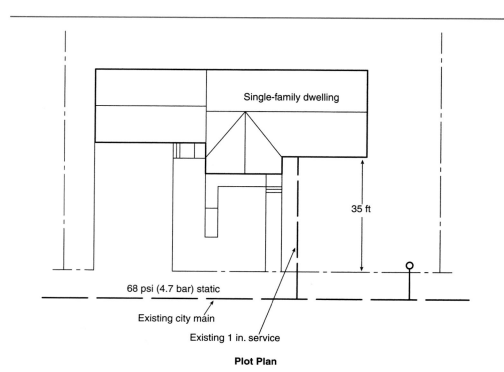

Single-family dwelling

35 ft

68 psi (4.7 bar) static

Existing city main

Existing 1 in. service

Plot Plan

For SI units, 1 in. = 25.4 mm; 1 ft = 0.305 m.

Lavatory

Laundry

Up ¾ in.

U

Unexcavated

Unexcavated

Up ¾ in.

10 ft

¾ in.

¾ in.

28 ft

1 in.

¾ in.

¾ in.

¾ in.

¾ in.

¾ in.

¾ in.

12 ft

¾ in.

1 in.

¾ in. 1 in.

Up ¾ in.

Beam

Recreation area

24 ft

¾ in.

1 in.

1 in.

10 ft

¾ in.

¾ in.

Up ¾ in.

Boiler room and workshop

16 ft

¾ in.

4 ft

¾ in.

Up
1 in.

Existing 1 in. line

Storage

12 ft

4 ft

Basement Plan

For SI units, 1 in. = 25.4 mm; 1 ft = 0.305 m.

EXHIBIT 8.3 *Basement Floor Plan for Sample Sprinkler Calculation.*

First-Floor Plan

For SI units, 1 in. = 25.4 mm; 1 ft = 0.305 m.

EXHIBIT 8.4 *First-Floor Plan for Sample Sprinkler Calculation.*

4. Type K copper tube is used.
5. The water pressure in the street was determined to be 68 psi (4.7 bar).

The calculation procedure is outlined in Exhibits 8.5 and 8.6. The farthest sprinkler in calculation example no. 2 is the farthest sprinkler in the only room having more than one sprinkler.

With regard to 8.4.4(8), the tables providing equivalent pipe length data for fittings and valves have been updated. Additional tables were created to address the different internal diameters of the three types of copper tubing.

8.4.5 Smaller pipe sizes than those determined by 8.4.4 shall be permitted where justified by calculations for systems connected to city water mains of at least 4 in. (102 mm) in diameter.

8.4.6 To size piping for systems with an elevated tank, pump, or pump–tank combination, the pressure at the water supply outlet shall be determined and the steps in 8.4.4(3), (4), (7), (8), (9), (10), and (11) shall be followed.

8.4.7 Hydraulic calculation procedures in accordance with NFPA 13, *Standard for the Installation of Sprinkler Systems,* shall be used for grid-type systems.

8.4.8 Hydraulic calculation procedures in accordance with NFPA 13, *Standard for the Installation of Sprinkler Systems,* shall be used for looped-type systems.

Where piping configurations are looped or gridded, calculations must be conducted in accordance with 8.4.3 and 8.4.9. Therefore, hydraulic calculations to size the piping must be done in accordance with the method described in NFPA 13, as stated in 8.4.8.

◄ **FAQ**
Where piping configurations are looped or gridded, are calculations required to be conducted in accordance with NFPA 13?

8.4.9 Hydraulic calculation procedures in accordance with NFPA 13, *Standard for the Installation of Sprinkler Systems,* shall be used for systems connected to city water mains of less than 4 in. (100 mm) in diameter.

EXHIBIT 8.5 Calculation
Example No. 1.

Calculation 1 at 18 gpm (21.3 psi) from Sprinkler A

1st Floor: Type K Copper Tube			Individual loss	Net total
a. Water pressure in street			_____	68
b. Arbitrarily selected pipe size 1 in. + ¾ in.				
c. Deduct meter loss (__¾ in.__ size)			4.0	64
d. Deduct loss for elevation System control valve* (__15__ ft × 0.434)			6.5	57.5

e. Deduct loss from city main to control valve

1 in.	tube	48	ft		
3	valves	3	ft		
3	elbows	9	ft		
1	tee	5	ft		
	Total	65	ft ×	0.09	5.9	51.6

f. Deduct loss for tubing: control valve to farthest sprinkler*

¾-in. tube: 19 ft	×	0.38	7.2	
1-in. tube: 35 ft	×	0.09	3.1	41.3

Size	Quantity	Description	Total equivalent ft		
	4	90-degree elbow	8		
	___	45-degree elbow	___		
¾ in.	___	tee	___		
	___	check valve	___		
	___	valve (___)	___		
		Total	8 ft × 0.38	= 3.0	38.3

Size	Quantity	Description	Total equivalent ft		
	1	90-degree elbow	3		
	___	45-degree elbow	___		
1 in.	1	tee	5		
	1	check valve	4		
	___	valve (___)	___		
		Total	12 ft × 0.09	= 1.1	37.2

This pressure exceeds 21.3 psi and design is acceptable.
Note: Repeat calculation for basement to verify adequacy of basement piping size.

Remaining pressure for sprinkler operations.
* Factors from Tables 8.4.4(a), 8.4.4(c), and 8.4.4(d).

For SI units, 1 in. = 25.4 mm; 1 ft = 0.305 m.

EXHIBIT 8.6 *Calculation Example No. 2.*

Calculation 2 at 26 gpm (11.1 psi) from Sprinklers B and C

1st Floor: Type K Copper Tube	Individual loss	Net total
a. Water pressure in street	————	6
b. Arbitrarily selected pipe size 1 in.+ ¾ in.		
c. Deduct meter loss (¾ in. size)	9.0	59.0
d. Deduct loss for elevation		
System control valve*		
(15 ft × 0.434)	6.5	52.5

e. Deduct loss from city main
to control valve

1 in.	tube	4 ft	
3	valves	8 ft	
3	elbows	3 ft	
1	tee	9 ft	
	Total	5 ft ×	0.20

	Individual loss	Net total
(Total 5 ft × 0.20)	13.0	39.5

f. Deduct loss for tubing: control
valve to farthest sprinkler*

			Individual loss	Net total
¾-in. tube: 12 ft	×	0.19	2.3	
1-in. tube: 14 ft	×	0.20	2.8	34.4

Size	Quantity	Description	Total equivalent ft		
	1	90-degree elbow	2		
	——	45-degree elbow	——		
¾ in.	——	tee	——		
	——	check valve	——		
	——	valve (——)	——		
		Total	2 ft × .27	.54	33.8

Size	Quantity	Description	Total equivalent ft		
	1	90-degree elbow	3		
	——	45-degree elbow	——		
1 in.	1	tee	5		
	1	check valve	4		
	——	valve (——)	——		
		Total	12 ft × 0.20	2.4	31.4

This pressure exceeds 11.1 psi and design is acceptable.
Note: Repeat calculation for basement to verify adequacy of basement piping size.

Remaining pressure for sprinkler operations.
* Factors from Table 8.4.4(a), 8.4.4(c), and 8.4.4(d).

For SI units, 1 in. = 25.4 mm; 1 ft = 0.305 m.

Because the approximation method of 8.4.4 relies on the static water supply pressure, it is restricted to city water mains with a 4-in. (100-mm) diameter or larger or to other water supply sources that utilize a captured supply, as indicated in 8.4.9.

8.5 Piping Configurations

8.5.1 The piping configuration shall be permitted to be looped.

8.5.2 The piping configuration shall be permitted to be gridded.

8.5.3 The piping configuration shall be permitted to be straight run.

8.5.4 The piping configuration shall be permitted to be a combination of the configurations permitted in 8.5.1 through 8.5.3.

8.6 Location of Sprinklers

8.6.1 Sprinklers shall be installed in all areas except where omission is permitted by 8.6.2 through 8.6.6.

Selective sprinkler omission from certain areas indicates that a level of protection less than that anticipated by NFPA 13D is being considered (see 8.6.1). NFPA 13D recognizes the presence and availability of the levels of protection concept that is included in other fire protection codes and standards.

FAQ ▶
How did the committee
determine from which areas
to omit sprinkler protection?

Areas mentioned in 8.6.2 through 8.6.6 are not selected at random but represent those areas in which fires do not result in a high percentage of fatalities. Table A.1.2(a) shows statistics for various fire deaths and their relation to the area of fire origin. In addition, the following is noted:

1. Combustible fuel loading in most bathrooms is typically low (see 8.6.2).
2. Small closets are usually impractical places to install sprinklers because of their relatively small size (see 8.6.3). The use of the closet is then limited. When heat-producing equipment is contained in the closet, the exception is no longer valid.
3. Mandatory sprinklering of the areas in 8.6.4 through 8.6.6 would necessitate the use of dry pipe systems where freezing weather is encountered. The use of dry systems would detract from the system's rapid response within the occupied areas of the dwelling and thus detract from, rather than enhance, life safety. The added cost to cover these areas must also be considered. A dry pipe system would be more costly.

Furthermore, most building codes require a 1-hour fire-rated separation between garages and other portions of the dwelling.

8.6.2 Sprinklers shall not be required in bathrooms of 55 ft^2 (5.1 m^2) and less.

8.6.3 Sprinklers shall not be required in clothes closets, linen closets, and pantries that meet all of the following conditions:

(1) The area of the space does not exceed 24 ft^2 (2.2 m^2).
(2) The least dimension does not exceed 3 ft (0.9 m).
(3) The walls and ceilings are surfaced with noncombustible or limited-combustible materials as defined in NFPA 220, *Standard on Types of Building Construction.*

8.6.4* Sprinklers shall not be required in garages, open attached porches, carports, and similar structures.

A.8.6.4 Although NFPA 13D does not require garages to be sprinklered, some authorities having jurisdiction take it upon themselves to add this requirement locally. In such circumstances, residential or quick-response sprinklers with a two-sprinkler design in the garage with the same piping used in the rest of the dwelling may be used. It is recognized that residential sprinklers have not been tested specifically for fires in garages, but field experience has shown that the sprinklers help to alert occupants to the fact that there is a fire, can reduce the possibility of flashover, and can improve the chances for occupants to escape.

8.6.5 Sprinklers shall not be required in attics, crawl spaces, and other concealed spaces that are not used or intended for living purposes.

8.6.6 Sprinklers shall not be required in covered unheated projections of the building at entrances/exits as long as there is another means of egress from the dwelling unit.

REFERENCES CITED IN COMMENTARY

National Fire Protection Association, 1 Batterymarch Park, P.O. Box 9101, Quincy, MA 02269-9101

NFPA 13, *Standard for the Installation of Sprinkler Systems,* 2002 edition

Underwriters Laboratories Inc., 333 Pfingsten Road, Northbrook, IL 60062

UL 1626, *Residential Sprinklers for Fire-Protection Service,* 2nd edition, 1994

Cote, A. E., "Final Report on Field Test and Evaluation of Residential Sprinkler Systems," National Fire Protection Association, Quincy, MA, July 1982

Cote, A., and Moore, D., "Field Test and Evaluation of Residential Sprinkler Systems, Los Angeles Test Series," National Fire Protection Association, Boston, MA, April 1980 (This report was done for the NFPA 13D subcommittee and included a series of fire tests in actual dwellings with sprinkler systems installed in accordance with the data resulting from all prior test work and the criteria included in the proposed 1980 revisions to NFPA 13D so as to evaluate the effectiveness of the system under conditions approaching actual use.)

Kung, H. C., Spaulding, R. D., Hill, E. E., Jr., and Symonds, A. P., "Technical Report Field Evaluation of Residential Prototype Sprinkler, Los Angeles Fire Test Program," Factory Mutual Research Corporation, Norwood, MA, February 1982

Moore, D., "Data Summary of the North Carolina Test Series of USFA Grant 79027 Field Test and Evaluation of Residential Sprinkler Systems," National Fire Protection Association, Boston, MA, September 1980 (This report was done for the NFPA 13D subcommittee and included a series of fire tests in actual mobile homes with sprinkler systems installed in accordance with the data resulting from prior test work and following criteria described in the 1980 edition of NFPA 13D in order to evaluate the effectiveness of the system under conditions approaching actual use.)

Explanatory Material

Annex A is not a part of the requirements of this NFPA document but is included for informational purposes only. This annex contains explanatory material, numbered to correspond with the applicable text paragraphs.

The material contained in Annex A of NFPA 13D is included within the text of this handbook and, therefore, is not repeated here.

Informational References

B.1 Referenced Publications

The following documents or portions thereof are referenced within this standard for informational purposes only and are thus not part of the requirements of this document unless also listed in Chapter 2.

B.1.1 NFPA Publications. National Fire Protection Association, 1 Batterymarch Park, P.O. Box 9101, Quincy, MA 02269-9101.

NFPA 13, *Standard for the Installation of Sprinkler Systems,* 2002 edition.

NFPA 13R, *Standard for the Installation of Sprinkler Systems in Residential Occupancies up to and Including Four Stories in Height,* 2002 edition.

NFPA 20, *Standard for the Installation of Stationary Pumps for Fire Protection,* 1999 edition.

NFPA 25, *Standard for the Inspection, Testing, and Maintenance of Water-Based Fire Protection Systems,* 1998 edition.

NFPA 72®, National Fire Alarm Code®, 2002 edition.

B.1.2 Other Publications.

B.1.2.1 ASTM Publications. American Society for Testing and Materials, 100 Barr Harbor Drive, West Conshohocken, PA 19428-2959.

ASTM D 3309, *Standard Specification for Polybutylene (PB) Plastic Hot- and Cold-Water Distribution Systems,* 1996.

ASTM F 437, *Standard Specification for Threaded Chlorinated Poly (Vinyl Chloride) (CPVC) Plastic Pipe Fittings, Schedule 80,* 1996.

ASTM F 438, *Standard Specification for Socket-Type Chlorinated Poly (Vinyl Chloride) (CPVC) Plastic Pipe Fittings, Schedule 40,* 1997.

ASTM F 439, *Standard Specification for Socket-Type Chlorinated Poly (Vinyl Chloride) (CPVC) Plastic Pipe Fittings, Schedule 80,* 1997.

ASTM F 442, *Standard Specification for Chlorinated Poly (Vinyl Chloride) (CPVC) Plastic Pipe (SDR-PR),* 1997.

ASTM SI 10, *Standard for Use of the International System of Units (SI): the Modernized Metric System,* 1997.

B.1.2.2 USFA Publication. U.S. Fire Administration, 16825 S. Seton Avenue, Emmitsburg, MD 21727.

Bill Jr., R. G., Kung, N. C., Brown, W. R., and Hill, E., "Effects of Cathedral and Beamed Ceiling Construction on Residential Sprinkler Performance," FMRC J.I. M3N5.RA(3). Prepared for U.S. Fire Administration, February 1988.

B.2 Informational References. (Reserved)

B.3 References for Extracts. (Reserved)

NFPA 13R,

Standard for the Installation of Sprinkler Systems in Residential Occupancies up to and Including Four Stories in Height,

2002 Edition, with Commentary

Part Three of this handbook includes the complete text and illustrations of the 2002 edition of NFPA 13R, *Standard for the Installation of Sprinkler Systems in Residential Occupancies up to and Including Four Stories in Height.* The text and illustrations from the standard are printed in black and are the official requirements of NFPA 13R. Line drawings and photographs from the standard are labeled "Figures."

Paragraphs that begin with the letter "A" are extracted from Annex A of the standard. Although printed in black ink, this nonmandatory material is purely explanatory in nature. For ease of use, this handbook places Annex A material immediately after the standard paragraph to which it refers.

In addition to the standard text and annexes, Part Three includes commentary that provides the history and other background information for specific paragraphs in the standard. This insightful commentary takes the reader behind the scenes, into the reasons underlying the requirements.

To make commentary material readily identifiable, commentary text, captions, and tables are printed in blue. Line drawings and photographs in the commentary are labeled "Exhibits."

CHAPTER 1

Administration

In 1989, the first edition of NFPA 13R, *Standard for the Installation of Sprinkler Systems in Residential Occupancies up to and Including Four Stories in Height,* was issued. Similar to NFPA 13D, *Standard for the Installation of Sprinkler Systems in One- and Two-Family Dwellings and Manufactured Homes,* NFPA 13R addressed cost-effective sprinkler protection with life safety as its primary goal and property protection as a secondary goal.

The development of NFPA 13D, along with continuing developments in residential sprinkler technology, sparked interest in expanding similar low-cost fire safety options to other types of low-rise residential occupancies such as apartments and condominiums. Many of the underlying fire safety objectives used to develop NFPA 13D were applied to these other larger residential occupancies. Fuel loading, basic room geometries, and subsequent fires in larger residential occupancies were observed to be similar to those anticipated in one- and two-family dwellings. Expanding public interest and the fact that some communities started developing their own installation standards for larger residential buildings made it clear that a national consensus standard such as NFPA 13R was needed.

The Technical Committee on Residential Sprinkler Systems intends that NFPA 13R provide an acceptable level of fire protection with respect to life safety and property protection. NFPA 13R provides a high, but not an absolute, level of life safety and a somewhat lesser degree of property protection. As with NFPA 13D systems, NFPA 13R permits the omission of sprinklers in certain areas of the building. A higher degree of life safety and property protection could be achieved by installing sprinklers throughout the premises in accordance with NFPA 13, *Standard for the Installation of Sprinkler Systems,* with residential sprinklers installed in the dwelling units. With sprinkler systems, life safety is generally more readily achievable than is property protection. In other words, a given system usually provides a higher degree of life safety than property protection. Where property protection is the primary objective, a stronger water supply and more complete sprinkler coverage among other factors as identified by NFPA 13 need to be considered for the type of hazard in question.

Although NFPA 13R differs from NFPA 13 in several areas, such as extent of sprinkler coverage and the mandatory use of residential sprinklers with certain exceptions, the documents have many similarities. Overall, NFPA 13R offers a cost advantage with respect to providing life safety in certain types of low-rise residential occupancies because the document was developed with this objective.

Various building codes have adopted NFPA 13R. However, certain restrictions could be imposed on buildings protected by NFPA 13R sprinkler systems with respect to height and area limitations, protection of attic spaces, and acceptable construction materials. Sprinkler coverage elimination in certain areas results in a reduced level of property protection. Property protection is a major function of building codes, so provisions in addition to those of NFPA 13R could be required.

NFPA 13R assumes that one or more smoke alarms are installed in accordance with *NFPA 72®, National Fire Alarm Code®.* Smoke alarms are a key component of a balanced fire protection system for residential occupancies. Alarms are intended to provide improved protection against smoldering fires and from fires that originate in areas not required to be protected by automatic sprinklers. Subsections 6.8.2 through 6.8.6 identify those areas not requiring sprinkler protection.

◀ FAQ
Does NFPA 13R assume the use of smoke alarms?

1.1* Scope

This standard shall cover the design and installation of automatic sprinkler systems for protection against fire hazards in residential occupancies up to and including four stories in height.

A.1.1 NFPA 13R is appropriate for use as an option to NFPA 13, *Standard for the Installation of Sprinkler Systems,* only in those residential occupancies, as defined in this standard, up to and including four stories in height. It is the intent of this standard that if NFPA 13R is appropriate for use, that it be used throughout the entire building. It is recognized that an occupancy incidental to the operations of the residential occupancy might exist within that residential occupancy. Such incidental occupancy would be considered part of the predominant (residential) occupancy and subject to the provisions of the predominant (residential) occupancy by 6.1.14.2 of NFPA *101®*, *Life Safety Code®*, and similar provisions in many local building and fire codes. Use of NFPA 13R throughout the entire building in this case is allowed.

Where buildings are greater than four stories in height, or where buildings are of mixed use where residential is not the predominant occupancy, residential portions of such buildings should be protected with residential or quick-response sprinklers in accordance with 8.4.5 of NFPA 13. Other portions of such buildings should be protected in accordance with NFPA 13. Where buildings of mixed use can be totally separated so that the residential portion is considered a separate building under the local code, NFPA 13R can be used in the residential portion, while NFPA 13 is used in the rest of the building.

The criteria in this standard are based on full-scale fire tests of rooms containing typical furnishings found in residential living rooms, kitchens, and bedrooms. The furnishings were arranged as typically found in dwelling units in a manner similar to that shown in Figure A.1.1(a), Figure A.1.1(b), and Figure A.1.1(c). Sixty full-scale fire tests were conducted in a two-story dwelling in Los Angeles, California, and 16 tests were conducted in a 14 ft (4.3 m)

FIGURE A.1.1(a) Bedroom.

FIGURE A.1.1(b) *Mobile Home Bedroom.*

FIGURE A.1.1(c) *Living Room.*

wide mobile home in Charlotte, North Carolina. Sprinkler systems designed and installed according to this standard are expected to prevent flashover within the compartment of origin where sprinklers are installed in the compartment. A sprinkler system designed and installed according to this standard cannot, however, be expected to completely control a fire involving fuel loads that are significantly higher than average for dwelling units [10 lb/ft^2 (49 kg/m^2)], configurations of fuels other than those with typical residential occupancies, or conditions where the interior finish has an unusually high flame spread rating (greater than 225).

To be effective, sprinkler systems installed in accordance with this standard need to open the sprinklers closest to the fire before the fire exceeds the ability of the sprinkler discharge to extinguish or control the fire. Conditions that allow the fire to grow beyond that point before sprinkler activation or that interfere with the quality of water distribution can produce conditions beyond the capabilities of the sprinkler system described in this standard. Unusually high ceilings or ceiling configurations that tend to divert the rising hot gases from sprinkler locations or change the sprinkler discharge pattern from its standard pattern can produce fire conditions that cannot be extinguished or controlled by the systems described in this standard.

 NFPA 13R is based in part on tests referenced in A.1.1. Those tests have demonstrated the ability of such residential systems to control fires that have growth rates similar to those involving residential furnishings. However, fire control depends on a sprinkler responding during the earliest stages of fire development. Curves indicating the energy release rates for different types of fires, including those using residential furnishings as the fuel package, are shown in Exhibit 1.1 [Nelson 1987]. The solid-line curves indicate a common means of categorizing the available heat release data. (See *NFPA 72* for additional information.)

FAQ ▶

Does NFPA 13R define the height of a story or the total height of a building?

NFPA 13R does not define the height of a story for use in determining overall building height. The building height is anticipated to be determined in accordance with the applicable building code (e.g., *NFPA 5000™, Building Construction and Safety Code™*) or NFPA *101®, Life Safety Code®*, each of which have their own method for determining building and story heights.

EXHIBIT 1.1 *Energy Release Time Curve.*

For SI units, 1 ft = 0.30 m.

As noted in 3.3.6, the use of the term *residential occupancies* for purposes of applying NFPA 13R differs from *residential occupancies* as defined in NFPA *101*. The NFPA 13R definition of *residential occupancies* is consistent with NFPA *101* except that three categories of board and care occupancies and one- and two-family dwellings are excluded.

The categories of board and care facilities are excluded due to a concern for overall building evacuation time and the fact that evacuation time in accordance with Chapters 32 and 33 of the 2000 edition of NFPA *101* is based on occupants reaching a point of safety that is not necessarily outside of the building. Because sprinklers are not required throughout the premises, NFPA 13R may not provide adequate protection for occupants who require an extended period of time to evacuate or who need to be protected in place. Based on the definitions in NFPA *101,* occupants who fall into the "slow" and the "impractical" evacuation capability are included. In general, this population group is not capable of self-preservation and must either be defended in place or must be assisted from the building. Because NFPA 13R allows the omission of sprinklers in certain areas, it is not well suited for those types of residential occupancies that contain population groups who are not readily capable of self-preservation.

One- and two-family dwellings are exempted from NFPA 13R because they are specifically addressed by NFPA 13D.

◀ FAQ
Are the definitions and use of the term *residential occupancies* **different between NFPA 13R and NFPA** *101*?

◀ FAQ
Are one- and two-family dwellings excluded from NFPA 13R?

1.2* Purpose

The purpose of this standard shall be to provide design and installation requirements for a sprinkler system to aid in the detection and control of fires in residential occupancies and thus provide improved protection against injury, life loss, and property damage. A sprinkler system designed and installed in accordance with this standard shall be expected to prevent flashover (total involvement) in the room of fire origin, where sprinklered, and to improve the chance for occupants to escape or be evacuated.

A.1.2 Various levels of sprinkler protection are available to provide life safety and property protection. This standard is designed to provide a high, but not absolute, level of life safety and a lesser level of property protection. Greater protection to both life and property could be achieved by sprinklering all areas in accordance with NFPA 13, *Standard for the Installation of Sprinkler Systems,* which permits the use of residential sprinklers in residential areas.

This standard recommends, but does not require, sprinklering of all areas in the building; it permits sprinklers to be omitted in certain areas. These areas have been proved by NFPA statistics to be those where the incidence of life loss from fires in residential occupancies is low. Such an approach provides a reasonable degree of fire safety. (*See Table A.1.2 for deaths and injuries in multifamily residential buildings.*)

It should be recognized that the omission of sprinklers from certain areas could result in the development of untenable conditions in adjacent spaces. Where evacuation times could be delayed, additional sprinkler protection and other fire protection features, such as detection and compartmentation, could be necessary.

The purpose of NFPA 13R is stated in Section 1.2. Both Underwriters Laboratories Inc. and FM Global have developed test standards for the evaluation of residential sprinklers. These standards have significantly different test parameters than those that apply to nonresidential sprinklers such as the standard spray sprinkler. The criteria used in UL 1626, *Residential Sprinklers for Fire-Protection Service,* for residential sprinklers during a fire test are as follows:

1. The maximum gas or air temperature adjacent to the sprinkler—3 in. (76.2 mm) below the ceiling and 8 in. (203 mm) horizontally away from the sprinkler—must not exceed 600°F (316°C).

TABLE A.1.2 *Fires and Associated Deaths and Injuries in Apartments by Area of Origin; Annual Average of 1986–1990 Structure Fires Reported to U.S. Fire Departments*

Area of Origin	Civilian Deaths	Civilian Percent	Fires	Percent	Injuries	Percent
Bedroom	309	33.9	17,960	15.8	1,714	27.2
Living room, family room, or den	308	33.8	10,500	9.3	1,272	20.2
Kitchen	114	12.5	46,900	41.4	1,973	31.2
Interior stairway	29	3.2	1,040	0.9	91	1.4
Hallway or corridor	23	2.6	3,130	2.8	165	2.6
Exterior balcony or open porch	17	1.8	1,880	1.7	69	1.1
Dining room	10	1.1	800	0.7	69	1.1
Closet	9	1.0	2,120	1.9	116	1.8
Multiple areas	9	1.0	780	0.7	38	0.6
Tool room or other supply storage room or area	8	0.9	1,250	1.1	53	0.8
Unclassified area	8	0.9	480	0.4	29	0.5
Exterior stairway	8	0.8	870	0.8	22	0.4
Bathroom	7	0.7	2,510	2.2	101	1.6
Heating equipment room or area	6	0.6	2,510	2.2	75	1.2
Exterior wall surface	5	0.5	2,150	1.9	26	0.4
Laundry room or area	4	0.4	3,380	3.0	89	1.4
Crawl space or substructure space	4	0.4	1,490	1.3	62	1.0
Wall assembly or concealed space	3	0.4	1,020	0.9	21	0.3
Attic or ceiling/roof assembly or concealed space	3	0.3	1,100	1.0	18	0.3
Ceiling/floor assembly or concealed space	3	0.3	560	0.5	18	0.3
Garage or carport*	3	0.3	1,290	1.1	36	0.6
Lobby or entrance way	3	0.3	670	0.6	31	0.5
Unclassified structural area	3	0.3	520	0.5	32	0.5
Unclassified storage area	3	0.3	430	0.4	22	0.3
Unclassified function area	3	0.3	250	0.2	13	0.2
Laboratory	2	0.3	80	0.1	3	0.0
Elevator or dumbwaiter	1	0.2	220	0.2	4	0.1
Sales or showroom area	1	0.2	110	0.1	3	0.1
Exterior roof surface	1	0.1	1,040	0.9	15	0.2
Unclassified means of egress	1	0.1	180	0.2	6	0.1
Office	1	0.1	120	0.1	4	0.1
Chimney	1	0.1	980	0.9	2	0.0
Personal service area	1	0.1	40	0.0	4	0.1
Library	1	0.1	10	0.0	0	0.0
Other known area	2	0.2	5,000	4.4	115	1.8
Total	912	100.0	113,390	100.0	6,313	100.0

Note: Fires are estimated to the nearest 10; civilian deaths and injuries are estimated to the nearest 1.

*Does not include dwelling garages coded as a separate property.

(Source: 1986–1990 NFIRS and NFPA survey.)

2. The maximum temperature—5 ft, 3 in. (1.6 m) above the floor and half the room length away from each wall—must be less than 200°F (93°C) during the entire test. This temperature must not exceed 130°F (54°C) for more than a 2-minute period.
3. The maximum temperature ¼ in. (6.3 mm) behind the finished surface of the ceiling material directly above the test fire must not exceed 500°F (260°C).
4. No more than two residential sprinklers in the test enclosure can operate.

EXHIBIT 1.2 Simulated Fuel Package for UL 1626. (Courtesy of Underwriters Laboratories Inc.)

The UL 1626 fuel package and test procedure was recently revised to (1) enhance the reproducibility of the tests and (2) increase the similarity between the fire performance of the fuel package used in the standard tests and that of the fuel packages used as part of the principle residential sprinkler research effort.

The details of the UL 1626 simulated furniture are shown in Exhibit 1.2. The fuel package is composed of several different components: a wood crib, two simulated sofa ends covered with foam, two sheets of ¼ in. (6.3 mm) Douglas fir plywood, a pan with heptane, and two heptane-soaked cotton wicks. The arrangement of the fuel package within the test room is shown at the upper left of the exhibit.

The three fire test configurations are shown in Exhibits 1.3 through 1.5. Exhibit 1.3 shows the configuration used to test pendent, upright, flush, recessed pendent, and concealed sprinklers. Exhibits 1.4 and 1.5 present the configurations used to test sidewall sprinklers; in the first case the sprinklers are located opposite the fuel package and in the second case the sprinklers are located on the same wall as the fuel package.

EXHIBIT 1.3 *Fire Test Arrangement for UL 1626 for Pendent, Upright, Flush, Recessed Pendent, and Concealed Sprinklers.*

These criteria are the same as those discussed in Chapter 1 of NFPA 13D concerning the testing and listing of residential sprinklers.

The intent of the preceding criteria is to show the following:

1. Flashover does not occur.
2. The environment through which occupants must evacuate is tenable.
3. Items (1) and (2) of this list can be accomplished with a limited water supply.
4. Proper wall-wetting characteristics occur.

The concept of levels of protection as identified in A.1.2 was developed so that low-cost sprinkler systems would become a viable and attractive option for certain types of residential facilities and so that installing dry pipe sprinkler systems in cold climates would not be a necessity. The areas where sprinkler omission is permitted in accordance with 6.8.2 through 6.8.6 of NFPA 13R are those where statistical analysis supports such omission. (See Table A.1.2.)

The Technical Committee on Residential Sprinkler Systems believes that dry pipe systems are not as effective as wet systems for life safety because of the associated delay in the sprinkler discharge application. (This delay was noted in early FM Global tests and substantiated in the fire tests done in Los Angeles and Charlotte, NC [Cote 1980, Cote 1982, Kung 1982,

◄ **FAQ**
Why are dry systems prohibited from protecting inside the dwelling unit?

EXHIBIT 1.5 *Fire Test Arrangement from UL 1626 for Sidewall Sprinklers, Test Arrangement 2.*

Moore 1980].) The key to achieving control of the residential fire is the rapid application of water. Residential systems also must be relatively simple systems and easy to maintain. These features are not characteristic of dry pipe systems.

Table A.1.2 contains data on life safety and not necessarily property protection. Reductions in building code criteria related to property protection need to be evaluated when the sprinkler system is installed in accordance with NFPA 13R. Areas of sprinkler omission would be of particular interest. Although fires that occur in nonsprinklered areas might not necessarily result in fatalities, such fires could result in serious property damage. (See 6.8.2 through 6.8.6 for areas not requiring sprinkler protection.)

1.3 Retroactivity

The provisions of this standard reflect a consensus of what is necessary to provide an acceptable degree of protection from the hazards addressed in this standard at the time the standard was issued. Unless otherwise specified, the provisions of this standard shall not apply to facilities, equipment, structures, or installations that existed or were approved for construction or installation prior to the effective date of the standard. Where specified, the provisions of this standard shall be retroactive. In those cases where the authority having jurisdiction determines that the existing situation presents an unacceptable degree of risk, the authority having jurisdiction shall be permitted to apply retroactively any portions of this standard deemed appropriate. The retroactive requirements of this standard shall be permitted to be modified if their application clearly would be impractical in the judgment of the authority having jurisdiction, and only where it is clearly evident that a reasonable degree of safety is provided.

1.4 Equivalency

Nothing in this standard is intended to restrict new technologies or alternative arrangements, provided that the level of safety prescribed by the standard is not reduced.

1.5 Units

1.5.1* Metric units of measurement in this standard shall be in accordance with the modernized metric system known as the International System of Units (SI).

A.1.5.1 For additional conversions and information, see ASTM SI 10, *Standard for Use of the International System of Units (SI): the Modern Metric System.*

1.5.2 The liter and bar units shall be permitted to be used in this standard.

1.5.3 The conversion factors for liter, pascal, and bar shall be in accordance with Table 1.5.3.

TABLE 1.5.3 *Metric Conversions*

Name of Unit	Unit Symbol	Conversion Factor
liter	L	1 gal = 3.785 L
pascal	Pa	1 psi = 6894.757 Pa
bar	bar	1 psi = 0.0689 bar
bar	bar	1 bar = 10^5 Pa

1.5.4* Where a value for measurement as specified in this standard is followed by an equivalent value in other units, the first stated value shall be regarded as the requirement.

A.1.5.4 A given equivalent value is considered to be approximate.

The International System of Units (SI) is typically rounded off to the nearest whole number (see 1.5.4).

1.5.5 The equivalent value for a measurement in SI shall be converted by multiplying the value by the conversion factor and then rounding the result to the appropriate number of significant digits.

REFERENCES CITED IN COMMENTARY

National Fire Protection Association, 1 Batterymarch Park, P.O. Box 9101, Quincy, MA 02269-9101

NFPA 13, *Standard for the Installation of Sprinkler Systems,* 2002 edition
NFPA 13D, *Standard for the Installation of Sprinkler Systems in One- and Two-Family Dwellings and Manufactured Homes,* 2002 edition
NFPA 72®, National Fire Alarm Code®, 2002 edition
NFPA *101®, Life Safety Code®,* 2000 edition
NFPA 5000™, Building Construction and Safety Code™, 2003 edition

Underwriters Laboratories Inc., 333 Pfingsten Road, Northbrook, IL 60062

UL 1624, *Residential Sprinklers for Fire-Protection Service,* 1994

Cote, A. E., "Final Report on Field Test and Evaluation of Residential Sprinkler Systems," National Fire Protection Association, Quincy, MA, July 1982
Cote, A. E., and Moore, D., "Field Test and Evaluation of Residential Sprinkler Systems, Los Angeles Test Series," National Fire Protection Association, Boston, MA, April 1980
Factory Mutual Research Corporation, "Approval Standard—Residential Automatic Sprinklers, Class No. 2030," Norwood, MA, September 1983
Kung, H. C., Spaulding, R. D., Hill, E. E., Jr., and Symonds, A. P., "Technical Report, Field Evaluation of Residential Prototype Sprinkler, Los Angeles Fire Test Program," Factory Mutual Research Corporation, Norwood, MA, February 1982
Moore, D., "Data Summary of the North Carolina Test Series of USFA Grant 79027 Field Test and Evaluation of Residential Sprinkler Systems," National Fire Protection Association, Boston, MA, September 1980
Nelson, H. E., "An Engineering Analysis of the Early Stages of Fire Development—The Fire at the Dupont Plaza Hotel and Casino Dec. 31, 1986," National Bureau of Standards, Gaithersburg, MD, 1987
Underwriters Laboratories Inc., Proposed First Edition of the Standard for Residential Sprinklers for Fire Protection Service, UL 1626, Northbrook, IL, April 1986

CHAPTER 2

Referenced Publications

2.1 General

The documents or portions thereof listed in this chapter are referenced within this standard and shall be considered part of the requirements of this document.

2.2 NFPA Publications

National Fire Protection Association, 1 Batterymarch Park, P.O. Box 9101, Quincy, MA 02269-9101.

NFPA 13, *Standard for the Installation of Sprinkler Systems,* 2002 edition.

NFPA 20, *Standard for the Installation of Stationary Pumps for Fire Protection,* 1999 edition.

NFPA 22, *Standard for Water Tanks for Private Fire Protection,* 1998 edition.

NFPA 25, *Standard for the Inspection, Testing, and Maintenance of Water-Based Fire Protection Systems,* 1998 edition.

NFPA *101*®, *Life Safety Code*®, 2000 edition.

NFPA 220, *Standard on Types of Building Construction,* 1999 edition.

NFPA 251, *Standard Methods of Tests of Fire Endurance of Building Construction and Materials,* 1999 edition.

2.3 Other Publications

2.3.1 ANSI Publication. American National Standards Institute, Inc., 11 West 42nd Street, 13th floor, New York, NY 10036.

ANSI B36.10M, *Welded and Seamless Wrought Steel Pipe,* 1996.

2.3.2 ASME Publications. American Society of Mechanical Engineers, Three Park Avenue, New York, NY 10016-5990.

ASME B16.1, *Cast Iron Pipe Flanges and Flanged Fittings,* 1989.

ASME B16.3, *Malleable Iron Threaded Fittings,* 1992.

ASME B16.4, *Gray Iron Threaded Fittings,* 1992.

ASME B16.5, *Pipe Flanges and Flanged Fittings,* 1996.

ASME B16.9, *Factory-Made Wrought Steel Buttwelding Fittings,* 1993.

ASME B16.11, *Forged Fittings, Socket-Welding and Threaded,* 1996.

ASME B16.18, *Cast Copper Alloy Solder Joint Pressure Fittings,* 1984.

ASME B16.22, *Wrought Copper and Copper Alloy Solder Joint Pressure Fittings,* 1995.

ASME B16.25, *Buttwelding Ends,* 1997.

2.3.3 ASTM Publications. American Society for Testing and Materials, 100 Barr Harbor Drive, West Conshohocken, PA 19428-2959.

ASTM A 53, *Standard Specification for Pipe, Steel, Black and Hot-Dipped, Zinc-Coated, Welded and Seamless,* 1998.

ASTM A 135, *Standard Specification for Electric-Resistance-Welded Steel Pipe,* 1997.

ASTM A 234, *Standard Specification for Piping Fittings of Wrought Carbon Steel and Alloy Steel for Moderate and Elevated Temperatures,* 1997.

ASTM A 795, *Standard Specification for Black and Hot-Dipped Zinc-Coated (Galvanized) Welded and Seamless Steel Pipe for Fire Protection Use,* 1997.

ASTM B 32, *Standard Specification for Solder Metal,* 1996.

ASTM B 88, *Standard Specification for Seamless Copper Water Tube,* 1996.

ASTM B 251, *Standard Specification for General Requirements for Wrought Seamless Copper and Copper-Alloy Tube,* 1997.

ASTM B 813, *Standard Specification for Liquid and Paste Fluxes for Soldering Applications of Copper and Copper-Alloy Tube,* 1993.

ASTM D 3309, *Standard Specification for Polybutylene (PB) Plastic Hot- and Cold-Water Distribution Systems,* 1996.

ASTM F 437, *Standard Specification for Threaded Chlorinated Poly (Vinyl Chloride) (CPVC) Plastic Pipe Fittings, Schedule 80,* 1996.

ASTM F 438, *Standard Specification for Socket-Type Chlorinated Poly (Vinyl Chloride) (CPVC) Plastic Pipe Fittings, Schedule 40,* 1997.

ASTM F 439, *Standard Specification for Socket-Type Chlorinated Poly (Vinyl Chloride) (CPVC) Plastic Pipe Fittings, Schedule 80,* 1997.

ASTM F 442, *Standard Specification for Chlorinated Poly (Vinyl Chloride) (CPVC) Plastic Pipe (SDR-PR),* 1997.

2.3.4 AWS Publication. American Welding Society, 550 N.W. LeJeune Road, Miami, FL 33126.

AWS A5.8, *Specification for Filler Metals for Brazing and Braze Welding,* 1992.

CHAPTER 3

Definitions

3.1 General

The definitions contained in this chapter shall apply to the terms used in this standard. Where terms are not included, common usage of the terms shall apply.

3.2 NFPA Official Definitions

3.2.1* Approved. Acceptable to the authority having jurisdiction.

A.3.2.1 Approved. The National Fire Protection Association does not approve, inspect, or certify any installations, procedures, equipment, or materials; nor does it approve or evaluate testing laboratories. In determining the acceptability of installations, procedures, equipment, or materials, the authority having jurisdiction may base acceptance on compliance with NFPA or other appropriate standards. In the absence of such standards, said authority may require evidence of proper installation, procedure, or use. The authority having jurisdiction may also refer to the listings or labeling practices of an organization that is concerned with product evaluations and is thus in a position to determine compliance with appropriate standards for the current production of listed items.

A common error is the assumption that the term *approved,* which is defined in 3.2.1, has the same meaning as the terms *listed,* which is defined in 3.2.4, or *labeled,* which is defined in 3.2.3. For NFPA 13R's purposes, approved means "that which is acceptable to the authority having jurisdiction." Although the authority having jurisdiction can use a listing or label to assist in approving an item, it should not be assumed that all approvals are based on a listing procedure. Some testing agencies use the terms *approved* or *approval* as their designation that a product is listed.

Paragraph 5.1.2 requires that only listed or approved devices and materials as indicated by NFPA 13R be used in sprinkler systems. Other sections require that specific components—for example, residential sprinklers and nonmetallic sprinkler pipe—be listed.

3.2.2* Authority Having Jurisdiction (AHJ). The organization, office, or individual responsible for approving equipment, materials, an installation, or a procedure.

A.3.2.2 Authority Having Jurisdiction (AHJ). The phrase "authority having jurisdiction," or its acronym AHJ, is used in NFPA documents in a broad manner, since jurisdictions and approval agencies vary, as do their responsibilities. Where public safety is primary, the authority having jurisdiction may be a federal, state, local, or other regional department or individual such as a fire chief; fire marshal; chief of a fire prevention bureau, labor department, or health department; building official; electrical inspector; or others having statutory authority. For insurance purposes, an insurance inspection department, rating bureau, or other insurance company representative may be the authority having jurisdiction. In many circumstances, the

◀ FAQ
What is the difference between Listed and Approved?

property owner or his or her designated agent assumes the role of the authority having jurisdiction; at government installations, the commanding officer or departmental official may be the authority having jurisdiction.

In the simplest terms, the authority having jurisdiction is the person or office enforcing the standard. The term *authority having jurisdiction,* which is defined in 3.2.2, is commonly associated with the fire marshal or building official. However, the authority having jurisdiction can also be a contract officer, design engineer, insurance company representative, facility owner, or other agency representative responsible for verifying that the standard's requirements are achieved.

3.2.3 Labeled. Equipment or materials to which has been attached a label, symbol, or other identifying mark of an organization that is acceptable to the authority having jurisdiction and concerned with product evaluation, that maintains periodic inspection of production of labeled equipment or materials, and by whose labeling the manufacturer indicates compliance with appropriate standards or performance in a specified manner.

3.2.4* Listed. Equipment, materials, or services included in a list published by an organization that is acceptable to the authority having jurisdiction and concerned with evaluation of products or services, that maintains periodic inspection of production of listed equipment or materials or periodic evaluation of services, and whose listing states that either the equipment, material, or service meets appropriate designated standards or has been tested and found suitable for a specified purpose.

A.3.2.4 Listed. The means for identifying listed equipment may vary for each organization concerned with product evaluation; some organizations do not recognize equipment as listed unless it is also labeled. The authority having jurisdiction should utilize the system employed by the listing organization to identify a listed product.

One prominent testing inspection agency laboratory uses the designation *classified* for pipe. Material with this designation meets the intent of the definition of *listed,* which is defined in 3.2.4. (Also see the commentary following the definition of *approved.*) Equipment critical to the system's proper performance and operation is typically listed. One such component is the sprinkler. Unless the component is evaluated for its performance under fire conditions and the quality control aspects of the manufacturing process can be assured, the device's level of reliability and expected performance cannot be affirmed.

3.2.5 Shall. Indicates a mandatory requirement.

3.2.6 Should. Indicates a recommendation or that which is advised but not required.

3.2.7 Standard. A document, the main text of which contains only mandatory provisions using the word "shall" to indicate requirements and which is in a form generally suitable for mandatory reference by another standard or code or for adoption into law. Nonmandatory provisions shall be located in an appendix or annex, footnote, or fine-print note and are not to be considered a part of the requirements of a standard.

3.3 General Definitions

 3.3.1* Bathroom. Within a dwelling unit, any room or compartment containing a lavatory dedicated to personal hygiene, or a water closet, or bathing capability such as a shower or tub, or any combination of facilities thereof.

 A.3.3.1 Bathroom. A room is still considered a bathroom if it contains just a toilet. Additionally, two bathrooms can be adjacent to each other and are considered separate rooms provided they are enclosed with the required level of construction.

3.3.2 Compartment. See Section 4.1.

3.3.3 Design Discharge. The rate of water discharged by an automatic sprinkler, expressed in gpm (mm/min).

The term *design discharge,* which is defined in 3.3.3, is used in the design approach for residential sprinklers. Although some sprinkler designs are based on their ability to achieve a certain density, residential sprinklers are listed to achieve a certain minimum flow rate. See 6.7.1.1 for more information on design discharge.

3.3.4 Dwelling Unit. One or more rooms, arranged for the use of one or more individuals living together, as in a single housekeeping unit, that normally have cooking, living, sanitary, and sleeping facilities.

For the purposes of NFPA 13R, a *dwelling unit,* which is defined in 3.3.4, includes hotel and motel rooms and suites, dormitory rooms, apartments, condominiums, sleeping rooms and most common areas in board and care facilities, and similar living units. In general, a dwelling unit consists of any part of a structure that is normally occupied and has fuel loading that is indicative of a residential environment. A dwelling unit also includes the corridor that leads to the guest rooms in a hotel- or motel-type facility.

◄ **FAQ**
What does NFPA 13R define as a dwelling unit?

3.3.5 Multipurpose Piping System. A piping system within a residential occupancy intended to serve both domestic and fire protection needs.

3.3.6 Residential Occupancies. Occupancies, as specified in the scope of this standard, that include the following, as defined in NFPA *101®*, *Life Safety Code®*: (1) Apartment buildings, (2) Lodging and rooming houses, (3) Board and care facilities (prompt and slow evacuation type), and (4) Hotels, motels, and dormitories.

For purposes of applying NFPA 13R, the definition of *residential occupancies,* which is contained in 3.3.6, differs from the definition used in NFPA *101®*, *Life Safety Code®*. Specifically, the definition in NFPA 13R does not include the following occupancies, which are considered residential occupancies by NFPA *101*:

◄ **FAQ**
What is meant by the definition of residential occupancies in NFPA 13R?

1. One- and two-family dwellings, including manufactured homes
2. Small board and care facilities, which have sleeping accommodations for not more than 16 residents, with impractical evacuation capability
3. Large board and care facilities with slow evacuation capability
4. Large board and care facilities with impractical evacuation capability

The commentary to Section 1.1 provides more information on the differences between the occupancies.

3.3.7 Sprinkler.

3.3.7.1 Automatic Sprinkler. A fire suppression or control device that operates automatically when its heat-actuated element is heated to its thermal rating or above, allowing water to discharge over a specific area.

Depending on the type used, automatic sprinklers, which are defined in 3.3.7.1, are intended to achieve fire control or fire suppression. Additionally, automatic sprinklers can be used for property protection or life safety, or both. Residential sprinklers are specifically listed as such and are intended to achieve life safety as their primary objective. NFPA 13 provides more information on the different types and styles of automatic sprinklers.

3.3.7.2 Residential Sprinkler. A type of fast-response sprinkler that meets the criteria of NFPA 13, *Standard for the Installation of Sprinkler Systems,* that has been specifically investigated for its ability to enhance survivability in the room of fire origin and is listed for use in the protection of dwelling units.

Residential sprinklers, which are defined in 3.3.7.2, are specifically listed by Underwriters Laboratories and FM Global for residential service and have been tested for compliance with NFPA

13D. Their primary purpose is to achieve life safety in residential occupancies. Residential sprinklers contain fast-response operating elements and can be an upright, pendent, or sidewall configuration, but no upright devices are available at this time. The discussion on sprinkler sensitivity in the commentary to 3.6.1 of NFPA 13 provides additional information on sprinklers with fast-response operating elements.

 3.3.8 Sprinkler System. For fire protection purposes, an integrated system of underground and overhead piping designed in accordance with fire protection engineering standards. The installation includes one or more automatic water supplies. The portion of the sprinkler system aboveground is a network of specially sized or hydraulically designed piping installed in a building, structure, or area, generally overhead, and to which sprinklers are attached in a systematic pattern. The valve controlling each system riser is located in the system riser or its supply piping. Each sprinkler system riser includes a device for actuating an alarm when the system is in operation. The system is usually activated by heat from a fire and discharges water over the fire area.

The definition of *sprinkler system,* which is contained in 3.3.8, addresses water supplies and underground piping. When tanks, pumps, and underground piping installation and design requirements covered by standards other than NFPA 13 are used in connection with overhead sprinkler piping, they become an integral part of the sprinkler system. Because these components are considered critical to system performance, they are treated as part of the system.

 3.3.8.1 Dry Pipe Sprinkler System. A sprinkler system employing automatic sprinklers that are attached to a piping system that contains air or nitrogen under pressure, the release of which (as from the opening of a sprinkler) permits the water pressure to open a valve known as a dry pipe valve, and the water then flows into the piping system and out the opened sprinkler.

FAQ ▶
Why are dry systems prohibited from protecting inside the dwelling unit?

Dry pipe sprinkler system is defined in 3.3.8.1. Because of the concern for delayed water delivery and the fact that no residential sprinklers are listed for dry system application, dry systems are not allowed for protection inside the dwelling unit. However, dry systems are permitted to be installed in areas outside the dwelling unit. See 6.7.2 with regard to the design criteria for areas outside the dwelling unit.

 3.3.8.2 Preaction Sprinkler System. A sprinkler system employing automatic sprinklers that are attached to a piping system containing air that might or might not be under pressure, with a supplemental detection system installed in the same areas as the sprinklers.

 3.3.8.3 Wet Pipe Sprinkler System. A sprinkler system employing automatic sprinklers attached to a piping system containing water and connected to a water supply so that water discharges immediately from sprinklers opened by heat from a fire.

3.3.9 System Working Pressure. The maximum anticipated static (nonflowing) or flowing pressure applied to sprinkler system components exclusive of surge pressures.

The definition of *system working pressure,* which is contained in 3.3.9, was added to the 1999 edition to clearly indicate that this pressure pertains to the installed system. Maximum static pressure could be the result of surge pressures held in a system by a check valve or back flow preventer.

  3.3.10 Thermal Barrier. A material that limits the average temperature rise of an unexposed surface to not more than 250°F (121°C) for a specified fire exposure complying with the standard time–temperature curve of NFPA 251, *Standard Methods of Tests of Fire Endurance of Building Construction and Materials.*

Construction materials that provide a 15-minute thermal barrier, which is defined in 3.3.10, must be used in bathrooms if sprinkler protection is not provided. (See 6.8.2 through 6.8.6.) The primary method of determining whether a material qualifies is to check the assembly's finish rating. This information can usually be found in fire resistance directories that are published by listing organizations.

3.3.11 Valve.

3.3.11.1 Check Valve. A valve that allows flow in one direction only.

3.3.11.2 Control Valve. An indicating valve employed to control (shut) a supply of water to a sprinkler system.

Control valve is defined in 3.3.11.2. The control valve used should be an indicating type—that is, one that has some external means to indicate that the valve is in the open position.

3.3.12 Waterflow Alarm. A sounding device activated by a waterflow detector or alarm check valve.

3.3.13 Waterflow Detector. An electric signaling indicator or alarm check valve actuated by waterflow in one direction only.

REFERENCES CITED IN COMMENTARY

National Fire Protection Association, 1 Batterymarch Park, P.O. Box 9101, Quincy, MA 02269-9101

NFPA *101®*, *Life Safety Code®*, 2000 edition

Factory Mutual Research Corporation, "Approval Standard—Residential Automatic Sprinklers, Class No. 2030," Norwood, MA, September 1983
Underwriters Laboratories Inc., Proposed First Edition of the Standard for Residential Sprinklers for Fire Protection Service, UL 1626, Northbrook, IL, April 1986

CHAPTER 4

General Requirements

4.1 Compartments

4.1.1 A compartment, for the purposes of this standard, shall be a space that is completely enclosed by walls and a ceiling.

4.1.2 A compartment enclosure shall be permitted to have openings in walls, provided the openings have a minimum lintel depth of 8 in. (203 mm) from the ceiling.

A room compartment, which is addressed in 4.1.2, is defined by the enclosing walls or a soffit or lintel that forms a definite barrier at the ceiling of a room opening. [See Figures A.6.7.1.2(a) and A.6.7.1.2(b).] In open-plan configurations, compartment boundaries can be determined by soffits or lintels over doorways as well as by walls or partitions. The 8-in. (203-mm) minimum depth ensures that heat will collect in the room of fire origin and activate the sprinklers over the fire rather than allowing sprinklers outside the room to activate.

It is not the intent of NFPA 13R that the number of sprinklers limits the size of a compartment—that is, a compartment can have more than four sprinklers installed in it. The size of the compartment or the number of sprinklers allowed in that compartment is not limited.

◄ **FAQ**
How is a room compartment defined?

◄ **FAQ**
Is it the intent of NFPA 13R that the number of sprinklers limits the maximum size of a compartment?

4.2 Tube

Wherever the word pipe is used in this standard, it shall also mean tube.

For the purposes of NFPA 13R, the term *pipe,* which is specified in Section 4.2, refers to any conduit for transporting water.

CHAPTER 5

System Components

5.1 General

5.1.1 Only new sprinklers shall be installed in sprinkler systems.

The sprinkler must operate properly and effectively when a fire occurs. It should not leak, rupture, or operate for any reason other than in response to a fire. For these performance reasons and because of sprinklers' relatively low cost, new sprinklers are required by 5.1.1. Additionally, the performance of used sprinklers is not easily verified, and their reliability can be questioned. The installation of new, listed residential sprinklers provides a higher degree of reliability.

5.1.2 Only listed or approved devices and materials as specified in this standard shall be used in sprinkler systems.

Any device critical to system operation or performance must be listed, as required by 5.1.2. Any device that does not directly affect system performance only needs to be approved. For example, the sprinkler must be listed because it is a critical device that initiates system operation. A drain valve only needs to be approved because it is not critical to system operation during a fire.

5.1.3 Sprinkler system components shall be rated for a working pressure of not less than 175 psi (12.1 bar).

Many sprinklers are currently rated for a working pressure of 175 psi (12.1 bar). Paragraph 5.1.3 allows for the event that higher pressure–rated sprinklers need to be used due to high system working pressures. Where the system working pressures are expected to be greater than 175 psi (12.1 bar), high-pressure components need to be used.

5.2 Piping

5.2.1* Pipe or tube used in sprinkler systems shall be of the materials specified in Table 5.2.1 or in accordance with 5.2.2.

NFPA 13R recognizes the use of nonmetallic piping products (see 5.2.1). As with ferrous materials and copper products, nonmetallic pipe standards exist and are used as the basis for the manufacture and production of polybutylene (PB) and chlorinated polyvinyl chloride (CPVC) pipe. Subsection 5.2.1 sets performance criteria for the piping products that are currently allowed in NFPA 13R systems. Pipe materials must conform to specific industry standards, and the materials must be capable of withstanding a working pressure of 175 psi (12.1 bar). These criteria apply to most ferrous, copper, PB, and CPVC pipe.

◀ **FAQ**
Are nonmetallic piping products permitted by NFPA 13R?

TABLE 5.2.1 *Pipe or Tube Materials and Dimensions*

Materials and Dimensions	Standard
Specification for Black and Hot-Dipped Zinc-Coated (Galvanized) Welded and Seamless Steel Pipe for Fire Protection Use	ASTM A 795
Specification for Welded and Seamless Pipe	ASTM A 53
Wrought Steel Pipe	ANSI B36.10M
Specification for Electric-Resistance-Welded Steel Pipe	ASTM A 135
Specification for Seamless Copper Water Tube [Copper Tube (Drawn, Seamless)]	ASTM B 88
Specification for General Requirements for Wrought Steamless Copper and Copper-Alloy Tube	ASTM B 251
Fluxes for Soldering Applications of Copper and Copper-Alloy Tube	ASTM B 813
Specification for Filler Metals for Brazing and Braze Welding (Classification BCuP-3 or BCuP-4)	AWS A5.8
Specification for Solder Metal [95-5 (Tin-Antimony-Grade 95TA)]	ASTM B 32

A.5.2.1 This standard anticipates that the water supply for the system is in compliance with the governing plumbing code for the jurisdiction. It is intended that any pipe material or diameter permitted for multiple family dwellings in the plumbing code and satisfying the hydraulic criteria of NFPA 13R is considered to be in compliance.

FAQ ▶
Does NFPA 13R require that the underground supply meet the requirements of NFPA 24?

NFPA 13R permits the underground supply pipe to conform to local plumbing code requirements (see A.5.2.1). Provided the pipe is sized to accommodate system flow rates and conforms to all local requirements, it is acceptable by NFPA 13R.

5.2.1.1 The chemical properties, physical properties, and dimensions of pipe materials shall be at least equivalent to the standards cited in Table 5.2.1.

5.2.1.2 Pipe shall be designed to withstand a working pressure of not less than 175 psi (12.1 bar).

5.2.1.3 When nonmetallic pipe is used, the pipe shall be designed to withstand a working pressure of not less than 175 psi (12.1 bar) at 120°F (49°C).

5.2.2 Types of pipe other than those specified in Table 5.2.1 shall be permitted to be used where listed for sprinkler system use.

NFPA 13R does not prohibit the use of any material, as long as it is listed for use in sprinkler systems. Subsection 5.2.2 is intended to encourage development of more effective materials in terms of either their function or cost.

Because alternative materials are available and used extensively, reference to such pipe or tube is included to aid the design professional, the installing contractor, and the authority having jurisdiction. Prior to installation, it must be verified that specially listed piping material is permitted to be used. Additionally, restrictions on its use and any special installation procedures must be identified.

FAQ ▶
What types of synthetic piping materials are applicable for NFPA 13R applications?

At present the only two synthetic piping materials that are listed for use in sprinkler systems are CPVC and PB.

Additionally, specially listed metallic pipe such as thin-wall steel pipe also exists. These materials often include restrictions with regard to their use and application. For example, PB pipe cannot be left exposed. The listing criteria are specific and indicate for which standard

(e.g., NFPA 13D, *Standard for the Installation of Sprinkler Systems in One- and Two-Family Dwellings and Manufactured Homes,* or NFPA 13R) or hazard classification (e.g., light hazard in accordance with NFPA 13, *Standard for the Installation of Sprinkler Systems*) the pipe is listed. This listing information as well as the manufacturer's installation instructions needs to be consulted for proper installation and application.

As noted in 5.2.2, not all pipe is required to be listed. Listed piping is identified by the listing agency's logo. Similar piping manufactured with less exacting quality control must not be used in sprinkler systems. This qualification essentially means that "garden variety" PB or polyvinyl chloride (PVC) pipe materials found at a building supply store are not eligible for use in sprinkler systems. A 1993 fire investigation conducted by NFPA in a board and care facility uncovered a system installed with PVC plumbing pipe. Although it was not apparent that the use of PVC pipe contributed to the two fatalities in this fire, its use was indicative of the installer's general lack of knowledge about sprinkler system design.

PB pipe is no longer manufactured due to problems associated with its use in domestic plumbing systems, not because of its use in fire protection systems. The development of other flexible pipe is being pursued as an alternative to PB pipe.

◀ **FAQ**
Is PB pipe still manufactured?

5.2.2.1 Pipe differing from those specified in Table 5.2.1 shall be installed in accordance with their listings and the manufacturers' installation instructions.

5.2.2.2* Chlorinated polyvinyl chloride (CPVC) and polybutylene (PB) pipe shall comply with the portions of the American Society for Testing and Materials (ASTM) standards specified in Table 5.2.2.2 that apply to fire protection service.

TABLE 5.2.2.2 *Specially Listed Pipe or Tube Materials and Dimensions*

Materials and Dimensions	Standard
Nonmetallic Piping	
Specification for Chlorinated Polyvinyl Chloride (CPVC) Pipe	ASTM F 442
Specification for Polybutylene (PB) Pipe	ASTM D 3309

A.5.2.2.2 Not all pipe or tube made to ASTM D 3309, *Standard Specification for Polybutylene (PB) Plastic Hot- and Cold-Water Distribution Systems,* and ASTM F 442, *Standard Specification for Chlorinated Poly (Vinyl Chloride) (CPVC) Plastic Pipe (SDR-PR),* as described in 5.2.2.2 is listed for fire sprinkler service. Listed pipe is identified by the logo of the listing agency.

5.2.3 Pipe having a wall thickness less than that of Schedule 30 pipe shall not be joined by fittings utilizing cut grooves where the pipe is 8 in. (203 mm) nominal or larger in size.

5.2.4 Pipe having a wall thickness less than that of Schedule 40 pipe shall not be joined by fittings utilizing cut grooves where the pipe is less than 8 in. (203 mm) nominal in size.

When grooves are cut, material is lost, and the use of thin-wall steel pipe could result in too little material remaining between the inside diameter and the root diameter of the groove. Based on a listing from a testing laboratory, 5.2.4 permits an innovative threaded assembly for use with thin-walled steel pipe.

Subsection 6.6.6 requires the piping support to be in accordance with NFPA 13.

5.2.5 Pipe joined with mechanical fittings using cut or rolled grooves shall be joined by a listed combination of fittings, gaskets, and grooves.

5.2.6 Grooves cut or rolled on pipe shall be dimensionally compatible with the fittings.

5.2.7 Fittings used in sprinkler systems shall be of the materials listed in Table 5.2.7 or in accordance with 5.2.10.

Fittings of the types and materials indicated in Table 5.2.7 must be manufactured to the standards indicated or to other standards that meet or exceed the intent of the standards referenced

TABLE 5.2.7 *Fitting Materials and Dimensions*

Materials and Dimensions	Standard
Cast Iron	
Cast Iron Threaded Fittings (Class 125 and 250)	ASME B16.4
Cast Iron Pipe Flanges and Flanged Fittings	ASME B16.1
Malleable Iron	
Malleable Iron Threaded Fittings	ASME B16.3
Steel	
Factory-Made Wrought Steel Buttwelding Fittings	ASME B16.9
Buttwelding Ends	ASME B16.25
Specification for Piping Fittings of Wrought Carbon Steel and Alloy Steel for Moderate and Elevated Temperatures	ASTM A 234
Pipe Flanges and Flanged Fittings (Nickel Alloy and Other Special Alloys)	ASME B16.5
Forged Fittings, Socket-Welding and Threaded	ASME B16.11
Copper	
Wrought Copper and Copper Alloy Solder Joint Pressure Fittings	ASME B16.22
Cast Copper Alloy Solder Joint Pressure Fittings	ASME B16.18

in NFPA 13R. Any fitting for use in a sprinkler system must be designed for a working pressure of at least 175 psi (12.1 bar). The same principles that apply to the quality control of piping materials also apply to pipe fittings.

5.2.7.1 The chemical properties, physical properties, and dimensions of fitting materials shall be at least equivalent to the standards cited in Table 5.2.7.

5.2.7.2 Fittings used in sprinkler systems shall be designed to withstand a working pressure of not less than 175 psi (12.1 bar).

5.2.7.3 When nonmetallic fittings are used, the fittings shall be designed to withstand a working pressure of not less than 175 psi (12.1 bar) at 120°F (49°C).

5.2.8 Joints for the connection of copper pipe shall be brazed on dry pipe and preaction systems.

5.2.9 Joints for the connection of copper pipe for wet systems shall use solder joints with 95-5 solder metal or be brazed.

 NFPA 13R does not recognize 50-50 solder, which was prohibited for use in plumbing systems by the 1986 amendments to the *Federal Safe Drinking Water Act* (see 5.2.9). Although the prohibition does not specifically extend to residential sprinkler systems, the Technical Committee on Residential Sprinkler Systems considered it a good practice to discontinue using this leaded solder in such close proximity to a potable water system.

5.2.10 Types of fittings other than those specified in Table 5.2.7 shall be permitted to be used where listed for sprinkler system use.

5.2.10.1 Fittings differing from those specified in Table 5.2.7 shall be installed in accordance with their listings and the manufacturers' installation instructions.

5.2.10.2* Chlorinated polyvinyl chloride (CPVC) and polybutylene (PB) fittings shall comply with the portions of the American Society for Testing and Materials (ASTM) standards specified in Table 5.2.10.2 that apply to fire protection service.

 A.5.2.10.2 Not all fittings made to ASTM F 437, *Standard Specification for Threaded Chlorinated Poly (Vinyl Chloride) (CPVC) Plastic Pipe Fittings, Schedule 80*; ASTM F 438, *Stan-*

TABLE 5.2.10.2 Specially Listed Fittings and Dimensions

Materials and Dimensions	Standard
Specification for Schedule 80 CPVC Threaded Fittings	ASTM F 437
Specification for Schedule 40 CPVC Socket-Type Fittings	ASTM F 438
Specification for Schedule 80 CPVC Socket-Type Fittings	ASTM F 439

dard Specification for Socket-Type Chlorinated Poly (Vinyl Chloride) (CPVC) Plastic Pipe Fittings, Schedule 40; and ASTM F 439 *Standard Specification for Socket-Type Chlorinated Poly (Vinyl Chloride) (CPVC) Plastic Pipe Fittings, Schedule 80,* as described in 5.2.10.2 are listed for fire sprinkler service. Listed fittings are identified by the logo of the listing agency.

The types of pipe and fittings that are described in 5.2.10.1 and listed in Table 5.2.10.2 are those that have been found satisfactory either due to their service record or based on their evaluation by a listing agency. Sections 6.3 and 6.5 of NFPA 13 contain additional information on pipe and fittings, respectively. Paragraph 5.2.10.1 of NFPA 13R allows for the development of new types of fittings. However, their performance must be evaluated.

The listing procedure for the materials in Tables 5.2.7 and 5.2.10.2 is performed as an assembly. The manufacturers of these materials have established a procedure for connecting fittings to the pipe to ensure that the system is reliable. Listing procedures are unique to each type of material. Special tools, bonding agents, and fittings are part of the tested assembly. The listing procedure's comprehensive methodology helps to ensure a reliable installation.

5.3 System Types

5.3.1 A wet pipe system shall be used where piping is installed in areas that can be maintained reliably above 40°F (4°C).

Wet pipe systems, which are addressed in 5.3.1, tend to be the most reliable and simplest of all sprinkler systems, because no equipment other than the sprinklers need to operate in order to activate the system. Only those sprinklers operated by the fire's heat discharge water. Wet pipe systems are recommended wherever possible.

5.3.2* Piping in areas that cannot be maintained reliably above 40°F (4°C) shall be protected by use of one of the following methods:

(1)* Antifreeze system
(2) Dry pipe system
(3) Preaction system
(4) Listed standard dry-pendent, dry-upright, or dry-sidewall sprinklers extended from pipe in heated areas

A.5.3.2 Piping covered by insulation, as shown in Figure A.5.3.2(a) through Figure A.5.3.2(e), is considered part of the area below the ceiling and not part of the unheated attic area.

A.5.3.2(1) Antifreeze solutions can be used for maintaining automatic sprinkler protection in small, unheated areas. Because of the cost of refilling the system or replenishing small leaks, antifreeze solutions are recommended only for systems not exceeding 40 gal (151 L).

Listed CPVC sprinkler pipe and fittings should be protected from freezing only with glycerine. The use of diethylene, ethylene, or propylene glycols is specifically prohibited. Laboratory testing shows that glycol-based antifreeze solutions present a chemical environment

Caution: It is important that the insulation be installed tight against the joists. In unheated areas, any spaces or voids between the insulation and the joists cause the water in the fire sprinkler piping to freeze.

FIGURE A.5.3.2(a) *Insulation Recommendations—Arrangement 1.*

Caution: For areas having temperatures of 0°F (−18°C) or lower, an additional batt of insulation covering the joist and the fire sprinkler piping should be used. If this is not done, freeze-ups can occur in the sprinkler piping.

FIGURE A.5.3.2(b) *Insulation Recommendations—Arrangement 2.*

Caution: Boring holes in the joist is one method of locating the fire sprinkler piping in the ceiling. As an alternative, when temperatures are expected to be 0°F (−18°C) or lower, loose pieces of insulation should be stuffed in the bored holes around the piping.

FIGURE A.5.3.2(c) *Insulation Recommendations—Arrangement 3.*

Caution: Care should be taken to avoid compressing the insulation. This reduces its *R* value. To prevent potential freeze-ups of the sprinkler piping, the insulation should be installed tight against the joists.

FIGURE A.5.3.2(d) *Insulation Recommendations—Arrangement 4.*

Caution: Care should be taken to avoid compressing the insulation. This reduces its *R* value. To prevent potential freeze-ups of the sprinkler piping, the insulation should be installed tight against the joists.

FIGURE A.5.3.2(e) *Insulation Recommendations—Arrangement 5.*

detrimental to CPVC. Listed polybutylene sprinkler pipe and fittings can be protected with glycerine, diethylene glycol, ethylene glycol, or propylene glycol.

The information in A.5.3.2 was added to ensure that the design professional and installing contractor are aware of the limitations associated with CPVC piping when used for antifreeze systems.

    With regard to antifreeze systems, state or local plumbing and health regulations may not allow the introduction of foreign materials into piping systems connected to public water. Where these regulations are in effect, the use of antifreeze and the type of solution permitted should be verified by local authorities. Antifreeze systems might be permitted where piping arrangements make contamination of public water highly unlikely. Where antifreeze systems are installed, many health authorities require the use of a reduced-pressure zone (RPZ) back-flow prevention device. In many instances, antifreeze systems offer the most attractive solution for a small unheated or cold storage area of a building.

    Dry pipe systems are installed in lieu of wet pipe systems where piping is subject to freezing. Dry pipe systems should not be used for the purpose of reducing water damage from pipe breakage or leakage, because the systems operate too quickly to be of value for this purpose.

    Because of the concern for delayed water delivery and the fact that no residential sprinklers are listed for dry system application, dry pipe systems are not allowed for protection inside dwelling units. However, dry pipe systems can be installed in areas outside dwelling units in accordance with 6.7.2 and NFPA 13.

◀ **FAQ**
Why are dry pipe systems prohibited from protection inside the dwelling unit?

    Dry pendent, dry upright, and dry sidewall sprinklers are specially designed to prevent water from entering the pipe between the sprinkler supply pipe (branch line) and the sprinkler's operating mechanism. These sprinklers can be used on wet pipe systems where individual sprinklers are extended into spaces subject to freezing.

◀ **FAQ**
How can small spaces subject to freezing be addressed with a wet pipe system?

5.3.3 Where antifreeze systems, dry pipe systems, and preaction systems are installed, they shall be installed in accordance with NFPA 13, *Standard for the Installation of Sprinkler Systems.*

Tables 7.5.2.2 and 7.5.2.3 in NFPA 13 list antifreeze concentrates that are permitted, depending on whether or not the sprinkler system is supplied by potable water (see 5.3.3). The concentrates for those systems attached to potable water systems are chemically pure, food-grade additives. Even so, a backflow device is still required by most water utilities.

REFERENCES CITED IN COMMENTARY

National Fire Protection Association, 1 Batterymarch Park, P.O. Box 9101, Quincy, MA 02269-9101

NFPA 13, *Standard for the Installation of Sprinkler Systems,* 2002 edition
NFPA 13D, *Standard for the Installation of Sprinkler Systems in One- and Two-Family Dwellings and Manufactured Homes,* 2002 edition
NFPA 24, *Standard for the Installation of Private Fire Service Mains and Their Appurtenances,* 2002 edition

U.S. Government, U.S. Government Printing Office, Washington, DC 20402

Federal Safe Drinking Water Act, 1974

CHAPTER 6

Working Plans, Design, Installation, Acceptance Tests, and Maintenance

6.1 Working Plans

Working plans, which are covered in Section 6.1, are prepared primarily for system installers. The plans also serve to protect the owner's interest, usually owners who are not knowledgeable in sprinkler system installations and consequently rely on others to check the plans for conformance to NFPA 13R. Various authorities having jurisdiction will likely be used to review the plans to ensure that the interests of society, the owner, and any other concerned parties, such as the insurance company, have been properly addressed.

When the installation is completed, it is checked against the plans to determine compliance with the approved plans and NFPA 13R. The owner should retain working plans and specifications to refer to in the future and to assist in the periodic maintenance program. In the event that future alterations are undertaken, a good deal of expense and time can be saved if accurate working plans and documentation are available since these systems are to be hydraulically calculated.

The symbols commonly used in working plans can be found in NFPA 170, *Standard for Fire Safety Symbols.* NFPA 13, *Standard for the Installation of Sprinkler Systems,* provides further information and examples of symbols and abbreviations commonly used on sprinkler system plans.

6.1.1 Working plans shall be submitted for approval to the authority having jurisdiction before any equipment is installed or remodeled.

6.1.2 Deviations from approved plans shall require permission of the authority having jurisdiction.

6.1.3 Working plans shall be drawn to a specified scale.

6.1.4 Sprinkler plans shall be drawn on sheets of uniform size.

6.1.5 Sprinkler plans shall provide a plan of each floor.

6.1.6 Sprinkler plans shall be capable of being easily duplicated.

6.1.7 Sprinkler plans shall indicate the following:

(1) Name of owner and occupant
(2) Location, including street address
(3) Point of compass
(4) Ceiling construction
(5) Full height cross section

(6)   Location of fire walls

(7)   Location of partitions

(8)   Occupancy of each area or room

(9)   Location and size of concealed spaces, attics, closets, and bathrooms

(10)   Any small enclosures in which no sprinklers are to be installed

(11)   Size of the city main in the street, pressure, whether dead-end or circulating and, if dead-end, the direction and distance to the nearest circulating main, and the city main test results including elevation of the test hydrant

(12)   Make, manufacturer, type, heat-response element, temperature rating, and nominal orifice size of the sprinkler

(13)   Temperature rating and location of high-temperature sprinklers

(14)   Number of sprinklers on each riser, per floor

(15)   Kind and location of alarm bells

(16)   Type of pipe and fittings

(17)   Type of protection for nonmetallic pipe

(18)*   Nominal pipe size with lengths shown to scale

 A.6.1.7(18) Where typical branch lines prevail, it will be necessary to size only one line.

(19)   Location and size of riser nipples

(20)   Types of fittings and joints and the locations of all welds and bends

(21)   Types and locations of hangers, sleeves, and braces, and methods of securing sprinklers, where applicable

(22)   All control valves, check valves, drain pipes, and test connections

(23)   Underground pipe size, length, location, weight, material, and point of connection to the city main; type of valves, meters, and valve pits; and depth at which the top of the pipe is laid below grade

(24)   In the case of hydraulically designed systems, the material to be included on the hydraulic data nameplate

(25)   Name and address of the contractor

The information required in 6.1.7(1) through 6.1.7(25) helps expedite the review process and saves time during the installation. Most of these items are easy to determine and result in a system design and installation that provides the protection level intended by NFPA 13R.

With regard to 6.1.7(13), consideration must be given to the sprinklers' location with respect to heat sources. The information in 6.6.7.1.5.3 and the manufacturer's literature contain guidance on positioning sprinklers near heat sources.

Where typical branch lines prevail, it will be necessary to size only one line with regard to 6.1.7(18).

With regard to 6.1.7(21), nonmetallic pipe has necessitated the securing of sprinklers to the ceiling. Refer to the manufacturer's listing information.

6.2 Approval of Sprinkler Systems

6.2.1 The installer shall perform all required acceptance tests *(see Section 6.3)* prior to asking for approval of the installation.

6.2.2 The installer shall complete the contractor's material and test certificate(s) *(see Figure 6.2.2)* prior to asking for approval of the installation.

A contractor's material and test certificate (see Figure 6.2.2) acknowledges that materials used and tests made are in accordance with the requirements of the approved plans. The certificate also provides a record of the test results, which can be used for comparison with tests conducted as part of a system maintenance program. The certificate also verifies that the system design and installation are completed in accordance with NFPA 13R.

Contractor's Material and Test Certificate for Aboveground Piping

PROCEDURE

Upon completion of work, inspection and tests shall be made by the contractor's representative and witnessed by an owner's representative. All defects shall be corrected and system left in service before contractor's personnel finally leave the job.

A certificate shall be filled out and signed by both representatives. Copies shall be prepared for approving authorities, owners, and contractor. It is understood the owner's representative's signature in no way prejudices any claim against contractor for faulty material, poor workmanship, or failure to comply with approving authority's requirements or local ordinances.

Property name					Date	

Property address

Plans	Accepted by approving authorities (names)					
	Address					
	Installation conforms to accepted plans			☐ Yes	☐ No	
	Equipment used is approved If no, explain deviations			☐ Yes	☐ No	

Instructions	Has person in charge of fire equipment been instructed as to location of control valves and care and maintenance of this new equipment? If no, explain	☐ Yes	☐ No
	Have copies of the following been left on the premises?		
	1. System components instructions	☐ Yes	☐ No
	2. Care and maintenance instructions	☐ Yes	☐ No
	3. NFPA 25	☐ Yes	☐ No

Location of system	Supplies buildings

Sprinklers	Make	Model	Year of manufacture	Orifice size	Quantity	Temperature rating

Pipe and fittings	Type of pipe _____ Type of fittings _____

Alarm valve or flow indicator	Alarm device			Maximum time to operate through test connection	
	Type	Make	Model	Minutes	Seconds

Dry pipe operating test	Dry valve			Q. O. D.		
	Make	Model	Serial no.	Make	Model	Serial no.

		Time to trip through test connection†		Water pressure	Air pressure	Trip point air pressure	Time water reached test outlet†		Alarm operated properly	
		Minutes	Seconds	psi	psi	psi	Minutes	Seconds	Yes	No
	Without Q.O.D.									
	With Q.O.D.									
	If no, explain									

† Measured from the time inspector's test connection is opened

FIGURE 6.2.2 *Contractor's Material and Test Certificate for Aboveground Piping.*

(Continues)

Deluge and preaction valves	Operation ☐ Pneumatic ☐ Electric ☐ Hydraulic						

Deluge and preaction valves

Operation   ☐ Pneumatic   ☐ Electric   ☐ Hydraulic

Piping supervised   ☐ Yes   ☐ No   Detecting media supervised   ☐ Yes   ☐ No

Does valve operate from the manual trip, remote, or both control stations?   ☐ Yes   ☐ No

Is there an accessible facility in each circuit for testing?   ☐ Yes   ☐ No   If no, explain

Make	Model	Does each circuit operate supervision loss alarm?		Does each circuit operate valve release?		Maximum time to operate release	
		Yes	No	Yes	No	Minutes	Seconds

Pressure reducing valve test

Location and floor	Make and model	Setting	Static pressure		Residual pressure (flowing)		Flow rate
			Inlet (psi)	Outlet (psi)	Inlet (psi)	Outlet (psi)	Flow (gpm)

Test description

Hydrostatic: Hydrostatic tests shall be made at not less than 200 psi (13.6 bar) for 2 hours or 50 psi (3.4 bar) above static pressure in excess of 150 psi (10.2 bar) for 2 hours. Differential dry-pipe valve clappers shall be left open during the test to prevent damage. All aboveground piping leakage shall be stopped.

Pneumatic: Establish 40 psi (2.7 bar) air pressure and measure drop, which shall not exceed 1½ psi (0.1 bar) in 24 hours. Test pressure tanks at normal water level and air pressure and measure air pressure drop, which shall not exceed 1½ psi (0.1 bar) in 24 hours.

Tests

All piping hydrostatically tested at _____ psi (___ bar) for _____ hours   If no, state reason
Dry piping pneumatically tested   ☐ Yes   ☐ No
Equipment operates properly   ☐ Yes   ☐ No

Do you certify as the sprinkler contractor that additives and corrosive chemicals, sodium silicate or derivatives of sodium silicate, brine, or other corrosive chemicals were not used for testing systems or stopping leaks?
☐ Yes   ☐ No

Drain test	Reading of gauge located near water supply test connection: _____ psi (___ bar)	Residual pressure with valve in test connection open wide: _____ psi (___ bar)

Underground mains and lead-in connections to system risers flushed before connection made to sprinkler piping verified by a copy of the "Contractor's Material and Test Certificate for Underground Piping."   ☐ Yes   ☐ No   Other   Explain

Flushed by installer of underground sprinkler piping   ☐ Yes   ☐ No

If powder-driven fasteners are used in concrete, has representative sample testing been satisfactorily completed?   ☐ Yes   ☐ No   If no, explain

Blank testing gaskets

Number used	Locations	Number removed

Welding

Welding piping   ☐ Yes   ☐ No

If yes . . .

Do you certify as the sprinkler contractor that welding procedures comply with the requirements of at least AWS B2.1?   ☐ Yes   ☐ No

Do you certify that the welding was performed by welders qualified in compliance with the requirements of at least AWS B2.1?   ☐ Yes   ☐ No

Do you certify that the welding was carried out in compliance with a documented quality control procedure to ensure that all discs are retrieved, that openings in piping are smooth, that slag and other welding residue are removed, and that the internal diameters of piping are not penetrated?   ☐ Yes   ☐ No

Cutouts (discs)

Do you certify that you have a control feature to ensure that all cutouts (discs) are retrieved?   ☐ Yes   ☐ No

Figure 6.2.2.2 Continued

Hydraulic data nameplate	Nameplate provided ☐ Yes ☐ No	If no, explain
Remarks	Date left in service with all control valves open	

Signatures	Name of sprinkler contractor		
	Tests witnessed by		
	For property owner (signed)	Title	Date
	For sprinkler contractor (signed)	Title	Date

Additional explanations and notes

Figure 6.2.2.2 Continued

6.2.3 The installer shall forward the certificate(s) to the authority having jurisdiction prior to asking for approval of the installation.

6.2.4 Where the authority having jurisdiction requires to be present during the conducting of acceptance tests, the installer shall provide advance notification of the time and date the testing will be performed.

Frequently the authority having jurisdiction wants to be present when acceptance tests are conducted, as indicated in 6.2.4. The installer should be aware of the policies or procedures of the authority having jurisdiction with respect to witnessing acceptance tests. When the authority having jurisdiction desires to witness the tests, the installer should provide sufficient advance notice. Failure to do so may require that the tests be repeated.

6.3 Acceptance Tests

6.3.1* Flushing of Underground Connections.

A.6.3.1 Underground mains and lead-in connections to system risers are required to be flushed before a connection is made to sprinkler piping in order to remove any foreign materials that have entered the underground piping during the course of the installation.

6.3.1.1 Underground mains and lead-in connections to system risers shall be flushed before a connection is made to sprinkler piping.

Flushing is specified in 6.3.1.1. Stones, gravel, blocks of wood, bottles, work tools, work clothes, and other objects have been found in piping when flushing was performed. Also, objects in underground piping quite remote from the sprinkler installation, which otherwise would remain stationary, will sometimes be forced into sprinkler system piping when sprinkler systems operate. Sprinkler systems can draw greater flows than normal domestic systems. Fire department pumpers, when taking suction from hydrants for pumping into sprinkler systems, tend to augment this effect by increasing the velocity of water flow through underground piping.

Because the size of sprinkler system piping typically gets smaller starting at the water supply's point of connection, objects that are forced from underground piping into the sprinkler system risers are likely to become lodged at a point in the system where they totally obstruct the water's passage.

6.3.1.2 The flushing operation shall be continued until the water issuing from the main is clear.

6.3.1.3 The flushing operation shall be performed at the hydraulically calculated water demand rate of the system.

Because only the design flow rate is anticipated, the calculated water demand rate is to be used for flushing, as stated in 6.3.1.3. Overall field experience with NFPA 13 systems indicates that flushing is normally accomplished at the maximum flow rate available from the water supply.

6.3.1.4 The flushing operation shall be performed such that the disposal of water issuing from the test outlets does not damage the property.

6.3.2* Hydrostatic Pressure Tests.

A.6.3.2 Testing of a system can be accomplished by pressurizing the system with water and checking visually for leakage at each joint or coupling.

Where pressure testing systems have rigid thermoplastic piping, such as listed CPVC, or flexible piping, such as listed polybutylene, the sprinkler system should be filled with water. The air should be bled from the highest and farthest sprinklers before the test pressure is applied. Compressed air or compressed gas never should be used for pressure testing CPVC piping. Testing with air pressure is permitted for polybutylene piping where conducted in accordance with the testing procedures of 16.2.2.1 of NFPA 13, *Standard for the Installation of Sprinkler Systems.*

Fire department connections are not required for all systems covered by this standard but can be installed at the discretion of the owner. In these cases, hydrostatic tests in accordance with NFPA 13 are required.

Dry systems also should be tested by placing the system under air pressure. Any leak that results in a drop in system pressure greater than 2 psi (0.14 bar) in 24 hours should be corrected. Leaks should be identified using soapy water brushed on each joint or coupling. The presence of bubbles indicates a leak. This test should be made prior to concealing the piping.

6.3.2.1 Systems having more than 20 sprinklers or having a fire department connection shall pass a hydrostatic pressure test performed for the aboveground piping system in accordance with NFPA 13, *Standard for the Installation of Sprinkler Systems.*

FAQ ▶
Are NFPA 13R sprinkler systems required to be hydrostatically tested to a pressure of at least 200 psi (13.8 bar)?

FAQ ▶
During a hydrostatic test, where should the test pressure be measured?

All NFPA 13R sprinkler systems must be hydrostatically tested to a pressure of at least 200 psi (13.8 bar) in accordance with NFPA 13, unless the system has 20 or fewer sprinklers with no fire department connection, as stated in 6.3.2.1.

This requirement ensures that pipe joints can withstand this working pressure without coming apart or leaking. Although the purpose of this test is to check the quality of the installation, it can also uncover defective components such as cracked fittings and leaky sprinklers.

The hydrostatic test pressure measurement is taken at the lowest elevation within the system or portion of the system being tested. Testing at the system's high point is not considered necessary because the system usually experiences the highest pressure at the lower elevation.

The measure of success for interior sprinkler piping under a hydrostatic test is no visible leakage. Often a very small bead of water forms on a fitting during the test. Unless the bead continues to grow and drip, it is not considered visible leakage.

6.3.2.2 Systems having both fewer than 20 sprinklers and no fire department connection shall pass a hydrostatic pressure test performed for the aboveground piping system at 50 psi higher than the maximum system pressure using the hydrostatic test procedure specified in NFPA 13, *Standard for the Installation of Sprinkler Systems.*

Paragraph 6.3.2.2 allows for lower hydrostatic pressure tests on small NFPA 13R systems. When a fire department connection is not installed and the system has no more than 20 sprinklers, the hydrostatic test pressure can be reduced to 50 psi (3.4 bar) above the maximum system design pressure. Where a fire department connection is not installed, the likelihood of the system experiencing very high pressures is rather remote.

   In accordance with 6.6.4, a fire department connection is not required for systems installed in buildings in certain remote areas or in single-story buildings 2000 ft² (186 m²) or less in area.

   The special precautions required for hydrostatic testing of systems using rigid thermoplastic piping such as chlorinated polyvinyl chloride (CPVC) or flexible piping such as polybutylene (PB) are described in A.6.3.2.

6.4 Design and Installation

6.4.1 At least three spare sprinklers of each type, temperature rating, and orifice size used in the system shall be installed on the premises.

Three spare sprinklers of each type used in the design are required to be kept on site, as stated in 6.4.1. This provision helps ensure that spare sprinklers are immediately available and that the system can be put back into service with minimal delay. NFPA 13R also clarifies that replacement sprinklers must be the same type—that is, have the same thermal operating characteristics.

   When a sprinkler needs to be replaced because it has operated or has been damaged, the orifice size, temperature rating, deflector configuration, and sprinkler type of the replacement sprinkler should be the same as the original sprinkler. Many sprinklers have unique operating characteristics, and some have special area of coverage limitations. The differences between the various residential sprinklers are not obvious, so care must be used when replacing them.

◄ **FAQ**
How many spare sprinklers are required for an NFPA 13R installation?

6.4.2 Where solvent cement is used as the pipe and fittings bonding agent, sprinklers shall not be installed in the fittings prior to the fittings being cemented in place.

The installation requirement in 6.4.2 was added to the 1999 edition to ensure that solvent cement does not drip into the piping drop and obstruct or clog the sprinkler.

◄ **FAQ**
Why do the requirements of 6.4.2 require that the sprinklers be installed after the fittings have been cemented in place?

6.4.3 A test connection shall be installed that permits the testing of the alarm mechanisms.

The test connection described in 6.4.3 is used to verify operation of the waterflow device and gives an indication of the available water supply characteristics. The test connection can indicate the presence of large obstructions in the water supply or a closed control valve. However, the test is not sensitive enough to determine if a valve is partially closed or if a portion of pipe is only partially obstructed.

6.5 Water Supply

6.5.1 Every sprinkler system shall have at least one automatic water supply.

6.5.2 The water supply shall be capable of supplying the system demand for at least 30 minutes. *(See 6.7.1.2.)*

The sprinkler system's effectiveness greatly depends on its water supply, which must be automatic and reliable (see 6.5.2). The adequacy of a public water supply is determined in accordance with 6.5.2, 6.7.2, and 6.7.4. If a stored water supply such as a tank is used, the amount of water should provide at least 30-minute duration at the required flow rate. The 30-minute requirement parallels the NFPA 13 criteria for light hazard occupancies.

6.5.3* The water supply source shall be one of the following:

(1) A connection to a reliable waterworks system with or without a pump, as required
(2) An elevated tank
 (3) A pressure tank installed in accordance with NFPA 13, *Standard for the Installation of Sprinkler Systems,* and NFPA 22, *Standard for Water Tanks for Private Fire Protection*
(4) A stored water source with an automatically operated pump

 A.6.5.3 The connection to city mains for fire protection is often subject to local regulation of metering and backflow prevention requirements. Preferred and acceptable water supply arrangements are shown in Figure A.6.5.3(a), Figure A.6.5.3(b), and Figure A.6.5.3(c). Where it is necessary to use a meter between the city water main and the sprinkler system supply, an acceptable arrangement as shown in Figure A.6.5.3(c) can be used. Under these circumstances, the flow characteristics of the meter are to be included in the hydraulic calculation of the system. Where a tank is used for both domestic and fire protection purposes, a low water alarm that actuates when the water level falls below 110 percent of the minimum quantity specified in 6.5.2 should be provided.

 FAQ ▶
Where fire pumps are required, are they required to meet the requirements of NFPA 20?

Although editions of NFPA 13R prior to 1996 did not specifically state that fire pumps be installed in accordance with NFPA 20, *Standard for the Installation of Stationary Pumps for Fire Protection,* this was always the intent. The 1996 edition made this requirement explicit in 6.5.4.

Figures A.6.5.3(a), A.6.5.3(b), and A.6.5.3(c) show the preferred and acceptable arrangements of connections to city mains and include control valves, meters, domestic takeoffs, waterflow detectors, pressure gauges, and check valves appropriately located. When the local

* Rubber-faced check valves are optional.

FIGURE A.6.5.3(a) Preferable Arrangement.

* Rubber-faced check valves are optional.
† Optional valve: See 6.6.1.2.

FIGURE A.6.5.3(b) Acceptable Arrangement with Valve Supervision (see 6.6.1.2).

* Rubber-faced check valves are optional.
† Optional valve: See 6.6.1.2.

FIGURE A.6.5.3(c) Acceptable Arrangement with Valve Supervision (see 6.6.1.2).

water company mandates back flow prevention devices, the devices will normally be located in the position where the rubber-faced check valve is shown on the diagrams. The piping arrangement, including valves and fittings, must be taken into account when performing the calculations for system adequacy.

From a fire protection standpoint, meters are not desirable because of their high friction loss characteristics. However, many water authorities require metering of the fire protection water supply connection. The friction loss must be accounted for through the system's hydraulic calculations. Table 8.4.4(g) of NFPA 13D, *Standard for the Installation of Sprinkler Systems in One- and Two-Family Dwellings and Manufactured Homes,* provides some friction loss values for water meters.

An elevated tank can serve as the water supply. With this arrangement the tank must have sufficient elevation to provide the required pressure for the system. Subsection 15.2.3 of NFPA 13 provides more information in this regard. When a pressure tank is used for water supply, the amount of water and the air pressure in the tank are determined using 15.2.3.3 and A.15.2.3.3 of NFPA 13.

A stored water source with an automatically operated pump must have a capacity sufficient to meet the system's demand as determined by 6.5.2 and 6.7. In addition, the stored water source must have adequate pressure determined in accordance with 6.7.4.

6.5.4 Where a fire pump is installed, the fire pump shall be installed in accordance with NFPA 20, *Standard for the Installation of Stationary Pumps for Fire Protection.*

A connection to the waterworks system might require a booster pump to provide the pressures required in accordance with 6.7.4. NFPA 13R is more restrictive than NFPA 13D with respect to a stored water source with a pump because NFPA 13R requires the pump to comply with NFPA 20. The Technical Committee on Residential Sprinkler Systems believes that the reliability features associated with NFPA 20 fire pump installations are necessary to achieve the objectives of NFPA 13R.

◀ FAQ

Where fire pumps are required, are they required to meet the requirements of NFPA 20?

A number of pump manufacturers and pump controller manufacturers have responded to this provision. Fire pumps with capacities as low as 25 gpm (95 L/min) are now commercially available. Listed limited service fire pump controllers are also available for use with these pumps.

6.5.5* Domestic demand shall be included as part of the overall system demand for systems with common domestic/fire mains where no provisions are made to prevent the domestic water flow upon sprinkler system activation.

 A.6.5.5 Table A.6.5.5(a) and Table A.6.5.5(b) can be used to determine a domestic design demand. Using Table A.6.5.5(a), the total number of water supply fixture units downstream of any point in the piping serving both sprinkler and domestic needs is determined. Using Table A.6.5.5(b), the appropriate total flow allowance is determined and added to the sprinkler demand at the total pressure required for the sprinkler system at that point.

Because domestic demand could occur at the same time as sprinkler system operation, the system design must include such demand if the provision in 6.5.5 is utilized. Tables A.6.5.5(a) and A.6.5.5(b) provide guidance on water demand of domestic plumbing facilities and their impact on hydraulic calculations. The tables are based on values found in plumbing codes published by the model code organizations. If the building being protected is of new construction, the domestic design demand should be readily available from the plumbing design documents and should not require additional effort from the sprinkler system installer.

As indicated in Figure A.6.5.3(9) the preferred arrangement is to combine underground supply piping for domestic and sprinkler systems. The Technical Committee on Residential Sprinkler Systems feels that such an arrangement increases the sprinkler system's overall reliability. In a residential occupancy, if water is not available for normal usage such as for toilets, the impairment to the water supply system is likely to be investigated and repaired in a timely fashion. However, the technical committee also recognizes that local plumbing or

TABLE A.6.5.5(a) *Fixture Load Values*

Facility Type	Unit
Private Facilities (those within individual dwelling units)	
Bathroom group with flush tank (including lavatory, water closet, and bathtub with shower)	6
Bathroom group with flush valve	8
Bathtub	2
Dishwasher	1
Kitchen sink	2
Laundry trays	3
Lavatory	1
Shower stall	2
Washing machine	2
Water closet with flush valve	6
Water closet with flush tank	3
Public Facilities	
Bathtub	4
Drinking fountain	0
Kitchen sink	4
Lavatory	2
Service sink	3
Shower head	4
Urinal with 1-in. (25.4-mm) flush valve	10
Urinal with ¾-in. (19-mm) flush valve	5
Urinal with flush tank	3
Washing machine [8 lb (17.6 kg)]	3
Washing machine [16 lb (35.2 kg)]	4
Water closet with flush valve	10
Water closet with flush tank	5

TABLE A.6.5.5(b) *Total Estimated Domestic Demand*

| Total Fixture Load Units [from Table A.6.5.5(a)] | Total Demand | | | |
| | For Systems with Predominately Flush Tanks | | For Systems with Predominately Flush Valves | |
	gpm	L/min	gpm	L/min
1	3	11.25	—	—
2	5	18.75	—	—
5	10	37.5	15	56
10	15	56	25	94
20	20	75	35	13
35	25	94	45	169
50	30	113	50	187
70	35	131	60	225
100	45	169	70	262
150	55	200	80	300
200	65	244	90	337
250	75	261	100	375
350	100	375	125	469
500	125	469	150	562
750	175	656	175	656
1000	200	750	200	750
1500	275	1031	275	1031
2000	325	1219	325	1219
3500	500	1875	500	1875

health regulations can place restrictions on such combined systems because trapped piping sections at the end of a sprinkler system are frequent. This occurrence is not normally permitted by such codes. Furthermore, some plumbing regulations permit piping materials and methods of lesser quality than prescribed by NFPA 13R.

Some components such as meters, valves, backflow devices, and relief valves have associated flow limits. Exceeding these values could result in improper system operation. Therefore, the designer must investigate whether the use of any system components is restricted by its flow limitation.

6.5.6 Sprinkler systems with non-fire protection connections shall comply with Section 7.6 of NFPA 13, *Standard for the Installation of Sprinkler Systems.*

For many years, making use of the sprinkler piping, which normally stands idle, for a more active purpose has been considered feasible (see 6.5.6). One such use is a circulating closed loop used for a heat pump system, in which water circulates through heating and air-conditioning equipment using sprinkler pipe as the primary conductors. Section 7.6 of NFPA 13 provides the basic criteria so that the auxiliary functions do not reduce the sprinkler system's effectiveness.

6.6 Installation of System Components

6.6.1 Valves.

6.6.1.1 A single control valve arranged to shut off both the domestic system and the sprinkler system shall be installed for systems with common sprinkler/domestic mains unless a separate shutoff valve for the sprinkler system is installed in accordance with 6.6.1.2.

6.6.1.2 The sprinkler system piping shall not have a separate control valve installed unless supervised by one of the following methods:

(1) Central station, proprietary, or remote station alarm service
(2) Local alarm service that causes the sounding of an audible signal at a constantly attended location
(3) Valves that are locked open

A control valve, which is specified in 6.6.1.2, permits the system to be shut off for sprinkler replacement or other maintenance functions.

FAQ ▶
Why is one control valve for domestic and sprinkler systems preferred?

The control valve must be in the open position at all other times. With one control valve serving both the domestic and sprinkler systems, the possibility of inadvertently shutting off the sprinkler system is greatly reduced, because inoperative plumbing will prompt immediate action to restore the system back into service. A separate valve for the sprinkler system is acceptable only when the valve is adequately supervised against inadvertent shutoff.

6.6.1.3 A separate shutoff valve shall be installed for the domestic water supply in installations having a common sprinkler/domestic main.

6.6.2* Drains.

A.6.6.2 These connections should be installed so that the valve can be opened fully and for a sufficient time period to ensure a proper test without causing water damage. The test connection should be designed and sized to verify the sufficiency of the water supply and alarm mechanisms.

The drain connections addressed in 6.6.2.3 are used to drain the system when repairs are necessary and to indicate that the water supply is available at the system riser and on the system side of all check valves, the control valve, and underground piping. The maintenance program should include the proper documentation and test records to permit detection of possible water supply deterioration or valves that may have been closed.

6.6.2.1 Each sprinkler system shall have a drain on the system side of the control valve.

6.6.2.2 The drain pipe shall be at least 1 in. (25 mm) nominal diameter.

6.6.2.3 A valve shall be installed in the drain piping.

6.6.2.4 A ½-in. (13-mm) drain shall be installed for each trapped portion of a dry system that is subject to freezing temperatures.

Because dry systems are normally installed in areas subject to freezing, trapped areas must have drain valves to allow water to be promptly removed, as indicated in 6.6.2.4. Water can enter the system by either activation of the dry pipe valve tripping or condensation of moisture from the pressurized air in the system. Additional guidance on auxiliary drains for dry systems can be found in Chapters 7 and 8 of NFPA 13. Condensate nipples are not required because the capacity of trapped sections is assumed to generally be small.

Auxiliary drains are not required for wet pipe systems because trapped sections of piping in a wet system rarely need to be drained. However, arrangements should be made to drain all portions of trapped piping if the following situations occur.

1. The building is used for seasonal occupancy.
2. The water system is shut off during periods of nonoccupancy (a practice that is discouraged by other NFPA codes and standards).
3. The authority having jurisdiction has permitted a wet pipe system to be installed in accordance with NFPA 13R.

For additional guidance on auxiliary drains, see 8.15.2.5 of NFPA 13.

6.6.3* Test Connection.

A.6.6.3 These connections should be installed so that the valve can be opened fully and for a sufficient time period to ensure a proper test without causing water damage. The test connection should be designed and sized to verify the sufficiency of the water supply and alarm mechanisms.

6.6.3.1 Each sprinkler system shall have a test connection.

6.6.3.2 The test connection pipe shall be at least 1 in. (25 mm) nominal diameter.

6.6.3.3 A valve shall be installed in the test connection piping.

6.6.3.4 When the drain required in 6.6.2.1 is arranged as a test connection, a separate test connection shall not be required.

6.6.4 Fire Department Connection.

6.6.4.1 At least one fire department connection shall be provided for buildings accessible by a fire department that exceed 2000 ft² (186 m²) or are more than a single story.

Fire department connections, which are addressed in 6.6.4.1, are an important supplement to normal water supplies because they allow the fire department to bypass a closed control valve in most instances. Even where gravity tanks, pressure tanks, or other stored water sources are the sole source of supply, fire department connections should be included. The connection allows the fire department to pump from engines, tankers, or some other water source into the system, thereby either increasing the supply or adding to the tank's supply prior to its depletion, or both.

Section 6.8 of NFPA 13 provides additional requirements on the arrangement of the fire department connection on wet pipe systems with a single riser, which is the most common system installed in accordance with NFPA 13R. The connection should be made to the riser on the system side of indicating, check, and alarm valves if provided. This placement reduces the likelihood that a valve can be closed and render the fire department connection ineffective. For this reason, the fire department connection should not have a shutoff valve.

Approved check valves are to be provided in the fire department connection as near as practicable to the point where it joins the system. The check valve should be installed to permit flow into the system and restrict waterflow from the system into the fire department connection. An approved automatic drip should be provided in the fire department connection where the piping is subject to freezing. The drip permits draining of water between the hose connection and the check valve. The drain should be located at the lowest point of the fire department connection piping to allow complete drainage.

All hose coupling threads on the fire department connection should match the threads used by the local fire department. The hose connections should be equipped with plugs or caps to prevent tampering with the fire department connection pipe.

The first two editions of NFPA 13R did not require the fire department connection unless the system had 20 or more sprinklers.

The 2002 edition of NFPA 13R now only requires fire department connections for buildings that are accessible to the fire department and that exceed 2000 ft² (186 m²) or are more than a single story.

◀ **FAQ**
When applying the requirements of NFPA 13R, where are fire department connections required?

Paragraph 6.6.4.1 allows the device to be omitted if there is no access for fire department vehicle support. Although this situation is not found in urban areas, it is likely to be common in rural areas, such as a ski resort or campground.

The limit of 2000 ft² (186 m²) is considered a reasonable size limitation. The limit represents the maximum size of a small structure where adequate accessibility is provided to enter any part of the building during fireground operations.

6.6.4.2 Fire department connections shall be at least 1½ in. (38 mm).

6.6.5 Pressure Gauges.

6.6.5.1 A pressure gauge shall be provided to indicate pressure of the supply.

6.6.5.2 A pressure gauge shall be provided to indicate pressure of the system.

Pressure gauges, which are addressed in 6.6.5.1 and 6.6.5.2, allow for routine observation and verification of proper water pressure and, in dry systems, proper air pressure. This type of visual inspection is recommended in A.6.9 and required by NFPA 25, *Standard for the Inspection, Testing, and Maintenance of Water-Based Fire Protection Systems.*

6.6.6* Piping Support. Piping hanging and bracing methods shall comply with NFPA 13, *Standard for the Installation of Sprinkler Systems.*

A.6.6.6 Sprinkler piping should be adequately secured to restrict the movement of piping upon sprinkler operation. The reaction forces caused by the flow of water through the sprinkler could result in displacement of the sprinkler, thereby adversely affecting sprinkler discharge. Listed CPVC pipe and listed PB pipe have specific requirements for piping support to include additional pipe bracing at sprinklers.

Piping support is covered in 6.6.6. Chapter 9 of NFPA 13 provides the minimum requirements for supporting sprinkler system piping. Section 9.3 of NFPA 13 contains provisions for protection against seismic events. The use of nonmetallic pipe can require that sprinklers be secured to the ceiling. The pipe manufacturer's listing information should be consulted in this regard.

The Technical Committee on Residential Sprinkler Systems believes that the pipe sizes and pipe lengths used in NFPA 13R systems and the occurrence of short-term pressure surges and water hammer necessitate the need for the pipe hanging and bracing requirements of NFPA 13. The provisions of NFPA 13D are not considered to be adequate. In addition, flow rates through systems designed in accordance with NFPA 13R are similar to the flow rates anticipated by NFPA 13 for light hazard occupancies.

6.6.7 Sprinklers.

6.6.7.1 Inside the Dwelling Units.

6.6.7.1.1 Listed residential sprinklers shall be used unless another type is permitted by 6.6.7.1.3 or 6.6.7.1.4.

Underwriters Laboratories Inc. and FM Global have standards for the testing and evaluation of residential sprinklers (see 6.6.7.1.1). The standards require that the sprinklers undergo room fire tests and have fast-response characteristics. Standard sprinklers of the type used in NFPA 13 sprinkler systems do not meet the criteria for residential sprinklers and should not be used except as specifically permitted by NFPA 13R. (See commentary to A.1.2 for a

EXHIBIT 6.1 Viking Model M-1 Horizontal Sidewall Residential Sprinkler. (Courtesy of Viking)

EXHIBIT 6.2 *Viking Model M-1 Pendent-Mounted Residential Sprinkler Shown in an Inverted Position with Glass Bulb and Orifice Cover Removed. (Courtesy of Viking)*

EXHIBIT 6.3 *Viking Model M Vertical Sidewall Quick-Response Sprinkler. (Courtesy of Viking)*

EXHIBIT 6.4 *Viking Model M Pendent-Mounted Quick-Response Sprinkler. (Courtesy of Viking)*

further discussion of the differences in the test criteria.) Residential sprinklers are permitted to be used in the corridor of a residential structure that serves the individual dwelling units. Exhibits 6.1 through 6.4 show different types of residential sprinklers.

6.6.7.1.2 Residential sprinklers shall not be used on systems other than wet pipe systems unless specifically listed for use on that particular type of system.

The requirement in 6.6.7.1.2 is based on the concern for the expected delay in water delivery inherent with dry pipe systems and is included because no residential sprinklers are listed for this application.

6.6.7.1.3 Listed quick-response sprinklers shall be permitted to be installed in dwelling units meeting the definition of a compartment, as defined in Section 4.1, where no more than four sprinklers are located in the dwelling unit.

The requirement in 6.6.7.1.3 permits the use of quick-response sprinklers in applications where the desired performance can be achieved without the wall-wetting characteristics associated with residential sprinklers. The requirement also permits systems to be installed in instances where room layout or ceiling configuration can restrict the use of residential sprinklers [Bill 1988]. For example, a hotel room could be protected with quick-response extended coverage sidewall sprinklers, which are not listed as residential sprinklers. An arrangement using quick-response sprinklers is considered to provide an acceptable level of protection for NFPA 13R systems. Exhibit 6.5 illustrates an example of the application of 6.6.7.1.3.

Previous editions of NFPA 13R allowed four standard response sprinklers to be used. However, quick-response sprinklers provide a more effective means of achieving life safety than do standard response sprinklers. This philosophy also holds true in NFPA 13, which now requires that listed quick-response or residential sprinklers be installed in light hazard occupancies. Additionally, when the exception for the standard response sprinklers was first

EXHIBIT 6.5 Dwelling Unit Protected with Quick-Response Sprinklers.

Clothes closet

Bathroom

Living/dining area

○ 4

Kitchen

Bedroom

○
1

○ 3

Clothes closet

○ Sprinkler location
▢ Smoke detector

accepted in 1988, listed quick-response sprinklers were not as readily available as they are today.

6.6.7.1.4 Quick-response sprinklers shall be permitted to be used in mechanical closets.

6.6.7.1.5 Temperature Ratings.

6.6.7.1.5.1* Sprinklers installed where maximum ambient ceiling temperatures do not exceed 100°F (38°C) shall be ordinary temperature–rated sprinklers unless modified by 6.6.7.1.5.3.

A.6.6.7.1.5.1 Sprinklers having a temperature rating of 135°F to 170°F (57°C to 77°C) are classified as ordinary temperature–rated sprinklers.

The maximum ambient temperature in a residential environment should be no more than 35°F (19°C) less than the temperature rating of the installed residential sprinkler (see 6.6.7.1.5.1). If higher temperatures are expected, then higher temperature–rated sprinklers should be used. The temperature ratings of residential sprinklers currently range from 135°F to 170°F (57°C to 77°C).

6.6.7.1.5.2* Sprinklers installed where maximum ambient ceiling temperatures are between 101°F and 150°F (39°C and 66°C) shall be intermediate temperature–rated sprinklers unless modified by 6.6.7.1.5.3.

A.6.6.7.1.5.2 Sprinklers having a temperature rating of 175°F to 225°F (79°C to 107°C) are classified as intermediate temperature–rated sprinklers.

6.6.7.1.5.3 The following practices shall be observed when installing residential sprinklers unless higher expected ambient temperatures require a higher temperature rating.

(A) Sprinklers under glass or plastic skylights exposed to direct rays of the sun shall be of intermediate temperature classification.

(B) Sprinklers in an unventilated concealed space under uninsulated roof or in an unventilated attic shall be of intermediate temperature classification.

(C) Sprinklers installed near specific heat sources that are identified in Table 6.6.7.1.5.3 shall be of the temperature rating indicated in Table 6.6.7.1.5.3 unless sprinklers are listed for positioning closer to the heat source.

TABLE 6.6.7.1.5.3 *Minimum Distances for Ordinary and Intermediate Temperature Residential Sprinklers*

Heat Source	From Edge of Source to Ordinary Temperature Sprinkler		From Edge of Source to Intermediate Temperature Sprinkler	
	in.	*mm*	*in.*	*mm*
Side of open or recessed fireplace	36	914	12	305
Front of recessed fireplace	60	1524	36	914
Coal- or wood-burning stove	42	1067	12	305
Kitchen range	18	457	9	229
Wall oven	18	457	9	229
Hot air flues	18	457	9	229
Uninsulated heat ducts	18	457	9	229
Uninsulated hot water pipes	12	305	6	152
Side of ceiling- or wall-mounted hot air diffusers	24	607	12	305
Front of wall-mounted hot air diffusers	36	914	18	457
Hot water heater or furnace	6	152	3	76
Light fixture:				
0 W – 250 W	6	152	3	76
250 W – 499 W	12	305	6	152

Areas containing hot water heaters, heating equipment, and other similar heat-producing devices require some special treatment (see 6.6.7.1.5.3). In addition, sprinklers that are installed in the vicinity of a fireplace or wood-burning stove can also be exposed to relatively high temperatures. The requirements of 6.6.7.1.5.2 and 6.6.7.1.5.3, as well as the manufacturer's instructions, need to be followed with regard to sprinkler temperature classification and placement where high ambient temperatures are expected.

With regard to 6.6.7.1.5.3(A), the temperature of the air surrounding a sprinkler can exceed 100°F (38°C) when a skylight permits direct sun exposure to that area. Also, unventilated attics tend to develop rather high temperatures in the summer months. Thus, a similar precaution to prevent false activation in attics should be undertaken. Selecting the appropriate temperature rating for a given environment is always important. The correct temperature rating helps to ensure that sprinklers will not operate prematurely and that an excessive number of sprinklers will not operate during the fire.

Positioning sprinklers closer than that allowed by Table 6.6.7.1.5.3 is likely to result in false activation of the sprinkler. Paragraph 6.6.7.1.5.3(C) allows for closer distances than indicated in Table 6.6.7.1.5.3 where sprinklers are specifically listed for this distance.

6.6.7.1.5.4 All sprinklers within a compartment shall have the same temperature classification except where required by 6.6.7.1.5.3 for a specific location.

A number of factors influence the operating time of a sprinkler, such as the sprinkler's location with respect to the fire, the air flow's temperature and velocity, the sprinkler's operating mechanism, and the sprinkler's position below the ceiling surface. A variation of any of the factors could result in a measurable difference in the operating time of the sprinkler. In order to establish some control over these related items, residential sprinklers with the same temperature classification are required in the compartment by 6.6.7.1.5.4. This requirement helps to ensure that sprinklers located closest to the fire will operate first.

This requirement also allows the designer more flexibility when placing sprinklers in odd-shaped compartments. For example, a room can be protected with two residential

◀ FAQ
What factors affect the operating time of sprinklers?

sprinklers—one with an extended area of coverage and one with a 144-ft^2 (13-m^2) area of coverage. Finding sprinklers with these different areas of coverage and an identical temperature rating may not be possible. As long as devices with the same temperature classification are used, the concern with skipping or reverse order of operation is alleviated.

Sprinklers can be of different temperature classifications as permitted in 6.6.7.1.5.3.

6.6.7.1.6 Where escutcheon plates are used, they shall be part of a listed sprinkler assembly.

Although 6.7.1.5 indicates the minimum distances a sprinkler deflector should be placed below ceilings, these provisions are not always followed. Sprinklers with small frames that are used with incompatible escutcheons can have their performance adversely affected. Unless properly evaluated, the escutcheon can severely obstruct the spray pattern and delay the sprinkler's activation. Therefore, escutcheons need to be listed, as required in 6.6.7.1.6.

6.6.7.1.7* **Painting and Ornamental Finishes.** Sprinkler frames shall not be painted or enameled unless applied by the manufacturer and the sprinkler has been listed with such finishes.

 A.6.6.7.1.7 Decorative painting of a residential sprinkler is not to be confused with the temperature identification colors as referenced in 6.2.5 of NFPA 13, *Standard for the Installation of Sprinkler Systems.*

It is extremely important that only sprinkler manufacturers apply paint or ornamental finishes to their sprinklers, as required in 6.6.7.1.7. Painting done by others could seriously impair the sprinkler's operation or could render the sprinkler inoperable.

 6.6.7.2 **Outside the Dwelling Unit.**

 6.6.7.2.1 Sprinklers outside of the dwelling units shall be quick response and selection shall be based on the requirements of NFPA 13, *Standard for the Installation of Sprinkler Systems,* except where permitted by 6.6.7.2.2.

Standard sprinklers are listed, but not in accordance with the criteria for residential sprinklers (see 6.6.7.2.1). See commentary to A.1.2.

 6.6.7.2.2 Residential sprinklers shall be permitted to be used in corridors leading to dwelling units and in areas covered by 6.7.2.2, 6.7.2.3 and 6.7.3.3.

 FAQ ▶
Are residential sprinklers permitted in adjoining corridors and lobbies?

Residential sprinklers, which are addressed in 6.6.7.2.2, are appropriate for use where the fire threat is similar to that expected in a dwelling unit. The fuel loading in a corridor adjoining the dwelling units is substantially lower than that found in the dwelling unit. Corridors and lobbies with ceiling heights of 10 ft (3.0 m) or less can be similar to hallways and living rooms within dwelling units. The criteria for a flat, smooth ceiling are consistent with the listing limitations of residential sprinklers [Bill 1988].

6.6.8 **Alarms.**

6.6.8.1 A local waterflow alarm shall be provided on all sprinkler systems.

6.6.8.2 Where a building fire alarm system is provided, the local waterflow alarms shall be connected to the building fire alarm system.

 FAQ ▶
Is the waterflow alarm required by NFPA 13R intended to be the building's evacuation alarm?

NFPA 13R requires a waterflow alarm for all systems to sound on the premises (see 6.6.8.1 and 6.6.8.2). The alarm's purpose is to indicate water flow through the sprinkler system. The waterflow alarm is not required by NFPA 13R to be part of the building's evacuation alarm. Other supplemental alarm systems are not required by NFPA 13 but are likely to be required by other regulations such as NFPA *101®*, *Life Safety Code®*. Where other regulations require a fire alarm system in the building, then the waterflow device usually needs to be connected to the building's fire alarm system.

6.7 System Design

System design is covered in Section 6.7. Systems installed in accordance with NFPA 13R must be hydraulically designed. The calculation procedure must be as outlined in Chapter 14 of NFPA 13. The design criteria of NFPA 13R sprinkler systems usually consist of two parts—those areas within the dwelling unit and those areas outside the dwelling unit.

In many instances, because of the size of the dwelling units, the systems can be designed with a maximum of four sprinklers operating. However, smaller dwelling units could require less.

6.7.1 Design Criteria—Inside Dwelling Unit.

Section 6.7 provides the design criteria for sprinklers protecting areas within the dwelling unit. Public corridors that serve areas other than dwelling units, lounges, and other areas outside the dwelling unit need to be protected in accordance with 6.7.2.

The information provided in 6.7.1.1, 6.7.1.3.1.1, 6.7.1.3.1.2, 6.7.1.3.1.3, and 6.7.1.3.1.4 is based on the "prototype" residential sprinkler that was used in the Los Angeles and Charlotte, NC, development tests. Listed residential sprinklers are still manufactured to these exact criteria, but other devices exist that cover larger areas, have different spacing criteria, and discharge greater or lesser amounts of water than that specified in 6.7.1. Residential sprinklers of this type are permitted to be used by 6.7.1.3.2.

6.7.1.1 Design Discharge.

6.7.1.1.1 Sprinklers That Have Not Been Listed with Specific Discharge Criteria.

6.7.1.1.1.1 The system shall provide a discharge of not less than 13 gpm (49 L/min) per sprinkler simultaneously to all of the design sprinklers.

6.7.1.1.1.2 The system shall provide a discharge of not less than 18 gpm (68 L/min) to any sprinkler in the system.

Paragraphs 6.7.1.1.1.1 and 6.7.1.1.1.2 prescribe a minimum discharge of 18 gpm (68 L/min) for a single operating sprinkler and 13 gpm (49 L/min) per sprinkler for multiple sprinklers within a compartment. The definition of a *compartment* is provided in Section 4.1. The water-flow criteria translate to a minimum density of 0.125 gpm/ft^2 (5.1 L/min · m^2) for one sprinkler and 0.09 gpm/ft^2 (3.7 L/min · m^2) for multiple sprinklers, assuming the maximum area coverage of 144 ft^2 (13.4 m^2) per sprinkler. The test data indicate that the primary criterion should be flow rate rather than density for a residential sprinkler system [Cote 1980, Cote 1982, Kung 1982, Moore 1980].

Because sprinklers other than residential sprinklers are to be provided within certain dwelling units, such sprinklers must only be used in accordance with their listing. Depending on the type of sprinkler used, the basis of design can be a minimum operating pressure or a minimum flow rate.

6.7.1.1.2* Sprinklers That Have Been Listed with Specific Discharge Criteria.

A.6.7.1.1.2 The minimum pressure and flow requirements need to be satisfied while also meeting the requirements of the formula $q = K(p)^{0.5}$. If a sprinkler with a K-factor of 4.3 is listed to cover an area of 18 ft × 18 ft at 16.2 gpm, the minimum pressure is required to be 14.2 psi so that the flow is achieved. Likewise, if a sprinkler with a K-factor of 5.6 is covering an area 12 ft × 12 ft, the minimum flow is required to be 14.8 gpm (the flow at 7 psi) even though a flow of 7.2 gpm will satisfy the density criteria.

6.7.1.1.2.1 The system shall provide at least the flow required for the multiple and single sprinkler operating criteria specified by the sprinkler listing.

6.7.1.1.2.2* The system shall provide at least the flow required to produce a minimum discharge density of 0.05 gpm/ft^2 (2.04 mm/min) to the design sprinklers.

 A.6.7.1.1.2.2 Sprinklers need to be used in accordance with their listed areas and density. (*See Figure A.6.7.1.1.2.2*).

Sprinkler 1, 4, 5, 6 — 16 ft × 16 ft coverage used to determine flow
Sprinkler 2, 3 — 14 ft × 14 ft coverage used to determine flow

FIGURE A.6.7.1.1.2.2 *Determining Required Flow.*

FAQ ▶
Why was the water spray density of 0.05 gpm/ft^2 (2.0 L/m^2) for sprinklers added to the 2002 edition of NFPA 13R?

With the 2002 edition, a minimum water spray density of 0.05 gpm/ft^2 (2.0 L/m^2) for sprinklers is required by 6.7.1.1.2.2 for systems designed according to this standard. The Technical Committee on Residential Sprinkler Systems proposed this change after considering (1) laboratory test data by Underwriters Laboratories and FM Global, (2) the variability of fire challenges, (3) the excellent residential sprinkler system performance record in field installations, and (4) the need for cost-effective sprinkler protection to encourage the use of sprinklers in residential occupancies.

6.7.1.2* Number of Design Sprinklers. The number of design sprinklers under flat, smooth, horizontal ceilings shall include all sprinklers within a compartment, up to a maximum of four sprinklers, that requires the greatest hydraulic demand.

A.6.7.1.2 It is intended that the design area is to include up to four adjacent sprinklers that produce the greatest water demand within the compartment. [*See Figure A.6.7.1.2(a) and Figure A.6.7.1.2(b).*]

Residential sprinklers are currently listed for use under flat, smooth, horizontal ceilings only. Sloped, beamed, and pitched ceilings could require special design features such as larger flows or a design for five or more sprinklers to operate in the compartment.

The NFPA 13D design criteria, which are based on a maximum of two sprinklers operating, are not considered adequate for NFPA 13R systems (see 6.7.1.2).

FAQ ▶
Why does NFPA 13R require a maximum four-sprinkler design?

The maximum four-sprinkler design criterion required by NFPA 13R incorporates a factor of safety that takes into consideration characteristics relative to larger multifamily residential occupancies, such as the wide range of occupant evacuation capabilities and a much larger number of occupants.

FAQ ▶
Where can a design include less than the four-sprinkler design?

When all compartments are protected with fewer than four sprinklers, the maximum number of sprinklers within a single compartment must define the design area. This requirement means that some NFPA 13R systems might only require two or three sprinklers as part of the operating area. In a highly compartmented structure, only a single design sprinkler might be needed. A compartment is defined in 4.1.1 for purposes of applying this design rule.

FIGURE A.6.7.1.2(a) *Sprinkler Design Areas for Typical Residential Occupancy—without Lintel.*

FIGURE A.6.7.1.2(b) *Sprinkler Design Areas for Typical Residential Occupancy—with Lintel.*

When a compartment contains two or more sprinklers, the designer must perform multiple sets of calculations. The single sprinkler design point and the multiple—that is, up to a maximum of four—sprinkler criteria must both be verified.

A room compartment is defined by the enclosing walls or a soffit or lintel that forms a definite barrier at the ceiling of a room opening. [See Figures A.6.7.1.2(a) and A.6.7.1.2(b).] In open-plan configurations, compartment boundaries can be determined by soffits or lintels over doorways as well as by walls or partitions. The 8-in. (203-mm) minimum depth ensures that heat will collect in the room of fire origin and activate the sprinklers over the fire rather than allowing sprinklers outside the room to activate.

◄ **FAQ**
How is a room compartment defined?

It is not the intent of NFPA 13R that the number of sprinklers limit the size of a compartment—that is, a compartment can have more than four sprinklers installed in it. The size of the compartment or the number of sprinklers allowed in that compartment is not limited.

◄ **FAQ**
Is it the intent of NFPA 13R that the number of sprinklers limit the maximum size of a compartment?

6.7.1.3 Sprinkler Coverage.

6.7.1.3.1 Residential Sprinklers That Have Not Been Listed with Specific Coverage Criteria.

6.7.1.3.1.1 Sprinklers shall be spaced so that the maximum area protected by a single sprinkler does not exceed 144 ft² (13.4 m²).

The design area for a single residential sprinkler should not exceed 144 ft² (13.4 m²), as stated in 6.7.1.3.1.1.

Larger spacings are permitted when evaluated and listed for such spacing in accordance with 6.7.1.3.2.

◄ **FAQ**
Are large spacings permitted by NFPA 13R?

6.7.1.3.1.2 The maximum distance between sprinklers shall not exceed 12 ft (3.7 m).

6.7.1.3.1.3 The maximum distance from the sprinkler to a wall or partition shall not exceed 6 ft (1.8 m).

The 6 ft (1.8 m) distance required by 6.7.1.3.1.3 acts to provide adequate coverage to the floor and to ensure that the high wall-wetting characteristics of residential sprinklers are maintained.

6.7.1.3.1.4 The minimum distance between sprinklers within a compartment shall be 8 ft (2.4 m).

A minimum distance of 8 ft (2.4 m), which is required by 6.7.1.3.1.4, is necessary to prevent cold soldering of adjacent residential sprinklers. If sprinklers are located too close to one another, then the discharge from one sprinkler could cool the area surrounding an adjacent sprinkler and prevent its proper activation. Some residential sprinklers with large areas of coverage might require an even greater minimum separation between devices for the same reason.

6.7.1.3.2 Residential Sprinklers That Have Been Listed with Specific Coverage Criteria. Sprinklers shall be installed in accordance with the coverage criteria specified by the listing.

 The limitations on spacing were determined by the Los Angeles and Charlotte, NC, fire tests (see 6.7.1.3.2) [Cote 1980, Cote 1982, Kung 1982, Moore 1980]. Although these tests were conducted with prototype fast-response residential sprinklers, the Technical Committee on Residential Sprinkler Systems recognized that other residential sprinklers can be developed that will operate properly with different spacing limitations. In fact, some currently listed residential sprinklers have a coverage area of 20 ft × 20 ft (6.1 m × 6.1 m). Such sprinklers can be used provided that spacing differing from that prescribed in NFPA 13R is justified based on testing conducted by a testing and inspection agency/laboratory.

When coverage areas are extended, the minimum flow rates required by the sprinkler's listing must be used. As areas of coverage increase, the minimum flow rates also usually increase. However, improvements and refinements to sprinkler deflectors and their operating elements have produced listed residential sprinklers that can cover areas greater than 12 ft × 12 ft (3.7 m × 3.7 m) yet discharge quantities of water that are less than the 18-gpm (68-L/min) and 13-gpm (49-L/min) flows established in 6.7.1.1. The minimum operating pressure requirement of 7 psi (0.5 bar) has been included in NFPA 13R. In this regard, NFPA 13R is in agreement with NFPA 13 and NFPA 13D.

 6.7.1.3.3 Non-Residential Sprinklers. Sprinklers other than residential sprinklers shall be installed in accordance with the coverage criteria specified by NFPA 13, *Standard for the Installation of Sprinkler Systems.*

6.7.1.4 Operating Pressure. The minimum operating pressure of any sprinkler shall be the higher of the minimum operating pressure specified by the listing or 7 psi (0.5 bar).

6.7.1.5 Position of Residential Sprinklers.

6.7.1.5.1 Pendent and Upright Sprinklers.

6.7.1.5.1.1 Pendent and upright sprinklers that have not been listed with specific positioning criteria shall be positioned so that the deflectors are within 1 in. to 4 in. (25.4 mm to 102 mm) from the ceiling.

 To allow the sprinkler to operate in a timely manner, the deflector's position below the ceiling is limited to ensure the sprinkler is placed where the thermal layer is expected to accumulate (see 6.7.1.5.1.1). This limitation is based on the results of the Los Angeles and Charlotte, NC, fire tests [Cote 1980, Cote 1982, Kung 1982, Moore 1980].

6.7.1.5.1.2 Pendent and upright sprinklers that have been listed with specific positioning criteria shall be positioned in accordance with the listing.

6.7.1.5.2 Sidewall Sprinklers.

6.7.1.5.2.1 Sidewall sprinklers that have not been listed with specific positioning criteria shall be positioned so that the deflectors are within 4 in. to 6 in. (102 mm to 152 mm) from the ceiling.

Dead-air spaces in corners can affect a sprinkler's operation time. The 4-in to 6-in. (102-mm to 152-mm) limitation in 6.7.1.5.2.1 ensures that the sprinkler will operate properly.

6.7.1.5.2.2 Sidewall sprinklers that have been listed with specific positioning criteria shall be positioned in accordance with the listing.

6.7.1.5.3* Sprinklers shall be positioned so that the response time and discharge are not unduly affected by obstructions such as ceiling slope, beams, or light fixtures.

A.6.7.1.5.3 Fire testing has indicated the need to wet walls in the area protected by residential sprinklers at a level closer to the ceiling than that accomplished by standard sprinkler distribution. Where beams, light fixtures, sloped ceilings, and other obstructions occur, additional residential sprinklers could be necessary to achieve proper response and distribution, and a greater water supply could be necessary.

Small areas created by architectural features such as planter box windows, bay windows, and similar features can be evaluated as follows:

(1) Where no additional floor area is created by the architectural feature, no additional sprinkler protection is required.

(2) Where additional floor area is created by an architectural feature, no additional sprinkler protection is required, provided all of the following conditions are met:

  (a) The floor area does not exceed 18 ft² (1.7 m²).

  (b) The floor area is not greater than 2 ft (0.65 m) in depth at the deepest point of the architectural feature to the plane of the primary wall where measured along the finished floor.

  (c) The floor is not greater than 9 ft (2.9 m) in length where measured along the plane of the primary wall.

Measurement from the deepest point of the architectural feature to the sprinkler should not exceed the maximum listed spacing of the sprinkler. The hydraulic design is not required to consider the area created by the architectural feature.

The installation of residential sprinklers under beamed, sloped, or cathedral ceilings is essentially prohibited by 6.7.1.5.3 because of a lack of information about response times and distribution patterns under such conditions.

Ceiling fans can create another obstruction problem. Although not specifically evaluated as a part of the listing for a residential sprinkler, a limited number of demonstration tests were conducted in Cobb County, GA, in 1985 to determine the effect of fans on sprinklers. Essentially, this demonstration indicated that no adverse effects occur as a result of the ceiling fan's rotation in either direction. The motor housing is the primary element that can impede the spray pattern and must be considered. The vertical obstruction rules in NFPA 13 can be used to minimize the motor's impact as an obstruction.

◄ FAQ
How can ceiling fans be addressed?

Paragraph A.6.7.1.5.3 includes additional information on sprinkler positioning in relation to planter box windows, bay windows, and similar architectural features. Overall, these features are usually smaller in area than a closet and, in some cases, do not add floor space. Therefore, these small architectural features are not anticipated to significantly increase the fire hazard of a residence nor to adversely impact sprinkler performance.

Furthermore, adherence to the spacing rules of NFPA 13R often cannot be achieved without placing a sprinkler within the bay window or planter box window. An alternative evaluation procedure has been added because sprinkler locations within these spaces raises concerns about system performance.

Small bay windows protected with sprinklers usually require piping run along an outside wall to feed the sprinkler in the bay window. Because the bay window is added onto the side of the house, the space is subject to greater temperature fluctuations that insulation cannot always protect against. This temperature fluctuation increases the potential of freezing during cold temperatures. Additionally, in areas where warmer climates prevail, solar heating of the window glass creates the potential for false actuation of the sprinkler. An increased number of sprinklers operating within the compartment is also a concern. Activating more sprinklers than anticipated by the design in a compartment can overtax the water supply and reduce the effectiveness of the sprinkler system.

◄ FAQ
Why are small bay windows addressed differently when determining sprinkler requirements?

6.7.1.5.4 In closets and storage areas with both a volume no larger than 300 ft³ (8.93 m³) and a ceiling height less than 5 ft (1.5 m) at the lowest ceiling, a single sprinkler located at the highest ceiling shall be permitted to protect that space.

Closets less than 5 ft (1.5 m) in height at the lowest ceiling and less than 300 ft³ (8.93 m³) in volume only need a single sprinkler located at the highest ceiling to achieve fire control, as stated in 6.7.1.5.4. These closet types are typically found under stairs and roofs. In some cases, multiple sprinklers are installed within a single closet or storage compartment in order to ensure proper floor coverage. Experience suggests that fire development within a small confined space, such as a closet, is not comparable with that of a larger space. Fire control in these smaller compartments results primarily from the buildup of steam and the associated cooling of the space. Also, the presence of a sprinkler on lower ceiling surfaces within the closet can create the potential for unsatisfactory sprinkler activation and operation. This requirement identifies the closets that can be satisfactorily protected by a single sprinkler.

6.7.2* Design Criteria—Outside Dwelling Unit.

 A.6.7.2 It is only the intent of NFPA 13R to reference the sprinkler discharge (flow and pressure), number of design sprinklers and position of sprinklers (distance from walls, ceilings, and other sprinklers) requirements of NFPA 13. Other rules from NFPA 13 such as sprinklering of combustible concealed spaces, hose stream demand and water supply duration are not intended to be referenced by 6.7.2. It is also the intent of 6.7.2 to apply to those systems or portions of systems that are outside the dwelling unit, but have been determined to be considered residential or incidental to residential and within the scope of this standard. (*Also see A.1.1.*)

Subsection 6.7.2 contains the design criteria for sprinklers protecting areas outside the dwelling unit, such as lobbies, corridors, halls, and foyers that are not contained within dwelling units; basements and storage areas; inside stairwells; and equipment, furnace, trash, laundry, and linen rooms. Paragraph 6.7.2.1 refers the user of NFPA 13R to NFPA 13. However, it should be noted that 6.7.4 requires the system to be hydraulically calculated.

In many cases, a design criterion based on four sprinklers will be possible to maintain in accordance with 6.7.2.1 through 6.7.2.3.

 6.7.2.1 For areas outside the dwelling unit, the following criteria shall comply with specifications in NFPA 13, *Standard for the Installation of Sprinkler Systems*, unless permitted by 6.7.2.2 and 6.7.2.3:

(1) Design discharge
(2) Number of design sprinklers
(3) Sprinkler coverage
(4) Position of sprinklers

 6.7.2.2 The system demand of areas outside the dwelling unit shall be permitted to be limited to the number of sprinklers in the compartmented area but shall not be greater than the demand for a total of four sprinklers where all of the following conditions are met:

(1) The area is compartmented into areas of 500 ft² (46 m²) or less by 30-minute fire-rated construction.
(2) The area is protected by quick-response or residential sprinklers not exceeding 130 ft² (12 m²) per sprinkler for ordinary hazard, 225 ft² (20.9 m²) for light hazard, or the allowable coverage of the sprinkler listing.
(3) Openings have a lintel at least 8 in. (203 mm) in depth.
(4) The total area of openings does not exceed 50 ft² (4.6 m²) for each compartment.
 (5) Discharge densities are in accordance with NFPA 13, *Standard for the Installation of Sprinkler Systems*.

Paragraph 6.7.2.2 provides an alternative to the design area criteria of NFPA 13. This alternative is an adaptation of the room design method of 11.2.3.3 of NFPA 13. The 130-ft^2 (12-m^2) area of coverage in 6.7.2.2(2) is based in part on the assumption that areas that will be protected in accordance with 6.7.2.2 the exception will be ordinary hazard areas.

6.7.2.3 The following types of spaces are permitted to be protected by residential sprinklers where they have flat, smooth ceilings not exceeding 10 ft (3.0 m) in height and are protected in accordance with the requirements for residential sprinklers:

(1) Lobbies not in hotels and motels
(2) Foyers
(3) Corridors
(4) Halls
(5) Lounges
(6) Other areas with fire loads similar to residential

Paragraph 6.7.2.3 underscores the fact that residential sprinklers can only be used under certain conditions. These conditions include certain construction features such as maximum ceiling heights of 10 ft (3.0 m) and smooth ceiling configurations and anticipated fire hazards such as those typically presented in residential occupancies. Hotel and motel lobbies do not fall within the scope of this exception because the fire hazard in these spaces is no longer residential in nature. Such lobbies often have adjacent or connecting spaces used for gift shops, restaurants, and small displays.

6.7.3 Design Criteria—Garages.

6.7.3.1 Garages that are completely separated from the residential portion of the building by fire resistive construction sufficient to have them considered separate buildings under the local code shall be protected in accordance with NFPA 13, *Standard for the Installation of Sprinkler Systems.*

6.7.3.2 Garages that are accessible by people from more than one dwelling unit, and are not covered by 6.7.3.1, shall be considered part of the building and shall be protected in accordance with 6.7.2. Garage doors shall not be considered obstructions and shall be permitted to be ignored for placement and calculation of sprinklers.

6.7.3.3* Garages that are only accessible from a single dwelling unit shall be considered as part of that dwelling unit. Such garages shall be sprinklered with residential sprinklers in accordance with 6.7.1 or quick-response sprinklers designed to provide a density of 0.05 gpm/ft^2 (2.04 mm/min) over the area of the garage, but not to exceed four sprinklers. Garage doors shall not be considered obstructions and shall be permitted to be ignored for placement and calculation of sprinklers.

A.6.7.3.3 Residential sprinklers and quick-response sprinklers at 0.05 gpm/ft^2 densities have not been tested for use in garages, however, field experience has shown that they will activate, sound an alarm, and provide water distribution that will assist in controlling a fire.

The last sentence of 6.7.3.3 addresses the practicality and cost of installing additional sprinklers in garages to minimize obstructions caused by overhead garage doors. While in the up position, the garage door will likely cause an obstruction to a sprinkler located above the door. However, garage doors are usually left in the closed position for the types of residential occupancies addressed by NFPA 13R. The likelihood of a deadly fire occurring in the garage while the door is in the open position falls within the level of protection concept employed by NFPA 13R.

A common mistake is made in the application of the location (e.g., combustible concealed spaces) rules from NFPA 13. Paragraph 6.7.2.1 of NFPA 13R only requires that the design discharge, number of design sprinklers, sprinkler coverage, and position of sprinklers be applied from NFPA 13. The location requirements for sprinklers in NFPA 13R applications are located in Section 6.8 and are applicable to areas inside and outside of the dwelling unit.

When applying the design criteria for areas outside the dwelling unit, is it the intent to apply the location requirements (e.g., combustible concealed spaces) for NFPA 13 to NFPA 13R applications?

◄ FAQ

6.7.4 Pipe Sizing. Piping shall be sized using hydraulic calculation procedures in accordance with NFPA 13, *Standard for the Installation of Sprinkler Systems.*

FAQ ▶
Are hydraulic calculations required to be completed in accordance with NFPA 13?

Hydraulic calculations must be prepared in accordance with Chapter 14 of NFPA 13, and all appropriate provisions of NFPA 13 must apply, as stated in 6.7.4. The different criteria for inside and outside dwelling units (see 6.7.1) as well as the dual discharge criteria of 6.7.1.1 require at least two and often three separate sets of calculations.

6.8 Location of Sprinklers

Section 6.8 is a departure from NFPA 13. The location of sprinklers is the primary area where the life safety goal is paramount to the property protection goal when compared to NFPA 13. The areas listed in 6.8.2 through 6.8.6 reflect spaces where fatalities are less likely to occur when a fire originates in one of them.

FAQ ▶
How did the committee determine from which areas to omit sprinkler protection?

The basis for sprinkler omission in 6.8.2 through 6.8.6 has been previously described under Section 1.2 and is based on NFPA statistics provided in Table A.1.2. The spaces in 6.8.2 through 6.8.6 are the ones shown to result in a low incidence of life loss from fires in dwellings.

With respect to 6.8.2, the combustible load in bathrooms is normally extremely low, especially when the ceiling and wall materials are not likely to contribute to the fire's growth. This requirement reflects the concern that a fire in an unsprinklered bathroom could enter unsprinklered concealed spaces. The additional requirement for floors, walls, and ceilings to provide a 15-minute thermal barrier was added to meet this concern.

With regard to 6.8.4 and 6.8.5, mandatory sprinklering of these areas would necessitate the use of dry pipe systems in areas where freezing weather is encountered. However, it should be noted where the spaces described in 6.8.5 contain fuel-fired equipment, sprinklers are required.

The word *open* in 6.8.4 is intended to apply to areas that are open to the outside atmosphere. An example of an open corridor is one that empties to an outside stairway and has no doors attached to it. Another example is an exterior wraparound corridor that is typical in a two- or three-story motel.

FAQ ▶
Are garages required to sprinklered?

One additional exception that users of NFPA 13R expect to see in Section 6.8 but does not appear is for garages. The Technical Committee on Residential Sprinkler Systems is of the opinion that a large number of building occupants can reside in the residential occupancies addressed by NFPA 13R and that a fire originating in an unsprinklered garage could quickly get out of control prior to evacuation of the building's occupants. Requirements for garages are addressed in 6.7.3.

With regard to 6.8.6, closets on exterior balconies used either for storage or as a mechanical space do not require sprinklers provided that they meet the conditions of 6.8.3 or 6.8.6. Where mechanical equipment in the closet penetrates into the living area, fire dampers or other fire penetration protection is required if the closet space is not sprinklered.

6.8.1 Sprinklers shall be installed in all areas except where omission is permitted by 6.8.2 through 6.8.6.

6.8.2* Sprinklers shall not be required in bathrooms where both of the following conditions are met:

(1) The bathroom area does not exceed 55 ft^2 (5.1 m^2).
(2) The walls and ceilings, including walls and ceilings behind fixtures, are of noncombustible or limited-combustible materials providing a 15-minute thermal barrier.

A   **A.6.8.2** A room is still considered a bathroom if it contains just a toilet. Additionally, two bathrooms can be adjacent to each other and are considered separate rooms provided they are enclosed with the required level of construction.

6.8.3 Sprinklers shall not be required in clothes closets, linen closets, and pantries within the dwelling units that meet all of the following conditions:

(1) The area of the space does not exceed 24 ft² (2.2 m²).
(2) The least dimension does not exceed 3 ft (0.91 m).
(3) The walls and ceilings are surfaced with noncombustible or limited-combustible materials as defined by NFPA 220, *Standard on Types of Building Construction.*

6.8.4 Sprinklers shall not be required in any porches, balconies, corridors, and stairs that are open and attached.

6.8.5 Sprinklers shall not be required in attics, penthouse equipment rooms, elevator machine rooms, concealed spaces dedicated exclusively to and containing only dwelling unit ventilation equipment, crawl spaces, floor/ceiling spaces, elevator shafts, and other concealed spaces that are not used or intended for living purposes or storage and do not contain fuel-fired equipment.

6.8.6 Sprinklers shall not be required in closets on exterior balconies, regardless of size, as long as there are no doors or unprotected penetrations from the closet directly into the dwelling unit.

6.9* Maintenance

A.6.9 The responsibility for properly maintaining a sprinkler system is that of the owner or manager, who should understand the sprinkler system operation. A minimum monthly maintenance program should include the following:

(1) Visual inspection of all sprinklers to insure against obstruction of spray.
(2) Inspection of all valves to ensure that they are open.
(3) Testing of all waterflow devices.
(4) Testing of the alarm system, where installed. Note that where it is likely that the test will result in a fire department response, notification to the fire department should be made prior to the test.
(5) Operation of pumps, where employed. (*See NFPA 20, Standard for the Installation of Stationary Pumps for Fire Protection.*)
(6) Checking of the pressure of air used with dry systems.
(7) Checking of the water level in tanks.
(8) Special attention to ensure that sprinklers are not painted either at the time of installation or during subsequent redecoration. When sprinkler piping or areas next to sprinklers are being painted, the sprinklers should be protected by covering them with a bag, which should be removed immediately after painting is finished.

For further information, see NFPA 25, *Standard for the Inspection, Testing, and Maintenance of Water-Based Fire Protection Systems.*

Maintenance is covered in Section 6.9. Due to the passive nature of systems, their proper maintenance is important for effective sprinkler system performance in a fire. NFPA 13R mandates, therefore, that the owner be responsible for a proper preventive maintenance program involving inspection, testing, and maintenance. A system not maintained in normal operating condition is not in compliance with NFPA 13R.

NFPA 25 contains numerous requirements on the inspection, testing, and maintenance of automatic sprinklers and sprinkler system components. The monthly maintenance program outlined in A.6.9 represents what the Technical Committee on Residential Sprinkler Systems considers to be a minimum acceptable program.

6.9.1 The owner shall be responsible for the condition of a sprinkler system and shall keep the system in normal operating condition.

 6.9.2 Sprinkler systems shall be inspected, tested, and maintained in accordance with NFPA 25, *Standard for the Inspection, Testing, and Maintenance of Water-Based Fire Protection Systems.*

FAQ ▶
How should damaged or painted sprinklers be treated?

Underwriters Laboratories Inc. has conducted a program in which to test field samples of automatic sprinklers to determine their operating characteristics. Results from this program have shown that, when a sprinkler has been damaged or painted after leaving the factory, it is unlikely to operate properly and should be replaced. Obviously, a sprinkler that has operated must also be replaced.

REFERENCES CITED IN COMMENTARY

National Fire Protection Association, 1 Batterymarch Park, P.O. Box 9101, Quincy, MA 02269-9101

NFPA 13, *Standard for the Installation of Sprinkler Systems,* 2002 edition
NFPA 13D, *Standard for the Installation of Sprinkler Systems in One- and Two-Family Dwellings and Manufactured Homes,* 2002 edition
NFPA 20, *Standard for the Installation of Stationary Pumps for Fire Protection,* 1999 edition
NFPA 25, *Standard for the Inspection, Testing, and Maintenance of Water-Based Fire Protection Systems,* 2002 edition
NFPA *101®, Life Safety Code®,* 2000 edition
NFPA 170, *Standard for Fire Safety Symbols,* 2002 edition

Bill, R. G., Jr., Kung, H. C., Brown, W. R., and Hill, E. E., Jr., "Effects of Cathedral and Beamed Ceiling Construction on Residential Sprinkler Performance," Factory Mutual Research Corporation, Norwood, MA, February 1988
Cote, A. E., "Final Report on Field Test and Evaluation of Residential Sprinkler Systems," National Fire Protection Association, Quincy, MA, July 1982
Cote, A. E., and Moore, D., "Field Test and Evaluation of Residential Sprinkler Systems, Los Angeles Test Series," National Fire Protection Association, Boston, MA, April 1980
Factory Mutual Research Corporation, "Approval Standard—Residential Automatic Sprinklers, Class No. 2030," Norwood, MA, September 1983
Kung, H. C., Spaulding, R. D., Hill, E. E., Jr., and Symonds, A. P., "Technical Report, Field Evaluation of Residential Prototype Sprinkler, Los Angeles Fire Test Program," Factory Mutual Research Corporation, Norwood, MA, February 1982
Moore, D., "Data Summary of the North Carolina Test Series of USFA Grant 79027 Field Test and Evaluation of Residential Sprinkler Systems," National Fire Protection Association, Boston, MA, September 1980
Underwriters Laboratories Inc., Proposed First Edition of the Standard for Residential Sprinklers for Fire Protection Service, UL 1626, Northbrook, IL, April 1986

Explanatory Material

Annex A is not a part of the requirements of this NFPA document but is included for informational purposes only. This annex contains explanatory material, numbered to correspond with the applicable text paragraphs.

The material contained in Annex A of NFPA 13R is included within the text of this handbook and, therefore, is not repeated here.

Informational References

B.1 Referenced Publications

The following documents or portions thereof are referenced within this standard for informational purposes only and are thus not part of the requirements of this document unless also listed in Chapter 2.

B.1.1 NFPA Publications. National Fire Protection Association, 1 Batterymarch Park, P.O. Box 9101, Quincy, MA 02269-9101.

NFPA 13, *Standard for the Installation of Sprinkler Systems,* 2002 edition.

NFPA 20, *Standard for the Installation of Stationary Pumps for Fire Protection,* 1999 edition.

NFPA 25, *Standard for the Inspection, Testing, and Maintenance of Water-Based Fire Protection Systems,* 1998 edition.

B.1.2 Other Publications.

B.1.2.1 ASTM Publications. American Society for Testing and Materials, 100 Barr Harbor Drive, West Conshohocken, PA 19428-2959.

ASTM D 3309, *Standard Specification for Polybutylene (PB) Plastic Hot- and Cold-Water Distribution Systems,* 1995.

ASTM F 437, *Standard Specification for Threaded Chlorinated Poly (Vinyl Chloride) (CPVC) Plastic Pipe Fittings, Schedule 80,* 1996.

ASTM F 438, *Standard Specification for Socket-Type Chlorinated Poly (Vinyl Chloride) (CPVC) Plastic Pipe Fittings, Schedule 40,* 1997.

ASTM F 439, *Standard Specification for Socket-Type Chlorinated Poly (Vinyl Chloride) (CPVC) Plastic Pipe Fittings, Schedule 80,* 1997.

ASTM F 442, *Standard Specification for Chlorinated Poly (Vinyl Chloride) (CPVC) Plastic Pipe (SDR-PR),* 1997.

ASTM SI 10, *Standard for Use of the International System of Units (SI): the Modern Metric System,* 1997.

B.2 Informational References. (Reserved)

B.3 References for Extracts. (Reserved)

PART FOUR

Supplements

The three supplements included in Part Four of the handbook provide additional information as well as supporting reference material to assist users and enforcers of NFPA 13, *Standard for the Installation of Sprinkler Systems*. The supplements are not part of NFPA 13 or the commentary presented in the previous part of this book. The supplements are as follows:

1   A Brief History of Sprinklers, Sprinkler Systems, and the NFPA Sprinkler Standards
2   The Effect of Large Orifice Sprinklers on High Challenge Fires
3   Microbiologically Influenced Corrosion in Fire Sprinkler Systems

Supplement 1

A Brief History of Sprinklers, Sprinkler Systems, and the NFPA Sprinkler Standards

Rolf Jensen, P.E.

Editor's Note: Perhaps no system has been more important in the effort to protect lives and property from fire than the automatic sprinkler system. For more than 100 years, National Fire Protection Association (NFPA) sprinkler standards have guided sprinkler system technology, design, and installation. This supplement traces the history of the development of the early sprinklers and sprinkler systems, the origin of the first sprinkler standard, and the influences of changes in technology on sprinkler systems and NFPA sprinkler standards.

EARLY HISTORY: 1870–1900

In the beginning, four interdependent paths led to the development of the early sprinkler systems, and eventually initiated the creation of the first edition of NFPA 13 in 1896. NFPA 13's original title was *Rules and Regulations of the National Board of Fire Underwriters for Sprinkler Equipments, Automatic and Open Systems.*

The first path was the invention of the automatic sprinkler by Henry S. Parmelee in 1874. The first practical, usable sprinkler was manufactured in 1875.

The second path was the development of the original configurations and pipe size schedules. These were based on pipe arrangements by Parmelee and the Providence Steam and Gas Pipe Company (PSGP), which later became the Grinnell Corporation. The pipe schedules were refined later in tests on automatic sprinklers by C. J. H. Woodbury and in experiments on the hydraulics of nozzles and fire streams by John R. Freeman. Both

Woodbury and Freeman were with the Factory Mutuals. [1,2,3][a]

The third path was the development of alarm valves and dry valves needed to control and detect waterflow and sound an alarm.

The fourth path was the recognition of the need for such systems initially by users, which were mostly textile manufacturers. Insurance companies subsequently recognized the benefit in the reduction of losses and catalyzed

---

[a]Many organizations have been referred to as "the Factory Mutuals." Some of these organizations are insurance companies and others are research organizations or product testing and approval organizations. It is beyond the scope of this supplement to attempt to trace the history or organizational structure of any of the Factory Mutual organizations. The names used in various sections are those that were commonly used to identify each company or organization at a point in time.

Rolf Jensen, P.E., was the founder of Rolf H. Jensen & Associates and served on the Technical Committee on Automatic Sprinklers for over 35 years.

the use of this important fire safety system by offering more insurance coverage or insurance rate reductions.

The Sprinkler

The automatic sprinkler of today is a far different device than the first sprinkler developed in 1874. (See Exhibit S1.1.) Several versions of the early Parmelee sprinklers were developed. The first version, Parmelee A, may not actually have been used, because it depended on a jute string to function. The second version, Parmelee 1, was actually installed in Parmelee's Mathushek Piano Factory in Providence, RI, possibly to achieve lower insurance rates but was replaced a year later with the Parmelee 3.

The Parmelee 1 sprinkler consisted of a perforated distributor and a valve, which was held in place by a spindle that rested against a lever. One end of the lever was pivoted and the other was attached to the casting with a heavy spring and a fusible link. Often referred to as a *salt shaker* sprinkler, the Parmelee 3 had a brass cap soldered in place over a distributor. The Parmelee 3's only similarity to modern sprinklers was that it was operated by a fusible element. [1,3,4]

Conceived in 1873 by Charles E. Buell although not installed until 1881, the Buell was the first sprinkler with an external deflector and the first to use a cap and seal to close the waterway. (See Exhibit S1.2.)

Regardless of the importance of the inventions of Parmelee, Buell, and others, it was Frederick Grinnell's sprinkler, patented in 1881, that was the first sensitive

EXHIBIT S1.2 *Buell Sprinkler.*

sprinkler. Grinnell followed with several improvements leading to the Grinnell Glass Disc Sprinkler in July 1890. This sprinkler was the earliest that had substantial similarity to those in modern use. [4]

Piping Systems

Early piping configurations evolved from perforated pipe systems that were supplied by a vertical riser for each floor because they were manually operated. Parmelee and Grinnell later originated a so-called "tree" system. In the system's original configuration, main feed pipes were placed about 20 ft (6.1 m) apart, and 5-ft (1.5-m) long branch lines of ¾-in. pipe were spaced about 10 ft (3 m) apart on the feed pipe. The concept was that by placing each sprinkler on a dead-end pipe the sprinkler would not be cooled by water flowing past it in the event of a fire.

The first pipe schedule, the 1-3-6 Pipe Schedule, was developed by PSGP. Until 1896, a variety of pipe size and spacing rules were used mostly in New England. As an outgrowth of experiments on hydraulics (circa 1888–1895), John R. Freeman proposed a 1-2-3 Pipe Schedule and suggested a staggered arrangement of sprinklers under joisted construction for better distribution. The demand for uniformity, however, led to the adoption of a 1-2-4 Pipe Schedule in the first NFPA sprinkler standard in 1896. Table S1.1 compares these very early schedules. Also see Table S1.2. [1,2,3]

EXHIBIT S1.1 *The First Sprinkler, Which Was Invented by Henry S. Parmelee.*

TABLE S1.1 Early Pipe Schedules

Nominal Pipe Size (in.)	Maximum Number of Sprinklers Allowed				
	Pre-1892	Freeman 1892	Freeman 1895	NFPA 13 1896	NFPA 13 1896*
¾	1	1	1	1	1
1	3	2	2	2	2
1¼	6	3	3	4	4
1½	10	5	5	8	6
2	18	10	10	16	8
2½	28	20	20	28	16
3	48	40	36	48	28
3½	78	60	55	78	
4	115	120	80	110	
5	150	150	140	150	
6	200	300	200	200	

For SI units, 1 in. = 25.4 mm.
*More than six sprinklers on a branch line.

TABLE S1.2 Sprinkler Pipe Schedules

Nominal Pipe Size (in.)	Maximum Number of Sprinklers Allowed						
	1940 Standard			1905 to 1940 1-2-3 System		Original NFPA Standard 1896 to 1905 1-2-4 System	Providence Steam and Gas Pipe Co. 1878 to 1896 1-3-6 System
	Light Hazard	Ordinary Hazard	Extra Hazard	Class A	Class B*		
¾	Eliminated			1	1	1	1
1	2	2	1	2	2	2	3
1¼	3	3	2	3	3	4	6
1½	5	5	5	5	5	8	10
2	10	10	8	10	10	16	18
2½	40	20	15	20		28	28
3		40	27	36		48	48
3½		65	40	55		78	78
4		100	55	80		110	115
5		160	90	140		150	150
6		250	150	200		200	200
8				400			

For SI units, 1 in. = 25.4 mm.
*Added in 1931.

Valves

The early alarm valves used a mechanical attachment to the hinge pin to detect clapper movement and thus detect waterflow. The first valve was patented by J. C. Meloon of PSGP in Providence, RI, in 1881, followed by the Buell valve in 1884. The first grooved seat ring alarm valve was developed in England and patented in the United States in 1888 by R. Dowson and J. Taylor. The valve was manufactured by PSGP and later by PSGP's successor, the General Fire Extinguisher Co. None of the valves had retarding devices and most were not too reliable. [3]

Although several earlier dry valves were developed, the first to be used in practice was the "bellows type" invented by Grinnell in 1885. The first differential-type valve, the Grinnell #12 (1890), was the first to be widely used. [3]

The Need

Parmelee developed his first sprinkler for his piano factory. Many of the early sprinklers were developed by textile manufacturers who recognized they needed to cope with their fire problems. The owners of textile mills also started many of the early mutual insurance companies, and most of the members of their boards of directors came from the textile industry. For example, Zachariah Allen, the owner of a woolen mill, founded the first Factory Mutual Insurance Company in 1835. The origin of the Factory Mutual System can best be related to Allen's formation of a second mutual company in 1848 and his promotion of cooperation with other mutual companies as they were formed over the next 30 years mostly in New England. The most important encouragement to the development of automatic sprinkler systems undoubtedly came in 1880 when the companies of the Factory Mutual System began to request installation of sprinkler systems in textile mills. [1,5]

The First Sprinkler Standard: 1896 [6]

In 1895, a group of men gathered in the Boston office of Everett U. Crosby, manager of the Underwriters' Bureau of New England, which later became the Fire Insurance Rating Bureau of New England. E. U. Crosby later also became the first secretary of the NFPA. It was obvious that these men representing fire insurance and sprinkler manufacturing interests had a common problem to solve. The group felt that automatic sprinklers, while proving their worth as extinguishing devices, were being installed in too many different ways. [7]

In his book *Men Against Fire*, Percy Bugbee, general manager of the NFPA from 1939 to 1969, lists the attendees at this meeting. "Attending that meeting in the Underwriters Bureau of New England office of the host, E. U. Crosby, were Uberto C. Crosby, Chairman of the Factory Improvement Committee of the New England Insurance Exchange; W. H. Stratton of the Factory Insurance Association; John R. Freeman of the Factory Mutual Insurance Companies; Frederick Grinnell of the Providence Steam and Gas Pipe Company; and F. Eliot Cabot of the Boston Board of Fire Underwriters." [7]

Grinnell told of the successful performance of sprinkler systems, and Freeman reported on Factory Mutual's success in insuring sprinklered properties. Thus the representatives of the stock insurance companies could see that action was required. In December 1895, a small group of inspection bureau men met in New York to prepare some sprinkler rules. The group met again in March 1896 to complete the work. The first "Report of Committee on Automatic Sprinkler Protection" was adopted at a conference held in New York on March 18 and 19, 1896. [6,7,8]

This first NFPA sprinkler standard came into being concurrent with the formation of the NFPA on November 6, 1896.[b] Several of the original officers of the NFPA were also the first sprinkler committee members.[c] In effect the NFPA may have been founded by stock insurance bureaus to meet Factory Mutual competition. [7]

The 1896 sprinkler standard was concerned with sprinklers, valves, hangers, piping, and pumps. Occupancy groups, calculations, and other requirements came later. Revisions were made in 58 successive editions. The most important of these revisions are as follows:

1. New pipe schedules in 1905
2. Separate standard on Class B systems in 1930
3. Class B standard merged into the standard in 1931
4. Three occupancy classes in 1940
5. Spray sprinklers in 1953 to 1958
6. Hydraulic calculations in 1966
7. Design curves in 1973 and 1974
8. Early suppression fast-response sprinklers (ESFR) in 1989
9. Complete reorganization in 1991
10. The standards 100-year anniversary in 1996
11. Consolidation of all sprinkler system design requirements in 1999

This first standard contained requirements for sprinkler positioning (upright was preferred), distance of deflectors from bottom of joists or ceilings [3 in. to 10 in. (76 mm to 250 mm)], and full sprinkler coverage throughout a building. The standard also required a sprinkler orifice to produce 12 gpm (45 L/min) at 5 psi (0.34 bar) (K = 5.4) and a minimum static pressure of 25 psi (1.7 bar) at the highest sprinklers. Only "tree" systems were permit-

---

[b]Concurrently, the Underwriters Electrical Bureau, which later became Underwriters Laboratories Inc. (UL), was formed in Chicago by William H. Merrill. A few years later, the National Board of Fire Underwriters (NBFU) provided financial support, and the name was changed to the Electrical Bureau of Fire Underwriters. In about 1900, the NFPA formed a Committee on Devices and Materials to cover the field of fire protection appliances with W. C. Robinson as chairman and Merrill as secretary. Robinson and Fitzhugh Taylor soon joined Merrill to be in charge of fire protection engineering and initiated the testing of automatic sprinkler equipment by UL. [9]

[c]The NFPA Technical Correlating Committee on Automatic Sprinkler Systems as it is currently named has had several names over time. Though the name has varied, the term *automatic sprinkler* has always been part of the name. In a similar way the structure of the committee has changed as technology has required the committee to consider varied approaches to the types of sprinklers in use, the variety of hardware needed or used to build a system, and the applications for which sprinkler systems were used.

ted with center/center or side/center feed recommended. Other requirements controlled spacing for mill construction, joists, bays, and pitched roofs.

Two water supplies, which could be steam pumps, public supply, elevated tanks, or pressure tanks, were deemed essential. The rules for rotary and steam fire pumps were in the sprinkler standard as were those for elevated and pressure tanks. The use of meters in a water supply connection required special consent. Pipe had to be securely supported; however, no detailed requirements were given.

Though dry systems were discouraged, they were preferred to system shutdown in cold weather. If there were more than 500 sprinklers, "water should be supplied through two or more dry valves—system divided horizontally," according to the standard. [6]

Some of the sprinklers illustrated in the 1896 sprinkler standard included the Buell of 1892 (see Exhibit S1.2), the Mackey of 1887, the Neracher of 1888, the Harkness of 1890, the New York and New Haven of 1889, the early Grinnells, and the Kane of 1888. See Exhibits S1.3 through S1.8.

In this era many highly inventive approaches were made towards automatic sprinkler design. Most early designers believed that the key to successful design was distribution of water and an automatic, thermally sensitive releasing element.

Most early sprinklers were a form of link and lever. In a link and lever design, the sprinkler cap is held closed against the water pressure by the mechanical advantage (generally about 20:1) of the sprinkler levers which, in turn, are held closed by the soldered link. In these early sprinklers, the first true eutectic alloys (the first solder-

(a) Closed position   **(b) Open position**

EXHIBIT S1.4 Neracher Sprinkler.

EXHIBIT S1.5 Harkness Sprinkler.

(a) Closed position   **(b) Open position**

EXHIBIT S1.3 Mackey Sprinkler.

EXHIBIT S1.6 Elbow Head of New York and New Haven Sprinkler.

FRONT VIEW   SIDE VIEW

EXHIBIT S1.7 Early Grinnell Sprinklers.

EXHIBIT S1.9 Duraspeed Sprinkler. (Courtesy of Grinnell Corporation)

(a) Closed position   (b) Open position

EXHIBIT S1.8 Kane Sprinkler.

type sprinklers) and the first center strut sprinklers appeared. Even then, the potential for the thermal characteristics or low thermal inertia of quick-response sprinklers was present in some designs that isolated the link load from the frame load and the link or solder from the water.

These early designs were conceived long before the mechanics of a sprinkler frame were fully understood, which was revealed in a 1933 patent application that was issued in 1939 to Albert J. Lipsinger of Grinnell. Lipsinger was the inventor of the Grinnell Duraspeed sprinkler. See Exhibit S1.9.

Hydraulic calculations had not yet been developed in 1896, so design was based on preferred piping arrangements with no more than six sprinklers on a branch line.

All of the piping arrangements were tree systems. Because of hydraulic calculations, a contemporary designer can arrange piping in loops, compound loops, and grids and then size the piping to take full advantage of an existing water supply.

THE NEXT 50 YEARS: 1900 THROUGH WORLD WAR II

In 1905, a substantial change was made in the pipe schedules of NFPA 13 (see Table S1.2). The restrictions for the number of sprinklers on a branch line were removed and new rules were added to limit the number of sprinklers fed by a given pipe size, whether on branch lines or collectively. [10]

In the early standard editions, the need to securely support pipe was recognized. Hanger location rules appeared by 1920. Permitted types of hangers were U-type hangers made of wrought iron or malleable cast-iron, ring clips, or approved adjustable hangers. Flat U-type hangers were permitted if the metal was at least 3/16 in. (0.48 mm) thick. Drive screws were only allowed in a horizontal position such as in the side of a beam. [3]

In 1926, UL completed a series of tests on the distribution of water by automatic sprinkler systems. The results were published in the report "The Distribution of Water by Automatic Sprinkler Systems." These tests were under the direction of a subcommittee of the NFPA Committee on Automatic Sprinklers and representatives of the NBFU, the National Automatic Sprinkler Association, and Underwriters' Laboratories. The purpose was to evaluate the adequacy of the existing pipe schedules and spacing requirements of the NFPA sprinkler standard. Although the tests clearly showed that the existing pipe schedules created a wide variation in the discharge from the sprinklers on a branch line, no action was taken to modify the standard until the 1940 edition. [11,12]

In 1930, a separate standard was created for Class B systems, which later became light hazard. Even though this standard was combined with NFPA 13 in 1931, it was the first time that multiple hazard categories were recognized.

The following major new concepts appeared in the 1940 edition:

1. Three hazard categories (light, ordinary, and extra)
2. Looped piping systems
3. Changes in the staggered spacing rules
4. Elimination of the use of ¾-in. (1.9-mm) pipe
5. Expanded rules for deluge systems

The changes in hazard categories came from studies by Henry Fiske on the fire performance of sprinkler systems. Fiske was one of the three editors of the *Crosby-Fiske-Forster Handbook*.[d] The spacing and pipe size rules in 1940 were also influenced by the previously mentioned 1926 UL water distribution tests. [8,12]

During the 1920–1947 era, constant changes in sprinklers and sprinkler system equipment were made and test methods at the UL and FM laboratories were improved as the sprinkler industry developed. Developments such as centrifugal fire pumps, steel water tanks, and rate-of-rise supplemental operation of deluge systems took place. Major sprinkler improvements were made such as the first glass bulb sprinkler in 1921 and the Duraspeed sprinkler in 1933. Also during this era, UL and FM began to publish formal standards to describe the test methods by which sprinklers and sprinkler equipment are tested.

Hydraulic Calculations of Sprinkler and Water Spray Systems by Clyde Wood was published by the "Automatic" Sprinkler Corporation of America in the 1940s. General use of hydraulic calculations to design systems, however, did not begin until the middle 1950s. Much of the mathematics of hydraulic calculations came from knowledge developed by John R. Freeman in the very late 1800s or early 1900s. Wood reduced the mathematics to practice in the 1940s and concurrently published a complete set of tables to identify friction factors used in the flow calculations. In a talk before NFPA in 1953, Joe Johnson proposed that hydraulic calculations be included

in the sprinkler standard. A hydraulic design method[e] was first included in NFPA 13 in 1966. The method is now mandatory for most system design.

POST–WORLD WAR II ERA: 1947–1972

In 1947, shortly after the end of World War II, FM opened a new fire testing facility in Norwood, MA. The two fire testing buildings had an area of 2400 ft² (40 ft × 60 ft, 34 ft high) (223 m²) and 3600 ft² (60 ft × 60 ft, 18 ft high) (334 m²). UL opened their Northbrook, IL, testing station with two fire test buildings in 1954. One building had an area of 3600 ft² (60 ft × 60 ft, 16 ft 9 in. high) (334 m²). The other building had an area of 2442 ft² (37 ft × 66 ft, 23 ft high) (227 m²). The era of testing sprinkler performance on actual fires began with these facilities. Prior to this time, sprinklers were only tested for the manner in which water was distributed—no testing was done to evaluate the fire-extinguishing potential.

The Rockwood Sprinkler Company developed the T-1 and T-2 sprinklers—the first of the spray sprinklers—in approximately 1948.[f] Subsequent testing by FM established the value of this new approach. Another result of the spray sprinkler introduction was that both FM and UL introduced new methods for evaluating water distribution and included a fire testing requirement in their sprinkler testing requirements. All sprinkler manufacturers thereafter developed sprinklers with spray deflectors in both upright and pendent configurations. (The "old style" sprinkler, previously in general use, was used universally for both upright and pendent positions.) [15]

NFPA 13 required the use of spray sprinklers by 1955. The sprinkler types in use stayed constant until the introduction of a variety of new technical approaches started to appear in about 1981. At this point the definitions and

---

[d]The original *Fire Protection Handbook* was published as the *Handbook of the Underwriters' Bureau of New England.* This became the *Crosby-Fiske Handbook (second to seventh editions)* and then the *Crosby-Fiske-Forster Handbook (eighth and later editions).* This handbook is now the *Fire Protection Handbook* published by NFPA. [8,13].

[e]The industry and NFPA 13 still base hydraulic calculations of sprinkler systems on the work of John R. Freeman and Wood. Their work applied the Hazen-Williams formula. Later the Hardy-Cross method was adopted for gridded systems. The method was used mostly because the calculations are much easier to compute though less accurate than they would be using classic fluid mechanics. [14]

[f]Prior to 1953 all sprinklers, whether upright or pendent, were designed to discharge 40 percent of the water upward and 60 percent downward. The FM tests in the 1948–1953 era established that better fire control was achieved when all water was discharged downward in a finely divided spray pattern. In the 1953 edition, a new chapter permitted the use of the new spray sprinkler. In 1955, the new spray sprinkler was named the standard sprinkler, and the old conventional or regular sprinkler with the 40/60 discharge pattern was renamed the "old style" sprinkler. [15,16]

terminology of sprinklers and sprinkler systems began to change rapidly, which is discussed in later sections.

In 1958, the ordinary hazard occupancy group was split into three subgroups, apparently for insurance underwriting, to define their different water supplies. The subgrouping of ordinary hazard occupancies appears only in the water supply rules. Extra hazard occupancies were all in one class.

A chapter was added to NFPA 13 in 1966 to describe methods for the hydraulic calculation of system pipe sizes as an acceptable alternative to the rules for pipe schedule systems. This addition was made largely because then new storage standards required calculated systems. (See "Fire Testing for the Storage Standards.")

In the late 1960s, Gordon Price, chairman of the NFPA sprinkler committee, and Chester Schirmer, later to become chairman, were instructed by the NFPA Board of Directors to have the sprinkler committee work diligently to "keep the costs of automatic sprinkler protection economically justifiable to encourage the installation of these systems." Cost effectiveness thus became an important criterion for the committee in subsequent changes to the standard and remains so to this date. [17]

Permissive language was included in the 1961 edition of NFPA 13 that provided for the use of any type of piping system or joining method that was evaluated and listed by the approval laboratories. These guidelines permitted the use of piping systems other than wrought iron or steel for the first time. By 1968, NFPA 13 specifically provided for the use of listed copper piping systems. Shop-welding was permitted in the mid-60s, flexible couplings were permitted in the mid-70s, and lightweight steel piping systems were introduced in 1973. Also in 1973, valves controlling water supplies to sprinkler systems were required to be supervised in the open position. The following six methods were permitted:

1. Central station alarm system
2. Proprietary station alarm system
3. Remote station alarm system
4. A constantly attended local alarm system or other alarm service
5. Valves locked open
6. Valves sealed in the open position

Guidance for the protection of piping against damage due to earthquakes appeared in the 1947 edition and was improved in the 1951 edition. By then, NFPA 13 contained criteria for placement of longitudinal and lateral braces, maximum slenderness ratio of braces, and use of flexible couplings on risers. The stated intent was to brace the piping to withstand the horizontal force of half the weight of the water-filled piping and valves. Diagrams

were included to show locations of braces. Also, tables were included for maximum lengths of angles, rods, flats, and pipe used as braces. The key was to restrain and support the piping with flexibility.

Several major changes occurred in the 1970s as the industry moved from large, heavy flanged or screwed piping systems based on a pipe schedule approach, to hydraulically calculated systems using lightweight piping with screwed fittings or welded piping and fittings and grooved couplings. During this time period there were major improvements in hanging systems and material-handling methods. The changes in installation and fabrication methods had a significant impact on reducing or at least maintaining the installed cost of sprinkler systems in an era of substantial worldwide inflation.

In the 1972 edition, the committee introduced a chapter on system design for life safety and fire protection in high-rise buildings. This chapter was in response to a renewed recognition that such buildings constituted a unique fire problem and that fire fighting and evacuation in these buildings was difficult at best. These requirements were also in response to many building code changes that required such buildings to be sprinklered. The design methods permitted the combined use of risers for both sprinkler and standpipe systems and created a conflict about whether the NFPA sprinkler or standpipe standards should decide water supply requirements. This conflict was not fully resolved until 1983.

Fire Testing for the Storage Standards[g]

Beginning with the establishment of the FM (1947) and UL (1954) fire testing facilities, several series of fire tests were conducted to establish sprinkler system design characteristics for certain types of storage hazards. Included among these tests were rack and palletized storage of whiskey in barrels, palletized storage of rubber tires, and palletized storage of a variety of commodities normally found in general storage warehouses. These tests were extensively reported to the sponsoring agencies, which included the insurance companies and testing organizations of the Factory Mutual System, the NBFU, the Factory Insurance Association (FIA), and a number of cooperating industries and companies. Based on the test data and on insurance considerations, NBFU, FIA, and FM published

---

[g]Although the terms full scale and large scale are used somewhat interchangeably, it should be recognized that the original fire test facilities of UL and FM were about 2500 ft² to 3500 ft² (230 m² to 325 m²). FM began testing in a 50,000-ft² (4645-m²) facility in 1967, and UL began testing in a 14,400-ft² (1338-m²) facility in 1996.

several standards for general fire protection and sprinkler system design including rack whiskey warehouses, palletized whiskey warehouses, palletized rubber tire storage, and general storage warehouses.

The FM and UL tests also led to the publication of NFPA 231, *Standard for General Storage,* in 1965. NFPA 231 included an appendix with sprinkler system design requirements for palletized storage. The design requirements for storage heights less than 12 ft (3.6 m) were also included in the 1965 edition of NFPA 13. NFPA 13 thus became the first NFPA standard containing sprinkler system design requirements partly based on full-scale fire testing. From 1970 onward, revisions in NFPA 13 and NFPA 231 continued to be based on a combination of test data and insurance considerations.

In 1967, FM constructed a 50,000-ft^2 (250 ft × 200 ft) [4645-m^2 (76.2 m × 61 m)] fire testing facility at West Gloucester, RI. The building has two testing areas. One section is 100 ft × 200 ft × 30 ft (30 m × 61 m × 9 m) high and the other section is 200 ft × 150 ft × 60 ft (61 m × 46 m × 18.3 m) high. Both have flat ceilings. The primary purpose of this facility was full-scale fire testing of a variety of storage commodities and configurations. The need for such a test facility was clear—larger warehouses were being developed for the storage of a variety of products on pallets, in racks, in bulk, and bundled in a variety of new and imaginative ways. The insurance industry was faced with an increasing number of situations where conventional sprinkler system design could not cope with the magnitude of the fires. Storage areas reaching well over 500,000 ft^2 (46,450 m^2), racks up to 60 ft (18.3 m) in height, automated racking systems, special racks for carpets, hanging garments, aerosol storage, and many more specialized storage methods came into use. Industry was experiencing numerous large losses in warehouses protected by sprinkler systems previously thought to be adequate.

In August 1967, Roger M. L. Russell of the FIA persuaded the rack manufacturers, sprinkler industry, industrial and commercial users, and insurance interests to join forces to financially sponsor a large-scale fire testing program at the new FM research facility. Subsequently, the Rack Storage Fire Protection Committee was formed, consisting mostly of the research sponsors. The Rack Storage Test Planning Committee and its steering committee planned an extensive series of fire tests. Tests were initially conducted at an 8-ft (2.4-m) height to establish representative commodity classes. Following these tests, full-scale fire tests were conducted at storage heights from 15 ft to 50 ft (4.6 m to 15.2 m) with a variety of commodities.

The NFPA Technical Committee on Rack Storage of Materials was organized under the chairmanship of Russell in 1965. The committee developed the area/density

curves for the 1971 edition of NFPA 231C, *Standard for Rack Storage of Materials,* based on analyses of the test results. The resulting standard became the first NFPA sprinkler standard entirely supported by full-scale fire test data. This committee continued a policy that all changes to the standard must be supported by full-scale fire test data. This committee was merged into the NFPA 13 committee in 1998.

Additional full-scale fire testing continued throughout the late 1970s and into the 1990s. NFPA 231C was changed as additional test data became available. Substantive changes were made to NFPA 231C in regard to storage of empty pallets, recognition of sprinkler system design methods for storage heights greater than 25 ft (7.6 m) (1973), modified commodity classes, means to protect plastic storage (1986), and others. In 1974 a companion standard was developed for rubber tire storage (NFPA 231D, *Standard for Storage of Rubber Tires*), and in 1984 new standards were added for rolled paper (NFPA 231F, *Standard for the Storage of Rolled Paper*) and cotton storage (NFPA 231E, *Recommended Practice for the Storage of Baled Cotton*).

The storage standards were also substantially influenced by the development of quick-response sprinkler technology. System design based on the use of early suppression fast-response (ESFR) sprinklers, extra large orifice (ELO) sprinklers, and large drop sprinklers were included in the storage standards starting in 1986. See "New Technology." [18]

The Impact of Hydraulic Calculations

After the introduction of hydraulic calculations in the 1966 edition of NFPA 13, economics made it apparent that hydraulic design criteria were needed for NFPA 13 systems in all hazard categories. The original area/density design curves were developed by a water supply subcommittee of NFPA 13, consisting of Jack Wood and Lin McCool. The curves were based on analyses of various piping configurations including piping variations such as center/center, side/center, and end, all with long and short branch lines. The concept was that the existing pipe schedule systems had performed well in most hazards, so they were evaluated to determine the comparable hydraulic design. Curves were then prepared having a slope similar to those planned in the storage standards. The curves became part of NFPA 13 in 1972 for light hazard and ordinary hazard occupancies. In 1974 the curves in NFPA 13 and NFPA 231 were further modified, which provided a smooth transition between the standards based on hazard severity.

In 1978, area/density design curves for hydraulically designed extra hazard systems were included in the appendix of NFPA 13. These design curves were included in the body of the standard and thus became mandatory requirements in the 1983 edition.

The concept of sizing system piping and water supplies based on density[h] and area of expected sprinkler operation was introduced in the 1972 edition of NFPA 13. This concept was further modified in the 1974 edition to permit design based on the largest room being considered, provided it was enclosed with fire-rated construction equal to the duration of the water supply.

A small but important change was made in NFPA 13 in 1973. A section was added to permit the use of special sprinklers for "larger protection areas or distances between sprinklers…when such installations are made in accordance with approvals or listings of a nationally recognized testing laboratory." Although this requirement was modified substantially in subsequent editions, this change permitted the sprinkler industry to begin to innovate in sprinkler design. What followed was the development of fast-response, extended coverage, residential, large orifice, extra large orifice, and flow control sprinklers.

Residential and Quick-Response Sprinklers

At a meeting in Cleveland, OH, in 1967, Gordon Price suggested that faster responding sprinklers could greatly improve sprinkler system performance. Subsequently, a quick-response subcommittee was formed within the sprinkler committee. The subcommittee held several meetings through 1971 and concluded that a quick-response sprinkler was feasible and valuable for light hazard life safety situations.

In 1972, Rolf Jensen, a member of the sprinkler committee, was involved in the design of the fire protection systems for Water Tower Place, a 75-story, multiple-use, high-rise building in Chicago in which sprinklers were proposed for use in the hotel and residential portions of the building. Jensen wrote a specification for a quick-response apartment sprinkler that proposed that the sprinkler be fire tested in a room configuration using a simulated urethane-foamed plastic chair. The measurement criteria were formulated to assure that the sprinkler was evaluated for its ability to limit the accumulation of combustion products so that a person could survive in the test room environment for a reasonable period of time. The measurement criteria at the 5-ft 6-in. (1.7-m) and 3-ft (0.9-m) levels were as follows:

1. Temperature was to be controlled to a maximum of 150°F (65.6°C).

2. Carbon-monoxide was to be controlled to 900 ppm before sprinkler operation and 400 ppm after sprinkler operation.

3. Smoke obscuration was to be controlled to a maximum Ringleman number of 4.

4. Oxygen depletion was to be controlled to not less than 15 percent.

Though later refined and improved, these measurement criteria became the means by which residential sprinkler performance would later be evaluated in tests by UL, in research by the United States Fire Administration (USFA) and its various subcontractors, and in research on the development of residential sprinkler systems by Factory Mutual Research Corporation (FMRC). With modifications, these criteria also became the basis for the room fire test standards for residential sprinklers used by UL and FM. All residential sprinklers are thus tested to evaluate their ability to enhance survivability in the room of origin. See Exhibit S1.10.

In July 1973, the NFPA 13 Subcommittee on Residential Sprinkler Systems was formed. The subcommittee's work led to the publication of NFPA 13D, the *Standard for the Installation of Sprinkler Systems in One- and Two-Family Dwellings and Mobile Homes,* in 1975. Much of this first edition was based on the collective experience of the committee members; little was based on real-world fire testing.

Once published, NFPA 13D encouraged the USFA to sponsor extensive test programs to evaluate what impact residential sprinkler systems could have on the loss of life then occurring in dwellings. The USFA sponsored programs to develop a prototype residential sprinkler, to refine the methods by which residential sprinklers are tested, and to develop methods for the design of installed systems.

One study was to establish factors that influenced homeowners' acceptance of these systems, a second was to

EXHIBIT S1.10 *An Early Residential Sprinkler. (Courtesy of Grinnell Corporation)*

---

[h]NFPA 13 uses the term *density* to define the water application rate of a sprinkler system in gpm/ft^2 (L/min · m^2) as determined by hydraulic calculations.

evaluate design features such as waterflow rates and number of sprinklers to operate, a third was to check design for flaming fires, and a fourth was to evaluate design on smoldering fires. These studies suggested that good design could be based on waterflow rates as low as 0.05 gpm/ft^2 (2.04 L/min · m^2). The NFPA 13 subcommittee then asked for tests involving flaming ventilated fire configurations in a simulated living room with combustible walls and ceilings. The tests using standard thermal response sprinklers were not successful. Additional tests using simulated fast-response sprinklers (none were yet commercially available) were completed. Due to the efforts of Dr. Hsiang-Cheng Kung of FMRC, the tests proved that control of the environment in a residential fire scenario with combustible walls and ceilings could only be achieved with fast-response sprinklers having water distribution characteristics that assured wall wetting to a specified distance below the ceiling.

Under sponsorship of the USFA, FM, and the NFPA, the Los Angeles Fire Department and the residential sprinkler subcommittee joined in an effort to test prototype residential sprinkler systems in houses in Los Angeles destined for demolition. The accumulated data from these tests and the previous USFA programs became the basis for the 1980 edition of NFPA 13D. These development tests of a prototype sprinkler and sprinkler system established that a system designed by the methods described in NFPA 13D would provide a survivable environment both in the room of fire origin and in other areas of a one- or two-story dwelling permitting sufficient time to allow occupants to escape. At the time the 1980 edition of NFPA 13D was published by the NFPA, no residential sprinkler was commercially available even though the standard required their use. The first UL-listed residential sprinkler became available in 1981. [18,19]

USFA sponsorship of residential sprinkler testing programs continued at both FM and UL. Substantial refinements continue to be made in subsequent editions of NFPA 13D.

The sprinkler committee recognized a need for improved fire safety for dwelling units in hotels, apartments, condominiums, and nursing homes and developed requirements for the 1985 edition of NFPA 13. System design was based on the use of residential sprinklers and the operation of four sprinklers. This concept became the basis for NFPA 13R, *Standard for the Installation of Sprinkler Systems in Residential Occupancies up to and Including Four Stories in Height,* which was developed in 1989 for residential facilities up to four stories in height. NFPA 13R provides a greater level of reliability and fire protection than NFPA 13D but not as much as NFPA 13. An important philosophy in the evolution of residential

sprinkler systems was that both NFPA 13D and NFPA 13R permit water supplies smaller than those required by NFPA 13, omission of sprinklers in certain areas, and design based on fewer sprinklers than is required for NFPA 13 systems. These and other cost savings achieved in NFPA 13D and 13R systems are intended to encourage users to install sprinklers in residential facilities with *life safety* as the primary goal.

New Technology

In 1974, NFPA adopted a new standards-making system to better achieve due process and public exposure in consensus standards. This new method of processing changes and improvements to NFPA standards allowed the general public to submit proposed changes to NFPA standards and to comment on the manner by which technical committees disposed of these changes. Although the new procedures opened the standards-making process to full public disclosure and participation, it also placed a substantial burden on the technical committees in the processing of the public proposals and comments. Less time was thus available to the committees to develop their own changes in response to changes in technology.

During this same era, changes in building codes and the extensive development of high-rise, multiple-use, and large-scale buildings of all types demanded that sprinkler systems be installed for facilities not previously commonly sprinklered. As a result, many new technologies in sprinkler design, sprinkler systems, and related equipment were developed largely through fire research. Fabrication methods and hydraulic design approaches were also changing rapidly.

The NFPA sprinkler committee had a difficult time keeping up with both public proposals and the rapid changes in technology. Faced with this challenge, the committee chairman created a system of balanced task groups organized by technical disciplines and the needs of the committee. Each of these subgroups concentrated on a specific portion of NFPA 13, such as hydraulic calculations or earthquake requirements for pipe hangers.

The subgroup on new technology was charged with reviewing new technological challenges and proposing changes in an orderly fashion. (This group did not normally process routine proposals or comments.) The new technology group addressed such changes as quick-response, ESFR, extended coverage, extended coverage sidewall, large drop, large orifice, and extra large orifice sprinklers. They also addressed new piping methods such as lightweight steel and plastic.

Starting in the mid-1970s, sprinkler manufacturers and fire research organizations focused their research on sprinkler technology. Included in the research efforts were programs to develop quick-response sprinklers, programs to measure sprinkler responsiveness, and continuing research on sprinkler protection methods for storage hazards. One result was the previously mentioned development of fast-response residential sprinklers. Between 1975 and 1980, Heskestad and Smith of FMRC had developed a plunge test apparatus for measuring sprinkler sensitivity and proposed a formula for the measurement of the response time index (RTI) of a sprinkler. [20]

In the early 1980s FMRC also developed a new concept for fire control of storage hazards using ESFR sprinklers. In their research, they developed a large-capacity calorimeter and a special water applicator in order to measure the actual delivered density (ADD) of a sprinkler and the required delivered density (RDD) of a sprinkler. RTI, ADD, and RDD were discovered to be the three most important factors to achieve early fire suppression (the ESFR approach). [21]

FMRC continued extensive testing of this concept during the 1980s and 1990s, which included numerous tests of rack and palletized storage arrangements using a variety of commodities at variable storage heights. This research led to a new concept in sprinkler design for high-challenge fire hazards using ESFR sprinklers. In this approach, design is based on 12 sprinklers operating at a minimum pressure of 50 psi (3.4 bar). The concepts were included in NFPA 13 in 1989 and NFPA 231C in 1991.[i]

Continuing research at FM and UL refined these new design concepts for sprinkler system design for high-challenge fires and storage occupancies. Much of this resulted from sponsorship and funding of fire research by FMRC, other insurance interests, industrial and commercial users, the National Institute for Standards and Technology (NIST), National Fire Protection Research Foundation, and the sprinkler industry. Other research was directed to the development of fire modeling methods whereby fire growth could be better predicted, which is a necessity for more efficient system design.

In response, sprinkler manufacturers developed many new and innovative types of sprinklers that function more efficiently, effectively, and quickly to control fires. Many new sprinkler designs resulted with a wide variety of orifice sizes, thermal elements, special distribution patterns, and operating pressure restrictions. A typical sprinkler manufacturer could supply approximately 250 varieties of sprinklers in 1980. By 1996 the number had exceeded

2000 for some manufacturers. This large increase in the types of sprinklers in use has resulted in an increased level of complexity when sprinklers must be replaced. In the 1999 edition of NFPA 13, the committee included a new marking system that requires each sprinkler to be marked by a one- or two-character symbol followed by up to four numbers to identify each variation in orifice size, shape, deflector characteristic, and thermal sensitivity. This marking system became mandatory in January 2001.

Also during the 1980s, substantial changes were made to the methods of testing sprinklers at the UL and FM approval laboratories. For example, the UL sprinkler standard *Automatic Sprinklers for Fire-Protection Service,* UL 199, was first published in 1919 and next revised in 1966. From 1967 to 1977, eight more revisions were made in order to stay current with technological changes. The task of monitoring these changes so they were harmonized with the NFPA sprinkler standards was assigned to the new technology subcommittee. [16]

These developments in new technology led to a continuing series of changes in the sprinkler requirements of the NFPA sprinkler and storage standards during the 1980s. For example, in 1985 a chapter was added to NFPA 13 to provide requirements for large drop sprinklers. Similar requirements were added to NFPA 231C in 1986. With the appearance of many new types of special sprinklers, the NFPA 13 committee enlarged the section of NFPA 13 that permitted use of such sprinklers to provide more explicit direction for sprinkler testing and evaluation by UL and FM. Many new sprinklers, such as standard and sidewall extended coverage sprinklers, had to be included in the standard. Thus a rule was adopted in the 1987 edition to limit the maximum area covered by a single sprinkler to 400 ft^2 (37.2 m^2). The committee's reasoning was based on a concern for the size of fire that could develop if a single sprinkler failed to function.

Also during the 1980s the National Fire Protection Research Foundation established a technical advisory committee to plan and review research efforts by FMRC, UL, and other contractors to introduce quick-response sprinkler technology into NFPA 13. These included studies by FMRC, NIST, UL, Worcester Polytechnic Institute (WPI), and others. Although these studies showed that quick-response technology had application across the full range of hazards for which sprinkler systems were designed, they have not yet been fully implemented in NFPA 13. As with the FMRC research on ESFR sprinklers, a full treatment of this research is beyond the scope of this brief history.

Fire research efforts continue even today. In 1996, UL commissioned a new large-scale fire test facility of 14,400 ft^2 (120 ft × 120 ft × 54 ft high) [1338 m^2 (36.6 m × 36.6 m × 16.5 m high)], having a ceiling that can be ad-

---

[i]This brief history does not intend to describe the specifics of these research programs, which have been widely published by FMRC and others. [20,21]

justed from 5 ft to 48 ft (1.5 m to 14.6 m). Both UL and FMRC are continuing to explore better methods of measuring sprinkler distribution patterns with and without a fire plume present. Both testing laboratories also continue to conduct full-scale tests to better refine methods of sprinkler protection for many types of storage and other hazards. [22,23]

THE LAST 10 YEARS

Prior to the 1974 edition of NFPA 13, little guidance for protection of sprinkler piping due to earthquakes was available. Earthquake guidance rules first appeared in 1974. Thereafter, few changes were made until 1987 when a seismic map was included and guidance for hanging and bracing of piping was added.

The 1989 Loma Prieta and 1994 Northridge earthquakes in California permitted studies to be made of sprinkler system performance in actual seismic events. These analyses contributed to a series of enhancements in the earthquake protection rules in the 1989, 1994, and 1996 editions. Requirements for sway bracing, swing joints, and flexible couplings were modified, and a new velocity-based seismic map was added in 1994. Methods for installation of piping, clearances to the building structure (generally and at seismic joints), and hanger strap requirements were included.

Even with the revised requirements, NFPA 13 still addresses how to provide earthquake protection rather then when. The fundamental approach of NFPA 13 is to permit evaluation of how anticipated horizontal loads affect braces, their connections, and their fasteners. While NFPA 13 retains the baseline criterion that bracing is designed to withstand a horizontal load equal to one-half the weight of the water-filled pipe and valves, it allows the use of higher or lower loads based on site-specific conditions.

As a result of the substantial changes in the design and installation of sprinkler systems over the preceding generation, NFPA 13 was completely reorganized in 1991. Numerous changes and improvements were accomplished to achieve a more user-friendly standard. Overall, NFPA 13 was arranged to be in the order in which information is used in the design of a system. NFPA 13 was organized in the following order:

1. General information
2. System components and hardware
3. System requirements
4. Installation requirements
5. Design approaches
6. Plans and calculations
7. Water supplies
8. System acceptance
9. Maintenance

Definitions for the wide variety of sprinklers in use were improved and consolidated in the first chapter. The rules on the location and spacing of sprinklers were clarified and definitions of *obstructed construction* and *unobstructed construction* were adopted. The obstruction rules were organized to define obstructions based on the degree to which they materially affect or impede the sprinkler's ability to control or suppress a fire. Obstructions were categorized depending on whether they occur at the ceiling or below the sprinkler and whether they impede the sprinkler discharge horizontally or vertically.

Other important changes included combining ordinary hazard (Group 2 and Group 3) occupancies and their design curves because the difference in required water application rates was insignificant for hydraulically designed systems and nonexistent for pipe schedule systems. Hydraulic calculations for pipe sizing were effectively made mandatory for all new systems covering an area less than 5000 ft^2 (464.5 m^2), with some minor exceptions.

In the 1996 100th anniversary edition, a few significant changes were made. Quick-response types of sprinklers were defined as sprinklers that have an RTI of 50 (meters-seconds) as measured under standard test conditions. RTI is a measure of the sensitivity of the sprinkler's element as installed in a specific sprinkler. RTI is usually determined by plunging a sprinkler into a heated laminar-airflow within a test oven. The factors that determine the response of a sprinkler's thermal element to a fire include RTI, temperature rating, sprinkler position, rate of fire growth, and radiation. [20]

Certain design rules were changed in 1996 to encourage the use of quick-response technology by proving a substantial reduction in the required design area when fast-response sprinklers were used. A 30-percent increase in the design area was also required when standard upright and pendent sidewall, and large drop sprinklers are installed below sloped ceilings. These changes all lead in a direction whereby sprinkler systems of the future can be designed to extinguish, not just control, fires.

Of equal importance, the installation rules and the rules for obstructions to sprinkler discharge were rewritten to be specific for all types of sprinklers, including special sprinklers. A new chapter was added for design of marine systems, the sprinkler systems installed onboard ships.

CONSOLIDATION: THE 1999 EDITION

The increased use of sprinkler systems over the past 25 years and significant improvements in sprinkler technology led to a standard based on fire control and encouraged the use of fast-response technology. Recognition of these improvements also motivated many writers of fire safety codes and standards to include mandates for sprinkler system installation. In some cases sprinkler design criteria were included in other NFPA standards that either supplemented or in some cases overrode NFPA 13.

The NFPA Standards Council observed that "sprinkler design criteria has been spread out among numerous installation and occupancy documents, creating the potential for redundancies, conflicts and inconsistencies." A Standards Council task force chaired by Jennifer Nelson was charged to study the problem and recommend a solution. After initial public exposure of the proposed concept at the NFPA meeting in November 1996, the task force met and a report was issued in March 1997. Additional public hearings were held in May 1997. After these meetings, the Standards Council decided to move forward with a complete reorganization of the Sprinkler Project. A mandate was given to the sprinkler committee and other NFPA technical committees to consolidate all sprinkler design and installation standards into NFPA 13, NFPA 13D, or NFPA 13R.

The newly formed NFPA 13 Technical Correlating Committee on Automatic Sprinkler Systems (see Exhibit S1.11 for new committee organization) and its associated technical committees began their work in November 1997

and held numerous meetings in 1998 and 1999. The work was correlated with ongoing changes in the storage standards and in other NFPA standards on water-based extinguishing systems. Although the initial report of the Standards Council task force suggested that about 45 documents contained sprinkler system design criteria in 1997, subsequent analysis indicated that the number was much higher.

The 1999 edition of NFPA 13 had the sprinkler system design requirements from 39 other NFPA standards integrated into the standard so that a sprinkler system designer could find most necessary design criteria in one document. The included material was extracted from the following NFPA standards:

NFPA 30, *Flammable and Combustible Liquids Code*

NFPA 30B, *Code for the Manufacture and Storage of Aerosol Products*

NFPA 33, *Standard for Spray Application Using Flammable or Combustible Materials*

NFPA 36, *Standard for Solvent Extraction Plants*

NFPA 40, *Standard for the Storage and Handling of Cellulose Nitrate Motion Picture Film*

NFPA 42, *Code for the Storage of Pyroxylin Plastic*

NFPA 45, *Standard on Fire Protection for Laboratories Using Chemicals*

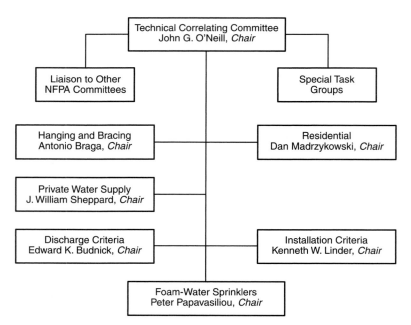

EXHIBIT S1.11 *Organization of NFPA 13's Technical Correlating Committee on Automatic Sprinkler Systems.*

NFPA 51, *Standard for the Design and Installation of Oxygen-Fuel Gas Systems for Welding, Cutting, and Allied Processes*

NFPA 51A, *Standard for Acetylene Cylinder Charging Plants*

NFPA 55, *Standard for the Storage, Use, and Handling of Compressed and Liquefied Gases in Portable Cylinders*

NFPA 59, *Standard for the Storage and Handling of Liquefied Petroleum Gases at Utility Gas Plants*

NFPA 59A, *Standard for the Production, Storage, and Handling of Liquefied Natural Gas (LNG)*

NFPA 75, *Standard for the Protection of Electronic Computer/Data Processing Equipment*

NFPA 82, *Standard on Incinerators and Waste and Linen Handling Systems and Equipment*

NFPA 86C, *Standard for Industrial Furnaces Using a Special Processing Atmosphere*

NFPA 96, *Standard for Ventilation Control and Fire Protection of Commercial Cooking Operations*

NFPA *101*®, *Life Safety Code*®

NFPA 130, *Standard for Fixed Guideway Transit Systems*

NFPA 150, *Standard on Fire Safety in Racetrack Stables*

NFPA 203, *Guide on Roof Coverings and Roof Deck Constructions*

NFPA 214, *Standard on Water-Cooling Towers*

NFPA 231, *Standard for General Storage*

NFPA 231C, *Standard for Rack Storage of Materials*

NFPA 231D, *Standard for Storage of Rubber Tires*

NFPA 231E, *Recommended Practice for the Storage of Baled Cotton*

NFPA 231F, *Standard for the Storage of Roll Paper*

NFPA 232, *Standard for the Protection of Records*

NFPA 307, *Standard for the Construction and Fire Protection of Marine Terminals, Piers, and Wharves*

NFPA 318, *Standard for the Protection of Cleanrooms*

NFPA 409, *Standard on Aircraft Hangars*

NFPA 415, *Standard on Airport Terminal Buildings, Fueling Ramp Drainage, and Loading Walkways*

NFPA 423, *Standard for Construction and Protection of Aircraft Engine Test Facilities*

NFPA 430, *Code for the Storage of Liquid and Solid Oxidizers*

NFPA 432, *Code for the Storage of Organic Peroxide Formulations*

NFPA 803, *Standard for Fire Protection for Light Water Nuclear Power Plants*

NFPA 804, *Standard for Fire Protection for Advanced Light Water Reactor Electric Generating Plants*

NFPA 850, *Recommended Practice for Fire Protection for Electric Generating Plants and High Voltage Direct Current Converter Stations*

NFPA 851, *Recommended Practice for Fire Protection for Hydroelectric Generating Plants*

NFPA 909, *Standard for the Protection of Cultural Resources, Including Museums, Libraries, Places of Worship, and Historic Properties*

In the process of integrating the new material, the correlating committee also reorganized the standard into the following chapters:

1. General information
2. Classification of occupancies and commodities
3. System components and hardware
4. System requirements
5. Installation requirements
6. Hanging, bracing, and restraint of systems
7. Design approaches
8. Plans and calculations
9. Water supplies
10. System acceptance
11. Marine systems
12. System inspection, testing, and maintenance

These changes better organized the material and made the new edition more user friendly.

Since the sprinkler committee's inception, 14 men have served as the chair for terms ranging from 3 to 24 years. (See Table S1.3.) The original driving force came from the insurance industry, but the interests that participate now are from a broad spectrum of interest groups including insurance, users, sprinkler industry, government, and special experts. (See Table S1.4.)

Moreover NFPA 13 would not be where it is today without the contributions of many other people. Some have served as committee members for extensive periods, some have worked in research and testing, and many have participated by making proposals for changes or improvements in the NFPA standards or by commenting on proposed changes. All have contributed to the evolution of this important standard, which is the best overall way of achieving cost-effective fire safety whether the goal is

TABLE S1.3 NFPA Sprinkler Committee Chairmen

Term	Chairman
1896–1901	U. C. Crosby
1902–1904	W. A. Anderson
1905–1909	W. C. Robinson
1910–1913	R. P. Boone
1914–1925	C. L. Scofield
1924–1927	F. B. Quackenboss
1928–1931	E. P. Boone
1932–1934	H. P. Smith
1935–1941	C. W. Johnson
1942–1956	K. W. Adkins
1957–1969	G. F. Price
1969–1972	I. L. Lamar
1973–1996	C. W. Schirmer
1997–	J. G. O'Neill

TABLE S1.4 NFPA 13's Voting Membership Interests

Interest	1960 Technical Committees	1969 Technical Committees	1974 Technical Committees	1989 Technical Committee	1999 Technical Committees	1999 Correlating Committee	2002 Technical Committees	2002 Correlating Committee
Insurance	16	13	9	4	14	3	24	6
Sprinkler industry	5	5	4	8	30	5	38	7
Consulting and miscellaneous	0	2	4	6	14	4	28	7
Industry	3	3	4	3	10	1	11	1
Fire service	2	1	1	3	4	3	11	2
Test lab	1	2	2	2	8	11	8	3
Government	0	0	0	3	5	1	3	0
Total	27	26	24	29	85	28	123	26

life safety, property protection, or assurance of business operation. NFPA 13 is a true story of success through concensus standards.

REFERENCES CITED IN SUPPLEMENT

National Fire Protection Association, 1 Batterymarch Park, P.O. Box 9101, Quincy, MA 02269-9101

NFPA 13, *Standard for the Installation of Sprinkler Systems,* 2002 edition

NFPA 13D, *Standard for the Installation of Sprinkler Systems in One- and Two-Family Dwellings and Manufactured Homes,* 2002 edition

NFPA 13R, *Standard for the Installation of Sprinkler Systems in Residential Occupancies up to and Including Four Stories in Height,* 2002 edition

NFPA 30, *Flammable and Combustible Liquids Code,* 2000 edition

NFPA 30B, *Code for the Manufacture and Storage of Aerosol Products,* 2002 edition

NFPA 33, *Standard for Spray Application Using Flammable or Combustible Materials,* 2000 edition

NFPA 36, *Standard for Solvent Extraction Plants,* 2001 edition

NFPA 40, *Standard for the Storage and Handling of Cellulose Nitrate Film,* 2001 edition

NFPA 42, *Code for the Storage of Pyroxylin Plastic,* 2002 edition

NFPA 45, *Standard on Fire Protection for Laboratories Using Chemicals,* 2000 edition

NFPA 51, *Standard for the Design and Installation of Oxygen–Fuel Gas Systems for Welding, Cutting, and Allied Processes,* 2002 edition

NFPA 51A, *Standard for Acetylene Cylinder Charging Plants,* 2001 edition

NFPA 55, *Standard for the Storage, Use, and Handling of Compressed Gases and Cryogenic Fluids in Portable and Stationary Containers, Cylinders, and Tanks,* 1998 edition

NFPA 59, *Utility LP-Gas Plant Code,* 2001 edition

NFPA 59A, *Standard for the Production, Storage, and Handling of Liquefied Natural Gas (LNG),* 2001 edition

NFPA 75, *Standard for the Protection of Information Technology Equipment,* 1999 edition

NFPA 82, *Standard on Incinerators and Waste and Linen Handling Systems and Equipment,* 1999 edition

NFPA 86C, *Standard for Industrial Furnaces Using a Special Processing Atmosphere,* 1999 edition

NFPA 96, *Standard for Ventilation Control and Fire Protection of Commercial Cooking Operations,* 2001 edition

NFPA *101®, Life Safety Code®,* 2000 edition

NFPA 130, *Standard for Fixed Guideway Transit and Passenger Rail Systems,* 2000 edition

NFPA 150, *Standard on Fire Safety in Racetrack Stables,* 2000 edition

NFPA 203, *Guide on Roof Coverings and Roof Deck Constructions,* 2000 edition

NFPA 214, *Standard on Water-Cooling Towers,* 2000 edition

NFPA 230, *Standard for Fire Protection of Storage,* 1999 edition

NFPA 232, *Standard for the Protection of Records,* 1995 edition

NFPA 307, *Standard for the Construction and Fire Protection of Marine Terminals, Piers, and Wharves,* 2000 edition

NFPA 318, *Standard for the Protection of Semiconductor Fabrication Facilities,* 2002 edition

NFPA 409, *Standard on Aircraft Hangars,* 2001 edition

NFPA 415, *Standard on Airport Terminal Buildings, Fueling Ramp Drainage, and Loading Walkways,* 2002 edition

NFPA 423, *Standard for Construction and Protection of Aircraft Engine Test Facilities,* 1999 edition

NFPA 430, *Code for the Storage of Liquid and Solid Oxidizers,* 2000 edition

NFPA 432, *Code for the Storage of Organic Peroxide Formulations,* 2002 edition

NFPA 804, *Standard for Fire Protection for Advanced Light Water Reactor Electric Generating Plants,* 2001 edition

NFPA 850, *Recommended Practice for Fire Protection for Electric Generating Plants and High Voltage Direct Current Converter Stations,* 2000 edition

NFPA 851, *Recommended Practice for Fire Protection for Hydroelectric Generating Plants,* 2000 edition

NFPA 909, *Standard for the Protection of Cultural Resources,* 2001 edition

Bibliography

1. *The Factory Mutuals 1835–1935,* Manufacturer's Mutual Insurance Co., Providence, RI, 1935.
2. Freeman, J. R. "Experiments Relating to Hydraulics of Fire Streams," *ASME Transactions,* 1889.
3. Gorham Dana, S. B., *Automatic Sprinkler Protection,* third edition, 1923.
4. Jerome S. Pepi, *The Early History of Grinnell Corporation and the Fire Sprinkler Industry,* Grinnell Corporation, Providence, RI, January 1996.
5. Edward B. French, *Factory Mutual Insurance,* Arkwright Mutual Fire Insurance Company, Boston, MA, 1912.
6. *NFPA sprinkler standards,* National Fire Protection Association, Quincy, MA, 1896–1999.
7. Percy Bugbee, *Men Against Fire,* National Fire Protection Association, Boston, MA, 1971.
8. E. U. Crosby, *Handbook of The Underwriters' Bureau of New England,* Boston, MA, 1896.
9. Merwin Brandon, *Reminiscences of Underwriters' Laboratories, Inc.,* Chicago, IL, 1964.
10. *NFPA Handbook of Fire Protection,* National Fire Protection Association, Boston, MA, 1914.
11. R. W. Hendricks, *The Distribution of Water by Automatic Sprinkler Systems,* Underwriters' Laboratories, Inc., Chicago, IL, 1926.
12. Henry A. Fiske, "Sprinkler Control—Pipe Sizes and Spacing," *NFPA Quarterly,* Boston, MA, 1927.
13. NFPA handbooks, National Fire Protection Association, Quincy, MA, 1940–present.
14. *Technical Bulletin #410,* Crane Co., Chicago, IL, 1957.
15. Norman J. Thompson, "Proving Spray Sprinkler Efficiency," *NFPA Quarterly,* Boston, MA, 1954.
16. UL199, *Standard for Automatic Sprinklers,* Underwriters' Laboratories, Inc., Chicago, IL, 1919.
17. Private phone conversation with Chester W. Schirmer, June 1999.
18. Russell B. Fleming, P.E., *Quick Response Sprinklers—A Technical Analysis,* National Fire Protection Research Foundation, Quincy, MA, 1985.
19. Arthur E. Cote, P.E., "Field Test and Evaluation of Residential Sprinkler Systems," National Fire Protection Association, Quincy, MA, July 1982.
20. Heskestad and Smith, "Plunge Test for Determination of Sprinkler Sensitivity," Factory Mutual Research Corporation, Norwood, MA, 1980.

21. James L. Lee, "Early Suppression Fast Response (ESFR) Program," Factory Mutual Research Corporation, Norwood, MA, 1984.

22. William M. Carey, "Report of the Quick Response Sprinkler Project, Group 2 Performance Tests, Phase I-RDD Tests," Underwriters Laboratories, Inc., Northbrook, IL, May 1988.

23. William M. Carey, "Report of the Quick Response Sprinkler Project, Group 2 Performance Tests, Phase II-ADD Tests," Underwriters Laboratories, Inc., Northbrook, IL, January 1989.

The Effect of Large Orifice Sprinklers on High Challenge Fires

Bill Thomas, P.E.

Bill Tomes

Editor's Note: Supplement 2 has been included to provide the reader with background information related to the development and application of large orifice sprinklers to high challenge fires. The information provided is intended to give the reader an overall understanding of the performance and effect large orifice sprinklers have in comparison to traditional orifice sizes. This supplement is not intended to provide any specific design guidance. For specific application and design requirements, see NFPA 13 and the sprinkler manufacturer's listing materials.

INTRODUCTION

With the completion of the FM test center in the late 1960s, the sprinkler industry had the opportunity to conduct more realistic tests. The test center was large enough to investigate many fire test variables not previously understood in smaller scale testing. For warehouse-type storage, high densities (those greater than 0.35) were found to be necessary, primarily because of the storage of plastics. As the density requirements increased up to 0.6 for certain high-challenge commodities, the use of ½-in. orifice and then ¹⁷⁄₃₂-in. orifice sprinklers required either higher pressures or closer spacing of the sprinklers. Both situations caused cold soldering or skipping to occur during critical stages of the test fires. (For information on skipping see A.12.1.13 of NFPA 13.) The high pressures created smaller droplets that were more easily carried to adjacent sprinklers. Close spacing (50 ft²) wet adjacent sprinklers even at lower pressures. Over the next years, the NFPA storage standards tried to combat the skipping by limiting the spacing to no less than 80 ft². With the advent of the large drop sprinkler in the 1970s and the ELO sprinkler

(0.64 in. orifice) in the 1980s, a better method of achieving high densities was born. This generation of sprinklers largely eliminated the skipping problem. Larger orifice sprinklers were then combined with other innovations, such as more sensitive sprinklers (quick response) and deflector designs that helped optimize the use of existing water supplies. In most cases, the larger the sprinkler orifice, the better the protection. Exhibit S2.1 shows the pressure requirements for various sized orifice sprinklers at various densities (all at 100-ft²-sprinkler spacing).

Each of the sprinkler K-factors identified in Exhibit S2.1 creates different combinations of droplet sizes ranging from very small to large. The larger K-factors result in an increase in the subsequent downward water force created by the velocity and size of the droplet that more effectively penetrates through fire updrafts. This result is true even if the sprinklers are operating at the same pressures. Each of the manufacturers of a specific size sprinkler has a different deflector, and each produced different combinations of small and large drop sprinklers throughout the pressure range of 7 psi (the minimum required by NFPA 13) to the upper limit of about 175 psi (normally

Bill Thomas, P.E., is executive vice president with TVA Fire and Life Safety Corporation in Chicago, IL.

Bill Tomes is chairman of TVA Fire and Life Safety Corporation in Chicago, IL.

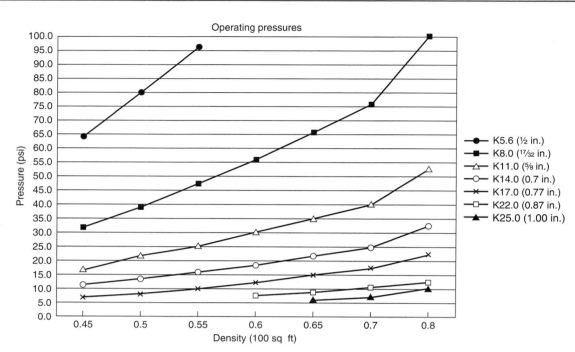

EXHIBIT S2.1 *Pressure Requirements for Various Sized Orifice Sprinklers at Various Densities.*

only produced with fire pump installations). Large drops with acceleration downward create bigger forces to penetrate fire updrafts than small droplets but do little cooling above the storage commodity. Small drops do not normally penetrate the storage fire plume and can do some harm by being blown onto adjacent sprinklers, delaying or preventing their operation. Conversely, small drops are good for cooling the ceiling area, depositing drops on exposed structural steel and helping to keep it cool.

LISTING/APPROVAL AGENCIES

At higher pressures (greater than 50 psi), more small droplets are created and less of the water reaches the top of storage and the burning commodity. The manufacturers, therefore, are presented with a dilemma—how much acceleration and downward force to impart versus how many small droplets to produce. Two of the major approval and listing agencies (Factory Mutual and Underwriters Laboratories) have tried to answer that question by requiring each sprinkler to undergo rigorous testing, including full-scale tests of the standard plastic commodity at various storage heights and clearances. The clearance effect will vary depending on the pressure on the sprinklers. Research has consistently shown that for the older, smaller orifice sprinklers, high pressure (greater than about 50 psi) is good if the clearance is small (less than 5 ft), as more water is able to reach the top of the storage and the

burning material below. However, high pressure is not as effective if the clearance is greater than about 5 ft and becomes increasingly ineffective as the clearance increases. Testing has also shown that the large clearance concern has been lessened with the use of larger orifice sprinklers (0.64 and larger). Listing/approval agencies' testing at various clearances has clearly demonstrated this.

Ignition location in relation to ceiling sprinkler has also been shown by the listing agencies as necessary to show the sprinklers' capability to control fires effectively when ignition occurs under one sprinkler, between two sprinklers, and between four sprinklers. As new commodities are stored and new storage arrangements are created, more large size testing will undoubtedly be needed to verify the proper combinations of large drop, small drops, downward force, and distribution.

Table S2.1 illustrates the effect changing K-factors has on a constant density fire test and the results of the fire test, including design pressure, steel peak temperature, sprinklers operated, and pallet loads of commodity consumed. The larger orifice sprinkler with lower pressures was able to penetrate the updraft and affect the fire faster than the smaller orifice sprinkler in this open rack arrangement

The larger orifice sprinkler in this palletized arrangement, as shown in Table S2.2, again reached the burning surfaces quicker via better penetration of the fire plume and produced a better result (both tests illustrated in Table S2.2 were successful).

TABLE S2.1 Constant Density Test Comparisons

Sprinkler	½ in.	⅝ in.
Commodity	Class II	Class II
Arrangement	Rack	Rack
Ceiling height	30 ft	30 ft
Storage height	20 ft	20 ft
Ignition location	4	4
Pressure	43 psi	11 psi
Steel peak temp	829°F	331°F
Density	0.37	0.37
Sprinklers operated	18	9
Pallet loads consumed	41	5

TABLE S2.2 Constant Density Test Comparisons

Sprinkler	$^{17}\!/_{32}$ in.	⅝ in.
Commodity	Plastic	Plastic
Arrangement	Palletized	Palletized
Ceiling height	25 ft	25 ft
Storage height	15 ft	15 ft
Ignition location	4	4
Pressure	36	19
Steel peak temp	Not measured	203°F
Density	0.6	0.6
Sprinklers operated	24	16
Pallet loads consumed	20	2

TABLE S2.3 Constant Density Test Comparisons

Sprinkler	$^{17}\!/_{32}$ in. (K-8)	⅝ in. (K-11)	0.77 in. (K-17)
Commodity	Plastic	Plastic	Plastic
Arrangement	Rack	Rack	Rack
Ceiling height	25 ft	25 ft	25 ft
Storage height	15 ft	15 ft	15 ft
Ignition location	4	4	4
Pressure	55 psi	29 psi	12.5 psi
Steel peak temp	Not measured	163°F	135°F
Sprinklers operated	29	4	4
Pallet loads consumed	26	2	4

The tests shown in Table S2.3 show a significant difference between the K-8 sprinkler and the other two. Obviously it was not possible in this comparison to show a better result than the K-11 sprinkler when using the larger orifice K-17. Other tests have shown a better result with the K-17 compared directly to the K-11.

The test results shown in Table S2.4 come from UL Report EX683-98NK7829 (sponsored by CHEP International and Central Sprinkler).

The difference between the two tests shown in Table S2.4 was the spread of fire. It was more easily diminished by the K-17, which operated less than half the number of sprinklers operated by the K-11 sprinkler.

Although it is feasible to find other direct comparisons showing the better results with a larger orifice sprinkler at the same density, Table S2.5 shows the last direct constant density comparison for this study.

This comparison in Table S2.5 shows the low-pressure requirement and much better results as demonstrated by the number of sprinklers operated and the pallet loads of commodity consumed with the larger orifice sprinkler.

Table S2.4 Constant Density Test Comparisons for Idle Pallet Storage

Sprinkler	⅝ in. (K-11)	0.77 in. (K-17)
Sprinkler temperature rating	165°F	155°F
Commodity	Idle 4-way wood pallets	Idle 4-way wood pallets
Arrangement	2 stacks × 3 stacks	2 stacks × 3 stacks
Storage height	12 ft	12 ft
Density	0.6	0.6
Steel peak temperature	201°F	129°F
Sprinklers operated	13	6
Approx. percentage of pallet damage	90%	23%

TABLE S2.5 Constant Density Test Comparisons

Sprinkler	½ in. (K-5.6)	0.77 in. (K-17)
Commodity	Plastic	Plastic
Arrangement	Rack	Rack
Ceiling height	30 ft	30 ft
Storage height	9 ft	9 ft
Density	0.45	0.45
Pressure	67 psi	7 psi
Sprinklers operated	29	5
Pallet loads consumed	14	2

SELF-REGULATING HIGH PRESSURES

Following is an actual approximation of a water supply curve with a pump that had a no control situation in a real-world hostile fire. With the pump running, the initial pressure was about 175 psi. The first few K-8 ($^{17}/_{32}$ in. orifice) sprinklers in the warehouse that operated apparently misted (almost all the drops were small), and the drops did not penetrate the fire plume and were carried upward and outward, thereby cooling adjacent sprinklers and preventing them from operating. The result was fire travel through much of the warehouse, destroying the product and causing a very large loss. Fire testing was initiated to determine if using a K-17 sprinkler would have helped the situation. Two of the tests showed these results as indicated in Table S2.6, including the peak steel temperature, number of sprinklers operated, and whether the fire spread was controlled.

Three benefits of the larger orifice sprinkler were obvious during the tests shown in Table S2.6, as follows:

1. The volume of water was greater. The K-8 sprinkler at 165 psi provides 103 gpm while the K-17 sprinkler at 130 psi provides 216 gpm.
2. With such high initial discharge rates, the friction loss on the supply pipes and sprinkler piping would be much greater with the K-17 sprinkler. This resulted in lower first operating sprinkler pressures with a

TABLE S2.6 Comparative Test Results

Sprinkler	$^{17}/_{32}$ in. (K-8)	0.77 in. (K-17)
Sprinkler temperature rating	286°F	155°F
Commodity	Class III	Class III
Ceiling height	31 ft	31 ft
Storage height	22 ft	22 ft
Pressure	165 psi	130 psi
Steel peak temperature	421°F	113°F
Sprinklers operated	2	2
Fire spread controlled?	No	Yes

greater rate of pressure reduction as more sprinklers operated, thus creating a self-regulated pressure reduction without a negative impact from high impact from high initial pressures.

3. The use of the lower temperature–rated sprinklers with the larger orifice sprinklers showed effective control of the spread of the fire and no need to use high-temperature sprinklers to reduce the number of sprinklers on the periphery of the fire.

Exhibit S2.2 highlights the differences of the K-8 and K-17 initial operating pressures.

It can be seen from Exhibit S2.2 that as more sprinklers operate, the K-17 sprinkler would move down the curve further with the same number of sprinkler operations, thus reducing the pressure and restricting the misting effect.

INITIAL DENSITY ADVANTAGES OF LARGER ORIFICE SPRINKLERS

In the real world, with sloping water supplies and pipe friction loss, higher initial pressures are inevitable. Since city water supplies vary considerably from being fairly flat to extremely steep, it is impossible to come up with a "typical" water supply. However, for storage occupancies, most NFPA requirements are for densities and pressures well above those required for most buildings. If the city water supply is flat, it usually requires a fire pump, boosting initial pressures. If the city water supply is steep, the higher initial pressures are already there. These high initial pressures can be anything over 50 psi up to close to 200 psi. For this example, 81 psi was chosen as a conservative point, the results of which are shown in Table S2.7.

Table S2.7 shows the distinct advantage of having larger sprinklers and high initial pressures. There is more

EXHIBIT S2.2 Differences Between K-8 and K-17 Initial Operating Pressures.

TABLE S2.7 81 PSI Initial Operating Pressure (10 ft × 10 ft Sprinkler Spacing)

K-5.6	K-8	K-11	K-14	K-17	K-22	K-25
$Q = K\sqrt{P}$	$Q = K\sqrt{P}$	$Q = K\sqrt{P}$	$Q = K\sqrt{P}$	$Q = K\sqrt{P}$	$Q = K\sqrt{P}$	$Q = K\sqrt{P}$
$Q = 5.6\sqrt{81}$	$Q = 8\sqrt{81}$	$Q = 11\sqrt{81}$	$Q = 14\sqrt{81}$	$Q = 17\sqrt{81}$	$Q = 22\sqrt{81}$	$Q = 25\sqrt{81}$
$Q = 50$ gpm	$Q = 72$ gpm	$Q = 99$ gpm	$Q = 126$ gpm	$Q = 153$ gpm	$Q = 198$ gpm	$Q = 225$ gpm

water on the fire and a much greater chance of operating fewer sprinklers away from the fire start area. Usually, that translates into a much smaller "normal loss expectancy." This smaller normal loss expectancy is good for the owner as well as the insurance companies.

USING THE QR LINK WITH LARGER ORIFICE SPRINKLERS

Over the last few years, the use of the quick response (QR) link in tests, even with the standard ½ in. and ¹⁷/₃₂-in. orifice sprinklers has been shown to work as well as or better than the standard response sprinklers. However, when the QR link was combined with a certain distribution pattern designed to suppress the fire, the ESFR sprinkler was born. It now made sense to put a lot of water on the fire quickly when the fire was small, allowing even less fire, smoke and water damage to occur than with large orifice sprinklers. The K-11 and K-14 upright ESFR sprinklers have been listed and/or approved by the testing agencies, as has the K-22 pendent ESFR, but have not been included in the following comparisons. At the time of this writing, two upright ESFRs and four pendent ESFRs are on the market. Table S2.8 shows the partial pressure requirements for each and again shows the advantages of the larger orifice sprinklers.

As the pressure requirements are reduced with the use of larger orifice sprinklers, there will be fewer and fewer requirements for fire pumps. Since city water supplies are normally more reliable than having to use a fire pump, a more reliable sprinkler system is normally used if larger orifice sprinklers are installed.

LARGER ORIFICE SPRINKLERS WITH SPECIAL DISTRIBUTION CAPABILITIES

Larger orifice sprinklers designed for high challenge fires with unique distribution methods have been created that produce special protection methods. One is the large drop sprinkler, and the other is the K-25 EC (extended coverage) sprinkler. The large drop sprinkler has certain pressure requirements for certain storage and ceiling heights that are able to produce water penetration capabilities above the norm for upright sprinklers. The K-25 EC can be spaced up to 14 ft by 14 ft and can be used as a density/area sprinkler creating the following three positive features:

1. A cheaper sprinkler piping system by eliminating some sprinkler lines (this usually offsets any possible increase in the cost of the sprinkler itself).
2. A wider distribution, so there is wetting ahead of the fire much quicker than with standard spaced sprinklers.

TABLE S2.8 Effect on Design Pressure Where Large Orifice Sprinklers are Utilized

Commodity	Maximum Staging Height	Maximum Ceiling Height	Nominal K-Factor	Minimum Pressure	In-Racks Required?
Cartoned unexpanded plastics	30	35	14	75	No
			17	52	No
			25	20	No
	35	40	14	75	No
			17	52	No
			25	25	No
	40	45	14	90	Yes
			17	63	Yes
			25	40	No

K-14 = 0.7 in. orifice
K-17 = 0.775 in. orifice
K-25 = 1.00 in. orifice

3. More initial water delivered to the fire area with the first few sprinklers at pressures that produce the optimum combination of large and small drops. This can be done because of the wide range of sprinkler spacing combinations.

LIMITATIONS OF LARGER ORIFICE SPRINKLERS

There is not one sprinkler that can be designed that is good for all field situations. Just designing for larger orifice sprinklers is not good enough. Sometimes the cheaper, better protection occurs with smaller orifice sprinklers. Larger orifice sprinklers are not normally suggested in the following situations:

1. When density requirements are less than 0.35 gpm/ft^2, as the minimum pressure requirement of 7 psi will cause overkill for these hazards.
2. For some specialty hazards that cause flash fires or hidden fast-spreading fires that normally require in-rack sprinkler protection, full-scale costly fire testing may be necessary for acceptance by the fire community.

Also in the larger orifice sprinkler categories there are many choices (⅝ in. to 1 in.). This means that careful study should be initiated to determine the proper sprinkler for each specific hazard and arrangement. Not everyone in the fire protection design industry is able to determine this. Therefore, some poor designs are more likely to occur.

TESTING LARGE ORIFICE SPRINKLERS

In the early testing of high-piled storage using ½-in. and $^{17}/_{32}$-in. sprinklers, almost all the comparison testing was done with constant densities. This meant that the first sprinkler operated at the same pressure as the last sprinkler. At the time, this was thought to be the conservative approach to testing, as a normal water supply would start at higher pressures and diminish as more sprinklers operated. This meant that in the real world, there would always be more water coming out of the sprinklers initially, and this would be a safety factor built into designs. Also, because public water supplies vary from very high initial pressures and step declines to very flat, testing engineers preferred constant densities so other variables could more easily be analyzed. These reasons for using constant density testing were good when testing at lower pressures and a minimum of 70 ft^2 to 80 ft^2 spacing. However, as pressures became

higher with the need for greater densities, these safety factors were found not to be conservative at all.

Today's testing with the larger orifice sprinklers has mostly been done by comparing the larger orifice sprinkler tests directly with the previously conducted ½-in. and $^{17}/_{32}$-in. orifice sprinkler tests—meaning constant densities throughout the test. This testing is correct, because it compares apples with apples, but it does not allow for the biggest advantages of the larger orifice sprinklers to be displayed. Future testing with large orifice sprinklers may determine the smallest anticipated initial densities for flat water supplies, and may use that density for the first four sprinklers operating during the test. If the water supply is known for the specific testing being conducted, of course that water supply may be followed throughout the test.

If the above procedure is followed, the true advantages of the larger orifice sprinklers will more easily be shown through the testing process. As the larger orifice sprinklers are used in the field, they will undoubtedly show the same advantages.

CONCLUSIONS

Larger orifice sprinklers are normally better for the higher hazard warehouse/storage protection schemes because of the following:

1. Lower pressures are feasible for the design, allowing fewer small drops to be produced, helping to eliminate skipping and causing better penetration through the commodity to the fire.
2. Higher initial densities with a given water supply put more water on the fire, causing an overkill that often produces fewer sprinkler operations outside the fire area. Also, the higher initial designs cause a quicker reduction in pressure for water supplies that normally produce very high pressures and misting with smaller orifice sprinklers. This again causes a self-regulating method of producing a better combination of large and small drops.
3. The combination of points (1) and (2) above will normally cause a hostile fire in the real world to be smaller in size, cause less smoke to be created, and cause less water damage than smaller orifice sprinklers. It can also, by eliminating the need for a fire pump, create a more reliable system that is less likely to fail.

For high-hazard applications with density demands higher than 0.35 gpm/ft^2 or higher, larger orifice sprinklers usually provided a more effective design.

Supplement 3

Microbiologically Influenced Corrosion in Fire Sprinkler Systems

Bruce H. Clarke

Anthony M. Aguilera

Editor's Note: Supplement 3 has been included to provide the user with background information related to microbiologically influenced corrosion or MIC. While MIC has been in existence for some time, it has recently become a maintenance problem, through recognition of the source of corrosion, for those involved in the maintenance of fire protection systems. The supplement discusses the microbial corrosion process and recognition and treatment of MIC for fire protection systems.

Beginning in the early 1990s, concerns were raised about multiple cases involving the abnormally rapid development of pinhole-sized leaks and highly obstructive interior growths in sprinkler systems, some less than a year old (Exhibits S3.1 and S3.2). Research into the cause of these leaks led to a growing awareness of the problem of microbiologically influenced corrosion (MIC), a localized electrochemical corrosion caused by bacterial activity. In just 10 years MIC has grown from a relatively unknown regional topic to one now generating widespread concern throughout several countries. MIC in fire protection systems also has become the subject of a wide array of speculation, debate, and, in some cases, gross inaccuracies.

At the time of this writing, few proven and universally accepted fire protection "best practices" were available to reference. Although MIC and biological growth

EXHIBIT S3.1 *Interior Pin Hole Leak.*

Bruce H. Clarke is manager of field services for GE Global Asset Protection Services and secretary of the Carolinas Chapter of the Society of Fire Protection Engineers.

Anthony M. Aguilera is manager of loss prevention for Honeywell Engines & Systems and vice chair of the Board of Directors for the Industrial Fire Protection Section of NFPA.

EXHIBIT S3.2 *Interior Tubercle.*

control have been extensively researched in many allied engineering fields for decades, treatment in fire sprinkler systems is relatively new. Although some currently available treatment systems may be effective or at least hold promise, there still is limited long-term data to support their overall effectiveness. This supplement will provide an overview of the MIC phenomenon in the fire protection industry and a review of the data and issues available at writing.

DEFINING CORROSION

General Corrosion

Specifically defining MIC is as complex as defining corrosion in general. One edition of *Webster's* defines *corrosion* as the wearing away of materials by chemical action(s). Another edition simply defines it as "the wearing away of material gradually." The on-line encyclopedia *Encarta* describes *corrosion* as "specifically being related to the gradual action of natural agents such as air or salt water on metals." All these definitions may be generally true but are anything but universally accurate. They certainly do not appear to be a definition of corrosion that is microbiological in nature. Even definitions presented by various corrosion engineers, though more detailed, can at times be somewhat contradictory and very confusing to the fire protection engineer.

Corrosion can occur from many biophysical reactions and be described from a multitude of scientific viewpoints. "General corrosion" typically refers to uniform corrosion that occurs on most unprotected metallic systems. This corrosion can be associated with the uniform "rust" layer seen on many steel structures. Besides rust from oxidation, several other types of general corrosion include stray current, uniform biological, galvanic, molten

salt, dealloying, chemical, high-temperature, and general carburization.

Microbiologically Influenced Corrosion

In contrast to general or "uniform" corrosion, MIC is a form of localized corrosion. Material is lost at discrete points instead of universally across an entire surface. There are several types of localized corrosion, including pitting, crevice, cratering, and filiform. Exhibit S3.3 illustrates MIC-induced pitting.

As with the various other types of corrosion, MIC can take many forms and affect different systems in unique ways. But, for the fire protection profession, an industry-specific definition can be developed. This definition captures both the causes and effects of this problem with several continuous generalities to avoid some of the current inaccuracies. Thus, microbiologically influenced corrosion in fire protection systems can be described as "an electrochemical corrosion process that is concentrated and accelerated by the activity of specific bacteria within a fire sprinkler system resulting in the premature failure of metallic system components." [1]

THE "CORROSION" PROBLEM

Concentrated and Accelerated Corrosion

All metallic systems normally begin to corrode to various degrees from the instant moisture contacts metal. Typically, this appears as general corrosion. By definition, in comparison, the MIC process is both *concentrated* and *accelerated*. With general corrosion, when moisture is introduced into a system, a thin layer of oxidation occurs relatively evenly throughout the pipe wall surface. This

EXHIBIT S3.3 *MIC-Induced Pitting.*

type of corrosion is typically not a significant concern in fire sprinkler systems and does not require treatment because it does not change a pipe's interior surface roughness (i.e., C-factor) unevenly. The rate of decay is also typically slow. A typical corrosion rate in sprinkler pipe is highly dependent on water quality, but with MIC, this relatively slow corrosion rate is abnormally accelerated.

MIC is the result of *specific* bacteria (see section on defining MIC). A multitude of bacteria are always omnipresent in all ecosystems, including the interior of sprinkler systems. Just as only a small number of bacteria on earth have the potential to cause human sickness, only a relatively small number of bacteria have the potential to cause the rapid system destruction currently linked to MIC. Thus, as defined, only a few *specific* bacteria *concentrate* and *accelerate* the general or uniform corrosion process.

The ultimate effect of MIC in fire protection systems is the premature failure of metallic components. Premature failure can take two forms, both requiring individual consideration. First is the failure of a system to hold water, in other words, pinhole leaks that require component replacement (Exhibit S3.4). Leaks can cause significant damage and require immediate action. Leaks can also lead to excessive direct and indirect costs, as well as inherent risks from repeated system impairments.

In one known case, MIC-related leaks resulted in the shutdown of an aerospace manufacturer's global computing center. [2] A pinhole leak developed in a wet-pipe sprinkler branch line located over the mainframe equipment of the computing center. Water from the leak not only damaged computing equipment but also resulted in over 5000 hours of lost operations time. Property damage from similar leaks at other sites have also been documented in the millions of dollars. [3,4]

The second and more concerning effect is the failure of a system to operate as designed to achieve fire control.

EXHIBIT S3.4 *Exterior Pinhole.*

This failure not only affects property loss but also could threaten lives. Several systems with MIC have been found with obstructed sprinkler drops, the result of debris generated as a byproduct of microbial activity (called biofilm or biosludge). Many in the industry have found systems with feed mains over 60 percent obstructed from biological growth. [4,5] This buildup of debris presents an obvious hydraulic concern as many affected sprinkler systems today will not provide fire control as the required discharge criteria, in terms of flow and pressure, is not available due to obstruction and associated frictional pressure loss.

Premature Failure

MIC causes systems to fail *prematurely.* What constitutes premature with regard to the integrity of specific system components has not officially been defined in the industry. Long-term warranties are not typical with system components, but with proper maintenance a sprinkler system is typically expected to last a minimum of 30 to 60 years before major repairs are required.

However, as discussed, premature failure is never considered acceptable when systems fail functionally. Any time a system is "in service" and fails to operate as designed, it has experienced an unacceptable "premature failure." Fire sprinkler systems are *always* expected to control a developing fire when properly designed, constructed, and maintained.

Extent of MIC in the Sprinkler Industry

Currently only limited study and anecdotal data exist. Complicating this lack of data, reported MIC cases rarely have secondary analysis to differentiate true MIC cases from other types of corrosion involving similar symptoms. Part of this problem is the complexity and cost of such additional testing. Due to the nature of electrochemical corrosion, most corrosion engineers agree that the degree to which MIC specifically increases or contributes to general corrosion can never be conclusively determined, as the complex biological interactions between bacteria and host materials are still not fully understood. There are simply too many variables and uncertainties that affect all corrosion reactions, especially those involving bacterial interactions. Thus, a "percentage of blame" or "rate of corrosion from MIC" cannot be numerically defined. And, any database generated at this point will likely list only reported cases, not confirmed cases.

Although several industry groups have been attempting to compile data on this problem for several years, to date only the results of two national studies have been published for the fire protection industry. [6,7] Thus the true extent and cost of the problem are not known. In

1996, the National Fire Sprinkler Association sent out a questionnaire in its quarterly membership magazine. These results yielded approximately 40 responses from across the United States and Canada, which appeared to indicate that MIC was a widespread problem. Due to the reasons previously stated, however, the quality of analytical techniques used by respondents claiming to have experienced MIC was never investigated or substantiated.

However, the results of MIC in other industries is well documented. The Energy and Power Research Institute has estimated that corrosion in the U.S. electric power industry costs $5 billion to $10 billion each year. Corrosion is said to be the culprit in half the forced outages each year in steam generating plants. [8] Data collected from before the 2001 "U.S. power shortage" showed corrosion to be the primary factor in more than 10 percent of U.S. power generation costs. [8] In the gas and nuclear industry, MIC is specifically said to account for 15 percent to 30 percent of corrosion-related failures. [9] To prevent such problems, North American companies spend in excess of $1.5 billion per year (over $7 billion globally) on treatment chemicals to prevent microbial corrosion and fouling.

Materials Affected by MIC

Although steel sprinkler pipe is the typically observed "first point of failure," sprinkler orifice caps, control valves, fittings, and supply tanks may also be subject to damage from MIC. All evidence suggests that only *metallic* components are susceptible to MIC. However, plastic components are subject to biofouling, or bacterial debris blockage from upstream corrosion activity. With the exception of a few time-proven metallic alloys, such as titanium, virtually all metallic materials are susceptible, including component materials typically used in sprinkler systems.

DEFINING MIC

Oxygen Tolerance

MIC-related bacteria are classified primarily by oxygen tolerance—that is, they are *aerobic* or *anaerobic*. *Aerobic* bacteria require oxygen to flourish and reproduce. *Anaerobic* bacteria do not require oxygen to flourish and reproduce. [6]

The most damaging MIC appears to take place within a highly complex community with multiple species of bacteria. This community includes not only aerobic and anaerobic bacteria, but also facultative bacteria, those MIC bacteria that function in both aerobic and anaerobic environments. All three types of bacteria can play a role in the somewhat random interactions that can occur in microbiologically influenced corrosion. [10]

Metabolism

In defining MIC bacteria further than previously done, classification is not absolute and can become confusing. The most commonly used method of categorizing bacteria associated with MIC is by metabolism. These categories are basically definitions of what each bacteria type eats (or metabolizes) and excretes as a byproduct. As these terms imply, where plants use photosynthesis (i.e., light) to develop energy, bacteria use chemosynthesis (i.e., eating/breathing various chemicals or minerals) to sustain life.

Metabolic classifications are not universally replicated among scientists and can be somewhat confusing. A single bacteria type may fall under more than one metabolic definition. Some of the commonly referenced categories include sulfur-reducing bacteria, metal-reducing bacteria, acid-producing bacteria, iron-depositing bacteria, low-nutrient bacteria, iron-related bacteria, iron-reducing bacteria, iron-oxidizing bacteria, sulfate-oxidizing bacteria, slime-forming bacteria, and iron bacteria. [2,6,10,11]

Scientific Nomenclature

Finally, all bacteria (i.e., all plants and animals) can be classified by their scientific name under phylum, class, order, family, genus, and species. For example, one type of sulfate-reducing bacteria is anaerobic and metabolizes sulfate to sulfide. The sulfate-reducing bacteria group includes the genera desulfovibrio, desulfobacter, and desulformaculum. [1] All are of the phylum Thiopneutes, which interestingly translates from Greek to "sulfur-breathers."

Sources of MIC Infection

Although there are no conclusive relational studies in the fire protection industry, as noted there are growing beliefs that a sprinkler system's water supply is not the only (and possibly primary) source of bacterial infection. Bacteria capable of causing MIC are potentially present in soil, air, and cutting oils, as well as water. Thus, the manufacture, shipping, storage, and flushing of system materials should be addressed in all MIC investigations.

MIC does not occur only in water-filled systems. Dry-pipe systems are also susceptible. Dry systems may even be more susceptible to damage than are wet systems, due to the humidified atmosphere that is created after trip testing. A trip test and subsequent drain can create the right atmospheric moisture content for some bacterial colonies to thrive. Complete drainage and the subsequent use of truly dried air or nitrogen gas appear to mitigate this problem. With regard to tubercle growth alone, dissolved oxygen content, not bacteria, may be the only considerable factor in prevention.

MIC Corrosion Process

As with other forms of corrosion, MIC removes material through a series of *electrochemical* interactions. As such, both an "electrical" and a "chemical" component occur with MIC. The electrical component occurs through electron transfer. Electron transfer removes pipe wall material one electron at a time. With MIC, this exact interaction is highly dependent on the specific bacteria involved. Within a sprinkler system, metallic parts become anodic in relation to the cathodic corrosion cell and surrounding water. Basic cathodic depolarization occurs as electrons are stripped away through various forms of oxidation and are "pulled" to an atom with another electrical potential.

Although many of the complex cellular interactions of bacteria are still unclear and can vary by system, there appear to be several somewhat universal steps in the MIC process. They are as follows: [1]

1. Bacteria enter the system, attach to metallic components, and begin to rapidly colonize and reproduce.
2. Aerobic colonies metabolize nutrients from the water and/or the metal surfaces they are attached to, and subsequently excrete a polymer film byproduct that bonds together to form crustaceous nodules called tubercles.
3. Tubercles and associated biofilms create microenvironments on the metallic material surface (under the tubercles). Tubercles are hard protective shells formed by biological activity. Tubercles typically have an open interior fluid cavity over the corrosion floor area.
4. The underdeposit area (i.e., under the tubercles) becomes oxygen-depleted (i.e., anaerobic and anodic) in relation to the surrounding system water or air, which remains aerobic and cathodic. Thus, electrons in the anodic metal flow to the cathode through a reduction reaction.
5. Underdeposit anaerobic bacteria metabolize pipe wall materials and excrete acids (such as acetic acid), as byproducts, which are very aggressive to the carbon steels used in sprinkler piping. Relative acidity and alkalinity levels within the tubercle shells are reduced to an approximate pH of 2 to 4, which chemically attacks the metallic component surface.

On painted sprinkler piping, it is common to observe blisters where through-wall penetration has occurred. Testing of the fluid within these blisters has shown a pH of less than 3.

The described corrosion process can continue indefinitely until the aerobic and anaerobic bacteria in the system are killed. The tubercles created from bacterial colonization must also be broken down to destroy the underdeposit microenvironment. Even without bacteria in the underdeposit of a corrosion cell, the process can continue indefinitely, as the corrosion chain in its final phases is no longer reliant on their activity.

TREATMENT

References from Allied Fields

Currently, the fire protection industry has a very limited number of directly usable references supported by scientific data. However, there is excellent information on data from other industries.

The National Association of Corrosion Engineers (NACE) has published multiple studies about MIC detection and treatment for many years. ASTM (American Society for Testing and Materials) offers several publications on proper bacterial testing practices.

Also, the American Water Works Association (AWWA) offers standards describing the proper management of the somewhat hazardous chemicals typically used in injection devices attached to sprinkler systems for microbial control.

Fire Protection Codes and Standards

The National Fire Protection Association (NFPA) also addresses MIC, although NFPA references are very limited. NFPA 25, *Standard for the Inspection, Testing, and Maintenance of Water-Based Fire Protection Systems,* discusses MIC treatment and detection in some detail. NFPA 13, *Standard for the Installation of Sprinkler Systems,* contains a requirement that provides more impact. In covering water supply treatment, NFPA 13 states: "In areas with water supplies known to have contributed to microbiologically influenced corrosion (MIC) of sprinkler system piping, water supplies shall be tested and appropriately treated prior to filling or testing of metallic piping systems."

Although this requirement has generated a flood of needed curiosity, it does little to address the resulting questions about proper treatment. First, there is no explanation as to what is considered an area "known to have contributed to microbiologically influenced corrosion." Data thus far on confirmed cases have been widely inconsistent, varying within city blocks and even within building complexes fed off common loops. Is the entire community served by the same water supply now considered a "biological activity area"?

The NFPA 13 mandate also requires users to be familiar with *all* the sources of their fire protection water. This can be very difficult as many municipalities switch between and blend multiple sources, such as canals, various wells, rivers, lakes, and reservoirs. The NFPA 13 requirement also does not address the fact that contamination can come from sources other than the water supply, as already discussed.

Finally, this section of NPFA 13 indicates that sprinkler systems "shall be tested and appropriately treated prior to filling." The who, how, and when are still in debate by those addressing this issue. *Who* is truly qualified to make the determination of *when* a failure is the result of MIC and if a biocidal treatment program will prevent all future failures? And *how* is a system best tested (i.e., most accurately and cost-effectively) to confirm MIC? Almost anything requiring laboratory work can be overtested—at a price. And undertesting can lead to a false sense of security. Answers to these questions are still evolving.

Upcoming changes to NFPA 25 are being included to provide better detection standards and data collection where MIC is suspected.

PREVENTION AND TREATMENT

Operational Considerations

As the industry continues to develop methods to treat and prevent MIC, building owners are faced with the challenge of managing associated risks to their assets and business operations. At-risk businesses should review the interdependence of various operations to identify critical locations.

Proper Diagnosis

The analysis required to properly select a course of action to address MIC is typically outside of the scope of most sprinkler contractors and engineers. Thus, until treatment methods become universally proven and standardized, the most critical step in proper mitigation begins with the selection of a qualified corrosion control consultant.

With the wrong choice, a large amount of money can be spent on a problem that may not be correctable. A poor treatment choice could actually accelerate the corrosion rate and increase the affected area beyond that experienced before treatment.

The company chosen to determine treatment must have detailed knowledge not only of microbial corrosion control but also of metallurgy and sprinkler system dynamics. Fire sprinkler systems have flow characteristics and concerns that are much different from other industrial processes and systems where MIC is typically addressed.

Specific Considerations for Fire Sprinkler Systems

Other industries deal with MIC in systems containing fluids that are either always static or always flowing, such as in cooling towers. Unlike sprinkler systems, dynamic systems have flow rates that are relatively constant, requiring that prescribed chemical dose rates be constant. A constant flow rate does not occur in sprinkler systems. Variable differences are seen with system drains and refills, inspector testing, and main drain tests. The dose rate for each of these flows must be considered to ensure that the chemical injection rate is always effective. Other industrial systems also have multiple points where biocidal chemicals can be injected. In contrast, sprinkler system water can realistically only be treated at system risers, backflow apparatus, or suction tanks.

Finally, it must again be stated that it is critical to understand that premature system failure can be a function of both bacterial infection and water quality that is incompatible with components. In the majority of premature system failure cases, water chemistry or poor design may be the only likely factors requiring consideration. A high bacterial count does not always indicate that MIC will occur, and conversely, a low bacterial count does not discount that MIC has occurred in the past, in a given system, and will not occur again in the near future.

Detection in Existing Systems

In existing systems suspected of being infected, the first step is to have all possible water supply sources (tank, city mains, ponds, rivers, etc.) and the interior of each system tested for bacterial levels and activity. Although current technology makes this detection easy, analysis of the results is somewhat complex. And, as previously stated, in determining treatment, bacterial detection is worthless without factoring in water quality.

The laboratory used for analysis should be capable of giving conclusive details of water supply mineral and chemical levels, pipe wall deposit compositions, and type-specific bacterial counts. Multiple tests are used in these analyses from simple bacterial incubation with visual inspection to sulfur print or DNA testing. Obviously, not all tests are required or are necessarily needed. Current preferred analysis methods run the spectrum, depending on the consultant chosen. Costs for such testing can also vary widely.

Mitigation in Affected Systems

When MIC is confirmed in operational systems, the building owner is first faced with a fundamental question. Can the system be salvaged (i.e., cleaned) or does it have to be replaced? Currently, this cost/benefit decision requires further study and is not supported one way or the other by documented best practices in the fire protection industry.

Pipe cleaning is typically an option when corrosion (i.e., pitting) is not excessive. However, *excessive* is a relative term. The after-cleaning quality of the pipe must be considered, both for future longevity and system hydraulics. The resulting frictional loss from numerous pits after cleaning could affect system performance. This, of course, is typically outside of the scope of work of most corrosion control consultants. When replacement materials are chosen that are different than those of the original system, they must also be accounted for in hydraulic analysis of the post-treated system. Case studies suggest that pipe cleaning may remove corrosion byproducts that are, in effect, stopping the flow of water through existing pipe penetrations, subsequently resulting in leaks. [10] Prudence dictates that complete mitigation must include some form of treatment once pipes are cleaned.

Prevention in New Systems

In new systems, it is critical that susceptibility be determined *before* any systems are filled or tested with *any* water. If water tests are positive for MIC-related bacteria, a chemical injection system must be installed and used from the first fill. This includes hydrostatic testing and preliminary fills. The treatment methodology must also consider that water delivery of treatment chemicals might not effectively treat "high" spots, remote areas, or areas that trap air within the system.

If MIC is anticipated, one form of risk reduction may be to specify thicker piping in the design. Although this option only tends to buy time, it may serve as a prudent measure until universally accepted treatment methods are developed. Thicker walls buy time, not because they are less susceptible to MIC—a point on which evidence to date is inconclusive—but simply because a thicker wall has more material to corrode before a through-wall leak develops.

Another possibility in design is to remove the risk of leaks before MIC treatment is even evaluated. Areas such as those occupied by critical energized equipment can often be addressed by removing overhead sprinkler piping and limiting leak exposure through use of sidewall sprinkler coverage. Where it is not feasible to relocate large feed mains, piping can be sleeved so as not to permit potential leaks to contact energized equipment. Although these efforts provide some measure of immediate relief, they do not address the root cause or present a long-term solution to the problem.

Finally, the frequency of sprinkler and water flow device testing must be addressed. Most agree that repeated draining and refilling of sprinkler systems can increase both biological and nonbiological forms of corrosion. Draining and refilling provide nutrients and oxygen to bacterial colonies and oxygen for general tuberculation. Some facilities have noted substantial reductions in the frequency of leaks by reducing the frequency of drain and alarm testing.

It is critical to note that once a system is filled with infected water, treatment can become exponentially more complex because any future treatment from a chemical injection system must now be effective in remote and stagnate system legs. In bacteria-positive areas, several additional water quality tests should be completed throughout the first year of service to ensure that contamination has not occurred from any other sources.

Chemical Injection

Once system components have been cleaned and sterilized or replaced, a chemical injection system must be installed to prevent recurrence. Once installed, this system will be required to be operational continuously. As with any other mechanical system, this will require continuous system preventive maintenance.

Several commercially available chemical injection systems have been specifically designed for installation on fire protection systems. Some simply use existing hardware and chemicals modified from MIC treatment in other utilities, such as cooling towers. At the time of this writing, none of the systems currently available was believed to be specifically listed or approved for use as a sprinkler system component. Although most systems appear to be effective when properly installed and maintained, reliability and effectiveness have not been time-proven when compared with other industrial system benchmarks. Past references should always be investigated with any choice.

Most injection systems currently available are designed to work with specific chemicals. These selected chemicals and dose rates are critical. Some bacteria can develop chemical resistance over time if doses are not strong enough and bacteria are not quickly killed. A small number of bacteria believed to be related to MIC (such as the genera Bacillus and Clostridium) are known to have the ability to convert to a spore state when they encounter adverse conditions that are not lethal. [1,12] Spores are impervious to penetration by most chemicals and can thus survive biocide treatments indefinitely. Although subsequent treatments may slow or stop their activity, spores will reappear if and when treatments are stopped, and resume colonization. With a weak chemical attack, bacteria may also become resistant to the chemicals chosen.

As with other factors involved in treatment, the choice of chemical depends on the consultant. These chemicals generally include penetrants and biodispersants to break up the tubercles that protect underdeposit colonies, a biocide to kill the bacteria in the colonies, and a corrosion inhibitor to protect the interior surfaces of the system.

When such a system is chosen, the applicable authority having jurisdiction (AHJ) should be consulted. In addition to frictional loss concerns mentioned from changes in pipe surface roughness, increased backflow prevention hardware may be required. This could mean a pressure drop of 10 psi (0.7 bar) or more to sprinkler systems in addition to that created by pitting if cleaning is chosen. In new system designs, added alarm system contacts should also be planned for to monitor injection system chemical levels, operational status, and trouble conditions such as loss of power. Many preengineered systems provide contact points for these signals. As with fire detection, the perceived "best choice" is at the discretion of the person choosing, and opinions on this subject are highly variable.

Unlike other industrial systems treated for MIC, several unique interactions must be considered. First, sprinkler systems are typically located directly over people. The chemicals used must therefore be nontoxic in contemplation of accidental discharge or exposure to fire fighters under fire conditions. The effect of chosen chemicals on fire fighting (i.e., heat absorption) and chemical reaction with fire (i.e., heat) also needs consideration. Second, system designs typically place water discharge (such as from an inspector's test ports) into foliage or biologically sensitive drains and dry wells. Most municipal wastewater treatment plants (to which typical drains ultimately flow) require bacterial activity to decompose waste. Too large a quantity of biocides in municipal drains could be a problem.

In conclusion, a complete toxicity review with the highest possible biocidal chemical concentration must be completed. As much as possible, these chemicals should be noncombustible, colorless, odorless, and nontoxic. These chemicals must also be nondeteriorating to rubbers and polymers such as those used on pipe couplings, sprinkler o-rings, and valves. Chemical storage should also be reviewed, as several chemicals currently in use degrade rapidly with heat and may create relatively toxic vapors.

Opinions of which chemicals are believed to be "most effective" in control vary. Choices are available from those currently used for treatment in cooling towers and boilers to specifically patented compounds for fire protection systems. Some of the more common chemicals currently in use specifically for microbial control in sprinkler systems include quaternary ammonium compounds, organosulfur compounds, bromines, carbamates, isothiazalone, phosphates, and chlorines. Sodium silicate is effectively used in bulk quantities by several municipalities as an inhibitor, but this should be avoided for individual systems due to the potential for sprinkler plugging that overdosing can cause. At the writing of this article, no chemical can conclusively be said to be proven as the "most effective." The chemical choice may greatly depend on the bacteria present and system water quality.

SUMMARY

Current testing and treatment options can be confusing. Treatment is slowly evolving and research is continuing. Several industry groups, allied groups, and insurance companies are looking at the problem and applicable solutions. Many universities, government, and private industry groups also continue to research microbial control in general industry, as they have for the past several decades. These efforts will continue to provide improved treatment options in our industry.

As the need to address this problem draws on the industry's creativity for resolution, prudent thinking requires us to evaluate each solution's impact on overall sprinkler system integrity and performance. In light of this problem, the overwhelming value of sprinkler systems should not be regarded as tarnished or tainted. Although some with repeated MIC problems may view sprinklers as a risk to property, the reduction of risk to life and property from fire these systems provide should never be overshadowed.

REFERENCES CITED IN SUPPLEMENT

1. Clarke, B., "Microbiologically Influenced Corrosion in Fire Protection Systems," Fire Protection Engineering, Society of Fire Protection Engineers, No. 9, Winter 2001, pp. 14–16.
2. Borenstein, S. W., *Microbiologically Influenced Corrosion Handbook,* Woodhead Publications Ltd., 1994.
3. Cappers, M. A., "Investigation of Microbiological Influenced Corrosion in Sprinkler Systems," *Proceedings* of Fire Suppression and Detection Research Application Symposium, Research and Practice: Bridging the Gap, February 12–14, 1997, Orlando, FL, National Fire Protection Research Foundation, Quincy, MA, 1997, pp. 69–81.
4. Kammen, J., "Bacteria Spell Doom for Fire Sprinklers," *The Arizona Republic,* October 24, 1999.
5. Shenkiryk, M., "Pipe-Klean Project—McCarran Airport," *HERC Products,* July 25, 1996.
6. Bsharat, T. K., "Detection, Treatment, and Prevention of Microbiologically Influenced Corrosion in Water Based Fire Protection Systems", National Fire Sprinkler Association, Inc., June 1998.
7. "Internal Corrosion in Automatic Sprinkler Systems," FM Global Property Loss Prevention Data Sheet, 2001.
8. Hoffman, S., *Bugging Water Systems for Corrosion Control,* Hoffman Publications, Inc., 1999.
9. "The Mitigation and Detection of Microbial Corrosion," Argonne National Laboratory, Programs and Capabilities Database No. 526-002, 1999.

10. Little, B. J., Ray, R. I., and Wagner, P. A., "Tame Microbiologically Influenced Corrosion," *Chemical Engineering Progress,* September 1998.
11. Pope, D. H., Duquette, D. J., Johannes, A. H., and Wayner, P. C., "Microbiologically Influenced Corrosion of Industrial Alloys," *Materials Performance,* July 1984.
12. Hero, H. M., *The Nalco Guide to Cooling Water System Failure Analysis,* McGraw-Hill, Inc., 1993.

NFPA Codes, Standards, and Recommended Practices

Reference to the following NFPA codes, standards, and recommended practices will provide further information on fire pumps discussed in this supplement. (See the latest version of *The NFPA Catalog* for availability of current editions of the following documents.)

NFPA 13, *Standard for the Installation of Sprinkler Systems*

NFPA 25, *Standard for the Inspection, Testing, and Maintenance of Water-Based Fire Protection Systems*

Additional Readings

Dickinson, W. H., and Lewandowski, Z., "Electrochemical Concepts and Techniques in the Study of Stainless Steel Ennoblement," *Biodegradation,* Vol. 9, No. 1, 1998, pp. 11–21.

Garlock, C., "Microbiologically Influenced Corrosion: The Spreading of Cancer or the Big Myth," *Sprinkler Age,* Vol. 20, No. 6, 2001, pp. 17–18.

Haagensen, D., "Microbiologically Influenced Corrosion in Fire Sprinkler Systems," *NFPA Journal,* Vol. 94, No. 6, 2000, pp. 69–70.

Huggins, R. J., "MIC and NFPA Standards," *Sprinkler Age,* Vol. 20, No. 5, 2001, p. 17.

Huggins, R. J., "Microbiological Influenced Corrosion: What It Is and How It Works," *Sprinkler Age,* Vol. 16, No. 7, 1997, p. 16.

Marshall, R., "Iowa Authorities Suspects M.I.C." *Sprinkler Age,* Vol. 17, No. 9, 1998.

Pope, D. H., "Testing for and Treating MIC: Monitor for MIC to Help Prevent Long-Term Effects," *Sprinkler Age,* Vol. 16, No. 12, 1997, p. 22.

Index

Generators
Emergency, electric generating plants, **13,** A.13.31.1(14),
A.13.32.1(6)
ESFR sprinklers, **13,** 12.3.2.3.2
Standby emergency, **13,** 12.3.2.3.2, 13.29.1.7
Turbine, *see* Turbine-generators
Glycerine, 13, 7.5.2.1, 7.5.2.2, **13D,** 8.3.3.2.2 to 8.3.3.2.4, A.8.3.3.2
Graph sheets, 13, 14.3.4, A.14.3.4
Gratings, sprinklers under, 13, 8.5.5.3.3, 8.6.5.3.3, 8.6.5.3.5,
8.7.5.3.2, 8.8.5.3.2, 8.8.5.3.4, 8.9.5.3.2, 8.10.6.3.2, 8.10.6.3.4,
8.10.7.3.2, 8.11.5.3.3, 8.12.5.3.4, A.6.2.8, A.12.3.2.5.1.1
Gravity chutes, 13, 13.15.2.1.1
Gravity tanks, 13, 8.15.1.1.5, 11.2.3.1.8(11), 15.2.4, A.8.15.1.1.5
Gridded systems
Definition, **13,** 3.4.6, Fig. A.3.4.6
Hydraulic calculation procedures, **13,** 14.4.4.2, A.14.4.4.2
Preaction systems, **13,** 7.3.2.5
Groove joining methods, 13, 6.5.3, 10.3.3, 10.8.1.2
Ground floors, spaces under, 13, 8.14.6
Guards, sprinkler, 13, 6.2.8, A.6.2.8

H

Hangars, aircraft, 13, 13.24
Hangers, 13, 6.6, 9.1, A.6.6, A.9.1
Branch lines, location on, **13,** 9.2.3, A.9.2.3
Component material, **13,** 9.1.1.5
Distance between, maximum, **13,** 9.2.2, A.9.2.2
Earthquakes, subject to, **13,** 9.3.7
Expansion shields, **13,** 9.1.3
Fasteners
In concrete, **13,** 9.1.3, A.9.1.3.9.3
In steel, **13,** 9.1.4, A.9.1.4.1
In wood, **13,** 9.1.5
Installation, **13,** 9.2, A.9.2
Mains, location on, **13,** 9.2.4
Marine systems, **13,** 17.2.5.1(5), 17.2.5.1(6), 17.2.5.3, A.17.2.5.3
Non-system components, support of, **13,** 9.1.1.7, A.9.1.1.7
Powder-driven and welding studs, **13,** 9.1.3.9, 9.1.4.1, 9.3.7.8,
9.3.7.9, A.9.1.3.9.3, A.9.1.4.1
Risers supported by, **13,** 9.2.5
Rods, *see* Rods
Trapeze, **13,** 9.1.1.6, 9.2.1.3.2, 9.2.4.5, A.9.1.1.6
U-hooks, *see* U-hooks
Hardware, 13, Chap. 6
Hazardous areas, protection of piping in, 13, 8.15.3.3
Hazen-Williams formula, 13, 14.4.2.1.1, 14.4.3.2, 14.4.4.5, B.2.1.3
Heat detectors, 13, 13.21.2.8
Heating systems
Sprinklers near components, **13,** 8.3.2.5(2)
Unit heaters, sprinklers installed below, **13,** 8.12.5.2(1)
Heat-responsive devices, preaction and deluge systems, 13, 7.3.1.4
Heat-sensitive materials, 13, 17.4.10, A.17.4.10.1(4)
Definition, **13,** 3.14(4), 17.1.3(4), A.3.14(4), A.17.1.3(4)
Heel angle (definition), 13, 3.14(6), 17.1.3(6)
Heel (definition), 13, 3.14(5), 17.1.3(5)
Hexagonal bushings, 13, 8.14.19.2
High-challenge fire hazard (definition), 13, 3.3.11
High-expansion foam systems, 13, 12.1.11
Palletized, solid pile, bin box, or shelf storage, **13,** 12.2.1.3
Plastic pallets, protection of, **13,** 12.1.9.2.2(1)(c)
Rack storage, **13,** 12.3.1.8, 12.3.2.5.2, 12.3.4.5.1, A.12.3.1.8.1,
A.12.3.2.5.2.2

Roll paper storage, **13,** 12.6.1.3, 12.6.2.1.6, 12.6.2.1.7
Rubber tire storage, **13,** 12.4.1.3, 12.4.4
High-piled storage, 13, 8.2.1(4), 8.2.3, 8.4.9.2(4), 8.8.2.1.3
Definition, **13,** 3.3.12
High-rise buildings, *see* Buildings, multistory
High temperature-rated sprinklers, 13, 8.3.2.3 to 8.3.2.5,
8.13.2.2, 11.2.3.2.6, 12.3.2.5.1.2(1), A.12.2.3.1.1
Ceiling sprinklers, rack storage, **13,** 12.3.1.4, 12.3.1.5,
12.3.4.1.1, A.12.3.4.1.1, C.19
Plastic pallets, protection of, **13,** 12.1.9.2.2(2)(c)
Protection criteria, **13,** 12.2.2.1.5
Roll paper storage, **13,** 12.6.2.1.4, A.12.6.2.1.4
High voltage direct current converter stations, 13, A.13.31,
A.13.31.1, A.13.31.2
High water level device, dry pipe systems, 13, 7.2.5.5
Hoods
Electrical equipment protection, **13,** 8.14.10.2
Sprinklers in, **13,** 7.9.2.1, 7.9.4 to 7.9.7
Horizontal barriers, 13, 12.3.1.12, A.12.3.1.12
Definition, **13,** 3.10.6
Horizontal ceiling, *see* Ceilings
Horizontal channels (definition), 13, 3.11.2
Hose, 13, 9.3.2.3(5)
Hydraulic calculations, **13,** 11.2.3.1.3, 11.2.3.1.4
Outside, *see* Outside hose
Palletized, solid pile, bin box, or shelf storage, **13,** 12.2.1.2.1,
12.2.1.2.2
Rack storage, **13,** 12.3.1.3
Small, **13,** 8.16.5.1, 12.1.3, 12.6.1.2, A.8.16.5.1.1, A.8.16.5.1.4, C.1
Hose connections, 13, 8.16.5, A.8.16.5, C.5
Fire department, *see* Fire department connections
Marine systems, **13,** 17.4.9, 17.8.1
One-and-one-half-inch, *see* Hose, small
Hose stations, 13, 8.16.5.1.3(2), 8.16.5.1.4, 11.2.3.1.8(7), A.8.16.5.1.4
Hose streams
Baled cotton storage, **13,** 12.5.1.2
Marine systems, **13,** 17.5.3, A.17.5.3
Miscellaneous storage, **13,** 12.1.10.2
Nuclear power plants, **13,** 13.29.1.1, 13.30.1(2), A.13.29.1.1
Palletized, solid pile, bin box, or shelf storage, **13,** 12.2.1.2,
12.2.2.2.5, 12.2.3.2.2.4, A.12.2.1.2, C.8
Plastics storage, **13,** 12.2.3.2.2.4, 12.3.3.1.11, 12.3.3.2.3.4,
12.3.5.1.3, A.12.3.3.1.11, C.8
Rack storage systems, **13,** 12.3.2.1.7, Table 12.3.2.1.7,
Table 12.3.2.2.1(a), 12.3.2.2.3.4, 12.3.3.1.11, 12.3.3.2.3.4,
12.3.4.1.5, 12.3.4.2.3.4, 12.3.5.1.3, A.12.3.2.1.7,
A.12.3.3.1.11, C.6, C.8
Residential sprinklers, **13,** 11.2.3.5.5
Roll paper storage, **13,** 12.6.1.2, 12.6.1.3
Water-cooling towers, **13,** 13.21.1.7.3
Hose valves, 13, 11.2.3.1.8(8)
Hydrants, 13, 8.16.5.1.3(1), 10.7.1, 10.7.3, 10.7.5, 10.10.2.2.4(3),
16.2.3.5
Hydraulically designed systems; *see also* Hydraulic calculations
Circulating closed-loop systems, **13,** 7.6.1.2, A.7.6.1.2
Definition, **13,** 3.3.13
Deluge systems, **13,** 7.3.3.2, 14.6
Exposure systems, **13,** 11.2.3.7, A.11.2.3.7.1
Extra hazard occupancies, **13,** 14.5.4, A.14.5.4
Fire department connections, **13,** 8.16.2.3(3)
Information signs, **13,** 16.5, Fig. A.16.5
In-rack sprinklers, **13,** 12.3.1.11.1, 14.8
Marine systems, **13,** 17.5.1.1

About the Editor

Christian Dubay is a Senior Fire Protection Engineer at NFPA, where he is responsible for NFPA 13, *Standard for the Installation of Sprinkler Systems;* NFPA 13R, *Standard for the Installation of Sprinkler Systems in Residential Occupancies up to and Including Four Stories in Height;* NFPA 13D, *Standard for the Installation of Sprinkler Systems in One- and Two-Family Dwellings and Manufactured Homes;* NFPA 24, *Standard for the Installation of Private Fire Service Mains and Their Appurtenances;* NFPA 291, *Recommended Practice for Fire Flow Testing and Marking of Hydrants;* and NFPA 750, *Standard on Water Mist.* Mr. Dubay regularly writes and speaks about these topics, and participates in fire investigations where these applications are involved. He instructs NFPA's sprinkler systems, inspection, testing, and maintenance and fire pump seminars.

Mr. Dubay holds a Bachelor of Science degree in Fire Protection Engineering from the University of Maryland. He is a registered professional engineer in fire protection engineering in the State of Connecticut and a member of the Society of Fire Protection Engineers and the International Association of Arson Investigators. Mr. Dubay currently serves as the Chair of the American Water Works Associations Fire Protection Committee and is a member of the Board of Directors for the International Water Mist Association. Prior to joining NFPA, Mr. Dubay worked as a Fire Protection Engineer for the U.S. Navy and as a research assistant for the University of Maryland's Fire Protection Engineering Department. Mr. Dubay also served as a fire fighter and emergency medical technician for 10 years in Connecticut and Maryland.